THE FOOD ADDITIVES BOOK

THE FOOD ADDITIVES BOOK

Nicholas Freydberg, Ph.D.,
and Willis A. Gortner, Ph.D.

CONSUMERS UNION
Mount Vernon, New York

The Food Additives Book is a Consumer Reports Book published by Consumers Union, the nonprofit organization that publishes Consumer Reports, the monthly magazine of test reports, product Ratings, and buying guidance. Established in 1936, Consumers Union is chartered under the Not-For-Profit Corporation Law of the State of New York.

The purposes of Consumers Union, as stated in its charter, are to provide consumers with information and counsel on consumer goods and services, to give information on all matters relating to the expenditure of the family income, and to initiate and to cooperate with individual and group efforts seeking to create and maintain decent living standards.

Consumers Union derives its income solely from the sale of Consumer Reports and other publications. In addition, expenses of occasional public service efforts may be met, in part, by noncommercial contributions, grants, and fees. Consumers Union accepts no advertising or product samples and is not beholden in any way to any commercial interest. Its Ratings and reports are solely for the use of the readers of its publications. Neither the Ratings nor the reports nor any Consumers Union publication, including this book, may be used in advertising or for any commercial purpose. Consumers Union will take all steps open to it to prevent such uses of its material, its name, or the name of Consumer Reports.

This special Consumers Union edition of *The Food Additives Book*
has been published by arrangement with Bantam Books, Inc.

Consumers Union edition
First printing, December 1982
Library of Congress Catalog Card Number: 81-15044
ISBN: 0-89043-122-1

Grateful acknowledgment is made for permission to include the following copyrighted material:

Information on sugar content in cereals reprinted from *Brand Name Guide to Sugar* by Ira L. Shannon, Copyright © 1977 by Ira L. Shannon. Used by permission of Nelson-Hall Publishers, Chicago.

Information from table 2-5 of "Gas-Liquid Chromatographic Analysis of Sugars in Ready-to-Eat Breakfast Cereals", *Journal of Food Science,* Vol. 45, No. 1, pp. 138-141. Reprinted by permission. Copyright © 1980 by Institute of Food Technologists.

ACKNOWLEDGMENTS

Many people have helped us in preparing this book. Our Dedication of the book acknowledges our great debt to the many scientists in the FASEB Select Committee on GRAS Substances and the Life Sciences Research Office. Miss Christine Aylor has helped keep us abreast of the scientific reports on additives issuing from that office.

The staff of the Bureau of Foods of the Food and Drug Administration, and especially Drs. Sanford A. Miller, F. Edward Scarbrough, and Corbin Miles; and of the Human Nutrition Center of the U.S. Department of Agriculture, particularly Drs. Frank Hepburn, Wayne R. Wolf, and John L. Weihrauch, have been most helpful and supportive in tracing some of the scientific details important in our assessment of various of the food additives.

Drs. Horace L. Sipple, Byron T. Webb, Mildred Rodriguez, and Steven R. Tannenbaum provided valuable assistance as scientific consultants.

Our research associates, Barbara Schlesinger, Elizabeth Vizza, and Margaret Curtin, bore the major share of the formidable task of purchasing the thousands of brands of food that were required, traveling to distant parts of the country for that purpose, and extracting the information from their labels needed for the Inventory-of-Brands Section and preparing it for publication. It would be difficult to duplicate their enthusiasm and standards of accuracy during the many months it took to accomplish this work. The authors, besides, are grateful for their many valuable suggestions which have contributed materially to making this volume more useful for the reader.

Acknowledgment of our debt to others would be incomplete without expressing our indebtedness to Judy Knipe, the editor assigned to us by our publisher. Her perceptive queries, insightful challenges, her rewritings and rearrangements have been of inestimable value toward achieving a clarity of presentation necessary for our objective—a readily understandable, helpful, and accurate guide to additives and branded foods for the food shopper.

DEDICATION

This work is dedicated to the distinguished scientists, researchers, and scholars, who, as the FASEB Select Committee on GRAS Substances (SCOGS) or as the staff of the FASEB Life Sciences Research Office (LSRO), devoted their expertise and time for a decade (1971–81) to the collection and the assessment of the bulk of the information used by the authors.

In a true sense, we, as the authors-of-record, regard these individuals as ''co-authors,'' and justly so, considering that the data and judgments contained in this volume would have been inconceivable to collect and present here without the benefit of their efforts.

Now, at last, in large measure because of them, the American public has available to it the relevant knowledge it needs in an area of vital significance, that of food additives, in an understandable and reliable form, and easy to put into practice.

Richard G. Allison, Ph.D. (LSRO).
Aaron M. Altschul, Ph.D. (SCOGS), Professor of Community Medicine and International Health, Georgetown University School of Medicine.
Sue Ann Anderson, Ph.D. (LSRO).
Joseph F. Borzelleca, Ph.D. (SCOGS), Professor of Pharmacology, Virginia Commonwealth University Medical College.
C. Jelleff Carr, Ph.D. (Director, LSRO 1972–77).
Herman I. Chinn, Ph.D. (LSRO).
Harry G. Day, Sc.D. (SCOGS), Professor Emeritus of Chemistry, Indiana University.
Samuel B. Detwiler, M.A. (LSRO).
Kenneth D. Fisher, Ph.D. (Director, LSRO 1977–).
Samuel J. Fomon, M.D. (SCOGS), Professor of Pediatrics, College of Medicine, University of Iowa.
Andrew F. Freeman, B.S. (LSRO).
George W. Irving, Jr., Ph.D. (Chairman, SCOGS).
Bert N. La Du, Jr., M.D. (SCOGS), Chairman, Department of Pharmacology, University of Michigan.
John R. McCoy, V.M.D. (SCOGS), Professor of Comparative Pathology, College of Medicine and Dentistry, Jersey-Rutgers Medical School.
Sanford A. Miller, Ph.D. (SCOGS), Professor of Nutritional Biochemistry, Massachusetts Institute of Technology.
Gabriel L. Plaa, Ph.D. (SCOGS), Chairman, Department of Pharmacology, University of Montreal.
Frederic R. Senti, Ph.D. (Associate Director, LSRO).
Michael B. Shimkin, M.D. (SCOGS), Professor of Community Medicine and Oncology, University of California School of Medicine at San Diego.
R. G. H. Siu, Ph.D. (SCOGS), Consultant.
Marian E. Swendseid, Ph.D. (SCOGS), Professor of Nutrition and Biological Chemistry, University of California School of Public Health at Los Angeles.
John M. Talbot, M.D. (LSRO).
Michael J. Wade, Ph.D. (LSRO).
John L. Wood, Ph.D. (SCOGS), Distinguished Service Professor of Biochemistry, University of Tennessee Center for Health Sciences.

CONTENTS

FOREWORD TO THE CONSUMERS UNION EDITION

For years, the safety of the additives contained in processed foods has been a major concern to many Americans. Some additives, like saccharin, have captured headline attention because of their suggested link to cancer. And some have been implicated in headaches, allergies, and other ailments. Increasing concern about additives in food has swelled the ranks of food shoppers who read the label before they buy the product. By examining the label on a package or can of food, they can find out some of the additives that are present. But then what? Few people are familiar with the names of many additives, or know which are safe to eat and which may be hazardous.

It is to help careful shoppers make judgments about additives in food that we commend to you *The Food Additives Book*. Organized in two main parts, the book begins with a section on brand-name products—listing additives of health concern, if any, that they contain—presented in twenty-three broad groupings. Each additive of health concern is categorized in one of two ways: as an additive of concern to all, or as an additive of concern to some. The second part of the book, a "Dictionary of Food Additives," describes individual food additives, assesses their safety, and rates each on a scale of comparative safety.

At the request of the authors, we have provided for this Consumers Union edition of the book a new Foods Index at the end of the book. The Foods Index enhances the usefulness of the book by helping you locate types of food more readily than if you were to rely on the table of contents alone.

We like the way the authors compiled the data for this book. Labels were checked on products bought especially for this project from supermarket chains, neighborhood markets, and health food stores used by ordinary consumers. Quite properly, readers are warned that ingredients may have changed since the samples were bought and the labels examined. Readers are urged to take nothing for granted and to continue to check labels: A safe product can become suspect—and the reverse could be true as well. We also like the authors' explanation of why they did not strive to include every known brand of food and of how you can extrapolate what you need to know about an unlisted brand from information about brands that are included (see page 3).

The authors are candid in laying out their sources and even tabulate how their ratings differ from those of SCOGS (the Select Committee on GRAS Substances).* Our technical reviewers found the rating procedure used in *The Food Additives Book* to be sensible, easy to understand, and somewhat more flexible than systems used by other groups of experts.

As with all Consumer Reports Books not of our own making, *The Food Additives Book* represents the research and thinking of its authors. It should not be assumed that Consumers Union concurs with every one of their views. We believe, however, that *The Food Additives Book* is an excellent source of information, clearly presented. It will help you to make informed decisions about the foods you eat. We are confident that this book will be a useful reference work for you and your family.

The Editors of Consumer Reports Books

---

*For an explanation of SCOGS and GRAS, see pages xiii-xiv.

WHAT THIS BOOK IS ALL ABOUT

Some of us have become confused about and fearful of a wide range of chemicals that are being added to our foods. Our distress has been accentuated by the continuing stream of *new research findings,* some adverse, others exaggerated by the media, which have fueled the concerns of consumers about the safety of foods available in the marketplace.

Our authoritative sources of information are not always of much help; they too have contributed to the uncertainty with conflicting advice. In 1980 the Departments of Health, Welfare & Education and Agriculture set dietary guidelines for us, only to have these disputed by the Food and Nutrition Board of the National Research Council. It didn't end there, for nutrition experts in the government, in turn, challenged these revisions. Our *experts* have been at loggerheads about saccharin, disputing whether this synthetic sweetener, which has caused cancer in laboratory animals, is a sufficient hazard to bar it in human food. They differ as well on whether excessive intake of cholesterol contributes to the occurrence of heart attacks.

As an increasingly urbanized society, we are becoming less and less able as individuals to grow our own food in sufficient quantity and variety. Some people have questioned whether the wide range of additives employed for many purposes is really needed. It is difficult to quarrel with the necessity of additives to preserve processed foods during their manufacture and shipment and while stored on grocery shelves for a reasonable period of time. Nor can we contest their "usefulness" if they enhance flavor, appearance, create satisfactory and appetizing textures, and so on, *as long as they are safe.*

What is difficult for a food consumer to be able to determine, within the limits of current knowledge, is which additives are safe, which are not, and which are questionable as to safety. This volume, the authors believe, will provide you with the necessary scientific and technological information to make those determinations for the additives you will find listed on the labels of branded food items. It should enable you to put this knowledge into practice with ease when you shop for food.

The safety ratings which this volume provides reflect the risks a consumer may face from including in his diet, at times frequently, certain food additives. They do *not* consider the possible benefits. The safety of ferric salts, for example, is questioned here because of insufficient information and poor biological availability. They are used as iron supplements and have nutritional benefits, as does calcium caseinate, whose use is also cautioned because of the possible presence of a substance which may (it is not certain) have an adverse effect on humans. The *risks* can be judged objectively; experimental studies can provide information on the nature of a possible hazard and the likelihood of it. By contrast, the *benefits* will vary for each person, depending on individual needs. With this in mind, the book tells why the additive has been used in formulating the food, and enables the reader to make an informed choice based on its value to him for a wholesome, satisfying, and safe diet.

A relevant question then is: Why hasn't the information contained in this volume been made available to the general public earlier? A Presidential Directive in 1969, tacitly acknowledging the need, ordered this done; and commencing in 1971, the massive task of evaluating the safety of hundreds of food additives was undertaken by a group of distinguished scientists. Collection of the worldwide experimental and clinical information has been ongoing for a decade, as have the assessments of safety.

You may have noted earlier that this volume is dedicated to this remarkable group of scientists (referred to as SCOGS—Select Committee on GRAS Substances). They were selected from the variety of disciplines concerned with food: biochemistry, organic chemistry, pathology, physiology, nutrition, food science, oncology, pharmacology, human and veterinary medicine. Their effort may have no parallel in science. The project has been conducted under the authority and direction of the Federation of American Societies for Experimental Biology (FASEB), a consortium of six scientific associations who bore the responsibility for the selection of the participants and provided their own research facility, the Life Sciences Research Office (LSRO), as a functioning staff.

The authors, on their part, have devoted over two years to winnowing the vast amounts of material provided in the reports issued by SCOGS, in order to make the information readily comprehensible to the layman. These reports provide a major part of the material contained in the second half of this volume. As the SCOGS reports did not cover all of the substances permitted as additives in food—those omitted were principally ones which the FDA had not classified "generally recognized as safe" (GRAS)*—the additional additives have been reviewed by the authors, or commissioned to qualified scientists for that purpose; and these too are included here.

For the most part, the safety assessments made by the authors have conformed with the judgments arrived at by the Select Committee. In some instances they have not, and, when in disagreement, SCOGS has arrived at a somewhat more severe rating in twice the number of instances as *The Food Additives Book*. (For this comparison, see p. 715.) The authors, of course, acknowledge their full responsibility for the judgments made in the book, irrespective of whether or not they are in agreement with SCOGS.

With the intention of making it easy to put the knowledge contained here into practice, an Inventory-of-Brands has been provided. It covers over 100 food categories, lists more than 6000 branded foods, and alongside each you will find any additives contained in it which are regarded in this volume as of possible concern to health. An explanatory introduction to this section follows immediately. It can be used as a basic shopping list and, at the least, as a means whereby ingredients to avoid in a specific category of food can be quickly identified.

---

*The 1958 Food Additives Amendments to the Food, Drug and Cosmetic Act of 1938 exempted from prior approval by the FDA substances which were "generally recognized as safe" by experts. These became known as GRAS substances. The amendments did require prior approval by the FDA for new commercially added food ingredients based on proof of safety.

THE INVENTORY OF BRANDS

THE PURPOSE OF THE INVENTORY OF BRANDS

The purpose of this section is to make it easy to apply the information on additives supplied in the dictionary section of this book when you go to market: to select foods both wisely and safely.

It can enable you to determine beforehand whether a specific food item included here contains an additive that may be of concern to your health; and if it does, to look for similar items which do not.

However, you are not likely to find every brand of food you prefer contained in the inventory section. To do so for all of the readers of this book would have required listing almost everything carried on grocery store shelves, possibly 25,000 items in all. We've compromised on about a quarter of this number, mostly best-sellers; otherwise the size of the book would make it unmanageable and its cost prohibitive.

If a food item of interest to you is not here, the inventory nevertheless should enable you to know what additives-of-concern to look for in that item. For example, if you fail to find a preferred soup included, you can easily determine the additives-of-concern to watch out for when shopping for it; they are likely to be the ones present with some frequency in the soups that are listed. By means of a breakdown of items into over 100 product categories, you have available sufficient representation in each to gain an excellent idea of the additives to avoid. And if you do come across an additive still different from these, you always can turn to the dictionary portion of this book to find what you'll need to know about it. The INVENTORY OF BRANDS covers:

- nationally distributed brands
- regional brands
- supermarket private brands
- brands in health food stores

All of these have representation here and are identified in each product category, the idea being to enable you to make comparisons and find purchasing alternatives. The national brands usually are best-sellers. Brands of regional origin (indicated by "R" on the left margin), usually perishable foods, are of significance in categories such as baked goods and dairy products. Again, space restrictions permitted representation of a limited number of supermarket chains, but these are among the largest in the country. Items sold in health food stores are becoming an increasingly important source for many shoppers, in part because of concern about additives. It has not been possible to determine whether these are regional or national in distribution.

It is of relevance to note here that all of the foods listed in this inventory were purchased by the authors at retail outlets, and none was obtained by other means; their selection was determined solely on their popularity or the requirements of a well-rounded representation.

Be certain to take note of this column heading, which is present in each product category:

ADDITIVES-OF-CONCERN
BOLD —CONCERN TO ALL
LIGHT —CONCERN TO SOME

It has been possible to differentiate, based on research and clinical experience, between additives that are of concern to all of us, and those which are of concern to some people and not to others. If any additives-of-concern are contained in an item, you'll find them listed alongside in this column.

It may startle you, at first, to find that so many food items contain a number of additives-of-concern. But note that the ones in light type are of relevance only to limited groups of people; for instance, to those allergic to certain ingredients in grains (gluten), or to dairy products (albumin, whey); or to women who are pregnant or lactating; or to anyone afflicted with high blood pressure. There should be little reason for others to avoid these additives.

When you find an additive-of-concern listed alongside a brand, it is suggested that you refer to the review of the additive in the dictionary section, where you will find the scientific evidence for the assessment of caution, and the identification of those individuals who should avoid a particular additive and why.

THE EXTENT OF THE PRESENCE OF ADDITIVES-OF-CONCERN IN THE FOOD ITEMS LISTED IN THE INVENTORY OF BRANDS*

The Inventory-of-Brands contains 6,212 items of branded, packaged foods that were purchased in grocery and health food stores. They provide representation in over 100 food product categories.

Half of these (50 percent) contain one or more ingredients regarded in this volume to be additives-of-concern to the health of all consumers.† Another 11 percent contain ingredients regarded here as additives-of-concern to some (but not all) consumers. In all, 6 out of 10 of these branded items contained substances of health concern to some or all of the U.S. public.

A significant difference exists in this respect between food items distributed through the usual food outlets and those distributed through health food stores. Sixty-five percent of the items that were purchased in grocery stores contained additives-of-concern (A-O-C), compared to 31 percent in health food stores, or more than double proportionally.

TYPE OF RETAIL OUTLET		TOTAL ITEMS	W/A-O-C FOR ALL	W/A-O-C FOR SOME	W/NO A-O-C
Grocery	Number	5420	2938	582	1900
	Percent	100%	54%	11%	35%
Health Food	Number	792	155	89	548
	Percent	100%	20%	11%	69%
Total Both	Number	6212	3093	671	2448
	Percent	100%	50%	11%	39%

These totals obscure substantial differences in the incidence of additives-of-concern between product categories. For in-

*The claim is not made here that the items listed in the Inventory-of-Brands section are a representative cross section of all of the packaged foods to be found on retailers' shelves. The objectives that guided our selection were inclusion of the more popular, nationally distributed brands, and, in addition, examples of regional and supermarket private brands which would enable the reader to make comparisons. Because of this bias in selection, the extent of the presence of additives-of-concern found in these items cannot be assumed to be an accurate reflection of all processed foods available to the U.S. consumer.

†These items in some instances also contained additives-of-concern to some (not all) consumers.

stance, relatively few sweet spreads, vegetables, baking ingredients, fruit and fruit juices, and drinks sold in grocery outlets contain additives-of-concern; on the average less than two out of ten do. In contrast, eight out of ten packaged dinners, baked goods, soups, and low-calorie foods and beverages, on the average, contain additives of concern; these foods are not commonly found in health food stores.

The table which follows provides this information for each of twenty-three major food groups contained in the Inventory of Brands section for both grocery and health food outlets.

Presence or Absence of Additives-of-Concern in items sold in grocery and health food stores by major food product categories (arranged in descending order of absence of additives-of-concern in grocery store items)

	GROCERY STORES National, Regional, and Private Brands				HEALTH FOOD STORES Items sold in these outlets			
Major Categories	TOTAL NUMBER OF ITEMS	% WITH A-O-C FOR ALL	% WITH A-O-C FOR SOME	% WITH NO A-O-C	TOTAL NUMBER OF ITEMS	% WITH A-O-C FOR ALL	% WITH A-O-C FOR SOME	% WITH NO A-O-C
Jellies & Other Sweet Spreads; Nut & Seed Butters	200	6%	1%	93%	65	-%	-%	100%
Vegetable Juices & Vegetables	434	17	1	82	48	-	10	90
Baking Ingredients	99	20	-	80	31	3	3	94
Fruit, Fruit Drinks, Fruit Juices	336	22	1	77	82	5	7	88
Pasta; Potatoes (Instant); Rice	118	53	3	44	35	6	23	71
Baby Foods	202	44	14	42	2	*	*	*
Beverage Mixes & Beverages	256	53	9	38	24	4	13	83
Snack Items	187	60	6	34	46	20	4	76
Bread & Bread Products; Crackers	580	38	29	33	61	8	21	71
Fish & Shellfish	139	58	10	32	12	*	*	*
Cereal, Cereal Bars (Breakfast & Snack)	110	65	5	30	27	30	11	59
Dairy Products & Substitutes	598	55	15	30	88	50	9	41
Gravies, Sauces, & Seasonings	138	65	7	28	28	7	21	71
Candy & Gum	144	65	13	22	35	20	6	74
One-Course Dinners	179	75	7	18	44	23	9	68
Pickles, Salad Dressings, & Other Condiments	147	73	13	14	45	40	18	42
Baked Sweet Goods, Not Frozen or Refrigerated	507	74	14	12	19	58	21	21
Low-Calorie Beverages & Foods	202	84	6	10	-	-	-	-
Baking Mixes, Dessert Toppings, Gelatin, Pudding	279	89	2	9	17	23	12	65
Soups	164	59	32	9	40	5	17	78
Meat & Poultry & Substitutes	163	85	7	8	29	62	3	35

Major Categories	GROCERY STORES National, Regional, and Private Brands TOTAL NUMBER OF ITEMS	% WITH A-O-C FOR ALL	% WITH A-O-C FOR SOME	% WITH NO A-O-C	HEALTH FOOD STORES Items sold in these outlets TOTAL NUMBER OF ITEMS	% WITH A-O-C FOR ALL	% WITH A-O-C FOR SOME	% WITH NO A-O-C
Baked Goods, Frozen & Refrigerated	138	83	11	6	7	*	*	*
Frozen Dinners, Pizza, Pot Pies	100	91	5	4	7	*	*	*
Total All Categories	5420	54%	11%	35%	792	20%	11%	69%

*Insufficient representation for percentages to be meaningful

THE LIMITATIONS OF FOOD LABELS FOR IDENTIFYING ADDITIVES-OF-CONCERN

The Food and Drug legislation presently permits exemptions in the requirement that specific additives be listed on a label when contained in some foods. In such instances, a means has been devised in the inventory to alert you when an additive-of-concern may be present.

- Artificial color and some natural colors.

When a certified (FD & C) artificial color is used, the actual color used need not be identified; only "artificial color" or some variant of the term must appear on the label, unless evidence exists that a specific one used is a proven hazard. In that case, it must be listed. FD & C Yellow No. 5 (Tartrazine) is the only artificial color at present subjected to this requirement, as it causes an allergic reaction in some people. Disagreement, however, exists concerning the possibility of harmful effects caused by some other artificial colors; and to caution about it, artificial color when noted on a label will appear in the additives-of-concern column. A rule-of-thumb method proposed here for assessing whether disputed artificial colors may be present is by the color of the food. If the color of the food is red, orange, or violet, these disputed food colors may be in it. Whatever the colors, children, especially hyperactive ones, are cautioned to avoid artificial color additives until questions concerning their effects are resolved. A detailed discussion is available under Food Colors in the dictionary section (see p. 534).

Dairy products like cheese and frozen desserts are exempted

by law from the necessity of even declaring that they contain artificial color, except in such instances as FD & C Yellow No. 5. Some manufacturers now voluntarily state the presence of artificial color on the label, or its absence. However, if not listed, or unless specifically stated as not being present, it remains uncertain whether artificial color has been used in these foods. A notation has been placed at the beginning of these product categories to alert the reader to the possibility of the presence of artificial color when it does not appear in the additives-of-concern column.

A few natural colors, too, can be of concern to health, such as carmine or saffron. When "natural color," but no *specific* natural color, appears on an ingredient label, you'll find it noted in the additives-of-concern column. Unfortunately, no method has been devised here to help determine whether or not it refers to a possibly harmful natural color.

• Artificial flavor and natural flavor.

The flavors used in foods may be derived from natural or synthetic substances; mostly they consist of complicated combinations of these, perhaps a dozen or more. The flavor chemist can choose from almost 2000 compounds for this purpose; by law, an individual listing of these substances is not required, and it is most unlikely to be revealed, for these combinations are regarded as valuable trade secrets. With no way to determine which components have been used from the formidable number that are available, it has not been possible to provide safety assessments for flavors identified as "artificial" or "natural." It is the only instance in this volume where we have been unable to do so. When a single flavor is reported as present, such as ethyl methyl phenylglycidate or ionone, an assessment is possible, and has been noted in the additives-of-concern column whenever the evidence indicates it to be warranted.

• Fats and oils.

A manufacturer is permitted by FDA regulations to identify in the ingredient list the range of fats and oils which may have been used, but one cannot be certain of the ones that actually are in the food. For example, the label on Dolly Madison Cinnamon Rolls lists these fats and oils that may be present:

> . . . vegetable and/or animal shortening (may contain one or more of the following: soya oil, beef fat, lard, partially

hydrogenated [soya oil, cottonseed oil, palm oil, coconut oil, palm kernel oil, beef fat and/or lard]) . . .

You will find this reduced list of animal fats and vegetable oils appearing in the additives-of-concern column alongside this Dolly Madison breakfast pastry:

(BEEF FAT, LARD; COCONUT, PALM KERNEL OILS)

The procedure followed in these instances is to extract the ones that are highly saturated, either naturally or by processing (hydrogenation), and in sufficient quantity if present in the food to be regarded as of possible health concern. An explanation of the method for determining quantity will be found in both Animal Fats (see p. 479) and Vegetable Oils (see p. 660) in the dictionary section.

- Inadequate identification of ingredients.

At times, a general rather than a specific term is used for an ingredient on a label, such as shortening instead of coconut oil, or natural color rather than saffron. This general term can refer to any of a number of ingredients and poses a problem for its safety evaluation when some of these possibilities are of concern and others are not. Thirteen general terms found on labels to which this applies are:

Animal fats; cellulose derivatives; coloring, food colors; natural colors, vegetable colors; seaweed; shortening, vegetable oils; softeners, stabilizers, thickeners, vegetable gums

The inability to determine the specific ingredient that may be present has led, for reasons of caution, to the placement of these terms in the additives-of-concern column when they appear on a label. A listing of the specific ingredients they can have reference to follows, separated into those regarded as additives-of-concern and those that are not.

Additives-of-Concern	*Not Additives-of-Concern*
ANIMAL FATS	
Beef fat (tallow); butter (butter fat); lard (pork fat); mutton (fat); stearic acid; calcium stearate	Marine (fish) oil; poultry fat and skin

Additives-of-Concern	*Not Additives-of-Concern*
CELLULOSE DERIVATIVES	
Hydroxypropyl cellulose; methyl ethyl cellulose	Cellulose derivatives *other than* hydroxypropyl cellulose, methyl ethyl cellulose
COLORING, FOOD COLORS	
Artificial color; certified color; FD & C colors; cochineal and carmine; paprika, turmeric, and their oleoresins; saffron	Natural color *other than* cochineal and carmine; paprika, turmeric, and their oleoresins; saffron
NATURAL COLORS, VEGETABLE COLORS	
Cochineal and carmine; paprika, turmeric, and their oleoresins; saffron	Natural color *other than* cochineal and carmine; paprika, turmeric and their oleoresins; saffron
SEAWEED	
Alginates; carrageenan and furcelleran; dulse and kelp	Agar-agar
SHORTENING, VEGETABLE OILS	
Coconut oil; hydrogenated vegetable oils; palm kernel oil; rapeseed oil	Non- and partially hydrogenated vegetable oils *other than* coconut, palm kernel, and rapeseed oils
SOFTENERS, STABILIZERS, THICKENERS, VEGETABLE GUMS	
Alginates; carrageenan and furcelleran; dulse and kelp; glycerol esters of wood rosin; gum arabic; gum tragacanth; guar gum; hydroxypropyl cellulose; locust bean gum; methyl ethyl cellulose; modified starch	Agar-agar; cellulose derivatives *other than* hydroxypropyl cellulose, methyl ethyl cellulose; unmodified or gelatinized starch; xanthan gum

Evidence regarding the safety of each of the ingredients listed in both columns is presented in the dictionary section of this volume.

Another situation of inadequate identification arises when an ingredient specified on a label contains a component which, if listed by itself, would have been identified as an additive-of-concern. This is true of a number of substances extracted from milk (buttermilk solids, milk derivatives, milk protein, milk solids, sour milk or cream solids) which may contain casein, lactalbumin, or whey, all viewed here as additives-of-concern.* A similar circumstance occurs in "high protein flour" which can contain albumin, casein, or gluten, all warranting caution for some people. These milk extractives and the flour will appear in the additives-of-concern column when present in a food.

- Absence of ingredient lists on labels.

Some manufacturers state on the label only that their product is "pure" fruit juice or "100%" coffee, or whatever, and do not supply a formal list of ingredients. They may make no reference whatever to ingredients, assuming perhaps that the content of foods like frozen fish fillets, simple frozen vegetables, and, on occasion, frozen and refrigerated meats, is self-evident. Pastas, nuts, dried and frozen fruits not infrequently will omit an ingredient list. It has made common sense to us to consider these products as additive-free, and they have been identified in the inventory as containing no additives-of-concern.

THE OMISSION OF SODIUM CHLORIDE (TABLE SALT) FROM THE ADDITIVES-OF-CONCERN COLUMN

Sodium chloride is regarded as an additive-of-concern in the review of this substance in the dictionary section, because anyone with high blood pressure or a family history of this tendency, or normal infants (in their prepared food) should avoid an excess. In spite of this, you will not find salt in the additives-of-concern column alongside items that contain it. It is present in so many foods that, regrettably, its constant repetition might serve little purpose except to obscure the crucial fact that it is the amount and not its mere presence which is important.

We have no way of determining from the label the amount of sodium chloride there is in a food item. Its order in the list of ingredients does provide a coarse measurement, as the largest

---

*Milk itself is considered a food, not an additive. It is not included as an additive-of-concern in this book, although some people may have a milk intolerance.

quantity of a substance in a food will come first in the list, the next in amount second, and so on.

In comparison with the ingredients which precede it on the list, the relatively small amount of salt used in foods would usually place it at, or near, the bottom. For this reason, the position of salt on the ingredients list makes it a doubtful means for determining the actual amount present or for discriminating between similar food items. To demonstrate the difficulty, a comparison is available between two well-known white breads, each of which lists salt as 6th in the ingredient order. Two slices of one of these is reported as containing 335 milligrams, while two slices of the other brand contains less than a quarter of this amount, 81 milligrams.

Perhaps more important for this book's purposes, although salt may be well down in the order of ingredients, there is no assurance that the amount is not a hazard to vulnerable consumers. It is eighth on the list of a popular frozen macaroni and cheese dish; yet a small serving of 6 ounces contains 780 milligrams, a substantial amount, and especially so if one is tempted to take another helping.

Guidance on the amount of sodium in common foods is available from the booklet "The Sodium Content of Your Food," prepared under the auspices of the U.S. Department of Agriculture and available from Superintendent of Documents, U.S. Printing Office, Washington, D.C. 20402. It lists the sodium content of an extensive range of common foods, not by brands but by food categories (carbonated beverages, coffee, fruit drinks and juices, specific cheeses, other dairy products, and so on).

• A caution: check the food label

THE INGREDIENTS MAY HAVE CHANGED.

The items listed in this inventory were purchased from September 1979 to February 1981. Food processors do change ingredients, and for certainty inspect the list on the label of an item you may wish to purchase to determine whether any additives regarded here as of concern have been removed or added in the interim.

GUIDE TO STYLE OF PRESENTATION IN THE INVENTORY OF BRANDS

In order to provide accurately and concisely the information on additives of concern which may be present in any of the thousands of items listed in this inventory, it has been necessary to adopt a terse styling procedure which is explained below:

FOOD BRANDS AND ITEMS

	TYPE FACE
PRODUCER AND/OR BRAND	
SWANSON	BOLD FACE
RELATED ITEMS SAME BRAND	
GERBER	
—HIGH MEAT DINNER	LIGHT FACE ITALICS,
BEEF W/ VEGETABLES; CHICKEN W/ VEGETABLES	LIGHT FACE
SINGLE ITEMS	
SWANSON	
FRENCH TOAST W/ SAUSAGES	LIGHT FACE
SUPERMARKET	
STOP & SHOP	BOLD FACE
SUPERMARKET PRIVATE BRAND—PRIVATE LABEL	
STOP & SHOP	BOLD FACE
—OUR FAMOUS	BOLD FACE

ADDITIVES-OF-CONCERN

ADDITIVES-OF-CONCERN TO ALL	
CARRAGEENAN	BOLD FACE
SODIUM NITRATE	
ADDITIVES-OF-CONCERN TO SOME PEOPLE	
GLUTEN	LIGHT FACE
SODIUM ALGINATE	

WORDS IN PARENTHESES AFTER AN ADDITIVE-OF-CONCERN

Some additives appear on labels in a number of ways. An attempt has been made to standardize these by placing the basic term first, followed in parentheses by any others appearing with it on the ingredient list.

GLUTEN (WHEAT)
WHEY (SWEET DAIRY)
BUTTER (GRADE AA)

GLUTEN (VITAL WHEAT)
WHEY (DRIED OR MODIFIED)
BUTTER (SWEET CREAM)

WORDS IN BRACKETS AFTER AN ADDITIVE-OF-CONCERN

These have been added to complete the proper name of an additive incompletely stated on the label, or to clarify what the substance is.

LOCUST BEAN [GUM]
BEEF OIL [FAT]

SPELLING AND PUNCTUATION OF BRANDS AND ITEMS

These are presented *exactly* as they appear on the label, even if they appear to have been mispelled or seem to be inconsistent.

Super-Stix
Cocoa Chp 'N Nut
Oatmeal N' Molasses

Hi-Proteen
Parmagian
Parmigiana (in another instance)

FD&C PRECEDING A COLOR ADDITIVE

FD & C preceding a color indicates that it is permitted in food, drugs and cosmetics. On occasions it is omitted in ingredients lists, but any artificial color permitted in food *must* be an FD & C color. To avoid confusion, it has been added in those instances when it had been absent.

TWO SPECIAL CASES

ARTIFICIAL COLORS

Artificial color without specification of all of the colors that are used is regarded in this volume as an additive of general concern. It appears in a variety of ways in an ingredient list; at times by itself, at times along with one or more of the colors that have been used but not necessarily limited to these. The examples below demonstrate what had been listed on the label and what has appeared in this book.

AS LISTED ON THE LABEL	AS LISTED IN THIS BOOK
Artificial Color (including FD & C Yellow No. 5)	**ARTIFICIAL COLOR** W/ FD & C YELLOW NO. 5
Artificial Color, FD & C Yellow No. 5	**ARTIFICIAL COLOR,** FD & C YELLOW NO. 5

Another variation apparently indicates that the associated color is the *sole* artificial color that has been used. This color in the example shown below is of concern to some people but not others. Artificial color, therefore, appears in very light capital letters, as does the specified color.

ON LABEL	IN BOOK
Artificial Color (FD & C Blue No. 1)	ARTIFICIAL COLOR FD & C BLUE NO. 1

ANIMAL FATS AND VEGETABLE OILS

Highly saturated fats and oils, either alone or as part of a blend (such as a shortening), when present in sufficient quantity in a food are regarded as additives of concern for all consumers.

If one of these fats or oils is listed by itself, it is certain to be in the food.

SATURATED FATS OR OILS LISTED SEPARATELY

TALLOW
PALM KERNEL OIL
BEEF FAT

But when one or more of these are part of a blend, at this writing the producer is permitted to list the range of fats and oils which *may* have been used, but one cannot be certain of the ones that actually are in the food. Considering the objectives of this volume and the possibility that these substances can be present, it is believed that a caution is needed.

SATURATED FATS AND/OR OILS AS PART OF A BLEND

Blend as listed on a label	Fats and oils in blend listed in book
Animal and/or vegetable shortening (contains one or more of the following: beef fat, partially hydrogenated soybean, coconut, palm kernel and palm oils)	**(BEEF FAT; COCONUT, PALM KERNEL OILS)**

TABLE OF CONTENTS

INVENTORY OF BRANDS

I. BABY FOODS

INFANT BISCUITS, COOKIES, TOAST

BRANDS	ADDITIVES-OF-CONCERN BOLD—CONCERN TO ALL LIGHT—CONCERN TO SOME
GERBER TEETHING BISCUITS; "ANIMAL SHAPED" COOKIES	WHEY (DAIRY)
ZWIEBACK TOAST	**MACE; NUTMEG**
NABISCO NATIONAL ARROWROOT BISCUIT	CASEIN
ZWIEBACK TOAST	EGG WHITES; LACTALBUMIN; **MACE; NUTMEG**

INFANT CEREALS

BRANDS	ADDITIVES-OF-CONCERN
BEECH-NUT HONEY MIXED; MIXED; RICE	NO ADDITIVES OF CONCERN
FAMILIA SWISS BABY FOOD	NO ADDITIVES OF CONCERN
GERBER HIGH PROTEIN; MIXED; MIXED CEREAL W/ BANANA; OATMEAL; OATMEAL W/ BANANA; RICE	NO ADDITIVES OF CONCERN

BRANDS	ADDITIVES-OF-CONCERN **BOLD—CONCERN TO ALL** LIGHT—CONCERN TO SOME
ITEMS IN HEALTH FOOD STORES HEALTH VALLEY NATURAL BABY FOOD BROWN RICE CEREAL W/ FRUIT	NO ADDITIVES OF CONCERN

INFANT FRUIT JUICE

BRANDS	ADDITIVES-OF-CONCERN
BEECH-NUT APPLE; MIXED FRUIT; ORANGE; ORANGE PINEAPPLE	NO ADDITIVES OF CONCERN
GERBER APPLE; APPLE-PLUM; MIXED FRUIT; ORANGE; ORANGE-APPLE-BANANA	NO ADDITIVES OF CONCERN
HEINZ APPLE; APPLE-PRUNE; MIXED FRUIT; ORANGE-APPLE-BANANA	NO ADDITIVES OF CONCERN

INFANT FORMULA

BRANDS	ADDITIVES-OF-CONCERN
ENFAMIL CONCENTRATED LIQUID; READY TO	**CARRAGEENAN; COCONUT OIL**

(continues)

BRANDS	ADDITIVES-OF-CONCERN BOLD—CONCERN TO ALL LIGHT—CONCERN TO SOME
USE; W/ IRON CONCENTRATED LIQUID; W/ IRON READY TO USE	
PRO SOBEE	
MILK-FREE FORMULA CONCENTRATED LIQUID	**CARRAGEENAN**
MILK-FREE FORMULA READY TO USE	**CARRAGEENAN**; GUAR GUM
SIMILAC	
CONCENTRATED LIQUID; READY TO FEED; W/ IRON CONCENTRATED LIQUID; W/ IRON READY TO FEED	**CARRAGEENAN; COCONUT OIL**
ISOMIL CONCENTRATED LIQUID	**CARRAGEENAN; MODIFIED CORN STARCH**
ISOMIL LIQUID READY TO FEED	**CARRAGEENAN**
SMA	
CONCENTRATED LIQUID; READY TO FEED	**CALCIUM CARRAGEENAN;** WHEY (ELECTRODIALIZED DEMINERALIZED)

BRANDS	ADDITIVES-OF-CONCERN BOLD—CONCERN TO ALL LIGHT—CONCERN TO SOME

INFANT STRAINED CEREALS, MEATS, VEGETABLES

BEECH-NUT	
BEEF & EGG NOODLE DINNER; MACARONI, TOMATO & BEEF DINNER; RICE CEREAL W/ APPLESAUCE & BANANAS; TURKEY RICE DINNER	**MODIFIED CORN STARCH**
CARROTS; GARDEN VEGETABLES; GREEN BEANS; VEAL; VEGETABLE LAMB DINNER	NO ADDITIVES OF CONCERN
COTTAGE CHEESE W/ PINEAPPLE JUICE	**MODIFIED TAPIOCA STARCH**
SWEET POTATOES IN BUTTER SAUCE	**BUTTER**
VEGETABLE BACON DINNER	**MODIFIED CORN STARCH; SMOKED BACON;* SMOKED YEAST***
VEGETABLE HAM DINNER	**MODIFIED CORN STARCH; SMOKED YEAST***
GERBER	
BEEF; CARROTS; GREEN BEANS; HAM; *(continues)*	NO ADDITIVES OF CONCERN

*Although "smoked" does not refer to a specific additive, it represents a process utilizing wood smoke, as "smoke flavoring" does, and therefore the food may contain some cancer-causing benzopyrene chemicals. For this reason, when a food or any of its constituents have been smoked, this has been noted in the additives-of-concern column.

BRANDS	ADDITIVES-OF-CONCERN **BOLD—CONCERN TO ALL** LIGHT—CONCERN TO SOME
LAMB; MIXED CEREAL W/ APPLESAUCE & BANANAS; MIXED VEGETABLES; PEAS; PORK; RICE CEREAL W/ APPLESAUCE & BANANAS; SWEET POTATOES; TURKEY; VEAL	
BEEF & EGG NOODLES W/ VEGETABLES; CHICKEN & NOODLES; CREAMED CORN; MACARONI-TOMATO W/ BEEF; TURKEY & RICE W/ VEGETABLES; VEGETABLES & BEEF; VEGETABLES & TURKEY	**MODIFIED CORN STARCH**
CREAMED SPINACH	MILK SOLIDS (WHOLE)
VEGETABLES & BACON	**NATURAL SMOKE FLAVORING**
—HIGH MEAT DINNER	
BEEF W/ VEGETABLES; CHICKEN W/ VEGETABLES	NO ADDITIVES OF CONCERN
HEINZ	
BEEF; CARROTS; CHICKEN; GREEN BEANS; LAMB;	NO ADDITIVES OF CONCERN

(continues)

BRANDS	ADDITIVES-OF-CONCERN BOLD—CONCERN TO ALL LIGHT—CONCERN TO SOME
HEINZ *(Continued)*	
SQUASH; SWEET POTATOES	NO ADDITIVES OF CONCERN
BEEF & EGG NOODLES; CHICKEN NOODLE DINNER; CREAMED PEAS; TURKEY RICE DINNER W/ VEGETABLES; VEGETABLES & BACON; VEGETABLES, EGG NOODLES, & TURKEY; VEGETABLES & HAM; VEGETABLES & LAMB	**MODIFIED CORN STARCH**
CREAMED CORN; MACARONI, TOMATOES, & BEEF	MILK SOLIDS (WHOLE); **MODIFIED CORN STARCH**
OATMEAL W/ APPLES & BANANAS; RICE CEREAL W/ APPLES & BANANAS	**FERRIC ORTHOPHOSPHATE**
VEGETABLES, DUMPLINGS, & BEEF	**MODIFIED CORN STARCH; PAPRIKA; SMOKED YEAST;* TURMERIC**

*Although "smoked" does not refer to a specific additive, it represents a process utilizing wood smoke, as "smoke flavoring" does, and therefore the food may contain some cancer-causing benzopyrene chemicals. For this reason, when a food or any of its constituents have been smoked, this has been noted in the additives-of-concern column.

BRANDS	ADDITIVES-OF-CONCERN BOLD—CONCERN TO ALL LIGHT—CONCERN TO SOME

INFANT STRAINED DESSERTS, FRUITS

BEECH-NUT APPLES & APRICOTS; APPLESAUCE; APPLESAUCE & BANANAS; PEACHES; PEARS	NO ADDITIVES OF CONCERN
APRICOTS W/ TAPIOCA & APPLE JUICE; BANANAS W/ TAPIOCA & APPLE JUICE; FRUIT DESSERT	**MODIFIED TAPIOCA STARCH**
GERBER APPLE BLUEBERRY; APPLESAUCE; PEACHES; PEARS	NO ADDITIVES OF CONCERN
APRICOTS W/ TAPIOCA; BANANAS W/ PINEAPPLE & TAPIOCA; PLUMS W/ TAPIOCA	**MODIFIED TAPIOCA STARCH**
CHOCOLATE CUSTARD PUDDING; DUTCH APPLE DESSERT; FRUIT DESSERT; PEACH COBBLER; VANILLA CUSTARD PUDDING	**MODIFIED CORN STARCH**
HEINZ APPLESAUCE; PEACHES; PEARS; PEARS & PINEAPPLE	NO ADDITIVES OF CONCERN

BRANDS	ADDITIVES-OF-CONCERN BOLD—CONCERN TO ALL LIGHT—CONCERN TO SOME
HEINZ *(Continued)*	
BANANAS & PINEAPPLE & TAPIOCA; PINEAPPLE ORANGE	**MODIFIED CORN & TAPIOCA STARCHES**
CUSTARD PUDDING; TUTTI FRUTTI	**MODIFIED CORN STARCH**
DUTCH APPLE DESSERT; PEACH COBBLER	**MODIFIED TAPIOCA STARCH**

JUNIOR & TODDLER CEREALS, MEATS, VEGETABLES

BRANDS	ADDITIVES-OF-CONCERN
BEECH-NUT *JUNIOR*	
CHICKEN NOODLE DINNER; TURKEY RICE DINNER; VEGETABLE BEEF DINNER	**MODIFIED CORN STARCH**
CARROTS; CHICKEN; GREEN BEANS; LAMB; SWEET POTATOES	NO ADDITIVES OF CONCERN
SPAGHETTI, TOMATO, & BEEF DINNER	**MODIFIED CORN STARCH;** WHEY (DRY)
SPLIT PEAS & HAM DINNER	**MODIFIED CORN STARCH; SMOKED YEAST***

BRANDS	ADDITIVES-OF-CONCERN **BOLD—CONCERN TO ALL** LIGHT—CONCERN TO SOME
VEGETABLE BACON DINNER	**MODIFIED CORN STARCH; SMOKED BACON;* SMOKED YEAST***
GERBER	
—JUNIOR	
BEEF; CARROTS; CHICKEN; LAMB; OATMEAL W/ APPLESAUCE & BANANAS; SWEET POTATOES; TURKEY & RICE W/ VEGETABLES; VEAL; VEGETABLES & BEEF	NO ADDITIVES OF CONCERN
BEEF & EGG NOODLES W/ VEGETABLES; MACARONI-TOMATO W/ BEEF; VEGETABLES & TURKEY	**MODIFIED CORN STARCH**
RICE CEREAL W/ MIXED FRUIT	**MODIFIED TAPIOCA STARCH**
VEGETABLES & BACON	**NATURAL SMOKE FLAVORING**
VEGETABLES & CHICKEN	**TURMERIC**

*Although "smoked" does not refer to a specific additive, it represents a process utilizing wood smoke, as "smoke flavoring" does, and therefore the food may contain some cancer-causing benzopyrene chemicals. For this reason, when a food or any of its constituents have been smoked, this has been noted in the additives-of-concern column.

BRANDS	ADDITIVES-OF-CONCERN **BOLD—CONCERN TO ALL** LIGHT—CONCERN TO SOME
GERBER *(Continued)*	
—HIGH MEAT DINNER BEEF W/ VEGETABLES; HAM W/ VEGETABLES; TURKEY W/ VEGETABLES	NO ADDITIVES OF CONCERN
—TODDLER MEAL BEEF STEW; CHICKEN STEW	**MODIFIED CORN STARCH**
HEINZ *JUNIOR* CARROTS; LAMB; SWEET POTATOES	NO ADDITIVES OF CONCERN
CEREAL & EGGS; CHICKEN NOODLE DINNER; MACARONI, TOMATOES, & BEEF; CREAMED PEAS; TURKEY RICE DINNER W/ VEGETABLES; VEGETABLES & BEEF	**MODIFIED CORN STARCH**
CREAMED CORN	MILK SOLIDS (WHOLE); **MODIFIED CORN STARCH**
CREAMED GREEN BEANS	MILK SOLIDS (WHOLE); **MODIFIED CORN STARCH; SMOKED YEAST***
VEGETABLES & BACON	**MODIFIED CORN STARCH; SMOKED YEAST***

*Although "smoked" does not refer to a specific additive, it represents a process utilizing wood smoke, as "smoke flavoring" does, and therefore the food may contain some cancer-causing benzopyrene chemicals. For this reason, when a food or any of its constituents have been smoked, this has been noted in the additives-of-concern column.

BRANDS	ADDITIVES-OF-CONCERN BOLD—CONCERN TO ALL LIGHT—CONCERN TO SOME

JUNIOR DESSERTS, FRUITS

BEECH-NUT APPLESAUCE & RASPBERRIES; PEACHES; PEARS	NO ADDITIVES OF CONCERN
APRICOTS W/ TAPIOCA; PLUMS W/ TAPIOCA & APPLE JUICE	**MODIFIED TAPIOCA STARCH**
BANANA DESSERT & APPLE JUICE; CUSTARD PUDDING	**MODIFIED CORN STARCH**
GERBER APPLE BLUEBERRY; APPLESAUCE; PEACHES; PEARS	NO ADDITIVES OF CONCERN
APPLE RASPBERRY	**MACE**
APRICOTS W/ TAPIOCA	**MODIFIED CORN STARCH; MODIFIED TAPIOCA STARCH**
BANANAS W/ PINEAPPLE & TAPIOCA; PLUMS W/ TAPIOCA	**MODIFIED TAPIOCA STARCH**
FRUIT DESSERT; RASPBERRY DESSERT W/ YOGURT; VANILLA CUSTARD PUDDING	**MODIFIED CORN STARCH**

BRANDS	ADDITIVES-OF-CONCERN BOLD—CONCERN TO ALL LIGHT—CONCERN TO SOME
HEINZ APPLES & CRANBERRIES W/ TAPIOCA; APRICOTS W/ TAPIOCA; BANANAS & PINEAPPLE W/ TAPIOCA	**MODIFIED CORN STARCH; MODIFIED TAPIOCA STARCH**
APPLES & PEARS; APPLESAUCE & APRICOTS; PEACHES; PEARS	NO ADDITIVES OF CONCERN
CUSTARD PUDDING; FRUIT DESSERT; PINEAPPLE ORANGE	**MODIFIED CORN STARCH**
DUTCH APPLE DESSERT; PEACH COBBLER	**MODIFIED TAPIOCA STARCH**

II. BAKED GOODS, FROZEN & REFRIGERATED

FROZEN BAGELS, BREAD DOUGH, MUFFINS, ROLLS

BRANDS	ADDITIVES-OF-CONCERN BOLD—CONCERN TO ALL LIGHT—CONCERN TO SOME
HOWARD JOHNSON'S *TOASTEES* BLUEBERRY	**BHA**
CORN	NO ADDITIVES OF CONCERN
LENDER'S *BAGELS* EGG FLAVORED; ONION; PLAIN; RAISIN 'N HONEY; WHEAT 'N HONEY	GLUTEN (VITAL WHEAT GLUTEN OR HI-GLUTEN FLOUR OR UNBLEACHED GLUTEN FLOUR)
PEPPERIDGE FARM *MUFFINS* BLUEBERRY; BRAN W/ RAISINS; CORN	**MODIFIED FOOD STARCH**
RHODES FROZEN BREAD DOUGH/WHITE	WHEY
RICH'S WHITE BREAD DOUGH	WHEY (DRIED)
SARA LEE PARKER HOUSE ROLLS	CASEIN; WHEY

BRANDS	ADDITIVES-OF-CONCERN BOLD—CONCERN TO ALL LIGHT—CONCERN TO SOME
STOUFFER'S PARTY GARLIC BREAD	**HYDROGENATED SOYBEAN OIL;** MONOSODIUM GLUTAMATE
SUPERMARKET PRIVATE BRANDS	
A & P	
—**ANN PAGE** BREAD DOUGH	NO ADDITIVES OF CONCERN

FROZEN BREAKFAST FOODS (EGG SUBSTITUTES, FRENCH TOAST, PANCAKES, WAFFLES)

AUNT JEMIMA	
—FRENCH TOAST	
CINNAMON SWIRL	**ARTIFICIAL COLOR FD & C** BLUE NO. 1, **RED NO. 3,** YELLOW NO. 5 & NO. 6; **BHA; BHT;** WHEY
PLAIN	**BHA; BHT;** WHEY
—PANCAKE BATTER	
BLUEBERRY; BUTTERMILK; PLAIN	NO ADDITIVES OF CONCERN
—WAFFLES	
BLUEBERRY	ARTIFICIAL COLOR FD & C BLUE NO. 2, YELLOW NO. 5 & NO. 6; MONOSODIUM GLUTAMATE; WHEY
ORIGINAL	ARTIFICIAL COLOR FD & C YELLOW NO. 5 & NO. 6; MONOSODIUM GLUTAMATE; WHEY

BRANDS	ADDITIVES-OF-CONCERN BOLD—CONCERN TO ALL LIGHT—CONCERN TO SOME
DOWNYFLAKE	
PANCAKES	**ARTIFICIAL COLOR** W/ FD & C YELLOW NO. 5; **(HYDROGENATED COTTONSEED, PALM OILS);*** WHEY SOLIDS
WAFFLES	**ARTIFICIAL COLOR** W/ FD & C YELLOW NO. 5; WHEY
EGGO *WAFFLES*	
BRAN	WHEY (DRIED DAIRY)
PLAIN; W/ IMITATION BLUEBERRIES	**ARTIFICIAL COLORING;** WHEY
FLEISCHMANN'S EGG BEATERS	**ARTIFICIAL COLORS; CALCIUM & SODIUM CASEINATES;** EGG WHITES; **FERRIC ORTHOPHOSPHATE;** WHEY
MORNINGSTAR FARMS SCRAMBLERS	**ARTIFICIAL COLORS; CALCIUM CASEINATE;** CAROB BEAN GUM; EGG WHITES; **FERRIC ORTHOPHOSPHATE;** GUAR GUM; **MODIFIED CORN STARCH**
ROMAN MEAL	
WAFFLES	WHEY SOLIDS
SWANSON	
FRENCH TOAST W/ SAUSAGES	**CALCIUM CASEINATE;** WHEY

*Blend may contain one or more of these saturated oils.

BRANDS	**ADDITIVES-OF-CONCERN** **BOLD—CONCERN TO ALL** LIGHT—CONCERN TO SOME
SWANSON *(Continued)*	
PANCAKES W/ SAUSAGES	**CALCIUM CASEINATE; SODIUM CASEINATE;** WHEY
SUPERMARKET PRIVATE BRANDS	
A & P	
—ANN PAGE WAFFLES	**ARTIFICIAL COLOR** W/ FD & C YELLOW NO. 5; WHEY
FIRST NATIONAL	
—EDWARDS-FINAST WAFFLES	**ARTIFICIAL COLOR** W/ FD & C YELLOW NO. 5; WHEY
—FINAST WAFFLES	**ARTIFICIAL COLOR** W/ FD & C YELLOW NO. 5; WHEY
SAFEWAY	
—BEL-AIR *WAFFLES*	
BUTTERMILK ROUND	**ARTIFICIAL COLOR** W/ FD & C YELLOW NO. 5; **(HYDROGENATED COTTONSEED, PALM OILS)***
PLAIN	**ARTIFICIAL COLOR;** WHEY
—LUCERNE	
BREAKFAST TREAT EGG SUBSTITUTE	**ARTIFICIAL COLOR; CALCIUM CARRAGEENAN;** EGG WHITES; MONOSODIUM GLUTAMATE
STOP & SHOP	
—STOP & SHOP WAFFLES	**ARTIFICIAL COLOR** W/ FD & C YELLOW NO. 5; WHEY

BRANDS	ADDITIVES-OF-CONCERN **BOLD—CONCERN TO ALL** LIGHT—CONCERN TO SOME

FROZEN CAKES, DOUGHNUTS, PASTRIES

CHOCK FULL O' NUTS *CAKE* MARBLE; POUND	EGG WHITES
DRESSEL'S *CAKE* SPECIAL PARTY FUDGE; WHIPPED CREAM BIRTHDAY FUDGE	**ARTIFICIAL COLOR; CONFECTIONER'S GLAZE;** GUM ARABIC; **MODIFIED FOOD STARCH;** WHEY
MORTON *DONUT SHOP* HONEY BUNS	**ARTIFICIAL COLOR; (BEEF FAT, LARD);*** GUAR GUM; GUM ACACIA
JELLY DONUTS	**ARTIFICIAL COLOR; MODIFIED FOOD STARCH;** SODIUM ALGINATE
SUGAR 'N SPICE MINI-DONUTS	**(BEEF FAT, LARD);*** CASEIN; **MODIFIED FOOD STARCH;** WHEY
PEPPERIDGE FARM *—CAKE SUPREME* BANANA	**MODIFIED FOOD STARCH;** WHEY
BOSTON CREME; CHOCOLATE; WALNUT	**MODIFIED FOOD STARCH; (PALM KERNEL OIL)***

*Blend may contain one or more of these saturated fats and/or oils.

BRANDS	**ADDITIVES-OF-CONCERN** **BOLD—CONCERN TO ALL** LIGHT—CONCERN TO SOME
PEPPERIDGE FARM—*CAKE SUPREME (Continued)*	
LEMON COCONUT	EGG WHITES; **MODIFIED FOOD STARCH**
—LAYER CAKE	
DEVIL'S FOOD; GERMAN CHOCOLATE; GOLDEN; VANILLA	**CALCIUM CASEINATE; (PALM KERNEL OIL);* MODIFIED FOOD STARCH; SODIUM CASEINATE;** WHEY
—MISCELLANEOUS CAKES	
APPLE-WALNUT W/ RAISINS	**MODIFIED FOOD STARCH; NUTMEG**
CARROT	**NUTMEG**
POUND	**BUTTER (SWEET CREAM)**
RICH'S CHOCOLATE ECLAIRS	**ARTIFICIAL COLOR; (COCONUT, PALM KERNEL OILS);* SODIUM CASEINATE**
SARA LEE	
—CHEESE CAKE	
CHERRY CREAM	**CALCIUM CARRAGEENAN;** LOCUST BEAN GUM; **MODIFIED FOOD STARCH;** PROPYLENE GLYCOL ALGINATE; **U.S. CERTIFIED FOOD COLOR**
FRENCH	GUAR GUM; **MODIFIED FOOD STARCH; TURMERIC EXTRACT**

*Blend may contain one or more of these saturated oils.

BRANDS	**ADDITIVES-OF-CONCERN** **BOLD—CONCERN TO ALL** LIGHT—CONCERN TO SOME
ORIGINAL CREAM	GUAR GUM; GUM ARABIC; LOCUST BEAN GUM; **MODIFIED FOOD STARCH**
—ORIGINAL BUTTER RECIPE CAKE	
APPLE WALNUT; CARROT; COCONUT	**BUTTER (GRADE AA); MODIFIED FOOD STARCH**
CHOCOLATE BROWNIES; FRESH ORANGE	NO ADDITIVES OF CONCERN
FRESH BANANA	GUM ARABIC
—MISCELLANEOUS CAKES	
BLACK FOREST; STRAWBERRY SHORT	**CALCIUM CARRAGEENAN;** GUAR GUM; GUM TRAGACANTH; LOCUST BEAN GUM; **MODIFIED FOOD STARCH;** PROPYLENE GLYCOL ALGINATE; WHEY
CHOCOLATE BAVARIAN	EGG WHITES; **MODIFIED FOOD STARCH**
ORIGINAL POUND	NO ADDITIVES OF CONCERN
RAISIN POUND	**MODIFIED FOOD STARCH**
—MISCELLANEOUS COFFEE CAKES, DANISH, ROLLS	
ALMOND LIGHT COFFEE RING; APPLE CRUNCH ROLLS;	CASEIN; GUAR GUM; **MODIFIED FOOD STARCH**

(continues)

BRANDS	ADDITIVES-OF-CONCERN BOLD—CONCERN TO ALL LIGHT—CONCERN TO SOME
SARA LEE *(Continued)*	
BLUEBERRY LIGHT COFFEE RING; RASPBERRY LIGHT COFFEE RING	CASEIN; GUAR GUM; **MODIFIED FOOD STARCH**
APPLE DANISH	**CALCIUM CARRAGEENAN;** LOCUST BEAN GUM; **MODIFIED FOOD STARCH**
BUTTER STREUSEL COFFEE CAKE	**BUTTER (GRADE AA)**
HONEY ROLLS	CASEIN; GUAR GUM; GUM ARABIC; **MODIFIED FOOD STARCH**
STOUFFER'S	
BOSTON CREAM CUPCAKES; YELLOW CUPCAKES	**ARTIFICIAL COLOR; MODIFIED CORN STARCH**
CHOCOLATE CHIP CRUMB CAKES; POUND CAKE	**ARTIFICIAL COLOR**
CREAM FILLED CUPCAKES	**ARTIFICIAL COLOR; (COCONUT, PALM KERNEL OILS);* CONFECTIONER'S GLAZE; MODIFIED CORN STARCH**
SUPERMARKET PRIVATE BRANDS	
SAFEWAY	
—BEL-AIR *DONUTS*	
GLAZED	**(BEEF TALLOW, COCONUT OIL, LARD);* MODIFIED FOOD STARCH; SODIUM CASEINATE;** WHEY

BRANDS	ADDITIVES-OF-CONCERN BOLD—CONCERN TO ALL LIGHT—CONCERN TO SOME
JELLY	**ARTIFICIAL COLOR; (BEEF TALLOW, COCONUT OIL, LARD);* SODIUM CASEINATE;** WHEY
ITEMS IN HEALTH FOOD STORES	
BARBARA'S	
CAROB MACAROON; COCONUT MACAROON	EGG WHITES
CHOCOLATE BROWNIE	NO ADDITIVES OF CONCERN
FOOD FOR LIFE *CAKE*	
BANANA; CARROT; POUND	NO ADDITIVES OF CONCERN
DATE-NUT	**NUTMEG**

FROZEN PIE CRUST, PIES, TARTS, TURNOVERS

MORTON *GREAT LITTLE DESSERTS PIE*	
APPLE	**(COCONUT OIL, LARD);* MODIFIED FOOD STARCH**

*Blend may contain one or more of these saturated fats and/or oils.

BRANDS	ADDITIVES-OF-CONCERN BOLD—CONCERN TO ALL LIGHT—CONCERN TO SOME
MORTON *GREAT LITTLE DESSERTS PIE (Continued)*	
BANANA CREAM; CHOCOLATE CREAM	**ARTIFICIAL COLOR; (BEEF FAT, LARD; HYDROGENATED COCONUT, COTTONSEED, PALM KERNEL, SOYBEAN OILS);* HYDROXYPROPYL CELLULOSE;** GUAR GUM; **MODIFIED FOOD STARCH; SODIUM CASEINATE**
BLUEBERRY	**MODIFIED FOOD STARCH**
MRS. SMITH'S	
BOSTON CREAM PIE	**ARTIFICIAL COLOR; CALCIUM CARRAGEENAN; MODIFIED FOOD STARCH; SODIUM CASEINATE**
LEMON MERINGUE PIE	**ARTIFICIAL COLOR;** EGG WHITES; LOCUST BEAN GUM; **MODIFIED FOOD STARCH**
—DEEP DISH PIE	
APPLE; GOLDEN DELUXE APPLE; BLUEBERRY; DUTCH APPLE CRUMB	**ARTIFICIAL COLOR; MODIFIED FOOD STARCH**
PUMPKIN CUSTARD	**ARTIFICIAL COLOR; CALCIUM CARRAGEENAN;** LOCUST BEAN GUM; **MODIFIED FOOD STARCH**
WALNUT	**ARTIFICIAL COLOR**
ORONOQUE ORCHARDS PIE CRUSTS	NO ADDITIVES OF CONCERN

BRANDS	ADDITIVES-OF-CONCERN **BOLD—CONCERN TO ALL** LIGHT—CONCERN TO SOME
PEPPERIDGE FARM	
APPLE CRISS-CROSS PASTRY; APPLE PIE TARTS; APPLE TURNOVERS; BLUEBERRY TURNOVERS; RASPBERRY TURNOVERS	**MODIFIED FOOD STARCH**
APPLE STRUDEL	**(COCONUT OIL);*** EGG WHITES; **MODIFIED FOOD STARCH**
PATTY SHELLS	NO ADDITIVES OF CONCERN
SARA LEE *PIE*	
APPLE	**MODIFIED FOOD STARCH**
PUMPKIN	**CALCIUM CARRAGEENAN;** LOCUST BEAN GUM; **MODIFIED FOOD STARCH;** WHEY
SUPERMARKET PRIVATE BRANDS	
SAFEWAY	
—BEL-AIR	
BLUEBERRY PIE; BOYSENBERRY PIE; CHERRY PIE	**ARTIFICIAL COLOR; (LARD);* MODIFIED STARCH;** WHEY (SWEET)
DEEP DISH PIE CRUST SHELLS	**ARTIFICIAL COLOR; (BEEF FAT, LARD; HYDROGENATED PALM, SOYBEAN OILS);* BHA; BHT;** WHEY SOLIDS

*Blend may contain one or more of these saturated fats and/or oils.

BRANDS	ADDITIVES-OF-CONCERN BOLD—CONCERN TO ALL LIGHT—CONCERN TO SOME
—BEL-AIR *(Continued)*	
DUTCH APPLE PIE	**ARTIFICIAL COLOR; MODIFIED STARCH;** WHEY (SWEET)
WINN DIXIE	
—DIXIANA PIE CRUST SHELLS	**ARTIFICIAL COLOR** W/ FD & C YELLOW NO. 5; **(BEEF FAT, LARD; HYDROGENATED PALM, SOYBEAN OILS);* BHA; BHT;** WHEY SOLIDS

REFRIGERATED DOUGH PRODUCTS (BISCUITS, COOKIES, DANISH, ROLLS)

BRANDS	ADDITIVES-OF-CONCERN
PILLSBURY	
—*BISCUITS*	
BUTTERMILK; COUNTRY STYLE	**BHA**
1869 BRAND BAKING POWDER; HUNGRY JACK BUTTERMILK FLAKY	**(BEEF FAT; HYDROGENATED PALM, SOYBEAN OILS);* BHA**
1869 BRAND BUTTERMILK	**(HYDROGENATED PALM, SOYBEAN OILS)***
HUNGRY JACK BUTTER TASTIN'	**ARTIFICIAL COLOR; (BEEF FAT; HYDROGENATED PALM, SOYBEAN OILS);* BHA**

BRANDS	ADDITIVES-OF-CONCERN BOLD—CONCERN TO ALL LIGHT—CONCERN TO SOME
—DINNER ROLLS	
BUTTERFLAKE	**(BEEF FAT; HYDROGENATED PALM, SOYBEAN OILS);* BHA; BUTTER**
CRESCENT	**(BEEF FAT; HYDROGENATED PALM, SOYBEAN OILS);* BHA;** GLUTEN (VITAL WHEAT)
—SLICE 'N BAKE COOKIES	
CHOCOLATE CHIP; OATMEAL RAISIN; SUGAR	**(BEEF FAT; HYDROGENATED COTTONSEED, PALM, SOYBEAN OILS);* BHA; CARRAGEENAN**
—DANISH & TURNOVERS	
APPLE FLAKY TURNOVER PIES	**ARTIFICIAL COLOR; (BEEF FAT; HYDROGENATED PALM, SOYBEAN OILS);* BHA; MODIFIED CORN STARCH; NUTMEG;** PROPYLENE GLYCOL ALGINATE
CARAMEL DANISH; ORANGE DANISH	**ARTIFICIAL COLOR; (BEEF FAT; HYDROGENATED PALM, SOYBEAN OILS);* BHA**

*Blend may contain one or more of these saturated fats and/or oils.

BRANDS	**ADDITIVES-OF-CONCERN** **BOLD—CONCERN TO ALL** LIGHT—CONCERN TO SOME
PILLSBURY *(Continued)*	
CINNAMON RAISIN DANISH	**ARTIFICIAL COLOR; (BEEF FAT; HYDROGENATED PALM, SOYBEAN OILS);* BHA; CARRAGEENAN;** MILK PROTEIN; **SODIUM CASEINATE;** WHEY
SUPERMARKET PRIVATE BRANDS	
FIRST NATIONAL	
—EDWARDS CRESCENT DINNER ROLLS	**BEEF FAT; (HYDROGENATED COTTONSEED, PALM, SOYBEAN OILS);* BHA; BHT**
HOMESTYLE BISCUITS; TEXAS STYLE OLD FASHIONED BISCUITS	**BEEF FAT; BHA; BHT;** WHEY SOLIDS
—FINAST BUTTERMILK BISCUITS	**BEEF FAT; BHA; BHT;** WHEY SOLIDS
LUCKY	
—LADY LEE BUTTERMILK BISCUITS	**BEEF TALLOW** OR **LARD;** BUTTERMILK SOLIDS; **CARRAGEENAN;** GUAR GUM; WHEY
HOMESTYLE BISCUITS	**BEEF TALLOW** OR **LARD; CARRAGEENAN;** GUAR GUM; WHEY
SAFEWAY	
—MRS. WRIGHT'S BUTTERMILK BISCUITS	**BEEF TALLOW** OR **LARD;** BUTTERMILK SOLIDS; **CARRAGEENAN;** GUAR GUM; WHEY

BRANDS	ADDITIVES-OF-CONCERN BOLD—CONCERN TO ALL LIGHT—CONCERN TO SOME
CRESCENT DINNER ROLLS	**BEEF FAT; BHA; BHT (HYDROGENATED COTTONSEED, PALM, SOYBEAN OILS)***
HOMESTYLE BISCUITS	**BEEF TALLOW** OR **LARD; CARRAGEENAN;** GUAR GUM; WHEY

*Blend may contain one or more of these saturated fats and/or oils.

III. BAKED SWEET GOODS, NOT FROZEN OR REFRIGERATED

R alongside a brand indicates regional (not national) distribution, based on shopping experience.

BISCUITS & COOKIES

BRANDS	ADDITIVES-OF-CONCERN BOLD—CONCERN TO ALL LIGHT—CONCERN TO SOME
ARCHWAY *—FAMILY STYLE* COCONUT CHOCOLATE CHIP; OATMEAL N' NUT; PECAN CRUNCH	NO ADDITIVES OF CONCERN
—HOME STYLE APRICOT FILLED; BLUEBERRY FILLED; RASPBERRY FILLED; STRAWBERRY FILLED	**ARTIFICIAL COLOR** OR **COLORS; (HYDROGENATED COTTONSEED, PALM OILS);* MODIFIED FOOD STARCH**
CHERRY NOUGAT; ICED MOLASSES; MERRY MINTS; NEW ORLEANS CAKE	**ARTIFICIAL COLOR**
CHOCOLATE CHIP DROP; CHOCOLATE CHIP SUPREME; COOKIE JAR HERMIT; *(continues)*	NO ADDITIVES OF CONCERN

BRANDS	ADDITIVES-OF-CONCERN BOLD—CONCERN TO ALL LIGHT—CONCERN TO SOME
DATE FILLED OATMEAL; DATE 'N NUT; DUTCH COCOA; FUDGE NUT BAR; GRANDMA'S MOLASSES; PEANUT BUTTER 'N CHIPS; RUTH'S GOLDEN OATMEAL	
COCOA SPRINKLES	**ARTIFICIAL COLOR; CONFECTIONER'S SHELLAC; VEGETABLE GUM**
FROSTED FINGERS	**ARTIFICIAL COLOR; CONFECTIONER'S SHELLAC;** EGG WHITES; **VEGETABLE GUM**
HOLIDAY SUGAR	FD & C BLUE COLOR NO. 1, **RED NO. 3 & NO. 40,** YELLOW NO. 5 & NO. 6
BURRY	
BURRY'S BEST CHOCOLATE CHIP; BURRY'S BEST SUGAR FUDGE	**(HYDROGENATED PALM OIL);*** WHEY (DAIRY OR DRIED DAIRY)
BURRY'S BEST COCONUT MACAROON	WHEY (DRIED DAIRY)
BURRY'S BEST WALNUT FUDGE; *(continues)*	**(HYDROGENATED PALM OIL)***

*Blend may contain one or more of these saturated oils.

BRANDS	ADDITIVES-OF-CONCERN BOLD—CONCERN TO ALL LIGHT—CONCERN TO SOME
BURRY *(Continued)*	
OXFORD VANILLA SANDWICH CREMES	**(HYDROGENATED PALM OIL)***
BUTTER FLAVORED	ARTIFICIAL COLOR FD & C YELLOW NO. 5 & NO. 6; **(HYDROGENATED PALM OIL)***
CINNAMON SHORTBREAD; SUGAR SHORTBREAD	EGG WHITES (DRIED); **(HYDROGENATED PALM OIL);*** WHEY (DRIED DAIRY)
FUDGETOWN (CHOCOLATE)	**(HYDROGENATED PALM OIL, LARD)***
FUDGETOWN (VANILLA); HAPPYNIKS	**ARTIFICIAL COLOR; (HYDROGENATED PALM OIL, LARD)***
GAUCHO	EGG WHITES (DRIED); WHEY (DRIED DAIRY)
MR CHIPS	**ARTIFICIAL COLOR; (PALM KERNEL, HYDROGENATED PALM OILS);*** WHEY (DRIED DAIRY)
SCOOTER-PIE DEVIL'S FOOD; SCOOTER-PIE ORIGINAL	MILK PROTEIN (HYDROLYZED)
CARR'S	
ASSORTED BISCUITS FOR CHEESE; WHEATMEAL BISCUITS	**(COCONUT, PALM KERNEL OILS)***

BRANDS	ADDITIVES-OF-CONCERN BOLD—CONCERN TO ALL LIGHT—CONCERN TO SOME
R **DUTCH TWINS**	
SUGAR WAFERS	**ARTIFICIAL COLORS; (COCONUT OIL)***
ENTENMANN'S	
BUTTER (APRICOT JELLY)	**BUTTER; MODIFIED CORN STARCH**
CHOCOLATE CHIP	NO ADDITIVES OF CONCERN
FFV	
FANCY TART	**ARTIFICIAL COLOR; CERTIFIED COLOR**
MINT SANDWICH	**ARTIFICIAL COLOR; (BEEF FAT);*** WHEY POWDER
PEANUT BUTTER SANDWICH	**(BEEF FAT)***
SPRINKLED MALLOWS	**ARTIFICIAL COLOR;** WHEY
STRIPED MALLOWS	WHEY
FIRESIDE	
CHOCOLATE CHIP	**ARTIFICIAL COLOR; (BEEF FAT, LARD; COCONUT, PALM KERNEL OILS);*** WHEY
GÖTEBORGS	
SWEDISH GINGER SNAPS	NO ADDITIVES OF CONCERN

*Blend may contain one or more of these saturated fats and/or oils.

BRANDS	ADDITIVES-OF-CONCERN BOLD—CONCERN TO ALL LIGHT—CONCERN TO SOME
JACOBS BISCUITS FOR CHEESE	BEEF FAT, HYDROGENATED COCONUT, MARINE, PALM KERNEL OILS; BHA; WHEY POWDER
KEEBLER	
CHOCOLATE FUDGE SANDWICH	ARTIFICIAL COLORING; (BEEF FAT, COCONUT OIL, LARD);* WHEY
DELUXE GRAHAMS; VANILLA CREMES	ARTIFICIAL COLORING; (LARD; COCONUT, PALM KERNEL OILS);* WHEY
DOUBLE NUTTY; ICED RAISIN BAR; PITTER PATTER	WHEY
FUDGE CREMES	(COCONUT OIL, LARD);* WHEY
FUDGE MARSHMALLOW	(BEEF FAT, LARD; COCONUT, PALM KERNEL OILS)*
FUDGE STICKS	ARTIFICIAL COLORING; (COCONUT, PALM KERNEL OILS);* WHEY
PECAN SANDIES OLD FASHION OATMEAL;	NO ADDITIVES OF CONCERN
RICH 'N CHIPS	ARTIFICIAL COLOR W/ FD & C YELLOW NO. 5; (BEEF FAT; COCONUT, PALM KERNEL OILS);* WHEY

	BRANDS	ADDITIVES-OF-CONCERN **BOLD—CONCERN TO ALL** LIGHT—CONCERN TO SOME
	VANILLA WAFERS	**(BEEF FAT);*** WHEY
	LITTLE BROWNIE	
	ASSORTED CREMES; LEMON CREMES; PEANUT BUTTER CREMES	**ARTIFICIAL COLOR; (BEEF OIL [FAT])***
	GINGER SNAPS	**(BEEF OIL [FAT])***
	LITTLE DEBBIE	
	NUTTY BAR; PEANUT BARS; SUPER-STIX	WHEY
	MASTER SUGAR CINNAMON TOAST	NO ADDITIVES OF CONCERN
R	**MAURICE LENELL**	
	BUTTERSCOTCH OATMEAL	**NUTMEG**
	BUTTERSCOTCH; PEANUT BUTTER STARS	**VEGETABLE SHORTENING**
	CHINESE ALMOND	NO ADDITIVES OF CONCERN
	FAMILY ASSORTMENT	**U.S. CERTIFIED COLOR WHEN USED**
	MC VITIES	
	WHEATOLO BISCUITS	**(BEEF FAT; COCONUT, PALM KERNEL OILS)***

*Blend may contain one or more of these saturated fats and/or oils.

	BRANDS	ADDITIVES-OF-CONCERN **BOLD—CONCERN TO ALL** LIGHT—CONCERN TO SOME
R	MOTHERS	
	CHOCOLATE CHIP ANGEL; FUDGE 'N CHIPS; ICED OATMEAL; OATMEAL	NO ADDITIVES OF CONCERN
	CIRCUS ANIMAL; ICED RAISIN	**ARTIFICIAL COLOR; (COCONUT, PALM KERNEL OILS)***
	CLASSIC; COOKIE PARADE ASSORTMENT; FLAKY FLIX FUDGE CREME WAFERS; FLAKY FLIX VANILLA CREME WAFERS	**ARTIFICIAL COLOR; (COCONUT, PALM KERNEL OILS);*** WHEY
	PEANUT BUTTER; SUGAR	WHEY
	STRIPED SHORTBREAD	ARTIFICIAL COLOR FD & C YELLOW NO. 5; WHEY
	WHOLE WHEAT FIG BARS	**ARTIFICIAL COLOR;** EGG WHITES; WHEY
	—BAKERY WAGON	
	DATE FILLED OATMEAL; HONEY FRUIT BARS	NO ADDITIVES OF CONCERN
	FROSTED LEMON	**ARTIFICIAL COLOR;** WHEY
	RANGER BARS	**ARTIFICIAL COLOR; BHA**
	RASPBERRY FILLED	**ARTIFICIAL COLOR; MODIFIED CORN STARCH**

BRANDS	ADDITIVES-OF-CONCERN BOLD—CONCERN TO ALL LIGHT—CONCERN TO SOME
R MURRAY	
BIG BOY ASSORTED	**ARTIFICIAL COLOR; (BEEF TALLOW, PALM KERNEL OIL);* BHA**
BIG BOY DUPLEX; BIG BOY VANILLA	**(BEEF TALLOW, PALM KERNEL OIL);* BHA; BHT**
CHOCOLATE CHIP; COCONUT MACAROON; FUDGE NUT; PEANUT BUTTER CREMES; VANILLA CREMES	**(BEEF TALLOW, PALM KERNEL OIL);* BHA; BHT;** WHEY
FIG BARS	**BHA; BHT;** WHEY
PEANUT BUTTER JOYS	**ARTIFICIAL COLOR** W/ FD & C YELLOW NO. 5; **(BEEF TALLOW, PALM KERNEL OIL);* BHA; BHT;** WHEY
NABISCO	
BISCOS SUGAR WAFERS; BISCOS TRIPLE DECKER; BUTTER FLAVORED; CHIPS AHOY!; COCOANUT BARS; FIG NEWTONS; IDEAL CHOCOLATE PEANUT BARS; MALLOMARS; PEANUT CREME; RAISIN FRUIT BISCUIT	WHEY
BISCOS WAFFLE CREMES	**ARTIFICIAL COLOR;** WHEY

*Blend may contain one or more of these saturated fats and/or oils.

BRANDS	ADDITIVES-OF-CONCERN BOLD—CONCERN TO ALL LIGHT—CONCERN TO SOME
NABISCO *(Continued)*	
BROWN EDGE WAFERS; FAMOUS CHOCOLATE WAFERS; FUDGE FUDGE; NILLA WAFERS; OREO	**(LARD);*** WHEY
CAMEO	**(LARD);* SODIUM CASEINATE;** WHEY
CHOCOLATE CHIP SNAPS; CHOCOLATE CHOCOLATE CHIP; DEVIL'S FOOD CAKES; GINGER SNAPS	NO ADDITIVES OF CONCERN
COCOANUT CHOCOLATE CHIP; OATMEAL; PECAN SHORTBREAD; SUGAR RINGS	**(LARD)***
FAMOUS COOKIE ASSORTMENT	**(BEEF FAT, LARD);*** EGG WHITES; WHEY
FANCY DIP GRAHAMS; MYSTIC MINT;	**(LARD, PALM KERNEL OIL);*** WHEY
LORNA DOONE; SOCIAL TEA BISCUITS	**(BEEF FAT, LARD);*** WHEY
NATIONAL ARROWROOT BISCUIT	CASEIN
NUTTER BUTTER	**(HYDROGENATED PEANUT OIL, LARD);*** WHEY

BRANDS	ADDITIVES-OF-CONCERN **BOLD—CONCERN TO ALL** LIGHT—CONCERN TO SOME
UNEEDA BISCUIT	**(HYDROGENATED COTTONSEED, PALM OILS)***
VANILLA CREME SANDWICH	**(LARD);* TURMERIC OLEORESIN**
PEEK FREANS ARROWROOT BISCUITS; GINGER CRISP BISCUITS	NO ADDITIVES OF CONCERN
FRUIT CREME BISCUITS	**ARTIFICIAL COLOR; (BEEF FAT)***
LEMON PUFF	**ARTIFICIAL COLOR; PALM KERNEL OIL;** WHEY POWDER
"NICE" BISCUITS	**ARTIFICIAL COLOR**
PETIT BEURRE	**BUTTER**
RICH TEA BISCUITS; SHORTCAKE BISCUITS; SWEET MEAL BISCUITS	**(BEEF FAT)***
PEPPERIDGE FARM BORDEAUX; CHAMPAGNE; FAVORITES W/ CHIPS & NUTS; PIROUETTES CHOCOLATE LACED; SEVILLE; SHORTBREAD; SOUTHPORT	**(COCONUT OIL);*** EGG WHITES

*Blend may contain one or more of these saturated fats and/or oils.

	BRANDS	ADDITIVES-OF-CONCERN BOLD—CONCERN TO ALL LIGHT—CONCERN TO SOME
	PEPPERIDGE FARM *(Continued)*	
	BROWNIE CHOCOLATE NUT; CAPRI; CINNAMON SUGAR; FAVORITES W/ SUGAR & SPICE; LIDO; MOLASSES CRISPS; OATMEAL RAISIN; SUGAR	**(COCONUT OIL)***
	BRUSSELS; CHOCOLATE CHIP; MILANO; ORLEANS SANDWICH	EGG WHITES
	BUTTER; CHESSMEN; KITCHEN HEARTH DATE-NUT GRANOLA; ST. MORITZ	**BUTTER**
	GINGER-MAN; NASSAU; PEANUT; TAHITI; ZANZIBAR	NO ADDITIVES OF CONCERN
	IRISH OATMEAL	**(COCONUT OIL);* NUTMEG**
	MINT MILANO	**(COCONUT, PALM KERNEL OILS);*** EGG WHITES
R	**RIPPIN' GOOD**	
	CHIP-CHIP	**(BEEF FAT, COCONUT, PALM KERNEL OILS)***
	PICADILLY JELLY	ALGIN; **STABILIZERS; U.S. CERTIFIED COLOR;** WHEY (DAIRY)
	SANDWICH	**(BEEF FAT);* U.S. CERTIFIED COLOR;** WHEY (DAIRY)

*Blend may contain one or more of these saturated fats and/or oils.

BRANDS	ADDITIVES-OF-CONCERN BOLD—CONCERN TO ALL LIGHT—CONCERN TO SOME
SALERNO GINGER SNAPS	NO ADDITIVES OF CONCERN
STELLA D'ORO	
ALMOND TOAST (MANDEL); ANGELICA GOODIES; ANGINETTI; ANISETTE SPONGE; ANISETTE TOAST; BREAKFAST TREATS; FRUIT CRESCENTS; GOLDEN BARS; THE HOSTESS W/ THE MOSTEST ASSORTMENT; LADY STELLA ASSORTMENT; MARGHERITE COMBINATION; SESAME (REGINA)	**ARTIFICIAL COLOR** OR **COLORS**
CHINESE DESSERT; EGG JUMBO; ROMAN EGG BISCUITS (RUM & BRANDY); ROMAN EGG BISCUITS (VANILLA); SPICE DROPS PFEFFERNUSSE; SUGARED EGG BISCUITS	NO ADDITIVES OF CONCERN
COMO DELIGHT	**ARTIFICIAL COLOR; MACE**
SUNSHINE	
BUTTER FLAVORED; CHIP A ROOS; GINGER SNAPS; GOLDEN FRUIT; TOY; VANILLA WAFERS	WHEY OR DAIRY WHEY

BRANDS	ADDITIVES-OF-CONCERN BOLD—CONCERN TO ALL LIGHT—CONCERN TO SOME
SUNSHINE *(Continued)*	
CHOCOLATE FUDGE; HYDROX; VANILLA HYDROX; VIENNA FINGERS	**(COCONUT OIL);*** WHEY
CHOCOLATE NUGGETS; OATMEAL W/ GROUND RAISINS; OATMEAL PEANUT SANDWICH	NO ADDITIVES OF CONCERN
FIG BARS; PEANUT BUTTER WAFERS	**ARTIFICIAL COLOR;** WHEY
HYDE PARK ASSORTMENT	**ARTIFICIAL COLORS; (COCONUT, PALM KERNEL OILS);*** WHEY
MARSHMALLOW BARS	**ARTIFICIAL COLOR; MODIFIED FOOD STARCH**
SPRINKLES	**ARTIFICIAL COLOR; FOOD SHELLAC**
SUGAR WAFERS	**ARTIFICIAL COLOR; (COCONUT OIL);*** WHEY
SWISSTYLE GRAHAMS	**(COCONUT, PALM KERNEL OILS; HYDROGENATED COTTONSEED, PALM, SOYBEAN OILS);*** WHEY
R TOGGENBURGER	
CHOCOLATE CREAM FILLED SNACK WAFERS	**VEGETABLE SHORTENING**

*Blend may contain one or more of these saturated oils.

	BRANDS	ADDITIVES-OF-CONCERN BOLD—CONCERN TO ALL LIGHT—CONCERN TO SOME
R	**VAN DE KAMP'S**	
	ALMOND ICE BOX; DUTCH CRISP; DUTCH SHORTBREAD BARS; LEMON SNACK; MAPLE PECAN; SPRITZ SHORTBREAD	MILK PROTEIN
	COCONUT MACAROONS	EGG WHITES; GUM TRAGACANTH
R	**WALKERS**	
	SHORTBREAD FINGERS	**BUTTER**
	SUPERMARKET PRIVATE BRANDS	
	A & P	
	—A & P	
	BUTTER FLAVORED; CHOCOLATE CHIP; VANILLA WAFERS	WHEY
	—ANN PAGE	
	BUTTER PECAN	WHEY (SWEET DAIRY)
	CHOCOLATE SANDWICH CREME; VANILLA SANDWICH CREME	**ARTIFICIAL COLORS**
	OLD FASHIONED CHOCOLATE CHIP; OLD FASHIONED FUDGE SUGAR; OLD FASHIONED OATMEAL; OLD FASHIONED SUGAR	NO ADDITIVES OF CONCERN

BRANDS	**ADDITIVES-OF-CONCERN** **BOLD—CONCERN TO ALL** LIGHT—CONCERN TO SOME
FIRST NATIONAL **—FINAST** FIG BARS	NO ADDITIVES OF CONCERN
SAFEWAY **—BUSY BAKER** ANIMAL; COCONUT; VANILLA SNAPS	**(HYDROGENATED SOYBEAN OIL);*** WHEY OR WHEY SOLIDS
CHOCOLATE SNAPS; FAMILY ASSORTMENT; VANILLA WAFERS	**ARTIFICIAL COLOR** OR **COLORS; (HYDROGENATED SOYBEAN OIL);*** WHEY
RAISIN BRAN FRUIT BARS	WHEY
—BUSY BAKER *GOOD OLD FASHIONED* CHOCOLATE CHIP; OATMEAL	**(HYDROGENATED SOYBEAN OIL)***
COCOA CHIPS; PINK SUGAR WAFERS	**ARTIFICIAL COLOR; (BEEF FAT);*** WHEY
DUTCH APPLE BARS; FIG BARS; MARSHMALLOW PUFFS	**ARTIFICIAL COLOR;** WHEY
LEMON CREMES	**ARTIFICIAL COLOR; (BEEF FAT)***
PEANUT BUTTER CREME; WHOLE WHEAT FIG BARS	WHEY

BRANDS	**ADDITIVES-OF-CONCERN** **BOLD—CONCERN TO ALL** LIGHT—CONCERN TO SOME
—SCOTCH BUY	
COCOA DROP	**ARTIFICIAL COLOR; (COCONUT, PALM KERNEL OILS)***
STOP & SHOP	
—STOP & SHOP	
CHOCO CHIP; FIG BARS; FIG SQUARES; REGULAR HERMITS	NO ADDITIVES OF CONCERN
—SUN GLORY	
BUTTER PECAN	WHEY (SWEET DAIRY)
CHOCOLATE CHIP; CHOCOLATE SQUARES; COCONUT BARS; FUDGE SUGAR; LEMON CUSTARD SQUARES; OATMEAL; PEANUT BUTTER SQUARES	**ARTIFICIAL COLOR**
ICED FUDGIES	**ARTIFICIAL COLOR;** EGG WHITES; WHEY (SWEET DAIRY)
ICED OATMEAL 'N RAISIN	EGG WHITES
ICED SPICE; SUGAR	**ARTIFICIAL COLOR; NUTMEG**
VANILLA SQUARES	NO ADDITIVES OF CONCERN
WINN DIXIE	
—CRACKIN GOOD	
ACE ASSORTMENT	**ARTIFICIAL COLOR; (BEEF FAT, LARD);* BHA;** WHEY (DAIRY)

*Blend may contain one or more of these saturated fats and/or oils.

BRANDS	ADDITIVES-OF-CONCERN BOLD—CONCERN TO ALL LIGHT—CONCERN TO SOME
WINN DIXIE—CRACKIN GOOD *(Continued)*	
ALMOND CRUNCH; ANIMAL; BUTTER; CHOCOLATE CHIP; COCONUT CREMES; FROSTED FRUIT; FUDGE RIPPLES; LEMON COCONUT ROUNDS; OATMEAL; VANILLA WAFERS	**(BEEF FAT, LARD);* BHA;** WHEY (DAIRY)
ASSORTED CREMES; BIG 60 SANDWICH CREMES; LEMON CREMES	**ARTIFICIAL COLOR** W/ FD & C YELLOW NO. 5; **(BEEF FAT, LARD);* BHA;** WHEY (DAIRY)
COCOA CHIP 'N NUT; FIG-BARS; GINGER CRISPS; VANILLA KREMO	**BHA;** WHEY (DAIRY OR POWDERED)
DEVILSFOOD CAKES	WHEY
ICED APPLESAUCE; PEANUT BUTTER; PECAN JOY	**(BEEF FAT, LARD);* BHA**
ICED SUGAR CRISPS	**(BEEF FAT, LARD);* BHA; MACE;** WHEY (DAIRY)
PEANUT BUTTER WAFERS	**ARTIFICIAL COLOR;** WHEY
ITEMS IN HEALTH FOOD STORES	
DONNA'S	
GOURMET NATURAL HONEY SNACK HAWAIIAN	NO ADDITIVES OF CONCERN

BRANDS	ADDITIVES-OF-CONCERN **BOLD—CONCERN TO ALL** LIGHT—CONCERN TO SOME
—NATURAL HONEY COOKIE BROWNIE; RAISIN NUT	NO ADDITIVES OF CONCERN
EL MOLINO MILLS HONEY ANIMAL	NO ADDITIVES OF CONCERN
HEALTH VALLEY OATMEAL; PEANUT BUTTER; WHEAT GERM & MOLASSES	**PURE CREAMERY BUTTER**; WHEY POWDER
RAISIN BRAN	**PURE CREAMERY BUTTER**
—NATURAL SNAPS CAROB & HONEY; COCONUT & HONEY; GINGER & HONEY; LEMON & HONEY; YOGURT & HONEY	**PURE CREAMERY BUTTER**; WHEY POWDER
HOFFMAN'S ENERGY-PLUS; HI-PROTEEN	**SODIUM CASEINATE**
SOVEX COCONUT; MOLASSES; PEANUT BUTTER	WHEY
GRANOLA	EGG WHITES; WHEY

*Blend may contain one or more of these saturated fats.

	BRANDS	ADDITIVES-OF-CONCERN **BOLD—CONCERN TO ALL** LIGHT—CONCERN TO SOME

BREAKFAST PASTRIES, BROWNIES, CAKES, SNACK CAKES

	BRANDS	ADDITIVES-OF-CONCERN
R	BUTTERMAID FARMCREST ECLAIRS	**ARTIFICIAL COLOR;** GUAR GUM; **(LARD);*** LOCUST BEAN GUM; **MODIFIED FOOD STARCH**
	COUNTRY GOOD DANISH BEAR CLAW	**ARTIFICIAL COLORINGS;** LOCUST BEAN GUM
R	DOLLY MADISON ANGEL FOOD CAKE	EGG WHITES
	CINNAMON ROLLS	**ARTIFICIAL COLOR; (BEEF FAT, LARD; COCONUT, PALM KERNEL OILS);*** LOCUST BEAN GUM; **MODIFIED CORN STARCH;** WHEY
	CREME CAKES	**ARTIFICIAL COLOR; CALCIUM CASEINATE;** GUAR GUM; **MODIFIED CORN STARCH;** SODIUM ALGINATE; **SODIUM CASEINATE;** WHEY
	DANISH ROLLS RASPBERRY	**ARTIFICIAL COLOR; (COCONUT, PALM KERNEL OILS; HYDROGENATED COTTONSEED, SOYBEAN OILS);*** LOCUST BEAN GUM; **MODIFIED CORN STARCH;** SODIUM ALGINATE; WHEY

BRANDS	ADDITIVES-OF-CONCERN BOLD—CONCERN TO ALL LIGHT—CONCERN TO SOME
DESSERT ROLL	**ARTIFICIAL COLOR; CALCIUM CASEINATE;** SODIUM ALGINATE; **SODIUM CASEINATE;** WHEY
POUND CAKE	**ARTIFICIAL COLOR; (BEEF FAT, LARD);* CALCIUM CASEINATE;** EGG WHITES; **SODIUM CASEINATE;** WHEY
ZINGERS (VANILLA)	**ARTIFICIAL COLOR; CALCIUM CASEINATE;** EGG WHITES; GUAR GUM; LOCUST BEAN GUM; **MODIFIED CORN STARCH;** SODIUM ALGINATE; **SODIUM CASEINATE;** WHEY
DRAKES	
COFFEE CAKE JR.	**ARTIFICIALLY COLORED WITH VEGETABLE COLORS; CALCIUM CASEINATE;** EGG WHITES; **SODIUM CASEINATE;** WHEY
CREME FINGERS	**ARTIFICIALLY COLORED WITH VEGETABLE COLORS; CALCIUM CASEINATE;** EGG WHITES; **MODIFIED CORN STARCH; SODIUM CASEINATE;** WHEY

*Blend may contain one or more of these saturated fats and/or oils.

BRANDS	ADDITIVES-OF-CONCERN BOLD—CONCERN TO ALL LIGHT—CONCERN TO SOME
DRAKES *(Continued)*	
DEVIL DOGS	**CALCIUM CASEINATE; SODIUM CASEINATE;** WHEY
MARBLE POUND CAKE JR.; POUND CAKE JR.	**CALCIUM CASEINATE; SODIUM CASEINATE;** WHEY
RING DING; SWISS ROLL; YODELS	**CALCIUM CASEINATE;** EGG WHITES; **(PALM KERNEL OIL);* SODIUM CASEINATE;** WHEY
ENTENMANN'S	
ALL BUTTER POUND CAKE; APPLE PUFFS; BANANA CRUNCH LOAF; CHEESE BUNS; CHOCOLATE CHIP CRUMB LOAF; FUDGE CAKE; MARSHMALLOW FUDGE SQUARE	**MODIFIED CORN STARCH**
APRICOT CRUMB SQUARE; RASPBERRY DANISH TWIST; STRAWBERRY CHEESE DANISH; WALNUT DANISH TWIST	**ARTIFICIAL COLOR; COLORING**

	BRANDS	**ADDITIVES-OF-CONCERN** BOLD—CONCERN TO ALL LIGHT—CONCERN TO SOME
	CHEESE COFFEE CAKE; CINNAMON DANISH TWIST; CINNAMON FILBERT; CRUMB COFFEE CAKE; PECAN RAISIN LOAF; WALNUT DANISH RING	**COLORING**
	MARBLE LOAF; PUMPKIN WALNUT CAKE	NO ADDITIVES OF CONCERN
R	HOLSUM ANGELFOOD CAKE	EGG WHITES
	APPLE STREUDEL	**ARTIFICIAL COLOR;** FD & C YELLOW NO. 5; **(BEEF FAT);*** CASEIN; **MODIFIED FOOD STARCH**
	CINNAMON ROLLS (PECAN, PLAIN, RAISIN)	**ARTIFICIAL COLOR;** GUAR GUM; WHEY
	COCONUT LAYER CAKE	**ARTIFICIAL COLOR;** EGG WHITES; LOCUST BEAN GUM; WHEY
	DEVIL'S DELITE	**ARTIFICIAL COLOR;** EGG WHITES; **MODIFIED FOOD STARCH;** WHEY

*Blend may contain one or more of these saturated fats and/or oils.

BRANDS	ADDITIVES-OF-CONCERN **BOLD—CONCERN TO ALL** LIGHT—CONCERN TO SOME
HOLSUM *(Continued)*	
DEVIL'S FOOD LAYER CAKE	EGG WHITES; LOCUST BEAN GUM; WHEY
FUDGE BAR	**(BEEF TALLOW, LARD);*** EGG WHITES
PECAN SPINS	**ARTIFICIAL COLOR; (BEEF FAT, LARD);*** WHEY
POUND CAKE	**ARTIFICIAL COLOR;** EGG WHITES; WHEY
HOSTESS	
BIG WHEELS	**(BEEF FAT, LARD);* MODIFIED FOOD STARCH; SODIUM CASEINATE;** WHEY
BREAKFAST BAKE SHOP ICED HONEY BUN	**ARTIFICIAL COLOR; (BEEF FAT, LARD);*** LOCUST BEAN GUM
FILLED CUP CAKES	**MODIFIED FOOD STARCH; SODIUM CASEINATE;** WHEY
SUZY Q'S	**SODIUM CASEINATE;** WHEY
TWINKIES	**ARTIFICIAL COLOR; MODIFIED FOOD STARCH; SODIUM CASEINATE;** WHEY
R **KING'S** FUDGE FROSTEES	**ARTIFICIAL COLORS;** EGG WHITES; WHEY

	BRANDS	ADDITIVES-OF-CONCERN BOLD—CONCERN TO ALL LIGHT—CONCERN TO SOME
R	**KITCHEN PRIDE**	
	APPLE SANDWICH CAKES	**ARTIFICIAL COLOR; MODIFIED CORN STARCH;** WHEY SOLIDS
	LITTLE DEBBIE	
	APPLE DELIGHTS; NUTTY BARS	WHEY
	APPLE SPICE CAKES	**ARTIFICIAL COLORS;** EGG WHITES
	FUDGE ROUNDS CAKE; SWISS CAKE ROLLS	**ARTIFICIAL COLOR** OR **COLORS;** WHEY
	JEL-CREME ROLLS	**ARTIFICIAL COLORS;** EGG WHITES; **MODIFIED FOOD STARCH;** WHEY
	PEANUT BUTTER BROWNIES	EGG WHITES; WHEY
R	**MICKEY CAKES**	
	APPLE WALNUT	**(BEEF TALLOW, LARD)***
	CARROT CAKE	LOCUST BEAN GUM
	FUDGE BAR	LOCUST BEAN GUM; **(PALM KERNEL OIL)***
R	**NISSEN**	
	COCOA SNAX	WHEY SOLIDS
	COFFEE CAKE	**ARTIFICIAL COLOR;** EGG WHITES; GLUTEN (WHEAT); GUAR GUM; WHEY

*Blend may contain one or more of these saturated fats and/or oils.

	BRANDS	ADDITIVES-OF-CONCERN **BOLD—CONCERN TO ALL** LIGHT—CONCERN TO SOME
	NISSEN *(Continued)*	
	CREME HORNS	**ARTIFICIAL COLOR;** LOCUST BEAN [GUM]; **TALLOW**
	FUDGE CAKE	**ARTIFICIAL COLOR;** EGG WHITES; GLUTEN (WHEAT); GUAR GUM; LOCUST BEAN GUM; WHEY
R	**REGENT** FUDGE BROWNIE	EGG WHITES; **(SATURATED COTTONSEED, PALM OILS);*** WHEY POWDER
	STELLA D'ORO LADY FINGERS	NO ADDITIVES OF CONCERN
R	**SVENHARD'S**	
	APPLE ROLLS; BEAR CLAWS; BREAKFAST CLAWS; BREAKFAST HORNS; BUTTER CRUNCH ROLLS; CINNAMON HORNS; FUDGE-ETTES; HORNS A PLENTY; LEMON ROLLS; RAISIN-ETTES; RAISIN SNAILS; WALNUT ROLLS	**ARTIFICIAL COLOR** OR **COLORS**
	APPLE STREUDEL	**MODIFIED CORN STARCH**
R	**TABLE TALK**	
	GOLDEN FUDGE CAKE	**ARTIFICIAL COLORS;** EGG WHITES; GUAR GUM; **MODIFIED FOOD STARCH**
	SOUR CREAM POUND CAKE	**MODIFIED FOOD STARCH**

BRANDS	ADDITIVES-OF-CONCERN **BOLD—CONCERN TO ALL** LIGHT—CONCERN TO SOME
R VACHON	
HALF MOON SPONGE CAKES W/ CREAMED FILLING	**ARTIFICIAL COLOR; SODIUM CASEINATE**
POPOVER PUFF W/ STRAWBERRY FILLING	**ARTIFICIAL COLOR; (BEEF TALLOW, LARD);*** SODIUM ALGINATE
R VAN DE KAMP'S	
ANGEL FOOD LOAF	EGG WHITES
APPLE MUFFINS; BANANA NUT LOAF; HONEY BRAN MUFFINS; LADY FINGERS	NO ADDITIVES OF CONCERN
APPLE PUFFS	**ARTIFICIAL COLOR; MODIFIED FOOD STARCH; PARTIALLY HYDROGENATED VEGETABLE SHORTENING**
APPLESAUCE CAKE	**ARTIFICIAL COLOR**
BLUEBERRY MUFFINS	**SODIUM CASEINATE**
BUTTERHORNS; PINEAPPLE SWIRLS	**ARTIFICIAL COLOR;** GUM TRAGACANTH
CARROT CAKE	**CARRAGEENAN; PARTIALLY HYDROGENATED VEGETABLE SHORTENING**
CHOCOLATE ICED ANGEL FOOD CAKE	**CARRAGEENAN;** EGG WHITES; **PARTIALLY HYDROGENATED VEGETABLE SHORTENING**

*Blend may contain one or more of these saturated fats and/or oils.

BRANDS	**ADDITIVES-OF-CONCERN** **BOLD—CONCERN TO ALL** LIGHT—CONCERN TO SOME
VAN DE KAMP'S *(Continued)*	
CINNAMON ROLLS	EGG WHITES; **ENZYME OF ASPERGILLUS ORYZAE;** GUM TRAGACANTH; WHEY
DATE NUT LOAF	**VEGETABLE SHORTENING**
GOLDEN CHOCOLATE CAKE	**ARTIFICIAL COLOR;** EGG WHITES; **MODIFIED FOOD STARCH; PARTIALLY HYDROGENATED VEGETABLE SHORTENING;** WHEY
MILK CHOCOLATE CUPCAKES	**MODIFIED FOOD STARCH;** WHEY
RASPBERRY ROLLS	**ARTIFICIAL COLOR; ENZYME OF ASPERGILLUS ORYZAE;** GUM TRAGACANTH
WALNUT SWIRLS	**ARTIFICIAL COLOR;** EGG WHITES; GUM TRAGACANTH; WHEY
SUPERMARKET PRIVATE BRANDS	
PUBLIX	
—**PUBLIX** FRUIT CAKE	**ARTIFICIAL COLOR**
STOP & SHOP	
—(NO BRAND NAME)	
APPLE SWEET ROLL; PECAN COFFEE RING	ALGIN; **ARTIFICIAL COLOR;** LOCUST BEAN GUM; **MODIFIED FOOD STARCH;** WHEY

BRANDS	ADDITIVES-OF-CONCERN BOLD—CONCERN TO ALL LIGHT—CONCERN TO SOME
CINNAMON RAISIN COFFEE RING; CINNAMON RAISIN ROLL	**ARTIFICIAL COLOR;** LOCUST BEAN GUM; WHEY
LADY FINGERS	NO ADDITIVES OF CONCERN
PECAN TWIRLS	**ARTIFICIAL COLOR;** FD & C YELLOW NO. 5
—OUR FAMOUS FUDGE CAKE	LOCUST BEAN GUM; WHEY
—OUR OWN ANGEL CAKE; SPONGE CAKE FEATHERLIGHT	EGG WHITES
MAPLE WALNUT CAKE	LOCUST BEAN GUM; WHEY
MARBLE PARTY BAR; MARBLE POUND CAKE	**ARTIFICIAL COLOR;** EGG WHITES; **MODIFIED FOOD STARCH;** WHEY
RASPBERRY FILLED FUN-BALLS	ALGIN; **ARTIFICIAL COLOR; CARRAGEENAN; MODIFIED FOOD STARCH;** WHEY
SPONGE CAKE	WHEY
—STOP & SHOP CHOCOLATE CHIP BUTTERSCOTCH BROWNIES; CREME FILLED COCOA ROLL	WHEY OR WHEY SOLIDS

BRANDS	**ADDITIVES-OF-CONCERN** **BOLD—CONCERN TO ALL** LIGHT—CONCERN TO SOME
—STOP & SHOP *(Continued)*	
GOLDEN CIRCLE CAKE; MARBLE CIRCLE CAKE	**ARTIFICIAL COLOR;** EGG WHITES; **MODIFIED FOOD STARCH;** WHEY
JELLY ROLL	**ARTIFICIAL COLORS; VEGETABLE GUM;** WHEY SOLIDS
WALNUT CHOCOLATE BROWNIES	GUAR GUM
WINN DIXIE	
—CRACKIN GOOD	
OATMEAL SNACK CAKES	**BHA;** EGG WHITES (DRIED); SODIUM ALGINATE; WHEY (DAIRY)
RAISIN SNACK CAKES	**ARTIFICIAL COLOR;** WHEY (DRIED)
ROYAL STRIPED MALLOWS	**ARTIFICIAL COLORS** W/ FD & C YELLOW NO. 5; **(BEEF FAT, LARD);* BHA;** SODIUM ALGINATE; WHEY (DAIRY)
—DIXIE DARLING	
ANGEL FOOD CAKE	EGG WHITES
PECAN TWIRLS	**ARTIFICIAL COLOR;** FD & C YELLOW NO. 5

DOUGHNUTS

ENTENMANN'S	
COUNTRY STYLE; CRUMB	**ARTIFICIAL COLOR; COLORING**

BRANDS		ADDITIVES-OF-CONCERN **BOLD—CONCERN TO ALL** LIGHT—CONCERN TO SOME
R	**HOLSUM**	
	DONUTS	**ARTIFICIAL COLOR; BHA; BHT; SHORTENING; SODIUM CASEINATE**
	CHOCOLATE COATED	**ARTIFICIAL COLOR; (BEEF TALLOW, LARD; COCONUT, PALM KERNEL OILS);* MACE; NUTMEG;** WHEY
	SUGAR	**ARTIFICIAL COLOR; MACE; NUTMEG**
	HOSTESS	
	DONETTE GEMS; FROSTED DONETTE GEMS	**ARTIFICIAL COLOR; (BEEF FAT, LARD);* SODIUM CASEINATE**
	—BREAKFAST BAKE SHOP	
	FINER DONUTS ASSORTMENT; FINER DONUTS FAMILY PAK; FROSTED	**ARTIFICIAL COLOR; (BEEF FAT, LARD);*** GUAR & KARAYA GUMS
R	**MICKEY** *MINI-DONUTS*	
	CHOCOLATE COATED	**ARTIFICIAL COLOR; (BEEF TALLOW, LARD; COCONUT, PALM KERNEL OILS);* MACE; NUTMEG;** WHEY
	CRUNCH; SUGAR COATED	**ARTIFICIAL COLOR; MACE; NUTMEG**

*Blend may contain one or more of these saturated fats and/or oils.

BRANDS	ADDITIVES-OF-CONCERN BOLD—CONCERN TO ALL LIGHT—CONCERN TO SOME
R **MOTHER PARKER'S**	
OLD FASHIONED	NO ADDITIVES OF CONCERN
R **NISSEN**	
ASSORTED; CINNAMON; PLAIN	**ARTIFICIAL COLOR;** GUAR & KARAYA GUMS
CHOCOLATE COCOANUT	**ARTIFICIAL COLOR**
R **VAN DE KAMP'S**	
CHOCOLATE ICED OLD FASHIONED	**VEGETABLE GUMS;** WHEY
GLAZED OLD FASHIONED	**MODIFIED FOOD STARCH; VEGETABLE GUMS;** WHEY
OLD FASHIONED	**ARTIFICIAL COLOR; BHA; BHT**
RAISED	**ARTIFICIAL COLOR;** GLUTEN (WHEAT)
SUPERMARKET PRIVATE BRANDS	
LUCKY	
—HARVEST DAY	
CHOCOLATE COATED	**ARTIFICIAL COLOR; (COCONUT, PALM KERNEL OILS);* MACE; NUTMEG;** WHEY
PLAIN; POWDERED SUGAR	**ARTIFICIAL COLOR; MACE; NUTMEG**
SAFEWAY	
—MRS. WRIGHT'S	
CHOCOLATE FLAVOR FROSTED	**ARTIFICIAL COLOR; (BEEF FAT, LARD);*** GUAR GUM; WHEY

BRANDS	**ADDITIVES-OF-CONCERN** **BOLD—CONCERN TO ALL** LIGHT—CONCERN TO SOME
DONUTS (FROSTED); DONUTS (PLAIN)	**ARTIFICIAL COLOR; (BEEF FAT, LARD);*** GUAR GUM; **MODIFIED FOOD STARCH;** WHEY
STOP & SHOP	
—STOP & SHOP BAKERY	
SNACK PACK (PLAIN)	EGG WHITES; GUAR GUM; **PAPRIKA; SODIUM CASEINATE; TURMERIC;** WHEY
SOUR CREME OLD FASHION	**ARTIFICIAL COLOR; MODIFIED WHEAT STARCH;** WHEY
—DAISY DONUTS	
CHOCOLATE COVERED; W/ CINNAMON; W/ POWDERED SUGAR; FROSTED	EGG WHITES; GUAR GUM; **PAPRIKA; SODIUM CASEINATE; TURMERIC;** WHEY
COUNTRY STYLE (W/ CINNAMON); COUNTRY STYLE (W/ POWDERED SUGAR)	**PAPRIKA; TURMERIC;** WHEY
GLAZED	**ARTIFICIAL COLOR; (BEEF FAT);* SODIUM CASEINATE;** WHEY
WINN DIXIE	
—WINN DIXIE	
GLAZED	**ARTIFICIAL COLOR; FUNGAL PROTEASE OBTAINED FROM ASPERGILLUS ORYZAE;** GUAR GUM; WHEY

*Blend may contain one or more of these saturated fats and/or oils.

BRANDS	**ADDITIVES-OF-CONCERN** BOLD—CONCERN TO ALL LIGHT—CONCERN TO SOME

PIES

DOLLY MADISON CHOCOLATE SNACK PIE	**ARTIFICIAL COLOR; (BEEF FAT, LARD; COCONUT, PALM KERNEL OILS);* CALCIUM CASEINATE;** LOCUST BEAN GUM; **MODIFIED CORN STARCH;** SODIUM ALGINATE; **SODIUM CASEINATE;** WHEY
—FRUIT PIE APPLE	**(BEEF FAT, LARD; COCONUT, PALM KERNEL OILS);* CALCIUM CASEINATE;** LOCUST BEAN GUM; **MODIFIED CORN STARCH; SODIUM CASEINATE;** WHEY
LEMON	**ARTIFICIAL COLOR; (BEEF FAT, LARD; COCONUT, PALM KERNEL OILS);* CALCIUM CASEINATE;** LOCUST BEAN GUM; **MODIFIED CORN STARCH; SODIUM CASEINATE; SODIUM NITRATE;** WHEY
DRAKE'S APPLE	CAROB BEAN GUM; EGG ALBUMIN; **MODIFIED CORN STARCH;** SODIUM ALGINATE; WHEY

	BRANDS	ADDITIVES-OF-CONCERN **BOLD—CONCERN TO ALL** LIGHT—CONCERN TO SOME
	ENTENMANN'S	
	APPLE; APPLE CRUMB	**MODIFIED CORN STARCH**
	HOSTESS *FRUIT PIE*	
	APPLE	**ARTIFICIAL COLOR; (BEEF FAT, LARD);* MODIFIED FOOD STARCH; NUTMEG**
	BLUEBERRY; CHERRY; LEMON	**ARTIFICIAL COLOR; (BEEF FAT, LARD);* MODIFIED FOOD STARCH**
R	**TABLE TALK**	
	BLUEBERRY	EGG WHITES; **LARD; MODIFIED FOOD STARCH; SODIUM CASEINATE;** WHEY
	BOSTON CREAM	**ARTIFICIAL COLOR; CARRAGEENAN; (COCONUT, PALM KERNEL OILS);*** LOCUST BEAN GUM; WHEY
	CHOCOLATE CREAM	**ARTIFICIAL COLOR; METHYL ETHYL CELLULOSE; MODIFIED FOOD STARCH; SODIUM CASEINATE;** WHEY
	LEMON MERINGUE	**ARTIFICIAL COLORS;** EGG WHITES; LOCUST BEAN GUM; **MODIFIED FOOD STARCH;** WHEY
	SQUASH	**ARTIFICIAL COLOR;** EGG WHITES; **SODIUM CASEINATE;** WHEY

*Blend may contain one or more of these saturated fats and/or oils.

	BRANDS	ADDITIVES-OF-CONCERN **BOLD—CONCERN TO ALL** LIGHT—CONCERN TO SOME
	R TABLE TALK *(Continued)*	
	—JUNIOR PIES	
	APPLE	**ARTIFICIAL COLORS; LARD; MODIFIED FOOD STARCH;** WHEY
	BLUEBERRY	**LARD; MODIFIED FOOD STARCH;** WHEY
	CHOCOLATE ECLAIR	**ARTIFICIAL COLORS;** GUAR GUM; **LARD;** LOCUST BEAN GUM; **MODIFIED FOOD STARCH;** WHEY
R	VAN DE KAMP'S	
	APPLE; BERRY	**ARTIFICIAL COLOR;** GUAR GUM; **MODIFIED STARCH**
	CHERRY; LEMON	**ARTIFICIAL COLOR; MODIFIED FOOD STARCH**
	HIGH TOP APPLE	LOCUST BEAN GUM; WHEY
	LEMON MERINGUE	**ARTIFICIAL COLOR;** EGG WHITES; LOCUST BEAN GUM; **MODIFIED FOOD STARCHES;** WHEY
	PEACH	LOCUST BEAN GUM; **MODIFIED FOOD STARCH;** WHEY
	SUPERMARKET PRIVATE BRANDS	
	STOP & SHOP	
	—OUR OWN	
	APPLE; BLUEBERRY; CHERRY; PINEAPPLE	**MODIFIED FOOD STARCH**
	CUSTARD	**ARTIFICIAL COLOR; PAPRIKA; TURMERIC**

BRANDS	**ADDITIVES-OF-CONCERN** **BOLD—CONCERN TO ALL** LIGHT—CONCERN TO SOME
ECLAIR	LOCUST BEAN GUM
HOLIDAY MINCE	NO ADDITIVES OF CONCERN
LEMON	**ARTIFICIAL COLOR; MODIFIED FOOD STARCH;** SODIUM ALGINATE
SQUASH	**CARRAGEENAN;** LOCUST BEAN GUM; **MODIFIED FOOD STARCH; NUTMEG**
—STOP & SHOP FRUIT PIE LEMON	**ARTIFICIAL COLOR;** GUM ARABIC; **MODIFIED FOOD STARCH;** SODIUM ALGINATE; **SODIUM CASEINATE**
WINN DIXIE **—CRACKIN GOOD** BANANA; DEVIL FOOD	**ARTIFICIAL COLOR** OR **COLORS** W/ FD & C YELLOW NO. 5; **(BEEF FAT, LARD);* BHA;** SODIUM ALGINATE; WHEY (DAIRY)
CHOCOLATE; COCONUT	**(BEEF FAT, LARD);* BHA;** SODIUM ALGINATE; WHEY (DAIRY)
OATMEAL CREME	**ARTIFICIAL COLOR;** MILK SOLIDS; WHEY SOLIDS
WILD CHERRY	**ARTIFICIAL COLOR; (BEEF FAT, LARD);* BHA;** SODIUM ALGINATE; WHEY (DAIRY)

*Blend may contain one or more of these saturated fats.

IV. BAKING INGREDIENTS

ALMOND PASTE, BAKING CHOCOLATE, CAROB POWDER, COCONUT, FLAVORED CHIPS

BRANDS	ADDITIVES-OF-CONCERN BOLD—CONCERN TO ALL LIGHT—CONCERN TO SOME
BAKER'S	
ANGEL FLAKE COCONUT; GERMAN'S SWEET CHOCOLATE; SEMI-SWEET CHOCOLATE; UNSWEETENED CHOCOLATE	NO ADDITIVES OF CONCERN
CHOCOLATE FLAVOR BAKING CHIPS	MILK DERIVATIVE; **PALM KERNEL OIL**
HERSHEY'S	
BAKING CHOCOLATE UNSWEETENED; COCOA; REAL CHOCOLATE MINI CHIPS	NO ADDITIVES OF CONCERN
NESTLÉ	
BUTTERSCOTCH ARTIFICIAL FLAVORED MORSELS	**ARTIFICIAL COLORS; PALM KERNEL OIL**
CHOCO BAKE	**BHA; HYDROGENATED COTTONSEED OIL**

BRANDS	ADDITIVES-OF-CONCERN BOLD—CONCERN TO ALL LIGHT—CONCERN TO SOME
MILK CHOCOLATE MORSELS; SEMI-SWEET CHOCOLATE TOLL HOUSE MORSELS	NO ADDITIVES OF CONCERN
ODENSE ALMOND PASTE	NO ADDITIVES OF CONCERN
REESE'S PEANUT BUTTER FLAVORED CHIPS	**(PALM KERNEL OIL)***
SUPERMARKET PRIVATE BRANDS	
A & P	
—ANN PAGE	
BUTTERSCOTCH CHIPS	**ARTIFICIAL COLOR**
SEMI-SWEET CHOCOLATE CHIPS	**PALM KERNEL OIL**
SAFEWAY	
—TOWN HOUSE	
SEMI-SWEET CHOCOLATE CHIPS; SWEETENED FANCY SHRED COCONUT; SWEETENED FLAKED COCONUT	NO ADDITIVES OF CONCERN
ITEMS IN HEALTH FOOD STORES	
CARA COA CAROB POWDER	NO ADDITIVES OF CONCERN
NIBLACK CAROB POWDER	NO ADDITIVES OF CONCERN

*Blend may contain this saturated oil.

BRANDS	ADDITIVES-OF-CONCERN BOLD—CONCERN TO ALL LIGHT—CONCERN TO SOME

EXTRACTS, FLAVORS, & FOOD COLORS

DURKEE	
IMITATION BUTTER FLAVOR	**CERTIFIED FOOD COLOR; VEGETABLE GUM**
CHOCOLATE FLAVOR; IMITATION PEPPERMINT EXTRACT	**CERTIFIED FOOD COLOR**
IMITATION COCONUT FLAVOR	**VEGETABLE GUM**
IMITATION MAPLE FLAVOR; IMITATION RUM FLAVOR	NO ADDITIVES OF CONCERN
McCORMICK	
PURE ALMOND EXTRACT; PURE ANISE EXTRACT; PURE MINT & PEPPERMINT EXTRACT; PURE ORANGE EXTRACT	NO ADDITIVES OF CONCERN
IMITATION RUM EXTRACT	**FD & C RED NO. 40** & YELLOW NO. 5
IMITATION STRAWBERRY EXTRACT	**ETHYL METHYL PHENYL GLYCIDATE; FD & C RED NO. 40;** IONONE

BRANDS	**ADDITIVES-OF-CONCERN** **BOLD—CONCERN TO ALL** LIGHT—CONCERN TO SOME
SUPERMARKET PRIVATE BRANDS **A & P** **—ANN PAGE** PURE ALMOND EXTRACT; PURE LEMON EXTRACT; PURE VANILLA EXTRACT	NO ADDITIVES OF CONCERN
FIRST NATIONAL **—EDWARDS** PURE VANILLA EXTRACT	NO ADDITIVES OF CONCERN
LUCKY **—LADY LEE** PURE VANILLA EXTRACT	NO ADDITIVES OF CONCERN
SAFEWAY **—CROWN COLONY** ALMOND EXTRACT; LEMON EXTRACT; PEPPERMINT EXTRACT; VANILLA EXTRACT	NO ADDITIVES OF CONCERN
ARTIFICIAL BANANA FLAVOR; ARTIFICIAL BUTTER FLAVOR; GREEN FOOD COLOR; RED FOOD COLOR; YELLOW FOOD COLOR	**ARTIFICIAL COLORING**
CHOCOLATE EXTRACT	**ARTIFICIAL COLORS;** PROPYLENE GLYCOL ALGINATE

BRANDS	ADDITIVES-OF-CONCERN BOLD—CONCERN TO ALL LIGHT—CONCERN TO SOME
—SCOTCH BUY ARTIFICIAL VANILLA FLAVORING	NO ADDITIVES OF CONCERN
STOP & SHOP —STOP & SHOP PURE LEMON EXTRACT; PURE VANILLA EXTRACT	NO ADDITIVES OF CONCERN
ITEMS IN HEALTH FOOD STORES WALNUT ACRES PURE VANILLA EXTRACT	NO ADDITIVES OF CONCERN

FLOURS & LEAVENING AGENTS, STABILIZERS

Most of the items in this section did not contain any additives of concern, and these appear first, without an additives-of-concern column.

The items that do contain additives of concern follow, in the usual style.

FLOUR

GOLD MEDAL ALL PURPOSE BLEACHED; SELF-RISING BLEACHED; WHOLE WHEAT; WONDRA BLEACHED

KING ARTHUR UNBLEACHED

PILLSBURY'S BEST ALL PURPOSE BLEACHED; MEDIUM RYE; SELF RISING BLEACHED; UNBLEACHED; WHOLE WHEAT

SWANS DOWN BLEACHED CAKE

—SUPERMARKET PRIVATE BRANDS
A & P ANN PAGE ALL PURPOSE BLEACHED

FIRST NATIONAL FINAST ALL PURPOSE BLEACHED

LUCKY LADY LEE ALL PURPOSE BLEACHED

SAFEWAY MRS. WRIGHT'S BLEACHED; KITCHEN CRAFT BLEACHED

STOP & SHOP ALL PURPOSE BLEACHED

WINN DIXIE THRIFTY MAID ALL PURPOSE BLEACHED; BLEACHED (SELF-RISING)

—ITEMS IN HEALTH FOOD STORES
EREWHON BROWN RICE; BUCKWHEAT DARK; RYE; SOYBEAN

OLDE MILL WHOLE WHEAT PASTRY; WHOLE WHEAT STONE GROUND

SHILOH FARMS BUCKWHEAT; CORN; OAT

WALNUT ACRES GRAHAM; OAT

LEAVENING AGENTS
ARM & HAMMER BAKING SODA

CALUMET BAKING POWDER

DAVIS BAKING POWDER

RUMFORD BAKING POWDER

—SUPERMARKET PRIVATE BRANDS
FIRST NATIONAL EDWARDS BAKING SODA

FIRST NATIONAL FINAST BAKING SODA

STOP & SHOP BAKING SODA

—ITEMS IN HEALTH FOOD STORES
EL MOLINO MILLS ACTIVE DRY YEAST

EREWHON AGAR

RED STAR DRY YEAST

WALNUT ACRES BAKON YEAST

The following items contain additives of concern.

BRANDS	**ADDITIVES-OF-CONCERN** BOLD—CONCERN TO ALL LIGHT—CONCERN TO SOME
FLEISCHMANN'S ACTIVE DRY YEAST	**BHA**
ITEMS IN HEALTH FOOD STORES **SHILOH FARMS** NATURAL STABILIZER #2	GUAR [GUM]; LOCUST BEAN [GUM]

OILS & SHORTENINGS

CRISCO OIL; VEGETABLE SHORTENING	NO ADDITIVES OF CONCERN
FILIPPO BERIO OLIO D'OLIVA	NO ADDITIVES OF CONCERN
HOLLYWOOD SAFFLOWER OIL	NO ADDITIVES OF CONCERN
MAZOLA CORN OIL; NO STICK VEGETABLE SPRAY-ON	NO ADDITIVES OF CONCERN
PAM VEGETABLE COOKING SPRAY	NO ADDITIVES OF CONCERN
PLANTERS PEANUT OIL	NO ADDITIVES OF CONCERN

BRANDS	ADDITIVES-OF-CONCERN **BOLD—CONCERN TO ALL** LIGHT—CONCERN TO SOME
WESSON VEGETABLE OIL	NO ADDITIVES OF CONCERN
SUPERMARKET PRIVATE BRANDS	
A & P	
—A & P DEXOLA VEGETABLE OIL	**BHA; BHT**
—ANN PAGE	
OLIVE OIL; PURE CORN OIL	NO ADDITIVES OF CONCERN
FIRST NATIONAL	
—FINAST	
VEGETABLE OIL	NO ADDITIVES OF CONCERN
VEGETABLE SHORTENING	**BHA; BHT**
LUCKY	
—HARVEST DAY	
SHORTENING	**BHA; BHT; MEAT FATS & VEGETABLE OILS**
—LADY LEE	
ALL PURPOSE VEGETABLE OIL; CORN OIL; PAN COATING	NO ADDITIVES OF CONCERN
SAFEWAY	
—EMPRESS OLIVE OIL	NO ADDITIVES OF CONCERN
—NUMADE	
VEGETABLE OIL; VEGETABLE SHORTENING	NO ADDITIVES OF CONCERN

BRANDS	**ADDITIVES-OF-CONCERN** **BOLD—CONCERN TO ALL** LIGHT—CONCERN TO SOME
STOP & SHOP **—STOP & SHOP** CORN OIL; SALAD OIL	NO ADDITIVES OF CONCERN
WINN DIXIE **—ASTOR** SHORTENING	NO ADDITIVES OF CONCERN
ITEMS IN HEALTH FOOD STORES **ARROWHEAD MILLS** *OIL* BLENDED; PEANUT; SOYBEAN	NO ADDITIVES OF CONCERN
EREWHON *OIL* CORN; SAFFLOWER	NO ADDITIVES OF CONCERN
HAIN *OIL* ALL BLEND; CORN; OLIVE; SAFFLOWER; SUNFLOWER; WALNUT	NO ADDITIVES OF CONCERN
COCOANUT	**COCONUT OIL**

V. BAKING MIXES, DESSERT TOPPINGS, GELATIN, & PUDDING

BISCUIT, BREAD, & MUFFIN BAKING MIXES

BRANDS	ADDITIVES-OF-CONCERN BOLD—CONCERN TO ALL LIGHT—CONCERN TO SOME
AUNT JEMIMA CORN BREAD MIX	NO ADDITIVES OF CONCERN
BISQUICK	
BUTTERMILK BAKING MIX	**(BEEF FAT, LARD);* BHA; BHT**
BETTY CROCKER	
MUFFIN MIX	
CORN	**(BEEF TALLOW, LARD);* BHA; BHT**
WILD BLUEBERRY	**BHA; BHT; MODIFIED CORN STARCH**
CRUTCHFIELD'S	
BRAN MUFFIN MIX	**BHA; BHT**
POPOVER MIX	NO ADDITIVES OF CONCERN
DUNCAN HINES	
WILD BLUEBERRY MUFFIN MIX	NO ADDITIVES OF CONCERN

*Blend may contain one or more of these saturated fats.

BRANDS	ADDITIVES-OF-CONCERN BOLD—CONCERN TO ALL LIGHT—CONCERN TO SOME
FLAKO CORN MUFFIN MIX	NO ADDITIVES OF CONCERN
POPOVER MIX	**LARD**
JIFFY BISCUIT BAKING MIX	**BHA; BHT; CALCIUM CASEINATE; (LARD, TALLOW);*** WHEY
—*MUFFIN MIX* APPLE-CINNAMON; BLUEBERRY	**ARTIFICIAL COLOR; BHA; BHT; (LARD, TALLOW)***
BRAN W/ DATES	**BHA; BHT; (LARD, TALLOW)***
PILLSBURY HOT ROLL MIX	**(BEEF FAT, LARD; HYDROGENATED COTTONSEED, PALM, SOYBEAN OILS);* BHA; BHT;** WHEY
—*QUICK BREAD MIX* APRICOT NUT; BANANA	**(BEEF FAT, HYDROGENATED SOYBEAN OIL, LARD);* BHA; BHT**
BLUEBERRY NUT	**ARTIFICIAL COLOR; (BEEF FAT, HYDROGENATED SOYBEAN OIL, LARD);* BHA; BHT;** SODIUM ALGINATE

BRANDS	ADDITIVES-OF-CONCERN BOLD—CONCERN TO ALL LIGHT—CONCERN TO SOME
CHERRY NUT	**ARTIFICIAL COLOR; (BEEF FAT, HYDROGENATED SOYBEAN OIL, LARD);* BHA; BHT; MODIFIED FOOD STARCH**
DATE; NUT	**BHA; BHT**
SUPERMARKET PRIVATE BRANDS WINN DIXIE —DIXIE DARLING	
BRAN MUFFIN MIX	**BHA;** WHEY (DRIED SWEET DAIRY)
BUTTERMILK BISCUIT MIX	**(BEEF FAT);* BHA;** WHEY (DRIED SWEET DAIRY)
CORN BREAD MIX	**BHA**
ITEMS IN HEALTH FOOD STORES ARROWHEAD MILLS *MIX*	
MULTIGRAIN CORN BREAD; STONE GROUND WHOLE WHEAT BREAD; WHOLE GRAIN BISCUIT; WHOLE GRAIN BRAN MUFFIN	NO ADDITIVES OF CONCERN
JOLLY JOAN *MIX*	
BARLEY	NO ADDITIVES OF CONCERN

*Blend may contain one or more of these saturated fats and/or oils.

BRANDS	ADDITIVES-OF-CONCERN BOLD—CONCERN TO ALL LIGHT—CONCERN TO SOME
JOLLY JOAN *MIX (Continued)*	
LOW PROTEIN BREAD	**CARRAGEENAN; MODIFIED VEGETABLE GUM**
WALNUT ACRES	
CORNELL BREAD FLOUR MIX	NO ADDITIVES OF CONCERN

DESSERT BAKING MIXES (BROWNIES, CAKES, COOKIES, PIE CRUSTS, PIES, & SIMILAR ITEMS)

AUNT JEMIMA	
COFFEE CAKE EASY MIX	NO ADDITIVES OF CONCERN
BETTY CROCKER	
BOSTON CREAM PIE MIX	**ARTIFICIAL COLOR; (BEEF TALLOW, LARD);* BHA; BHT; CALCIUM CASEINATE;** GUAR GUM; SODIUM ALGINATE; WHEY
COCONUT MACAROON MIX	NO ADDITIVES OF CONCERN
GINGERBREAD MIX	**(BEEF TALLOW, LARD);* BHA; BHT**
PIE CRUST MIX; PIE CRUST STICKS	**(BEEF TALLOW, LARD);* BHA; BHT; MODIFIED CORN STARCH; SODIUM CASEINATE; TURMERIC EXTRACT**

BRANDS	ADDITIVES-OF-CONCERN **BOLD—CONCERN TO ALL** LIGHT—CONCERN TO SOME
—BIG BATCH COOKIE MIX	
DOUBLE CHOCOLATE; PEANUT BUTTER	NO ADDITIVES OF CONCERN
SUGAR	WHEY
—BROWNIE MIX	
CHOCOLATE CHIP BUTTERSCOTCH	**BHA; BHT**
FUDGE	**ARTIFICIAL COLOR; (BEEF TALLOW, LARD);* BHA; BHT**
WALNUT	**BHA; BHT;** EGG WHITES; **SODIUM CASEINATE**
—CAKE MIX	
ANGEL FOOD	EGG WHITES; **MODIFIED CORN STARCH**
CHOCOLATE PUDDING	**(BEEF TALLOW, LARD);* BHA; BHT**
GOLDEN POUND	**TURMERIC EXTRACT**
LEMON PUDDING	**ARTIFICIAL COLOR; (BEEF TALLOW, LARD);* BHA; BHT**
—SNACKIN' CAKE MIX	
APPLESAUCE RAISIN; GOLDEN CHOCOLATE CHIP	**BHA**

*Blend may contain one or more of these saturated fats.

BRANDS	ADDITIVES-OF-CONCERN BOLD—CONCERN TO ALL LIGHT—CONCERN TO SOME
BETTY CROCKER—*SNACKIN' CAKE MIX (Continued)*	
BANANA WALNUT; COCONUT PECAN	**ARTIFICIAL COLOR; BHA**
—STIR 'N FROST MIX	
CHOCOLATE CAKE/CHOCOLATE FROSTING	**BHA; BHT; SODIUM CASEINATE**
LEMON CAKE/LEMON FROSTING	**ARTIFICIAL COLOR; (BEEF TALLOW, LARD);* BHA; BHT;** EGG WHITES; **MODIFIED CORN STARCH**
YELLOW CAKE/CHOCOLATE FROSTING	**(BEEF TALLOW, LARD);* BHA; BHT; MODIFIED CORN STARCH; TURMERIC EXTRACT**
—SUPER MOIST CAKE MIX	
CHERRY CHIP	**ARTIFICIAL COLOR; (BEEF TALLOW, LARD);* BHA; BHT;** EGG WHITES; **MODIFIED CORN STARCH**
CHOCOLATE FUDGE; DEVIL'S FOOD	**(BEEF TALLOW; LARD);* BHA; BHT;** EGG WHITES; GUAR GUM; **MODIFIED CORN STARCH**
MARBLE; YELLOW	**(BEEF TALLOW, LARD);* BHA; BHT;** EGG WHITES; **MODIFIED CORN STARCH; TURMERIC EXTRACT**

BRANDS	ADDITIVES-OF-CONCERN **BOLD—CONCERN TO ALL** LIGHT—CONCERN TO SOME
WHITE	**(BEEF TALLOW, LARD);* BHA; BHT;** EGG WHITES; **MODIFIED CORN STARCH**
DROMEDARY	
GINGERBREAD MIX	**BHA**
POUND CAKE MIX	**(BEEF FAT, LARD);* BHA**
DUNCAN HINES	
ANGEL FOOD DELUXE CAKE MIX	EGG WHITES (DRIED); **MODIFIED FOOD STARCH**
DOUBLE FUDGE BROWNIE MIX	NO ADDITIVES OF CONCERN
MOIST & EASY SPICY APPLE RAISIN SNACK CAKE MIX	**ARTIFICIAL COLORING;** EGG WHITES (DRIED); **MODIFIED FOOD STARCH**
—DELUXE II CAKE MIX	
BANANA SUPREME; FUDGE MARBLE; LEMON SUPREME; YELLOW	**ARTIFICIAL COLORING; MODIFIED FOOD STARCH**
DEEP CHOCOLATE; DEVIL'S FOOD	**ARTIFICIAL COLORING; MODIFIED FOOD STARCH;** WHEY SOLIDS (DRIED)
STRAWBERRY SUPREME	**ARTIFICIAL COLORING; CONFECTIONER'S GLAZE;** WHEY SOLIDS (DRIED)
SWISS CHOCOLATE	**MODIFIED FOOD STARCH**

*Blend may contain one or more of these saturated fats.

BRANDS	**ADDITIVES-OF-CONCERN** **BOLD—CONCERN TO ALL** LIGHT—CONCERN TO SOME
DUNCAN HINES—*DELUXE II CAKE MIX (Continued)*	
WHITE	GUAR GUM; **MODIFIED FOOD STARCH;** WHEY SOLIDS (DRIED)
—PUDDING RECIPE CAKE MIX DEVIL'S FOOD	GUAR GUM; **MODIFIED FOOD STARCH;** WHEY SOLIDS (DRIED)
GERMAN CHOCOLATE	**MODIFIED FOOD STARCH**
LEMON; YELLOW	**ARTIFICIAL COLOR; MODIFIED FOOD STARCH**
JELL-O CHEESECAKE MIX	**ARTIFICIAL COLOR; BHA; MODIFIED TAPIOCA STARCH; SODIUM CASEINATE;** WHEY
JIFFY FUDGE BROWNIE MIX	**BHA; BHT; (TALLOW)***
PIE CRUST MIX	**BHA; BHT; (LARD, TALLOW)***
—CAKE MIX DEVIL'S FOOD; WHITE	**BHA; BHT; CALCIUM CASEINATE; (LARD, TALLOW);*** WHEY
GOLDEN YELLOW	**BHA; BHT; CALCIUM CASEINATE;** FD & C YELLOW NO. 5; **(LARD, TALLOW);*** WHEY

BRANDS	**ADDITIVES-OF-CONCERN** BOLD—CONCERN TO ALL LIGHT—CONCERN TO SOME
NESTLÉ *COOKIE MIX*	
CHOCOLATE CHIP; PEANUT BUTTER	NO ADDITIVES OF CONCERN
SUGAR	**(HYDROGENATED COTTONSEED, PALM, SOYBEAN OILS);*** WHEY
PILLSBURY	
DELUXE FUDGE BROWNIE MIX	**BEEF FAT; BHA**
PIE CRUST MIX	**ARTIFICIAL COLOR; (BEEF FAT, LARD);* BHA; BHT**
SOUR CREAM COFFEE CAKE MIX	**(BEEF FAT, HYDROGENATED SOYBEAN OIL, LARD);* BHA; BHT**
—BUNDT CAKE FILLING AND GLAZE MIX	
FUDGE NUT CROWN	**ARTIFICIAL COLOR; (BEEF FAT, LARD; HYDROGENATED COCONUT, COTTONSEED, PALM, SOYBEAN OILS);* BHA; BHT; MODIFIED TAPIOCA STARCH**
LEMON BLUEBERRY	**ARTIFICIAL COLOR; BHA; BHT; MODIFIED TAPIOCA STARCH**

*Blend may contain one or more of these saturated fats and/or oils.

BRANDS	ADDITIVES-OF-CONCERN BOLD—CONCERN TO ALL LIGHT—CONCERN TO SOME
PILLSBURY *(Continued)*	
—PLUS CAKE MIX	
DARK CHOCOLATE	**(BEEF FAT, LARD; HYDROGENATED COTTONSEED, PALM, SOYBEAN OILS);* BHA; BHT; MODIFIED TAPIOCA STARCH;** WHEY PROTEIN
FUDGE MARBLE; LEMON; YELLOW	**ARTIFICIAL COLOR; (BEEF FAT, LARD; HYDROGENATED COTTONSEED, PALM, SOYBEAN OILS);* BHA; BHT; MODIFIED TAPIOCA STARCH**
WHITE	**(BEEF FAT, LARD; HYDROGENATED COTTONSEED, PALM, SOYBEAN OILS);* BHA; BHT;** EGG WHITES; **MODIFIED TAPIOCA STARCH**
—STREUSEL SWIRL CAKE MIX	
CINNAMON; LEMON SUPREME	**ARTIFICIAL COLOR; (BEEF FAT, LARD; HYDROGENATED COCONUT, COTTONSEED, SOYBEAN OILS);* BHA; BHT; MODIFIED TAPIOCA STARCH;** WHEY PROTEIN

BRANDS	ADDITIVES-OF-CONCERN BOLD—CONCERN TO ALL LIGHT—CONCERN TO SOME
FUDGE MARBLE	**ARTIFICIAL COLOR; (BEEF FAT, LARD; HYDROGENATED COCONUT, COTTONSEED, PALM, SOYBEAN OILS);* BHA; BHT; MODIFIED TAPIOCA STARCH;** WHEY PROTEIN
ROYAL REAL CHEESE CAKE MIX	**ARTIFICIAL COLOR; MODIFIED FOOD STARCH; SODIUM CASEINATE;** WHEY
QUAKER *COOKIE MIX*	
CHOCOLATE CHIP	WHEY (DRIED)
OATMEAL	NO ADDITIVES OF CONCERN
SUPERMARKET PRIVATE BRANDS	
FIRST NATIONAL	
—EDWARDS-FINAST	
FUDGE BROWNIE MIX	**ARTIFICIAL COLOR; (BEEF FAT, LARD);* BHA; MODIFIED CORN STARCH**
—DELUXE CAKE MIX	
FUDGE MARBLE; LEMON; YELLOW	**ARTIFICIAL COLOR; (BEEF FAT, LARD);* BHA;** GUAR GUM; **MODIFIED CORN STARCH**
WHITE	**(BEEF FAT, LARD);* BHA;** GUAR GUM; **MODIFIED CORN STARCH;** WHEY
—FINAST FLAKY PIE CRUST MIX	**COCONUT OIL**

*Blend may contain one or more of these saturated fats and/or oils.

BRANDS	ADDITIVES-OF-CONCERN BOLD—CONCERN TO ALL LIGHT—CONCERN TO SOME
LUCKY —LADY LEE *CAKE MIX*	
DEVIL'S FOOD; WHITE	**CALCIUM CASEINATE;** GUAR GUM; **SODIUM CASEINATE;** WHEY (SWEET)
LEMON; YELLOW	**ARTIFICIAL COLORING; CALCIUM CASEINATE;** GUAR GUM; **MODIFIED WHEAT STARCH; SODIUM CASEINATE;** WHEY (SWEET)
SAFEWAY —MRS. WRIGHT'S *CAKE MIX*	
BUTTER RECIPE	**ARTIFICIAL COLOR; (BEEF FAT, LARD);* BHA; MODIFIED CORN STARCH**
PUDDING DELIGHT DEVIL'S FOOD	**(BEEF FAT, LARD);* BHA; MODIFIED FOOD STARCH**
—*DELUXE CAKE MIX*	
ANGEL FOOD	EGG WHITES
DEVIL'S FOOD	**BHA;** GUAR GUM; **MODIFIED CORN STARCH**
LEMON; YELLOW	**ARTIFICIAL COLOR; (BEEF FAT, LARD);* BHA;** GUAR GUM; **MODIFIED CORN STARCH**
WHITE	**(BEEF FAT, LARD);* BHA;** GUAR GUM; **MODIFIED CORN STARCH;** WHEY

BRANDS	ADDITIVES-OF-CONCERN **BOLD—CONCERN TO ALL** LIGHT—CONCERN TO SOME
STOP & SHOP —STOP & SHOP FUDGE BROWNIE MIX	**ARTIFICIAL COLOR; (BEEF FAT, LARD);* BHA; MODIFIED CORN STARCH**
—DELUXE CAKE MIX DEVIL'S FOOD	**BHA;** GUAR GUM; **MODIFIED CORN STARCH**
FUDGE MARBLE; LEMON	**ARTIFICIAL COLOR; (BEEF FAT, COCONUT OIL, LARD);* BHA; BHT;** GUAR GUM; **MODIFIED CORN STARCH**
WHITE	**(BEEF FAT, COCONUT OIL, LARD);* BHA; BHT;** GUAR GUM; **MODIFIED CORN STARCH;** WHEY
WINN DIXIE **—DIXIE DARLING** FUDGE BROWNIE MIX	**(BEEF FAT, COCONUT OIL, LARD);* BHA; BHT; COLOR; MODIFIED CORN STARCH**
—CAKE MIX DEVIL'S FOOD	GUAR GUM; **MODIFIED CORN STARCH**
LEMON; YELLOW	**ARTIFICIAL COLOR; (BEEF FAT, COCONUT OIL, LARD);* BHA; BHT;** GUAR GUM; **MODIFIED CORN STARCH**

*Blend may contain one or more of these saturated fats and/or oils.

BRANDS	ADDITIVES-OF-CONCERN **BOLD—CONCERN TO ALL** LIGHT—CONCERN TO SOME
ITEMS IN HEALTH FOOD STORES	
ARROWHEAD MILLS	
WHOLE GRAIN CAROB CAKE	NO ADDITIVES OF CONCERN
FEARN *CAKE MIX*	
CAROB	WHEY (SWEET DAIRY)
CARROT; SPICE	**NUTMEG;** WHEY (SWEET DAIRY)

DESSERT TOPPINGS (OTHER THAN WHIPPED CREAM OR WHIPPED-CREAM SUBSTITUTES)

EVAN'S WALNUT DESSERT TOPPING	NO ADDITIVES OF CONCERN
JOHNSTON'S	
BUTTERSCOTCH-READY TOPPING	NO ADDITIVES OF CONCERN
KRAFT *TOPPING*	
BUTTERSCOTCH; STRAWBERRY; WALNUT	**ARTIFICIAL COLOR**
CHOCOLATE	WHEY
PINEAPPLE	NO ADDITIVES OF CONCERN
SMUCKER'S *TOPPING*	
BUTTERSCOTCH; PINEAPPLE	**ARTIFICIAL COLOR**
CHOCOLATE FUDGE	NO ADDITIVES OF CONCERN

BRANDS	**ADDITIVES-OF-CONCERN** **BOLD—CONCERN TO ALL** LIGHT—CONCERN TO SOME

FROSTINGS (CANNED & MIXES)

BRANDS	ADDITIVES-OF-CONCERN
BETTY CROCKER *—FROSTING MIX* CHOCOLATE FUDGE	**BHA; BHT**
FLUFFY WHITE	EGG WHITES; **MODIFIED CORN STARCH**
—CREAMY DELUXE READY TO SPREAD FROSTING CHOCOLATE	**(BEEF TALLOW, LARD);* BHA; BHT**
SOUR CREAM WHITE; SUNKIST LEMON	**ARTIFICIAL COLOR; (BEEF TALLOW, LARD);* BHA; BHT**
JIFFY *FROSTING MIX* FUDGE	**BHA; BHT; (TALLOW);*** WHEY
WHITE	**BHA; BHT; CALCIUM CASEINATE; (TALLOW);*** WHEY
PILLSBURY *—READY TO SPREAD FROSTING SUPREME* CHOCOLATE FUDGE; MILK CHOCOLATE	**(BEEF FAT, HYDROGENATED COTTONSEED, PALM, SOYBEAN OILS);* BHA; BHT;** GUAR GUM

*Blend may contain one or more of these saturated fats and/or oils.

BRANDS	ADDITIVES-OF-CONCERN BOLD—CONCERN TO ALL LIGHT—CONCERN TO SOME
PILLSBURY *(Continued)*	
VANILLA	**ARTIFICIAL COLOR; (BEEF FAT, HYDROGENATED COTTONSEED, PALM, SOYBEAN OILS);* BHA; BHT;** GUAR GUM
SUPERMARKET PRIVATE BRANDS	
A & P	
—ANN PAGE	
FROSTING MIX	
CHOCOLATE FUDGE; MILK CHOCOLATE	NO ADDITIVES OF CONCERN
CREAMY WHITE	**ARTIFICIAL COLOR**
FIRST NATIONAL	
—EDWARDS	
FROSTING	
CREAMY FUDGE; CREAMY WHITE	**ARTIFICIAL COLOR; (BEEF FAT, COCONUT OIL, LARD);* BHA; MODIFIED FOOD STARCH**
LUCKY	
—LADY LEE	
CREAMY WHITE FROSTING MIX	**ARTIFICIAL COLORING**
SAFEWAY	
—MRS. WRIGHT'S	
FROSTING MIX	
CHOCOLATE FUDGE	**BHA**
WHITE	**ARTIFICIAL COLOR; (BEEF FAT, LARD);* BHA; MODIFIED CORN STARCH**

BRANDS	ADDITIVES-OF-CONCERN BOLD—CONCERN TO ALL LIGHT—CONCERN TO SOME
STOP & SHOP —STOP & SHOP *DELUXE FROSTING MIX*	
CHOCOLATE FUDGE	**BHA**
CREAMY WHITE	**ARTIFICIAL COLOR; (BEEF FAT, COCONUT OIL, LARD);* BHA; BHT**
—READY TO SPREAD FROSTING	
CHOCOLATE; VANILLA	**ARTIFICIAL COLOR; (BEEF FAT, COCONUT OIL, LARD);* BHA; MODIFIED FOOD STARCH**
WINN DIXIE —DIXIE DARLING *FROSTING MIX*	
FUDGE	**BHA; BHT**
WHITE	**ARTIFICIAL COLOR; BHA; BHT; MODIFIED CORN STARCH**

GELATIN & GELATIN DESSERTS

JELL-O *GELATIN DESSERT*	
APRICOT; CHERRY; PEACH; RASPBERRY; STRAWBERRY; STRAWBERRY/BANANA	**ARTIFICIAL COLOR**
LEMON; LIME; MIXED FRUIT; ORANGE	**ARTIFICIAL COLOR; BHA**

*Blend may contain one or more of these saturated fats and/or oils.

BRANDS	ADDITIVES-OF-CONCERN BOLD—CONCERN TO ALL LIGHT—CONCERN TO SOME
KNOX	
ORANGE DRINKING GELATINE	**ARTIFICIAL COLOR;** GUM ARABIC
UNFLAVORED GELATINE	NO ADDITIVES OF CONCERN
ROYAL *GELATIN DESSERT*	
CHERRY; LEMON; ORANGE; PEACH; RASPBERRY; STRAWBERRY	**ARTIFICIAL COLOR**
SUPERMARKET PRIVATE BRANDS	
A & P	
—ANN PAGE	
UNFLAVORED GELATIN	NO ADDITIVES OF CONCERN
—GELATIN DESSERT	
APRICOT; CHERRY; RED RASPBERRY	**ARTIFICIAL COLOR**
LEMON; LIME	**ARTIFICIAL COLOR; BHA**
LUCKY	
—LADY LEE *GELATIN DESSERT*	
LEMON; LIME; ORANGE; RASPBERRY; STRAWBERRY	**ARTIFICIAL COLOR** OR **COLORS**
SAFEWAY	
—JELL-WELL *GELATIN DESSERT*	
BLACK RASPBERRY;	**ARTIFICIAL COLOR**

(continues)

BRANDS	ADDITIVES-OF-CONCERN **BOLD—CONCERN TO ALL** LIGHT—CONCERN TO SOME
CHERRY; LEMON; MIXED-FRUIT; ORANGE; RASPBERRY; STRAWBERRY	**ARTIFICIAL COLOR**
STOP & SHOP —STOP & SHOP KITCHENS *GELATIN DESSERT*	
CHERRY APPLE; FRUIT SALAD; PINEAPPLE CARROT	**ARTIFICIAL COLOR**

PANCAKE & WAFFLE MIXES

AUNT JEMIMA *PANCAKE & WAFFLE MIX*	
BUCKWHEAT	NO ADDITIVES OF CONCERN
BUTTERMILK	**ARTIFICIAL COLORING;** BUTTERMILK SOLIDS (DRIED)
BUTTERMILK COMPLETE	**ARTIFICIAL COLORING;** BUTTERMILK SOLIDS (DRIED); **CARRAGEENAN;** WHEY (DRIED)
COMPLETE	**ARTIFICIAL COLORING;** WHEY (DRIED)
LOG CABIN	
COMPLETE PANCAKE & WAFFLE MIX	WHEY

BRANDS	**ADDITIVES-OF-CONCERN** BOLD—CONCERN TO ALL LIGHT—CONCERN TO SOME
PILLSBURY *HUNGRY JACK* COMPLETE PANCAKE MIX	EGG WHITES; **HYDROGENATED SOYBEAN OIL; SODIUM CASEINATE**
EXTRA LIGHTS PANCAKE & WAFFLE MIX	NO ADDITIVES OF CONCERN
SUPERMARKET PRIVATE BRANDS	
FIRST NATIONAL —EDWARDS-FINAST	
PANCAKE & WAFFLE MIX	
BUTTERMILK	**MODIFIED CORN STARCH**
COMPLETE	**BHA;** EGG WHITES; WHEY
OLD FASHIONED	**ARTIFICIAL COLOR**
STOP & SHOP —STOP & SHOP	
PANCAKE & WAFFLE MIX	
COMPLETE	**BHA; BHT;** EGG WHITES; WHEY
OLD FASHIONED	**ARTIFICIAL COLOR**
ITEMS IN HEALTH FOOD STORES	
ARROWHEAD MILLS	
MULTIGRAIN PANCAKE & WAFFLE MIX	NO ADDITIVES OF CONCERN

BRANDS	ADDITIVES-OF-CONCERN BOLD—CONCERN TO ALL LIGHT—CONCERN TO SOME
FEARN SOY/O *PANCAKE MIX* BUCKWHEAT; WHOLE WHEAT	NO ADDITIVES OF CONCERN
JOLLY JOAN WHEAT & SOY PANCAKE & WAFFLE MIX	BUTTERMILK SOLIDS (DRY); MILK SOLIDS (NONFAT DRY); WHEY (SWEET DAIRY)
KRUSTEAZ WHOLE WHEAT 'N HONEY COMPLETE PANCAKE MIX	**CALCIUM CASEINATE; CALCIUM STEARATE; CARRAGEENAN;** EGG WHITES; **SODIUM CASEINATE;** WHEY (SWEET)
SHILOH FARMS WHOLE WHEAT PANCAKE MIX	NO ADDITIVES OF CONCERN

PIE & PUDDING FILLINGS (CANNED & MIXES)

BRANDS	ADDITIVES-OF-CONCERN
BETTY CROCKER *PUDDING* CHOCOLATE; TAPIOCA	**ARTIFICIAL COLOR; MODIFIED TAPIOCA STARCH**
RICE	**ARTIFICIAL COLOR; MODIFIED CORN STARCH**
BORDEN NONE SUCH MINCE MEAT	**MODIFIED FOOD STARCH**
COMSTOCK APPLE PIE FILLING	**MODIFIED FOOD STARCH; TURMERIC**

BRANDS	ADDITIVES-OF-CONCERN BOLD—CONCERN TO ALL LIGHT—CONCERN TO SOME
DEL MONTE *PUDDING CUP*	
CHOCOLATE; VANILLA	**ARTIFICIAL COLOR;** FD & C YELLOW NO. 5; **MODIFIED FOOD STARCH**
HUNT'S *SNACK PACK PUDDING*	
BUTTERSCOTCH; TAPIOCA; VANILLA	**ARTIFICIAL COLORS; MODIFIED FOOD STARCH**
CHOCOLATE; CHOCOLATE FUDGE	**MODIFIED FOOD STARCH**
JELL-O	
—AMERICANA	
CHOCOLATE TAPIOCA PUDDING	NO ADDITIVES OF CONCERN
GOLDEN EGG CUSTARD	**ARTIFICIAL COLOR; BHA; CALCIUM CARRAGEENAN;** WHEY
RICE PUDDING	**ARTIFICIAL COLOR; CALCIUM CARRAGEENAN**
—INSTANT PUDDING & PIE FILLING	
BUTTERSCOTCH; VANILLA	**ARTIFICIAL COLOR; BHA; MODIFIED CORN & TAPIOCA STARCHES**
CHOCOLATE; CHOCOLATE FUDGE	**BHA; MODIFIED CORN & TAPIOCA STARCHES**
—PUDDING & PIE FILLING	

(continues)

BRANDS	**ADDITIVES-OF-CONCERN** **BOLD—CONCERN TO ALL** LIGHT—CONCERN TO SOME
BANANA CREAM; BUTTERSCOTCH; COCONUT CREAM; VANILLA	**ARTIFICIAL COLOR; CALCIUM CARRAGEENAN; MODIFIED CORN STARCH**
CHOCOLATE; CHOCOLATE FUDGE	**CALCIUM CARRAGEENAN; MODIFIED CORN STARCH**
LEMON	**ARTIFICIAL COLOR; BHA; MODIFIED TAPIOCA STARCH**
JUNKET	
DANISH DESSERT PUDDING-PIE FILLING RASPBERRY-CURRANT; RENNET CUSTARD RASPBERRY	**ARTIFICIAL COLOR** OR **COLORS**
RENNET CUSTARD VANILLA	NO ADDITIVES OF CONCERN
MINUTE TAPIOCA	NO ADDITIVES OF CONCERN
MY-T-FINE *PUDDING & PIE FILLING*	
CHOCOLATE; VANILLA	**ARTIFICIAL COLOR; CALCIUM CARRAGEENAN; MODIFIED CORN STARCH**
LEMON	**ARTIFICIAL COLOR; MODIFIED TAPIOCA STARCH**
ROYAL	
TAPIOCA VANILLA PUDDING	**ARTIFICIAL COLOR**

BRANDS	ADDITIVES-OF-CONCERN **BOLD—CONCERN TO ALL** LIGHT—CONCERN TO SOME
ROYAL *(Continued)*	
—INSTANT PUDDING & PIE FILLING	
BUTTERSCOTCH	**ARTIFICIAL COLOR; MODIFIED FOOD STARCH;** SODIUM ALGINATE
CHOCOLATE; DARK 'N' SWEET CHOCOLATE	**ARTIFICIAL COLOR; MODIFIED FOOD STARCH**
—PIE FILLING	
KEY LIME; LEMON	**ARTIFICIAL COLOR; CALCIUM CARRAGEENAN; MODIFIED TAPIOCA STARCH**
—PUDDING & PIE FILLING	
BUTTERSCOTCH; CHOCOLATE; VANILLA	**ARTIFICIAL COLOR; CALCIUM CARRAGEENAN**
THANK YOU *PUDDING*	
BUTTERSCOTCH; TAPIOCA	**ARTIFICIAL COLORING** W/ FD & C YELLOW NO. 5; **MODIFIED FOOD STARCH**
CHOCOLATE FUDGE	**MODIFIED FOOD STARCH**
WYMAN'S *PIE FILLING*	
APPLE; WILD BLUEBERRY	NO ADDITIVES OF CONCERN
STRAWBERRY	**ARTIFICIAL COLORING**
SUPERMARKET PRIVATE BRANDS	
A & P	
—ANN PAGE	
EGG CUSTARD MIX	**ARTIFICIAL COLORS; CALCIUM CARRAGEENAN;** MILK SOLIDS (NONFAT DRY)

BRANDS	ADDITIVES-OF-CONCERN BOLD—CONCERN TO ALL LIGHT—CONCERN TO SOME
—INSTANT PUDDING BUTTERSCOTCH; CHOCOLATE; TOASTED COCONUT; VANILLA	**ARTIFICIAL COLOR; MODIFIED STARCH (PRECOOKED)**
—PUDDING & PIE FILLING BANANA CREAM; BUTTERSCOTCH; CHOCOLATE; LEMON; VANILLA	**ARTIFICIAL COLOR**
COCONUT	**ARTIFICIAL COLOR; CALCIUM CARRAGEENAN**
—TAPIOCA PUDDING CHOCOLATE; VANILLA	**ARTIFICIAL COLOR**
SAFEWAY —JELL-WELL *INSTANT PUDDING & PIE FILLING* CHOCOLATE	**BHA;** MILK SOLIDS (NONFAT); **MODIFIED CORN & TAPIOCA STARCHES**
LEMON; PISTACHIO; VANILLA	**ARTIFICIAL COLOR; BHA;** MILK SOLIDS (NONFAT); **MODIFIED CORN & TAPIOCA STARCHES**

BRANDS	ADDITIVES-OF-CONCERN BOLD—CONCERN TO ALL LIGHT—CONCERN TO SOME
—TOWN HOUSE *PUDDING* BUTTERSCOTCH; RICE; TAPIOCA; VANILLA	**ARTIFICIAL COLOR; MODIFIED FOOD STARCH**
CHOCOLATE	**MODIFIED FOOD STARCH**
WINN DIXIE —THRIFTY MAID *PUDDING SNACK* BUTTERSCOTCH; VANILLA	**ARTIFICIAL COLOR; MODIFIED FOOD STARCH**
CHOCOLATE; CHOCOLATE FUDGE	**MODIFIED FOOD STARCH**

VI. BEVERAGE MIXES & BEVERAGES

CARBONATED BEVERAGES

Sugars like sucrose (cane and beet sugar), corn sweeteners (corn syrup, dextrose, fructose, etc.), and honey have not been treated in this volume as additives of concern in the amounts they are used as additives in many foods. However, when they comprise a substantial percentage of a food, a caution is warranted and has been noted for candy and gum, ready-to-eat cereals, carbonated beverages, and jellies and other sweet spreads. A Department of Agriculture study (Nutrient Composition Laboratory, USDA, June 10, 1980, news release) revealed a sugar content of 1 to 1½ ounces per 12-ounce can of some sodas. In almost all sodas the most abundant ingredient next to water was sugar, except for plain club soda, which did not contain sugar.

BRANDS	**ADDITIVES-OF-CONCERN** BOLD—CONCERN TO ALL LIGHT—CONCERN TO SOME
BARRELHEAD ROOT BEER	ACACIA GUM
CANADA DRY CLUB SODA; COLLINS MIXER; GINGER ALE	NO ADDITIVES OF CONCERN
HALF & HALF	**ESTER GUM**
JAMAICA COLA	ACACIA GUM; CAFFEINE
ORANGE SODA	**ARTIFICIAL COLORING; ESTER GUM**
TONIC WATER	QUININE
COCA-COLA	CAFFEINE

BRANDS	ADDITIVES-OF-CONCERN **BOLD—CONCERN TO ALL** LIGHT—CONCERN TO SOME
COTT	
COLA	ACACIA GUM; CAFFEINE
CREAM SODA; DRY GINGER ALE; SPARKLING WATER	NO ADDITIVES OF CONCERN
ENERGADE; HALF & HALF	ACACIA GUM; **BROMINATED VEGETABLE OIL; GLYCERYL ABIETATE**
ORANGE SODA; FRUIT PUNCH SODA	ACACIA GUM; **ARTIFICIAL COLOR; BROMINATED VEGETABLE OIL; GLYCERYL ABIETATE**
TONIC WATER	EXTRACT OF QUININE
CRUSH ORANGE SODA	ACACIA GUM; **ARTIFICIAL COLOR; BROMINATED VEGETABLE OIL; GLYCEROL ESTER OF WOOD ROSIN**
DR PEPPER	CAFFEINE
HIRES ROOT BEER	NO ADDITIVES OF CONCERN
KEEFERS	
CLUB SODA BUBBLY WATER; GINGER ALE	NO ADDITIVES OF CONCERN
TONIC MIXER QUININE WATER	QUININE SALTS
MELLO YELLO	
CITRUS SODA	ACACIA GUM; **ARTIFICIAL COLOR; BROMINATED VEGETABLE OIL;** CAFFEINE; LOCUST BEAN GUM

BRANDS	ADDITIVES-OF-CONCERN **BOLD—CONCERN TO ALL** LIGHT—CONCERN TO SOME
MOUNTAIN DEW	**BROMINATED VEGETABLE OIL;** CAFFEINE; FD & C YELLOW NO. 5; GUM ARABIC
PEPSI-COLA	CAFFEINE
SCHWEPPES	
BITTER LEMON	QUININE
CLUB SODA; GINGER ALE; ROOT BEER	NO ADDITIVES OF CONCERN
ORANGE	**ARTIFICIAL COLOR**
TONIC WATER	QUININE
7-UP	NO ADDITIVES OF CONCERN
SUNKIST ORANGE SODA	ACACIA GUM; **ARTIFICIAL COLOR; BHA;** CAFFEINE; **GLYCERYL ABIETATE**
WELCH'S GRAPE SODA	**ARTIFICIAL COLORS**
SUPERMARKET PRIVATE BRANDS	
A & P	
—YUKON	
COLA	CAFFEINE; GUM ARABIC
GINGER ALE	NO ADDITIVES OF CONCERN
ORANGE SODA	**ARTIFICIAL COLOR; BROMINATED VEGETABLE OIL; GLYCERYL ABIETATE;** GUM ARABIC
LUCKY	
—LADY LEE	
BLACK CHERRY SODA	ACACIA GUM; **ARTIFICIAL COLOR**

BRANDS	**ADDITIVES-OF-CONCERN** **BOLD—CONCERN TO ALL** LIGHT—CONCERN TO SOME
—LADY LEE *(Continued)*	
COLA	CAFFEINE
CREME SODA; GINGER ALE	NO ADDITIVES OF CONCERN
ORANGE SODA	ACACIA GUM; **ARTIFICIAL COLOR; BROMINATED VEGETABLE OIL; GLYCERYL ABIETATE**
ROOT BEER	**MODIFIED FOOD STARCH**
PUBLIX	
—PIX	
BLACK CHERRY SODA; STRAWBERRY SODA	**ARTIFICIAL COLOR**
COLA	ACACIA [GUM]; CAFFEINE
CREAM SODA; GINGER ALE; LEMON-HI SODA	NO ADDITIVES OF CONCERN
GRAPE SODA	ACACIA [GUM]; **ARTIFICIAL COLOR**
ORANGE SODA	ACACIA [GUM]; **ARTIFICIAL COLOR; BROMINATED VEGETABLE OIL; GLYCEROL ESTER OF WOOD ROSIN**
QUININE TONIC WATER	QUININE

BRANDS	ADDITIVES-OF-CONCERN BOLD—CONCERN TO ALL LIGHT—CONCERN TO SOME
SAFEWAY —CRAGMONT	
BLACK CHERRY SODA; CHERRY COLA; GRAPE SODA; STRAWBERRY SODA	**ARTIFICIAL COLOR** OR **COLORING;** GUM ARABIC
COLLINS MIX	**BROMINATED VEGETABLE OIL; GLYCERYL ABIETATE;** GUM ARABIC
CREAM SODA; GINGER ALE; LEMON LIME SODA	NO ADDITIVES OF CONCERN
ORANGE SODA; SPARKLING PUNCH	**ARTIFICIAL COLOR; BROMINATED VEGETABLE OIL; GLYCERYL ABIETATE;** GUM ARABIC
TONIC MIX	QUININE HYDROCHLORIDE
STOP & SHOP —SUN GLORY	
COLA	ACACIA GUM; CAFFEINE
CREME SODA; GINGER ALE; SQUEEZ O' LEMON SODA	NO ADDITIVES OF CONCERN
LEMON & LIME SODA; ORANGE SODA	ACACIA GUM; **ARTIFICIAL COLOR; BROMINATED VEGETABLE OIL; GLYCERYL ABIETATE**
ROOT BEER	ACACIA GUM
WINN DIXIE —CHEK COLA	CAFFEINE

BRANDS	**ADDITIVES-OF-CONCERN** BOLD—CONCERN TO ALL LIGHT—CONCERN TO SOME
WINN DIXIE—CHEK *(Continued)*	
CREME SODA; GINGER ALE; LEMON LIME SODA; ROOT BEER	NO ADDITIVES OF CONCERN
GRAPE SODA	ACACIA GUM; **ARTIFICIAL COLOR**
ORANGE SODA	**ARTIFICIAL COLOR; BROMINATED VEGETABLE OIL; GLYCEROL ESTER OF WOOD ROSIN**
ITEMS IN HEALTH FOOD STORES	
CORR'S GINSENG RUSH	NO ADDITIVES OF CONCERN
DR. TIMA KOLA	NO ADDITIVES OF CONCERN
HANSEN'S *SODA*	
GRAPEFRUIT; LEMON LIME	NO ADDITIVES OF CONCERN
HEALTH VALLEY	
HONEY PINEAPPLE SODA; IMITATION CREME COLA	NO ADDITIVES OF CONCERN
HONEY PURE	
ENGLISH GINGER; MOUNTAIN ROOT BEER	NO ADDITIVES OF CONCERN
NECTAREL	
LIME ORANGE; ROOT BEER	NO ADDITIVES OF CONCERN
ORIGINAL	**TURMERIC**
SOHO BLACK CHERRY SODA	NO ADDITIVES OF CONCERN

BRANDS	ADDITIVES-OF-CONCERN BOLD—CONCERN TO ALL LIGHT—CONCERN TO SOME

CHOCOLATE DRINKS, INSTANT BREAKFAST MIXES, LIQUID MEALS, MILK MODIFIERS (COCOA MIXES, SYRUPS)

BOSCO CHOCOLATE FLAVORED SYRUP	**ARTIFICIAL COLOR**
CARNATION	
—INSTANT BREAKFAST	
EGGNOG	**AMMONIUM CARRAGEENAN; ARTIFICIAL COLOR; FERRIC ORTHOPHOSPHATE; SODIUM CASEINATE**
CHOCOLATE; CHOCOLATE MALT	**AMMONIUM CARRAGEENAN; FERRIC ORTHOPHOSPHATE; SODIUM CASEINATE**
COFFEE; VANILLA	**AMMONIUM CARRAGEENAN; FERRIC ORTHOPHOSPHATE**
—INSTANT HOT COCOA MIX	
COCO SUPREME; RICH CHOCOLATE	**SODIUM CASEINATE**
W/ MINI-MARSHMALLOWS	**ARTIFICIAL COLOR; SODIUM CASEINATE**
HERSHEY'S	
HOT COCOA MIX	**ARTIFICIAL COLORING; SODIUM CASEINATE; STABILIZERS**

BRANDS	ADDITIVES-OF-CONCERN BOLD—CONCERN TO ALL LIGHT—CONCERN TO SOME
HERSHEY'S *(Continued)*	
INSTANT; SYRUP CHOCOLATE	NO ADDITIVES OF CONCERN
MILK MATE	
CHOCOLATE SYRUP	**ARTIFICIAL COLOR; MODIFIED FOOD STARCH**
NESTLÉ	
QUIK CHOCOLATE	NO ADDITIVES OF CONCERN
QUIK STRAWBERRY	**ARTIFICIAL COLOR**
HOT COCOA MIX	WHEY
HOT COCOA MIX W/ MINI-MARSHMALLOWS	**ARTIFICIAL COLOR;** WHEY
NUTRAMENT	
DUTCH CHOCOLATE	**ARTIFICIAL COLOR; CALCIUM CASEINATE; CARRAGEENAN; SODIUM CASEINATE**
VANILLA	**CALCIUM CASEINATE; CARRAGEENAN; SODIUM CASEINATE**
OVALTINE	
CHOCOLATE; MALT	**FERRIC SODIUM PYROPHOSPHATE;** WHEY
HOT COCOA MIX	**ARTIFICIAL COLOR; CARRAGEENAN; (COCONUT OIL);* FERRIC SODIUM PYROPHOSPHATE; SODIUM CASEINATE;** WHEY

*Blend may contain this saturated oil.

BRANDS	**ADDITIVES-OF-CONCERN** **BOLD—CONCERN TO ALL** LIGHT—CONCERN TO SOME
PARTY TIME CHOCOMITE	**ARTIFICIAL COLOR; CARRAGEENAN; COCONUT FAT [OIL];** GUAR GUM; **SODIUM CASEINATE**
PDQ CHOCOLATE MILK FLAVORING	**ARTIFICIAL COLOR**
QWIP CHOCOLATE SHAKE	**CARRAGEENAN; COCONUT OIL;** WHEY
SWISS MISS *HOT COCOA MIX* LITE; MILK CHOCOLATE; W/ MINI-MARSHMALLOWS	NO ADDITIVES OF CONCERN
SUPERMARKET PRIVATE BRANDS	
FIRST NATIONAL —FINAST INSTANT CHOCOLATE FLAVORED MIX	WHEY SOLIDS
PUBLIX —DAIRI-FRESH CHOCOLATE DRINK	**CARRAGEENAN;** GUAR GUM; **SODIUM CASEINATE;** WHEY
SAFEWAY —LUCERNE *INSTANT BREAKFAST* CHOCOLATE MALT; COFFEE; VANILLA	**CARRAGEENAN**
CHOCOLATE FUDGE; EGGNOG; STRAWBERRY	**ARTIFICIAL COLOR; CARRAGEENAN**

BRANDS	ADDITIVES-OF-CONCERN BOLD—CONCERN TO ALL LIGHT—CONCERN TO SOME
—LUCERNE *INSTANT HOT COCOA MIX* (REGULAR); W/ MINI-MARSHMALLOWS	**ARTIFICIAL COLOR; SODIUM CASEINATE**
STOP & SHOP	
—STOP & SHOP	
HOT COCOA MIX	**ARTIFICIAL COLOR; SODIUM CASEINATE**
INSTANT CHOCOLATE FLAVORED MIX	NO ADDITIVES OF CONCERN
—FLAVORED SYRUP	
COFFEE	NO ADDITIVES OF CONCERN
FRUIT PUNCH; GRAPE; ORANGE	**U.S. CERTIFIED FOOD COLORS**
WINN DIXIE	
—SUPERBRAND	
CHOCO-RIFFIC DRINK	**ARTIFICIAL COLORS; CARRAGEENAN;** GUAR GUM; **SODIUM CASEINATE;** WHEY
ITEMS IN HEALTH FOOD STORES	
CHRISTOPHER'S	
MALTED MILK	
CAROB	MILK PROTEIN; SODIUM ALGINATE
VANILLA	ALGIN
HORLICKS INSTANT MALTED MILK	NO ADDITIVES OF CONCERN

COFFEE BEVERAGES & COFFEE SUBSTITUTES, DECAFFEINATED COFFEE, GROUND & INSTANT COFFEE

Most of the items in this section did not contain any additives of concern, and these appear first, without an additives-of-concern column.

The items that do contain additives of concern follow, in the usual style.

Regular and instant coffees—and some coffee substitutes—contain a significant amount of caffeine as a natural component, not as an additive. Whether present naturally or added, caffeine is believed to be of concern to the health of some individuals.

BRIM DECAFFEINATED; FREEZE-DRIED DECAFFEINATED
CHOCK FULL O' NUTS ALL-METHOD GRIND; INSTANT
FOLGER'S FLAKED; REGULAR
FRENCH MARKET COFFEE & CHICORY
HILLS BROS. REGULAR
KAVA INSTANT
MAXIM FREEZE-DRIED
MAX-PAX REGULAR
MAXWELL HOUSE INSTANT; REGULAR
MEDAGLIA D'ORO CAFFÉ ESPRESSO
MELLOW ROAST INSTANT; REGULAR
NESCAFÉ DECAFFEINATED INSTANT; INSTANT
PARADE DELUXE BLEND REGULAR; INSTANT
POSTUM ARTIFICIAL COFFEE FLAVOR; REGULAR
SANKA FREEZE-DRIED INSTANT; INSTANT; REGULAR
SUNRISE INSTANT COFFEE MELLOWED W/ CHICORY
TASTER'S CHOICE FREEZE-DRIED; FREEZE-DRIED DECAFFEINATED
YUBAN INSTANT; REGULAR/DRIP

SUPERMARKET PRIVATE BRANDS

FIRST NATIONAL FINAST DRIP GRIND; ELECTRIC PERK; FREEZE DRIED; INSTANT; REGULAR GRIND
LUCKY LADY LEE DRIP-FILTER GRIND; ELECTRIC PERK; FREEZE-DRIED; REGULAR GRIND
PUBLIX BREAKFAST CLUB 100% COLOMBIAN ALL PURPOSE GRIND

SAFEWAY ALL-PURPOSE GRIND; INSTANT
SAFEWAY EDWARDS DRIP OR FINE GRIND; FOR ELECTRIC PERCOLATORS; REGULAR GRIND; FLAKE GRIND; WHOLE-BEAN
SAFEWAY SCOTCH BUY INSTANT
STOP & SHOP DECAFFEINATED ALL METHOD GRIND; DRIP GRIND; ELECTRIC PERCOLATOR GRIND; INSTANT PRESIDENT'S BLEND; NEW; REGULAR GRIND
STOP & SHOP SUN GLORY ALL METHOD GRIND
WINN DIXIE ASTOR INSTANT

ITEMS IN HEALTH FOOD STORES
BAMBU SWISS COFFEE-SUBSTITUTE
CAFIX NATURAL CEREAL BEVERAGE
PERO INSTANT CEREAL BEVERAGE
PIONIER INSTANT SWISS COFFEE SUBSTITUTE

The following items contain additives of concern.

BRANDS	**ADDITIVES-OF-CONCERN** BOLD—CONCERN TO ALL LIGHT—CONCERN TO SOME
GENERAL FOODS *—INTERNATIONAL COFFEES*	
CAFÉ FRANÇAIS; CAFÉ VIENNA; ORANGE CAPPUCCINO; SUISSE MOCHA	**COCONUT OIL; SODIUM CASEINATE SOLIDS**
IRISH MOCHA MINT	**CARRAGEENAN; COCONUT OIL; SODIUM CASEINATE SOLIDS**
HILLS BROS.	
BAVARIAN MINT; CAFE MOCHA	**CARRAGEENAN; SODIUM CASEINATE**
ITEMS IN HEALTH FOOD STORES	
SYMINGTONS	
HON-Y-CUP	WHEY

BRANDS	**ADDITIVES-OF-CONCERN** **BOLD—CONCERN TO ALL** LIGHT—CONCERN TO SOME

FRUIT DRINK MIXES & CONCENTRATES

COUNTRY TIME	
LEMONADE; PINK LEMONADE	**ARTIFICIAL COLOR; BHA; MODIFIED CORN & TAPIOCA STARCHES**
HAWAIIAN PUNCH	
CHERRY; GRAPE; RED; STRAWBERRY	**ARTIFICIAL COLOR**
LEMONADE	**ARTIFICIAL COLOR; BHA; BHT**
HI-C	
FRUIT PUNCH; LEMONADE; ORANGE	**ARTIFICIAL COLOR; MODIFIED CORN STARCH**
KOOL-AID	
UNSWEETENED TROPICAL PUNCH	**ARTIFICIAL COLOR; BHA; MODIFIED CORN & TAPIOCA STARCHES**
—*SUGAR SWEETENED*	
CHERRY; ORANGE; STRAWBERRY	**ARTIFICIAL COLOR; BHA**
GRAPE	**ARTIFICIAL COLOR**
LEMONADE	**ARTIFICIAL COLOR; BHA; MODIFIED CORN & TAPIOCA STARCHES**
MINUTE MAID	
LEMONADE CRYSTALS	NO ADDITIVES OF CONCERN
TANG ORANGE	**ARTIFICIAL COLOR; BHA**

BRANDS	**ADDITIVES-OF-CONCERN** **BOLD—CONCERN TO ALL** LIGHT—CONCERN TO SOME
WELCH'S GRAPE	**U.S. CERTIFIED ARTIFICIAL COLORS**
WYLER'S	
CHERRY; GRAPE; PINK LEMONADE	**ARTIFICIAL COLOR** OR **U.S. CERTIFIED ARTIFICIAL COLORS**
LEMONADE	**ARTIFICIAL COLOR; CARRAGEENAN**
SUPERMARKET PRIVATE BRANDS	
A & P	
—ANN PAGE	
LEMONADE SUPREME	**ARTIFICIAL COLOR**
TROPICAL FRUIT PUNCH W/ SUGAR	ACACIA GUM; **ARTIFICIAL COLOR; COCONUT OIL**
—CHEERI AID	
CHERRY; GRAPE	**ARTIFICIAL COLOR; DIOCYTL SODIUM SULFOSUCCINATE (DSS)**
IMITATION LEMONADE; ORANGE	**ARTIFICIAL COLOR; BHA; DIOCYTL SODIUM SULFOSUCCINATE (DSS)**
STRAWBERRY	**ARTIFICIAL COLOR**
—CHEERI AID COMPLETE W/ SUGAR	
IMITATION LEMONADE; RASPBERRY; STRAWBERRY	**ARTIFICIAL COLOR**

BRANDS	ADDITIVES-OF-CONCERN BOLD—CONCERN TO ALL LIGHT—CONCERN TO SOME
TROPICAL FRUIT PUNCH	ACACIA GUM; **ARTIFICIAL COLOR; COCONUT OIL**
FIRST NATIONAL	
—EDWARDS	
INSTANT BREAKFAST DRINK ORANGE	ARTIFICIAL COLOR FD & C YELLOW NO. 5 & NO. 6
LUCKY	
—LADY LEE	
CHERRY; GRAPE; ORANGE; PUNCH	**ARTIFICIAL FOOD COLOR**
LEMONADE	**ARTIFICIAL FOOD COLOR; VEGETABLE GUM**
PUBLIX	
—FLAVOR PERFECT	
CHERRY; GRAPE	**ARTIFICIAL COLOR; BHA;** GUM ARABIC
FRUIT PUNCH	**ARTIFICIAL COLOR; BHA**
IMITATION LEMONADE	**ARTIFICIAL COLOR; BHA; CARRAGEENAN;** GUM ARABIC
SAFEWAY	
—CRAGMONT	
CHERRY; GRAPE; STRAWBERRY	**ARTIFICIAL COLOR**
LEMONADE	**ARTIFICIAL COLOR; BHA**
ORANGE	**BHA**
—TOWN HOUSE	
INSTANT BREAKFAST DRINK ORANGE	**ARTIFICIAL COLORS** W/ FD & C YELLOW NO. 5; **MODIFIED FOOD STARCH**

BRANDS	ADDITIVES-OF-CONCERN **BOLD—CONCERN TO ALL** LIGHT—CONCERN TO SOME
STOP & SHOP **—STOP & SHOP** CHERRY; GRAPE; STRAWBERRY	**U.S. CERTIFIED ARTIFICIAL COLOR**
FRUIT PUNCH; IMITATION PINK LEMONADE	**MODIFIED FOOD STARCH; U.S. CERTIFIED ARTIFICIAL COLOR; VEGETABLE GUMS**
IMITATION LEMONADE; ORANGEADE	**MODIFIED FOOD STARCH; U.S. CERTIFIED ARTIFICIAL COLOR**
ITEMS IN HEALTH FOOD STORES **HAIN** *CONCENTRATE* APRICOT; BLACK CHERRY; RED RASPBERRY; STRAWBERRY	NO ADDITIVES OF CONCERN

INSTANT ICED TEA & TEA MIXES

FANTA ICED TEA LEMON FLAVORED*	NO ADDITIVES OF CONCERN
LIPTON ICED TEA LEMON FLAVORED*	**ARTIFICIAL COLOR**
ICED TEA MIX LEMON FLAVOR & SUGAR; INSTANT LEMON FLAVORED	NO ADDITIVES OF CONCERN
NESTEA ICED TEA MIX SUGAR & LEMON FLAVORED	NO ADDITIVES OF CONCERN

BRANDS	ADDITIVES-OF-CONCERN **BOLD—CONCERN TO ALL** LIGHT—CONCERN TO SOME
ICED TEA SUGAR & LEMON FLAVOR*	**MODIFIED FOOD STARCH**
INSTANT TEA MIX LEMON FLAVOR	GUM ARABIC
TETLEY	
ICED TEA MIX SUGAR & LEMON FLAVOR	**BHA; CERTIFIED FOOD COLORING**
SUPERMARKET PRIVATE BRANDS	
A & P	
—OUR OWN	
ICED TEA MIX LEMON FLAVORED W/ SUGAR	**ARTIFICIAL COLOR; BHA**
FIRST NATIONAL	
—FINAST	
ICED TEA MIX W/ SUGAR & LEMON FLAVOR	**ARTIFICIAL FOOD COLOR**
INSTANT TEA	NO ADDITIVES OF CONCERN
LUCKY	
—LADY LEE	
ICED TEA MIX SUGAR & LEMON FLAVOR	**ARTIFICIAL FOOD COLOR**
PUBLIX	
—FLAVOR PERFECT	
ICED TEA MIX SUGAR & LEMON FLAVOR	**BHA; CERTIFIED FOOD COLORING**
SAFEWAY	
—CROWN COLONY	
ICED TEA MIX LEMON FLAVORED W/ SUGAR	**ARTIFICIAL FOOD COLOR**

*Noncarbonated, in can.

BRANDS	**ADDITIVES-OF-CONCERN** **BOLD—CONCERN TO ALL** LIGHT—CONCERN TO SOME
STOP & SHOP **—STOP & SHOP** INSTANT ICED TEA MIX	**BHA**
WINN DIXIE **—ASTOR** ICED TEA MIX W/ SUGAR & LEMON FLAVOR	**ARTIFICIAL FOOD COLOR**

VII. BREAD & BREAD PRODUCTS; CRACKERS

R alongside a brand indicates regional (not national) distribution, based on shopping experience.

BAGELS, BUNS, MUFFINS, ROLLS

	BRANDS	ADDITIVES-OF-CONCERN BOLD—CONCERN TO ALL LIGHT—CONCERN TO SOME
	ARNOLD	
	BRAN'NOLA MUFFINS W/ BRAN; DUTCH EGG SANDWICH BUNS; SOFT SANDWICH ROLLS	GLUTEN (VITAL WHEAT)
	DELI-TWIST ROLLS	GLUTEN (WHEAT); **VEGETABLE SHORTENING (LIQUID)**
	DINNER PARTY ROLLS; DINNER PARTY PARKERHOUSE ROLLS; EXTRA CRISP MUFFINS	NO ADDITIVES OF CONCERN
R	AUGUST BROS.	
	ASSORTED DINNER ROLLS; EGG ROLLS; ONION ROLLS	**PAPRIKA; TURMERIC**
	JR. BAGELS	HIGH GLUTEN FLOUR (BLEACHED)
R	COLOMBO	
	SOUR FRENCH ROLLS; SOUR *(continues)*	NO ADDITIVES OF CONCERN

	BRANDS	ADDITIVES-OF-CONCERN BOLD—CONCERN TO ALL LIGHT—CONCERN TO SOME
	COLUMBO *(Continued)*	
	SANDWICH ROLLS; SWEET SANDWICH ROLLS	NO ADDITIVES OF CONCERN
R	**COUNTRY FAIR**	
	BUNS	GLUTEN (WHEAT); **LARD**
	ENGLISH MUFFINS	GLUTEN (WHEAT)
R	**DANDEE** BROWN 'N SERVE ROLLS	NO ADDITIVES OF CONCERN
	FRANCISCO	
	FRENCH ROLLS; SANDWICH ROLLS; SOUR DOUGH FRENCH ROLLS	NO ADDITIVES OF CONCERN
R	**GREEN FREEDMAN**	
	ONION DELI ROLLS	**PAPRIKA; TURMERIC**
R	**HOLSUM**	
	BAKE & SERVE ONION HOT BREAD	NO ADDITIVES OF CONCERN
	BAKE & SERVE CINNAMON HOT BREAD	EGG WHITES (DRIED); GLUTEN; GUAR GUM; **MODIFIED FOOD STARCH**
	BRAN GRANOLA ENGLISH MUFFINS; BROWN 'N SERVE ROLLS	GLUTEN OR WHEAT GLUTEN
	SOF-BUNS; YOU'LL LIKE BAHAMA BUNS	**CALCIUM PEROXIDE;** GLUTEN (WHEAT)
R	**MERITA** GOLDEN HONEY BUNS	GLUTEN (WHEAT)

BRANDS		ADDITIVES-OF-CONCERN **BOLD—CONCERN TO ALL** LIGHT—CONCERN TO SOME
R	**NISSEN**	
	BAKE 'N BROWN BUNS	ARTIFICIAL COLOR FD & C YELLOW NO. 5; EGG WHITES; GLUTEN (WHEAT)
	BLUEBERRY MUFFINS	EGG WHITES; GLUTEN (WHEAT); GUAR GUM; WHEY (MILK)
	BROWN 'N SERVE ROLLS (WHITE)	**(BEEF TALLOW, LARD);* CALCIUM PEROXIDE;** EGG WHITES; GLUTEN (WHEAT)
	CRANBERRY-ORANGE MUFFINS; HAMBURGER BUNS	NO ADDITIVES OF CONCERN
	NEW ENGLAND STYLE FRANKFURT ROLLS	**(BEEF TALLOW, LARD)***
R	**OLD COUNTRY**	
	DINNER ROLLS	**ARTIFICIAL COLOR; PAPRIKA; TURMERIC**
	EGG TWIST ROLLS; HARD ROLLS	NO ADDITIVES OF CONCERN
	PEPPERIDGE FARM	
	BUTTER CRESCENT ROLLS; GOLDEN TWIST ROLLS BROWN & SERVE	**BUTTER**
	CINNAMON RAISIN MUFFINS; HAMBURGER ROLLS; SOFT FAMILY ROLLS	GLUTEN (WHEAT)

*Blend may contain one or more of these saturated fats.

	BRANDS	ADDITIVES-OF-CONCERN **BOLD—CONCERN TO ALL** LIGHT—CONCERN TO SOME
	PEPPERIDGE FARM *(Continued)*	
	CLUB ROLLS BROWN & SERVE; FRENCH ROLLS; WHITE SANDWICH POCKETS	NO ADDITIVES OF CONCERN
	ENGLISH MUFFINS	WHEY
	OLD FASHIONED ROLLS; PARKER HOUSE ROLLS; PARTY ROLLS	EGG WHITES
R	SUNBEAM	
	ENGLISH MUFFIN LOAF	WHEY (DRIED)
	ENGLISH MUFFINS	NO ADDITIVES OF CONCERN
	FRANKFURTER ROLLS; SLICED ROLLS	**(LARD)***
	THOMAS'	
	BRAN TOAST-R-CAKES W/ RAISINS; ENGLISH MUFFINS	WHEY SOLIDS
	WHEAT ENGLISH MUFFINS	NO ADDITIVES OF CONCERN
R	TOSCANA'S	
	ALL PURPOSE SAN'WICH ROLLS; CLUSTER ROLLS; ONION ROLLS; SEEDED ROLLS	NO ADDITIVES OF CONCERN

*Blend may contain this saturated fat.

BRANDS	ADDITIVES-OF-CONCERN **BOLD—CONCERN TO ALL** LIGHT—CONCERN TO SOME
WONDER	
BROWN N SERVE ROLLS	NO ADDITIVES OF CONCERN
ENGLISH MUFFINS	GLUTEN (WHEAT); WHEY
HOT DOG BUNS	GLUTEN (WHEAT); **LARD**
SUPERMARKET PRIVATE BRANDS	
FIRST NATIONAL —FINAST	
BAKE & SERVE CINNAMON HOT BREAD	EGG WHITES (DRIED); GLUTEN; GUAR GUM; **MODIFIED FOOD STARCH**
LUCKY —HARVEST DAY	
ENGLISH MUFFINS; SOURDOUGH MUFFINS	**ENZYME FROM ASPERGILLUS ORYZAE;** GLUTEN (WHEAT)
GOURMET ROLLS	ARTIFICIAL COLOR FD & C YELLOW NO. 5; WHEY
RAISIN MUFFINS	NO ADDITIVES OF CONCERN
SESAME BUNS; SLICED BUNS	WHEY
—BROWN 'N SERVE	
BUTTERMILK TWINS ROLLS	NO ADDITIVES OF CONCERN
CLOVERLEAF ROLLS; FLAKY GEMS ROLLS	WHEY
PUBLIX —BREAKFAST CLUB	
HAMBURGER BUNS	NO ADDITIVES OF CONCERN

BRANDS	ADDITIVES-OF-CONCERN BOLD—CONCERN TO ALL LIGHT—CONCERN TO SOME
—THE DELI AT PUBLIX	
DINNER ROLLS	GLUTEN (VITAL WHEAT)
EGG BAGELS; GARLIC BAGELS; ONION BAGELS; PUMPERNICKEL BAGELS	NO ADDITIVES OF CONCERN
ONION ROLLS	GLUTEN (VITAL WHEAT); **MODIFIED STARCH;** WHEY
SAFEWAY	
—MRS. WRIGHT'S	
CRUSHED WHEAT HAMBURGER BUNS	**CALCIUM PEROXIDE;** GLUTEN (WHEAT)
ENGLISH MUFFINS; SOURDOUGH MUFFINS	NO ADDITIVES OF CONCERN
HONEY WHEAT BERRY ROLLS	GLUTEN (WHEAT)
HAMBURGER BUNS; HOT DOG BUNS; SESAME ENRICHED ROLLS	**CALCIUM PEROXIDE;** GLUTEN (WHEAT); WHEY
SWEET FARMSTYLE ROLLS	WHEY
STOP & SHOP	
—(NO BRAND NAME)	
DINNER ROLLS	**PAPRIKA; TURMERIC**
GRINDER ROLLS	NO ADDITIVES OF CONCERN

BRANDS	ADDITIVES-OF-CONCERN **BOLD—CONCERN TO ALL** LIGHT—CONCERN TO SOME
—OUR OWN	
BRAN TOASTIES; CORN TOASTIES; NEWFANGLED CORN MUFFINS	WHEY
NEWFANGLED BLUEBERRY MUFFINS	**MODIFIED FOOD STARCH;** WHEY
—STOP & SHOP	
BIG BURGERS SANDWICH ROLLS; FRANKFURTER ROLLS; SLICED ONION ROLLS; SLICED SESAME ROLLS; WHEATBERRY ENGLISH MUFFINS	GLUTEN (WHEAT)
BLUEBERRY FLAVORED ENGLISH MUFFINS	**ARTIFICIAL COLOR;** SODIUM ALGINATE; WHEY
BULKIE ROLLS	NO ADDITIVES OF CONCERN
BUTTER ENGLISH MUFFINS	**BUTTER; PAPRIKA; TURMERIC**
ENGLISH MUFFINS	**ARTIFICIAL COLOR;** WHEY
WINN DIXIE	
—DIXIE DARLING	
CLUSTER BROWN 'N SERVE ROLLS; HAMBURGER BUNS; TWIN BROWN 'N SERVE ROLLS	**CALCIUM PEROXIDE;** GLUTEN (VITAL WHEAT)

BRANDS	ADDITIVES-OF-CONCERN **BOLD—CONCERN TO ALL** LIGHT—CONCERN TO SOME
—DIXIE DARLING *(Continued)*	
SEEDED FRENCH BROWN 'N SERVE HARD ROLLS	NO ADDITIVES OF CONCERN
—PRESTIGE	
BISCUITS MADE W/ BUTTERMILK BROWN 'N SERVE	**ARTIFICIAL COLOR;** WHEY
BONANZA STEAK ROLLS; ONION ROLLS	NO ADDITIVES OF CONCERN
BROWN 'N SERVE ROLLS	GLUTEN (VITAL WHEAT)
ENGLISH MUFFINS	MILK SOLIDS (NONFAT DRY)
WEINER BUNS	**CALCIUM PEROXIDE; PAPRIKA; TURMERIC**
ITEMS IN HEALTH FOOD STORES	
GIUSTO'S VITA-GRAIN	
HONEY-PRO DINNER ROLLS	HI PROTEIN FLOUR (UNBLEACHED)
SOYA BUNS; WHOLE WHEAT DINNER ROLLS	NO ADDITIVES OF CONCERN
MATTHEW'S *WHOLE WHEAT ENGLISH MUFFINS*	
CINNAMON RAISIN; PLAIN	NO ADDITIVES OF CONCERN
STAFF OF LIFE	
SESAME WHOLE WHEAT ROLLS	NO ADDITIVES OF CONCERN

	BRANDS	ADDITIVES-OF-CONCERN **BOLD—CONCERN TO ALL** LIGHT—CONCERN TO SOME
	VITAL VITTLES REAL BREAD ROLLS	NO ADDITIVES OF CONCERN

BREAD

	BRANDS	ADDITIVES-OF-CONCERN
	ANADAMA CORNMEAL & MOLASSES	GLUTEN (VITAL WHEAT)
	ARNOLD BRICK OVEN 100% WHOLE WHEAT; BRICK OVEN WHITE; MELBA THIN DIETSLICE 100% WHOLE WHEAT; MELBA THIN DIETSLICE WHITE	NO ADDITIVES OF CONCERN
	JEWISH RYE W/ CARAWAY SEEDS; NATURÉL; PUMPERNICKLE; RAISIN TEA LOAF; STONE GROUND 100% WHOLE WHEAT	GLUTEN (VITAL WHEAT)
R	**AUGUST BROS.** GENUINE JEWISH RYE; ITALIAN; ONION RYE; PITA; SLICED PUMPERNICKLE	NO ADDITIVES OF CONCERN
	STONE GROUND 100% WHOLE WHEAT	GLUTEN FLOUR (WHEAT)
	BRAN'NOLA (OROWEAT) COUNTRY OAT; HEARTY WHEAT	GLUTEN (VITAL WHEAT); WHEY

	BRANDS	ADDITIVES-OF-CONCERN **BOLD—CONCERN TO ALL** LIGHT—CONCERN TO SOME
	BRAN'NOLA *(Continued)*	
	GOLDEN SESAME	WHEY
	YOGURT	GLUTEN (VITAL WHEAT)
	BREADS INTERNATIONAL GERMAN PUMPERNICKEL; JEWISH RYE	NO ADDITIVES OF CONCERN
	SAN FRANCISCO SOURDOUGH	EGG WHITES; GLUTEN (WHEAT)
R	**COLOMBO** ENRICHED FRENCH SWEET	NO ADDITIVES OF CONCERN
R	**COTE'S** STONE GROUND WHEAT	**CALCIUM PEROXIDE;** GLUTEN (WHEAT)
	COUNTY FAIR KING SIZE SANDWICH	WHEY
	COUNTRY HEARTH BRAN 'N HONEY; 7 WHOLE GRAIN	GLUTEN (WHEAT)
	BUTTERSPLIT; MOUNTAIN MEAL; OLD FASHIONED WHITE	GLUTEN (WHEAT); WHEY (SWEET DAIRY)
R	**FLOWERS** BUTTERMAID; DANDEE OLD FASHIONED WHITE; NEW YORK JEWISH RYE	NO ADDITIVES OF CONCERN

	BRANDS	ADDITIVES-OF-CONCERN **BOLD—CONCERN TO ALL** LIGHT—CONCERN TO SOME
	NEW ORLEANS STYLE VIENNA	EGG WHITES; GLUTEN (WHEAT)
	—*NATURE'S OWN*	
	BUTTERBREAD; OLD FASHIONED WHITE; REAL BRAN 'N HONEY	NO ADDITIVES OF CONCERN
	HONEY WHEAT; REAL GRAIN	GLUTEN (WHEAT); WHEY
	FRANCISCO	
	FRENCH STYLE; VIENNA FRENCH SLICED	NO ADDITIVES OF CONCERN
R	**GREEN FREEDMAN**	
	CARAWAY RYE; RUSSIAN RYE	NO ADDITIVES OF CONCERN
R	**GROSSINGER'S**	
	PUMPERNICKEL; RYE NO SEEDS	HIGH PROTEIN WHEAT FLOUR
	HOLLYWOOD	
	DARK	GLUTEN (WHEAT); KELP (DEHYDRATED)
	LIGHT	GLUTEN (WHEAT); KELP (DEHYDRATED); WHEY
R	**HOLSUM**	
	SANDWICH THIN	WHEY
	WHITE NO SALT	**CALCIUM PEROXIDE**
	BAHAMA	**CALCIUM PEROXIDE;** GLUTEN (WHEAT); WHEY

	BRANDS	ADDITIVES-OF-CONCERN **BOLD—CONCERN TO ALL** LIGHT—CONCERN TO SOME
	HOME PRIDE BUTTER TOP; WHEAT BUTTER TOP	**CALCIUM CASEINATE;** GLUTEN (WHEAT); WHEY
R	JOSEPH'S MIDDLE EAST STYLE SYRIAN	NO ADDITIVES OF CONCERN
R	KASANOF'S GENUINE LIGHT RYE; GENUINE PUMPERNICKEL RYE; JEWISH CARAWAY RYE; RUSSIAN BLACK RYE	NO ADDITIVES OF CONCERN
R	MERITA OLD FASHIONED	WHEY
R	MONK'S HI-FIBRE; RAISIN; WHITE	WHEY (DRIED SWEET DAIRY)
R	MUNZENMAIER'S KÜMMELBROT SEEDED RYE	HIGH GLUTEN WHEAT FLOUR
	RUSSIAN PUMPERNICKEL	NO ADDITIVES OF CONCERN
R	NISSEN BRAN; BUTTER TOP OATMEAL; CANADIAN BROWN; HONEY TOP CRACKED WHEAT	GLUTEN (WHEAT)
	BUTTER TOP; OLD SETTLER WHITE; RYE; TENDER CRUST GIANT WHITE	NO ADDITIVES OF CONCERN

BRANDS		ADDITIVES-OF-CONCERN BOLD—CONCERN TO ALL LIGHT—CONCERN TO SOME
	CINNAMON W/ RAISINS	GUM ARABIC; WHEY
	ITALIAN; TENDER CRUST GIANT SANDWICH WHITE; VIENNA	**(BEEF TALLOW, LARD)***
R	**OLD COUNTRY**	
	FRENCH; ITALIAN; ONION RYE; PUMPERNICKEL	NO ADDITIVES OF CONCERN
	OROWEAT	
	RUSSIAN RYE; SCHWARZWÄLDER DARK RYE; SPROUTED WHEAT	GLUTEN (VITAL WHEAT)
	PEPPERIDGE FARM	
	CORN & MOLASSES; HONEY BRAN; ITALIAN BROWN & SERVE; 100% WHOLE WHEAT; RAISIN W/ CINNAMON; SANDWICH RYE; WHITE	NO ADDITIVES OF CONCERN
	CRACKED WHEAT; FAMILY RYE W/ SEEDS; HONEY WHEAT BERRY; OATMEAL; PUMPERNICKEL; SEEDLESS RYE; WHEAT	GLUTEN (WHEAT)

*Blend may contain one or more of these saturated fats.

	BRANDS	ADDITIVES-OF-CONCERN **BOLD—CONCERN TO ALL** LIGHT—CONCERN TO SOME
	ROMAN MEAL BREAD	GLUTEN (VITAL WHEAT); WHEY SOLIDS
R	**SUNBEAM** BATTER WHIPPED	**(LARD);* SODIUM CASEINATE;** WHEY
	BUTTERTOP OATMEAL	GLUTEN (WHEAT)
	BUTTERTOP WHEAT	**CALCIUM PEROXIDE;** GLUTEN (WHEAT)
	HONEY CRUSHED WHEAT	NO ADDITIVES OF CONCERN
	VIENNA	**(LARD)***
R	**THOMAS'** PROTEIN	GLUTEN FLOUR
R	**TOSCANA'S** ENRICHED FRENCH SWEET	NO ADDITIVES OF CONCERN
R	**WEIGHT WATCHERS** THIN SLICED	GLUTEN (WHEAT); WHEY
R	**WONDER** ENRICHED	WHEY

*Blend may contain this saturated fat.

BRANDS	ADDITIVES-OF-CONCERN **BOLD—CONCERN TO ALL** LIGHT—CONCERN TO SOME
GOLDEN WHEAT; BEEFSTEAK SOFT RYE	GLUTEN (WHEAT)
100% WHOLE WHEAT	GLUTEN (WHEAT); WHEY
SUPERMARKET PRIVATE BRANDS	
LUCKY	
—LADY LEE	
PREMIUM SANDWICH WHEAT	NO ADDITIVES OF CONCERN
PREMIUM SANDWICH WHITE	MILK SOLIDS (NONFAT DRY)
—HARVEST DAY	
CHUCK WAGON; LARGE DELUXE WHITE; VIENNA	MILK SOLIDS (NONFAT DRY); WHEY
CRUSHED WHEAT SANDWICH; THIN SLICED SANDWICH	WHEY
DARK THINLY SLICED SLIMLINE; LIGHT THINLY SLICED SLIMLINE	**CALCIUM CASEINATE;** GLUTEN (WHEAT); WHEY
LA TORTILLA CORN TORTILLAS; MADE W/ BUTTERMILK; 100% WHOLE WHEAT; POTATO	NO ADDITIVES OF CONCERN
LA TORTILLA FLOUR TORTILLAS	**LARD;** LOCUST BEAN GUM
RAISIN; RYE	GLUTEN (WHEAT)

BRANDS	ADDITIVES-OF-CONCERN **BOLD—CONCERN TO ALL** LIGHT—CONCERN TO SOME
LUCKY—HARVEST DAY *(Continued)*	
SPLIT TOP WHITE	**ARTIFICIAL COLOR; BUTTER**
PUBLIX	
—BREAKFAST CLUB	
WHITE	NO ADDITIVES OF CONCERN
—PUBLIX *SPECIAL RECIPE*	
BUTTER CRUST WHITE; HONEY WHEAT; THIN SLICED STONE GROUND WHEAT; 100% WHOLE WHEAT STONE GROUND	NO ADDITIVES OF CONCERN
—THE DELI AT PUBLIX	
CHALLAH EGG TWIST; ITALIAN; PUMPERNICKLE	GLUTEN (VITAL WHEAT)
FRENCH; NATURAL WHEAT ITALIAN	**MODIFIED STARCH**
JEWISH STYLE ONION RYE	NO ADDITIVES OF CONCERN
SAFEWAY	
—MRS. WRIGHT'S	
BUTTER & EGG; HOMESTYLE BUTTER TOP; 100% WHOLE WHEAT; SPLIT TOP WHITE	WHEY
CRUSHED WHEAT; ENRICHED	NO ADDITIVES OF CONCERN

(continues)

BRANDS	ADDITIVES-OF-CONCERN **BOLD—CONCERN TO ALL** LIGHT—CONCERN TO SOME
BUTTERMILK; HOMESTYLE WHITE; MALT-O-WHEAT; OATMEAL; OLD FASHIONED ITALIAN; POTATO; RAISIN NUT; SANDWICH RYE W/ SEEDS; SOURDOUGH WHITE ENRICHED	NO ADDITIVES OF CONCERN
ENGLISH MUFFIN STYLE; GRAIN BELT; GRANOLA BRAN; RAISIN; SPECIAL FORMULA DARK STYLE	GLUTEN (WHEAT)
SANDWICH WHEAT; SUPER SOFT WHEAT	**CALCIUM PEROXIDE;** GLUTEN (WHEAT)
SUPER SOFT SANDWICH WHITE; SUPER SOFT WHITE	**CALCIUM PEROXIDE**
—(NO BRAND NAME)	
7 GRAIN; SOYA; STONE GROUND WHOLE WHEAT; WHEAT GERM	NO ADDITIVES OF CONCERN
STONEHEDGE FARM WHOLE WHEAT	**BUTTER;** WHEY
—SAFEWAY	
PREMIUM WHEAT	WHEY
PREMIUM WHITE THIN SLICED SANDWICH	**CALCIUM PEROXIDE;** WHEY

BRANDS	**ADDITIVES-OF-CONCERN** **BOLD—CONCERN TO ALL** LIGHT—CONCERN TO SOME
STOP & SHOP —OUR OWN BANANA TEA	**ARTIFICIAL COLOR**
CRANBERRY NUT	NO ADDITIVES OF CONCERN
DATE NUT	EGG WHITES
—STOP & SHOP HOT CINNAMON LOAF BAKE AT HOME	EGG WHITES (DRIED); GLUTEN; GUAR GUM; **MODIFIED FOOD STARCH**
ITALIAN BROWN 'N' SERVE; MINI LOAVES BROWN 'N' SERVE WHITE	NO ADDITIVES OF CONCERN
—STOP & SHOP BAKERY BUTTER TOP; DAISY; YAH YAH BUTTERCREST WHITE	WHEY
BUTTER TOP HONEY WHEAT; CHEESE;* ENGLISH MUFFIN LOAF; HIGH FIBER WHEAT W/ BRAN; HOME KITCHEN; SANDWICH; ITALIAN; PLAIN RYE	GLUTEN (WHEAT)

*By law, at this writing, it is not required of a manufacturer to state whether cheeses contain artificial colors, unless the color is FD & C Yellow No. 5 (Tartrazine). Their presence in bread containing cheese therefore remains an uncertainty, unless it is voluntarily declared on the label that artificial colors have been used or have not. For a more detailed explanation of artificial color in cheese, refer to the beginning of the cheese section in "Dairy Products & Substitutes."

BRANDS	**ADDITIVES-OF-CONCERN** **BOLD—CONCERN TO ALL** LIGHT—CONCERN TO SOME
CANADIAN STYLE OATMEAL; FRENCH STICKS; KOSHER PUMPERNICKEL; KOSHER RYE; MADE W/ BUTTERMILK; OATMEAL N' MOLASSES; 100% WHOLE WHEAT; SWEDISH	NO ADDITIVES OF CONCERN
CRACKED WHEAT; OATMEAL; VIENNA	GLUTEN (WHEAT); WHEY
LOTS 'O RAISIN	GLUTEN (WHEAT); **PAPRIKA; TURMERIC**
WINN DIXIE —DIXIE DARLING	
BERMUDA	GLUTEN (VITAL WHEAT)
LARGE WHITE; WHITE; WHITE MADE W/ BUTTERMILK	**CALCIUM PEROXIDE**
—PRESTIGE	
COUNTRY WHITE; VERY THIN WHITE	WHEY SOLIDS
DELUXE	**CALCIUM PEROXIDE; PAPRIKA; TURMERIC**
NATURAL FIBER; 100% WHOLE WHEAT	GLUTEN (VITAL WHEAT OR WHEAT)
RAISIN	GLUTEN (VITAL WHEAT); **MACE**
V-10 PROTEIN	GLUTEN (WHEAT); **SODIUM CASEINATE;** WHEY

BRANDS	ADDITIVES-OF-CONCERN BOLD—CONCERN TO ALL LIGHT—CONCERN TO SOME
ITEMS IN HEALTH FOOD STORES	
BALDWIN HILL *NATURAL SOURDOUGH* RYE; WHOLE WHEAT	NO ADDITIVES OF CONCERN
EREWHON MIDDLE EASTERN WHOLE WHEAT; 100% STONE GROUND WHOLE WHEAT	NO ADDITIVES OF CONCERN
FOOD FOR LIFE BAKING BRAN FOR LIFE	GLUTEN (VITAL WHEAT); MILK SOLIDS
7-GRAIN SPROUTED WHEAT	GLUTEN (VITAL WHEAT)
GARDEN OF EATIN' BIBLE; CORNTILLAS	NO ADDITIVES OF CONCERN
GIUSTO'S VITA-GRAIN HI PROTEIN GLUTEN; HI PROTEIN GLUTEN & SOYA	GLUTEN FLOUR
HI PROTEIN WHEAT; SOURDOUGH WHOLE WHEAT & CORN	HIGH PROTEIN FLOUR (UNBLEACHED OR WHOLE WHEAT)
—UNSALTED LOW SODIUM WHEAT; WHITE	NO ADDITIVES OF CONCERN
LIFESTREAM ESSENE; ESSENE RAISIN	NO ADDITIVES OF CONCERN

BRANDS	ADDITIVES-OF-CONCERN BOLD—CONCERN TO ALL LIGHT—CONCERN TO SOME
QUEBRADA	
OATMEAL; RAISIN WHOLE WHEAT; VITA-LOAF	NO ADDITIVES OF CONCERN
SPRUCE TREE	
ONION RYE; WHOLE WHEAT	NO ADDITIVES OF CONCERN
STAFF OF LIFE	
APPLE; SOURDOUGH RYE; VEGETABLE HERB; WHEATLESS PUMPERNICKEL RYE; WHOLE WHEAT	NO ADDITIVES OF CONCERN
THE GRAIN-BIN	
CASHEW DATE; WHOLE WHEAT	NO ADDITIVES OF CONCERN
VITAL VITTLES	
BUTTERMILK CORNBREAD; REAL LITTLE; REAL SESAME-MILLET; SOURDOUGH	NO ADDITIVES OF CONCERN

BREAD & CORN-FLAKE CRUMBS; CRACKER MEAL

ARNOLD	
ALL PURPOSE BREAD CRUMBS	GLUTEN (VITAL WHEAT)
ITALIAN BREAD CRUMBS	GLUTEN (VITAL WHEAT); MONOSODIUM GLUTAMATE

	BRANDS	ADDITIVES-OF-CONCERN **BOLD—CONCERN TO ALL** LIGHT—CONCERN TO SOME
R	**COLOMBO** BREAD CRUMBS; BREAD CRUMBS W/ ITALIAN SEASONING	**VEGETABLE SHORTENING**
R	**COLONNA** FLAVORED BREAD CRUMBS	MILK SOLIDS; **SHORTENING**
	CONTADINA SEASONED BREAD CRUMBS	NO ADDITIVES OF CONCERN
	DEVONSHEER PLAIN BREAD CRUMBS	NO ADDITIVES OF CONCERN
	SEASONED BREAD CRUMBS	MONOSODIUM GLUTAMATE
R	**4C** BREAD CRUMBS PLAIN	NO ADDITIVES OF CONCERN
	BREAD CRUMBS REDI-FLAVORED	MONOSODIUM GLUTAMATE
R	**INTROVIGNE'S** "5 in 1" MIX FLAVORED BREAD CRUMBS	NO ADDITIVES OF CONCERN
R	**JASON** READY FLAVORED BREAD CRUMBS	MILK SOLIDS
	KELLOGG'S CORN FLAKE CRUMBS	**BHA**

	BRANDS	ADDITIVES-OF-CONCERN **BOLD—CONCERN TO ALL** LIGHT—CONCERN TO SOME
	NABISCO CRACKER MEAL	NO ADDITIVES OF CONCERN
R	**NISSEN**	
	BREAD CRUMBS	WHEY
	FLAVORED BREAD CRUMBS	MONOSODIUM GLUTAMATE; **PAPRIKA;** WHEY
R	**OLD LONDON**	
	BREAD CRUMBS ITALIAN	MONOSODIUM GLUTAMATE; WHEY
	BREAD CRUMBS REGULAR	WHEY
R	**PASTENE** ITALIAN BREAD CRUMBS	MONOSODIUM GLUTAMATE
R	**PRINCE** ITALIAN BREAD CRUMB MIX	MONOSODIUM GLUTAMATE
	PROGRESSO	
	ITALIAN BREAD CRUMBS	MONOSODIUM GLUTAMATE; **PAPRIKA;** WHEY
	PLAIN BREAD CRUMBS	WHEY
R	**VIGO**	
	ITALIAN BREAD CRUMBS	MONOSODIUM GLUTAMATE

BRANDS	ADDITIVES-OF-CONCERN BOLD—CONCERN TO ALL LIGHT—CONCERN TO SOME
SUPERMARKET PRIVATE BRANDS	
FIRST NATIONAL —FINAST	
BREAD CRUMBS	**SHORTENING**
BREAD CRUMBS FLAVORED	MONOSODIUM GLUTAMATE
STOP & SHOP —STOP & SHOP	
FLAVORED BREAD CRUMBS	MONOSODIUM GLUTAMATE; WHEY
TOASTED BREAD CRUMBS	WHEY
ITEMS IN HEALTH FOOD STORES	
BALDWIN HILL	
NATURAL SOURDOUGH WHOLE WHEAT BREAD CRUMBS	NO ADDITIVES OF CONCERN

BREADSTICKS

BRANDS	ADDITIVES-OF-CONCERN
ANGONOA'S	
CHEESE	**ARTIFICIAL COLOR;** WHEY
GARLIC; ITALIAN; SESAME ROYALE	NO ADDITIVES OF CONCERN
R BEST QUALITY	
SESAME	NO ADDITIVES OF CONCERN
R COLOMBO ITALIAN STYLE	GLUTEN (WHEAT)

BRANDS	ADDITIVES-OF-CONCERN **BOLD—CONCERN TO ALL** LIGHT—CONCERN TO SOME
R GARDETTO'S CHEESE;* GARLIC; ONION; SALTED	NO ADDITIVES OF CONCERN
R PAN D'OR SLIM ITALIAN	NO ADDITIVES OF CONCERN
PEPPERIDGE FARM LIGHTLY SALTED SNACK STICKS; PUMPERNICKEL SNACK STICKS; SESAME SNACK STICKS	**COCONUT OIL;** GLUTEN (WHEAT)
STELLA D'ORO BREADSTICKS; DIETETIC FOR SODIUM RESTRICTED DIETS SESAME; SESAME	NO ADDITIVES OF CONCERN
R TOSCANA'S BREAD STICKS	NO ADDITIVES OF CONCERN
ITEMS IN HEALTH FOOD STORES	
DE BOLES ARTI-SESAME-STIX	HIGH GLUTEN FLOUR; **100% PURE VEGETABLE OIL**

*By law, at this writing, it is not required of a manufacturer to state whether cheeses contain artificial colors, unless the color is FD & C Yellow No. 5 (Tartrazine). Their presence in breadsticks containing cheese therefore remains an uncertainty, unless it is voluntarily declared on the label that artificial colors have been used or have not. For a more detailed explanation of artificial color in cheese, refer to the beginning of the cheese section of "Dairy Products & Substitutes."

BRANDS	ADDITIVES-OF-CONCERN BOLD—CONCERN TO ALL LIGHT—CONCERN TO SOME

CRACKERS

By law, at this writing, it is not required of a manufacturer to state whether cheeses contain artificial colors, unless the color is FD & C Yellow No. 5 (Tartrazine). Their presence in crackers containing cheese therefore remains an uncertainty, unless it is voluntarily declared on the label that artificial colors have been used or have not. For a more detailed explanation of artificial color in cheese, refer to the beginning of the cheese section of "Dairy Products & Substitutes."

	BRANDS	ADDITIVES-OF-CONCERN
	BREMNER	
	POPPYSEED; WAFERS	**(BEEF FAT, LARD)***
	BURRY	
	EUPHRATES	**(COCONUT, HYDROGENATED PALM OILS);*** WHEY (DRIED DAIRY)
	MARINER SEA	**(HYDROGENATED PALM OIL)***
	CARR'S TABLE WATER	**(COCONUT, PALM KERNEL OILS)***
R	**CELLU** LOW SODIUM UNSALTED	**(LARD)***
	CHE-CRI CHEESE CRISPIES	**(COCONUT OIL; HYDROGENATED PALM, SOYBEAN OILS)***
	CRAQUELINS	
	SESAME & ONION	**COCONUT OIL**
	STONED WHEAT THINS	WHEY

BRANDS	ADDITIVES-OF-CONCERN **BOLD—CONCERN TO ALL** LIGHT—CONCERN TO SOME
DEVONSHEER GARLIC ROUNDS; ONION ROUNDS; PLAIN MELBA TOAST; PLAIN MELBA TOAST NO SALT; RYE MELBA TOAST; SESAME MELBA ROUNDS; UNSALTED PLAIN MELBA TOAST; WHEAT MELBA TOAST	NO ADDITIVES OF CONCERN
FFV APPETIZER THINS	**(BEEF FAT, COCONUT OIL)***
BLEU CHEESE	**(BEEF FAT, COCONUT OIL);*** MONOSODIUM GLUTAMATE; WHEY
OCEAN CRISP UNSALTED TOPS	NO ADDITIVES OF CONCERN
ONION STIX	**ARTIFICIAL COLORS; (BEEF FAT, COCONUT OIL);* PAPRIKA**
STONED WHEAT	**(BEEF FAT);*** WHEY
WHEAT	**(BEEF FAT, COCONUT OIL);*** MONOSODIUM GLUTAMATE
FINN CRISP LIGHT; DARK W/ CARAWAY	NO ADDITIVES OF CONCERN

*Blend may contain one or more of these saturated fats and/or oils.

	BRANDS	ADDITIVES-OF-CONCERN **BOLD—CONCERN TO ALL** LIGHT—CONCERN TO SOME
	FIRESIDE ANIMAL	**(BEEF FAT, LARD);*** WHEY
	SALTINE	**(COCONUT OIL, LARD)***
	SUGAR HONEY GRAHAM	NO ADDITIVES OF CONCERN
	FLAVOR TREE CHEDDAR CHIPS; SESAME CHIPS	NO ADDITIVES OF CONCERN
	FRENCH ONION CRISPS; PARTY MIX	**TURMERIC**
	GOODMAN'S CARAWAY & RYE MATZOS	NO ADDITIVES OF CONCERN
R	GRIELLE CRISP TOAST W/ GLUTEN	GLUTEN FLOUR; **RAPESEED OIL**
	CRISP TOAST TOASTED WHEATBREAD	**RAPESEED OIL**
	HOROWITZ MARGARETEN UNSALTED MATZOHS	NO ADDITIVES OF CONCERN
R	HOVIS EXTRA WHEAT GERM	**BUTYLATED HYDROXYANISOLE; (COCONUT, PALM KERNEL OILS; HYDROGENATED PALM OIL, LARD);*** WHEY (DRIED SALT)

BRANDS	ADDITIVES-OF-CONCERN BOLD—CONCERN TO ALL LIGHT—CONCERN TO SOME
IDEAL CRISPBREAD WAFERS ULTRA-THIN; CRISPBREAD WAFERS WHOLE GRAIN	NO ADDITIVES OF CONCERN
JACOB'S CREAM	**BHA; (COCONUT OIL, HYDROGENATED MARINE OIL)***
KAVLI NORWEGIAN FLATBREAD THIN	NO ADDITIVES OF CONCERN
KEEBLER ANIMAL; ZESTA SALTINE	**(BEEF FAT, LARD)***
CHEESE SHINDIGS	**ARTIFICIAL COLORING; (COCONUT OIL, LARD);*** MONOSODIUM GLUTAMATE; WHEY
CINNAMON CRISP	WHEY
CLUB; ONION TOAST; SESAME STICKS; WHEAT TOAST	**(COCONUT OIL, LARD);*** WHEY
HONEY GRAHAMS	**LARD**
RYE TOAST; SESAME TOAST; TOWN HOUSE	**(COCONUT OIL, LARD)***

*Blend may contain one or more of these saturated fats and/or oils.

BRANDS		ADDITIVES-OF-CONCERN BOLD—CONCERN TO ALL LIGHT—CONCERN TO SOME
	KEEBLER *(Continued)*	
	SOUR CREAM & ONION SHINDIGS	**(COCONUT OIL, LARD);*** MILK SOLIDS (NONFAT); MONOSODIUM GLUTAMATE; **PAPRIKA;** SOUR CREAM SOLIDS; WHEY
	WHEAT CRISPS	**(COCONUT OIL, LARD);*** GLUTEN (WHEAT); MONOSODIUM GLUTAMATE
R	**KINGS BREAD** CRISP BREAD BROWN	NO ADDITIVES OF CONCERN
	KITANIHON	
	SEAWEED CRUNCH	NORI
	SHRIMP RICE CRUNCH	**ARTIFICIAL COLOR FD & C RED NO. 3**
	MANISCHEWITZ	
	MATZO-THINS; UNSALTED MATZOS; WHOLE WHEAT MATZOS	NO ADDITIVES OF CONCERN
	GARLIC TAMS; ONION TAMS; TAM TAM	**(COCONUT, HYDROGENATED COTTONSEED, SOYBEAN OILS)***
R	**MARUKAI**	
	SESAME RICE	**SEAWEED**
	CHEESE RICE	**U.S. CERTIFIED COLOR**
	MASTER	
	HOL-RY	**COCONUT OIL**

BRANDS	ADDITIVES-OF-CONCERN **BOLD—CONCERN TO ALL** LIGHT—CONCERN TO SOME
LOW SODIUM RYE; LOW SODIUM TOAST; OLD COUNTRY HARDTACK RYE	NO ADDITIVES OF CONCERN
NABISCO	
BACON FLAVORED THINS	**(COCONUT OIL, LARD);* NATURAL SMOKE FLAVOR;** WHEY
BARNUM'S ANIMALS	WHEY
BUTTERY SESAME; TRISCUIT WAFERS	**(COCONUT OIL)***
CHEESE NIPS; NABS CHEESE SANDWICH	**ARTIFICIAL COLOR; (COCONUT OIL, LARD);*** MONOSODIUM GLUTAMATE; **PAPRIKA;** WHEY
CHICKEN IN A BISKIT; DIP IN A CHIP	**(COCONUT OIL, LARD);*** MONOSODIUM GLUTAMATE; WHEY
CINNAMON TREATS GRAHAM; PREMIUM SALTINE; RITZ; SOCIABLES; WAVERLY WAFERS	**(COCONUT OIL, LARD)***
CROWN PILOT CHOWDER; DANDY SOUP & OYSTER; HONEY MAID GRAHAM; *(continues)*	**(LARD)***

*Blend may contain one or more of these saturated fats and/or oils.

BRANDS	ADDITIVES-OF-CONCERN BOLD—CONCERN TO ALL LIGHT—CONCERN TO SOME
NABISCO *(Continued)*	
OYSTERETTES; ROYAL LUNCH MILK	**(LARD)***
DIXIES	**(COCONUT OIL, LARD);*** EGG WHITES; MONOSODIUM GLUTAMATE; **NATURAL SMOKE FLAVOR; TURMERIC OLEORESIN;** WHEY
NABS CHEESE PEANUT BUTTER SANDWICH	**ARTIFICIAL COLOR; (COCONUT, HYDROGENATED PEANUT OILS, LARD);* PAPRIKA**
NABS MALTED MILK & PEANUT BUTTER SANDWICH	**(COCONUT, HYDROGENATED PEANUT OILS, LARD)***
GRAHAM; SEA ROUNDS	NO ADDITIVES OF CONCERN
SESAME MEAL MATES	**(COCONUT OIL);*** KARAYA GUM
SESAME WHEATS!	**(COCONUT OIL, LARD);* TURMERIC OLEORESIN;** WHEY
SWISS CHEESE	**(COCONUT OIL, LARD);* MODIFIED CORN STARCH;** MONOSODIUM GLUTAMATE; WHEY
WHEATSWORTH	GLUTEN (WHEAT)

BRANDS	ADDITIVES-OF-CONCERN **BOLD—CONCERN TO ALL** LIGHT—CONCERN TO SOME
WHEAT THINS	**ARTIFICIAL COLOR; (COCONUT OIL, LARD)***
ZWIEBACK TOAST	EGG WHITES; LACTALBUMIN; **MACE; NUTMEG**
OLD LONDON	
RYE MELBA TOAST; SESAME MELBA TOAST; WHITE MELBA TOAST	**PROTEOLYTIC ENZYMES DERIVED FROM ASPERGILLUS ORYZAE**
WHITE MELBA TOAST UNSALTED	**(HYDROGENATED COTTONSEED, PALM, SOYBEAN OILS)***
PEEK FREANS	
CRACKERS FOR SNACKERS	**BHA; (COCONUT, RAPESEED OILS)***
PEPPERIDGE FARM	
BUTTER THINS	**BUTTER; COCONUT OIL**
CHEDDAR CHEESE GOLDFISH; LIGHTLY SALTED GOLDFISH	**COCONUT OIL**
GOLDFISH THINS RYE	**MODIFIED FOOD STARCH**
GOLDFISH THINS LIGHTLY SALTED	**(COCONUT OIL);* MODIFIED FOOD STARCH**
GOLDFISH THINS CHEESE; MIXED SUITS SNACK HERB; MIXED SUITS SNACK SESAME	**COCONUT OIL; MODIFIED FOOD STARCH**

*Blend may contain one or more of these saturated fats and/or oils.

BRANDS	ADDITIVES-OF-CONCERN BOLD—CONCERN TO ALL LIGHT—CONCERN TO SOME
PEPPERIDGE FARM *(Continued)*	
PRETZEL GOLDFISH	**(COCONUT OIL)***
TACO GOLDFISH	**COCONUT OIL; PAPRIKA**
RY KRISP	
NATURAL	NO ADDITIVES OF CONCERN
SEASONED	**BHA; COCONUT OIL**
SOME OF EACH	
CRACKED WHEAT/RYE/GOLDEN	**ARTIFICIAL COLOR; (BEEF FAT, COCONUT OIL, LARD);*** MONOSODIUM GLUTAMATE
SUNSHINE	
ANIMAL; KRISPY SALTINE; OYSTER & SOUP	WHEY
CHEEZ-IT	**(COCONUT OIL);* PAPRIKA**
WHEAT WAFERS	**(COCONUT OIL)***
HI-HO	**(COCONUT OIL);*** WHEY (DAIRY)
CINNAMON GRAHAM; HONEY GRAHAM; KRISPY UNSALTED TOPS	NO ADDITIVES OF CONCERN
VENUS	
CRACKED WHEAT WAFERS; CRACKED *(continues)*	NO ADDITIVES OF CONCERN

*Blend may contain one or more of these saturated fats and/or oils.

BRANDS	ADDITIVES-OF-CONCERN **BOLD—CONCERN TO ALL** LIGHT—CONCERN TO SOME
WHEAT WAFERS NO SALT; NEW ENGLAND SODA; WHEAT WAFERS	
WASA	
CRISP RYE BREAD HEARTY RYE; SOURDOUGH TOAST; SWEDISH CRISPBREAD SEASONED; SWEDISH CRISPBREAD SESAME	NO ADDITIVES OF CONCERN
R WESTON	
ONION STIX	**ANIMAL & VEGETABLE SHORTENING; ARTIFICIAL FOOD COLOR;** MONOSODIUM GLUTAMATE
WHEAT O'S	**(BEEF TALLOW, LARD; COCONUT OIL, VEGETABLE OIL SHORTENING);*** WHEY (DRIED)
SUPERMARKET PRIVATE BRANDS	
A & P	
—A & P	
ANIMAL; SOUP & OYSTER	NO ADDITIVES OF CONCERN
CHEESE	**ARTIFICIAL COLOR;** FD & C YELLOW NO. 5; **(COCONUT OIL)***
GRAHAM	**ARTIFICIAL COLOR;** FD & C YELLOW NO. 5

*Blend may contain one or more of these saturated fats and/or oils.

BRANDS	ADDITIVES-OF-CONCERN BOLD—CONCERN TO ALL LIGHT—CONCERN TO SOME
—A & P *(Continued)*	
SALTINES; SNACK	**(COCONUT OIL)***
FIRST NATIONAL	
—EDWARDS OYSTER	NO ADDITIVES OF CONCERN
—FINAST ANIMAL	NO ADDITIVES OF CONCERN
SAFEWAY	
—BUSY BAKER	
BACON	**(COCONUT OIL, HYDROGENATED SOYBEAN OIL);* NATURAL SMOKE FLAVORED YEAST;** WHEY
GARDEN VEGETABLE	**(COCONUT, HYDROGENATED SOYBEAN OILS);* TURMERIC**
ONION; RYE; SESAME; WHEAT	**(COCONUT, HYDROGENATED SOYBEAN OILS)***
SESAME CHEDDAR	**(COCONUT, HYDROGENATED SOYBEAN OILS);* PAPRIKA**
STOP & SHOP	
—STOP & SHOP	
ANIMAL; SALTINES; SOUP & OYSTER	NO ADDITIVES OF CONCERN
CHEESE	**ARTIFICIAL COLOR;** FD & C YELLOW NO. 5; **(COCONUT OIL)***
SUGAR HONEY GRAHAM	**ARTIFICIAL COLOR;** FD & C YELLOW NO. 5

BRANDS	**ADDITIVES-OF-CONCERN** BOLD—CONCERN TO ALL LIGHT—CONCERN TO SOME
WINN DIXIE —CRACKIN GOOD	
BLEU CHEESE	**ARTIFICIAL COLOR** W/ FD & C YELLOW NO. 5; **(BEEF FAT, LARD);* BHA; COCONUT OIL;** MONOSODIUM GLUTAMATE; WHEY (DAIRY)
CHEEZ BITS	**ARTIFICIAL COLOR** W/ FD & C YELLOW NO. 5; **(BEEF FAT, LARD);* BHA; COCONUT OIL; PAPRIKA;** WHEY (DAIRY)
SUGAR HONEY GRAHAM	**BHA**
ORLEANS WAFERS; SALTINES	**(BEEF FAT, LARD);* BHA;** WHEY (DAIRY)
WHEAT BITS	**ARTIFICIAL COLOR; (BEEF FAT, LARD);* BHA;** WHEY (DAIRY)
ITEMS IN HEALTH FOOD STORES	
CHICO-SAN *RICE CAKES*	
SALTED W/ MILLET ADDED; UNSALTED	NO ADDITIVES OF CONCERN
EL MOLINO MILLS	
HONEY BRAN	GLUTEN FLOUR; WHEY POWDER
EREWHON	
BROWN RICE TAMARI FLAVORED; KOISHI RICE	NO ADDITIVES OF CONCERN

*Blend may contain one or more of these saturated fats and oils.

BRANDS	ADDITIVES-OF-CONCERN **BOLD—CONCERN TO ALL** LIGHT—CONCERN TO SOME
EREWHON *(Continued)*	
NORI MAKI RICE	NORI SEAWEED
HEALTH VALLEY	
CHEESE	**PAPRIKA**
HERB; SESAME; WHOLE WHEAT; YOGURT	NO ADDITIVES OF CONCERN
HONEY GRAHAM	WHEY POWDER
HUG DAR-VIDA SWISS WHOLE-WHEAT BREAD	**VEGETABLE SHORTENING**
MI-DEL HONEY GRAHAMS	NO ADDITIVES OF CONCERN
SOKEN-SHA	
BROWN RICE	NO ADDITIVES OF CONCERN
SEAWEED CRUNCH	GREEN NORI; HIJIKI SEAWEED; KOMBU SEAWEED; WAKAME SEAWEED
SOVEX *PROTHINS SNACK CHIPS*	
BARBEQUE	**HICKORY SMOKED TORULA YEAST;*** KELP; **PAPRIKA**

*Although "smoked" does not refer to a specific additive, it represents a process utilizing wood smoke, as "smoke flavoring" does, and therefore the foods may contain some cancer-causing benzopyrene chemicals. For this reason, when a food or any of its constituents have been smoked, this has been noted in the additives-of-concern column.

BRANDS	ADDITIVES-OF-CONCERN BOLD—CONCERN TO ALL LIGHT—CONCERN TO SOME
CELERY; ONION	KELP
SPIRAL BRAND SALTED RICE CAKES	NO ADDITIVES OF CONCERN

CROUTONS

By law, at this writing, it is not required of a manufacturer to state whether cheeses contain artificial colors, unless the color is FD & C Yellow No. 5 (Tartrazine). Their presence in croutons containing cheese therefore remains an uncertainty, unless it is voluntarily declared on the label that artificial colors have been used or have not. For a more detailed explanation of artificial color in cheese, refer to the beginning of the cheese section of "Dairy Products & Substitutes."

BRANDS	ADDITIVES-OF-CONCERN
ARNOLD CANADIAN CHEESE GARLIC; SPICY ITALIAN SALAD FIXIN'S	**ARTIFICIAL COLOR; BHA;** MONOSODIUM GLUTAMATE; WHEY
FRENCH GARLIC	**BHA**
BROWNBERRY BLEU CHEESE; TOASTED	**BHA;** WHEY (DRIED)
CAESAR SALAD	WHEY (DRIED)
ONION & GARLIC; SEASONED	MONOSODIUM GLUTAMATE; WHEY (DRIED)
DEVONSHEER CHEESE & GARLIC; ONION & GARLIC; SEASONED	MONOSODIUM GLUTAMATE; WHEY

BRANDS	**ADDITIVES-OF-CONCERN** **BOLD—CONCERN TO ALL** LIGHT—CONCERN TO SOME
DEVONSHEER *(Continued)*	
PLAIN	NO ADDITIVES OF CONCERN
FRANCISCO	
CHEESE & GARLIC	**VEGETABLE OIL**
SEASONED	**(COCONUT OIL);*** MONOSODIUM GLUTAMATE; WHEY (SWEET DAIRY)
FRENCH'S BEL-AIR CHEESE & GARLIC	**ARTIFICIAL COLOR; COCONUT OIL**
KELLOGG'S	
CROUTETTES STUFFING HERB SEASONED	**BHA;** MONOSODIUM GLUTAMATE
PEPPERIDGE FARM	
CHEDDAR & ROMANO CHEESE; CHEESE & GARLIC; ONION & GARLIC; SEASONED	**COCONUT OIL**
SALAD CRISPINS	
FRENCH STYLE	**ARTIFICIAL COLOR;** BUTTERMILK SOLIDS; **PAPRIKA;** WHEY
ITALIAN STYLE	**ARTIFICIAL COLOR; (HYDROGENATED COTTONSEED, PALM, SOYBEAN OILS);* PAPRIKA**
SUPERMARKET PRIVATE BRANDS	
LUCKY	
—HARVEST DAY CROUTON STUFFING MIX	NO ADDITIVES OF CONCERN

BRANDS	**ADDITIVES-OF-CONCERN** BOLD—CONCERN TO ALL LIGHT—CONCERN TO SOME
SAFEWAY —MRS. WRIGHT'S HERB SEASONED	**ARTIFICIAL COLOR;** BUTTERMILK SOLIDS; **LARD;** MONOSODIUM GLUTAMATE; WHEY
UNSEASONED BREAD CUBES	NO ADDITIVES OF CONCERN
STOP & SHOP —STOP & SHOP CROUTONS	WHEY

CRUMB COATING MIXES

	GOLDEN DIPT *MIX* BATTER	**CALCIUM CASEINATE;** SODIUM ALGINATE; WHEY
	BREADING SEASONED COATING	**OLEORESIN PAPRIKA**
	SPOON 'N FRY DONUT BATTER	EGG WHITES; **SODIUM CASEINATE;** WHEY
	SEAFOOD SEASONED COATING	NO ADDITIVES OF CONCERN
R	KRISPPE BATTER MIX	WHEY
	FRYING BATTER MIX	**CERTIFIED COLOR;** WHEY
	FRYING BREADER	MONOSODIUM GLUTAMATE; **PAPRIKA;** WHEY

BRANDS	ADDITIVES-OF-CONCERN **BOLD—CONCERN TO ALL** LIGHT—CONCERN TO SOME
OVEN FRY *COATING FOR CHICKEN*	
CRISPY CRUMB RECIPE	MONOSODIUM GLUTAMATE; **PAPRIKA**
HOME STYLE FLOUR RECIPE	**ARTIFICIAL COLOR; MODIFIED CORN STARCH; PAPRIKA**
SHAKE 'N BAKE *—SEASONED COATING MIX*	
BARBEQUE CHICKEN	**ARTIFICIAL COLOR;** GUM TRAGACANTH; **MODIFIED CORN STARCH;** MONOSODIUM GLUTAMATE; **PAPRIKA (& EXTRACTIVES);** WHEY
BARBEQUE PORK & RIBS	**MODIFIED CORN STARCH**
CHICKEN ORIGINAL	**ARTIFICIAL COLOR;** MONOSODIUM GLUTAMATE; **NATURAL HICKORY SMOKE FLAVOR; PAPRIKA**
FISH	**ARTIFICIAL COLOR; BHA;** MONOSODIUM GLUTAMATE
PORK	**ARTIFICIAL COLOR; MODIFIED CORN STARCH;** MONOSODIUM GLUTAMATE
SUPERMARKET PRIVATE BRANDS	
SAFEWAY —MRS. WRIGHT'S	
POULTRY, MEAT & FISH DRESSING	NO ADDITIVES OF CONCERN

BRANDS	ADDITIVES-OF-CONCERN **BOLD—CONCERN TO ALL** LIGHT—CONCERN TO SOME
ITEMS IN HEALTH FOOD STORES	
DR. TIMA SEASONED COATING MIX	**PAPRIKA**

QUICK STUFFING & STUFFING MIXES

	BRANDS	ADDITIVES-OF-CONCERN
	ARNOLD	
	GREAT STUFF CHICKEN STUFFING MIX	**BHA; MODIFIED CORN STARCH;** MONOSODIUM GLUTAMATE; **TURMERIC**
	SEASONED STUFFIN'	**BHA;** GLUTEN (VITAL WHEAT); MONOSODIUM GLUTAMATE
R	BELL'S	
	PAN TO TABLE QUICK STUFFING MIX CHICKEN	MONOSODIUM GLUTAMATE; **TURMERIC**
	STUFFING	MONOSODIUM GLUTAMATE
R	GOLDEN DIPT	
	SEASONED STUFFIN' DRESSING	**(COCONUT, HYDROGENATED SOYBEAN OILS);*** MSG
	PEPPERIDGE FARM	
	CHICKEN & HERB PAN STYLE STUFFING MIX	MONOSODIUM GLUTAMATE
	CORN BREAD STUFFING; HERB SEASONED STUFFING	NO ADDITIVES OF CONCERN
	SEASONED PAN STYLE STUFFING MIX	MONOSODIUM GLUTAMATE; **NATURAL SMOKE FLAVOR**

*Blend may contain one or more of these saturated oils.

BRANDS	ADDITIVES-OF-CONCERN BOLD—CONCERN TO ALL LIGHT—CONCERN TO SOME
STOVE TOP *STUFFING MIX* CHICKEN FLAVOR; FOR PORK; W/ RICE	**BHA; MODIFIED WHEAT STARCH;** MONOSODIUM GLUTAMATE; **TURMERIC;** WHEY
CORNBREAD	**ARTIFICIAL COLOR; BHA;** GLUTEN (WHEAT); **MODIFIED WHEAT STARCH;** MONOSODIUM GLUTAMATE; **TURMERIC**
UNCLE BEN'S STUFF 'N SUCH STUFFING MIX TRADITIONAL SAGE	**FERRIC ORTHOPHOSPHATE;** MONOSODIUM GLUTAMATE; **TURMERIC**
SUPERMARKET PRIVATE BRANDS SAFEWAY —MRS. WRIGHT'S CORNBREAD STUFFING MIX	**(HYDROGENATED SOYBEAN OIL);*** MSG

*Blend may contain this saturated oil.

VIII. CANDY & GUM

Although sugars (both sucrose and corn sweeteners) and honey are not treated as additives of concern in this volume when present in moderate amounts as additives, excessive amounts of these or other carbohydrates in the diet can be of health concern. Confections, including chewing gum (other than sugar-less gum), are likely to consist of from 20% to 75% sugar.

CANDY BARS

BRANDS	**ADDITIVES-OF-CONCERN** **BOLD—CONCERN TO ALL** LIGHT—CONCERN TO SOME
BABY RUTH	**ARTIFICIAL COLOR;** WHEY (DAIRY)
CADBURY'S	
CARAMELLO	WHEY
PEPPERMINT	**ARTIFICIAL COLOR**
—MILK CHOCOLATE	
BRAZIL NUT; FRUIT & NUT; HAZEL NUT; REGULAR	NO ADDITIVES OF CONCERN
CHARLESTON CHEW!	
BITE SIZE; VANILLA	**(COCONUT, PALM KERNEL OILS);*** EGG ALBUMIN; MILK SOLIDS (NONFAT)
CHUNKY	NO ADDITIVES OF CONCERN
FOREVER YOURS	EGG WHITES
HEATH ENGLISH TOFFEE	NO ADDITIVES OF CONCERN

*Blend may contain one or more of these saturated oils.

BRANDS	ADDITIVES-OF-CONCERN BOLD—CONCERN TO ALL LIGHT—CONCERN TO SOME
HERSHEY'S KRACKEL; MILK CHOCOLATE; MILK CHOCOLATE W/ ALMONDS; MR. GOODBAR	NO ADDITIVES OF CONCERN
KIT KAT	NO ADDITIVES OF CONCERN
MILKY WAY	EGG WHITES
NECCO SKY BAR	EGG WHITES
NESTLÉ CHOCO'LITE; CRUNCH; MILK CHOCOLATE; $100,000	NO ADDITIVES OF CONCERN
PETER PAUL ALMOND JOY	EGG WHITES; WHEY
MOUNDS	EGG WHITES
SNICKERS	EGG WHITES
3 MUSKETEERS	EGG WHITES
ITEMS IN HEALTH FOOD STORES **APLETS**	NO ADDITIVES OF CONCERN
BURRY HEALTH FOODS CAROB CRUNCH; CAROB MINT	**FRACTIONATED PALM KERNEL OIL**
CAROB MILK	NO ADDITIVES OF CONCERN

BRANDS	ADDITIVES-OF-CONCERN BOLD—CONCERN TO ALL LIGHT—CONCERN TO SOME
CAROB CRUNCH	NO ADDITIVES OF CONCERN
GRAPELETS	NO ADDITIVES OF CONCERN
HALVAH CAROB-SESAME; SESAME-HONEY	NO ADDITIVES OF CONCERN
HOFFMAN'S CAROB CLUSTER	**VEGETABLE OIL**
HI-PROTEEN ENERGY	EGG WHITES (DRIED)
SUPER HI-PROTEEN DIET	EGG WHITES (DRIED); **SODIUM CASEINATE**
LIFESTREAM CASHEW HALVAH; HIKERS; RASPBERRY DELITE; SESAME DREAM; SUNSHINE HONEY	NO ADDITIVES OF CONCERN
NATURE'S FANTASY	NO ADDITIVES OF CONCERN
NATURE NOUGATS	WHEY
TANIA'S *CHEWS* MAPLE NUT; SESAME COCONUT	NO ADDITIVES OF CONCERN
WHA GURU CHEW CASHEW-ALMOND; ORIGINAL; SESAME-ALMOND	NO ADDITIVES OF CONCERN

BRANDS	ADDITIVES-OF-CONCERN **BOLD—CONCERN TO ALL** LIGHT—CONCERN TO SOME

CANDY: OTHER (CHOCOLATE, HARD CANDIES, JELLIED & OTHER SOFT CANDIES, MARSHMALLOWS, MINTS, NUT CANDIES)

BRANDS	ADDITIVES-OF-CONCERN
ANDES CREME DE MENTHE'S	**CERTIFIED COLORS;** MILK SOLIDS (NONFAT & WHOLE); **PALM KERNEL OIL**
BORDEN CAMPFIRE MINIATURE MARSHMALLOWS	**ARTIFICIAL COLOR**
BRACH'S	
BURGUNDY; ROYALS	**ARTIFICIAL COLORS;** FD & C YELLOW NO. 5; **BHA;** EGG WHITES; **MODIFIED STARCH**
LICORICE TWISTS	**ARTIFICIAL COLOR**
CLARK PEANUT BUTTER LOGS	**ARTIFICIAL COLOR**
HERSHEY'S KISSES	NO ADDITIVES OF CONCERN
KRAFT	
BUTTER MINTS	**ARTIFICIAL COLOR; BHA; BUTTER**
FUDGIES	WHEY
JETS MARSHMALLOWS	**MODIFIED FOOD STARCH**

BRANDS	ADDITIVES-OF-CONCERN BOLD—CONCERN TO ALL LIGHT—CONCERN TO SOME
MINIATURE MARSHMALLOWS (LEMON, LIME, ORANGE, STRAWBERRY)	**ARTIFICIAL COLOR; MODIFIED FOOD STARCH**
TOFFEE	NO ADDITIVES OF CONCERN
LIFE SAVERS	
BREATH SAVERS WINTERGREEN	ACACIA [GUM]; **ARTIFICIAL COLOR; CALCIUM STEARATE**
BUTTER RUM; FIVE FLAVOR; STIKOPEP; TROPICAL FRUITS	**ARTIFICIAL COLORS**
CRYSTOMINT; PEPOMINT; WINTOGREEN	NO ADDITIVES OF CONCERN
M & M'S *CHOCOLATE CANDIES*	
PEANUT; PLAIN	**ARTIFICIAL COLORS**
NECCO	
ASSORTED WAFERS	**ARTIFICIAL COLORS;** GUM ARABIC; GUM TRAGACANTH
CANADA MINTS	GUM TRAGACANTH
CANADA SPEARMINT; CANADA WINTERGREEN	**ARTIFICIAL COLOR** OR **COLORS;** GUM TRAGACANTH
PEARSON	
CARAMEL NIP; COFFEE NIP	WHEY (DAIRY)

BRANDS	ADDITIVES-OF-CONCERN BOLD—CONCERN TO ALL LIGHT—CONCERN TO SOME
PEARSON *(Continued)*	
CHOCOLATE PARFAIT	**(COCONUT, PALM KERNEL, HYDROGENATED SOYBEAN OILS);*** WHEY (DAIRY)
PETER PAUL YORK PEPPERMINT PATTIE	EGG WHITES
REESE'S PEANUT BUTTER CUP	NO ADDITIVES OF CONCERN
RICHARDSON CLUB MINTS; PARTY JELLIES; PASTEL MINTS	**ARTIFICIAL COLORS**
ROLO	NO ADDITIVES OF CONCERN
SOPHIE MAE PEANUT BRITTLE	NO ADDITIVES OF CONCERN
SPANGLER DUM-DUM POPS	**ARTIFICIAL COLOR**
STARBURST FRUIT CHEWS	**ARTIFICIAL COLORS; MODIFIED FOOD STARCH; PALM KERNEL OIL**
TOOTSIE ROLL POP DROPS	**ARTIFICIAL COLORS; (COCONUT OIL);*** WHEY
ROLL; ROLL MIDGEES	WHEY
ROLL POPS	**ARTIFICIAL COLOR;** WHEY

*Blend may contain one or more of these saturated oils.

BRANDS	ADDITIVES-OF-CONCERN **BOLD—CONCERN TO ALL** LIGHT—CONCERN TO SOME
SUPERMARKET PRIVATE BRANDS A & P —ANN PAGE	
BUTTERSCOTCH; CLEARMINTS; 50 POPS; FILLED BERRIES; JELLY BEANS; LICORICE GUMS; MINT PUFFS; PEPPERMINT LOZENGES; SALT WATER TAFFY; SOUR BALLS; SPEARMINT LEAVES; SPICE DROPS; STRAWBERRY LACES	**ARTIFICIAL COLOR (COLORS)** OR **CERTIFIED COLOR** OR **U.S. CERTIFIED COLOR (COLORS)**
ASSORTED TOFFEES	**ARTIFICIAL COLORS;** EGG ALBUMIN; WHEY SOLIDS
BLACK LACES; CARAMELS; MARY JANES; MILK CHOCOLATE STARS; MINT WAFERS; PEANUT CLUSTERS	NO ADDITIVES OF CONCERN
BUTTERMINTS	**ARTIFICIAL COLOR; BHA; BUTTER**
CANDY CORN	**CONFECTIONER'S GLAZE;** EGG ALBUMIN; **U.S. CERTIFIED COLORS**
CHOCOLATE BRIDGE MIX	**ARTIFICIAL COLOR;** EGG WHITES (DRIED); GUM ARABIC; **RESINOUS GLAZE**
CHOCOLATE PEANUTS	**BHA; HYDROGENATED VEGETABLE OIL;** WHEY POWDER

BRANDS	ADDITIVES-OF-CONCERN BOLD—CONCERN TO ALL LIGHT—CONCERN TO SOME
—ANN PAGE *(Continued)*	
CREAM DROPS; THIN MINTS	EGG WHITES (DRIED)
LICORICE DROPS	**ARTIFICIAL COLORS; BUTTER**
MALTED MILK BALLS	**CONFECTIONER'S GLAZE; HYDROGENATED VEGETABLE OIL**
PEANUT BUTTER KISSES	**ARTIFICIAL COLOR; BHA**
STOP & SHOP	
—STOP & SHOP	
CARAMEL RUM	**ARTIFICIAL COLOR; BUTTER**
DUTCHESS MIX; MINT MOLASSES; PEPPERMINT STARLITES; ROOT BEER; SOUR BALLS	**ARTIFICIAL COLOR**
FRUIT & SPICE; ORANGE SLICES; SPEARMINT LEAVES	**ARTIFICIAL COLORS** W/ FD & C YELLOW NO. 5
ITEMS IN HEALTH FOOD STORES	
BARBARA'S	
DELICIOUS FUDGE; DELICIOUS SESAME CRUNCH; PEANUT BRITTLE	NO ADDITIVES OF CONCERN

BRANDS	ADDITIVES-OF-CONCERN **BOLD—CONCERN TO ALL** LIGHT—CONCERN TO SOME
NIK'S SWEETS *TREATS* BARLEY; GINGER; PEANUT	NO ADDITIVES OF CONCERN
PANDA LICORICE ALL NATURAL	NO ADDITIVES OF CONCERN
YINNIES CARAMEL CANDY; TAFFY	NO ADDITIVES OF CONCERN

CHEWING GUM

Chewing-gum base: Chewing gum contains chewing-gum base; 18 specific bases are used, and a few (for example, glycerol esters of wood rosin) are regarded as additives of concern when identified on labels of other foods. Since there is no way of determining which base has been used in a particular gum, and the likelihood of much being ingested is minimal, chewing-gum bases are not noted in the additives-of-concern column.

BRANDS	ADDITIVES-OF-CONCERN
BEECH-NUT SPEARMINT	**ARTIFICIAL COLORS; BHA**
BUBBLE YUM *BUBBLE GUM* REGULAR; SPEARMINT	**ARTIFICIAL COLORS; BHA; SOFTENERS**
GRAPE	**ARTIFICIAL COLORS; BHT; SOFTENERS**
BUBBLICIOUS *SOFT BUBBLE GUM*	**ARTIFICIAL COLOR; SOFTENERS**

BRANDS	ADDITIVES-OF-CONCERN BOLD—CONCERN TO ALL LIGHT—CONCERN TO SOME
CARE-FREE *SUGARLESS GUM* BUBBLE	**ARTIFICIAL COLORS; BHA; SOFTENER**
CINNAMON	**ARTIFICIAL COLORS; SOFTENER**
FRUIT; PEPPERMINT; SPEARMINT	**SOFTENER**
CHICLETS FRUIT FLAVORS; SPEARMINT; TINY SIZE FLAVOR COATED	**ARTIFICIAL COLORS**
PEPPERMINT	NO ADDITIVES OF CONCERN
CLORETS	**ARTIFICIAL COLORS**
DENTYNE REGULAR	**ARTIFICIAL COLORS; SOFTENERS**
SPEARMINT	**ARTIFICIAL COLORS**
FRESHEN-UP CINNAMON; SPEARMINT	**ARTIFICIAL COLORS; SOFTENERS**
ORBIT *SUGAR FREE GUM* CINNAMON	**ARTIFICIAL COLORS; BHA; SOFTENERS**
PEPPERMINT; SPEARMINT	**SOFTENERS**

BRANDS	ADDITIVES-OF-CONCERN **BOLD—CONCERN TO ALL** LIGHT—CONCERN TO SOME
TRIDENT *SUGARLESS GUM*	
BUBBLE; SPEARMINT	ACACIA [GUM]; **ARTIFICIAL COLOR** OR **COLORS**
CINNAMON; FRUIT FLAVOR	ACACIA [GUM]; **ARTIFICIAL COLORS; XYLITOL**
ORIGINAL FLAVOR	ACACIA [GUM]
WRIGLEY'S	
BIG RED	**ARTIFICIAL COLORS; SOFTENERS**
DOUBLEMINT; JUICY FRUIT; SPEARMINT	**SOFTENERS**
FREEDENT PEPPERMINT; FREEDENT SPEARMINT	**ARTIFICIAL COLORS; BHA; SOFTENERS**
ITEMS IN HEALTH FOOD STORES	
XYLITOL	
CINNAMON	GUM ARABIC; **XYLITOL**
PEPPERMINT; SPEARMINT	**XYLITOL**

IX. CEREAL, CEREAL BARS (BREAKFAST & SNACK)

CEREAL: HOT

BRANDS	**ADDITIVES-OF-CONCERN** **BOLD—CONCERN TO ALL** LIGHT—CONCERN TO SOME
MAYPO	
30-SECOND OATMEAL W/ MAPLE FLAVOR; VERMONT STYLE HOT OAT CEREAL	**FERRIC ORTHOPHOSPHATE**
NABISCO	
INSTANT CREAM OF WHEAT	NO ADDITIVES OF CONCERN
QUICK CREAM OF WHEAT	**IRON PHOSPHATE**
—MIX 'N EAT CREAM OF WHEAT	
PLAIN	**BHA;** GUAR GUM; **IRON PHOSPHATE**
BANANA & SPICE	**BHA;** GUAR GUM; **IRON PHOSPHATE; NUTMEG**
PILLSBURY FARINA	NO ADDITIVES OF CONCERN
QUAKER	
ENRICHED WHITE HOMINY GRITS; OLD FASHIONED OATS; QUICK OATS	NO ADDITIVES OF CONCERN
INSTANT GRITS	**BHA**

BRANDS	ADDITIVES-OF-CONCERN BOLD—CONCERN TO ALL LIGHT—CONCERN TO SOME
—INSTANT OATMEAL	
APPLES & CINNAMON; MAPLE & BROWN SUGAR; REGULAR FLAVOR	GUAR GUM
RALSTON INSTANT	**BHA**
WHEATENA	NO ADDITIVES OF CONCERN
SUPERMARKET PRIVATE BRANDS	
LUCKY	
—LADY LEE QUICK OATS	NO ADDITIVES OF CONCERN
SAFEWAY	
—MRS. WRIGHT'S HOMINY GRITS	NO ADDITIVES OF CONCERN
STOP & SHOP	
—STOP & SHOP QUICK OATS	NO ADDITIVES OF CONCERN
ITEMS IN HEALTH FOOD STORES	
CREAM OF RYE	NO ADDITIVES OF CONCERN
EREWHON	
BROWN RICE CREAM; SCOTCH OATS; SWEET CREAM CEREAL	NO ADDITIVES OF CONCERN
ROMAN MEAL 5 MINUTE	NO ADDITIVES OF CONCERN

BRANDS	ADDITIVES-OF-CONCERN BOLD—CONCERN TO ALL LIGHT—CONCERN TO SOME

CEREAL: READY-TO-EAT; WHEAT GERM

When used in reasonable amounts, sugars have not been treated here as additives of concern. However, when they are present as a sizable proportion of the total content of a cereal, a caution may be warranted. Percentages of sugar content have been provided in parentheses for the cereals below for which information was available.

FAMILIA	NO ADDITIVES OF CONCERN
GENERAL MILLS BOO BERRY (46);* CHEERIOS (3); LUCKY CHARMS (39); TRIX (31)	**ARTIFICIAL COLOR** OR **COLORS**
BUC WHEATS (11); COCOA PUFFS (34); COUNT CHOCULA (37); GOLDEN GRAHAMS (29); KIX (3)	NO ADDITIVES OF CONCERN
CRAZY COW (CHOCOLATE) (44)	**ARTIFICIAL COLOR; CARRAGEENAN;** GUAR GUM
NATURE VALLEY GRANOLA CINNAMON & RAISINS; NATURE VALLEY GRANOLA TOASTED OAT MIXTURE	**COCONUT OIL**

BRANDS	ADDITIVES-OF-CONCERN **BOLD—CONCERN TO ALL** LIGHT—CONCERN TO SOME
TOTAL (7); WHEATIES (8)	**BHT**
KELLOGG'S	
ALL-BRAN (19); BRAN BUDS (30);* 40% BRAN FLAKES (16);* RAISIN BRAN (29); SUGAR SMACKS (54)	NO ADDITIVES OF CONCERN
APPLE JACKS (52); FROOT LOOPS (48)	**ARTIFICIAL COLORING; BHA**
COCOA KRISPIES (41)	**BHA;** WHEY
CORN FLAKES (5); CRACKLIN' BRAN (28); FROSTED MINI-WHEATS BROWN SUGAR CINNAMON (16);* FROSTED MINI-WHEATS SUGAR FROSTED (34);* FROSTED RICE (34); PRODUCT 19 (10); RICE KRISPIES (7); SUGAR CORN POPS *(continues)*	**BHA**

*Source of sugar content (sucrose only): Ira L. Shannon, *Brand Name Guide to Sugar* (Nelson-Hall Publishers, 1977). Source for unstarred entries (sucrose and corn sweeteners): B. W. Li and P. J. Shuhmann, *Gas-Liquid Chromatographic Analysis of Sugars in Ready-to-Eat Breakfast Cereals* (Institute of Food Technologists; reprinted in *J. Food Science,* 45:138-141, 1980).

BRANDS	ADDITIVES-OF-CONCERN BOLD—CONCERN TO ALL LIGHT—CONCERN TO SOME
KELLOGG'S *(Continued)*	
(44); SUGAR FROSTED FLAKES (38); TOASTED MINI-WHEATS PLAIN	**BHA**
SPECIAL K (5)	**BHA; CALCIUM CASEINATE;** GLUTEN (WHEAT); WHEY
—NUTRI-GRAIN	
BARLEY; CORN; RYE; WHEAT	**BHA**
KRETSCHMER	
WHEAT GERM REGULAR; WHEAT GERM W/ SUGAR & HONEY	NO ADDITIVES OF CONCERN
NABISCO	
100% BRAN (19)	NO ADDITIVES OF CONCERN
SHREDDED WHEAT (1)	**BHT**
TEAM (13)	**BHT; IRON PHOSPHATE**
POST	
ALPHA-BITS (35)	**ARTIFICIAL COLOR; BHA**
C. W. POST (27); C. W. POST W/ RAISINS (27)	WHEY
COCOA PEBBLES (41)	**(COCONUT, PALM KERNEL OILS)***
FORTIFIED OAT FLAKES (18)	**BHA;** MILK PROTEIN

*Blend may contain one or more of these saturated oils.

BRANDS	ADDITIVES-OF-CONCERN **BOLD—CONCERN TO ALL** LIGHT—CONCERN TO SOME
40% BRAN FLAKES (12); GRAPE-NUTS FLAKES (12); HONEY-COMB (36)	**BHA**
FRUITY PEBBLES (41)	**ARTIFICIAL COLOR; (COCONUT, PALM KERNEL OILS)***
GRAPE-NUTS (7); RAISIN BRAN (28); SUPER SUGAR CRISP (45)	NO ADDITIVES OF CONCERN
QUAKER	
LIFE (15)	**ARTIFICIAL COLORING; BHA;** CASEIN
LIFE CINNAMON FLAVOR (21)	**ARTIFICIAL COLOR; BHA;** LACTALBUMIN
PUFFED RICE (0.1); PUFFED WHEAT (0.5)	NO ADDITIVES OF CONCERN
—CAP'N CRUNCH	
CRUNCH BERRIES (43)	**ARTIFICIAL COLORING; BHA;** WHEY (DRIED)
PEANUT BUTTER (31)	**BHA**
REGULAR (39)	**ARTIFICIAL COLOR; BHA**
CORN BRAN	**ARTIFICIAL COLOR** FD & C BLUE NO. 1, **RED NO. 3,** YELLOW NO. 5 & NO. 6
—100% NATURAL CEREAL	
REGULAR; W/ APPLES & CINNAMON (17);* W/ RAISINS & DATES	NO ADDITIVES OF CONCERN

BRANDS	ADDITIVES-OF-CONCERN BOLD—CONCERN TO ALL LIGHT—CONCERN TO SOME
RALSTON PURINA *—CHEX* BRAN; CORN (3); RICE (4); WHEAT (4)	**BHA**
—COOKIE CRISP CHOCOLATE CHIP (41)	**ARTIFICIAL COLOR;** FD & C YELLOW NO. 5; **BHT**
OATMEAL COOKIE (40)	**ARTIFICIAL COLORS; BHT**
SUPERMARKET PRIVATE BRANDS **LUCKY** **—LADY LEE** CRISPY RICE; RAISIN BRAN;	**BHT**
SUGAR FROSTED FLAKES	**BHT; IRON PHOSPHATE**
TASTEEOS	**ARTIFICIAL COLOR;** FD & C YELLOW NO. 5; **BHA; BHT**
—SAFEWAY CORN FLAKES; CRISPY RICE	**BHT; IRON PHOSPHATE**
TASTEEOS	**ARTIFICIAL COLOR;** FD & C YELLOW NO. 5; **BHA; BHT**

*Source of sugar content (sucrose only): Ira L. Shannon, *Brand Name Guide to Sugar* (Nelson-Hall Publishers, 1977). Source for unstarred entries (sucrose and corn sweeteners): B. W. Li and P. J. Shuhmann, *Gas-Liquid Chromatographic Analysis of Sugars in Ready-to-Eat Breakfast Cereals* (Institute of Food Technologists; reprinted in *J. Food Science,* 45:138-141, 1980).

BRANDS	ADDITIVES-OF-CONCERN BOLD—CONCERN TO ALL LIGHT—CONCERN TO SOME
STOP & SHOP —STOP & SHOP CORN FLAKES; CRISPY RICE; SUGAR FROSTED FLAKES	**BHT; IRON PHOSPHATE**
—SUN GLORY PUFFED RICE	ACACIA GUM; **FERRIC ORTHOPHOSPHATE**
ITEMS IN HEALTH FOOD STORES	
EL MOLINO PUFFED CORN; PUFFED WHEAT	NO ADDITIVES OF CONCERN
EREWHON SUNFLOWER CRUNCH	**UNREFINED VEGETABLE OIL**
—*GRANOLA* CAROB COCONUT; DATE NUT; MAPLE; NUMBER 9 SALT-FREE; SPICED APPLE	**UNREFINED VEGETABLE OIL**
HONEY ALMOND	NO ADDITIVES OF CONCERN
FAMILIA SWISS GRANOLA	NO ADDITIVES OF CONCERN
FEARN SOY/O WHEAT CEREAL & SOYA	NO ADDITIVES OF CONCERN
GOOD SHEPHERD ALMONDS 'N' MOLASSES	**COCONUT OIL**
TRADITIONAL W/ ADDED BRAN	NO ADDITIVES OF CONCERN

BRANDS	ADDITIVES-OF-CONCERN BOLD—CONCERN TO ALL LIGHT—CONCERN TO SOME
GOOD SHEPARD *(Continued)*	
UNSWEETENED GRANOLA	**COCONUT OIL;** WHEY
—8 GRAIN CEREAL 'N' SNACK	
APPLE CINNAMON; RAISIN CINNAMON	WHEY
HEALTH VALLEY	
BRAN W/ APPLES & CINNAMON; ORANGEOLA; SPROUTS 7	NO ADDITIVES OF CONCERN
ROSE ENRIGHT	
GREAT GRAINS 'N HONEY	NO ADDITIVES OF CONCERN
SOVEX	
HONEY ALMOND GRANOLA	NO ADDITIVES OF CONCERN
MAPLE WALNUT TRITICALE	WHEY

CEREAL BARS (BREAKFAST & SNACK)

BRANDS	ADDITIVES-OF-CONCERN
CARNATION	
BREAKFAST BAR	
CHOCOLATE CHIP	**CALCIUM CASEINATE;** MONOSODIUM GLUTAMATE
PEANUT BUTTER CRUNCH	**CALCIUM CASEINATE**

BRANDS	ADDITIVES-OF-CONCERN **BOLD—CONCERN TO ALL** LIGHT—CONCERN TO SOME
CRUNCHOLA PEANUT BUTTER & GRANOLA BARS CHOCOLATE CHIP	**HYDROGENATED PALM OIL; PALM KERNEL OIL; U.S. CERTIFIED COLOR;** WHEY
LITTLE DEBBIE GRANOLA BARS	NO ADDITIVES OF CONCERN
NATURE VALLEY *GRANOLA BARS* CINNAMON; COCONUT; OATS 'N HONEY	**COCONUT OIL**

X. DAIRY PRODUCTS & SUBSTITUTES

R alongside a brand indicates regional (not national) distribution, based on shopping experience.

Note on Cheese; Cheese: Cottage & Ricotta; Cheese: Cream (& Imitations). Declaration of the presence of artificial color in these dairy products by the manufacturer is not required unless the FDA has sufficient evidence that there is a question of safety, in which case the specific color must be identified. FD & C Yellow No. 5 (Tartrazine) is the only artificial color now subjected to this requirement. There is disagreement about the possibility of harmful effects caused by other artificial colors. When artificial color appears on a label, this has been noted in the additives-of-concern column. But when it does not, its absence remains uncertain unless it is voluntarily declared on the label that artificial color has or has not been used.

It may be helpful to compare the color of cheese with milk, its basic component, taking into account that an animal's diet, if rich in grass and other greens, can cause a light yellow hue. Also, a color derived from annatto seed, which produces a yellow to orange hue, is frequently added to cheese: it is not regarded here as an additive of concern. For a review and assessment of food colors, see page 534.

CHEESE

BRANDS	**ADDITIVES-OF-CONCERN** **BOLD—CONCERN TO ALL** LIGHT—CONCERN TO SOME
ALOUETTE W/ GARLIC & SPICES	LOCUST BEAN GUM
AUSTRIAN ALPS SWISS SLICED	NO ADDITIVES OF CONCERN
BORDEN GRATED PARMESAN; LITE-LINE SINGLE WRAP SLICES; *(continues)*	NO ADDITIVES OF CONCERN

BRANDS	ADDITIVES-OF-CONCERN BOLD—CONCERN TO ALL LIGHT—CONCERN TO SOME
MOZZARELLA SLICED; ROQUEFORT;	
—PASTEURIZED PROCESS AMERICAN EASY-PEEL SLICES (ORANGE)	**ARTIFICIALLY COLORED**
EASY-PEEL SLICES (WHITE)	NO ADDITIVES OF CONCERN
CHEESE FOOD SINGLE WRAP SLICES (ORANGE)	**ARTIFICIALLY COLORED;** WHEY & MODIFIED WHEY SOLIDS
—SKIM AMERICAN PASTEURIZED PROCESS CHEESE PRODUCT SINGLE WRAP SLICES (ORANGE)	**ARTIFICALLY COLORED;** CAROB BEAN GUM; GUAR GUM
SINGLE WRAP SLICES (WHITE)	CAROB BEAN GUM; GUAR GUM
CASINO BRICK; MONTEREY JACK; MOZZARELLA; MUENSTER; ROMANO	NO ADDITIVES OF CONCERN
CHURNY CHEESE BALL COLD PACK CHEESE FOOD W/ ALMONDS	GUAR GUM; WHEY
RUGGED SHARP CHEDDAR	NO ADDITIVES OF CONCERN
SMOKSTIK	**HICKORY SMOKED***

	BRANDS	ADDITIVES-OF-CONCERN **BOLD—CONCERN TO ALL** LIGHT—CONCERN TO SOME
R	**COON BRAND** EXTRA SHARP CHEDDAR	NO ADDITIVES OF CONCERN
	CRACKER BARREL EXTRA SHARP CHEDDAR	**ARTIFICIAL COLOR**
	EXTRA SHARP-WHITE CHEDDAR; MELLO-WHITE CHEDDAR; MILD-WHITE CHEDDAR; SHARP-WHITE CHEDDAR	NO ADDITIVES OF CONCERN
	SHARP CHEDDAR COLD PACK CHEESE FOOD	**ARTIFICIAL COLOR;** GUAR GUM; WHEY
	KAUKAUNA KLUB CHEDDAR; CHEDDAR (WINE)	**ARTIFICIAL COLOR;** GUAR GUM; WHEY
	KRAFT AGED SWISS SLICED; MOZZARELLA; NEW YORK EXTRA SHARP CHEDDAR IN WAX; 100% GRATED PARMESAN; SWITZERLAND SWISS	NO ADDITIVES OF CONCERN

*Although "smoked" does not refer to a specific additive, it represents a process utilizing wood smoke, as "smoke flavoring" does, and therefore may contain some cancer-causing benzopyrene chemicals. For this reason, when a food or any of its constituents have been smoked, this has been noted in the additives-of-concern column.

BRANDS	ADDITIVES-OF-CONCERN **BOLD—CONCERN TO ALL** LIGHT—CONCERN TO SOME
PROVOLONE SLICED	**SMOKE FLAVOR**
—CHEESE SPREAD PASTEURIZED NEUFCHÂTEL	
W/ OLIVE & PIMIENTO; W/ PINEAPPLE	CAROB BEAN GUM; WHEY
—CHEESE SPREAD PASTEURIZED PROCESS	
CHEEZ WHIZ; VELVEETA	**ARTIFICIAL COLOR;** WHEY
SHARP OLD ENGLISH; W/ BACON	**ARTIFICIAL COLOR**
—PASTEURIZED PROCESS AMERICAN	
CHEESE FOOD SINGLES (ORANGE)	**ARTIFICIAL COLOR;** WHEY
CHEESE FOOD SINGLES (WHITE)	WHEY
DELUXE CHOICE (ORANGE); DELUXE CHOICE SHARP OLD ENGLISH; DELUXE CHOICE (WHITE)	NO ADDITIVES OF CONCERN
LIGHT N' LIVELY AMERICAN FLAVORED CHEESE PRODUCT	**ARTIFICIAL COLOR;** SODIUM ALGINATE; WHEY

BRANDS	ADDITIVES-OF-CONCERN BOLD—CONCERN TO ALL LIGHT—CONCERN TO SOME
LAUGHING COW CHEEZBITS	NO ADDITIVES OF CONCERN
MAY-BUD EDAM; GOUDA	NO ADDITIVES OF CONCERN
PARADE AMERICAN SLICES SINGLE WRAPPED (ORANGE); AMERICAN SLICES SINGLE WRAPPED (WHITE)	**ARTIFICIAL COLOR;** GUAR GUM; WHEY & MODIFIED WHEY
EXTRA SHARP CHEDDAR; MILD CHEDDAR	NO ADDITIVES OF CONCERN
RONDELÉ SPICED W/ GARLIC & HERBS; SPICED W/ PEPPER	NO ADDITIVES OF CONCERN
SARGENTO PROVOLONE SLICES; SHREDDED CHEDDAR; SHREDDED MOZZARELLA FOR PIZZA	NO ADDITIVES OF CONCERN
STELLA CRUMBLED BLUE; MOZZARELLA; PARMESAN; ROMANO	NO ADDITIVES OF CONCERN
SWISS KNIGHT (ASSORTED CHEESES)	NO ADDITIVES OF CONCERN

BRANDS	ADDITIVES-OF-CONCERN **BOLD—CONCERN TO ALL** LIGHT—CONCERN TO SOME
WEIGHT WATCHERS	
PASTEURIZED PROCESS CHEESE PRODUCT	**ARTIFICIAL COLOR**
WISPRIDE *COLD PACK CHEESE FOOD*	
HICKORY SMOKED	**ARTIFICIAL COLOR;** GUAR GUM; **SMOKE FLAVOR;** WHEY SOLIDS (CHEESE)
SHARP CHEDDAR; W/ PORT WINE	**ARTIFICIAL COLOR** OR **COLORING;** GUAR GUM; WHEY SOLIDS (CHEESE)
WOODY'S *COLD PACK CHEESE FOOD*	
SHARP CHEDDAR; W/ PORT WINE	**ARTIFICIAL COLOR;** GUAR GUM; WHEY
SUPERMARKET PRIVATE BRANDS	
A & P	
—ANN PAGE	
GRATED PARMESAN; NATURAL MUENSTER; NATURAL SHARP CHEDDAR (ORANGE); NATURAL SHARP CHEDDAR (WHITE)	NO ADDITIVES OF CONCERN
—AMERICAN PASTEURIZED PROCESS	
CHED-O-BIT CHEESE FOOD	**ARTIFICIALLY COLORED;** WHEY & MODIFIED WHEY SOLIDS

BRANDS	**ADDITIVES-OF-CONCERN** **BOLD—CONCERN TO ALL** LIGHT—CONCERN TO SOME
ANN PAGE—*PASTEURIZED PROCESS (Continued)*	
CHED-O-BIT WHITE CHEESE FOOD	WHEY & MODIFIED WHEY SOLIDS
MEL-O-BIT; MEL-O-BIT PIMENTO	NO ADDITIVES OF CONCERN
FIRST NATIONAL	
—EDWARDS	
MOZZARELLA	NO ADDITIVES OF CONCERN
—FINAST	
DELUXE AMERICAN PASTEURIZED PROCESS (ORANGE)	**ARTIFICIALLY COLORED**
DELUXE WHITE AMERICAN PASTEURIZED PROCESS	NO ADDITIVES OF CONCERN
LUCKY	
—LADY LEE	
COLBY; LONGHORN CHEDDAR; MEDIUM TILAMOOK CHEDDAR; MILD CHEDDAR; MONTEREY JACK; MOZZARELLA (SHREDDED); MUENSTER; 100% GRATED PARMESAN; PEPPER JACK; SWISS	NO ADDITIVES OF CONCERN
LONGHORN STYLE CHEDDAR; MILD LONGHORN STYLE CHEDDAR	**ARTIFICIAL COLOR**

BRANDS	**ADDITIVES-OF-CONCERN** **BOLD—CONCERN TO ALL** LIGHT—CONCERN TO SOME
—PASTEURIZED PROCESS SLICES AMERICAN	**ARTIFICIAL COLOR**
SLICES AMERICAN CHEESE SPREAD	**ARTIFICIAL COLOR;** GUAR GUM; WHEY
SLICES SWISS	NO ADDITIVES OF CONCERN
SAFEWAY **—LUCERNE** MELLOW SHREDDED CHEDDAR; SHARP SHREDDED CHEDDAR	**COLORING**
SHREDDED MOZZARELLA; SWISS	NO ADDITIVES OF CONCERN
—MIDGET LONGHORN NATURAL CHEDDAR; NATURAL COLBY	**COLORING**
—PASTEURIZED PROCESS CHEESE FOOD SINGLE SLICES PIMENTO	**ARTIFICIAL COLOR;** WHEY
—(NO BRAND NAME) EXTRA SHARP NATURAL CHEDDAR; LONGHORN STYLE NATURAL CHEDDAR; MEDIUM NATURAL CHEDDAR; MILD NATURAL CHEDDAR; MUENSTER; SHARP NATURAL CHEDDAR	**COLORING**

BRANDS	ADDITIVES-OF-CONCERN BOLD—CONCERN TO ALL LIGHT—CONCERN TO SOME
SAFEWAY—(NO BRAND NAME) *(Continued)*	
KUMINOST SPICED; MILD CHEDDAR CLUB	NO ADDITIVES OF CONCERN
—(NO BRAND NAME) *PASTEURIZED PROCESS* SMOKED CHEDDAR; SMOKED SWISS	**SMOKED***
—SAFEWAY SWISS (UNSLICED)	NO ADDITIVES OF CONCERN
—*PASTEURIZED PROCESS* AMERICAN; SLICES SHARP AMERICAN	**ARTIFICIAL COLOR**
SWISS	NO ADDITIVES OF CONCERN
STOP & SHOP —STOP & SHOP *PASTEURIZED PROCESS* AMERICAN CHEESE FOOD (ORANGE)	**ARTIFICIAL COLOR;** WHEY

*Although "smoked" does not refer to a specific additive, it represents a process utilizing wood smoke, as "smoke flavoring" does, and therefore the food may contain some cancer-causing benzopyrene chemicals. For this reason, when a food or any of its constituents have been smoked, this has been noted in the additives-of-concern column.

BRANDS	**ADDITIVES-OF-CONCERN** **BOLD—CONCERN TO ALL** LIGHT—CONCERN TO SOME
AMERICAN CHEESE FOOD (WHITE)	WHEY
ITEMS IN HEALTH FOOD STORES	
ALTA-DENA	
MONTEREY JACK; NATURAL SWISS; RAW MILK MILD CHEDDAR; RENNETLESS MILD CHEDDAR	NO ADDITIVES OF CONCERN
CABOT	
NATURAL CHEDDAR	NO ADDITIVES OF CONCERN
VERMONT SMOKED NATURAL CHEDDAR	**NATURAL SMOKE FLAVORING**
GREENBANK FARMS	
—RAW MILK RENNETLESS NATURAL	
JALAPEÑO JACK; LOW SALT JACK; MILD CHEDDAR; MUENSTER; SWISS; TACO CHEDDAR	NO ADDITIVES OF CONCERN
REDWOOD	
—NATURAL RAW WHOLE MILK CHEESE	
LONGHORN CHEDDAR; MEDIUM CHEDDAR; MONTEREY JACK; MUENSTER; SWISS	NO ADDITIVES OF CONCERN

BRANDS	ADDITIVES-OF-CONCERN **BOLD—CONCERN TO ALL** LIGHT—CONCERN TO SOME
TILLAMOOK MEDIUM AGED CHEDDAR	**VEGETABLE COLORING**

CHEESE: COTTAGE & RICOTTA

BELLA COTTA RICOTTA	WHEY (DRY)
COLOMBO RICOTTA	NO ADDITIVES OF CONCERN
HOOD *COTTAGE CHEESE* W/ PINEAPPLE	CAROB BEAN GUM; WHEY (COTTAGE CHEESE)
NUFORM LOWFAT	CAROB BEAN GUM; **CARRAGEENAN;** GUAR GUM; WHEY (COTTAGE CHEESE)
—ALL NATURAL COTTAGE CHEESE CHIVE; GARDEN SALAD; PLAIN LARGE CURD; PLAIN SMALL CURD	CAROB BEAN GUM; WHEY (COTTAGE CHEESE)
THE SEWARD FAMILY VERMONT HILL COUNTRY COTTAGE CHEESE	**CARRAGEENAN;** GUAR GUM

BRANDS	ADDITIVES-OF-CONCERN **BOLD—CONCERN TO ALL** LIGHT—CONCERN TO SOME
SUPERMARKET PRIVATE BRANDS	
A & P	
—A & P *COTTAGE CHEESE*	
SMALL CURD	CAROB [BEAN] GUM; WHEY (COTTAGE CHEESE)
FIRST NATIONAL	
—FINAST *COTTAGE CHEESE*	
LARGE CURD; SMALL CURD	**CARRAGEENAN;** LOCUST BEAN GUM
LUCKY	
—LADY LEE *COTTAGE CHEESE*	
LARGE CURD; LOWFAT; LOWFAT W/ CHIVES; SMALL CURD	NO ADDITIVES OF CONCERN
PUBLIX	
—DAIRI-FRESH *COTTAGE CHEESE*	
CHIVES; LARGE CURD	**CARRAGEENAN;** GUAR GUM; LOCUST BEAN GUM
LOWFAT	NO ADDITIVES OF CONCERN
PINEAPPLE	**CARRAGEENAN;** GUAR GUM; LOCUST BEAN GUM; **MODIFIED STARCH**
SAFEWAY	
—LUCERNE *COTTAGE CHEESE*	
FRUIT SALAD	**MODIFIED STARCH**
PINEAPPLE	GUAR GUM

BRANDS	ADDITIVES-OF-CONCERN BOLD—CONCERN TO ALL LIGHT—CONCERN TO SOME
STOP & SHOP —STOP & SHOP ALL NATURAL RICOTTA	NO ADDITIVES OF CONCERN
—COTTAGE CHEESE LARGE CURD; LOWFAT; SMALL CURD	NO ADDITIVES OF CONCERN
WINN DIXIE —SUPERBRAND COUNTRY STYLE COTTAGE CHEESE	**CARRAGEENAN;** GUAR GUM
ITEMS IN HEALTH FOOD STORES	
CABOT COTTAGE CHEESE	NO ADDITIVES OF CONCERN
NANCY'S CULTURED RENNETLESS COTTAGE CHEESE	NO ADDITIVES OF CONCERN
ROSEDALE BRAND COTTAGE CHEESE DRY CURD; RICOTTA	NO ADDITIVES OF CONCERN
VALLEY GOLD *COTTAGE CHEESE* LARGE CURD; SMALL CURD	NO ADDITIVES OF CONCERN
LOWFAT	**CARRAGEENAN;** GUAR GUM; LOCUST BEAN GUM
ZAUSNER'S COTTAGE CHEESE	**CARRAGEENAN**

BRANDS	ADDITIVES-OF-CONCERN BOLD—CONCERN TO ALL LIGHT—CONCERN TO SOME

CHEESE: CREAM (& IMITATIONS)

BORDEN LITE-LINE NEUFCHÂTEL	CAROB BEAN GUM
KING SMOOTHIE	
IMITATION	**ARTIFICIAL COLOR; CARRAGEENAN; (COCONUT OIL);*** GUAR GUM; **SODIUM CASEINATE**
PHILADELPHIA	
IMITATION; PLAIN; W/ CHIVES	CAROB BEAN GUM
—WHIPPED	
CREAM CHEESE & BLUE CHEESE; PLAIN; W/ BACON & HORSERADISH; W/ CHIVES; W/ PIMENTOS	CAROB BEAN GUM; GUAR GUM
W/ ONION	CAROB BEAN GUM; GUAR GUM; **TURMERIC;** WHEY
W/ SMOKED SALMON	CAROB BEAN GUM; GUAR GUM; MONOSODIUM GLUTAMATE; **PAPRIKA; SMOKED SALMON†**

*Blend may contain this saturated oil.

†Although "smoked" does not refer to a specific additive, it represents a process utilizing wood smoke, as "smoke flavoring" does, and therefore the food may contain some cancer-causing benzopyrene chemicals. For this reason, when a food or any of its constituents have been smoked, this has been noted in the additives-of-concern column.

BRANDS	ADDITIVES-OF-CONCERN **BOLD—CONCERN TO ALL** LIGHT—CONCERN TO SOME
SUPERMARKET PRIVATE BRANDS	
LUCKY	
—LADY LEE CREAM CHEESE	CAROB BEAN GUM
WINN DIXIE	
—SUPERBRAND	
CREAM CHEESE	CAROB BEAN GUM
ITEMS IN HEALTH FOOD STORES	
ZAUSNER'S WHIPPED CREAM CHEESE & CHIVES	**VEGETABLE GUM**

CREAM, HALF & HALF, WHIPPED CREAM

R	**BORDEN** LIGHT	NO ADDITIVES OF CONCERN
	WHIPPING	SODIUM ALGINATE
R	**DAIRI PRIDE**	
	FOUNT-WIP WHIPPED CREAM	**CARRAGEENAN;** MILK SOLIDS (NONFAT)
	HALF & HALF	NO ADDITIVES OF CONCERN
	WHIPPING	ALGIN
R	**DAIRYLEA**	
	HALF & HALF; HEAVY; LIGHT	**CALCIUM CARRAGEENAN**
R	**HOME** HEAVY WHIPPING	SODIUM ALGINATE

	BRANDS	ADDITIVES-OF-CONCERN **BOLD—CONCERN TO ALL** LIGHT—CONCERN TO SOME
R	**HOOD**	
	HALF & HALF; LIGHT	NO ADDITIVES OF CONCERN
	HEAVY; WHIPPING	SODIUM ALGINATE
	HUNT'S	
	REDDI WIP INSTANT WHIPPED CREAM	**CARRAGEENAN;** MILK SOLIDS (NONFAT)
R	**McARTHUR DAIRY**	
	HEAVY WHIPPING	SODIUM ALGINATE
	LIGHT	MILK SOLIDS (NONFAT)
R	**SEALTEST**	
	HALF & HALF	NO ADDITIVES OF CONCERN
	LIGHT; WHIPPING	SODIUM ALGINATE
	SUPERMARKET PRIVATE BRANDS	
	FIRST NATIONAL —FINAST	
	HALF & HALF; HEAVY; LIGHT	**CALCIUM CARRAGEENAN**
	LUCKY —LADY LEE	
	HALF & HALF	NO ADDITIVES OF CONCERN
	CREAM TOPPING	**CARRAGEENAN;** WHEY
	HEAVY WHIPPING; WHIPPING	**CARRAGEENAN;** GUAR [GUM]
	PUBLIX —DAIRI-FRESH	
	COFFEE; WHIPPING	ALGIN

BRANDS	**ADDITIVES-OF-CONCERN** **BOLD—CONCERN TO ALL** LIGHT—CONCERN TO SOME
PUBLIX—DAIRY-FRESH *(Continued)*	
HALF & HALF	NO ADDITIVES OF CONCERN
SAFEWAY —LUCERNE	
CREAM TOPPING	**ARTIFICIAL COLOR; CARRAGEENAN;** MILK SOLIDS (NONFAT)
HALF & HALF	NO ADDITIVES OF CONCERN
WHIPPING	**CARRAGEENAN**
STOP & SHOP —STOP & SHOP	
HALF & HALF; LIGHT	NO ADDITIVES OF CONCERN
HEAVY; WHIPPING	ALGIN
ITEMS IN HEALTH FOOD STORES	
VALLEY GOLD	
HALF & HALF; WHIPPING CREAM	NO ADDITIVES OF CONCERN

CREAM: NONDAIRY; WHIPPED-CREAM SUBSTITUTES

BORDEN CREMORA	**(COCONUT, PALM KERNEL OILS);* SODIUM CASEINATE**
CARNATION	
COFFEE-MATE	**ARTIFICIAL COLORS; (COCONUT, PALM KERNEL OILS);* SODIUM CASEINATE**

*This blend may contain one or more of these saturated oils.

BRANDS	ADDITIVES-OF-CONCERN **BOLD—CONCERN TO ALL** LIGHT—CONCERN TO SOME
COOL WHIP NON-DAIRY WHIPPED TOPPING	**ARTIFICIAL COLOR; COCONUT & PALM KERNEL OILS;** GUAR GUM; **SODIUM CASEINATE**
DREAM WHIP WHIPPED TOPPING MIX	**ARTIFICIAL COLOR; BHA; PALM KERNEL OIL; SODIUM CASEINATE;** WHEY
KRAFT WHIPPED TOPPING	**ARTIFICIAL COLOR; CALCIUM & SODIUM CASEINATE;** GUAR GUM; **PALM KERNEL OIL;** SODIUM ALGINATE
LUCKY WHIP DESSERT TOPPING	**COCONUT OIL; SODIUM CASEINATE**
MITCHELL'S PERX	**COCONUT OIL; SODIUM CASEINATE**
PARADE NON-DAIRY CREAMER	**ARTIFICIAL COLORS; COCONUT OIL; SODIUM CASEINATE**
RICH'S COFFEE RICH	**ARTIFICIAL COLOR; COCONUT OIL**
WHIPPED TOPPING (CAN)	**ARTIFICIAL COLOR; COCONUT & PALM KERNEL OILS; METHYL ETHYL CELLULOSE**

BRANDS	ADDITIVES-OF-CONCERN BOLD—CONCERN TO ALL LIGHT—CONCERN TO SOME
RICH'S *(Continued)*	
WHIPPED TOPPING SPOON 'N SERVE	**ARTIFICIAL COLOR; COCONUT & PALM KERNEL OILS;** GUAR GUM; **SODIUM CASEINATE**
SUPERMARKET PRIVATE BRANDS	
A & P—A & P	
NON-DAIRY CREAMER	**ARTIFICIAL COLOR; COCONUT OIL**
EIGHT O'CLOCK NON-DAIRY CREAMER	**ARTIFICIAL COLOR; (COCONUT, PALM KERNEL OILS);* SODIUM CASEINATE**
—ANN PAGE	
HANDI WHIP NON-DAIRY WHIPPED TOPPING	**COCONUT & PALM KERNEL OILS;** GUAR GUM; **SODIUM CASEINATE**
FIRST NATIONAL	
—EDWARDS	
NON-DAIRY COFFEE CREAMER	**ARTIFICIAL COLORS; (COCONUT, PALM KERNEL OILS);* SODIUM CASEINATE**
—FINAST CREEM RITE	**ARTIFICIAL COLORS; CASEINATE; COCONUT OIL**
LUCKY	
—LADY LEE	
NON-DAIRY CREAMER	**ARTIFICIAL COLOR; (COCONUT, PALM KERNEL OILS);* SODIUM CASEINATE**
NON-DAIRY PRODUCT FOR CEREAL OR COFFEE	NO ADDITIVES OF CONCERN

BRANDS	ADDITIVES-OF-CONCERN **BOLD—CONCERN TO ALL** LIGHT—CONCERN TO SOME
NON-DAIRY WHIPPED TOPPING	**(COCONUT, PALM KERNEL OILS);*** GUAR GUM; **SODIUM CASEINATE**
PUBLIX	
—FLAVOR PERFECT	
NON-DAIRY CREAMER	**ARTIFICIAL COLOR; (COCONUT, PALM KERNEL OILS);* SODIUM CASEINATE**
SAFEWAY	
—BLOSSOM TIME	
DESSERT TOPPING	**CALCIUM & SODIUM CASEINATE;** GUAR GUM; **PALM KERNEL OIL;** SODIUM ALGINATE
—LUCERNE	
CEREAL BLEND	NO ADDITIVES OF CONCERN
COFFEE TONE	**ARTIFICIAL COLORS; (COCONUT, PALM KERNEL OILS);* SODIUM CASEINATE**
WHIPPING BLEND	**ARTIFICIAL COLOR; HYDROXYPROPYL CELLULOSE; PALM KERNEL OIL; SODIUM CASEINATE**
STOP & SHOP	
—STOP & SHOP	
COFFEE CREAMER	**ARTIFICIAL COLORS; (COCONUT, PALM KERNEL OILS);* SODIUM CASEINATE**

*This blend may contain one or more of these saturated oils.

BRANDS	ADDITIVES-OF-CONCERN BOLD—CONCERN TO ALL LIGHT—CONCERN TO SOME
WINN DIXIE —ASTOR NON-DAIRY CREAMER	ARTIFICIAL COLORS; (COCONUT, PALM KERNEL OILS);* SODIUM CASEINATE

ICE CREAM & NONDAIRY ICE-CREAM SUBSTITUTES

Note on Ice Cream and Nondairy Ice-Cream Substitutes; Ice-Cream Bars, Cake Rolls, Pies, Popsicles, Sandwiches; Ice Milk, Ices, Yogurt (Frozen); Juice Bars; Sherbet; Yogurt Bars: Declaration of the presence of artificial color in these dairy products by the manufacturer is not required unless the FDA has sufficient evidence that there is a question of safety, in which case the specific color must be identified. FD & C Yellow No. 5 (Tartrazine) is the only artificial color now subjected to this requirement. There is disagreement about the possibility of harmful effects caused by other artificial colors. When artificial color appears on a label, this has been noted in the additives-of-concern column. But when it does not, its presence remains uncertain unless it is voluntarily declared on the label that artificial color has or has not been used.

	BRANDS	ADDITIVES-OF-CONCERN
R	BORDEN COFFEE; DUTCH CHOCOLATE CHIP; VANILLA	ARTIFICIAL COLOR; CARRAGEENAN; GUAR GUM; LOCUST BEAN GUM; WHEY
	—*ALL NATURAL* BUTTERED ALMOND; DUTCH CHOCOLATE; STRAWBERRIES 'N CREAM	CARRAGEENAN; GUAR GUM; LOCUST BEAN GUM

*Blend may contain one or more of these saturated oils.

BRANDS	ADDITIVES-OF-CONCERN **BOLD—CONCERN TO ALL** LIGHT—CONCERN TO SOME
CHERRY VANILLA	**CARRAGEENAN;** GUAR GUM; LOCUST BEAN GUM; **MODIFIED FOOD STARCH**
—LADY BORDEN BUTTER FUDGE SWIRL; VANILLA	**ARTIFICIAL COLOR; CARRAGEENAN;** GUAR GUM; LOCUST BEAN GUM
—OLD FASHIONED CHOCOLATE FUDGE SWIRL	**ARTIFICIAL COLOR; CARRAGEENAN;** GUAR GUM; LOCUST BEAN GUM; **MODIFIED FOOD STARCH;** WHEY
DUTCH CHOCOLATE	**CARRAGEENAN;** GUAR GUM; LOCUST BEAN GUM; WHEY
STRAWBERRIES 'N CREAM SWIRL	**ARTIFICIAL COLOR; CARRAGEENAN;** GUAR GUM; LOCUST BEAN GUM; WHEY
BREYERS	
BUTTER ALMOND; CHERRY VANILLA; CHOCOLATE; COFFEE; NATURAL MINT CHOCOLATE CHIP; NATURAL PEACH; NATURAL STRAWBERRY; NATURAL VANILLA; VANILLA FUDGE TWIRL	NO ADDITIVES OF CONCERN

	BRANDS	ADDITIVES-OF-CONCERN **BOLD—CONCERN TO ALL** LIGHT—CONCERN TO SOME
	ESKIMO	
	HALF N' HALF CHOCOLATE-VANILLA	**ARTIFICIAL COLOR; CARRAGEENAN;** GUAR GUM; LOCUST BEAN GUM; WHEY
	HÄAGEN-DAZS	
	CAROB; CHOCOLATE; COFFEE; HONEY; RUM RAISIN; STRAWBERRY; VANILLA	NO ADDITIVES OF CONCERN
R	HOOD	
	CHOCOLATE; COFFEE; HEAVENLY HASH	**CALCIUM CARRAGEENAN;** CAROB BEAN GUM; GUAR GUM; WHEY
	BUTTERSCOTCH WHIRL	**ARTIFICIAL COLOR; CALCIUM CARRAGEENAN;** CAROB BEAN GUM; GUAR GUM; **MODIFIED FOOD STARCH;** PROPYLENE GLYCOL ALGINATE; WHEY
	CHIPPEDY CHOCOLATY; PEANUT BUTTER CUP; VANILLA	**CALCIUM CARRAGEENAN;** CAROB BEAN GUM; FD & C YELLOW NO. 5 & NO. 6; GUAR GUM; WHEY
	HOODSIE CUPS CHOCOLATE & VANILLA; STRAWBERRY	**ARTIFICIAL COLOR; CALCIUM CARRAGEENAN;** CAROB BEAN GUM; GUAR GUM; WHEY

	BRANDS	ADDITIVES-OF-CONCERN **BOLD—CONCERN TO ALL** LIGHT—CONCERN TO SOME
	—CORONET BAVARIAN CHOCOLATE; BUTTER ALMOND	CAROB BEAN GUM
	HOWARD JOHNSON'S BURGUNDY CHERRY	**ARTIFICIAL COLOR; CARRAGEENAN;** GUAR GUM; LOCUST BEAN GUM; **MODIFIED FOOD STARCH**
	COFFEE; MOCHA CHIP; STRAWBERRY; VANILLA	**CARRAGEENAN;** GUAR GUM; LOCUST BEAN GUM
R	**JUBILEE** CHOCOLATE	**CARRAGEENAN;** GUAR GUM; LOCUST BEAN GUM; WHEY
	STRAWBERRY	**CARRAGEENAN; CERTIFIED COLOR;** GUAR GUM; LOCUST BEAN GUM; WHEY
	VANILLA	**CARRAGEENAN;** FD & C YELLOW NO. 5; GUAR GUM; LOCUST BEAN GUM; WHEY
R	**McARTHUR DAIRY** BUTTER PECAN; CHOCOLATE CHIP	**CARRAGEENAN;** FD & C YELLOW NO. 5; GUAR GUM; LOCUST BEAN GUM; WHEY
	STRAWBERRY	**CARRAGEENAN; CERTIFIED FOOD COLOR;** GUAR GUM; LOCUST BEAN GUM; WHEY

	BRANDS	ADDITIVES-OF-CONCERN **BOLD—CONCERN TO ALL** LIGHT—CONCERN TO SOME
R	McCARTHY'S *OLD FASHIONED* BUTTERCRUNCH; CHOCOLATE CHIP; COFFEE; STRAWBERRY; VANILLA	**CARRAGEENAN;** GUAR GUM; LOCUST BEAN GUM
	DOUBLE CHOCOLATE	**CARRAGEENAN;** GUAR GUM; LOCUST BEAN GUM; MILK SOLIDS (NONFAT)
R	RICH'S HALF & HALF CHOCOLATE-VANILLA	**ARTIFICIAL COLOR; CARRAGEENAN;** GUAR GUM; WHEY
	DELUXE STRAWBERRY	**ARTIFICIAL COLOR; CARRAGEENAN;** GUAR GUM; WHEY
	SEALTEST BUTTER BRICKLE; MAPLE WALNUT; VANILLA	**ARTIFICIAL COLOR;** CAROB BEAN GUM; **CARRAGEENAN;** GUAR GUM; WHEY
	CHOCOLATE CHIP	CAROB BEAN GUM; **CARRAGEENAN;** GUAR GUM; WHEY
	CHOCOLATE ECLAIR	**ARTIFICIAL COLOR; CALCIUM CASEINATE;** CAROB BEAN GUM; **CARRAGEENAN;** GUAR GUM; PROPYLENE GLYCOL ALGINATE; WHEY

BRANDS	ADDITIVES-OF-CONCERN BOLD—CONCERN TO ALL LIGHT—CONCERN TO SOME
FUDGE ROYALE	**ARTIFICIAL COLOR;** CAROB BEAN GUM; **CARRAGEENAN;** GUAR GUM; SODIUM ALGINATE; WHEY & MODIFIED WHEY
STRAWBERRY	**ARTIFICIAL COLOR;** CAROB BEAN GUM; **CARRAGEENAN;** GUAR GUM; GUM KARAYA; WHEY
SUPERMARKET PRIVATE BRANDS	
A & P	
—A & P	
BUTTER PECAN; CHOCOLATE	**CARRAGEENAN;** GUAR GUM; WHEY
VANILLA-CHOCOLATE-STRAWBERRY	**ARTIFICIAL COLOR; CARRAGEENAN;** GUAR GUM; WHEY
—ANN PAGE	
COFFEE; VANILLA	**CARRAGEENAN;** GUAR GUM; WHEY
FIRST NATIONAL	
—EDWARDS-FINAST	
FUDGE MARBLE	**CARRAGEENAN;** GUAR GUM; LOCUST BEAN GUM, **MODIFIED FOOD STARCH;** WHEY
NEAPOLITAN VANILLA/CHOCOLATE/STRAWBERRY	**CARRAGEENAN;** GUAR GUM; LOCUST BEAN GUM; WHEY

BRANDS	ADDITIVES-OF-CONCERN **BOLD—CONCERN TO ALL** LIGHT—CONCERN TO SOME
LUCKY —HARVEST DAY CHOCOLATE; NEAPOLITAN; VANILLA	**ARTIFICIAL COLOR** OR **COLORING; CARRAGEENAN;** GUAR GUM; WHEY
—LADY LEE CHOCOLATE MARSHMALLOW	CAROB [BEAN] GUM; GUAR GUM; WHEY (DRIED)
DUTCH CHOCOLATE; MAPLE NUT; STRAWBERRY	**CARRAGEENAN;** GUAR GUM; WHEY (DRIED)
ENGLISH TOFFEE	**BHA; CARRAGEENAN;** GUAR GUM; WHEY (DRIED)
MARBLE FUDGE	GUAR GUM; **MODIFIED FOOD STARCH;** WHEY (DRIED)
MINT CHOCOLATE CHIP	ARTIFICIAL COLORING FD & C BLUE NO. 1 & YELLOW NO. 5; **CARRAGEENAN;** GUAR GUM; WHEY (DRIED)
VANILLA	CAROB [BEAN] GUM; GUAR GUM
SAFEWAY —JOYETT *IMITATION* CHOCOLATE	**CALCIUM CARRAGEENAN;** GUAR GUM; **(COCONUT, HYDROGENATED COTTONSEED, SOYBEAN OILS);*** LOCUST BEAN GUM; WHEY

BRANDS	ADDITIVES-OF-CONCERN BOLD—CONCERN TO ALL LIGHT—CONCERN TO SOME
CHOCOLATE CHIP; VANILLA	**ARTIFICIAL COLOR; CALCIUM CARRAGEENAN;** GUAR GUM; **(COCONUT, HYDROGENATED COTTONSEED, SOYBEAN OILS);*** LOCUST BEAN GUM; WHEY
—LUCERNE	
BUTTER BRICKLE; CHOCOLATE CHIP; STRAWBERRY; VANILLA	**ARTIFICIAL COLOR; CALCIUM CARRAGEENAN;** GUAR GUM; LOCUST BEAN GUM
CHOCOLATE MARBLE	**ARTIFICIAL COLOR; CALCIUM CARRAGEENAN;** GUAR GUM; LOCUST BEAN GUM; **MODIFIED FOOD STARCH**
COFFEE	**CALCIUM CARRAGEENAN;** GUAR GUM; LOCUST BEAN GUM; **NATURAL COLOR**
NEAPOLITAN	**ARTIFICIAL COLOR; CALCIUM CARRAGEENAN;** GUAR GUM; LOCUST BEAN GUM; WHEY
—GOURMET	
BURGUNDY CHERRY	**ARTIFICIAL COLOR; CALCIUM CARRAGEENAN;** GUAR GUM; LOCUST BEAN GUM; **MODIFIED STARCH**

*This blend may contain one or more of these saturated oils.

BRANDS	ADDITIVES-OF-CONCERN **BOLD—CONCERN TO ALL** LIGHT—CONCERN TO SOME
—LUCERNE *GOURMET (Continued)*	
ROCKY ROAD	**CALCIUM CARRAGEENAN;** GUAR GUM; LOCUST BEAN GUM; **MODIFIED STARCH;** WHEY
—PARTY PRIDE	
CHOCOLATE FUDGE SUNDAE	**ARTIFICIAL COLOR; CALCIUM CARRAGEENAN;** GUAR GUM; LOCUST BEAN GUM; **MODIFIED FOOD STARCH;** WHEY
—SNOW STAR	
CHOCOLATE MARBLE	**ARTIFICIAL COLOR; CALCIUM CARRAGEENAN;** GUAR GUM; LOCUST BEAN GUM; **MODIFIED FOOD STARCH;** WHEY
STOP & SHOP	
—STOP & SHOP	
COFFEE; COUNTRY CLUB; HARLEQUIN; STRAWBERRY; VANILLA	**ARTIFICIAL COLOR;** CAROB BEAN GUM; **CARRAGEENAN;** GUAR GUM; WHEY
—100% NATURAL	
CHOCOLATE; CHUNKY CHOCOLATE CHIP; VANILLA BEAN	CAROB BEAN GUM; GUAR GUM
WINN DIXIE	
—KOUNTRY FRESH *PRESTIGE*	
BUTTER PECAN; CHOCOLATE CHIP; VANILLA	GUAR GUM; LOCUST BEAN GUM

BRANDS	ADDITIVES-OF-CONCERN **BOLD—CONCERN TO ALL** LIGHT—CONCERN TO SOME
—SUPERBRAND FUDGE ROYALE	**CARRAGEENAN;** GUAR GUM; LOCUST BEAN GUM; **MODIFIED FOOD STARCH;** WHEY
STRAWBERRY ROYALE	**ARTIFICIAL COLOR; CARRAGEENAN;** GUAR GUM; GUM KARAYA; LOCUST BEAN GUM; **MODIFIED FOOD STARCH;** WHEY
ITEMS IN HEALTH FOOD STORES	
DAMIAN'S CHICORY COFFEE; COUNTRY VANILLA; DANISH TOASTED ALMOND; NATURAL CHOCOLATE; PURE STRAWBERRY; VERMONT MAPLE WALNUT	**IRISH SEA MOSS**
FARM FOODS ICE BEAN HONEY VANILLA	**VEGETABLE GUM**
NATURAL NECTAR BRAZILIAN MOCHA; MAPLE ALMOND CRUNCH; ROYAL DUTCH COCOA; VANILLA	GUAR [GUM]; MILK SOLIDS

	BRANDS	ADDITIVES-OF-CONCERN BOLD—CONCERN TO ALL LIGHT—CONCERN TO SOME

ICE-CREAM BARS, CAKE ROLLS, PIES, POPSICLES, SANDWICHES; JUICE BARS; YOGURT BARS

	BRANDS	ADDITIVES-OF-CONCERN
R	CHARLIE FROZEN YOGURT ON-A-STICK RASPBERRY	NO ADDITIVES OF CONCERN
	DANNY SQUARES STRAWBERRY	NO ADDITIVES OF CONCERN
	—FROZEN LOWFAT YOGURT ON-A-STICK CAROB COATED BOYSENBERRY; PIÑA COLADA	NO ADDITIVES OF CONCERN
	CHOCOLATE COATED STRAWBERRY	MILK SOLIDS (NONFAT)
	ESKIMO THIN MINTS	**ARTIFICIAL COLOR; CARRAGEENAN;** GUAR GUM; LOCUST BEAN GUM; SKIM MILK-DERIVED SOLIDS; WHEY
	TOASTED ALMOND CRUNCH!	NO ADDITIVES OF CONCERN
	HIRES ROOT BEER FLOAT BARS	GUM TRAGACANTH; LOCUST BEAN GUM
R	HOOD FUDGSICLE	CAROB BEAN GUM; **CARRAGEENAN;** GUAR GUM; SODIUM ALGINATE; WHEY

BRANDS	ADDITIVES-OF-CONCERN **BOLD—CONCERN TO ALL** LIGHT—CONCERN TO SOME
POPSICLE	**ARTIFICIAL COLORS;** GUAR GUM; GUM TRAGACANTH
VANILLA ICE CREAM SANDWICHES	**ARTIFICIAL COLOR; CALCIUM CARRAGEENAN;** CAROB BEAN GUM; GUAR GUM; WHEY
—FIRM 'N FROSTY FROZEN YOGURT PUSHUPS	
ORANGE	BUTTERMILK SOLIDS; CAROB BEAN GUM
RASPBERRY; STRAWBERRY	CAROB BEAN GUM
R **KLONDIKES** KRISPY ICE CREAM BARS	**CARRAGEENAN;** GUAR GUM; LOCUST BEAN GUM
R **LIFESTYLE** VANILLA YOGURT BARS	**CARRAGEENAN; CERTIFIED COLOR;** GUAR GUM; WHEY
R **LOTTA POPS** SIX FLAVORS	**ARTIFICIAL COLOR;** GUAR GUM
R **NESTLÉ** CRUNCH VANILLA ICE CREAM BARS	**ARTIFICIAL COLOR; CARRAGEENAN;** GUAR GUM; LOCUST BEAN GUM; WHEY
R **RICH'S**	
ICE CREAM CAKE ROLL	NO ADDITIVES OF CONCERN
LIME JUICE BARS	ALGIN STABILIZER; **U.S. CERTIFIED COLOR**

BRANDS	ADDITIVES-OF-CONCERN BOLD—CONCERN TO ALL LIGHT—CONCERN TO SOME
RICH'S *(Continued)*	
ORANGE JUICE BARS	**CARRAGEENAN;** LOCUST BEAN GUM
SEALTEST	
FROZEN YOGURT STRAWBERRY BARS	CAROB BEAN GUM; GUAR GUM
—*SMACKERS*	
ASSORTED TWIN POPS	**ARTIFICIAL COLOR;** GUAR & KARAYA GUMS
BAVARIAN FUDGE KRUNCH BARS; ICE CREAM SANDWICHES; ORANGE TREAT BARS	**ARTIFICIAL COLOR;** CAROB BEAN GUM; **CARRAGEENAN;** GUAR GUM; WHEY
FUDGE BARS	CAROB BEAN GUM; **CARRAGEENAN;** GUAR GUM; WHEY & MODIFIED WHEY
R TUSCAN FARMS	
TUSCAN POPS FROZEN YOGURT ON A STICK CHOCOLATE	CAROB [BEAN] GUM; **CARRAGEENAN;** MILK SOLIDS (NONFAT)
SUPERMARKET PRIVATE BRANDS	
A & P	
—ANN PAGE	
POPSICLE TWIN TREATS	**ARTIFICIAL COLOR;** GUAR GUM
FUDGSICLE TREATS	ALGIN; **ARTIFICIAL COLOR; CARRAGEENAN;** GUAR GUM; LOCUST BEAN GUM; WHEY
VANILLA ICE CREAM BARS	**CARRAGEENAN;** GUAR GUM; WHEY

BRANDS	ADDITIVES-OF-CONCERN BOLD—CONCERN TO ALL LIGHT—CONCERN TO SOME
SAFEWAY —**BEL-AIR** FRUIT BARS	GUAR GUM; LOCUST BEAN GUM
—**PARTY PRIDE** ICE CREAM SANDWICHES VANILLA	**ARTIFICIAL COLOR; CALCIUM CARRAGEENAN;** GUAR GUM; LOCUST BEAN GUM; WHEY
MINI POPS ASSORTED FLAVORS	**ARTIFICIAL COLORS;** GUAR GUM
TOFFEE BRITTLE ICE CREAM BARS	**ARTIFICIAL COLOR; CALCIUM CARRAGEENAN;** GUAR GUM; LOCUST BEAN GUM; MILK SOLIDS (NONFAT & WHOLE); **MODIFIED FOOD STARCH;** WHEY
STOP & SHOP —**STOP & SHOP** CERT'NLY CITRUS JUICE STICKS	**ARTIFICIAL COLOR;** GUAR GUM
FUDGE & POP	ALGIN; **ARTIFICIAL COLORING; CARRAGEENAN;** GUAR GUM; LOCUST BEAN GUM; **SODIUM CASEINATE;** WHEY
WINN DIXIE —**SUPERBRAND** ASSORTED TWIN POPS	**ARTIFICIAL COLOR;** GUAR GUM

BRANDS	ADDITIVES-OF-CONCERN **BOLD—CONCERN TO ALL** LIGHT—CONCERN TO SOME
WINN DIXIE —SUPERBRAND *(Continued)*	
ICE CREAM BARS	**ARTIFICIAL COLOR; CARRAGEENAN;** GUAR GUM; LOCUST BEAN GUM; WHEY
ITEMS IN HEALTH FOOD STORES	
NATURAL NECTAR	
BANANA NUGGET; COCOA CHIP CRUNCH; YULOVIT	GUAR GUM; **IRISH MOSS;** LOCUST BEAN [GUM]; MILK SOLIDS
CAROB COATED VANILLA HONEY ICE CREAM BAR	GUAR [GUM]; MILK SOLIDS (& NONFAT)
INCREDIBLE EDIBLE; NECTAR PIE	GUAR [GUM]; **IRISH MOSS;** LOCUST BEAN [GUM]; MILK SOLIDS (FAT FREE AND/OR NONFAT)
MOCHA PIE	GUAR GUM; **IRISH MOSS;** LOCUST BEAN [GUM]; MILK SOLIDS (& FAT FREE)
—CREAM PIE	
BLUEBERRY CUSTARD	**CARRAGEENAN;** GUAR [GUM]; LOCUST BEAN GUM; MILK SOLIDS (FAT FREE); WHEY
CAPPUCCINO ESPRESSO; FRENCH PECAN	GUAR [GUM]; LOCUST BEAN [GUM]; MILK SOLIDS (FAT FREE); WHEY

	BRANDS	**ADDITIVES-OF-CONCERN** **BOLD—CONCERN TO ALL** LIGHT—CONCERN TO SOME

ICE MILK, ICES, YOGURT (FROZEN)

R	BORDEN NEAPOLITAN VANILLA-CHOCOLATE-STRAWBERRY ICE MILK	**ARTIFICIAL COLOR; CARRAGEENAN;** GUAR GUM; LOCUST BEAN GUM; WHEY
	DANNY *—IN-A-CUP FROZEN LOWFAT YOGURT* BANANA; CHERRY; LEMON; PINEAPPLE-ORANGE; RED RASPBERRY; VANILLA	NO ADDITIVES OF CONCERN
R	GUIDO'S *REAL ITALIAN ICES* CHERRY; LEMON	**ARTIFICIAL COLOR; VEGETABLE GUM**
R	HOOD VANILLA ICE MILK BARS	**ARTIFICIAL COLOR; CALCIUM CARRAGEENAN;** CAROB BEAN GUM; GUAR GUM; WHEY
	—FIRM 'N FROSTY FROZEN YOGURT BLUEBERRY; RASPBERRY	CAROB BEAN GUM
	—NUFORM *ICE MILK* CHIPPEDY CHOCOLATY; VANILLA CHOCOLATE STRAWBERRY	**ARTIFICIAL COLOR; CARRAGEENAN;** GUAR GUM

	BRANDS	ADDITIVES-OF-CONCERN BOLD—CONCERN TO ALL LIGHT—CONCERN TO SOME
R	LIFESTYLE *ICE MILK*	
	COFFEE	**CARRAGEENAN;** GUAR GUM; LOCUST BEAN GUM; WHEY
	VANILLA	**CARRAGEENAN;** FD & C YELLOW NO. 5; GUAR GUM; LOCUST BEAN GUM; WHEY
R	RICH'S *ICE MILK CAKE BARS*	
	CHOCOLATE SHORTCAKE	**ARTIFICIAL COLOR; CARRAGEENAN;** GUAR GUM; LOCUST BEAN GUM; WHEY
	STRAWBERRY SHORTCAKE	**ARTIFICIAL COLOR; VEGETABLE GUM STABILIZER**
	SEALTEST	
	ICE MILK FUDGE SUNDAE	**ARTIFICIAL COLOR;** CAROB BEAN GUM; **CARRAGEENAN;** GUAR GUM; SODIUM ALGINATE; WHEY & MODIFIED WHEY
	—FROZEN YOGURT	
	BLACK CHERRY; VANILLA BEAN	CAROB BEAN GUM; GUAR GUM
	—LIGHT N' LIVELY ICE MILK	
	CARAMEL NUT; VANILLA, CHOCOLATE, STRAWBERRY	CAROB BEAN GUM; **CARRAGEENAN;** GUAR GUM; WHEY
	CHOCOLATE MARSHMALLOW	CAROB BEAN GUM; **CARRAGEENAN;** EGG ALBUMIN; GUAR GUM; WHEY

BRANDS	**ADDITIVES-OF-CONCERN** **BOLD—CONCERN TO ALL** LIGHT—CONCERN TO SOME
SUPERMARKET PRIVATE BRANDS	
LUCKY	
—LADY LEE *ICE MILK*	
MARBLE FUDGE	**CARRAGEENAN;** GUAR GUM; **MODIFIED FOOD STARCH;** WHEY (DRIED)
NEAPOLITAN	**CARRAGEENAN;** GUAR GUM; WHEY (DRIED)
VANILLA FLAVORED ICE MILK	**CARRAGEENAN;** GUAR GUM; WHEY (DRIED)
SAFEWAY	
—LUCERNE *ICE MILK*	
ROCKY ROAD	**CALCIUM CARRAGEENAN;** GUAR GUM; LOCUST BEAN GUM; **MODIFIED STARCH;** WHEY
TRIPLE TREAT	**ARTIFICIAL COLOR** OR **COLORS; CALCIUM CARRAGEENAN;** GUAR GUM; LOCUST BEAN GUM; WHEY
—*LOWFAT FROZEN YOGURT DESSERT*	
LEMON; RED RASPBERRY	**ARTIFICIAL COLOR; CALCIUM CARRAGEENAN;** GUAR GUM; LOCUST BEAN GUM
STOP & SHOP	
—STOP & SHOP CHOC-LIT COVERS	**CARRAGEENAN;** GUAR GUM; LOCUST BEAN GUM; SKIM MILK SOLIDS

BRANDS	ADDITIVES-OF-CONCERN **BOLD—CONCERN TO ALL** LIGHT—CONCERN TO SOME
WINN DIXIE —THRIFTY MAID *ICE MILK*	
FUDGE ROYALE	**CARRAGEENAN;** GUAR GUM; LOCUST BEAN GUM; **MODIFIED FOOD STARCH;** WHEY
NEAPOLITAN	**ARTIFICIAL COLOR; CARRAGEENAN;** GUAR GUM; LOCUST BEAN GUM; WHEY
ITEMS IN HEALTH FOOD STORES SHILOH FARMS *FROZEN YOGURT*	
BLUEBERRY; HONEY; PEACH; RASPBERRY; STRAWBERRY	**CARRAGEENAN;** GUAR [GUM]; LOCUST BEAN [GUM]; MILK SOLIDS (NONFAT); WHEY POWDER

MARGARINE

Artificial color in margarine has not been noted because the coloring agent most often used, natural or synthetic beta carotene, is not regarded as an additive of concern. Beta carotene adds a yellowish-orange hue and a source of vitamin A to margarine.

AUTUMN NATURAL	NO ADDITIVES OF CONCERN
BLUE BONNET REGULAR; SOFT	**POTASSIUM CASEINATE;** WHEY
CHIFFON SOFT; WHIPPED	NO ADDITIVES OF CONCERN

BRANDS	ADDITIVES-OF-CONCERN BOLD—CONCERN TO ALL LIGHT—CONCERN TO SOME
FLEISCHMANN'S DIET IMITATION; SWEET UNSALTED	NO ADDITIVES OF CONCERN
CORN OIL; LIGHT CORN OIL SPREAD; SOFT	**POTASSIUM CASEINATE;** WHEY
IMPERIAL REGULAR; SOFT	**POTASSIUM CASEINATE;** WHEY
KRAFT PARKAY; SOFT PARKAY; SQUEEZE PARKAY	**POTASSIUM CASEINATE;** WHEY
LAND O LAKES CORN OIL; REGULAR; SOFT	NO ADDITIVES OF CONCERN
MAZOLA REGULAR; SWEET-UNSALTED	NO ADDITIVES OF CONCERN
MRS FILBERTS CORN OIL; SOFT GOLDEN; SPREAD 25	NO ADDITIVES OF CONCERN
GOLDEN QUARTERS; SOFT	**POTASSIUM CASEINATE;** WHEY
R **PROMISE** REGULAR	NO ADDITIVES OF CONCERN
R **SHEDD'S** SPREAD	NO ADDITIVES OF CONCERN
WEIGHT WATCHERS IMITATION	NO ADDITIVES OF CONCERN

BRANDS	**ADDITIVES-OF-CONCERN** **BOLD—CONCERN TO ALL** LIGHT—CONCERN TO SOME
SUPERMARKET PRIVATE BRANDS	
A & P	
—A & P	
CORN OIL; SOFT	NO ADDITIVES OF CONCERN
—ANN PAGE	
REGULAR	NO ADDITIVES OF CONCERN
FIRST NATIONAL	
—EDWARDS CORN OIL	MILK SOLIDS (NONFAT DRY)
—FINAST REGULAR	NO ADDITIVES OF CONCERN
LUCKY	
—LADY LEE	
CORN OIL; REGULAR; SOFT	**POTASSIUM CASEINATE;** WHEY
PUBLIX	
—BREAKFAST CLUB	
GOLDEN CORN OIL; REGULAR	NO ADDITIVES OF CONCERN
60% SPREAD	WHEY
SAFEWAY	
—EMPRESS CORN OIL	**POTASSIUM CASEINATE;** WHEY
—SCOTCH BUY	
REGULAR; SOFT	**POTASSIUM CASEINATE;** WHEY
SOFT SPREAD	NO ADDITIVES OF CONCERN
STOP & SHOP	
—STOP & SHOP	
REGULAR; SOFT	MILK SOLIDS (NONFAT DRY)

BRANDS	**ADDITIVES-OF-CONCERN** **BOLD—CONCERN TO ALL** LIGHT—CONCERN TO SOME
WINN DIXIE —SUPERBRAND LIGHT SPREAD; SOFT	NO ADDITIVES OF CONCERN
REGULAR	**POTASSIUM CASEINATE;** WHEY
ITEMS IN HEALTH FOOD STORES FRAZIER FARMS SOYBEAN OIL	NO ADDITIVES OF CONCERN
HAIN SAFFLOWER OIL	NO ADDITIVES OF CONCERN
SHEDD'S WILLOW RUN SOY BEAN	NO ADDITIVES OF CONCERN

BRANDS	ADDITIVES-OF-CONCERN BOLD—CONCERN TO ALL LIGHT—CONCERN TO SOME

MILK OTHER THAN WHOLE MILK* (ACIDOPHILUS & KEFIR, BUTTERMILK, CHOCOLATE, CONDENSED, EVAPORATED, LOW-FAT, NONFAT, NONFAT DRY, SKIM)

Note on Milk Other Than Whole Milk; Yogurt (Refrigerated): Declaration of the presence of artificial color in these dairy products by the manufacturer is not required unless the FDA has sufficient evidence that there is a question of safety, in which case the specific color must be identified. FD & C Yellow No. 5 (Tartrazine) is the only artificial color now subjected to this requirement. There is disagreement about the possibility of harmful effects caused by other artificial colors. When artificial color appears on a label, this has been noted in the additives-of-concern column. But when it does not, its presence remains uncertain unless it is voluntarily declared on the label that artificial color has or has not been used.

	BRANDS	ADDITIVES-OF-CONCERN
	ALBA NONFAT DRY	NO ADDITIVES OF CONCERN
R	BORDEN BUTTERMILK	MILK SOLIDS (NONFAT)
	DUTCH CHOCOLATE	**CARRAGEENAN;** GUAR GUM
	—EAGLE BRAND CONDENSED	NO ADDITIVES OF CONCERN
	CARNATION NONFAT DRY; EVAPORATED SKIMMED	NO ADDITIVES OF CONCERN

*Whole milk has not been included. Inspection of labels in various parts of the country found none that contained any additives of concern.

	BRANDS	ADDITIVES-OF-CONCERN BOLD—CONCERN TO ALL LIGHT—CONCERN TO SOME
	EVAPORATED	**CARRAGEENAN**
R	**FRIENDSHIP** BUTTERMILK	NO ADDITIVES OF CONCERN
R	**HOME** STA-TRIM LOWFAT	NO ADDITIVES OF CONCERN
	HOOD LOWFAT; SIL-OU-ET	NO ADDITIVES OF CONCERN
	CHOCOLATE LOWFAT	**CARRAGEENAN**
	NUFORM	MILK SOLIDS (NONFAT)
R	**McARTHUR DAIRY** BUTTERMILK	**CARRAGEENAN;** GUAR GUM; MILK SOLIDS (NONFAT)
	CHOCOLATE LOWFAT	**CARRAGEENAN**
	SWEET ACIDOPHILUS LOWFAT	NO ADDITIVES OF CONCERN
R	**McINTIRE DAIRY FARM** TRU FORM LOWFAT	NO ADDITIVES OF CONCERN
	MIX 'N DRINK NONFAT DRY	NO ADDITIVES OF CONCERN
	PARADE EVAPORATED	**CARRAGEENAN**
	PET EVAPORATED	**CARRAGEENAN**
	EVAPORATED SKIMMED	NO ADDITIVES OF CONCERN

BRANDS	ADDITIVES-OF-CONCERN BOLD—CONCERN TO ALL LIGHT—CONCERN TO SOME
SANALAC NONFAT DRY	NO ADDITIVES OF CONCERN
R SEALTEST	
CHOCOLATE LOWFAT	**CALCIUM CARRAGEENAN**
LIGHT 'N' LIVELY LOWFAT	NO ADDITIVES OF CONCERN
R T. G. LEE	
COUNTRY STYLE BUTTERMILK	NO ADDITIVES OF CONCERN
HI-LO LOWFAT	MILK SOLIDS (NONFAT)
SUPERMARKET PRIVATE BRANDS	
A & P	
—A & P	
LOOK FIT LOW FAT; NONFAT DRY	NO ADDITIVES OF CONCERN
NONFAT	MILK SOLIDS (NONFAT)
FIRST NATIONAL	
—FINAST	
EVAPORATED	**CARRAGEENAN**
LUCKY	
—LADY LEE	
BUTTERMILK	NO ADDITIVES OF CONCERN
LOWFAT W/ LACTOBACILLUS ACIDOPHILUS CULTURE ADDED; NONFAT	MILK SOLIDS (NONFAT)
EVAPORATED	**CARRAGEENAN**

BRANDS	ADDITIVES-OF-CONCERN BOLD—CONCERN TO ALL LIGHT—CONCERN TO SOME
SAFEWAY **—LUCERNE** BUTTERMILK; LOWFAT W/ LACTOBACILLUS ACIDOPHILUS CULTURE ADDED; NONFAT	MILK SOLIDS (NONFAT)
CHOCOLATE LOWFAT; EVAPORATED	**CARRAGEENAN**
STOP & SHOP **—STOP & SHOP** EVAPORATED	**CARRAGEENAN**
GREAT SHAPE LOWFAT; NONFAT	MILK SOLIDS (NONFAT)
ITEMS IN HEALTH FOOD STORES **ALTA-DENA** KEFIR BLACK CHERRY; PEACH; RED RASPBERRY	NO ADDITIVES OF CONCERN
PINEAPPLE	**TURMERIC EXTRACT**
EAST COAST KEFIR BLUEBERRY; RASPBERRY; STRAWBERRY	**VEGETABLE COLOR**
MAPLE SYRUP	NO ADDITIVES OF CONCERN

BRANDS	ADDITIVES-OF-CONCERN **BOLD—CONCERN TO ALL** LIGHT—CONCERN TO SOME

SHERBET*

	Brands	Additives-of-concern
R	BORDEN LIME; RAINBOW	**ARTIFICIAL COLOR; CARRAGEENAN;** GUAR GUM; WHEY
R	HÄAGEN-DAZS BOYSENBERRY	NO ADDITIVES OF CONCERN
R	HOOD LEMON-ORANGE-LIME	**ARTIFICIAL COLOR; CALCIUM CARRAGEENAN;** CAROB BEAN GUM; GUAR GUM; GUM KARAYA
R	McARTHUR DAIRY LIME	**ARTIFICIAL COLOR;** FD & C YELLOW NO. 5; GUAR GUM; LOCUST BEAN GUM; WHEY
	SEALTEST LEMON-LIME; ORANGE; RAINBOW	**ARTIFICIAL COLOR;** CAROB BEAN GUM; **CARRAGEENAN;** GUAR GUM; WHEY
	SUPERMARKET PRIVATE BRANDS A & P —A & P LEMON; LIME	**ARTIFICIAL COLOR;** GUAR GUM; LOCUST BEAN GUM; **TURMERIC** OR **TURMERIC COLOR**

*See note on page 222.

BRANDS	ADDITIVES-OF-CONCERN BOLD—CONCERN TO ALL LIGHT—CONCERN TO SOME
LUCKY —LADY LEE PINEAPPLE	CAROB [BEAN] GUM; GUAR GUM
RAINBOW	ARTIFICIAL COLORING FD & C BLUE NO. 1, YELLOW NO. 5 & NO. 6; CAROB [BEAN] GUM; GUAR GUM
RASPBERRY SHERBET/VANILLA ICE MILK	**CARRAGEENAN;** GUAR GUM; LOCUST BEAN GUM; WHEY (DRIED)
SAFEWAY —LUCERNE ORANGE; RASPBERRY; TRIPLE TREAT	**ARTIFICIAL COLOR** OR **COLORS; CALCIUM CARRAGEENAN;** GUAR GUM; LOCUST BEAN GUM
STOP & SHOP —STOP & SHOP ORANGE/LEMON/LIME; RASPBERRY	**ARTIFICIAL COLOR;** GUAR GUM; WHEY
WINN DIXIE —SUPERBRAND LIME; ORANGE	**ARTIFICIAL COLOR; CARRAGEENAN;** GUAR GUM; LOCUST BEAN GUM; WHEY

BRANDS	ADDITIVES-OF-CONCERN **BOLD—CONCERN TO ALL** LIGHT—CONCERN TO SOME
WINN DIXIE—SUPERBRAND *(Continued)*	
PINEAPPLE	**CARRAGEENAN;** GUAR GUM; LOCUST BEAN GUM; WHEY

SOUR CREAM & IMITATIONS

HOOD SOUR CREAM	LOCUST BEAN GUM
THE SEWARD FAMILY SOUR CREAM	**VEGETABLE GUM**
SUPERMARKET PRIVATE BRANDS	
A & P	
—A & P SOUR CREAM	**CARRAGEENAN;** LOCUST BEAN GUM
LUCKY	
—LADY LEE	
SOUR CREAM	**CARRAGEENAN;** LOCUST BEAN GUM; MILK SOLIDS (NONFAT); **MODIFIED STARCH**
SOUR DRESSING	**COCONUT OIL;** LOCUST BEAN GUM; **SODIUM CASEINATE;** WHEY SOLIDS
PUBLIX	
—DAIRI-FRESH	
SOUR CREAM; SOUR HALF & HALF	**CARRAGEENAN;** LOCUST BEAN GUM
SAFEWAY	
—LUCERNE	
IMITATION SOUR CREAM	**CARRAGEENAN; COCONUT OIL;** PROPYLENE GLYCOL ALGINATE

BRANDS	**ADDITIVES-OF-CONCERN** **BOLD—CONCERN TO ALL** LIGHT—CONCERN TO SOME
SOUR HALF & HALF	CAROB [BEAN] GUM; **CARRAGEENAN;** MILK SOLIDS (NONFAT); **MODIFIED STARCH**
ITEMS IN HEALTH FOOD STORES	
VALLEY GOLD SOUR CREAM	**CARRAGEENAN;** GUAR GUM; MILK SOLIDS (NONFAT DRY)

YOGURT (REFRIGERATED)*

BREYER'S PLAIN	NO ADDITIVES OF CONCERN
COLOMBO	
BLACK CHERRY; BLUEBERRY; PEACH MELBA; STRAWBERRY	MILK SOLIDS (NONFAT DRY); **MODIFIED FOOD STARCH**
NATURAL; VANILLA HONEY	MILK SOLIDS (NONFAT DRY)
DANNON	
BANANA; BLUEBERRY; COFFEE; DUTCH APPLE; PEACH; PLAIN; RED RASPBERRY; STRAWBERRY; VANILLA	MILK SOLIDS (NONFAT)
HOOD NUFORM	NO ADDITIVES OF CONCERN
KNUDSEN	
APRICOT PINEAPPLE	**ARTIFICIAL COLOR (VEGETABLE);** MILK SOLIDS (NONFAT); **MODIFIED FOOD STARCH**

*See note on page 222.

BRANDS	ADDITIVES-OF-CONCERN BOLD—CONCERN TO ALL LIGHT—CONCERN TO SOME
KNUDSEN *(Continued)*	
PLAIN	MILK SOLIDS (NONFAT)
RED RASPBERRY; STRAWBERRY	**ARTIFICIALLY COLORED; MODIFIED FOOD STARCH**
SPICED APPLE	MILK SOLIDS (NONFAT); **MODIFIED CORN STARCH**
NEW COUNTRY	
BLUEBERRY RIPPLE; PEACHES 'N CREAM	**MODIFIED FOOD STARCH**
HAWAIIAN SALAD	**MODIFIED FOOD STARCH; TURMERIC**
SIPPITY	
BLUEBERRY; PEACH; RASPBERRY	GUAR GUM; LOCUST BEAN GUM
SUPERMARKET PRIVATE BRANDS	
A & P	
—A & P	
APRICOT; BLUEBERRY; STRAWBERRY	MILK SOLIDS (NONFAT)
LUCKY	
—LADY LEE *BLENDED*	
CHERRY; LEMON; PEACH; RASPBERRY	**ARTIFICIAL COLOR;** CAROB [BEAN GUM]; MILK SOLIDS (NONFAT)
—FRUIT ON BOTTOM	
BLACKBERRY	**ARTIFICIALLY COLORED W/ VEGETABLE COLORS;** LOCUST BEAN GUM; MILK SOLIDS (NONFAT)

BRANDS	ADDITIVES-OF-CONCERN **BOLD—CONCERN TO ALL** LIGHT—CONCERN TO SOME
CHERRY; PEACH; STRAWBERRY	**ARTIFICIAL COLOR;** LOCUST BEAN GUM; MILK SOLIDS (NONFAT)
PUBLIX	
—DAIRI-FRESH	
PLAIN	LOCUST BEAN GUM; **MODIFIED STARCH**
—DAIRI-FRESH *SWISS STYLE*	
BLACK CHERRY; BOYSENBERRY; LEMON; MANDARIN ORANGE; PEACH; RASPBERRY	**CERTIFIED COLOR;** LOCUST BEAN GUM; **MODIFIED STARCH**
PRUNE	LOCUST BEAN GUM; **MODIFIED STARCH**
SAFEWAY	
—LUCERNE	
APRICOT-PINEAPPLE; LEMON	**TURMERIC COLOR**
BANANA; BLACKBERRY; BOYSENBERRY; ORANGE; PEACH; PLAIN; SPICED APPLE	NO ADDITIVES OF CONCERN
CHERRY; RED RASPBERRY; STRAWBERRY	**CARMINE COLOR**
CHERRY VANILLA	**CARMINE COLOR;** MILK SOLIDS (SKIM); **MODIFIED FOOD STARCH**

BRANDS	**ADDITIVES-OF-CONCERN** **BOLD—CONCERN TO ALL** LIGHT—CONCERN TO SOME
STOP & SHOP —STOP & SHOP APRICOT; BLUEBERRY; PEACH; PINEAPPLE; RASPBERRY; STRAWBERRY	NO ADDITIVES OF CONCERN
—SWISS STYLE BLUEBERRY; PEACH; PINEAPPLE; RASPBERRY; STRAWBERRY	**ARTIFICIAL COLOR;** MILK SOLIDS (NONFAT); **MODIFIED FOOD STARCH**
WINN DIXIE —SUPERBRAND *ALL NATURAL* MANDARIN ORANGE	**CARRAGEENAN**
VANILLA	NO ADDITIVES OF CONCERN
—SWISS STYLE CHERRY VANILLA; LEMON; RASPBERRY	**ARTIFICIAL COLOR; MODIFIED FOOD STARCH**
ITEMS IN HEALTH FOOD STORES ALTA-DENA *—MAYA* BLACK CHERRY; BLUEBERRY; BOYSENBERRY; RED RASPBERRY; STRAWBERRY	CAROB BEAN [GUM]; **CARRAGEENAN;** GUAR [GUM]; [GUM] TRAGACANTH
LEMON; PEACH	CAROB BEAN [GUM]; **CARRAGEENAN;** GUAR [GUM]; [GUM] TRAGACANTH; **TURMERIC EXTRACT**

BRANDS	**ADDITIVES-OF-CONCERN** **BOLD—CONCERN TO ALL** LIGHT—CONCERN TO SOME
PLAIN	**CARRAGEENAN**
—*NAJA LOWFAT* BLACK CHERRY; BLUEBERRY; PEACH; STRAWBERRY	CAROB BEAN [GUM]; **CARRAGEENAN;** GUAR [GUM]; [GUM] TRAGACANTH
LEMON	CAROB BEAN [GUM]; **CARRAGEENAN;** GUAR [GUM]; [GUM] TRAGACANTH; **TURMERIC EXTRACT**
PLAIN; VANILLA	**CARRAGEENAN**
BROWN COW FARM BLUEBERRY; PLAIN; STRAWBERRY; TUPELO HONEY; VANILLA	NO ADDITIVES OF CONCERN
MOONDANCE	WHEY SOLIDS

XI. FISH & SHELLFISH

CANNED FISH & SHELLFISH

BRANDS	**ADDITIVES-OF-CONCERN** BOLD—CONCERN TO ALL LIGHT—CONCERN TO SOME
BUMBLE BEE BRAND —*SALMON* ALASKAN SOCKEYE RED; PINK	NO ADDITIVES OF CONCERN
—*TUNA* CHUNK LIGHT; CHUNK WHITE; SOLID WHITE; SOLID WHITE IN WATER	NO ADDITIVES OF CONCERN
CHICKEN OF THE SEA *TUNA* CHUNK LIGHT	**VEGETABLE OIL**
CHUNK LIGHT IN WATER; SOLID WHITE IN WATER	NO ADDITIVES OF CONCERN
CONNORS KIPPERED SNACKS	**LIQUID SMOKE FLAVORED**
DOXSEE MINCED CLAMS	MONOSODIUM GLUTAMATE
DURKEE *SARDINES* GRANADAISA; KING DAVID	NO ADDITIVES OF CONCERN
EAST POINT SHRIMP	NO ADDITIVES OF CONCERN

BRANDS	ADDITIVES-OF-CONCERN **BOLD—CONCERN TO ALL** LIGHT—CONCERN TO SOME
EMPRESS WHOLE OYSTERS	NO ADDITIVES OF CONCERN
GEISHA KING CRABMEAT; NORWAY SARDINES; TINY SHRIMP; WHOLE OYSTERS	NO ADDITIVES OF CONCERN
—TUNA LIGHT IN WATER; SOLID WHITE IN WATER	NO ADDITIVES OF CONCERN
GORTON'S CODFISH CAKES	**MODIFIED FOOD STARCH**
MINCED CLAMS	MONOSODIUM GLUTAMATE
KING OSCAR KIPPER SNACKS; LIGHTLY SMOKED BRISLING SARDINES	**LIGHTLY SMOKED***
NORWAY SARDINES	**SMOKED***
NORSE PRINCE KIPPER SNACKS	**SMOKED***
NORWAY MAID *NORWEGIAN SARDINES* IN MUSTARD SAUCE; IN OIL; IN TOMATO SAUCE	NO ADDITIVES OF CONCERN

*Although "smoked" does not refer to a specific additive, it represents a process utilizing wood smoke, as "smoke flavoring" does, and therefore the food may contain some cancer-causing benzopyrene chemicals. For this reason, when a food or any of its constituents has been smoked, this has been noted in the additives-of-concern-column.

BRANDS	ADDITIVES-OF-CONCERN BOLD—CONCERN TO ALL LIGHT—CONCERN TO SOME
PORTLOCK SMOKED SALMON	**SMOKED***
ROMANOFF *ICELANDIC CAVIAR* BLACK LUMPFISH; RED LUMPFISH	**ARTIFICIAL COLOR**
SALTSEA MINCED CLAMS	NO ADDITIVES OF CONCERN
SNOW'S MINCED CLAMS	NO ADDITIVES OF CONCERN
STAR-KIST *TUNA* CHUNK LIGHT; CHUNK LIGHT IN SPRING WATER; CHUNK WHITE IN WATER	NO ADDITIVES OF CONCERN
SOLID WHITE TUNA	**VEGETABLE OIL**
UNDERWOOD SARDINES IN OIL	**SMOKED***
SUPERMARKET PRIVATE BRANDS	
A & P	
—**A & P** SOLID WHITE TUNA	NO ADDITIVES OF CONCERN

BRANDS	ADDITIVES-OF-CONCERN **BOLD—CONCERN TO ALL** LIGHT—CONCERN TO SOME
FIRST NATIONAL **—EDWARDS** CHUNK LIGHT TUNA	NO ADDITIVES OF CONCERN
—EDWARDS-FINAST CHUNK LIGHT TUNA	NO ADDITIVES OF CONCERN
SAFEWAY **—SEA TRADER** CHUNK LIGHT TUNA IN WATER	NO ADDITIVES OF CONCERN
STOP & SHOP **—STOP & SHOP** BRISLING SARDINES	NO ADDITIVES OF CONCERN
—TUNA CHUNK LIGHT; WHITE IN WATER	NO ADDITIVES OF CONCERN
ITEMS IN HEALTH FOOD STORES	
FEATHERWEIGHT PINK SALMON; UNSALTED LIGHT TUNA CHUNKS	NO ADDITIVES OF CONCERN
UNSALTED NORWAY SMOKED BRISLING SARDINES IN WATER	**SMOKED***

*Although "smoked" does not refer to a specific additive, it represents a process utilizing wood smoke, as "smoke flavoring" does, and therefore the food may contain some cancer-causing benzopyrene chemicals. For this reason, when a food or any of its constituents has been smoked, this has been noted in the additives-of-concern column.

BRANDS	ADDITIVES-OF-CONCERN **BOLD—CONCERN TO ALL** LIGHT—CONCERN TO SOME
HEALTH VALLEY BEST OF SEAFOOD ALASKAN PINK SALMON; RED SALMON; SOLID WHITE TUNA IN WATER	NO ADDITIVES OF CONCERN
SPRUCE ANCHOVIES	NO ADDITIVES OF CONCERN

FROZEN FISH & SHELLFISH (DINNERS & SINGLE ITEMS)

GORTON'S	
BAKED STUFFED SCROD	**BUTTER**
CRUNCHY FISH FILLETS	**MODIFIED CORN STARCH;** MONOSODIUM GLUTAMATE; SODIUM ALGINATE; WHEY
HADDOCK IN LEMON BUTTER; SOLE IN LEMON BUTTER	**BUTTER;** WHEY
TINY FISH CAKES	GUAR GUM; **MODIFIED CORN STARCH; PAPRIKA EXTRACT;** WHEY
—BATTER FRIED	
FISH & CHIPS; FISH KABOBS; SCALLOPS	**MODIFIED CORN STARCH;** MONOSODIUM GLUTAMATE; SODIUM ALGINATE; WHEY
—FISH STICKS	
REGULAR	**MODIFIED CORN STARCH;** MONOSODIUM GLUTAMATE; **PAPRIKA EXTRACT**

BRANDS	ADDITIVES-OF-CONCERN BOLD—CONCERN TO ALL LIGHT—CONCERN TO SOME
W/ SHRIMP STUFFING	**MODIFIED CORN STARCH;** MONOSODIUM GLUTAMATE; SODIUM ALGINATE; WHEY
HOWARD JOHNSON'S	
FRIED CLAMS	NO ADDITIVES OF CONCERN
HADDOCK AU GRATIN*	**PAPRIKA**
MATLAW'S STUFFED CLAMS	MONOSODIUM GLUTAMATE
MRS. PAUL'S	
BUTTERED FISH FILLETS	**BUTTER**
FISH CAKES	**SMOKE FLAVOR;** WHEY
FISH STICKS; FRIED FISH FILLETS; FRIED SCALLOPS	WHEY
FRIED CLAMS	NO ADDITIVES OF CONCERN
—LIGHT BATTER	
CLAM FRITTERS; FISH FILLETS; SCALLOPS	**MODIFIED FOOD STARCH**
STOUFFER'S	
ALASKA KING CRAB NEWBURG; LOBSTER NEWBURG	MONOSODIUM GLUTAMATE

*By law, at this writing, it is not required of a manufacturer to state whether cheeses contain artificial colors, unless the color is FD & C Yellow No. 5 (Tartrazine). Their presence in frozen fish dinners containing cheese therefore remains an uncertainty, unless it is voluntarily declared on the label that artificial colors have been used or have not. For a more detailed explanation of artificial color in cheese, refer to the beginning of the cheese section of "Dairy Products & Substitutes."

BRANDS	ADDITIVES-OF-CONCERN **BOLD—CONCERN TO ALL** LIGHT—CONCERN TO SOME
STOUFFER'S *(Continued)*	
SCALLOPS & SHRIMP MARINER W/ RICE	**MODIFIED CORN STARCH**
SWANSON	
FISH 'N' CHIPS DINNER	GLUTEN (WHEAT); **MODIFIED FOOD STARCH**
HUNGRY-MAN DINNER FISH 'N' CHIPS	GLUTEN (WHEAT); **MODIFIED FOOD STARCH;** WHEY POWDER
TASTE O' SEA	
FISH CAKES	**ARTIFICIAL COLOR; BHA; BHT; MODIFIED FOOD STARCH; OLEORESIN PAPRIKA;** WHEY
FRIED CLAMS	**OLEORESIN PAPRIKA;** WHEY
"KRUNCHEE" FISH PORTIONS; SEA SCALLOPS; SHRIMP	**ARTIFICIAL COLOR; OLEORESIN PAPRIKA;** WHEY
—BATTER DIPT	
FISH PORTIONS; FISH STICKS; SHRIMP	EGG WHITES; **MODIFIED FOOD STARCH;** MONOSODIUM GLUTAMATE; SODIUM ALGINATE; WHEY
—DINNER	
BATTER DIPT SCROD	EGG WHITES; **MODIFIED FOOD STARCH;** MONOSODIUM GLUTAMATE; SODIUM ALGINATE; WHEY

BRANDS	ADDITIVES-OF-CONCERN **BOLD—CONCERN TO ALL** LIGHT—CONCERN TO SOME
FISH; FLOUNDER; HADDOCK; SOLE	**MODIFIED FOOD STARCH; OLEORESIN PAPRIKA**
SCALLOP; SHRIMP	**ARTIFICIAL COLOR; OLEORESIN PAPRIKA;** WHEY
—NATURAL FILLETS	
COD; FILLET OF SOLE; HADDOCK	NO ADDITIVES OF CONCERN
—PLATTER	
SEAFOOD	**ARTIFICIAL COLOR; BHA; BHT; MODIFIED FOOD STARCH; OLEORESIN PAPRIKA;** WHEY
CLAM	**OLEORESIN PAPRIKA;** WHEY
VAN DE KAMP'S	
FISH FILLETS	ALGINATE; **MODIFIED STARCH;** MONOSODIUM GLUTAMATE; WHEY
FISH KABOBS	**MODIFIED STARCH;** MONOSODIUM GLUTAMATE; WHEY
FISH STICKS	EGG WHITES (PASTEURIZED); **MODIFIED FOOD STARCH;** MONOSODIUM GLUTAMATE; WHEY
WAKEFIELD *ALASKA CRABMEAT*	
KING	NO ADDITIVES OF CONCERN

BRANDS	ADDITIVES-OF-CONCERN BOLD—CONCERN TO ALL LIGHT—CONCERN TO SOME
WEIGHT WATCHERS	
FLOUNDER	CAROB BEAN GUM; GUAR GUM; GUM TRAGACANTH; **PAPRIKA**
HADDOCK	CAROB BEAN GUM; GUAR GUM; GUM TRAGACANTH
SUPERMARKET PRIVATE BRANDS	
A & P	
—A & P	
FLOUNDER FILLETS; HADDOCK FILLETS	NO ADDITIVES OF CONCERN
CRISPY SCALLOPS; CRISPY SHRIMP	GUAR GUM; **OLEORESIN PAPRIKA;** WHEY
FISH STICKS	**MODIFIED FOOD STARCH;** MONOSODIUM GLUTAMATE; **OLEORESIN PAPRIKA;** WHEY
SOLE IN LEMON BUTTER	**BUTTER;** MONOSODIUM GLUTAMATE; WHEY
—BATTER DIPPED	
COD PORTIONS; FISH & CHIPS; FISH PORTIONS; FISH STICKS	GUAR GUM; **MODIFIED FOOD STARCH;** MONOSODIUM GLUTAMATE; WHEY
FIRST NATIONAL	
—FINAST	
FISH STICKS	**MODIFIED FOOD STARCH;** MONOSODIUM GLUTAMATE; **OLEORESIN PAPRIKA;** WHEY

BRANDS	ADDITIVES-OF-CONCERN BOLD—CONCERN TO ALL LIGHT—CONCERN TO SOME
—BATTER DIPPED	
FISH & CHIPS; FISH FINGERS; FISH PORTIONS	GUAR GUM; **MODIFIED FOOD STARCH;** MONOSODIUM GLUTAMATE; WHEY
SAFEWAY —CAPTAIN'S CHOICE	
FISH & CHIPS	GUAR GUM; **MODIFIED FOOD STARCH;** MONOSODIUM GLUTAMATE; WHEY
GOURMET BREADED FANTAIL SHRIMP	MONOSODIUM GLUTAMATE; SODIUM ALGINATE; WHEY
GOURMET FANCY FRENCH FRIED SHRIMP	**ARTIFICIAL COLORING;** GUAR GUM; **OLEORESIN PAPRIKA**
SHRIMP SCAMPI	**BUTTER; MODIFIED FOOD STARCH;** MONOSODIUM GLUTAMATE; **OLEORESIN PAPRIKA;** WHEY
SOLE IN LEMON BUTTER SAUCE	**BUTTER;** MONOSODIUM GLUTAMATE; WHEY
—BATTER FRIED	
FISH STICKS	**MODIFIED FOOD STARCH;** MONOSODIUM GLUTAMATE; WHEY
SCALLOPS	GUAR GUM; **OLEORESIN PAPRIKA;** WHEY

BRANDS	ADDITIVES-OF-CONCERN BOLD—CONCERN TO ALL LIGHT—CONCERN TO SOME
SAFEWAY (Continued)	
—SCOTCH BUY	
BREADED FANTAIL SHRIMP	GUAR GUM
GOLDEN FRIED FISH STICKS	**MODIFIED FOOD STARCH;** MONOSODIUM GLUTAMATE; **OLEORESIN PAPRIKA;** WHEY
SEAFOOD ASSORTMENT	GUAR GUM; **MODIFIED FOOD STARCH;** MONOSODIUM GLUTAMATE; **OLEORESIN PAPRIKA;** SODIUM ALGINATE; WHEY
STOP & SHOP	
—STOP & SHOP	
BREADED SHRIMP; SALAD SHRIMP	NO ADDITIVES OF CONCERN
FISH-NICS	**MODIFIED FOOD STARCH; OLEORESIN PAPRIKA**
FRIED CLAMS	**OLEORESIN PAPRIKA;** WHEY
SCALLOPS	**ARTIFICIAL COLOR; OLEORESIN PAPRIKA;** WHEY
—BATTER DIPPED	
FISH NUGGETS; SCALLOPS	EGG WHITES; **MODIFIED FOOD STARCH;** MONOSODIUM GLUTAMATE; SODIUM ALGINATE; WHEY

BRANDS	ADDITIVES-OF-CONCERN **BOLD—CONCERN TO ALL** LIGHT—CONCERN TO SOME
—GOLDEN FRIED	
FISH CAKES; MINI FISH CAKES	**ARTIFICIAL COLOR; BHA; BHT; MODIFIED FOOD STARCH; OLEORESIN PAPRIKA;** WHEY
FISH "MIDGETS"	**ARTIFICIAL COLOR; OLEORESIN PAPRIKA;** WHEY
FISH STICKS	**MODIFIED FOOD STARCH; OLEORESIN PAPRIKA**
ITEMS IN HEALTH FOOD STORES	
BEST OF SEAFOOD (HEALTH VALLEY)	
ALASKAN FISH FILLETS; ALASKAN FISH STICKS; COOKED SHRIMP	**PAPRIKA**
ALASKAN SALMON STEAK	NO ADDITIVES OF CONCERN

REFRIGERATED FISH

SAU-SEA SHRIMP COCKTAIL	**MODIFIED FOOD STARCH**
VITA	
HERRING IN CREAM SAUCE	MILK SOLIDS (NONFAT)
HERRING PARTY SNACKS; TASTEE BITS	NO ADDITIVES OF CONCERN
HERRING SALAD	MONOSODIUM GLUTAMATE

XII. FROZEN DINNERS, PIZZA, POT PIES

FROZEN DINNERS

By law, at this writing, it is not required of a manufacturer to state whether cheeses contain artificial colors, unless the color is FD & C Yellow No. 5 (Tartrazine). Their presence in frozen dinners containing cheese therefore remains an uncertainty, unless it is voluntarily declared on the label that artificial colors have been used or have not. For a more detailed explanation of artificial color in cheese, refer to the beginning of the cheese section of "Dairy Products & Substitutes."

BRANDS	**ADDITIVES-OF-CONCERN** **BOLD—CONCERN TO ALL** LIGHT—CONCERN TO SOME
BANQUET	
—DINNER	
CHOPPED BEEF	**COLORING;** WHEY
FRIED CHICKEN	MONOSODIUM GLUTAMATE; WHEY
MEAT LOAF	**CALCIUM CASEINATE; PAPRIKA;** WHEY (DRIED)
—MAN-PLEASER DINNER	
CHOPPED BEEF	**ARTIFICIAL COLOR; COLORING; MODIFIED FOOD STARCH**
FRIED CHICKEN	**MODIFIED FOOD STARCH;** MONOSODIUM GLUTAMATE
TURKEY	**ARTIFICIAL COLOR; MODIFIED FOOD STARCH;** MONOSODIUM GLUTAMATE; **OLEORESIN OF TURMERIC; PAPRIKA**

BRANDS	ADDITIVES-OF-CONCERN **BOLD—CONCERN TO ALL** LIGHT—CONCERN TO SOME
VEAL PARMIGIAN	**ARTIFICIAL COLORS; BHA; CALCIUM CASEINATE; COLORING;** MONOSODIUM GLUTAMATE; **PAPRIKA; SODIUM CASEINATE;** WHEY & DRY WHEY
CHUN KING *DINNER*	
BEEF PEPPER ORIENTAL	**CALCIUM CASEINATE; MODIFIED FOOD STARCH;** MONOSODIUM GLUTAMATE; SODIUM ALGINATE; WHEY (DRIED)
CHICKEN CHOW MEIN	**CALCIUM CASEINATE; MODIFIED FOOD STARCH;** MONOSODIUM GLUTAMATE; **PAPRIKA;** SODIUM ALGINATE; WHEY (DRIED)
FREEZER QUEEN *ENTRÉE*	
BREADED VEAL PARMIGIAN	**MODIFIED FOOD STARCH;** MONOSODIUM GLUTAMATE; **OLEORESIN PAPRIKA & PAPRIKA**
GRAVY & SLICED BEEF	**HYDROGENATED SOYBEAN OIL; MODIFIED FOOD STARCH;** MONOSODIUM GLUTAMATE; **OLEORESIN PAPRIKA**

BRANDS	ADDITIVES-OF-CONCERN **BOLD—CONCERN TO ALL** LIGHT—CONCERN TO SOME
MORTON *—DINNER* BEEF; MEAT LOAF; SALISBURY STEAK; VEAL PARMIGIANA	**ARTIFICIAL COLOR; MODIFIED FOOD STARCH;** MONOSODIUM GLUTAMATE; WHEY SOLIDS
BONELESS CHICKEN	**ARTIFICIAL COLOR; BHA; MODIFIED FOOD STARCH;** MONOSODIUM GLUTAMATE; **PAPRIKA OLEORESIN; TURMERIC;** WHEY SOLIDS
MACARONI & CHEESE	**ARTIFICIAL COLOR; MODIFIED FOOD STARCH;** WHEY SOLIDS
TURKEY	**ARTIFICIAL COLOR; MODIFIED FOOD STARCH;** MONOSODIUM GLUTAMATE; **PAPRIKA OLEORESIN; TURMERIC;** WHEY SOLIDS
—COUNTRY TABLE ENTRÉE FRIED CHICKEN	**ARTIFICIAL COLOR; MODIFIED FOOD STARCH; PAPRIKA;** WHEY SOLIDS
SLICED TURKEY	**ARTIFICIAL COLOR; MODIFIED FOOD STARCH;** MONOSODIUM GLUTAMATE; **PAPRIKA OLEORESIN; TURMERIC;** WHEY SOLIDS
—STEAK HOUSE SIRLOIN STRIP STEAK; TENDERLOIN STEAK	**MODIFIED FOOD STARCH;** SODIUM ALGINATE

BRANDS	ADDITIVES-OF-CONCERN **BOLD—CONCERN TO ALL** LIGHT—CONCERN TO SOME
SWANSON	
—DINNER	
BEEF; TURKEY	**MODIFIED FOOD STARCH;** MONOSODIUM GLUTAMATE; WHEY POWDER
LOIN OF PORK; VEAL PARMIGIANA	**MODIFIED FOOD STARCH**
CRISPY FRIED CHICKEN; FRIED CHICKEN	**MODIFIED FOOD STARCH; VEGETABLE OIL;** WHEY POWDER
HAM	**MODIFIED FOOD STARCH; SODIUM NITRITE;** WHEY POWDER
MACARONI & CHEESE	**MODIFIED FOOD STARCH; OLEORESIN PAPRIKA**
POLYNESIAN STYLE	**MODIFIED FOOD STARCH;** MONOSODIUM GLUTAMATE
SALISBURY STEAK	**CALCIUM CASEINATE; MODIFIED FOOD STARCH;** WHEY & WHEY POWDER
—ENTRÉE	
CHICKEN NIBBLES; FRIED CHICKEN	**VEGETABLE OIL**
GRAVY & SLICED BEEF	**MODIFIED FOOD STARCH;** MONOSODIUM GLUTAMATE
MEATBALLS	**MODIFIED FOOD STARCH**
SALISBURY STEAK	**CALCIUM CASEINATE; SODIUM CASEINATE;** WHEY

BRANDS	ADDITIVES-OF-CONCERN BOLD—CONCERN TO ALL LIGHT—CONCERN TO SOME
SWANSON *(Continued)*	
—HUNGRY-MAN DINNER	
BONELESS CHICKEN; SLICED BEEF; TURKEY	**MODIFIED FOOD STARCH;** MONOSODIUM GLUTAMATE; WHEY POWDER
SALISBURY STEAK	**CALCIUM CASEINATE; MODIFIED FOOD STARCH; SODIUM CASEINATE;** WHEY & WHEY POWDER
VEAL PARMIGIANA	**MODIFIED FOOD STARCH; OLEORESIN PAPRIKA;** WHEY POWDER
—HUNGRY-MAN ENTRÉE	
FRIED CHICKEN	**VEGETABLE OIL**
LASAGNA W/ MEAT	**MODIFIED FOOD STARCH**
WEIGHT WATCHERS	
CHICKEN LIVERS & ONIONS	CAROB BEAN GUM; GUAR GUM; GUM TRAGACANTH; **MODIFIED FOOD STARCH; NUTMEG**
VEAL PARMIGIANA & ZUCCHINI IN SAUCE	CAROB BEAN GUM; GUAR GUM; GUM TRAGACANTH
SUPERMARKET PRIVATE BRANDS	
A & P	
—ANN PAGE *DINNER*	
BEEF	**MODIFIED FOOD STARCH**
FRIED CHICKEN	**PAPRIKA;** WHEY

BRANDS	ADDITIVES-OF-CONCERN **BOLD—CONCERN TO ALL** LIGHT—CONCERN TO SOME
MEAT LOAF	**CALCIUM CASEINATE;** MONOSODIUM GLUTAMATE; **PAPRIKA;** WHEY
TURKEY	**MODIFIED FOOD STARCH;** MONOSODIUM GLUTAMATE; **OLEORESIN OF PAPRIKA; TURMERIC**
SAFEWAY —BEL-AIR *DINNER* FRIED CHICKEN	BUTTERMILK SOLIDS; MONOSODIUM GLUTAMATE; **OLEORESIN PAPRIKA;** SODIUM ALGINATE; WHEY SOLIDS
MEAT LOAF	BUTTERMILK SOLIDS; WHEY SOLIDS
SALISBURY STEAK	MONOSODIUM GLUTAMATE; **PAPRIKA;** WHEY (DRIED)
SPAGHETTI & MEATBALLS	EGG WHITES; MILK SOLIDS (NONFAT DRY)
TURKEY	WHEY (DRIED)

BRANDS	ADDITIVES-OF-CONCERN BOLD—CONCERN TO ALL LIGHT—CONCERN TO SOME

FROZEN PIZZA

By law, at this writing, it is not required of a manufacturer to state whether cheeses contain artificial colors, unless the color is FD & C Yellow No. 5 (Tartrazine). Their presence in frozen pizza therefore remains an uncertainty, unless it is voluntarily declared on the label that artificial colors have been used or have not. For a more detailed explanation of artificial color in cheese, refer to the beginning of the cheese section of "Dairy Products & Substitutes."

CELESTE	
CHEESE	**MODIFIED FOOD STARCH**
CHEESE SICILIAN STYLE	**BHA; BHT;** GLUTEN; **MODIFIED FOOD STARCH**
PIZZA-FOR-ONE PEPPERONI	**BHA; BHT; MODIFIED FOOD STARCH; OLEORESIN OF PAPRIKA; SODIUM NITRITE**
ELLIO'S CHEESE	**MODIFIED FOOD STARCH**
JENO'S	
ITALIAN BREAD CHEESE	GLUTEN (WHEAT); **MODIFIED FOOD STARCH;** WHEY
CHEESE	**ARTIFICIAL COLOR;** LOCUST BEAN GUM; **MODIFIED FOOD STARCH;** WHEY POWDER
PIZZA SNACKS ASSORTED (SAUSAGE-PEPPERONI-CHEESE)	**ARTIFICIAL COLORING; BHA; BHT; CALCIUM & SODIUM CASEINATE;** LOCUST BEAN GUM;

(continues)

BRANDS	**ADDITIVES-OF-CONCERN** **BOLD—CONCERN TO ALL** LIGHT—CONCERN TO SOME
	MODIFIED FOOD STARCH; MONOSODIUM GLUTAMATE; **PAPRIKA (& OLEORESIN OF); SODIUM NITRITE**
JOHN'S HOMESTYLE THICK CRUST CHEESE; ORIGINAL CHEESE	**MODIFIED FOOD STARCH; PAPRIKA**
LA PIZZERIA CHEESE	NO ADDITIVES OF CONCERN
COMBINATION	**BHA; BHT; PAPRIKA; SODIUM NITRITE**
SALUTO *FRENCH BREAD PIZZA* CHEESE	NO ADDITIVES OF CONCERN
DELUXE; PEPPERONI	**BHA; BHT; PAPRIKA; SODIUM NITRITE**
STOUFFER'S *FRENCH BREAD PIZZA* CHEESE	**ARTIFICIAL COLOR; MODIFIED CORN STARCH;** MONOSODIUM GLUTAMATE
DELUXE SAUSAGE & PEPPERONI	**BHT; MODIFIED CORN STARCH;** MONOSODIUM GLUTAMATE; **OLEORESIN OF PAPRIKA; SODIUM NITRITE**
PEPPERONI	**MODIFIED CORN STARCH;** MONOSODIUM GLUTAMATE; **OLEORESIN OF PAPRIKA; SODIUM NITRITE**

BRANDS	ADDITIVES-OF-CONCERN BOLD—CONCERN TO ALL LIGHT—CONCERN TO SOME
SUPERMARKET PRIVATE BRANDS	
A & P—ANN PAGE	
CHEESE	GUAR GUM; GUM TRAGACANTH; **MODIFIED FOOD STARCH**
MINI	**ARTIFICIAL COLORING;** GUAR GUM; GUM TRAGACANTH; **MODIFIED FOOD STARCH;** RENNET CASEIN
SAFEWAY—BEL-AIR	
CHEESE	NO ADDITIVES OF CONCERN
CHEESE & PEPPERONI	**BHA; BHT; SODIUM NITRITE**
CHEESE & SAUSAGE	**SODIUM NITRATE; SODIUM NITRITE**
STOP & SHOP —STOP & SHOP	
CHEESE; SAUSAGE & CHEESE	**MODIFIED FOOD STARCH;** MONOSODIUM GLUTAMATE
CHEESE PIZZA 10 PAK	**MODIFIED FOOD STARCH; VEGETABLE OIL**
ITEMS IN HEALTH FOOD STORES	
PIZZA NATURALLY	
DELUXE VEGETABLE CHEESE	HIGH GLUTEN FLOUR
SHILOH FARMS	
WHOLE WHEAT PIZZA	
PLAIN; W/ SWEET PEPPERS; W/ SAUSAGE	GLUTEN (WHEAT OR VITAL WHEAT)

BRANDS	ADDITIVES-OF-CONCERN **BOLD—CONCERN TO ALL** LIGHT—CONCERN TO SOME
WORTHINGTON PIZZA ITALIANA	**ARTIFICIAL COLOR; CALCIUM CASEINATE;** EGG WHITES; GLUTEN (WHEAT); GUAR GUM; MONOSODIUM GLUTAMATE; **SODIUM CASEINATE;** WHEY

FROZEN POT PIES

BANQUET	
BEEF	NO ADDITIVES OF CONCERN
CHICKEN; TURKEY	MONOSODIUM GLUTAMATE; **PAPRIKA; OLEORESIN OF TURMERIC**
MORTON	
BEEF	**MODIFIED FOOD STARCH;** MONOSODIUM GLUTAMATE; **SHORTENING**
TURKEY	**BHA; MODIFIED FOOD STARCH;** MONOSODIUM GLUTAMATE; **OLEORESINS OF PAPRIKA & TURMERIC;** WHEY SOLIDS
STOUFFER'S	
BEEF	**MODIFIED CORN STARCH;** MONOSODIUM GLUTAMATE
CHICKEN; TURKEY	**MODIFIED CORN STARCH;** MONOSODIUM GLUTAMATE; **TURMERIC**

BRANDS	ADDITIVES-OF-CONCERN BOLD—CONCERN TO ALL LIGHT—CONCERN TO SOME
SWANSON	
BEEF	**MODIFIED FOOD STARCH**
CHICKEN; TURKEY	**MODIFIED FOOD STARCH;** MONOSODIUM GLUTAMATE
SUPERMARKET PRIVATE BRANDS	
A & P —ANN PAGE	
BEEF	**MODIFIED FOOD STARCH**
CHICKEN; TURKEY	**MODIFIED FOOD STARCH;** MONOSODIUM GLUTAMATE; **OLEORESIN OF PAPRIKA; TURMERIC**
FIRST NATIONAL —FINAST	
BEEF	**MODIFIED FOOD STARCH**
CHICKEN; TURKEY	**MODIFIED FOOD STARCH;** MONOSODIUM GLUTAMATE; **OLEORESIN OF PAPRIKA; TURMERIC**
SAFEWAY —MANOR HOUSE	
BEEF	**(BEEF FAT, LARD)***
CHICKEN	**(BEEF FAT, LARD);*** MONOSODIUM GLUTAMATE; **PAPRIKA; OLEORESIN OF TURMERIC**

*Blend may contain one or more of these saturated fats.

BRANDS	**ADDITIVES-OF-CONCERN** **BOLD—CONCERN TO ALL** LIGHT—CONCERN TO SOME
ITEMS IN HEALTH FOOD STORES	
WORTHINGTON *PIE*	
TUNO	**MODIFIED CORN STARCH; MODIFIED TAPIOCA STARCH;** MONOSODIUM GLUTAMATE; **TURMERIC**
VEGETARIAN	**ARTIFICIAL COLORS;** EGG WHITE SOLIDS; **MODIFIED CORN STARCH;** MONOSODIUM GLUTAMATE

XIII. FRUIT, FRUIT DRINKS, FRUIT JUICES

FRUIT: CANNED

Most of the items in this section do not contain any additives of concern, and these appear first, without an additives-of-concern column.

The items that do contain additives of concern follow, in the usual style.

DEL MONTE APRICOT HALVES; BARTLETT PEAR HALVES; ROYAL ANNE CHERRIES; SLICED PINEAPPLE; WHOLE FIGS; YELLOW CLING SLICED PEACHES

DOLE CHUNK PINEAPPLE IN HEAVY SYRUP; CHUNK PINEAPPLE IN UNSWEETENED PINEAPPLE JUICE

GEISHA MANDARIN ORANGE SEGMENTS

LIBBY'S GRAPEFRUIT SECTIONS; PEAR HALVES; YELLOW CLING SLICED PEACHES

MOTT'S APPLE SAUCE; APPLE SAUCE NATURAL STYLE

OCEAN SPRAY CRAN RASPBERRY JELLIED SAUCE; JELLIED CRANBERRY SAUCE; WHOLE BERRY CRANBERRY SAUCE

SENECA CINNAMON APPLESAUCE

STOKELY VAN CAMP'S APPLESAUCE; YELLOW CLING SLICED PEACHES

SUNSWEET COOKED PRUNES

3 DIAMONDS MANDARIN ORANGE SEGMENTS

VERYFINE APPLE SAUCE NATURAL STYLE; APPLE SAUCE 100% McINTOSH

SUPERMARKET PRIVATE BRANDS

A & P ANN PAGE APPLE SAUCE; PEACHES YELLOW CLING SLICED

FIRST NATIONAL FINAST APPLE SAUCE; APRICOT HALVES; BARTLETT PEARS; FANCY APPLE SAUCE; GRAPEFRUIT SECTIONS; YELLOW CLING PEACHES

LUCKY HARVEST DAY APPLE SAUCE; APRICOTS; FRUIT MIX; PEACHES; PEARS

LUCKY LADY LEE APPLE SAUCE; APRICOTS; BARTLETT PEAR HALVES; CRUSHED PINEAPPLE; FANCY GRAVENSTEIN APPLE SAUCE; FREESTONE PEACHES; MANDARIN ORANGES; PEACH HALVES; PEACH SLICES; PINEAPPLE CHUNKS; UNSWEETENED APPLE SAUCE; WHOLE CRANBERRY SAUCE

SAFEWAY SCOTCH BUY APPLE SAUCE; FRUIT MIX; HALVES BARTLETT PEARS; HALVES YELLOW CLING PEACHES; MANDARIN ORANGE SEGMENTS; UNPEELED HALVES APRICOTS; WHOLE & SPLIT KADOTA FIGS; YELLOW ELBERTA FREESTONE PEACHES

SAFEWAY TOWN HOUSE APPLE SAUCE; CRANBERRY SAUCE; CRUSHED PINEAPPLE; GRAPEFRUIT SECTIONS; GRAVENSTEIN APPLE SAUCE; HALVES BARTLETT PEARS; MANDARIN ORANGE SEGMENTS; PINEAPPLE CHUNKS IN HEAVY SYRUP; PINEAPPLE CHUNKS IN UNSWEETENED PINEAPPLE JUICE; RED SOUR PITTED CHERRIES; SLICED CLING PEACHES; WHOLE APRICOTS; WHOLE PURPLE PLUMS

STOP & SHOP APPLE SAUCE; APRICOT HALVES; BARTLETT PEARS; CHUNKY APPLE SAUCE; CLING PEACHES; CRANBERRY SAUCE; CRUSHED

(continues)

STOP & SHOP *(Continued)*

PINEAPPLE; ELBERTA PEACHES HALVES; GRAPEFRUIT & ORANGE SECTIONS IN LIGHT SYRUP; GRAPEFRUIT IN UNSWEETENED GRAPEFRUIT JUICE; PINEAPPLE CHUNKS; SLICED PEARS; SLICED PINEAPPLE IN HEAVY SYRUP

STOP & SHOP SUN GLORY HALVES PEACHES; SLICED PEACHES; SLICED PEARS

WINN DIXIE ASTOR APRICOTS; BARTLETT PEARS; CRUSHED PINEAPPLE; SLICED PINEAPPLE; YELLOW CLING PEACHES

WINN DIXIE THRIFTY MAID APPLE SAUCE; BARTLETT PEARS; GRAPEFRUIT SECTIONS; SLICED PINEAPPLE; YELLOW CLING SLICED PEACHES; WHOLE APRICOTS

ITEMS IN HEALTH FOOD STORES

CELLU BARTLETT PEARS

FEATHERWEIGHT KADOTA FIGS; SLICED PINEAPPLE; STEWED PRUNES

HEALTH VALLEY BARTLETT PEARS; CHUNK PINEAPPLE; FRUIT MIX; HALVES APRICOTS; HALVES PEACHES; SLICED PINEAPPLE

WALNUT ACRES CRANBERRY-HONEY SAUCE; WHOLE CRANBERRY SAUCE

The following items contain additives of concern.

BRANDS	**ADDITIVES-OF-CONCERN** BOLD—CONCERN TO ALL LIGHT—CONCERN TO SOME
DEL MONTE FRUIT COCKTAIL; FRUITS FOR SALAD; TROPICAL FRUIT SALAD	CHERRIES **ARTIFICIALLY COLORED RED**

BRANDS	ADDITIVES-OF-CONCERN BOLD—CONCERN TO ALL LIGHT—CONCERN TO SOME
LIBBY'S FRUIT COCKTAIL	CHERRIES **ARTIFICIALLY COLORED RED**
OCEAN SPRAY CRAN ORANGE RELISH	**MODIFIED STARCH**
ROYAL WILLAMETTE MARASCHINO CHERRIES	**ARTIFICIAL COLOR**
STOKELY VAN CAMP'S FRUIT COCKTAIL	CHERRIES **ARTIFICIALLY COLORED RED**
SUPERMARKET PRIVATE BRANDS	
A & P—ANN PAGE FRUIT COCKTAIL	CHERRIES **ARTIFICIALLY COLORED RED**
FIRST NATIONAL —FINAST FRUIT COCKTAIL	CHERRIES **ARTIFICIALLY COLORED RED**
LUCKY—LADY LEE FRUIT COCKTAIL	CHERRIES **ARTIFICIALLY COLORED RED**
SAFEWAY —TOWN HOUSE FRUIT COCKTAIL	CHERRIES **ARTIFICIALLY COLORED RED**
STOP & SHOP —STOP & SHOP FRUIT COCKTAIL	CHERRIES **ARTIFICIALLY COLORED RED**
MARASCHINO CHERRIES	**CERTIFIED COLOR**

BRANDS	ADDITIVES-OF-CONCERN BOLD—CONCERN TO ALL LIGHT—CONCERN TO SOME
WINN DIXIE —ASTOR FRUIT COCKTAIL	CHERRIES **ARTIFICIALLY COLORED RED**

FRUIT: DRIED*

DEL MONTE EVAPORATED APPLES; APRICOTS; LARGE PRUNES; SEEDLESS RAISINS

DROMEDARY CHOPPED DATES

SUN MAID GOLDEN RAISINS; RAISINS; ZANTE CURRANTS

SUNSWEET APRICOTS; LARGE PRUNES

SUPERMARKET PRIVATE BRANDS
LUCKY LADY LEE SEEDLESS RAISINS

SAFEWAY SCOTCH BUY DRIED FIGS

SAFEWAY TOWN HOUSE APPLES; LARGE PEACHES; LARGE PRUNES; MEDIUM APRICOTS; MEDIUM PRUNES; SEEDLESS GOLDEN RAISINS; SEEDLESS RAISINS

STOP & SHOP LARGE PRUNES; PITTED PRUNES; SEEDLESS RAISINS

ITEMS IN HEALTH FOOD STORES
BARBARA'S APPLES

*See note on page 280.

EREWHON BREAD DATES; APRICOT; BLACK MISSION FIGS

SONOMA PEARS; PINEAPPLE

The following item contains an additive of concern.

BRANDS	ADDITIVES-OF-CONCERN BOLD—CONCERN TO ALL LIGHT—CONCERN TO SOME
SUN MAID MUSCAT RAISINS	**TREATED W/ VEGETABLE OIL**

FRUIT: FROZEN

None of the items in this section contain any additives of concern, and all the items appear without an additives-of-concern column.

BIRDS EYE MIXED FRUIT; PEACHES; RED RASPBERRIES; WHOLE STRAWBERRIES

NATURIPE SLICED STRAWBERRIES

NEWTON ACRES MELON BALLS

STEWART'S MAINE WILD BLUEBERRIES

SUPERMARKET PRIVATE BRANDS
A & P SLICED STRAWBERRIES

LUCKY LADY LEE SLICED STRAWBERRIES

SAFEWAY BEL-AIR BLUEBERRIES; BOYSENBERRIES; MIXED MELON BALLS; RASPBERRIES; RHUBARB; SLICED PEACHES; STRAWBERRIES

BRANDS	**ADDITIVES-OF-CONCERN** **BOLD—CONCERN TO ALL** LIGHT—CONCERN TO SOME

FRUIT DRINKS: CANNED

DEL MONTE *JUICE DRINK*	
PINEAPPLE GRAPEFRUIT	NO ADDITIVES OF CONCERN
PINEAPPLE ORANGE	**ARTIFICIAL COLOR**
DOLE	
PINEAPPLE PINK GRAPEFRUIT JUICE-DRINK	**ARTIFICIAL COLORING;** GUM ARABIC
HAWAIIAN PUNCH *FRUIT PUNCH*	
GRAPE; ORANGE; RED; VERY BERRY	**ARTIFICIAL COLOR** OR **COLORS**
HI-C	
FRUIT PUNCH	**ARTIFICIAL COLORS**
—DRINK	
APPLE; CHERRY; CITRUS COOLER; GRAPE; ORANGE; WILD BERRY	**ARTIFICIAL COLOR** OR **COLORS**
LEMON TREE	
LEMONADE FLAVOR DRINK	ACACIA GUM; **ARTIFICIAL COLOR; BHA; GLYCERYL ABIETATE**
MOTT'S *FRUIT DRINK*	
A.M.	**ARTIFICIAL COLOR;** GUM ARABIC; GUM TRAGACANTH
P.M. APPLE-GRAPE	**ARTIFICIAL COLOR;** GUM ARABIC

BRANDS	ADDITIVES-OF-CONCERN **BOLD—CONCERN TO ALL** LIGHT—CONCERN TO SOME
MUSSELMAN'S BREAKFAST COCKTAIL ORANGE APRICOT FRUIT DRINK	**ARTIFICIAL COLORS; BHT;** GUM ARABIC
OCEAN SPRAY CRANAPPLE; CRANBERRY JUICE COCKTAIL; CRAN-GRAPE; CRANICOT	NO ADDITIVES OF CONCERN
PARADE CRANBERRY COCKTAIL	NO ADDITIVES OF CONCERN
STOKELY VAN CAMP'S GATORADE (LEMON-LIME); GATORADE (ORANGE)	**ARTIFICIAL COLOR** W/ FD & C YELLOW NO. 5; **ESTER GUM**
TROPI-CAL-LO ORANGE DRINK	**ARTIFICIAL COLOR; MODIFIED STARCH; SODIUM SACCHARIN; VEGETABLE GUMS**
TROPICANA GRAPE DRINK	**ARTIFICIAL COLOR; VEGETABLE GUMS**
WAGNER BREAKFAST GRAPEFRUIT DRINK	**MODIFIED FOOD STARCH; VEGETABLE GUM**
THIRST QUENCHER	**ARTIFICIAL COLOR;** GUAR GUM; **MODIFIED FOOD STARCH**

BRANDS	ADDITIVES-OF-CONCERN **BOLD—CONCERN TO ALL** LIGHT—CONCERN TO SOME
WELCHADE	
FRUIT PUNCH	**ESTER GUM;** GUM ARABIC; **U.S. CERTIFIED ARTIFICIAL COLOR**
GRAPE DRINK	**ARTIFICIAL COLOR**
SUPERMARKET PRIVATE BRANDS	
A & P	
—A & P CRANBERRY APPLE DRINK	NO ADDITIVES OF CONCERN
—ANN PAGE	
TROPICAL FRUIT PUNCH	**ARTIFICIAL COLOR**
DRINK	
APPLE	NO ADDITIVES OF CONCERN
CHERRY; GRAPE	**ARTIFICIAL COLOR**
CITRUS COOLER; ORANGE	**ARTIFICIAL COLOR;** GUM ARABIC; GUM TRAGACANTH
FIRST NATIONAL	
—EDWARDS *DRINK*	
CHERRY; GRAPE; ORANGE	**ARTIFICIAL COLOR; VEGETABLE GUM**
—FINAST *DRINK*	
CRANBERRY APPLE	NO ADDITIVES OF CONCERN
WILD BERRY	**U.S. CERTIFIED COLOR**
LUCKY	
—LADY LEE FRUIT PUNCH CONCENTRATE	**ARTIFICIAL COLOR**

BRANDS	ADDITIVES-OF-CONCERN **BOLD—CONCERN TO ALL** LIGHT—CONCERN TO SOME
SAFEWAY **—CRAGMONT** LEMONADE FLAVORED DRINK	**ARTIFICIAL COLOR; BROMINATED VEGETABLE OIL; GLYCEROL ESTER OF WOOD ROSIN;** GUM ARABIC
—SCOTCH BUY GRAPE DRINK	**ARTIFICIAL COLOR;** GUM ARABIC
—TOWN HOUSE CRAN-APPLE DRINK	NO ADDITIVES OF CONCERN
STOP & SHOP **—STOP & SHOP** TROPICAL PUNCH	**U.S. CERTIFIED COLOR**
DRINK APPLE	NO ADDITIVES OF CONCERN
GRAPE; PINEAPPLE GRAPEFRUIT JUICE	**ARTIFICIAL COLOR**
WINN DIXIE **—THRIFTY MAID** *DRINK* APPLE; PINEAPPLE GRAPEFRUIT	NO ADDITIVES OF CONCERN
FRUIT PUNCH; GRAPE; ORANGE	**ARTIFICIAL COLOR** OR **COLORS**

FRUIT DRINKS: FROZEN

BIRDS EYE AWAKE; ORANGE PLUS	**ARTIFICIAL COLOR; BHA; MODIFIED CORN OR FOOD STARCH**

BRANDS	ADDITIVES-OF-CONCERN **BOLD—CONCERN TO ALL** LIGHT—CONCERN TO SOME
COUNTRY TIME LEMONADE	**ARTIFICIAL COLOR; BHA; MODIFIED STARCHES**
HAWAIIAN PUNCH RED	**ARTIFICIAL COLOR**
MINUTE MAID LEMONADE; LIMEADE; PINK LEMONADE	NO ADDITIVES OF CONCERN
OCEAN SPRAY CRANBERRY JUICE COCKTAIL; CRANORANGE	NO ADDITIVES OF CONCERN
WELCHADE GRAPE DRINK	NO ADDITIVES OF CONCERN
SUPERMARKET PRIVATE BRANDS A & P —ANN PAGE LEMONADE	NO ADDITIVES OF CONCERN
PINK LEMONADE	**ARTIFICIALLY COLORED**
LUCKY —LADY LEE FRUIT PUNCH	ACACIA GUM; **ARTIFICIAL COLOR**
PINK LEMONADE	**U.S. CERTIFIED ARTIFICIAL COLOR**

BRANDS	**ADDITIVES-OF-CONCERN** **BOLD—CONCERN TO ALL** LIGHT—CONCERN TO SOME
SAFEWAY —BEL-AIR CONCENTRATE FOR LEMONADE; CONCENTRATE FOR LIMEADE	NO ADDITIVES OF CONCERN
FRUIT PUNCH	ACACIA GUM; **ARTIFICIAL COLOR; GLYCERYL ABIETATE**
PINK LEMONADE	**ARTIFICIAL COLOR**

FRUIT DRINKS: REFRIGERATED

HOOD ALL NATURAL LEMONADE	NO ADDITIVES OF CONCERN
FRUIT PUNCH	**ARTIFICIAL COLOR**
SUPERMARKET PRIVATE BRANDS LUCKY —LADY LEE FRUIT PUNCH; ORANGE DRINK	**ARTIFICIAL COLOR; GLYCERYL ABIETATE; MODIFIED FOOD STARCH**
SAFEWAY —LUCERNE *DRINK* LEMON; ORANGE	ACACIA ESTER GUM; **ARTIFICIAL COLOR**
GRAPE	**ARTIFICIAL COLOR; MODIFIED FOOD STARCH**

BRANDS	**ADDITIVES-OF-CONCERN** **BOLD—CONCERN TO ALL** LIGHT—CONCERN TO SOME
WINN DIXIE —SUPERBRAND SWANEE *DRINK* GRAPE; LEMON; ORANGE	**ARTIFICIAL COLOR**

FRUIT JUICES: CANNED

Most of the items in this section do not contain any additives of concern, and these appear first, without an additives-of-concern column.

The items that do contain additives of concern follow, in the usual style.

APPLE & EVE APPLE

BIG TEX GRAPEFRUIT RUBY RED

DEL MONTE PINEAPPLE UNSWEETENED

DOLE PINEAPPLE UNSWEETENED

GLORIETTA APRICOT NECTAR; PEAR NECTAR

HEART'S DELIGHT APRICOT NECTAR; PEACH NECTAR; PEAR NECTAR

JUICY JUICE *100% JUICES* GOLDEN; PURPLE

LIBBY'S APRICOT NECTAR; ORANGE UNSWEETENED

MOTT'S APPLE McINTOSH; APPLE NATURAL STYLE; PRUNE SUPER

OCEAN SPRAY GRAPEFRUIT UNSWEETENED

PARADE HAWAIIAN UNSWEETENED PINEAPPLE; UNSWEETENED APPLE; UNSWEETENED GRAPE;

(continues)

100% UNSWEETENED GRAPEFRUIT; 100% UNSWEETENED ORANGE; UNSWEETENED PRUNE

REALEMON RECONSTITUTED LEMON

REALIME RECONSTITUTED LIME

SENECA APPLE

SUNSWEET PRUNE UNSWEETENED

TREESWEET GRAPEFRUIT UNSWEETENED

WELCH'S GRAPE; GRAPE RED; WHITE GRAPE

SUPERMARKET PRIVATE BRANDS
A & P APPLE CIDER; CRANBERRY COCKTAIL

A & P ANN PAGE APPLE; 100% GRAPEFRUIT UNSWEETENED

FIRST NATIONAL EDWARDS GRAPE; RECONSTITUTED LEMON; UNSWEETENED GRAPEFRUIT

FIRST NATIONAL FINAST APPLE; CRANBERRY COCKTAIL; 100% GRAPEFRUIT UNSWEETENED; 100% ORANGE UNSWEETENED; UNSWEETENED PINK GRAPEFRUIT

LUCKY LADY LEE APRICOT NECTAR; CRANBERRY COCKTAIL; GRAPE; HAWAIIAN PINEAPPLE UNSWEETENED; 100% GRAPEFRUIT UNSWEETENED; PINK GRAPEFRUIT; PRUNE UNSWEETENED; PURE APPLE CIDER; PURE APPLE; RECONSTITUTED LEMON

SAFEWAY TOWN HOUSE APPLE; APPLE CIDER; APRICOT NECTAR; CRANBERRY COCKTAIL; GRAPEFRUIT 100% UNSWEETENED; ORANGE; ORANGE 100% UNSWEETENED; PINEAPPLE; PINK GRAPEFRUIT 100% UNSWEETENED; PRUNE; RECONSTITUTED LEMON

STOP & SHOP APRICOT NECTAR

WINN DIXIE ASTOR UNSWEETENED PRUNE

WINN DIXIE THRIFTY MAID CRANBERRY; 100% FLORIDA GRAPEFRUIT UNSWEETENED; 100% FLORIDA ORANGE & GRAPEFRUIT UNSWEETENED; 100% FLORIDA ORANGE UNSWEETENED; RECONSTITUTED LEMON; SWEET APPLE CIDER; UNSWEETENED APPLE; UNSWEETENED FANCY HAWAIIAN PINEAPPLE; UNSWEETENED GRAPE

ITEMS IN HEALTH FOOD STORES
AFTER THE FALL APPLE; APPLE-APRICOT; APPLE BLACKBERRY; APPLE-CHERRY; APPLE-GRAPE; APPLE-PINEAPPLE; APPLE RASPBERRY; APPLE STRAWBERRY; PEAR; PURE GRAPE

CHARISMA GRAPE; PRUNE

EREWHON APPLE; APPLE APRICOT; APPLE BANANA; APPLE CRANBERRY; APPLE LIME; APPLE RASPBERRY; APPLE STRAWBERRY

HAIKU GUAVA; GUAVA-BERRY; PAPAYA; PASSION

HAIN CRANBERRY COCKTAIL; FIG

HEALTH VALLEY APRICOT ZAPPER

HEINKE'S APPLE; APPLE-APRICOT BLEND; APRICOT; BLACK CHERRY; PEACH; PEAR; PLUM; POMEGRANATE

KEDEM GRAPE

KNUDSEN'S APPLE; APPLE-BOYSENBERRY; APPLE-STRAWBERRY; CONCORD GRAPE

LAKEWOOD APPLE LOGANBERRY; CARROT ORANGE; LEMON-LIME; "PINEAPPLE N' PAPAYA"; "SECOND WIND"; "STRAWBERRIES N' CREME"

LEHR'S PURE RED GRAPE

TAP 'N APPLE APPLE

WALNUT ACRES CRANBERRY NECTAR

WESTBRAE MACHU-PICCHU PUNCH

The following items contain additives of concern.

BRANDS	ADDITIVES-OF-CONCERN BOLD—CONCERN TO ALL LIGHT—CONCERN TO SOME
ITEMS IN HEALTH FOOD STORES	
LAKEWOOD	
BANANA COLADA; COCONUT MILK; PINA COLADA; PINEAPPLE AMBROSIA	**VEGETABLE GUM**
CRANBERRY; LOGANBERRY; MANGO; PASSION FRUIT; RED PAPAYA RICA; SÃO PAULO PUNCH	PACIFIC SEA KELP (ALGINATE)

FRUIT JUICES: FROZEN

None of the items in this section contain any additives of concern, and all the items appear without an additives-of-concern column.

DONALD DUCK ORANGE

MINUTE MAID GRAPE; 100% LEMON; ORANGE; PINEAPPLE; UNSWEETENED GRAPEFRUIT

SENECA APPLE; GRAPE

TREESWEET ORANGE

TROPICANA ORANGE

WELCH'S GRAPE

SUPERMARKET PRIVATE BRANDS
A & P ORANGE

LUCKY LADY LEE FROZEN CONCENTRATE FOR APPLE; 100% FROZEN CONCENTRATED ORANGE; SWEETENED CONCORD FROZEN CONCENTRATED GRAPE

SAFEWAY BEL-AIR FROZEN CONCENTRATED SWEETENED CONCORD GRAPE; FROZEN CONCENTRATE FOR APPLE; 100% FROZEN CONCENTRATED GRAPEFRUIT; 100% FROZEN CONCENTRATED ORANGE

SAFEWAY SCOTCH BUY 100% FROZEN CONCENTRATED ORANGE

FRUIT JUICES: REFRIGERATED

None of the items in this section contain any additives of concern, and all the items appear without an additives-of-concern column.

HOOD 100% PURE ORANGE

KRAFT ORANGE; UNSWEETENED GRAPEFRUIT

MINUTE MAID GRAPEFRUIT; ORANGE

TROPICANA GRAPEFRUIT; ORANGE

SUPERMARKET PRIVATE BRANDS
LUCKY LADY LEE REAL ORANGE

SAFEWAY LUCERNE GRAPEFRUIT; ORANGE

XIV. GRAVIES, SAUCES, & SEASONINGS

GLAZE & MARINADE MIXES

BRANDS	**ADDITIVES-OF-CONCERN** BOLD—CONCERN TO ALL LIGHT—CONCERN TO SOME
ADOLPH'S CHICKEN MARINADE	**MODIFIED FOOD STARCH; PAPRIKA; TURMERIC**
—MARINADE IN MINUTES BARBECUE FLAVOR	**EXTRACTIVES OF PAPRIKA; MODIFIED FOOD STARCH**
GARLIC FLAVOR	**MODIFIED FOOD STARCH**
STEAK SAUCE FLAVOR	**MODIFIED FOOD STARCH; NATURAL SMOKE FLAVOR**
TEMPO HAM GLAZE	NO ADDITIVES OF CONCERN
—CHICKEN GLAZE HERB HONEY; SAVORY ORANGE	NO ADDITIVES OF CONCERN

GRAVIES & GRAVY MIXES

DURKEE *—GRAVY MIX* BROWN; MUSHROOM	**MODIFIED FOOD STARCH;** MONOSODIUM GLUTAMATE

BRANDS	ADDITIVES-OF-CONCERN **BOLD—CONCERN TO ALL** LIGHT—CONCERN TO SOME
DURKEE *GRAVY MIX (Continued)*	
CHICKEN	BUTTERMILK SOLIDS; **MODIFIED FOOD STARCH;** MONOSODIUM GLUTAMATE; **TURMERIC**
FOR TURKEY	**ARTIFICIAL COLOR; MODIFIED FOOD STARCH;** MONOSODIUM GLUTAMATE
—ROASTIN' BAG GRAVY MIX	
FOR CHICKEN; POT ROAST	**MODIFIED FOOD STARCH;** MONOSODIUM GLUTAMATE
FRANCO-AMERICAN	
—GRAVY	
AU JUS; BEEF; BROWN W/ ONIONS; CHICKEN GIBLET	**MODIFIED FOOD STARCH;** MONOSODIUM GLUTAMATE
CHICKEN	MONOSODIUM GLUTAMATE; **OLEORESIN TURMERIC**
FRENCH'S	
GRAVY MAKINS MIX FOR TURKEY	**BHA; BHT; MODIFIED CORN STARCH;** MONOSODIUM GLUTAMATE; **PAPRIKA; SODIUM CASEINATE**
—GRAVY MIX	
BROWN	**LARD; MODIFIED CORN STARCH;** WHEY
MUSHROOM	**MODIFIED CORN STARCH;** MONOSODIUM GLUTAMATE; **SODIUM CASEINATE**

BRANDS	**ADDITIVES-OF-CONCERN** **BOLD—CONCERN TO ALL** LIGHT—CONCERN TO SOME
GRAVY MASTER SEASONING & BROWNING SAUCE	NO ADDITIVES OF CONCERN
HEINZ —*HOME STYLE* *GRAVY* CHICKEN	**MODIFIED FOOD STARCH;** MONOSODIUM GLUTAMATE; **PAPRIKA OLEORESIN; TURMERIC; SODIUM CASEINATE**
ONION	GUM ARABIC; **MODIFIED FOOD STARCH;** MONOSODIUM GLUTAMATE
McCORMICK GRAVY MIX FOR PORK	MILK SOLIDS (BLENDED); MONOSODIUM GLUTAMATE
SUPERMARKET PRIVATE BRANDS A & P —ANN PAGE *GRAVY* *MIX* BROWN	**BUTYLATED HYDROXYANISOLE; MODIFIED STARCH;** MONOSODIUM GLUTAMATE; WHEY SOLIDS
CHICKEN	**MODIFIED STARCH;** MONOSODIUM GLUTAMATE; **TURMERIC**
MUSHROOM	**HYDROGENATED SHORTENING; MODIFIED STARCH**

BRANDS	**ADDITIVES-OF-CONCERN** **BOLD—CONCERN TO ALL** LIGHT—CONCERN TO SOME
SAFEWAY —CROWN COLONY *GRAVY MIX* AU JUS	NO ADDITIVES OF CONCERN
CHICKEN	**ARTIFICIAL COLOR; BHA; MODIFIED WHEAT STARCH;** MONOSODIUM GLUTAMATE; **TURMERIC**
MUSHROOM	**MODIFIED WHEAT STARCH**
ONION	MILK SOLIDS (NONFAT); **MODIFIED WHEAT STARCH**

SAUCE MIXES & SAUCES

By law, at this writing, it is not required of a manufacturer to state whether cheeses contain artificial colors, unless the color is FD & C Yellow No. 5 (Tartrazine). Their presence in sauce mixes and sauces containing cheese therefore remains an uncertainty, unless it is voluntarily declared on the label that artificial colors have been used or have not. For a more detailed explanation of artificial color in cheese, refer to the beginning of the cheese section of "Dairy Products & Substitutes."

BRANDS	ADDITIVES-OF-CONCERN
A.1. STEAK SAUCE	NO ADDITIVES OF CONCERN
CHEF BOYARDEE SPAGHETTI SAUCE W/ GROUND BEEF	**MODIFIED FOOD STARCH**
CHUN KING SOY SAUCE	NO ADDITIVES OF CONCERN

BRANDS	**ADDITIVES-OF-CONCERN** **BOLD—CONCERN TO ALL** LIGHT—CONCERN TO SOME
CROSSE & BLACKWELL SEAFOOD COCKTAIL SAUCE	**MODIFIED FOOD STARCHES; PAPRIKA EXTRACT**
DAWN FRESH MUSHROOM STEAK SAUCE	**ARTIFICIAL COLOR; CARRAGEENAN; MODIFIED CORN STARCH**
DURKEE REDHOT! SAUCE	NO ADDITIVES OF CONCERN
—SAUCE MIX CHEESE	**MODIFIED FOOD STARCH**
HOLLANDAISE	**ARTIFICIAL COLORS** W/ FD & C YELLOW NO. 5; **MODIFIED FOOD STARCH**
SPAGHETTI	ALGIN; **MODIFIED FOOD STARCH;** MONOSODIUM GLUTAMATE; **PAPRIKA**
WHITE	**ARTIFICIAL COLOR; BHA; BHT; MODIFIED FOOD STARCH**
FRENCH'S WORCESTERSHIRE SAUCE; SLOPPY JOE SEASONING MIX	NO ADDITIVES OF CONCERN
HEINZ CHILI SAUCE; WORCESTERSHIRE SAUCE	NO ADDITIVES OF CONCERN

BRANDS	ADDITIVES-OF-CONCERN BOLD—CONCERN TO ALL LIGHT—CONCERN TO SOME
HEINZ *(Continued)*	
57 SAUCE	GUAR GUM; **TURMERIC**
HELLMAN'S BIG H	
BURGER SAUCE	**ARTIFICIAL COLOR;** PROPYLENE GLYCOL ALGINATE
HUNT'S *PRIMA SALSA SPAGHETTI SAUCE EXTRA THICK & ZESTY!*	
MEAT FLAVORED; (PLAIN); W/ MUSHROOMS	**MODIFIED FOOD STARCH;** MONOSODIUM GLUTAMATE
KIKKOMAN	
SOY SAUCE; TERIYAKI	NO ADDITIVES OF CONCERN
KRAFT *BARBECUE SAUCE*	
GARLIC FLAVORED; ONION BITS	CAROB BEAN GUM; **MODIFIED FOOD STARCH; PAPRIKA**
HICKORY SMOKE FLAVORED; (PLAIN)	CAROB BEAN GUM; **HICKORY SMOKE FLAVOR; MODIFIED FOOD STARCH; PAPRIKA**
LEA & PERRINS	
WORCESTERSHIRE SAUCE	NO ADDITIVES OF CONCERN
McCORMICK *SAUCE MIX*	
SPAGHETTI	**ARTIFICIAL COLORS;** MILK SOLIDS (BLENDED); **PAPRIKA**

BRANDS	ADDITIVES-OF-CONCERN BOLD—CONCERN TO ALL LIGHT—CONCERN TO SOME
WHITE	MONOSODIUM GLUTAMATE; **TURMERIC**
McILHENNY CO. TABASCO PEPPER SAUCE	NO ADDITIVES OF CONCERN
OPEN PIT ORIGINAL FLAVOR BARBECUE SAUCE	**ARTIFICIAL COLOR; MODIFIED TAPIOCA STARCH**
PRINCE ITALIAN COOKING SAUCE	NO ADDITIVES OF CONCERN
RAGU ITALIAN COOKING SAUCE; TABLE SAUCE	NO ADDITIVES OF CONCERN
—EXTRA THICK & ZESTY SPAGHETTI SAUCE (PLAIN); W/ MEAT; W/ MUSHROOMS	**MODIFIED FOOD STARCH**
—SPAGHETTI SAUCE (PLAIN); W/ MEAT; W/ MUSHROOMS & ONIONS	NO ADDITIVES OF CONCERN
SUPERMARKET PRIVATE BRANDS	
A & P—ANN PAGE SPAGHETTI SAUCE MIX	**CALCIUM STEARATE; MODIFIED STARCH;** MONOSODIUM GLUTAMATE
TARTAR SAUCE	NO ADDITIVES OF CONCERN

BRANDS	ADDITIVES-OF-CONCERN BOLD—CONCERN TO ALL LIGHT—CONCERN TO SOME
—ANN PAGE *(Continued)*	
—BARBEQUE SAUCE	
PLAIN; W/ MINCED ONIONS	**MODIFIED STARCH**
—SPAGHETTI SAUCE	
FLAVORED W/ MEAT; MARINARA; MEATLESS W/ MUSHROOMS	**MODIFIED STARCH**
LUCKY	
—LADY LEE	
SPAGHETTI SAUCE	
FLAVORED W/ MEAT; W/ MUSHROOMS	NO ADDITIVES OF CONCERN
SAFEWAY	
—CROWN COLONY	
SAUCE MIX	
SPAGHETTI	**PAPRIKA;** WHEY
SPAGHETTI ITALIAN STYLE W/ MUSHROOMS	**PAPRIKA**
—TOWN HOUSE	
CHILI SAUCE	NO ADDITIVES OF CONCERN
STOP & SHOP	
—STOP & SHOP	
CHILI SAUCE	NO ADDITIVES OF CONCERN
TARTAR SAUCE	**TURMERIC**
WINN DIXIE	
—DEEP SOUTH	
REGULAR BARBECUE SAUCE	**SMOKE FLAVOR**

BRANDS	ADDITIVES-OF-CONCERN **BOLD—CONCERN TO ALL** LIGHT—CONCERN TO SOME
—**THRIFTY MAID** *SPAGHETTI SAUCE* (PLAIN); W/ MEAT; W/ MUSHROOMS	**MODIFIED FOOD STARCH; PAPRIKA OLEORESIN**
ITEMS IN HEALTH FOOD STORES	
DE BOLES *SPAGHETTI SAUCE* IMITATION MEAT FLAVORED; MARINARA; MEATLESS; MUSHROOM	NO ADDITIVES OF CONCERN
ENRICO'S *SPAGHETTI SAUCE* NO SALT—ALL PURPOSE; (PLAIN); W/ MUSHROOMS	NO ADDITIVES OF CONCERN
FEATHERWEIGHT CHILI SAUCE	NO ADDITIVES OF CONCERN
HAIN NATURAL BAR-B-QUE SAUCE	ALGIN
SPAGHETTI SAUCE MIX	NO ADDITIVES OF CONCERN
JOHNSON'S SPAGHETTI SAUCE	NO ADDITIVES OF CONCERN
MARK'S NATURAL *SPAGHETTI SAUCE* (PLAIN); W/ ONION & MUSHROOMS	NO ADDITIVES OF CONCERN
SOKEN *SAUCE* BAR-B-QUE; PEANUT	NO ADDITIVES OF CONCERN

BRANDS	ADDITIVES-OF-CONCERN **BOLD—CONCERN TO ALL** LIGHT—CONCERN TO SOME

SEASONING MIXES & SEASONINGS

BRANDS	ADDITIVES-OF-CONCERN
ACCENT	MONOSODIUM GLUTAMATE
ADOLPH'S	
MEAT TENDERIZER SEASONED	**PAPRIKA**
SALT SUBSTITUTE	GLUTAMIC ACID; MONOPOTASSIUM GLUTAMATE
BELL'S SEASONING	NO ADDITIVES OF CONCERN
DURKEE	
BUTTER FLAVORED SALT	**ARTIFICIAL COLOR** W/ FD & C YELLOW NO. 5
IMITATION BACON BITS	**ARTIFICIAL COLORS**
INSTANT MEAT TENDERIZER; SLOPPY JOE SEASONING MIX	MONOSODIUM GLUTAMATE
KNORR SWISS	
AROMAT ALL PURPOSE SEASONING	MONOSODIUM GLUTAMATE; **TURMERIC**
LAWRY'S	
GARLIC SALT	**MODIFIED FOOD STARCH;** MONOSODIUM GLUTAMATE
GARLIC SPREAD	NO ADDITIVES OF CONCERN
SEASONED SALT	MONOSODIUM GLUTAMATE; **PAPRIKA; TURMERIC**

BRANDS	**ADDITIVES-OF-CONCERN** **BOLD—CONCERN TO ALL** LIGHT—CONCERN TO SOME
McCORMICK CINNAMON SUGAR	**MODIFIED CORN STARCH; VEGETABLE OIL**
FANCY PAPRIKA	**PAPRIKA**
GARLIC SALT; ONION SALT	**CALCIUM STEARATE; VEGETABLE GUM**
IMITATION BACON BITS	**BHA; BHT; FD & C RED NO. 3**
IMITATION BUTTER FLAVORED SALT	**COCONUT OIL;** FD & C YELLOW NO. 5; **MODIFIED CORN STARCH; SODIUM CASEINATE**
POULTRY SEASONING	**NUTMEG**
SLOPPY JOE'S SEASONING MIX	**ARTIFICIAL COLORS;** MONOSODIUM GLUTAMATE
MORTON SALT SUBSTITUTE	NO ADDITIVES OF CONCERN
SPICE ISLANDS SEASONING SALT	MONOSODIUM GLUTAMATE
SWEET 'N LOW **—NU SALT** SALT SUBSTITUTE	NO ADDITIVES OF CONCERN
SUPERMARKET PRIVATE BRANDS	
A & P **—ANN PAGE** CELERY SALT	NO ADDITIVES OF CONCERN
GARLIC SALT; ONION SALT	**CALCIUM STEARATE**

BRANDS	**ADDITIVES-OF-CONCERN** BOLD—CONCERN TO ALL LIGHT—CONCERN TO SOME
—ANN PAGE *(Continued)*	
HAMBURGER & MEAT LOAF SEASONING	MONOSODIUM GLUTAMATE
IMITATION BACON BITS	**U.S. CERTIFIED COLOR**
SALAD SEASONING	MONOSODIUM GLUTAMATE; **OLEORESIN PAPRIKA**
—*MEAT TENDERIZER*	
SEASONED; UNSEASONED	**CALCIUM STEARATE**
—*SEASONING MIX*	
CHILI; GROUND BEEF W/ ONIONS	**MODIFIED STARCH**
SLOPPY JOE	ALGIN DERIVATIVE
SAFEWAY	
—CROWN COLONY	
IMITATION BACON BITS	**ARTIFICIAL COLOR**
—*SEASONING MIX*	
BEEF STEW; SLOPPY JOE	MONOSODIUM GLUTAMATE; **PAPRIKA**
CHILI; ENCHILADA	NO ADDITIVES OF CONCERN
TACO	MONOSODIUM GLUTAMATE; **PAPRIKA;** WHEY
STOP & SHOP	
—STOP & SHOP	
GARLIC SALT; ONION SALT	NO ADDITIVES OF CONCERN

BRANDS	**ADDITIVES-OF-CONCERN** **BOLD—CONCERN TO ALL** LIGHT—CONCERN TO SOME
WINN DIXIE —ASTOR	
BARBEQUE SEASONING; LEMON & PEPPER SEASONING	MONOSODIUM GLUTAMATE
FLAVOR SALT; MEAT TENDERIZER	MONOSODIUM GLUTAMATE; **PAPRIKA**
GARLIC SALT; ONION SALT	NO ADDITIVES OF CONCERN
IMITATION BACON BITS	**CERTIFIED COLORS; VEGETABLE OIL**
ITEMS IN HEALTH FOOD STORES	
ATLANTIC MARICULTURE	
ATLANTIC KELP FLAKES; ATLANTIC KELP POWDER	KELP
BIOFORCE *HERB SEASONING SALT*	
HERBA-MARE; TROCO-MARE	KELP
CHICO SAN LIMA SOY SAUCE	NO ADDITIVES OF CONCERN
EREWHON	
NATURAL SHOYU; TAMARI	NO ADDITIVES OF CONCERN
HAIN VEGETABLE SEASONED SALT	DULSE; KELP

BRANDS	ADDITIVES-OF-CONCERN BOLD—CONCERN TO ALL LIGHT—CONCERN TO SOME
INDO FLAVORIZES-SEASONS-TENDERIZES	NO ADDITIVES OF CONCERN
MARUSAN TAMARI	NO ADDITIVES OF CONCERN
PRIDE OF SZEGED HUNGARIAN PAPRIKA	**PAPRIKA**
VEGE-SAL VEGETIZED SEASONER	**PACIFIC SEA GREENS (SEAWEED)**
WESTBRAE TAMARI	NO ADDITIVES OF CONCERN

XV. JELLIES & OTHER SWEET SPREADS; NUT & SEED BUTTERS

FRUIT BUTTERS

None of the items in this section contain any additives of concern, and all the items appear without an additives-of-concern column.

MUSSELMAN'S APPLE

SUPERMARKET PRIVATE BRANDS
LUCKY LADY LEE APPLE

SAFEWAY EMPRESS APPLE

SAFEWAY SCOTCH BUY APPLE

ITEMS IN HEALTH FOOD STORES
ARROWHEAD MILLS APPLE; APRICOT; PEACH; PLUM; RASPBERRY; STRAWBERRY

HAIN APPLE

KIMES APPLE

SORRELL RIDGE DAMSON PLUM

TAP 'N APPLE APPLE

WESTBRAE *BUTTER & HONEY* APPLE APRICOT; CHERRY; MACHU PICCHU FRUIT; PEACH; PLUM; STRAWBERRY

JAMS, JELLIES, MARMALADE, PRESERVES

Although sugars (both sucrose and corn sweeteners) and honey are not treated as additives of concern in this volume when present in moderate amounts as additives, excessive amounts of these or other carbohydrates in the diet can be of health concern. Sugars usually are listed in second and third positions in order of quantity among the ingredients in the jams, jellies, marmalade, and preserves represented here—an indication that sugars are present in considerable amounts.

Most of the items in this section do not contain any additives of concern, and these appear first, without an additives-of-concern column.

The items that do contain additives of concern follow, in the usual style.

CROSSE & BLACKWELL PURE ORANGE MARMALADE

KRAFT
ORANGE MARMALADE
—*JELLY* APPLE; GRAPE; RED CURRANT; STRAWBERRY
—*PRESERVES* APRICOT; RED RASPBERRY; STRAWBERRY

SMUCKERS
SWEET ORANGE MARMALADE
—*JAM* GRAPE; SEEDLESS RED RASPBERRY; STRAWBERRY
—*JELLY* APPLE; GRAPE; STRAWBERRY
—*PRESERVES* APRICOT; BLUEBERRY; CHERRY; PEACH; RED RASPBERRY; STRAWBERRY

WELCH'S GRAPE JAM; GRAPE JELLY; STRAWBERRY PRESERVES

SUPERMARKET PRIVATE BRANDS
A & P ANN PAGE
ORANGE MARMALADE
—*JAM* BLACK RASPBERRY; GRAPE
—*JELLY* APPLE; BLACK RASPBERRY; CRAB APPLE;

(continues)

CURRANT; GRAPE; RED RASPBERRY; STRAWBERRY; WILD ELDERBERRY
—*PRESERVES* BLACKBERRY; BLUEBERRY; CHERRY; DAMSON PLUM; PEACH; PINEAPPLE; RED RASPBERRY; STRAWBERRY

FIRST NATIONAL EDWARDS BLACKBERRY PRESERVES; STRAWBERRY JELLY

FIRST NATIONAL FINAST
ORANGE MARMALADE
—*JELLY* APPLE; CURRANT; GRAPE; RASPBERRY
—*PRESERVES* APRICOT; PEACH; PINEAPPLE; PLUM

LUCKY LADY LEE
ORANGE MARMALADE
—*JAM* BLACKBERRY; CONCORD GRAPE; PLUM
—*JELLY* APPLE; CONCORD GRAPE; CURRANT; MIXED FRUIT; STRAWBERRY
—*PRESERVES* APRICOT; APRICOT-PINEAPPLE; BOYSENBERRY; PEACH; RED RASPBERRY; STRAWBERRY

PUBLIX
ORANGE MARMALADE
—*JAM* GRAPE; RED RASPBERRY
—*JELLY* APPLE; CURRANT; GRAPE; RED RASPBERRY; STRAWBERRY
—*PRESERVES* APRICOT; BLACK RASPBERRY; CHERRY; DAMSON PLUM; PINEAPPLE; RED RASPBERRY; STRAWBERRY

SAFEWAY EMPRESS
—*JAM* CURRANT; PURE BLACKBERRY; PURE BLUEBERRY; PURE STRAWBERRY
—*JELLY* APPLE; BLACKBERRY; BLACK RASPBERRY; BOYSENBERRY; CONCORD GRAPE GUAVA; MIXED-FRUIT; PLUM; RED CURRANT; RED RASPBERRY; STRAWBERRY
—*MARMALADE* CALIFORNIA STYLE SWEET ORANGE; PURE SEVILLE ORANGE
—*PRESERVES* APRICOT; APRICOT-PINEAPPLE;

(continues)

SAFEWAY EMPRESS PRESERVES *(Continued)*

BLACKBERRY; BLACK CHERRY; BLACK RASPBERRY; BLUEBERRY; BOYSENBERRY; PEACH; PEACH-PINEAPPLE; PLUM; RED CHERRY; RED RASPBERRY; STRAWBERRY

SAFEWAY SCOTCH BUY GRAPE JAM; GRAPE JELLY; STRAWBERRY PRESERVES

STOP & SHOP
GRAPE JAM; ORANGE MARMALADE
—*JELLY* APPLE; CRABAPPLE; CURRANT; GRAPE; STRAWBERRY
—*PRESERVES* APRICOT; BLACKBERRY; BLACK RASPBERRY; PEACH; PINEAPPLE; RED RASPBERRY; STRAWBERRY

STOP & SHOP SUN GLORY
ORANGE MARMALADE
—*PRESERVES* RED RASPBERRY; STRAWBERRY

WINN DIXIE DEEP SOUTH
—*JAM* BLACKBERRY; DAMSON PLUM; GRAPE
—*JELLY* APPLE; BLACKBERRY; CURRANT; GRAPE; GUAVA; STRAWBERRY
—*PRESERVES* PEACH; PINEAPPLE; STRAWBERRY

ITEMS IN HEALTH FOOD STORES
ARROWHEAD MILLS
ORANGE MARMALADE
—*JAM* CHERRY; GRAPE

CHARISMA
ORANGE MARMALADE
—*JAM* APRICOT; CHERRY; GRAPE; PEACH; RASPBERRY; STRAWBERRY

HAIN
ORANGE MARMALADE
—*PRESERVES* APRICOT; BLACKBERRY; GRAPE; RASPBERRY; STRAWBERRY

SORRELL RIDGE
—*PURE PRESERVES* RASPBERRY; STRAWBERRY; WILD BLUEBERRY; WILD PARTRIDGEBERRY

TREE OF LIFE
—*PRESERVES* APRICOT; BLACKBERRY; BLUEBERRY; CHERRY; RASPBERRY; STRAWBERRY

WESTBRAE NATURAL
—*UNSWEETENED SPREAD* APRICOT; BOYSENBERRY; RASPBERRY

WM ESCOTT'S
ORANGE MARMALADE
—*PRESERVES* APRICOT-PINEAPPLE; BOYSENBERRY; FIG & DATE; RED RASPBERRY; STRAWBERRY

The following items contain additives of concern.

BRANDS	**ADDITIVES-OF-CONCERN** **BOLD—CONCERN TO ALL** LIGHT—CONCERN TO SOME
KRAFT MINT FLAVORED APPLE JELLY	**ARTIFICIAL COLOR**
RAFFETTO MINT W/ LEAVES	**ARTIFICIAL COLOR**
SUPERMARKET PRIVATE BRANDS	
A & P	
—ANN PAGE MINT FLAVORED IMITATION JELLY	**ARTIFICIAL COLOR; VEGETABLE GUM STABILIZER**
FIRST NATIONAL	
—FINAST MINT FLAVORED IMITATION JELLY	**U.S. CERTIFIED FOOD COLORING**

BRANDS	ADDITIVES-OF-CONCERN BOLD—CONCERN TO ALL LIGHT—CONCERN TO SOME
LUCKY	
—LADY LEE MINT FLAVORED APPLE JELLY	**ARTIFICIAL COLOR**
PUBLIX	
—PUBLIX MINT JELLY	**ARTIFICIAL COLOR**
SAFEWAY	
—EMPRESS MINT FLAVORED APPLE JELLY	**ARTIFICIAL COLORING**
STOP & SHOP	
—STOP & SHOP MINT JELLY	**ARTIFICIAL COLORING**
WINN DIXIE	
—DEEP SOUTH MINT FLAVORED IMITATION JELLY	**U.S. CERTIFIED COLOR**

MARSHMALLOW CREAM, MOLASSES, SYRUPS

Although sugars (both sucrose and corn sweeteners) and honey are not treated as additives of concern in this volume when present in moderate amounts as additives, excessive amounts of these or other carbohydrates can be of health concern. Some of the brands of syrups listed below report their sugar content, ranging from 84% to 99% of total content.

Most of the items in this section do not contain any additives of concern, and these appear first, without an additives-of-concern column.

The items that do contain additives of concern follow, in the usual style.

AUNT JEMIMA SYRUP

BRER RABBIT MOLASSES

GOLDEN GRIDDLE PANCAKE SYRUP

GRANDMA'S *MOLASSES* DARK, RICH ROBUST STYLE; THE FAMOUS "UNSULPHURED"

KARO *SYRUP* DARK CORN; LIGHT CORN

LOG CABIN *SYRUP* COUNTRY KITCHEN; REGULAR

VERMONT MAID SYRUP

SUPERMARKET PRIVATE BRANDS
A & P ANN PAGE *SYRUP* PANCAKE & WAFFLE; REGULAR

FIRST NATIONAL EDWARDS PANCAKE & WAFFLE SYRUP

LUCKY LADY LEE PANCAKE & WAFFLE SYRUP

SAFEWAY SCOTCH BUY WAFFLE & PANCAKE SYRUP

STOP & SHOP PANCAKE & WAFFLE SYRUP

ITEMS IN HEALTH FOOD STORES
CROSBY'S MOLASSES

McCLURE'S MAPLE SYRUP

NIBLACK PURE MALT SYRUP

OLD COLONY PURE MAPLE SYRUP

PLANTATION *MOLASSES* BARBADOS; BLACKSTRAP

WESTBRAE NATURAL MALTED GRAIN SYRUP

YINNIES RICE SYRUP

BRANDS	ADDITIVES-OF-CONCERN **BOLD—CONCERN TO ALL** LIGHT—CONCERN TO SOME

The following items contain additives of concern.

KRAFT MARSHMALLOW CREME	**ARTIFICIAL COLOR**; EGG WHITES
MRS BUTTERWORTH'S THICK 'N RICH SYRUP	ALGIN DERIVATIVE
SAFEWAY EMPRESS *SYRUP* BOYSENBERRY	**CALCIUM CARRAGEENAN**
RASPBERRY; STRAWBERRY	**ARTIFICIAL COLORING; CALCIUM CARRAGEENAN**

PEANUT BUTTER & OTHER NUT & SEED BUTTERS

None of the items in this section contain any additives of concern, and all the items appear without an additives-of-concern column.

JIF *PEANUT BUTTER* CREAMY; EXTRA CRUNCHY

PETER PAN *PEANUT BUTTER* CREAMY; CRUNCHY

SKIPPY *PEANUT BUTTER* CREAMY; SUPER CHUNK

SMUCKER'S NATURAL PEANUT BUTTER

SUPERMARKET PRIVATE BRANDS
A & P ANN PAGE *PEANUT BUTTER* CREAMY SMOOTH; KRUNCHY

FIRST NATIONAL EDWARDS OLD FASHIONED PEANUT BUTTER

FIRST NATIONAL EDWARDS-FINAST CRUNCHY PEANUT BUTTER

LUCKY LADY LEE *PEANUT BUTTER* CHUNK STYLE; CHUNKY; CREAMY

PUBLIX CRUNCHY PEANUT BUTTER

STOP & SHOP *PEANUT BUTTER* CHUNK; CREAMY

WINN DIXIE DEEP SOUTH SMOOTH PEANUT BUTTER

ITEMS IN HEALTH FOOD STORES

ARROWHEAD MILLS *DEAF SMITH PEANUT BUTTER* CRUNCHY; OLD FASHIONED

EREWHON *BUTTER* ALMOND; CASHEW; CREAMY & SALTED PEANUT; SESAME; SUNFLOWER

XVI. LOW-CALORIE BEVERAGES & FOODS

LOW-CALORIE BAKED GOODS (COOKIES & PASTRIES)

BRANDS	ADDITIVES-OF-CONCERN BOLD—CONCERN TO ALL LIGHT—CONCERN TO SOME
AMUROL *DIETETIC/LOW SODIUM* FILLED WAFERS	**ARTIFICIAL COLORS; (COCONUT OIL)***
LEMON COOKIES; VANILLA COOKIES	**CERTIFIED COLOR**
OATMEAL RAISIN COOKIES	NO ADDITIVES OF CONCERN
ESTEE *DIETETIC* ASSORTED FILLED WAFERS	**ARTIFICIAL COLORS; (COCONUT, PALM KERNEL OILS);*** WHEY
CHOCOLATE CHIP COOKIES; VANILLA THINS	**ARTIFICIAL COLOR;** WHEY
COCONUT COOKIES	**BHA**
FUDGE COOKIES	**ARTIFICIAL COLOR; BHA**
LEMON SANDWICH COOKIES	**ARTIFICIAL COLOR; (COCONUT OIL);*** GLUTEN FLOUR

*Blend may contain one or more of these saturated oils.

BRANDS	ADDITIVES-OF-CONCERN **BOLD—CONCERN TO ALL** LIGHT—CONCERN TO SOME
OATMEAL RAISIN COOKIES	NO ADDITIVES OF CONCERN
STELLA D'ORO *DIETETIC* APPLE PASTRY; PEACH-APRICOT PASTRY	**ARTIFICIAL COLOR;** GUAR & LOCUST BEAN GUMS; **MACE**
COCONUT COOKIES; EGG BISCUITS; LOVE COOKIES	NO ADDITIVES OF CONCERN
KICHEL	**ARTIFICIAL COLOR**

LOW-CALORIE BEVERAGE MIXES & BEVERAGES

ALBA *—'66 HOT COCOA MIX* CHOCOLATE & MARSHMALLOW; MILK CHOCOLATE	**SODIUM SACCHARIN;** WHEY SOLIDS (DAIRY)
—'77 FIT 'N FROSTY CHOCOLATE FLAVOR	**SODIUM SACCHARIN;** WHEY SOLIDS (DAIRY)
STRAWBERRY	**ARTIFICIAL COLOR; SODIUM SACCHARIN;** WHEY SOLIDS (DAIRY)

BRANDS	**ADDITIVES-OF-CONCERN** **BOLD—CONCERN TO ALL** LIGHT—CONCERN TO SOME
BARRELHEAD SUGAR FREE ROOT BEER	ACACIA GUM; **SODIUM SACCHARIN**
CANADA DRY *DIET* GINGER ALE	**SODIUM SACCHARIN**
ORANGE	ACACIA GUM; **ARTIFICIAL COLORING; ESTER GUM; SODIUM SACCHARIN**
TONIC WATER	QUININE; **SODIUM SACCHARIN**
COTT *SUGAR FREE* COLA	CAFFEINE; **SACCHARIN**
ORANGE; PINK GRAPEFRUIT	ACACIA GUM; **ARTIFICIAL COLOR; BROMINATED VEGETABLE OIL; GLYCERYL ABIETATE; SACCHARIN**
ROOT BEER	ACACIA GUM; **SACCHARIN**
DR PEPPER SUGAR FREE	CAFFEINE; **SODIUM SACCHARIN**
FRESCA SUGAR FREE	**ARTIFICIAL COLOR; BROMINATED VEGETABLE OIL; GLYCEROL ESTER OF WOOD ROSIN;** GUM ARABIC; **SODIUM SACCHARIN**
HAWAIIAN PUNCH LOW SUGAR FRUIT PUNCH	**ARTIFICIAL COLOR; SODIUM SACCHARIN**

BRANDS	ADDITIVES-OF-CONCERN BOLD—CONCERN TO ALL LIGHT—CONCERN TO SOME
LIPTON ICED TEA LEMON FLAVORED SUGAR FREE; ICED TEA MIX LOW CALORIE LEMON FLAVORED	**SODIUM SACCHARIN**
MOXIE SUGAR FREE	CAFFEINE; **SODIUM SACCHARIN**
NESTEA LIGHT ICED TEA MIX	NO ADDITIVES OF CONCERN
LOW CALORIE ICED TEA MIX	GUM ARABIC; **SODIUM SACCHARIN**
OCEAN SPRAY *LOW CALORIE* CRANAPPLE; CRANBERRY JUICE COCKTAIL	**CALCIUM SACCHARIN**
OVALTINE REDUCED CALORIE HOT COCOA MIX	**ARTIFICIAL COLOR; CARRAGEENAN; (COCONUT OIL);* FERRIC SODIUM PYROPHOSPHATE; SODIUM CASEINATE;** WHEY
PEPSI-COLA DIET	CAFFEINE; **SODIUM SACCHARIN**
PEPSI LIGHT	CAFFEINE; **SODIUM SACCHARIN**

*Blend may contain this saturated oil.

BRANDS	ADDITIVES-OF-CONCERN **BOLD—CONCERN TO ALL** LIGHT—CONCERN TO SOME
SALADA LIGHT ICED TEA MIX LEMON FLAVOR	**BHA**
SCHWEPPES DIET GINGER ALE	**SODIUM SACCHARIN**
7 UP SUGAR FREE	**SODIUM SACCHARIN**
SHASTA *DIET* BLACK CHERRY; GRAPE	**ARTIFICIAL COLOR;** GUM ARABIC; **SODIUM SACCHARIN**
COLA	**BROMINATED VEGETABLE OIL;** CAFFEINE; GUM ARABIC; **SODIUM SACCHARIN**
GINGER ALE; LEMON LIME	**SODIUM SACCHARIN**
ORANGE	**ARTIFICIAL COLOR; BROMINATED VEGETABLE OIL; GLYCEROL ESTER OF WOOD ROSIN;** GUM ARABIC; **SODIUM SACCHARIN**
SWEET 'N LOW *LO-CALORIE SOFT DRINK MIX* CHERRY; GRAPE	**CERTIFIED COLOR; SODIUM SACCHARIN**
TAB SUGAR FREE GINGER ALE	**SODIUM SACCHARIN**

BRANDS	ADDITIVES-OF-CONCERN **BOLD—CONCERN TO ALL** LIGHT—CONCERN TO SOME
REGULAR	CAFFEINE; **SODIUM SACCHARIN**
ROOT BEER	GUM ARABIC; **SODIUM SACCHARIN**
TROPI-CAL-LO ORANGE DRINK	**ARTIFICIAL COLOR; MODIFIED STARCH; SODIUM SACCHARIN; VEGETABLE GUMS**
SUPERMARKET PRIVATE BRANDS	
A & P—YUKON *SUGAR FREE DIET* COLA	CAFFEINE; **SACCHARIN**
GINGER ALE; ROOT BEER	**SODIUM SACCHARIN**
ORANGE SODA	**ARTIFICIAL COLOR; BROMINATED VEGETABLE OIL; GLYCERYL ABIETATE;** GUM ARABIC; **SODIUM SACCHARIN**
FIRST NATIONAL —FINAST *SUGAR FREE* COLA	CAFFEINE; **SODIUM SACCHARIN**
GINGER ALE; OLD FASHIONED ROOT BEER	**SODIUM SACCHARIN**
ORANGE SODA	**ESTER GUM;** GUM ARABIC; **SODIUM SACCHARIN; U.S. CERTIFIED COLOR**

BRANDS	ADDITIVES-OF-CONCERN BOLD—CONCERN TO ALL LIGHT—CONCERN TO SOME
LUCKY —LADY LEE *SUGAR FREE DIET* CREME SODA	**SODIUM SACCHARIN**
GRAPE SODA	**ARTIFICIAL COLOR; SODIUM SACCHARIN; VEGETABLE GUM**
ORANGE SODA	ACACIA GUM; **ARTIFICIAL COLOR; GLYCERYL ABIETATE; SODIUM SACCHARIN**
PUBLIX —PIX *DIET* BLACK CHERRY SODA; ORANGE SODA; ROOT BEER	**ARTIFICIAL COLOR; SODIUM SACCHARIN**
COLA; CREAM SODA	**SODIUM SACCHARIN**
SAFEWAY —CRAGMONT *SUGAR FREE DIET* BLACK CHERRY	**ARTIFICIAL COLOR;** GUM ARABIC; **SODIUM SACCHARIN**
COLA; ROOT BEER	GUM ARABIC; **SODIUM SACCHARIN**
CREAM; GINGER ALE; LEMON LIME	**SODIUM SACCHARIN**

BRANDS	ADDITIVES-OF-CONCERN BOLD—CONCERN TO ALL LIGHT—CONCERN TO SOME
ORANGE	**ARTIFICIAL COLOR; BROMINATED VEGETABLE OIL; GLYCERYL ABIETATE;** GUM ARABIC; **SODIUM SACCHARIN**
TONIC MIX	QUININE HYDROCHLORIDE; **SODIUM SACCHARIN**
STOP & SHOP —SUN GLORY *SUGAR FREE*	
CITRUS	ACACIA GUM; **ARTIFICIAL COLOR; BROMINATED VEGETABLE OIL; GLYCERYL ABIETATE; SACCHARIN**
COLA	CAFFEINE; **SACCHARIN**
GINGER	**SODIUM SACCHARIN**
RASPBERRY	**ARTIFICIAL COLOR; SACCHARIN**
ROOT BEER	ACACIA GUM; **SACCHARIN**
WINN DIXIE —CHEK *SUGAR FREE*	
COLA	CAFFEINE; **SODIUM SACCHARIN**
FRESHY	**ARTIFICIAL COLOR; BROMINATED VEGETABLE OIL; GLYCERYL ABIETATE; MODIFIED FOOD STARCH; SODIUM SACCHARIN**

BRANDS	ADDITIVES-OF-CONCERN **BOLD—CONCERN TO ALL** LIGHT—CONCERN TO SOME
WINN DIXIE—CHEK *SUGAR FREE (Continued)*	
GINGER ALE; ROOT BEER	**SODIUM SACCHARIN**

LOW-CALORIE CANNED FRUIT

DIET DELIGHT	
APPLE SAUCE; APRICOTS; BARTLETT PEARS PACKED IN JUICE; BARTLETT PEARS PACKED IN WATER; CHERRIES; CLING PEACHES PACKED IN JUICE; CLING PEACHES PACKED IN WATER; ELBERTA PEACHES; GRAPEFRUIT SECTIONS; MANDARIN ORANGE SECTIONS; PINEAPPLE TIDBITS; PURPLE PLUMS	NO ADDITIVES OF CONCERN
FRUIT COCKTAIL; FRUITS FOR SALAD	CHERRIES **ARTIFICIALLY COLORED RED**

BRANDS	ADDITIVES-OF-CONCERN **BOLD—CONCERN TO ALL** LIGHT—CONCERN TO SOME

LOW-CALORIE DESSERT TOPPINGS, FROZEN DIETARY DAIRY DESSERTS,* GELATIN DESSERTS, PUDDING

BRANDS	ADDITIVES-OF-CONCERN
BORDEN *FROZEN DIETARY DAIRY DESSERT*	
CHOCOLATE	**CARRAGEENAN**
VANILLA	**ARTIFICIAL COLOR; CARRAGEENAN**
DIA-MEL	
CHOCOLATE FLAVOR INSTANT PUDDING	**CARRAGEENAN; COLOR; SODIUM SACCHARIN**
RASPBERRY GELATIN DESSERT	**CALCIUM SACCHARIN; U.S. CERTIFIED COLOR**
DIET DELIGHT	
CHOCOLATE TOPPING	**MODIFIED CORN STARCH**
D-ZERTA	
LOW CALORIE WHIPPED TOPPING MIX	**ARTIFICIAL COLOR; BHA; COCONUT & HYDROGENATED SOYBEAN OILS; SODIUM CASEINATE; SODIUM SACCHARIN;** WHEY SOLIDS

*Declaration by the manufacturer of the presence of artificial color in some dairy products, including frozen desserts, is not required by law except for FD & C Yellow No. 5 (Tartrazine). The presence or absence of other artificial colors in low-calorie frozen dairy desserts, therefore, remains uncertain unless it is declared on the label.

BRANDS	ADDITIVES-OF-CONCERN **BOLD—CONCERN TO ALL** LIGHT—CONCERN TO SOME
D-ZERTA *(Continued)*	
—LOW CALORIE GELATIN DESSERT	
CHERRY; STRAWBERRY	**ARTIFICIAL COLOR; SODIUM SACCHARIN**
LEMON; ORANGE	**ARTIFICIAL COLOR; BHA; SODIUM SACCHARIN**
—LOW CALORIE PUDDING	
BUTTERSCOTCH; VANILLA	**ARTIFICIAL COLOR; BHA; CALCIUM CARRAGEENAN; SODIUM SACCHARIN;** WHEY SOLIDS
CHOCOLATE	**CALCIUM CARRAGEENAN; SODIUM SACCHARIN**
ESKIMO DIETETIC BAR	GUAR GUM; MILK SOLIDS (NONFAT)
ESTEE	
—GEL	
CHERRY; STRAWBERRY	**ARTIFICIAL COLOR;** LOCUST BEAN GUM; **POTASSIUM CARRAGEENAN**
—PUDDING	
CHOCOLATE	**CALCIUM CARRAGEENAN; MODIFIED CORN STARCH**
VANILLA	**ARTIFICIAL COLOR; CALCIUM CARRAGEENAN;** EGG ALBUMIN; **MODIFIED CORN STARCH**
FEATHERWEIGHT WHIPPED TOPPING	NO ADDITIVES OF CONCERN

BRANDS	ADDITIVES-OF-CONCERN **BOLD—CONCERN TO ALL** LIGHT—CONCERN TO SOME
—*GELATIN DESSERT* CHERRY; LEMON; STRAWBERRY	**ARTIFICIAL COLOR; CALCIUM SACCHARIN**
—*PUDDING* BUTTERSCOTCH; CHOCOLATE; VANILLA	**ARTIFICIAL COLOR; CALCIUM SACCHARIN; CARRAGEENAN; MODIFIED CORN STARCH**
HOWARD JOHNSON'S COFFEE FROZEN DIETARY DAIRY DESSERT	GUAR GUM; GUM ARABIC; LOCUST BEAN GUM
SWEET 'N LOW WHITE FROSTING MIX	**MODIFIED FOOD STARCH**
THIN N' CREAMIE *DIETARY FROZEN DESSERT* BUTTER ALMOND; CHOCOLATE MINT; CREAMY ORANGE; VANILLA FUDGE	**CARRAGEENAN;** LOCUST BEAN GUM
WEIGHT WATCHERS CHOCOLATE FROZEN DIETARY DAIRY DESSERT	**ARTIFICIAL COLOR; CARRAGEENAN**
SUPERMARKET PRIVATE BRANDS **SAFEWAY** **—LUCERNE** *DIETETIC ICE CREAM* CHOCOLATE	**CALCIUM CARRAGEENAN;** GUAR GUM; LOCUST BEAN GUM

BRANDS	ADDITIVES-OF-CONCERN **BOLD—CONCERN TO ALL** LIGHT—CONCERN TO SOME
SAFEWAY—LUCERNE *DIETETIC (Continued)*	
VANILLA	**ARTIFICIAL COLOR; CALCIUM CARRAGEENAN;** GUAR GUM; LOCUST BEAN GUM

LOW-CALORIE DIET MEALS (FROZEN DINNERS, FROZEN ONE-COURSE DISHES, LIQUID MEALS, MEAL BARS, POWDERED MIXES)

By law, at this writing, it is not required of a manufacturer to state whether cheeses contain artificial colors, unless the color is FD & C Yellow No. 5 (Tartrazine). Their presence in low-calorie diet meals containing cheese therefore remains an uncertainty, unless it is voluntarily declared on the label that artificial colors have been used or have not. For a more detailed explanation of artificial color in cheese, refer to the beginning of the cheese section of "Dairy Products & Substitutes."

BRANDS	ADDITIVES-OF-CONCERN
CARNATION SLENDER	
—*DIET MEAL BARS*	
CHOCOLATE; CHOCOLATE PEANUT BUTTER; VANILLA	**ARTIFICIAL COLOR; CALCIUM CASEINATE;** EGG WHITES; WHEY PROTEIN CONCENTRATE
—*LIQUID*	
CHOCOLATE FLAVOR; CHOCOLATE FUDGE FLAVOR; COFFEE FLAVOR	**ARTIFICIAL COLOR** OR **COLORS; CALCIUM CARRAGEENAN; FERRIC ORTHOPHOSPHATE; SODIUM CASEINATE**
—*POWDER MIX*	
CHOCOLATE; DUTCH CHOCOLATE	**AMMONIUM CARRAGEENAN; ARTIFICIAL COLOR**

BRANDS	**ADDITIVES-OF-CONCERN** **BOLD—CONCERN TO ALL** LIGHT—CONCERN TO SOME
COFFEE; FRENCH VANILLA	**AMMONIUM CARRAGEENAN**
WILD STRAWBERRY	**AMMONIUM CARRAGEENAN; ARTIFICIAL COLOR; BHA**
PILLSBURY FIGURINES	
CHOCOLATE	**COCONUT & PALM KERNEL OILS;** MILK PROTEIN; GLUTEN (VITAL WHEAT)
CHOCOLATE CARAMEL	**BHA; COCONUT & PALM KERNEL OILS;** GLUTEN (VITAL WHEAT); MILK PROTEIN
VANILLA	**ARTIFICIAL COLOR; BHA; COCONUT & PALM KERNEL OILS;** GLUTEN (VITAL WHEAT); MILK PROTEIN
WEIGHT WATCHERS *—FROZEN DINNERS*	
CHICKEN LIVERS & ONIONS	CAROB BEAN GUM; GUAR GUM; GUM TRAGACANTH; **MODIFIED FOOD STARCH; NUTMEG**
FLOUNDER	CAROB BEAN GUM; GUAR GUM; GUM TRAGACANTH; **PAPRIKA**
HADDOCK; VEAL PARMIGIANA & ZUCCHINI IN SAUCE	CAROB BEAN GUM; GUAR GUM; GUM TRAGACANTH

BRANDS	ADDITIVES-OF-CONCERN **BOLD—CONCERN TO ALL** LIGHT—CONCERN TO SOME
WEIGHT WATCHERS *(Continued)* *—FROZEN* *ONE-COURSE DISHES* CHEESE & TOMATO PIES	NO ADDITIVES OF CONCERN
CHICKEN CREOLE	**VEGETABLE STABILIZERS**
EGGPLANT PARMIGIANA; ZITI MACARONI W/ VEAL, CHEESE & SAUCE	CAROB BEAN GUM; GUAR GUM; GUM TRAGACANTH
VEAL STUFFED PEPPER	CAROB BEAN GUM; GUAR GUM; GUM TRAGACANTH; WHEY

LOW-CALORIE JAMS, JELLIES, PRESERVES, SYRUPS

BRANDS	ADDITIVES-OF-CONCERN
CARY'S LOW CALORIE SYRUP	MONOSODIUM GLUTAMATE; **SODIUM SACCHARIN**
DIET DELIGHT *LOW CALORIE* PANCAKE SYRUP	NO ADDITIVES OF CONCERN
—JAM BLACKBERRY; STRAWBERRY	**ARTIFICIAL COLOR; CARRAGEENAN**
FEATHERWEIGHT *LOW CALORIE IMITATION* CHERRY JELLY; GRAPE JELLY	**CARRAGEENAN; SEAWEED EXTRACT**
STRAWBERRY JELLY; STRAWBERRY PRESERVES	**ARTIFICIAL COLOR; CARRAGEENAN; SEAWEED EXTRACT**

BRANDS	ADDITIVES-OF-CONCERN BOLD—CONCERN TO ALL LIGHT—CONCERN TO SOME
SMUCKER'S SLENDERELLA *LOW CALORIE IMITATION* ORANGE MARMALADE; STRAWBERRY JAM	**ARTIFICIAL COLOR; CARRAGEENAN**
—JELLY BLACKBERRY; CHERRY; GRAPE	**CARRAGEENAN**

LOW-CALORIE MAYONNAISE & SALAD DRESSINGS

By law, at this writing, it is not required of a manufacturer to state whether cheeses contain artificial colors, unless the color is FD & C Yellow No. 5 (Tartrazine). Their presence in low-calorie mayonnaise and salad dressings containing cheese therefore remains an uncertainty, unless it is voluntarily declared on the label that artificial colors have been used or have not. For a more detailed explanation of artificial color in cheese, refer to the beginning of the cheese section of "Dairy Products & Substitutes."

BRANDS	ADDITIVES-OF-CONCERN
DIA-MEL MAYONNAISE	**VEGETABLE OIL**
DIET DELIGHT MAY-O-LITE	ALGIN DERIVATIVES; **MODIFIED CORN STARCH; PAPRIKA**
FEATHERWEIGHT *LOW CALORIE DRESSING* CREAMY ITALIAN	**BHA; BHT**
THOUSAND ISLAND	ALGIN DERIVATIVE; **BHA; BHT; MODIFIED CORN STARCH; SODIUM SACCHARIN; VEGETABLE GUM**

BRANDS	ADDITIVES-OF-CONCERN BOLD—CONCERN TO ALL LIGHT—CONCERN TO SOME
FRENCHETTE *LOW CALORIE DRESSING*	
ITALIAN	**ARTIFICIAL COLORING; BHA; BHT;** GUM TRAGACANTH
THOUSAND ISLAND	**BHA; BHT;** GUM TRAGACANTH; **MODIFIED FOOD STARCH; OLEORESIN OF PAPRIKA**
KRAFT *LOW CALORIE DRESSING*	
BLUE CHEESE	**MODIFIED FOOD STARCH**
CREAMY CUCUMBER	PROPYLENE GLYCOL ALGINATE
RUSSIAN	**ARTIFICIAL COLOR; OLEORESIN PAPRIKA;** PROPYLENE GLYCOL ALGINATE
ZESTY ITALIAN	**ARTIFICIAL COLOR**
WEIGHT WATCHERS	
CREAMY ITALIAN DRESSING	**MODIFIED FOOD STARCH**
IMITATION MAYONNAISE	**MODIFIED FOOD STARCH; NATURAL COLOR**
THOUSAND ISLAND DRESSING	**MODIFIED FOOD STARCH; NATURAL COLOR; PAPRIKA**

BRANDS	ADDITIVES-OF-CONCERN **BOLD—CONCERN TO ALL** LIGHT—CONCERN TO SOME
WISH-BONE *LOW CALORIE DRESSING* CHUNKY BLUE CHEESE	ALGIN DERIVATIVE; **VEGETABLE GUM**
CREAMY ITALIAN; THOUSAND ISLAND	ALGIN DERIVATIVE
FRENCH STYLE	**OLEORESIN PAPRIKA**
RUSSIAN	ALGIN DERIVATIVE; **ARTIFICIAL COLOR**
SUPERMARKET PRIVATE BRANDS	
A & P	
—ANN PAGE *LOW CALORIE DRESSING* BLUE CHEESE; IMITATION FRENCH STYLE	ALGIN DERIVATIVE
THOUSAND ISLAND	ALGIN DERIVATIVE; **ARTIFICIAL COLOR**
SAFEWAY	
—NUMADE *REDUCED CALORIE DRESSING* ITALIAN	**ARTIFICIAL COLOR**
1000 ISLAND DRESSING	**ARTIFICIAL COLOR;** PROPYLENE GLYCOL ALGINATE

LOW-CALORIE SUGAR SUBSTITUTES

DIA-MEL SUGAR-LIKE	**SACCHARIN**
SUCARYL	**SODIUM SACCHARIN**

BRANDS	ADDITIVES-OF-CONCERN BOLD—CONCERN TO ALL LIGHT—CONCERN TO SOME
SWAN	
SWEETEST EFFERVESCENT SACCHARIN	**SACCHARIN**
SWEET 'N LOW	
REGULAR	**SACCHARIN**
ZERO-CAL	**CALCIUM SACCHARIN**
WEIGHT WATCHERS	
SWEET'NER	**SODIUM SACCHARIN**

XVII. MEAT & POULTRY & SUBSTITUTES

CANNED MEAT & POULTRY & SUBSTITUTES

BRANDS	ADDITIVES-OF-CONCERN BOLD—CONCERN TO ALL LIGHT—CONCERN TO SOME
ARMOUR	
CORNED BEEF HASH	GUM ARABIC; **SODIUM NITRITE**
POTTED MEAT FOOD PRODUCT; VIENNA SAUSAGE	**SODIUM NITRITE**
TREET	**COLORING; SMOKE FLAVORING; SODIUM NITRITE**
CUDAHY BAR S HAM	**SODIUM NITRITE**
HORMEL	
CHOPPED HAM	**SODIUM NITRATE; SODIUM NITRITE**
HAM PATTIES	**HICKORY SMOKE FLAVORING; SODIUM NITRITE**
—DINTY MOORE	
BEEF STEW	**MODIFIED FOOD STARCH**
MEATBALL STEW	**MODIFIED FOOD STARCH;** MONOSODIUM GLUTAMATE

BRANDS	ADDITIVES-OF-CONCERN **BOLD—CONCERN TO ALL** LIGHT—CONCERN TO SOME
HORMEL *(Continued)*	
—*TENDER CHUNK* CHICKEN; TURKEY	MONOSODIUM GLUTAMATE
HAM	**SMOKE FLAVORING; SODIUM NITRITE**
KRAKUS POLISH HAM	**SODIUM NITRITE**
LIBBY'S	
CORNED BEEF; CORNED BEEF HASH	**SODIUM NITRITE**
SLOPPY JOE	**MODIFIED CORNSTARCH; PAPRIKA; TURMERIC**
MARY KITCHEN	
CORNED BEEF HASH	**SODIUM NITRITE**
ROAST BEEF HASH	NO ADDITIVES OF CONCERN
PLUMROSE DANISH HAM	**SODIUM NITRITE**
SELL'S LIVER PATÉ	NO ADDITIVES OF CONCERN
SPAM	
DEVILED LUNCHEON MEAT; REGULAR	**SODIUM NITRITE**
SWANSON	
BEEF STEW MAIN DISH; BONED CHICKEN; BONED TURKEY	NO ADDITIVES OF CONCERN
CHICKEN STEW MAIN DISH; CHUNK CHICKEN	MONOSODIUM GLUTAMATE

BRANDS	ADDITIVES-OF-CONCERN **BOLD—CONCERN TO ALL** LIGHT—CONCERN TO SOME
SWIFT PREMIUM	
CORNED BEEF	**SODIUM NITRITE**
UNDERWOOD	
CHUNKY CHICKEN SPREAD	**MODIFIED FOOD STARCH;** MONOSODIUM GLUTAMATE; **TURMERIC (& EXTRACTIVES OF)**
CORNED BEEF SPREAD; DEVILED HAM	**SODIUM NITRITE**
LIVERWURST SPREAD	**PORK FAT (COOKED)**
SUPERMARKET PRIVATE BRANDS	
SAFEWAY	
—SAFEWAY HAM PATTIES	**SMOKE FLAVORING; SODIUM NITRITE**
—TOWN HOUSE	
VIENNA SAUSAGE	**SODIUM NITRITE**
WINN DIXIE	
—THRIFTY MAID	
VIENNA SAUSAGE	**SODIUM NITRITE**
ITEMS IN HEALTH FOOD STORES	
FEATHERWEIGHT	
UNSALTED BONED CHICKEN	NO ADDITIVES OF CONCERN
SOVEX VEGE-PAT	NO ADDITIVES OF CONCERN
WORTHINGTON	
CHOPLETS	MONOSODIUM GLUTAMATE
SANDWICH SPREAD	CAROB BEAN & GUAR GUMS; **MODIFIED CORN STARCH**

BRANDS	ADDITIVES-OF-CONCERN **BOLD—CONCERN TO ALL** LIGHT—CONCERN TO SOME
WORTHINGTON *(Continued)*	
SOYAMEAT BEEF FLAVOR	**ARTIFICIAL COLOR;** EGG WHITES; GLUTEN (WHEAT); MONOSODIUM GLUTAMATE
SOYAMEAT CHICKEN FLAVOR	**ARTIFICIAL COLOR; CARRAGEENAN;** EGG WHITE SOLIDS; **MODIFIED CORN STARCH;** MONOSODIUM GLUTAMATE
SUPER-LINKS	**ARTIFICIAL COLORS;** EGG WHITES; GLUTEN (WHEAT); **MODIFIED CORN STARCH; NATURAL SMOKE FLAVOR; PAPRIKA**
209 SMOKED TURKEY FLAVOR	EGG WHITES; GLUTEN (WHEAT); MONOSODIUM GLUTAMATE; **NATURAL SMOKE FLAVOR**
VEJA-LINKS	**ARTIFICIAL COLORS; CARRAGEENAN;** EGG WHITES; GLUTEN (WHEAT); MONOSODIUM GLUTAMATE; **NATURAL SMOKE FLAVOR; PAPRIKA;** SODIUM ALGINATE

FROZEN MEAT & POULTRY & SUBSTITUTES

JONES	
COUNTRY PORK SAUSAGE; LITTLE PORK SAUSAGES; MINUTE BREAKFAST LINKS	NO ADDITIVES OF CONCERN

BRANDS	ADDITIVES-OF-CONCERN **BOLD—CONCERN TO ALL** LIGHT—CONCERN TO SOME
LOVITT'S SHAVED STEAK	NO ADDITIVES OF CONCERN
MAID-RITE	
BEEF PEPPER STEAKS	MONOSODIUM GLUTAMATE
BREADED VEAL STEAKS	MONOSODIUM GLUTAMATE; **PAPRIKA;** WHEY (DRIED)
VEAL STEAKS	NO ADDITIVES OF CONCERN
MORNINGSTAR FARMS	
BREAKFAST LINKS	EGG WHITES; GLUTEN (WHEAT); GUAR GUM; **MODIFIED CORN STARCH;** MONOSODIUM GLUTAMATE; **SODIUM CASEINATE**
BREAKFAST STRIPS	**ARTIFICIAL COLOR;** CAROB BEAN & GUAR GUMS; **CARRAGEENAN;** EGG WHITES; **MODIFIED CORN STARCH;** MONOSODIUM GLUTAMATE
SWIFT PREMIUM	
BROWN 'N SERVE SAUSAGE	
BACON 'N SAUSAGE	**BHA; BHT; SMOKE FLAVORING; SODIUM NITRITE**
BEEF; THE ORIGINAL	**BHA; BHT;** MONOSODIUM GLUTAMATE
HICKORY SMOKE FLAVORED	**BHA; BHT; HICKORY SMOKE FLAVORING;** MONOSODIUM GLUTAMATE

BRANDS	ADDITIVES-OF-CONCERN **BOLD—CONCERN TO ALL** LIGHT—CONCERN TO SOME
SWIFT PREMIUM *(Continued)*	
MAPLE FLAVORED	**BHA; BHT**
TABLE TREAT	
STEAK-UMM ALL BEEF SANDWICH STEAKS	NO ADDITIVES OF CONCERN
SUPERMARKET PRIVATE BRANDS	
SAFEWAY	
—MANOR HOUSE	
FRIED CHICKEN	
BREAST PORTIONS; FULLY COOKED ASSORTED PIECES; WING PORTIONS	MONOSODIUM GLUTAMATE
ITEMS IN HEALTH FOOD STORES	
HEALTH IS WEALTH	
BREADED TURKEY PATTIE; CHICK PUPS; TURKEY BREAST ROLL	NO ADDITIVES OF CONCERN
HEALTH VALLEY	
SLICED BREAKFAST BEEF; SLICED BREAKFAST PORK; WHOLE FRYING CHICKEN	NO ADDITIVES OF CONCERN
SMOKED DRIED BEEF	**SMOKED***

*Although "smoked" does not refer to a specific additive, it represents a process utilizing wood smoke, as "smoke flavoring" does, and therefore may contain some cancer-causing benzopyrene chemicals. For this reason, when a food or any of its constituents has been smoked, this has been noted in the additives-of-concern column.

BRANDS	ADDITIVES-OF-CONCERN BOLD—CONCERN TO ALL LIGHT—CONCERN TO SOME
—*NATURAL SPICE UNCURED COOKED SAUSAGE* BEEF WIENER FLAVORING; CHICKEN BOLOGNA FLAVORING; OUR SUPREME BRAND BEEF WIENER FLAVORING; TURKEY WIENER FLAVORING	**PAPRIKA**
SHILOH FARMS *SAUSAGE* BREAKFAST; UNCURED COOKED	NO ADDITIVES OF CONCERN
WORTHINGTON DINNER ROAST	**CALCIUM CASEINATE; CARRAGEENAN;** EGG WHITES; GLUTEN (WHEAT); **MODIFIED CORN STARCH; SODIUM CASEINATE; TURMERIC**
FILLETS	EGG WHITES; **MODIFIED CORN STARCH; MODIFIED TAPIOCA STARCH;** MONOSODIUM GLUTAMATE
FRI PATS	EGG WHITES; **MODIFIED TAPIOCA STARCH; SODIUM CASEINATE**
LUNCHEON SLICES SMOKED TURKEY-LIKE FLAVOR	EGG WHITES; GLUTEN (WHEAT); MONOSODIUM GLUTAMATE; **NATURAL SMOKE FLAVOR**

BRANDS	ADDITIVES-OF-CONCERN **BOLD—CONCERN TO ALL** LIGHT—CONCERN TO SOME
WORTHINGTON *(Continued)*	
MEATLESS CHICKEN	**ARTIFICIAL COLOR; CARRAGEENAN;** EGG WHITES; MONOSODIUM GLUTAMATE; **TURMERIC**
STAKELETS	EGG WHITE SOLIDS; **SODIUM CASEINATE**
STRIPPLES	**ARTIFICIAL COLOR; CARRAGEENAN;** EGG ALBUMIN (RECONSTITUTED); GLUTEN (WHEAT); **MODIFIED TAPIOCA STARCH; SODIUM CASEINATE**

REFRIGERATED MEAT & POULTRY

ARMOUR	
BACON; 1877 CANADIAN STYLE BACON	**SODIUM NITRITE**
BEEF HOT DOGS; HOT DOGS	**OLEORESIN OF PAPRIKA; SODIUM NITRITE**
CASERTA BRAND PEPERONI	**BHA; BHT; OLEORESIN OF PAPRIKA; SODIUM NITRATE; SODIUM NITRITE**
GENOA SALAMI; HARD SALAMI	**SODIUM NITRATE; SODIUM NITRITE**
CARL BUDDIG	
CORNED BEEF	MONOSODIUM GLUTAMATE; **SODIUM NITRITE**

BRANDS	ADDITIVES-OF-CONCERN BOLD—CONCERN TO ALL LIGHT—CONCERN TO SOME
SMOKED BEEF; SMOKED HAM; SMOKED PASTRAMI	MONOSODIUM GLUTAMATE; **SODIUM NITRITE; WOOD SMOKED***
SMOKED CHICKEN	**MODIFIED FOOD STARCH;** MONOSODIUM GLUTAMATE; **TURMERIC; WOOD SMOKED***
HEBREW NATIONAL	
BEEF FRANKFURTERS; BEEF SALAMI; PASTRAMI	**PAPRIKA; SODIUM NITRITE**
JONES SLICED BACON	**SODIUM NITRITE**
OSCAR MAYER	
BEEF BOLOGNA; BOLOGNA	**PAPRIKA; SODIUM NITRITE**
BEEF COTTO SALAMI; BRAUNSCHWEIGER; CHOPPED HAM; HARD SALAMI; WIENERS	**SODIUM NITRITE**
HAM STEAKS	**SMOKE FLAVORING; SODIUM NITRITE**
HONEY LOAF; OLD FASHIONED LOAF	**CALCIUM CASEINATE;** MONOSODIUM GLUTAMATE; **SODIUM NITRITE;** WHEY

*Although "smoked" does not refer to a specific additive, it represents a process utilizing wood smoke, as "smoke flavoring" does, and therefore the food may contain some cancer-causing benzopyrene chemicals. For this reason, when a food or any of its constituents has been smoked, this has been noted in the additives-of-concern column.

BRANDS	**ADDITIVES-OF-CONCERN** **BOLD—CONCERN TO ALL** LIGHT—CONCERN TO SOME
OSCAR MAYER *(Continued)* MORTADELLA	MONOSODIUM GLUTAMATE; **PORK FAT; SODIUM NITRITE**
OLIVE LOAF; PICKLE & PIMENTO LOAF	**CALCIUM CASEINATE; SODIUM NITRITE;** WHEY
PLUMROSE *PREMIUM* AMERICAN COOKED HAM; SLICED BACON	**SODIUM NITRITE**
SWIFT SIZZLEAN PORK BREAKFAST STRIPS	MONOSODIUM GLUTAMATE; **SMOKE FLAVORING; SODIUM NITRITE**
WEAVER CHICKEN FRANKS	**PAPRIKA; SODIUM NITRITE**
WHITE MEAT CHICKEN ROLL	MONOSODIUM GLUTAMATE
SUPERMARKET PRIVATE BRANDS **A & P—A & P** BOLOGNA; COOKED SALAMI; DANISH COOKED HAM; NEW ENGLAND BRAND SAUSAGE; SKINLESS BEEF FRANKS	**SODIUM NITRITE**
BRAUNSCHWEIGER	**PORK FAT; SODIUM NITRITE**
CHICKEN ROLL	EGG ALBUMIN
HARD SALAMI	**BHA; BHT; NATURAL SMOKE FLAVOR; SODIUM NITRITE**

BRANDS	ADDITIVES-OF-CONCERN BOLD—CONCERN TO ALL LIGHT—CONCERN TO SOME
PEPPERONI	**BHA; BHT; PAPRIKA; NATURAL SMOKE FLAVOR; SODIUM NITRITE**
TURKEY BREAST ROLL	NO ADDITIVES OF CONCERN
—*SMOKED SLICED* BEEF; HAM; TURKEY	MONOSODIUM GLUTAMATE; **SMOKED;* SODIUM NITRITE**
PASTRAMI	**PAPRIKA; SMOKED;* SODIUM NITRITE**
—**ANN PAGE** SLICED BACON	**SODIUM NITRITE**
FIRST NATIONAL **—EDWARDS-FINAST** SLICED BACON	**SODIUM NITRITE**
—FINAST BEEF FRANKS; COOKED SALAMI	**SODIUM NITRITE**
SPICED LUNCHEON LOAF	MONOSODIUM GLUTAMATE; **SODIUM NITRITE**
LUCKY—LADY LEE BOLOGNA; CHICKEN BOLOGNA	**PAPRIKA; SMOKE FLAVORING; SODIUM NITRITE**

*Although "smoked" does not refer to a specific additive, it represents a process utilizing wood smoke, as "smoke flavoring" does, and therefore the food may contain some cancer-causing benzopyrene chemicals. For this reason, when a food or any of its constituents has been smoked, this has been noted in the additives-of-concern column.

BRANDS	ADDITIVES-OF-CONCERN BOLD—CONCERN TO ALL LIGHT—CONCERN TO SOME
LUCKY—LADY LEE *(Continued)*	
BEEF SALAMI; COOKED SALAMI	**SMOKE FLAVORING; SODIUM NITRITE**
CHOPPED HAM; CHOPPED PORK; SLICED BACON	**SODIUM NITRITE**
GARLIC SAUSAGE; HOT SAUSAGE LINKS; KNOCKWURST	**PAPRIKA; HICKORY SMOKE FLAVORING; SODIUM NITRITE**
HOT PORK SAUSAGE	**BHA**
POLISH SAUSAGE	**HICKORY SMOKE FLAVORING; SODIUM NITRITE**
—FRANKS	
CHICKEN; REGULAR; TURKEY	**PAPRIKA; HICKORY SMOKE FLAVORING; SODIUM NITRITE**
SAFEWAY	
—SAFEWAY	
ALL VEAL STEAKS	NO ADDITIVES OF CONCERN
BEEF BACON; BRAUNSCHWEIGER	**NATURAL SMOKE FLAVOR** OR **SMOKE FLAVORING; SODIUM NITRITE**
BEEF BOLOGNA; BOLOGNA; COOKED HAM; COTTO SALAMI; GERMAN BRAND SAUSAGE; KNOCKWURST; THURINGER	**SODIUM NITRITE**

BRANDS	**ADDITIVES-OF-CONCERN** **BOLD—CONCERN TO ALL** LIGHT—CONCERN TO SOME
BEEF BREAKFAST STRIPS	**HICKORY SMOKE FLAVORING; SODIUM NITRITE**
CHOPPED HAM	MONOSODIUM GLUTAMATE; **SODIUM NITRITE**
COMBINATION LOAF; OLIVE LOAF	MONOSODIUM GLUTAMATE; **SODIUM CASEINATE; SODIUM NITRITE;** WHEY (SWEET DAIRY)
HOT PORK SAUSAGE WHOLE HOG; MEDIUM PORK SAUSAGE WHOLE HOG	MONOSODIUM GLUTAMATE
—MANOR HOUSE	
CHICKEN BOLOGNA	**SODIUM NITRITE**
—(NO BRAND NAME) *SMOKED-SLICED-CHOPPED-PRESSED-COOKED*	
BEEF; HAM; PASTRAMI	MONOSODIUM GLUTAMATE; **SMOKED;* SODIUM NITRITE**
CHICKEN; TURKEY	MONOSODIUM GLUTAMATE; **SMOKED;* SODIUM CASEINATE; SODIUM NITRITE**

*Although "smoked" does not refer to a specific additive, it represents a process utilizing wood smoke, as "smoke flavoring" does, and therefore the food may contain some cancer-causing benzopyrene chemicals. For this reason, when a food or any of its constituents has been smoked, this has been noted in the additives-of-concern column.

BRANDS	ADDITIVES-OF-CONCERN BOLD—CONCERN TO ALL LIGHT—CONCERN TO SOME
SAFEWAY *(Continued)*	
—TROPHY ITALIAN BRAND BREADED VEAL PATTIES	**ARTIFICIALLY COLORED;** MONOSODIUM GLUTAMATE
STOP & SHOP —STOP & SHOP BEEF BOLOGNA	**OLEORESIN PAPRIKA; SODIUM NITRITE**
CHOPPED HAM; LUNCHEON LOAF	MONOSODIUM GLUTAMATE; **SODIUM NITRITE**
POLISH BRAND LOAF	MONOSODIUM GLUTAMATE; **PORK FAT; SODIUM CASEINATE; SODIUM NITRITE;** WHEY (DRIED)
—BACON MAPLE SUGAR CURED; THICK SLICED SUGAR CURED	**SODIUM NITRITE**
—FRANKS BEEF SKINLESS; EXTRA MILD SKINLESS	**OLEORESIN OF PAPRIKA; SODIUM NITRITE**
GET-A-LONG-DOGGIE	**OLEORESIN OF PAPRIKA; PORK FAT; SODIUM NITRITE**
—SUN GLORY SUGAR CURED SLICED BACON	**SODIUM NITRITE**

BRANDS	ADDITIVES-OF-CONCERN **BOLD—CONCERN TO ALL** LIGHT—CONCERN TO SOME
WINN DIXIE —W-D	
BEEF BOLOGNA; CHOPPED HAM; COOKED HAM; COOKED SALAMI; PRESTIGE SLICED BACON; SOUSE	**SODIUM NITRITE**
LEBANON BOLOGNA	**POTASSIUM NITRATE**
SMOKED SAUSAGE; SMOKED PORK SHOULDER PICNIC	**SMOKED;* SODIUM NITRITE**
SPICED LUNCHEON LOAF	MONOSODIUM GLUTAMATE; **SODIUM CASEINATE; SODIUM NITRITE;** WHEY SOLIDS
—WINN DIXIE	
BREAKFAST SAUSAGE MADE FROM BEEF	MONOSODIUM GLUTAMATE

*Although "smoked" does not refer to a specific additive, it represents a process utilizing wood smoke, as "smoke flavoring" does, and therefore the food may contain some cancer-causing benzopyrene chemicals. For this reason, when a food or any of its constituents has been smoked, this has been noted in the additives-of-concern column.

XVIII. ONE-COURSE DISHES

CANNED ONE-COURSE DISHES (BEANS, ETHNIC FOODS)

By law, at this writing, it is not required of a manufacturer to state whether cheeses contain artificial colors, unless the color is FD & C Yellow No. 5 (Tartrazine). Their presence in one-course dishes containing cheese therefore remains an uncertainty, unless it is voluntarily declared on the label that artificial colors have been used or have not. For a more detailed explanation of artificial color in cheese, refer to the beginning of the cheese section of "Dairy Products & Substitutes."

BRANDS	**ADDITIVES-OF-CONCERN** **BOLD—CONCERN TO ALL** LIGHT—CONCERN TO SOME
B & M *BAKED BEANS*	
REGULAR; W/ RED KIDNEY BEANS; W/ YELLOW EYE BEANS	NO ADDITIVES OF CONCERN
BUITONI SPAGHETTI TWISTS	**MODIFIED FOOD STARCH**
CAMPBELL'S *BEANS*	
BARBEQUE	**OLEORESIN TURMERIC; SMOKE FLAVORING**
W/ FRANKS	**OLEORESIN PAPRIKA; MODIFIED FOOD STARCH; SODIUM NITRITE**
OLD FASHIONED	NO ADDITIVES OF CONCERN
W/ PORK	**MODIFIED FOOD STARCH; OLEORESIN PAPRIKA**

BRANDS	**ADDITIVES-OF-CONCERN** **BOLD—CONCERN TO ALL** LIGHT—CONCERN TO SOME
CHEF BOY-AR-DEE	
BEEFARONI; LASAGNA; MACARONI SHELLS	**MODIFIED FOOD STARCH**
BEEF RAVIOLI; CHEESE RAVIOLI IN SAUCE; ROLLER COASTERS; SPAGHETTI & MEAT BALLS	**MODIFIED FOOD STARCH;** MONOSODIUM GLUTAMATE
CHUN KING	
BEAN SPROUTS; CHOW MEIN NOODLES; CHOW MEIN VEGETABLES	NO ADDITIVES OF CONCERN
FRANCO-AMERICAN	
BEEF RAVIOLIOS	**MODIFIED FOOD STARCH; OLEORESIN PAPRIKA**
BEEFY MAC	MONOSODIUM GLUTAMATE; **OLEORESIN PAPRIKA**
ELBOW MACARONI & CHEESE	MONOSODIUM GLUTAMATE; **OLEORESIN PAPRIKA;** WHEY
SPAGHETTI; SPAGHETTIOS; SPAGHETTIOS W/ LITTLE MEATBALLS	NO ADDITIVES OF CONCERN
SPAGHETTI W/ MEATBALLS	MONOSODIUM GLUTAMATE
SPAGHETTIOS W/ SLICED FRANKS	**OLEORESIN PAPRIKA; SODIUM NITRITE**

BRANDS	ADDITIVES-OF-CONCERN **BOLD—CONCERN TO ALL** LIGHT—CONCERN TO SOME
HEINZ VEGETARIAN BEANS	**MODIFIED FOOD STARCH**
HORMEL	
BEEF TAMALES IN CHILI SAUCE	NO ADDITIVES OF CONCERN
CHILI NO BEANS	**MODIFIED FOOD STARCH;** MONOSODIUM GLUTAMATE
CHILI W/ BEANS; HOT CHILI W/ BEANS	**MODIFIED FOOD STARCH**
LIBBY'S	
CHILI W/ BEANS	NO ADDITIVES OF CONCERN
DEEP BROWN PORK & BEANS	**MODIFIED CORN STARCH**
STEWART'S	
SATURDAY SUPPER PEA BEANS & PORK	NO ADDITIVES OF CONCERN
SUPERMARKET PRIVATE BRANDS	
A & P	
—ANN PAGE	
BOSTON STYLE BEANS	**MODIFIED CORN STARCH**
PORK & BEANS IN TOMATO SAUCE	NO ADDITIVES OF CONCERN
FIRST NATIONAL	
—EDWARDS BROWN BEANS IN CHILI GRAVY	NO ADDITIVES OF CONCERN

BRANDS	ADDITIVES-OF-CONCERN **BOLD—CONCERN TO ALL** LIGHT—CONCERN TO SOME
LUCKY—LADY LEE	
CHILI W/ BEANS HOT	**MODIFIED FOOD STARCH; NATURAL COLORING; PAPRIKA**
CORNED BEEF HASH	**SODIUM NITRITE**
REFRIED BEANS	**LARD**
SAFEWAY —TOWN HOUSE	
BEEF STEW	**MODIFIED FOOD STARCH**
CHILI CON CARNE W/ BEANS	MONOSODIUM GLUTAMATE; **PAPRIKA**
CHILI CON CARNE W/ OUT BEANS	**MODIFIED FOOD STARCH;** MONOSODIUM GLUTAMATE; **PAPRIKA**
CORNED BEEF HASH	**SODIUM NITRITE**
PORK & BEANS	**EXTRACTIVES OF PAPRIKA; MODIFIED FOOD STARCH**
—STOP & SHOP	
SALAD	
MACARONI; OIL & VINEGAR POTATO	NO ADDITIVES OF CONCERN
POTATO	PROPYLENE GLYCOL ALGINATE
WINN DIXIE —THRIFTY MAID	
BEEF STEW; CHILI W/ BEANS; MEXICAN STYLE CHILI BEANS	NO ADDITIVES OF CONCERN

BRANDS	ADDITIVES-OF-CONCERN BOLD—CONCERN TO ALL LIGHT—CONCERN TO SOME
WINN DIXIE—THRIFTY MAID *(Continued)*	
HOT DOG CHILI SAUCE	**BEEF FAT; MODIFIED FOOD STARCH;** MONOSODIUM GLUTAMATE
MEAT RAVIOLI	**MODIFIED FOOD STARCH**
SPAGHETTI; SPAGHETTI RINGS	**MODIFIED FOOD STARCH; PAPRIKA**
ITEMS IN HEALTH FOOD STORES	
FEATHERWEIGHT	
UNSALTED	
BEEF RAVIOLI	EGG WHITES; **MODIFIED FOOD STARCH**
BEEF STEW; LAMB STEW	NO ADDITIVES OF CONCERN
DUMPLINGS W/ CHICKEN	**BHA; BHT; MODIFIED FOOD STARCH**
SPAGHETTI W/ MEATBALLS	**MODIFIED FOOD STARCH**
HEALTH VALLEY	
HONEY BAKED BEANS	NO ADDITIVES OF CONCERN
—*VEGETARIAN CHILI*	
MILD; SPICY	**PAPRIKA**
WALNUT ACRES CHILI CON CARNE	**PAPRIKA**

BRANDS	ADDITIVES-OF-CONCERN **BOLD—CONCERN TO ALL** LIGHT—CONCERN TO SOME

DRY MIXES FOR ONE-COURSE DISHES

By law, at this writing, it is not required of a manufacturer to state whether cheeses contain artificial colors, unless the color is FD & C Yellow No. 5 (Tartrazine). Their presence in dry mixes for one-course dishes containing cheese therefore remains an uncertainty, unless it is voluntarily declared on the label that artificial colors have been used or have not. For a more detailed explanation of artificial color in cheese, refer to the beginning of the cheese section of "Dairy Products & Substitutes."

BRANDS	ADDITIVES-OF-CONCERN
BETTY CROCKER NOODLES ROMANOFF	**ARTIFICIAL COLOR; BHA**
—HAMBURGER HELPER FOR BEEF NOODLE	MONOSODIUM GLUTAMATE
FOR BEEF ROMANOFF	**BHA; MODIFIED CORN STARCH;** MONOSODIUM GLUTAMATE; WHEY
FOR CHEESEBURGER MACARONI	**ARTIFICIAL COLOR; BHA; MODIFIED CORN STARCH; SODIUM CASEINATE**
FOR HAMBURGER POTATOES AU GRATIN	**ARTIFICIAL COLOR; BHA;** MONOSODIUM GLUTAMATE; WHEY
FOR RICE ORIENTAL	**BHT**
—MUG-O-LUNCH BEEF NOODLES & GRAVY	**MODIFIED CORN & TAPIOCA STARCHES;** MONOSODIUM GLUTAMATE
MACARONI & CHEESE	**ARTIFICIAL COLOR; MODIFIED CORN STARCH;** WHEY

BRANDS	**ADDITIVES-OF-CONCERN** **BOLD—CONCERN TO ALL** LIGHT—CONCERN TO SOME
BETTY CROCKER *(Continued)*	
—*TUNA HELPER* FOR CREAMY NOODLES 'N TUNA	**ARTIFICIAL COLOR; BHA; SODIUM CASEINATE**
FOR NOODLES, CHEESE SAUCE 'N TUNA	**ARTIFICIAL COLOR; BHA; MODIFIED CORN STARCH;** MONOSODIUM GLUTAMATE; **SODIUM CASEINATE;** WHEY
BELL'S MEATLOAF	**MODIFIED FOOD STARCH;** MONOSODIUM GLUTAMATE; **PAPRIKA**
CHEF BOY-AR-DEE COMPLETE CHEESE PIZZA; COMPLETE CHEESE PIZZA IN A SKILLET	GUAR GUM; **MODIFIED FOOD STARCH;** WHEY (DRIED)
SPAGHETTI DINNER W/ MEAT SAUCE	**MODIFIED FOOD STARCH**
CHUN KING ORIENTAL VEGETABLES & SAUCE MIX FOR STIR-FRY PEPPER STEAK	**MODIFIED FOOD STARCH;** MONOSODIUM GLUTAMATE
GOLDEN GRAIN MACARONI & CHEDDAR	**ARTIFICIAL COLOR;** WHEY
NOODLE RONI STROGANOFF	MONOSODIUM GLUTAMATE; **PAPRIKA;** WHEY
KRAFT *DINNERS* MACARONI & CHEESE DELUXE	**ARTIFICIAL COLOR;** SODIUM ALGINATE; WHEY

BRANDS	ADDITIVES-OF-CONCERN BOLD—CONCERN TO ALL LIGHT—CONCERN TO SOME
TANGY ITALIAN STYLE SPAGHETTI	**ARTIFICIAL COLOR; MODIFIED FOOD STARCH;** MONOSODIUM GLUTAMATE
LIPTON *LITE-LUNCH*	
BEEF; STOCKPOT VEGETABLE	**(HYDROGENATED COTTONSEED, PALM, SOYBEAN OILS);*** MONOSODIUM GLUTAMATE
CHICKEN	**(HYDROGENATED COTTONSEED, PALM, SOYBEAN OILS);*** MONOSODIUM GLUTAMATE; **TURMERIC OLEORESIN**
MACARONI & CHEESE	**ARTIFICIAL COLOR; MODIFIED TAPIOCA STARCH;** MONOSODIUM GLUTAMATE; WHEY SOLIDS
NESTLÉ *LUNCH TIME*	
EGG NOODLES BEEF	**MODIFIED TAPIOCA STARCH;** MONOSODIUM GLUTAMATE
EGG NOODLES CHICKEN	**MODIFIED TAPIOCA STARCH;** MONOSODIUM GLUTAMATE; **SODIUM CASEINATE; TURMERIC**
EGG NOODLES TUNA & CELERY	**MODIFIED TAPIOCA STARCH;** MONOSODIUM GLUTAMATE; **SODIUM CASEINATE**
MACARONI CHEESE & HAM	**ARTIFICIAL COLOR; MODIFIED TAPIOCA STARCH;** MONOSODIUM GLUTAMATE

*Blend may contain one or more of these saturated oils.

BRANDS	ADDITIVES-OF-CONCERN BOLD—CONCERN TO ALL LIGHT—CONCERN TO SOME
TEMPO	
ITALIAN MEAT BALL; MEAT LOAF	NO ADDITIVES OF CONCERN
SWEDISH MEAT BALL	MONOSODIUM GLUTAMATE
SUPERMARKET PRIVATE BRANDS	
A & P—ANN PAGE	
MACARONI & CHEESE DINNER	**ARTIFICIAL COLOR;** BUTTERMILK SOLIDS; WHEY SOLIDS
LUCKY —LADY LEE	
MACARONI & CHEESE DINNER	BUTTERMILK SOLIDS; **CERTIFIED FOOD COLOR;** WHEY SOLIDS
SAFEWAY —TOWN HOUSE	
MACARONI & CHEESE DINNER	**ARTIFICIAL COLOR; MODIFIED CORN STARCH;** WHEY
WINN DIXIE —THRIFTY MAID	
DINNER	
MACARONI & CHEESE; SHELLS & CHEDDAR; TWISTS & CHEDDAR	**ARTIFICIAL COLOR;** BUTTERMILK SOLIDS; **MODIFIED FOOD STARCH;** WHEY SOLIDS
ITEMS IN HEALTH FOOD STORES	
DE BOLES *DINNER*	
MACARONI & CHEESE; WHOLE WHEAT HIGH PROTEIN MACARONI & CHEESE	EGG WHITE SOLIDS; GLUTEN (WHEAT)

BRANDS	**ADDITIVES-OF-CONCERN** **BOLD—CONCERN TO ALL** LIGHT—CONCERN TO SOME
EARTHWONDER *NATURAL DINNER-IN-A-BOX* MILLET STEW; MUSHROOM WHEAT PILAF; QUICK CHILI	NO ADDITIVES OF CONCERN
FANTASTIC FOODS *MIX* FANTASTIC FALAFIL; NATURE'S BURGER; TEMPURA BATTER	NO ADDITIVES OF CONCERN
FEARN *MIX* BREAKFAST PATTY; BRAZIL NUT BURGER	NO ADDITIVES OF CONCERN
SESAME BURGER	GLUTEN (WASHED WHEAT); KELP POWDER
FRITINI SWISS READY MIX FOR VEGETABLE PATTIES	NO ADDITIVES OF CONCERN
MANNA MEALS OF MARYLAND SLOPPY JOE	NO ADDITIVES OF CONCERN
NEAR EAST *MIX* WHEAT PILAF; WHEAT SALAD TABOULEH	NO ADDITIVES OF CONCERN

BRANDS	ADDITIVES-OF-CONCERN BOLD—CONCERN TO ALL LIGHT—CONCERN TO SOME
SOKEN-SHA *SOKEN RAMEN UNBLEACHED NOODLES*	
SEA VEGETABLES W/ MISO FLAVOR	WAKAME SEAWEED
W/ SOUP BASE; W/ WHOLE WHEAT/ BROWN RICE GERM	NO ADDITIVES OF CONCERN

FROZEN ONE-COURSE DISHES

By law, at this writing, it is not required of a manufacturer to state whether cheeses contain artificial colors, unless the color is FD & C Yellow No. 5 (Tartrazine). Their presence in frozen one-course dishes containing cheese therefore remains an uncertainty, unless it is voluntarily declared on the label that artificial colors have been used or have not. For a more detailed explanation of artificial color in cheese, refer to the beginning of the cheese section of "Dairy Products & Substitutes."

BANQUET	
FRIED CHICKEN	MONOSODIUM GLUTAMATE
—*BUFFET SUPPER*	
CHICKEN & DUMPLINGS; GRAVY & SLICED TURKEY	MONOSODIUM GLUTAMATE; **PAPRIKA; TURMERIC**
GRAVY & SLICED BEEF	**BEEF FAT**
VEAL PARMIGIAN	**ARTIFICIAL COLORS; BHA;** MONOSODIUM GLUTAMATE; **PAPRIKA; SODIUM CASEINATE;** WHEY (DRY)

BRANDS	ADDITIVES-OF-CONCERN BOLD—CONCERN TO ALL LIGHT—CONCERN TO SOME
—COOKIN' BAG CHICKEN À LA KING	MONOSODIUM GLUTAMATE; **PAPRIKA**
CREAMED CHIPPED BEEF	**SODIUM NITRITE**
GRAVY & SLICED TURKEY	MONOSODIUM GLUTAMATE; **OLEORESIN OF TURMERIC; PAPRIKA**
MACARONI & CHEESE	**ARTIFICIALLY COLORED; COLORING; SODIUM CASEINATE;** WHEY
MEAT LOAF W/ TOMATO SAUCE	**CALCIUM CASEINATE; PAPRIKA;** WHEY
SALISBURY STEAK W/ GRAVY	**COLORING**
BUITONI	
BAKED ZITI; EGGPLANT PARMIGIANA	**MODIFIED FOOD STARCH; SODIUM/CALCIUM CASEINATE;** WHEY
CHEESE RAVIOLI; MANICOTTI	**FURCELLERAN; MODIFIED FOOD STARCH; SODIUM/CALCIUM CASEINATE;** WHEY
LASAGNE	**MODIFIED FOOD STARCH; SODIUM/CALCIUM CASEINATE; VEGETABLE GUM;** WHEY SOLIDS
MEAT RAVIOLI	NO ADDITIVES OF CONCERN

BRANDS	ADDITIVES-OF-CONCERN BOLD—CONCERN TO ALL LIGHT—CONCERN TO SOME
BUITONI *(Continued)*	
SAUSAGE & PEPPERS W/ MOSTACCIOLI RIGATI	**MODIFIED FOOD STARCH;** MONOSODIUM GLUTAMATE
VEAL PARMIGIANA W/ SPAGHETTI TWISTS	GLUTEN; **MODIFIED FOOD STARCH;** MONOSODIUM GLUTAMATE
CHUN KING CHICKEN CHOW MEIN; SHRIMP CHOW MEIN	**MODIFIED FOOD STARCH;** MONOSODIUM GLUTAMATE
FRIED RICE W/ PORK	NO ADDITIVES OF CONCERN
SHRIMP EGG ROLLS	**CALCIUM CASEINATE; EXTRACT OF PAPRIKA; MODIFIED FOOD STARCH;** MONOSODIUM GLUTAMATE; SODIUM ALGINATE; WHEY (DRIED)
FREEZER QUEEN BREADED VEAL PARMIGIANA	**MODIFIED FOOD STARCH;** MONOSODIUM GLUTAMATE; **PAPRIKA (& OLEORESIN)**
GRAVY & SALISBURY STEAK; GRAVY & SLICED BEEF; MUSHROOM GRAVY & CHAR BROILED BEEF PATTIES	**MODIFIED FOOD STARCH;** MONOSODIUM GLUTAMATE; **OLEORESIN PAPRIKA**
GRAVY & SLICED TURKEY	**MODIFIED FOOD STARCH;** MONOSODIUM GLUTAMATE; **OLEORESIN PAPRIKA; OLEORESIN TURMERIC**

BRANDS	ADDITIVES-OF-CONCERN **BOLD—CONCERN TO ALL** LIGHT—CONCERN TO SOME
SPAGHETTI W/ MEAT BALLS	**ARTIFICIAL COLOR; MODIFIED FOOD STARCH;** MONOSODIUM GLUTAMATE; **PAPRIKA (& OLEORESIN)**
GREEN GIANT	
CHICKEN & BISCUITS	GUAR GUM; **MODIFIED CORN STARCH;** MONOSODIUM GLUTAMATE; **TURMERIC**
LASAGNA	**MODIFIED FOOD STARCH;** MONOSODIUM GLUTAMATE
STUFFED GREEN PEPPERS	**MODIFIED FOOD STARCH;** MONOSODIUM GLUTAMATE; **PAPRIKA**
VEAL PARMIGIANA	**ARTIFICIAL COLOR; BHA; VEGETABLE SHORTENING**
HOWARD JOHNSON'S	
MACARONI & CHEESE	**PAPRIKA**
LA CHOY	
CHICKEN CHOW MEIN	**MODIFIED FOOD STARCH;** MONOSODIUM GLUTAMATE; **TURMERIC**
FRIED RICE W/ MEAT	MONOSODIUM GLUTAMATE
—EGG ROLLS	
CHICKEN; MEAT & SHRIMP; SHRIMP	**MODIFIED FOOD STARCH;** MONOSODIUM GLUTAMATE

BRANDS	ADDITIVES-OF-CONCERN **BOLD—CONCERN TO ALL** LIGHT—CONCERN TO SOME
MRS. PAUL'S EGGPLANT PARMESAN	NO ADDITIVES OF CONCERN
MORTON MACARONI & CHEESE	**ARTIFICIAL COLOR; MODIFIED FOOD STARCH;** WHEY SOLIDS
RONZONI FETTUCCINE ALFREDO	**BUTTER (U.S. GRADE A FRESH); MODIFIED FOOD STARCH**
STOUFFER'S BEEF STEW; MACARONI & CHEESE; ROAST BEEF HASH; TURKEY TETRAZZINI	MONOSODIUM GLUTAMATE
BEEF STROGANOFF W/ PARSLEY NOODLES	**MODIFIED CORN STARCH;** MILK SOLIDS (CULTURED NONFAT); MONOSODIUM GLUTAMATE; **PAPRIKA**
CHICKEN À LA KING W/ RICE; CHICKEN DIVAN; CREAMED CHICKEN	**MODIFIED CORN STARCH;** MONOSODIUM GLUTAMATE; **TURMERIC**
CREAMED CHIPPED BEEF	**BHA; BUTTER; MODIFIED CORN STARCH; SODIUM NITRITE**
GREEN PEPPER STEAK W/ RICE; SHORT RIBS OF BEEF	ALGIN; **MODIFIED CORN STARCH;** MONOSODIUM GLUTAMATE
LASAGNA	**MODIFIED CORN STARCH**

BRANDS	ADDITIVES-OF-CONCERN BOLD—CONCERN TO ALL LIGHT—CONCERN TO SOME
MACARONI & BEEF W/ TOMATOES; STUFFED GREEN PEPPERS	**MODIFIED CORN STARCH;** MONOSODIUM GLUTAMATE
TUNA NOODLE CASSEROLE	**ARTIFICIAL COLOR;** MONOSODIUM GLUTAMATE
NOODLES ROMANOFF SIDE DISH	**CARRAGEENAN; COCONUT OIL; PAPRIKA; SODIUM CASEINATE;** WHEY SOLIDS
SWANSON	
FRIED CHICKEN	NO ADDITIVES OF CONCERN
MACARONI & CHEESE	**MODIFIED FOOD STARCH;** MONOSODIUM GLUTAMATE; **OLEORESIN PAPRIKA**
WEAVER	
—BATTER DIPPED FRIED CHICKEN BREASTS; FRIED CHICKEN THIGHS & DRUMSTICKS	NO ADDITIVES OF CONCERN
—DUTCH ENTREE CHICKEN AU GRATIN	**ARTIFICIAL COLOR;** BUTTERMILK SOLIDS; **MODIFIED FOOD STARCH;** WHEY & MODIFIED WHEY
CHICKEN CROQUETTES	EGG WHITE SOLIDS; **MODIFIED FOOD STARCH;** MONOSODIUM GLUTAMATE; **OLEORESIN OF TURMERIC; PAPRIKA (& OLEORESIN OF);** SODIUM ALGINATE; WHEY

BRANDS	ADDITIVES-OF-CONCERN **BOLD—CONCERN TO ALL** LIGHT—CONCERN TO SOME
WEAVER *(Continued)*	
—DUTCH FRYE	
FRIED CHICKEN BREASTS	**MODIFIED FOOD STARCH; OLEORESIN PAPRIKA;** SODIUM ALGINATE
FRIED CHICKEN DRUMSTICKS	ALGIN GUM; **PAPRIKA;** WHEY (DRIED)
—TOUCH-O-HONEY	
FRIED CHICKEN BREAST, THIGHS, DRUMSTICKS	**MODIFIED FOOD STARCH;** MONOSODIUM GLUTAMATE; **OLEORESIN PAPRIKA;** SODIUM ALGINATE
WEIGHT WATCHERS	
CHEESE & TOMATO PIES	NO ADDITIVES OF CONCERN
CHICKEN CREOLE	**VEGETABLE STABILIZERS**
EGGPLANT PARMIGIANA; LASAGNA W/ CHEESE, VEAL & SAUCE; ZITI MACARONI W/ VEAL, CHEESE & SAUCE	CAROB BEAN GUM; GUAR GUM; GUM TRAGACANTH
SUPERMARKET PRIVATE BRANDS	
A & P	
—A & P MACARONI & CHEESE	**FOOD COLOR;** GUAR GUM; **MODIFIED STARCH;** MONOSODIUM GLUTAMATE; WHEY (SWEET DAIRY)
—ANN PAGE	
GRAVY & 6 CHICKEN CROQUETTES	**MODIFIED FOOD STARCH;** MONOSODIUM GLUTAMATE; **PAPRIKA; TURMERIC**

BRANDS	ADDITIVES-OF-CONCERN **BOLD—CONCERN TO ALL** LIGHT—CONCERN TO SOME
ONION GRAVY & 4 CHAR-BROILED PATTIES	**MODIFIED FOOD STARCH;** MONOSODIUM GLUTAMATE
TOMATO SAUCE & MEAT LOAF	**MODIFIED FOOD STARCH**
FIRST NATIONAL	
—FINAST MACARONI & CHEESE	BUTTERMILK SOLIDS; **MODIFIED FOOD STARCH;** WHEY SOLIDS (MODIFIED)
—FINAST	
BOIL-IN-BAG	
BREADED VEAL PARMIGIANA	**MODIFIED FOOD STARCH;** MONOSODIUM GLUTAMATE; **OIL EXTRACTIVES OF PAPRIKA**
CHICKEN A LA KING	**MODIFIED FOOD STARCH;** MONOSODIUM GLUTAMATE
GRAVY & SLICED BEEF	NO ADDITIVES OF CONCERN
SAFEWAY	
—SAFEWAY	
BEEF & BEAN GREEN CHILI BURRITO; RED HOT BEEF BURRITO	**MODIFIED FOOD STARCH**
—BEL-AIR	
BARBEQUE SAUCE & SLICED BEEF	**PAPRIKA; SMOKE FLAVORING; SMOKED YEAST;* TURMERIC**

*Although "smoked" does not refer to a specific additive, it represents a process utilizing wood smoke, as "smoke flavoring" does, and therefore the food may contain some cancer-causing benzopyrene chemicals. For this reason, when a food or any of its constituents has been smoked, this has been noted in the additives-of-concern column.

BRANDS	ADDITIVES-OF-CONCERN BOLD—CONCERN TO ALL LIGHT—CONCERN TO SOME
SAFEWAY—BEL-AIR *(Continued)*	
SALISBURY STEAK & GRAVY	NO ADDITIVES OF CONCERN
GRAVY & SLICED BEEF	**RENDERED BEEF FAT**
GRAVY & SLICED TURKEY	MONOSODIUM GLUTAMATE; **OLEORESIN OF TURMERIC; PAPRIKA**
STOP & SHOP —STOP & SHOP	
CHEESE RAVIOLI	NO ADDITIVES OF CONCERN
MEAT TORTELLINI	**BHA; BHT; MODIFIED CORN STARCH;** MONOSODIUM GLUTAMATE; **OLEORESINS OF PAPRIKA & TURMERIC**
ITEMS IN HEALTH FOOD STORES	
HEALTH VALLEY	
CHEDDAR CHICKEN; CHEESE EGGPLANT; EGG ROLLS; LOBSTER ROLLS; NUT ROLLS; SHRIMP ROLLS; STUFFED PEPPERS	NO ADDITIVES OF CONCERN
PIZZA NATURALLY	
EGGPLANT PARMIGIANA; WHOLE WHEAT BAKED ZITI; WHOLE WHEAT LASAGNE	NO ADDITIVES OF CONCERN

BRANDS	ADDITIVES-OF-CONCERN **BOLD—CONCERN TO ALL** LIGHT—CONCERN TO SOME
TUMARO'S TEYA'S STUFFED GOLDEN SOY BEAN CAKES; TAMALE; TAMALE W/ SOY PROTEIN ADDED	NO ADDITIVES OF CONCERN
WORTHINGTON EGG ROLLS	**ARTIFICIAL COLOR;** EGG WHITES; **MODIFIED CORN STARCH;** MONOSODIUM GLUTAMATE
STAKES AU SAUCE	**ARTIFICIAL COLOR; CALCIUM & POTASSIUM CASEINATE;** EGG WHITES; GLUTEN (WHEAT); **MODIFIED CORN & TAPIOCA STARCH;** MONOSODIUM GLUTAMATE; WHEY
VEELETS PARMESANO	**ARTIFICIAL COLOR; CALCIUM & POTASSIUM CASEINATE;** EGG WHITES; GLUTEN (WHEAT); **MODIFIED TAPIOCA STARCH;** MONOSODIUM GLUTAMATE; WHEY
VEGETARIAN LASAGNA	**CALCIUM CASEINATE; FERRIC ORTHOPHOSPHATE; MODIFIED CORN STARCH;** MONOSODIUM GLUTAMATE

XIX. PASTA; POTATOES (INSTANT); RICE

PASTA

BRANDS	ADDITIVES-OF-CONCERN BOLD—CONCERN TO ALL LIGHT—CONCERN TO SOME
MUELLER'S ELBOWS; LASAGNE; OLD FASHIONED EGG NOODLES; READY-CUT MACARONI; SEA SHELLS; THIN SPAGHETTI; VERMICELLI	NO ADDITIVES OF CONCERN
PARADE ELBOWS; RIGATONI; SHELLS MEDIUM; VERMICELLI; ZITI	**FERRIC ORTHOPHOSPHATE**
PENNSYLVANIA DUTCH BROAD EGG NOODLES	NO ADDITIVES OF CONCERN
PRINCE ALPHABETS; CURLY LASAGNE; EGG PASTINA; ELBOWS; MACARONI MACARONCELLI; MANICOTTI; ORZO; RIGATONI; SHELLS MEDIUM	**FERRIC ORTHOPHOSPHATE**

BRANDS	ADDITIVES-OF-CONCERN BOLD—CONCERN TO ALL LIGHT—CONCERN TO SOME
ENRICHED EGG NOODLES; LINGUINE; SPAGHETTI; VERMICELLI; ZITI	**SODIUM IRON PYROPHOSPHATE**
—*SUPERONI*	
ELBOW MACARONI	**FERRIC ORTHOPHOSPHATE;** GLUTEN (WHEAT)
RIGATONI; THIN SPAGHETTI; ZITI	**CALCIUM CASEINATE; FERRIC ORTHOPHOSPHATE;** GLUTEN (WHEAT)
RONZONI	
CURLY EDGE LASAGNE; FETTUCCINE; RIGATONI; SHELLS; VERMICELLI; ZITI	NO ADDITIVES OF CONCERN
SUPERMARKET PRIVATE BRANDS	
A & P	
—ANN PAGE	
EGG NOODLES; ELBOW MACARONI; LASAGNE; LINGUINE; SEA SHELLS; SPAGHETTI	NO ADDITIVES OF CONCERN
FIRST NATIONAL	
—EDWARDS-FINAST	
ELBOW MACARONI; LARGE SHELLS; LASAGNA; RIGATONI; SPAGHETTI; VERMICELLI; ZITI	NO ADDITIVES OF CONCERN

BRANDS	ADDITIVES-OF-CONCERN **BOLD—CONCERN TO ALL** LIGHT—CONCERN TO SOME
LUCKY **—LADY LEE** COIL VERMICELLI; CUT MACARONI; EGG BUTTERFLIES; FINE EGG NOODLES; LARGE SHELLS; LASAGNE; RIGATONI; SMALL ELBOWS; SPAGHETTI	NO ADDITIVES OF CONCERN
SAFEWAY **—TOWN HOUSE** CUT MACARONI; FINE EGG NOODLES; RIGATONI; SMALL ELBOWS; SMALL SHELLS; SPAGHETTI	NO ADDITIVES OF CONCERN
STOP & SHOP **—STOP & SHOP** SPAGHETTI; THIN SPAGHETTI; ZITI	**FERRIC ORTHOPHOSPHATE**
WINN DIXIE **—THRIFTY MAID** CURLY LASAGNA; ELBOWS; SPAGHETTI; VERMICELLI	**FERRIC ORTHOPHOSPHATE**
ITEMS IN HEALTH FOOD STORES **DE BOLES** CURLY LASAGNE; FETTUCCINE; RIGATONI; SPINACH FETTUCCINE	NO ADDITIVES OF CONCERN

BRANDS	ADDITIVES-OF-CONCERN **BOLD—CONCERN TO ALL** LIGHT—CONCERN TO SOME
—WHOLE WHEAT HIGH PROTEIN ELBOWS; LINGUINE; MEDIUM SHELLS; RICE SUBSTITUTE; THIN SPAGHETTI; ZITI MACARONI	EGG WHITE SOLIDS; GLUTEN (WHEAT)
EREWHON CHINESE PASTA ORIENTAL NOODLES W/ INSTANT BROTH	DRIED KOMBU (KELP)
JAPANESE PASTA	NO ADDITIVES OF CONCERN
—WHOLEWHEAT ELBOW MACARONI; ELBOW PASTA W/ MIXED VEGETABLE POWDERS; LASAGNA; SPAGHETTI W/ ARTICHOKE POWDER; SPINACH LASAGNA; SPIRAL PASTA W/ SESAME & BROWN RICE; THIN SPAGHETTI; ZITI	NO ADDITIVES OF CONCERN
HEALTH VALLEY *WHOLE WHEAT* ELBOW PASTA W/ WHEAT GERM & 4 VEGETABLES; LASAGNA W/ WHEAT GERM; PASTA W/ WHEAT GERM; SPINACH PASTA W/ WHEAT GERM	NO ADDITIVES OF CONCERN
WESTBRAE NATURAL EGG NOODLES; SPINACH LASAGNA	NO ADDITIVES OF CONCERN

BRANDS	ADDITIVES-OF-CONCERN **BOLD—CONCERN TO ALL** LIGHT—CONCERN TO SOME
WESTBRAE NATURAL *(Continued)*	
WHOLEWHEAT RAMEN	DRIED KOMBU
—WHOLE-WHEAT LASAGNE; SPAGHETTI; STUFFING SHELLS	NO ADDITIVES OF CONCERN

POTATOES (INSTANT)

BRANDS	ADDITIVES-OF-CONCERN
BETTY CROCKER	
AU GRATIN	**ARTIFICIAL COLOR;** MONOSODIUM GLUTAMATE; WHEY
HASH BROWN; POTATO BUDS MASHED	**BHA**
SCALLOPED	**ARTIFICIAL COLOR; BHA;** MONOSODIUM GLUTAMATE; **SODIUM CASEINATE;** WHEY
FRENCH'S	
IDAHO MASHED	**BHA; BHT**
—BIG TATE HASH BROWN	**BHT; PAPRIKA**
MASHED	**BHA**
SCALLOPED	**SODIUM CASEINATE;** WHEY
IDAHOAN MASHED	**BHA**

BRANDS	ADDITIVES-OF-CONCERN **BOLD—CONCERN TO ALL** LIGHT—CONCERN TO SOME
PILLSBURY HUNGRY JACK MASHED	**BHA; BHT**
SUPERMARKET PRIVATE BRANDS	
FIRST NATIONAL	
—EDWARDS AU GRATIN	**ARTIFICIAL COLOR;** GUAR GUM; **MODIFIED CORN STARCH;** MONOSODIUM GLUTAMATE; WHEY
—EDWARDS-FINAST INSTANT MASHED	**BHA**
LUCKY	
—LADY LEE MASHED	**BHA**
SAFEWAY	
—TOWN HOUSE	
AU GRATIN	**ARTIFICIAL COLOR;** MILK SOLIDS (NONFAT); **MODIFIED CORN STARCH;** WHEY (ACID & SWEET)
MASHED	**BHA**
SCALLOPED	MILK SOLIDS (NONFAT); **MODIFIED CORN STARCH;** WHEY (ACID & SWEET)
STOP & SHOP	
—STOP & SHOP MASHED	**BHA**
WINN DIXIE	
—ASTOR	
AU GRATIN; SCALLOPED	**ARTIFICIAL COLOR; MODIFIED CORN STARCH;** MONOSODIUM GLUTAMATE; WHEY

BRANDS	ADDITIVES-OF-CONCERN BOLD—CONCERN TO ALL LIGHT—CONCERN TO SOME
WINN DIXIE—ASTOR *(Continued)*	
HASH BROWN	NO ADDITIVES OF CONCERN
IDAHO MASHED	**BHA**
ITEMS IN HEALTH FOOD STORES	
BARBARA'S ORGANIC MASHED POTATOES	NO ADDITIVES OF CONCERN
PANNI BAVARIAN POTATO DUMPLING MIX	NO ADDITIVES OF CONCERN

RICE & RICE DISHES

BRANDS	ADDITIVES-OF-CONCERN
GOLDEN GRAIN *—RICE-A-RONI*	
BEEF FLAVOR	MONOSODIUM GLUTAMATE
CHICKEN FLAVOR; SAVORY RICE PILAF	**BHA;** MONOSODIUM GLUTAMATE; **TURMERIC**
FRIED RICE W/ ALMONDS	**BHA; BHT;** MONOSODIUM GLUTAMATE; **TURMERIC**
HERB & BUTTER	**BHA; BHT**
LONG GRAIN & WILD RICE	**BHT;** MONOSODIUM GLUTAMATE
STROGANOFF	MONOSODIUM GLUTAMATE; **PAPRIKA;** WHEY
MINUTE RICE	**FERRIC ORTHOPHOSPHATE**
—RICE MIX	
DRUMSTICK	**BHA; BHT;** MONOSODIUM GLUTAMATE; **TURMERIC**

BRANDS	ADDITIVES-OF-CONCERN **BOLD—CONCERN TO ALL** LIGHT—CONCERN TO SOME
FRIED; RIB ROAST	MONOSODIUM GLUTAMATE
NEAR EAST RICE PILAF	**TURMERIC**
SUCCESS RICE	NO ADDITIVES OF CONCERN
UNCLE BEN'S *RICE*	
BROWN	NO ADDITIVES OF CONCERN
CONVERTED; QUICK	**FERRIC ORTHOPHOSPHATE**
LONG GRAIN & WILD	**BHA; BHT; FERRIC ORTHOPHOSPHATE; HICKORY SMOKED TORULA YEAST;*** MONOSODIUM GLUTAMATE
FOR BEEF W/ MUSHROOMS	**BHA; BHT; FERRIC ORTHOPHOSPHATE; MODIFIED CORN STARCH;** MONOSODIUM GLUTAMATE; **PAPRIKA**
FOR CHICKEN W/ VEGETABLES	**BHA; BHT; FERRIC ORTHOPHOSPHATE;** MONOSODIUM GLUTAMATE; **SMOKED TORULA YEAST;* TURMERIC**
PILAF W/ ROSAMARINA & PEAS	**BHA; BHT; FERRIC ORTHOPHOSPHATE;** MONOSODIUM GLUTAMATE; **TURMERIC**

*Although "smoked" does not refer to a specific additive, it represents a process utilizing wood smoke, as "smoke flavoring" does, and therefore the food may contain some cancer-causing benzopyrene chemicals. For this reason, when a food or any of its constituents has been smoked, this has been noted in the additives-of-concern column.

BRANDS	ADDITIVES-OF-CONCERN BOLD—CONCERN TO ALL LIGHT—CONCERN TO SOME
SUPERMARKET PRIVATE BRANDS	
A & P	
—ANN PAGE	
RICE 'N EASY CHICKEN FLAVORED	**BHA; BHT;** MONOSODIUM GLUTAMATE; **TURMERIC**
LUCKY	
—LADY LEE	
ENRICHED LONG GRAIN RICE	NO ADDITIVES OF CONCERN
SAFEWAY	
—TOWN HOUSE *RICE*	
CALIFORNIA PEARL	NO ADDITIVES OF CONCERN
LONG GRAIN; MEDIUM GRAIN	**FERRIC ORTHOPHOSPHATE**
ITEMS IN HEALTH FOOD STORES	
NEAR EAST *PILAF MIX*	
LENTIL	NO ADDITIVES OF CONCERN
RICE	**TURMERIC**
SPANISH RICE	**PAPRIKA; TURMERIC**

XX. PICKLES, SALAD DRESSINGS, & OTHER CONDIMENTS

CATSUP

None of the items in this section contain any additives of concern, and all the items appear without an additives-of-concern column.

DEL MONTE TOMATO CATSUP

HEINZ TOMATO KETCHUP

HUNT'S TOMATO KETCHUP

SUPERMARKET PRIVATE BRANDS
A & P ANN PAGE TOMATO KETCHUP

LUCKY HARVEST DAY TOMATO CATSUP

LUCKY LADY LEE TOMATO CATSUP

SAFEWAY TOWN HOUSE TOMATO CATSUP

STOP & SHOP TOMATO KETCHUP

WINN DIXIE THRIFTY MAID TOMATO CATSUP

ITEMS IN HEALTH FOOD STORES

HAIN IMITATION CATSUP

BRANDS	ADDITIVES-OF-CONCERN **BOLD—CONCERN TO ALL** LIGHT—CONCERN TO SOME

MAYONNAISE & IMITATIONS

HELLMANN'S MAYONNAISE	NO ADDITIVES OF CONCERN
KRAFT MAYONNAISE	**PAPRIKA**
MIRACLE WHIP	**MODIFIED FOOD STARCH; PAPRIKA**
MRS FILBERTS IMITATION MAYONNAISE	**ARTIFICIAL COLOR; MODIFIED FOOD STARCH; NATURAL COLOR**
SUPERMARKET PRIVATE BRANDS **A & P** **—ANN PAGE** MAYONNAISE	NO ADDITIVES OF CONCERN
SALAD DRESSING; SANDWICH SPREAD	**MODIFIED CORN STARCH**
FIRST NATIONAL **—EDWARDS** SALAD DRESSING	**MODIFIED FOOD STARCH; OLEORESIN PAPRIKA**
—FINAST MAYONNAISE	NO ADDITIVES OF CONCERN
LUCKY **—LADY LEE** IMITATION MAYONNAISE	**ARTIFICIAL COLOR; MODIFIED FOOD STARCH; OLEORESIN OF PAPRIKA;** PROPYLENE GLYCOL ALGINATE
MAYONNAISE	**OLEORESIN PAPRIKA**

BRANDS	ADDITIVES-OF-CONCERN BOLD—CONCERN TO ALL LIGHT—CONCERN TO SOME
SALAD DRESSING	ALGIN DERIVATIVE; **MODIFIED FOOD STARCH; PAPRIKA**
PUBLIX	
—FLAVOR PERFECT	
MAYONNAISE	**OLEORESIN PAPRIKA**
SALAD DRESSING	**MODIFIED FOOD STARCH**
SAFEWAY	
—NUMADE	
REAL MAYONNAISE	NO ADDITIVES OF CONCERN
RELISH SANDWICH SPREAD; SALAD DRESSING	**MODIFIED FOOD STARCH; OLEORESIN OF PAPRIKA**
—SCOTCH BUY IMITATION MAYONNAISE	**ARTIFICIAL COLOR; MODIFIED FOOD STARCH; OLEORESIN PAPRIKA**
STOP & SHOP	
—STOP & SHOP	
IMITATION MAYONNAISE	**ARTIFICIAL COLOR; MODIFIED FOOD STARCH; OLEORESIN OF PAPRIKA**
MAYONNAISE	NO ADDITIVES OF CONCERN
SALAD DRESSING	**MODIFIED CORN STARCH**
WINN DIXIE	
—DEEP SOUTH	
MAYONNAISE	NO ADDITIVES OF CONCERN
SALAD DRESSING	**MODIFIED FOOD STARCH**
ITEMS IN HEALTH FOOD STORES	
HAIN *MAYONNAISE*	
EGGLESS IMITATION	ALGIN

BRANDS	ADDITIVES-OF-CONCERN BOLD—CONCERN TO ALL LIGHT—CONCERN TO SOME
HAIN *(Continued)*	
SAF-FLOWER; UNSALTED	NO ADDITIVES OF CONCERN
NORGANIC GOLDEN SOYA MAYONNAISE	NO ADDITIVES OF CONCERN
WALNUT ACRES MAYONNAISE	NO ADDITIVES OF CONCERN

MUSTARD

COLMAN'S HOT ENGLISH	**ARTIFICIAL COLORING**
FRANK'S MISTER	NO ADDITIVES OF CONCERN
FRENCH'S ONION BITS; REGULAR	**TURMERIC**
GREY-POUPON DIJON	NO ADDITIVES OF CONCERN
GULDEN'S DIABLO HOT; SPICY BROWN	**TURMERIC**
KRAFT REGULAR	**OLEORESINS OF PAPRIKA & TURMERIC; TURMERIC**
MAILLE DIJON	NO ADDITIVES OF CONCERN
NANCE'S REGULAR	PROPYLENE GLYCOL ALGINATE
PLOCHMAN'S REGULAR	**PAPRIKA; TURMERIC**

BRANDS	ADDITIVES-OF-CONCERN BOLD—CONCERN TO ALL LIGHT—CONCERN TO SOME
SUPERMARKET PRIVATE BRANDS	
A & P	
—ANN PAGE SALAD	**PAPRIKA; TURMERIC**
LUCKY	
—LADY LEE	
REGULAR	**TURMERIC**
SAFEWAY	
—TOWN HOUSE	
REGULAR	**PAPRIKA; TURMERIC**
STOP & SHOP	
—STOP & SHOP	
SALAD STYLE	**TURMERIC**
ITEMS IN HEALTH FOOD STORES	
EDEN HOT	NO ADDITIVES OF CONCERN
HAIN	NO ADDITIVES OF CONCERN
REINE DIJON NO SALT ADDED	NO ADDITIVES OF CONCERN

PICKLES

HEINZ	
GENUINE DILL	NO ADDITIVES OF CONCERN
HAMBURGER DILL SLICES	**ARTIFICIAL COLORING**
KOSHER DILL SPEARS; SWEET CUCUMBER SLICES; SWEET GHERKINS; SWEET MIXED	**TURMERIC OLEORESIN**

BRANDS	ADDITIVES-OF-CONCERN BOLD—CONCERN TO ALL LIGHT—CONCERN TO SOME
VLASIC	
KOSHER DILLS; KOSHER GHERKINS; POLISH SPEARS; SWEET BUTTER CHIPS; SWEET GHERKINS; SWEET MIX	**ARTIFICIAL COLOR**
SUPERMARKET PRIVATE BRANDS	
FIRST NATIONAL —EDWARDS	
HAMBURGER SLICES; KOSHER DILLS	**ARTIFICIAL COLOR**
SWEET GHERKINS; WHOLE SWEETS	**TURMERIC**
SAFEWAY —TOWN HOUSE	
HAMBURGER DILL CHIPS; SWEET; SWEET CUCUMBER CHIPS; WHOLE DILL; WHOLE KOSHER STYLE DILL	**ARTIFICIAL COLOR** OR **U.S. CERTIFIED COLOR; TURMERIC**
KOSHER STYLE DILL GHERKINS; POLISH STYLE WHOLE DILLS	**TURMERIC**
SWEET MIDGETS	FD & C YELLOW NO. 5
STOP & SHOP —STOP & SHOP	
CUCUMBER SLICES; HAMBURGER DILL SLICES;	**CERTIFIED FOOD COLOR**

(continues)

BRANDS	**ADDITIVES-OF-CONCERN** **BOLD—CONCERN TO ALL** LIGHT—CONCERN TO SOME
KOSHER DILLS; SWEET GHERKINS; SWEET MIXED	**CERTIFIED FOOD COLOR**
WINN DIXIE —DEEP SOUTH	
KOSHER DILL SPEARS; SWEET CUCUMBER CHIPS	FD & C YELLOW NO. 5
SWEET MIXED; WHOLE DILL; WHOLE SOUR	**ARTIFICIAL COLORS** W/ FD & C YELLOW NO. 5; **TURMERIC**
ITEMS IN HEALTH FOOD STORES	
FEATHERWEIGHT	
SLICED CUCUMBER; WHOLE DILL	**TURMERIC** OR **OIL OF TURMERIC**
HAIN NATURALS	
NATURAL KOSHER DILL CHIPS	NO ADDITIVES OF CONCERN
NEW ENGLAND ORGANIC PRODUCE CENTER —*THE PICKLE EATERS*	
CHIPS W/ HONEY; POOKIE SIZE	NO ADDITIVES OF CONCERN
WESTBRAE NATURAL	
KOSHER DILL	NO ADDITIVES OF CONCERN

RELISH

BENNETT'S CHILI SAUCE	NO ADDITIVES OF CONCERN

BRANDS	ADDITIVES-OF-CONCERN **BOLD—CONCERN TO ALL** LIGHT—CONCERN TO SOME
HEINZ HAMBURGER	NO ADDITIVES OF CONCERN
HOT DOG	[GUM] TRAGACANTH
SWEET	**TURMERIC OLEORESIN**
VLASIC HAMBURG; HOT DOG; SWEET	**ARTIFICIAL COLOR** OR **ARTIFICIALLY COLORED**
SUPERMARKET PRIVATE BRANDS	
A & P	
—ANN PAGE SWEET GARDEN	**TURMERIC**
FIRST NATIONAL	
—EDWARDS SWEET	**MODIFIED FOOD STARCH; TURMERIC**
SAFEWAY	
—TOWN HOUSE	
HAMBURGER	**MODIFIED FOOD STARCH; PAPRIKA; TURMERIC**
HOT DOG	**ARTIFICIAL COLOR; MODIFIED FOOD STARCH; PAPRIKA; TURMERIC**
STOP & SHOP	
—STOP & SHOP	
SWEET PICKLED	**TURMERIC**
ITEMS IN HEALTH FOOD STORES	
MRS. WOOD'S FARM	
SWEET RELISH	NO ADDITIVES OF CONCERN
NEW ENGLAND ORGANIC PRODUCE CENTER	
PICCALILLI RELISH	**IRISH MOSS**

BRANDS	ADDITIVES-OF-CONCERN **BOLD—CONCERN TO ALL** LIGHT—CONCERN TO SOME

SALAD DRESSINGS

By law, at this writing, it is not required of a manufacturer to state whether cheeses contain artificial colors, unless the color is FD & C Yellow No. 5 (Tartrazine). Their presence in salad dressings containing cheese therefore remains an uncertainty, unless it is voluntarily declared on the label that artificial colors have been used or have not. For a more detailed explanation of artificial color in cheese, refer to the beginning of the cheese section of "Dairy Products & Substitutes."

GOOD SEASONS *SALAD DRESSING MIX* BLEU CHEESE	**ARTIFICIAL COLOR;** MONOSODIUM GLUTAMATE; PROPYLENE GLYCOL ALGINATE
CHEESE ITALIAN	**ARTIFICIAL COLOR;** GUAR GUM; PROPYLENE GLYCOL ALGINATE
GARLIC	MONOSODIUM GLUTAMATE; **PAPRIKA;** PROPYLENE GLYCOL ALGINATE
ITALIAN	**BHA; CALCIUM CARRAGEENAN;** MONOSODIUM GLUTAMATE
RIVIERA FRENCH	**ARTIFICIAL COLOR; BHA;** GUAR GUM
HIDDEN VALLEY RANCH MILK RECIPE ORIGINAL RANCH	BUTTERMILK SOLIDS; **CALCIUM STEARATE;** CASEIN; MONOSODIUM GLUTAMATE; WHEY SOLIDS

BRANDS	ADDITIVES-OF-CONCERN BOLD—CONCERN TO ALL LIGHT—CONCERN TO SOME
KRAFT	
CATALINA; MIRACLE FRENCH	**OLEORESIN PAPRIKA**
COLESLAW; CREAMY CUCUMBER; ROKA BLUE CHEESE; THOUSAND ISLAND	PROPYLENE GLYCOL ALGINATE
CREAMY RUSSIAN; OIL & VINEGAR	**OLEORESIN PAPRIKA;** PROPYLENE GLYCOL ALGINATE
RED WINE VINEGAR & OIL	CAROB BEAN GUM; **OLEORESIN PAPRIKA**
ZESTY ITALIAN	**MODIFIED FOOD STARCH; OLEORESIN PAPRIKA**
PFEIFFER	
CAESAR	**MODIFIED FOOD STARCH**
CHEF ITALIAN; RED WINE VINEGAR & OIL	**ARTIFICIAL COLOR** OR **ARTIFICIAL FOOD COLORS**
ROQUEFORT CHEESE; THOUSAND ISLAND	PROPYLENE GLYCOL ALGINATE
RUSSIAN	**COLORING;** PROPYLENE GLYCOL ALGINATE
SPRING GARDEN	NO ADDITIVES OF CONCERN

BRANDS	ADDITIVES-OF-CONCERN BOLD—CONCERN TO ALL LIGHT—CONCERN TO SOME
SEVEN SEAS GREEN GODDESS	**ARTIFICIAL COLOR; CARRAGEENAN;** GUAR GUM; LOCUST BEAN GUM
RUSSIAN	NO ADDITIVES OF CONCERN
VIVA CAESAR	**ARTIFICIAL COLOR;** MONOSODIUM GLUTAMATE; **OXYSTEARIN**
VIVA ITALIAN!; VIVA RED WINE VINEGAR & OIL	**ARTIFICIAL COLOR; OXYSTEARIN**
WISH-BONE CALIFORNIA ONION; CHUNKY BLUE CHEESE; CREAMY GARLIC; CREAMY ITALIAN	ALGIN DERIVATIVE
DELUXE FRENCH; SWEET 'N SPICY FRENCH	ALGIN DERIVATIVE; **OLEORESIN PAPRIKA**
ITALIAN; RUSSIAN	NO ADDITIVES OF CONCERN
SUPERMARKET PRIVATE BRANDS **A & P** **—ANN PAGE** CAESAR; THOUSAND ISLAND	NO ADDITIVES OF CONCERN
FRENCH; ITALIAN	ALGIN DERIVATIVE
RED WINE VINEGAR & OIL	**ARTIFICIAL COLOR**

BRANDS	**ADDITIVES-OF-CONCERN** BOLD—CONCERN TO ALL LIGHT—CONCERN TO SOME
LUCKY —LADY LEE	
BLUE CHEESE	PROPYLENE GLYCOL ALGINATE
ITALIAN	**PAPRIKA**
THOUSAND ISLAND	ALGIN DERIVATIVE; **MODIFIED FOOD STARCH**
(REFRIGERATED) BLEU CHEESE; ROQUEFORT	**COCONUT OIL;** LOCUST BEAN GUM; MILK SOLIDS (NONFAT); MONOSODIUM GLUTAMATE; **SODIUM CASEINATE;** WHEY SOLIDS
1000 ISLAND	MONOSODIUM GLUTAMATE
SAFEWAY —NUMADE	
GREEN GODDESS	**ARTIFICIAL COLORS**
1000 ISLAND	NO ADDITIVES OF CONCERN
STOP & SHOP —STOP & SHOP	
BLEU CHEESE	NO ADDITIVES OF CONCERN
CREAMY ITALIAN; RED WINE VINEGAR & OIL	**ARTIFICIAL COLOR** OR **CERTIFIED FOOD COLOR**
FRENCH; RUSSIAN; THOUSAND ISLAND	**OLEORESIN PAPRIKA;** PROPYLENE GLYCOL ALGINATE
ITEMS IN HEALTH FOOD STORES	
HAIN	
BLEU CHEESE;	**VEGETABLE GUM**

(continues)

BRANDS	ADDITIVES-OF-CONCERN **BOLD—CONCERN TO ALL** LIGHT—CONCERN TO SOME
CREAMY FRENCH; GREEN GODDESS; HONEY & SESAME; ITALIAN; LEMON N HERB; REAL BLEU CHEESE BUTTERMILK; RUSSIAN; THOUSAND ISLAND	**VEGETABLE GUM**
GARLIC 'N OIL; OIL 'N VINEGAR	NO ADDITIVES OF CONCERN
HERB (UNSALTED)	SEA KELP
OLD WORLD FRENCH	ALGIN; WHEY
—SALAD DRESSING MIX	
BLEU CHEESE	WHEY
CAESAR; THOUSAND ISLAND	ALGIN; WHEY
FRENCH; ITALIAN	ALGIN; **PAPRIKA**
HONEY & LEMON	ALGIN
HEALTH VALLEY *DRESSING & DIP*	
AVOCADO; GREEN GODDESS; RUSSIAN	NO ADDITIVES OF CONCERN
FRENCH	ALGIN DERIVATIVE FROM SEAWEED
NORGANIC FRENCH	**VEGETABLE GUM**

BRANDS	ADDITIVES-OF-CONCERN BOLD—CONCERN TO ALL LIGHT—CONCERN TO SOME
WALNUT ACRES	
CREAMY FRENCH	CAROB [BEAN] GUM; **PAPRIKA**
CREAMY ITALIAN; CREAMY WATERCRESS; THOUSAND ISLAND	NO ADDITIVES OF CONCERN

XXI. SNACK ITEMS

CORN, POTATO, & TORTILLA CHIPS

By law, at this writing, it is not required of a manufacturer to state whether cheeses contain artificial colors, unless the color is FD & C Yellow No. 5 (Tartrazine). Their presence in corn, potato, and tortilla chips containing cheese therefore remains an uncertainty, unless it is voluntarily declared on the label that artificial colors have been used or have not. For a more detailed explanation of artificial color in cheese, refer to the beginning of the cheese section of "Dairy Products & Substitutes."

BRANDS	**ADDITIVES-OF-CONCERN** BOLD—CONCERN TO ALL LIGHT—CONCERN TO SOME
CAINS BARBEQUE POTATO	**MODIFIED WHEAT STARCH;** MONOSODIUM GLUTAMATE; **NATURAL HICKORY SMOKE FLAVOR; PAPRIKA**
POTATO	NO ADDITIVES OF CONCERN
SOUR CREAM & ONION RIPPLED POTATO	**MODIFIED FOOD STARCH;** MONOSODIUM GLUTAMATE; **SODIUM CASEINATE;** SOUR CREAM SOLIDS; WHEY POWDER
DORITOS NACHO CHEESE TORTILLA	**ARTIFICIAL COLOR;** MONOSODIUM GLUTAMATE; WHEY
FRITOS CORN	NO ADDITIVES OF CONCERN

BRANDS	**ADDITIVES-OF-CONCERN** **BOLD—CONCERN TO ALL** LIGHT—CONCERN TO SOME
KEYSTONE SNACKS	
CORN	**BUTYLATED HYDROXYTOLUENE; (COCONUT OIL)***
NACHO CHEESE TORTILLA	**(COCONUT OIL);* EXTRACTIVES OF PAPRIKA;** MONOSODIUM GLUTAMATE; **U.S. CERTIFIED FOOD COLOR;** WHEY POWDER
LAY'S POTATO	NO ADDITIVES OF CONCERN
NABISCO	
NACHO CHEESE TORTILLA	MILK SOLIDS (NONFAT); MONOSODIUM GLUTAMATE; **PAPRIKA; TURMERIC OLEORESIN;** WHEY SOLIDS
POTATO CHIPSTERS	**BHA; COCONUT OIL; TURMERIC OLEORESIN**
PARADE POTATO	**VEGETABLE OIL**
PRINGLE'S	
COUNTRY STYLE POTATO; ORIGINAL STYLE POTATO; RIPPLED STYLE POTATO	NO ADDITIVES OF CONCERN
TOSTITOS NACHO CHEESE TORTILLA	**ARTIFICIAL COLOR;** MONOSODIUM GLUTAMATE; WHEY

*Blend may contain this saturated oil.

BRANDS	ADDITIVES-OF-CONCERN BOLD—CONCERN TO ALL LIGHT—CONCERN TO SOME
WISE BARBEQUE POTATO	**ARTIFICIAL COLOR;** MONOSODIUM GLUTAMATE; **PAPRIKA**
CORN; POTATO	NO ADDITIVES OF CONCERN
—*BRAVOS* SOUR CREAM & ONION TORTILLA	MILK SOLIDS (CULTURED NONFAT); MONOSODIUM GLUTAMATE; SOUR CREAM SOLIDS
—*RIDGIES* SOUR CREAM & ONION POTATO	MONOSODIUM GLUTAMATE; **SODIUM CASEINATE;** WHEY
SUPERMARKET PRIVATE BRANDS	
A & P—ANN PAGE CORN; POTATO; RIPPLED POTATO	NO ADDITIVES OF CONCERN
LUCKY—LADY LEE DIP POTATO; POTATO	NO ADDITIVES OF CONCERN
SAFEWAY —(NO BRAND NAME) JALAPEÑO TORTILLA HOT	**PAPRIKA; TURMERIC**
—PARTY PRIDE BARBEQUE POTATO	**(HYDROGENATED COTTONSEED, PALM, SAFFLOWER OILS);* NATURAL HICKORY SMOKE FLAVOR; PAPRIKA (& EXTRACTIVES OF)**

*Blend may contain one or more of these saturated oils.

BRANDS	ADDITIVES-OF-CONCERN BOLD—CONCERN TO ALL LIGHT—CONCERN TO SOME
SAFEWAY—PARTY PRIDE *(Continued)*	
POTATO	**(HYDROGENATED CORN, COTTONSEED, PALM, PEANUT, SOYBEAN, SUNFLOWER OILS)***
TACO FLAVORED POTATO	NO ADDITIVES OF CONCERN
STOP & SHOP —STOP & SHOP	
CORN	NO ADDITIVES OF CONCERN
WINN DIXIE —CRACKIN GOOD	
CORN PLAIN; TACOS TORTILLA; WAVY	NO ADDITIVES OF CONCERN
ITEMS IN HEALTH FOOD STORES	
DR. BRONNER'S	
CORN & SESAME SNACK	NO ADDITIVES OF CONCERN
EREWHON *—AZTEC CORN*	
ONION & GARLIC; TAMARI; UNSALTED	NO ADDITIVES OF CONCERN
TACO	**PAPRIKA**
—ALL NATURAL POTATO	
NO SALT ADDED; SALTED; TAMARI	NO ADDITIVES OF CONCERN

*Blend may contain one or more of these saturated oils.

BRANDS	ADDITIVES-OF-CONCERN BOLD—CONCERN TO ALL LIGHT—CONCERN TO SOME
TACO	**PAPRIKA**
HAIN	
CHEESE SESAME TORTILLA	**PAPRIKA; TURMERIC;** WHEY
NATURAL POTATO	NO ADDITIVES OF CONCERN
VEGETIZED SESAME TORTILLA	DULSE; KELP
—SEVEN GRAIN	
W/ CINNAMON & RAISINS; W/ ONION & GARLIC	NO ADDITIVES OF CONCERN
—YOGURT	
W/ PEANUTS; W/ WHEAT GERM	NO ADDITIVES OF CONCERN
HEALTH VALLEY	
DIP POTATO CHIPS UNSALTED	NO ADDITIVES OF CONCERN
—CORN CHIPS	
UNSALTED; W/ CHEESE; W/ SESAME SEEDS	NO ADDITIVES OF CONCERN
—TORTILLA STRIPS	
CHEDDAR CHEESE; YOGURT	NO ADDITIVES OF CONCERN
MOTHER EARTH	
TAMARI TORTILLA	NO ADDITIVES OF CONCERN

BRANDS	ADDITIVES-OF-CONCERN **BOLD—CONCERN TO ALL** LIGHT—CONCERN TO SOME

DIPS & DIP MIXES

By law, at this writing, it is not required of a manufacturer to state whether cheeses contain artificial colors, unless the color is FD & C Yellow No. 5 (Tartrazine). Their presence in dips and dip mixes containing cheese therefore remains an uncertainty, unless it is voluntarily declared on the label that artificial colors have been used or have not. For a more detailed explanation of artificial color in cheese, refer to the beginning of the cheese section of "Dairy Products & Substitutes."

BRANDS	ADDITIVES-OF-CONCERN
BORDEN CLAM & LOBSTER DIP	**ARTIFICIAL COLOR;** CAROB BEAN GUM; **MODIFIED FOOD STARCH;** MONOSODIUM GLUTAMATE; WHEY
BREAKSTONE'S *DIP*	
CLAM; FRENCH ONION	CAROB BEAN GUM; **MODIFIED FOOD STARCH;** MONOSODIUM GLUTAMATE
FRITO-LAY *DIP MIX*	
GREEN GODDESS; ONION-BACON	**ARTIFICIAL COLOR** OR **COLORING;** MONOSODIUM GLUTAMATE
TOASTED ONION	**MODIFIED FOOD STARCH;** MONOSODIUM GLUTAMATE; **PAPRIKA**
FRITOS *DIP*	
BEAN	**LARD; PAPRIKA**
ENCHILADA	**LARD; MODIFIED FOOD STARCH;** MONOSODIUM GLUTAMATE; **PAPRIKA**

BRANDS	ADDITIVES-OF-CONCERN **BOLD—CONCERN TO ALL** LIGHT—CONCERN TO SOME
KRAFT *READY TO SERVE DIP*	
BLUE CHEESE	CAROB BEAN GUM; GUAR GUM
CREAMY CUCUMBER	**ARTIFICIAL COLOR;** CAROB BEAN GUM; **MODIFIED FOOD STARCH;** MONOSODIUM GLUTAMATE
ONION	CAROB BEAN GUM; GUAR GUM; **TURMERIC;** WHEY
SUPERMARKET PRIVATE BRANDS	
LUCKY	
—LADY LEE *DIP*	
AVOCADO; AVOCADO HOT	**ARTIFICIAL COLOR; COCONUT OIL;** GUAR GUM; MILK SOLIDS (NONFAT); **SODIUM CASEINATE;** WHEY SOLIDS
BACON & ONION; CLAM; FRENCH ONION	**COCONUT OIL;** MILK SOLIDS (NONFAT); PROPYLENE GLYCOL ALGINATE; WHEY SOLIDS
TORTILLA	**ARTIFICIAL COLOR; COCONUT OIL;** MILK SOLIDS (NONFAT); PROPYLENE GLYCOL ALGINATE; WHEY SOLIDS
PUBLIX	
—DAIRI-FRESH	
FRENCH ONION CHIP 'N DIP	**CARRAGEENAN;** LOCUST BEAN GUM

BRANDS	**ADDITIVES-OF-CONCERN** **BOLD—CONCERN TO ALL** LIGHT—CONCERN TO SOME
SAFEWAY —(NO BRAND NAME) *PARTY DIP*	
AVOCADO GUACAMOLE	ALGIN; **ARTIFICIAL COLOR;** GUAR GUM; MONOSODIUM GLUTAMATE; SODIUM ALGINATE; **SODIUM CASEINATE**
BLEU TANG; GARLIC	GUAR GUM; **MODIFIED FOOD STARCH;** MONOSODIUM GLUTAMATE; **SODIUM CASEINATE**
CHEDDAR CHEESE	BUTTERMILK SOLIDS; GUAR GUM; MONOSODIUM GLUTAMATE; **SODIUM CASEINATE;** WHEY
CLAM	FD & C YELLOW NO. 5; GUAR GUM; **SODIUM CASEINATE**
ITEMS IN HEALTH FOOD STORES	
HAIN *DIP*	
JALAPENO BEAN	**PAPRIKA**
ONION BEAN	NO ADDITIVES OF CONCERN
SEELECT VEGETABLE DIP MIX	NO ADDITIVES OF CONCERN

BRANDS	ADDITIVES-OF-CONCERN **BOLD—CONCERN TO ALL** LIGHT—CONCERN TO SOME

NUTS & SEEDS

BLUE DIAMOND *ALMONDS* CHEESE FLAVORED*	MONOSODIUM GLUTAMATE; **NATURAL SMOKE FLAVOR; VEGETABLE OIL;** WHEY (CHEDDAR CHEESE)
ROASTED BLANCHED SALTED	NO ADDITIVES OF CONCERN
SMOKEHOUSE	**NATURAL HICKORY SMOKE FLAVOR**
MAUNA LOA MACADAMIA NUTS	**COCONUT OIL**
PILLSBURY WHEAT NUTS	**ARTIFICIAL COLOR; HYDROGENATED SOYBEAN OIL; SODIUM CASEINATE**
PLANTERS COCKTAIL PEANUTS; MIXED NUTS; SALTED CASHEWS; SESAME NUT MIX; SUNFLOWER NUTS	**(COCONUT OIL)†**

*By law, at this writing, it is not required of a manufacturer to state whether cheeses contain artificial colors, unless the color is FD & C Yellow No. 5 (Tartrazine). Their presence in nuts and seeds containing cheese therefore remains an uncertainty, unless it is voluntarily declared on the label that artificial colors have been used or have not. For a more detailed explanation of artificial color in cheese, refer to the beginning of the cheese section of "Dairy Products & Substitutes."

†Blend may contain this saturated oil.

BRANDS	ADDITIVES-OF-CONCERN BOLD—CONCERN TO ALL LIGHT—CONCERN TO SOME
PLANTERS *(Continued)*	
RED PISTACHIOS	**ARTIFICIAL COLOR**
TAVERN NUTS	**MODIFIED FOOD STARCH**
—DRY ROASTED	
ALMONDS; CASHEWS; MIXED NUTS; PEANUTS; SPANISH PEANUTS; SUNFLOWER NUTS	GUM ARABIC; **MODIFIED FOOD STARCH;** MONOSODIUM GLUTAMATE; **PAPRIKA**
UNSALTED PEANUTS	NO ADDITIVES OF CONCERN
—SOUTHERN BELLE	
CASHEW HALVES; SUNFLOWER KERNELS	**(COCONUT OIL)***
SUNFLOWER SEEDS	NO ADDITIVES OF CONCERN
RIVER QUEEN	
CASHEW HALVES; SALTED MIXED NUTS	NO ADDITIVES OF CONCERN
SUPERMARKET PRIVATE BRANDS	
A & P	
—ANN PAGE	
ALMONDS; FANCY SALTED CASHEWS; FILBERTS; PECAN MEATS	NO ADDITIVES OF CONCERN
—DRY ROASTED	
CASHEWS; MIXED NUTS; PEANUTS	**MODIFIED STARCH;** MONOSODIUM GLUTAMATE

BRANDS	ADDITIVES-OF-CONCERN **BOLD—CONCERN TO ALL** LIGHT—CONCERN TO SOME
—SALTED FANCY MIXED NUTS; MIXED NUTS; PARTY PEANUTS; SPANISH PEANUTS	NO ADDITIVES OF CONCERN
FIRST NATIONAL —FINAST *DRY ROASTED* MIXED NUTS; PEANUTS	**PAPRIKA**
LUCKY —LADY LEE CASHEWS; MIXED NUTS W/ PEANUTS	**(COCONUT OIL)***
TOFFEE BUTTER PEANUTS	**BUTTER**
—DRY ROASTED CASHEWS; MIXED NUTS; PEANUTS	MONOSODIUM GLUTAMATE
SAFEWAY —PARTY PRIDE CASHEWS; DELUXE MIXED NUTS; PEANUTS	**(COCONUT OIL)***
—DRY ROASTED CASHEWS; MIXED NUTS; PEANUTS	MONOSODIUM GLUTAMATE

*Blend may contain this saturated oil.

BRANDS	ADDITIVES-OF-CONCERN **BOLD—CONCERN TO ALL** LIGHT—CONCERN TO SOME
STOP & SHOP —STOP & SHOP MIXED NUTS NO PEANUTS; SALTED PEANUTS	NO ADDITIVES OF CONCERN
—*DRY ROASTED* CASHEWS; MIXED NUTS; PEANUTS	GUM ARABIC; MONOSODIUM GLUTAMATE
UNSALTED PEANUTS	NO ADDITIVES OF CONCERN
ITEMS IN HEALTH FOOD STORES	
FLAVOR TREE NUT & SNACK MIX; SUNFLOWER & SESAME MIX	**TURMERIC**
HUNZA ALMONDS; WALNUTS	NO ADDITIVES OF CONCERN
NIK'S SNAKS RAISINS & RAW WALNUTS; TRAIL MIX	NO ADDITIVES OF CONCERN
—*DRY ROASTED* CASHEWS; MIXED NUTS; SPANISH PEANUTS; SUNFLOWER SEEDS	NO ADDITIVES OF CONCERN
—*RAW* MIXED NUTS; SUNFLOWER SEEDS; SUNFLOWER SEEDS & RAISINS	NO ADDITIVES OF CONCERN

BRANDS	ADDITIVES-OF-CONCERN **BOLD—CONCERN TO ALL** LIGHT—CONCERN TO SOME

POPCORN & POPCORN SNACKS

BANG-O *POPCORN* WHITE HULLESS; YELLOW HYBRID	NO ADDITIVES OF CONCERN
CRACKER JACK	NO ADDITIVES OF CONCERN
FIDDLE FADDLE	WHEY
FRANKLIN CRUNCH 'N MUNCH	NO ADDITIVES OF CONCERN
JIFFY-POP *POPCORN* BUTTER FLAVOR	**ARTIFICIAL VEGETABLE COLOR; BHA; BHT**
NATURAL FLAVOR	NO ADDITIVES OF CONCERN
ORVILLE REDENBACHER'S GOURMET POPPING CORN	NO ADDITIVES OF CONCERN
POPPYCOCK THE ORIGINAL	NO ADDITIVES OF CONCERN
SCREAMING YELLOW ZONKERS	**ARTIFICIAL COLOR**
TV TIME POPCORN	**ARTIFICIAL COLOR; COCONUT OIL**
WISE CHEEZ POP CORN	**ARTIFICIAL COLORS; (COCONUT OIL);*** MONOSODIUM GLUTAMATE

*Blend may contain this saturated oil.

BRANDS	ADDITIVES-OF-CONCERN BOLD—CONCERN TO ALL LIGHT—CONCERN TO SOME
SUPERMARKET PRIVATE BRANDS	
A & P	
—ANN PAGE	
CHEESE CORN	**ARTIFICIAL COLORING;** BUTTERMILK SOLIDS; **(COCONUT OIL);*** MONOSODIUM GLUTAMATE; WHEY SOLIDS
POPCORN	**ARTIFICIAL COLORING; (COCONUT OIL)***
LUCKY	
—LADY LEE	
POPCORN	NO ADDITIVES OF CONCERN
SAFEWAY	
—PARTY PRIDE	
POPCORN	**ARTIFICIAL COLOR; (COCONUT OIL)***
STOP & SHOP	
—STOP & SHOP	
CARAMEL CORN	NO ADDITIVES OF CONCERN

PRETZELS & MISCELLANEOUS SNACKS

DURKEE/O & C	
FRENCH FRIED ONIONS	**ARTIFICIAL COLOR; BHA;**
POTATO STICKS	**BHA**
GENERAL MILLS	
BUGLES	**BHA; BHT; COCONUT OIL**

*Blend may contain this saturated oil.

BRANDS	ADDITIVES-OF-CONCERN BOLD—CONCERN TO ALL LIGHT—CONCERN TO SOME
KEYSTONE SNACKS CHEESE CURLS	**ARTIFICIAL COLORING; (COCONUT OIL);*** WHEY
NABISCO CORN DIGGERS	**BHA; COCONUT OIL**
DOO-DADS	**ARTIFICIAL COLOR; BHA; (COCONUT OIL; LARD);*** MONOSODIUM GLUTAMATE; **PAPRIKA;** WHEY
—*MISTER SALTY* DUTCH PRETZELS	NO ADDITIVES OF CONCERN
VERI-THIN PRETZELS	**(LARD)***
WISE *CHEESE DOODLES* CRUNCHY	**ARTIFICIAL COLORS; (COCONUT OIL);* FERRIC ORTHOPHOSPHATE;** WHEY (ACID & SWEET)
PUFFED	**ARTIFICIAL COLOR; (COCONUT OIL);* FERRIC ORTHOPHOSPHATE; MODIFIED CORN STARCH;** MONOSODIUM GLUTAMATE; **SODIUM CASEINATE;** WHEY
SUPERMARKET PRIVATE BRANDS A & P —A & P BITE SIZE PRETZELS	NO ADDITIVES OF CONCERN

*Blend may contain one or more of these saturated fats and/or oil.

BRANDS	ADDITIVES-OF-CONCERN **BOLD—CONCERN TO ALL** LIGHT—CONCERN TO SOME
—ANN PAGE CHEESE TWISTS	**ARTIFICIAL COLORING;** BUTTERMILK SOLIDS; **(COCONUT OIL);*** MILK SOLIDS (NONFAT DRY); MONOSODIUM GLUTAMATE; WHEY SOLIDS
—ANN PAGE *PRETZELS* PETITE; RODS; STIX; TEENIES	NO ADDITIVES OF CONCERN
FIRST NATIONAL —FINAST *PRETZELS* RODS; STIX	NO ADDITIVES OF CONCERN
LUCKY —LADY LEE *PRETZELS* MINI-TWIST; ROD; STICK; TWIST	NO ADDITIVES OF CONCERN
SAFEWAY —PARTY PRIDE *PRETZELS* BAVARIAN; MINI TWIST; STICK	NO ADDITIVES OF CONCERN
STOP & SHOP —STOP & SHOP CORN Q'S	**ARTIFICIAL COLOR;** BUTTERMILK SOLIDS; **(COCONUT OIL);*** MONOSODIUM GLUTAMATE; WHEY SOLIDS
—STOP & SHOP *PRETZELS* RINGS; STIX; THINS	NO ADDITIVES OF CONCERN

*Blend may contain one or more of these saturated fats and/or oils.

BRANDS	ADDITIVES-OF-CONCERN BOLD—CONCERN TO ALL LIGHT—CONCERN TO SOME
WINN DIXIE —CRACKIN GOOD CHEESE BALLS	**ARTIFICIAL COLOR;** WHEY
PRETZELS RINGS; RODS	NO ADDITIVES OF CONCERN
ITEMS IN HEALTH FOOD STORES	
BARBARA'S PRETZELS	NO ADDITIVES OF CONCERN
SESAME BREADSTICKS	GLUTEN (WHEAT)
DR. BRONNER'S CHEEZON CORN-SNACK*	**COCONUT OIL;** MILK SOLIDS (NONFAT)
EREWHON PRETZELS	NO ADDITIVES OF CONCERN
FLAVOR TREE SESAME & BRAN STICKS; SESAME STICKS	**TURMERIC**
HEALTH VALLEY PRETZELS	NO ADDITIVES OF CONCERN

*By law, at this writing, it is not required of a manufacturer to state whether cheeses contain artificial colors, unless the color is FD & C Yellow No. 5 (Tartrazine). Their presence in snacks containing cheese therefore remains an uncertainty, unless it is voluntarily declared on the label that artificial colors have been used or have not. For a more detailed explanation of artificial color in cheese, refer to the beginning of the cheese section of "Dairy Products & Substitutes."

BRANDS	ADDITIVES-OF-CONCERN **BOLD—CONCERN TO ALL** LIGHT—CONCERN TO SOME

TOASTER PASTRIES

KELLOGG'S *—POP-TARTS* BLUEBERRY; CHERRY CHIP; STRAWBERRY	**ARTIFICIAL COLORING; BHA; (COCONUT OIL);*** WHEY
BROWN SUGAR-CINNAMON; CHOCOLATE CHIP	**BHA; (COCONUT OIL);*** EGG WHITES; WHEY
—FROSTED POP-TARTS CHOCOLATE FUDGE; CHOCOLATE-VANILLA CREME	**ARTIFICIAL COLORING; BHA; (COCONUT OIL);*** EGG WHITES; WHEY
NABISCO *TOASTETTES* BLUEBERRY; BROWN SUGAR CINNAMON; CHERRY; STRAWBERRY	**ARTIFICIAL COLOR; MODIFIED CORN STARCH; MODIFIED TAPIOCA STARCH;** WHEY
SUPERMARKET PRIVATE BRANDS FIRST NATIONAL —FINAST *TOASTER PASTRIES* BROWN SUGAR CINNAMON	**BHA; MODIFIED CORN STARCH;** WHEY SOLIDS
CHERRY; FROSTED STRAWBERRY; STRAWBERRY	**ARTIFICIAL COLORS; BHA;** WHEY SOLIDS

BRANDS	ADDITIVES-OF-CONCERN BOLD—CONCERN TO ALL LIGHT—CONCERN TO SOME
SAFEWAY —TOWN HOUSE *FROSTED TOASTER TARTS* FUDGE; STRAWBERRY	**ARTIFICIAL COLORS; BHA;** WHEY SOLIDS
STOP & SHOP —STOP & SHOP *TOASTER TARTS* BLUEBERRY; STRAWBERRY	**ARTIFICIAL COLORS; BHA;** WHEY SOLIDS
FROSTED TOASTER TARTS CINNAMON	**ARTIFICIAL COLORS; BHA; MODIFIED CORN STARCH;** WHEY SOLIDS
WINN DIXIE —CRACKIN GOOD *TOASTER PASTRIES* BLUEBERRY; STRAWBERRY	**ARTIFICIAL COLOR; (HYDROGENATED PALM, SOYBEAN OILS);*** WHEY SOLIDS
FROSTED TOASTER PASTRIES APPLE	**ARTIFICIAL COLOR; NUTMEG;** WHEY SOLIDS
BLUEBERRY; CHERRY; CINNAMON; GRAPE; STRAWBERRY	**ARTIFICIAL COLOR;** WHEY SOLIDS

*Blend may contain these saturated oils.

XXII. SOUPS

BOUILLON, KOJI, MISO

BRANDS	**ADDITIVES-OF-CONCERN** BOLD—CONCERN TO ALL LIGHT—CONCERN TO SOME
CAINS *BOUILLON CUBES*	
BEEF	NO ADDITIVES OF CONCERN
CHICKEN	**TURMERIC**
HERB-OX	
—*BOUILLON CUBES*	
BEEF; CHICKEN	NO ADDITIVES OF CONCERN
—*INSTANT BROTH*	
BEEF	NO ADDITIVES OF CONCERN
CHICKEN	**TURMERIC**
STEERO	
INSTANT BEEF BOUILLON	MONOSODIUM GLUTAMATE
—*BOUILLON CUBES*	
BEEF; CHICKEN	MONOSODIUM GLUTAMATE
WYLER'S	
—*BOUILLON CUBES*	
BEEF	**ARTIFICIAL COLOR;** MONOSODIUM GLUTAMATE
CHICKEN	**BHA; BHT;** MONOSODIUM GLUTAMATE; **TURMERIC**

BRANDS	ADDITIVES-OF-CONCERN **BOLD—CONCERN TO ALL** LIGHT—CONCERN TO SOME
—*INSTANT BOUILLON*	
BEEF	**ARTIFICIAL COLOR;** MONOSODIUM GLUTAMATE
CHICKEN	**BHA; BHT;** MONOSODIUM GLUTAMATE; **TURMERIC**
ITEMS IN HEALTH FOOD STORES	
COLD MOUNTAIN	
KOJI	**ASPERGILLUS ORYZAE MOLD**
—*MISO*	
MELLOW WHITE; RED MISO	NO ADDITIVES OF CONCERN
EREWHON *SOYBEAN PASTE*	
PLAIN; W/ BARLEY; W/ RICE	NO ADDITIVES OF CONCERN
HAUSER BROTH	NO ADDITIVES OF CONCERN
MARUSAN SOYBEAN PASTE MAME MISO	NO ADDITIVES OF CONCERN
MORGA VEGETABLE BOUILLON CUBES	NO ADDITIVES OF CONCERN
PLANTAFORCE	
VEGETABLE CONCENTRATE	KELP
VEGEX BOUILLON CUBES	NO ADDITIVES OF CONCERN
WESTBRAE NATURAL	
MELLOW WHITE MISO	NO ADDITIVES OF CONCERN

BRANDS	ADDITIVES-OF-CONCERN BOLD—CONCERN TO ALL LIGHT—CONCERN TO SOME

CANNED SOUP

CAMPBELL'S BEEF NOODLE; CHICKEN BARLEY; CHICKEN NOODLE; MEATBALL ALPHABET; MUSHROOM BARLEY; NEW ENGLAND CLAM CHOWDER; TURKEY NOODLE; VEGETABLE; VEGETARIAN VEGETABLE	MONOSODIUM GLUTAMATE
BEEFY MUSHROOM; CLAM CHOWDER MANHATTAN STYLE; CREAM OF SHRIMP	**MODIFIED FOOD STARCH;** MONOSODIUM GLUTAMATE
BLACK BEAN	MONOSODIUM GLUTAMATE; **OLEORESIN PAPRIKA**
CHEDDAR CHEESE*	**CALCIUM CASEINATE;** MONOSODIUM GLUTAMATE; **OLEORESIN PAPRIKA; SODIUM CASEINATE;** WHEY
CREAM OF ASPARAGUS	**CALCIUM CASEINATE;** MONOSODIUM GLUTAMATE; **SODIUM CASEINATE;** WHEY

*By law, at this writing, it is not required of a manufacturer to state whether cheeses contain artificial colors, unless the color is FD & C Yellow No. 5 (Tartrazine). Their presence in canned soup containing cheese therefore remains an uncertainty, unless it is voluntarily declared on the label that artificial colors have been used or have not. For a more detailed explanation of artificial color in cheese, refer to the beginning of the cheese section in "Dairy Products & Substitutes."

BRANDS	ADDITIVES-OF-CONCERN **BOLD—CONCERN TO ALL** LIGHT—CONCERN TO SOME
CREAM OF CELERY; CREAM OF MUSHROOM	**CALCIUM CASEINATE; MODIFIED FOOD STARCH;** MONOSODIUM GLUTAMATE; WHEY
CREAM OF CHICKEN	**CALCIUM CASEINATE;** MONOSODIUM GLUTAMATE; WHEY
GREEN PEA; PEPPER POT; TOMATO; TOMATO BISQUE	NO ADDITIVES OF CONCERN
OLD FASHIONED TOMATO RICE	**CALCIUM CASEINATE;** WHEY
—CHUNKY SOUP	
BEEF	NO ADDITIVES OF CONCERN
CHICKEN; CLAM CHOWDER MANHATTAN STYLE; TURKEY; VEGETABLE BEEF	MONOSODIUM GLUTAMATE
HAM 'N BUTTER BEAN; SPLIT PEA W/ HAM	MONOSODIUM GLUTAMATE; **SMOKE FLAVORING; SODIUM NITRITE**
—ONE OF THE LIGHT ONES	
BEEF BROTH; CHICKEN & STARS; CHICKEN BROTH; CHICKEN VEGETABLE; CHICKEN W/ RICE; CONSOMMÉ (BEEF); ONION; TURKEY VEGETABLE	MONOSODIUM GLUTAMATE

BRANDS	ADDITIVES-OF-CONCERN **BOLD—CONCERN TO ALL** LIGHT—CONCERN TO SOME
CAMPBELL'S *(Continued)*	
—ONE OF THE MANHANDLERS	
BEAN W/ BACON	**MODIFIED FOOD STARCH;** MONOSODIUM GLUTAMATE; **SMOKE FLAVORING**
BEEF W/ VEGETABLES & BARLEY; MINESTRONE; SCOTCH BROTH; VEGETABLE BEEF	MONOSODIUM GLUTAMATE
CHILI BEEF	**OLEORESIN PAPRIKA**
SPLIT PEA W/ HAM & BACON	**SMOKE FLAVORING**
—SOUP FOR ONE	
BURLY VEGETABLE BEEF	**MODIFIED FOOD STARCH;** MONOSODIUM GLUTAMATE
GOLDEN CHICKEN & NOODLES; OLD WORLD VEGETABLE	MONOSODIUM GLUTAMATE
SAVORY CREAM OF MUSHROOM	**CALCIUM CASEINATE; MODIFIED FOOD STARCH;** MONOSODIUM GLUTAMATE; **SODIUM CASEINATE;** WHEY
CROSSE & BLACKWELL	
BLACK BEAN; CONSOMMÉ; CREME MUSHROOM BISQUE; CURRIED CREAM OF CHICKEN; LOBSTER BISQUE; MINESTRONE	MONOSODIUM GLUTAMATE

BRANDS	ADDITIVES-OF-CONCERN **BOLD—CONCERN TO ALL** LIGHT—CONCERN TO SOME
CRAB	MONOSODIUM GLUTAMATE; **SMOKED YEAST FLAVOR**
GAZPACHO	**MODIFIED CORN STARCH;** MONOSODIUM GLUTAMATE
LENTIL	MONOSODIUM GLUTAMATE; **SMOKED HAM;* SMOKED YEAST;* SODIUM NITRITE**
ONION	NO ADDITIVES OF CONCERN
SPLIT GREEN PEA	MONOSODIUM GLUTAMATE; **NATURAL SMOKE FLAVORS; SMOKED HAM;* SODIUM NITRITE**
DOXSEE *CLAM CHOWDER*	
MANHATTAN	**MODIFIED FOOD STARCH;** MONOSODIUM GLUTAMATE; **PAPRIKA**
NEW ENGLAND	**MODIFIED FOOD STARCH;** MONOSODIUM GLUTAMATE
PEPPERIDGE FARM	
BACON, LETTUCE & TOMATO; WATERCRESS	**MODIFIED FOOD STARCH;** MONOSODIUM GLUTAMATE
BLACK BEAN	MONOSODIUM GLUTAMATE

*Although "smoked" does not refer to a specific additive, it represents a process utilizing wood smoke, as "smoke flavoring" does, and therefore the food may contain some cancer-causing benzopyrene chemicals. For this reason, when a food or any of its constituents has been smoked, this has been noted in the additives-of-concern column.

BRANDS	**ADDITIVES-OF-CONCERN** **BOLD—CONCERN TO ALL** LIGHT—CONCERN TO SOME
PEPPERIDGE FARM *(Continued)*	
CHICKEN CURRY	MONOSODIUM GLUTAMATE; **TURMERIC**
PROGRESSO	
BEAN & HAM	HYDROLYZED MILK PROTEIN; **MODIFIED FOOD STARCH;** MONOSODIUM GLUTAMATE; **NATURAL SMOKE FLAVORING**
CHICKARINA	EGG WHITES; MONOSODIUM GLUTAMATE; **TURMERIC**
GREEN SPLIT PEA	**NATURAL SMOKE FLAVOR**
LENTIL; MACARONI & BEAN; MINESTRONE; TOMATO	NO ADDITIVES OF CONCERN
SNOW'S	
OYSTER STEW	**GRADE AA BUTTER; MODIFIED FOOD STARCH;** MONOSODIUM GLUTAMATE
—CHOWDER	
CORN; MANHATTAN CLAM	**ARTIFICIAL COLORING; MODIFIED FOOD STARCH;** MONOSODIUM GLUTAMATE
FISH; SEAFOOD	**MODIFIED FOOD STARCH;** MONOSODIUM GLUTAMATE
NEW ENGLAND CLAM	MONOSODIUM GLUTAMATE
SUPERMARKET PRIVATE BRANDS	
A & P—ANN PAGE	
BEAN W/ BACON	**MODIFIED FOOD STARCH;** MONOSODIUM GLUTAMATE; **OLEORESIN OF PAPRIKA**

BRANDS	ADDITIVES-OF-CONCERN **BOLD—CONCERN TO ALL** LIGHT—CONCERN TO SOME
CHICKEN NOODLE; CHICKEN VEGETABLE; CHICKEN W/ RICE	MONOSODIUM GLUTAMATE
CREAM OF CELERY; CREAM OF CHICKEN	**MODIFIED STARCH;** MONOSODIUM GLUTAMATE; WHEY (DRIED OR POWDER)
TOMATO	NO ADDITIVES OF CONCERN
VEGETABLE BEEF; VEGETARIAN VEGETABLE	MONOSODIUM GLUTAMATE; **OLEORESIN OF PAPRIKA**
LUCKY	
—LADY LEE	
BEAN W/ BACON	MONOSODIUM GLUTAMATE
CREAM OF CHICKEN	**MODIFIED FOOD STARCH;** MONOSODIUM GLUTAMATE; **PAPRIKA; SODIUM CASEINATE**
SPLIT PEA W/ HAM	MONOSODIUM GLUTAMATE; **SMOKED HAM;* SMOKED YEAST***
VEGETABLE; VEGETABLE BEEF	MONOSODIUM GLUTAMATE; **PAPRIKA OLEORESIN**
—*CHUNKY* CHICKEN	**MODIFIED FOOD STARCH;** MONOSODIUM GLUTAMATE

*Although "smoked" does not refer to a specific additive, it represents a process utilizing wood smoke, as "smoke flavoring" does, and therefore the food may contain some cancer-causing benzopyrene chemicals. For this reason, when a food or any of its constituents has been smoked, this has been noted in the additives-of-concern column.

BRANDS	**ADDITIVES-OF-CONCERN** **BOLD—CONCERN TO ALL** LIGHT—CONCERN TO SOME
—LADY LEE *CHUNKY* *(Continued)*	
SIRLOIN BURGER	**MODIFIED FOOD STARCH;** MONOSODIUM GLUTAMATE; **OLEORESIN PAPRIKA; SMOKED YEAST***
SPLIT PEA W/ HAM	MONOSODIUM GLUTAMATE; **SODIUM NITRITE**
SAFEWAY	
—TOWN HOUSE	
CHICKEN W/ RICE	**MODIFIED FOOD STARCH;** MONOSODIUM GLUTAMATE
CREAM OF MUSHROOM	**CALCIUM CASEINATE; MODIFIED FOOD STARCH;** MONOSODIUM GLUTAMATE; WHEY
MINESTRONE	MONOSODIUM GLUTAMATE; **PAPRIKA OLEORESIN**
TOMATO	**MODIFIED FOOD STARCH**
CHUNKY	
SPLIT PEA W/ HAM	MONOSODIUM GLUTAMATE; **SODIUM NITRITE**
STOP & SHOP	
—STOP & SHOP	
CHICKEN NOODLE	**MODIFIED FOOD STARCH;** MONOSODIUM GLUTAMATE; **PAPRIKA**
CHICKEN VEGETABLE; TURKEY NOODLE	MONOSODIUM GLUTAMATE

*Although "smoked" does not refer to a specific additive, it represents a process utilizing wood smoke, as "smoke flavoring" does, and therefore the food may contain some cancer-causing benzopyrene chemicals. For this reason, when a food or any of its constituents has been smoked, this has been noted in the additives-of-concern column.

BRANDS	**ADDITIVES-OF-CONCERN** **BOLD—CONCERN TO ALL** LIGHT—CONCERN TO SOME
CREAM OF CELERY; CREAM OF MUSHROOM	**MODIFIED FOOD STARCH;** MONOSODIUM GLUTAMATE; **SODIUM CASEINATE**
VEGETABLE BEEF; VEGETARIAN VEGETABLE	MONOSODIUM GLUTAMATE; **PAPRIKA OLEORESIN**
WINN DIXIE —THRIFTY MAID	
CHICKEN NOODLE; CHICKEN RICE	**MODIFIED FOOD STARCH;** MONOSODIUM GLUTAMATE; **TURMERIC**
CREAM OF CHICKEN; VEGETABLE BEEF	**MODIFIED FOOD STARCH;** MONOSODIUM GLUTAMATE
CHUNKY	
BEEF	**MODIFIED FOOD STARCH**
CHICKEN	MONOSODIUM GLUTAMATE; **TURMERIC**
VEGETABLE	MONOSODIUM GLUTAMATE
ITEMS IN HEALTH FOOD STORES	
HEALTH VALLEY	
BEAN; CLAM CHOWDER; LENTIL; MINESTRONE; SPLIT PEA; VEGETABLE	NO ADDITIVES OF CONCERN
CHICKEN BROTH	**SPICE EXTRACTIVES OF TURMERIC**

BRANDS	ADDITIVES-OF-CONCERN **BOLD—CONCERN TO ALL** LIGHT—CONCERN TO SOME
WALNUT ACRES	
BEEF STEW; BLACK BEAN; CHICKEN CORN; FISH CHOWDER; MANHATTAN CLAM CHOWDER; TOMATO; VEGETABLE	NO ADDITIVES OF CONCERN

DEHYDRATED SOUP

CUP O' NOODLES	
BEEF; BEEF/ONION; SHRIMP	MONOSODIUM GLUTAMATE
PORK	MONOSODIUM GLUTAMATE; **NATURAL HICKORY SMOKE FLAVOR; VEGETABLE OIL**
KNORR SWISS *SOUPMIX*	
ASPARAGUS	**MODIFIED FOOD STARCH;** MONOSODIUM GLUTAMATE; **TURMERIC; VEGETABLE GUM**
ONION & DIP MIX	**MODIFIED FOOD STARCH;** MONOSODIUM GLUTAMATE
OXTAIL	**BEEF FAT;** MONOSODIUM GLUTAMATE; **VEGETABLE GUM**
LA CHOY *RAMEN NOODLES*	
BEEF	**BHA; BHT;** GUAR GUM; MONOSODIUM GLUTAMATE; **PAPRIKA**

BRANDS	ADDITIVES-OF-CONCERN BOLD—CONCERN TO ALL LIGHT—CONCERN TO SOME
CHICKEN	**BHA; BHT;** GUAR GUM; MONOSODIUM GLUTAMATE; **PAPRIKA; TURMERIC**
LIPTON	
—SOUP MIX	
BEEF FLAVOR MUSHROOM	BUTTERMILK SOLIDS; MONOSODIUM GLUTAMATE; WHEY SOLIDS
CHICKEN NOODLE	**COLORING;** MONOSODIUM GLUTAMATE
CHICKEN RICE	**COLORING;** EGG WHITE SOLIDS; MONOSODIUM GLUTAMATE
CHICKEN RIPPLE NOODLE	**BHA; COLORING;** MONOSODIUM GLUTAMATE
GIGGLE NOODLE	**(HYDROGENATED COTTONSEED, PALM, SOYBEAN OILS);*** MONOSODIUM GLUTAMATE; **OLEORESIN TURMERIC**
ONION	NO ADDITIVES OF CONCERN
VEGETABLE BEEF	MONOSODIUM GLUTAMATE; **PAPRIKA; VEGETABLE GUM**
—CUP-A-BROTH	
CHICKEN	MONOSODIUM GLUTAMATE; **OLEORESIN TURMERIC**

*Blend may contain these saturated oils.

BRANDS	ADDITIVES-OF-CONCERN **BOLD—CONCERN TO ALL** LIGHT—CONCERN TO SOME
LIPTON *(Continued)*	
—CUP-A-SOUP BEEF NOODLE; ONION	MONOSODIUM GLUTAMATE
CHICKEN NOODLE	**BHA; COLORING; MODIFIED CORN STARCH;** MONOSODIUM GLUTAMATE
CHICKEN VEGETABLE	**BHA; COLORING; MODIFIED FOOD STARCH;** MONOSODIUM GLUTAMATE
CREAM OF CHICKEN	BUTTERMILK SOLIDS; **COCONUT OIL;** MILK SOLIDS (NONFAT); **MODIFIED FOOD STARCH;** MONOSODIUM GLUTAMATE; **OLEORESIN TURMERIC; VEGETABLE GUM;** WHEY SOLIDS
GREEN PEA	**MODIFIED FOOD STARCH;** MONOSODIUM GLUTAMATE; **VEGETABLE GUM**
TOMATO	**MODIFIED FOOD STARCH;** MONOSODIUM GLUTAMATE; **PAPRIKA OLEORESIN**
NESTLÉ'S *SOUPTIME* CHICKEN NOODLE	**MODIFIED CORN STARCH;** MONOSODIUM GLUTAMATE; **TURMERIC**

BRANDS	ADDITIVES-OF-CONCERN **BOLD—CONCERN TO ALL** LIGHT—CONCERN TO SOME
CREAM OF CHICKEN; CREAM OF GARDEN VEGETABLE	**HYDROGENATED COTTONSEED & SOY OILS; MODIFIED CORN STARCH;** MONOSODIUM GLUTAMATE; **SODIUM CASEINATE; TURMERIC**
GREEN PEA	**ARTIFICIAL COLOR;** GUAR BEAN GUM; **HYDROGENATED COTTONSEED & SOY OILS; MODIFIED CORN STARCH; NATURAL SMOKE FLAVOR; SMOKED TORULA YEAST***
TOMATO	**MODIFIED TAPIOCA & CORN STARCHES;** WHEY
OODLES OF NOODLES	
BEEF; PORK	ALGINIC ACID; MONOSODIUM GLUTAMATE; **VEGETABLE OIL**
CHICKEN	ALGINIC ACID; GUM ARABIC; MONOSODIUM GLUTAMATE; **SOLUBLE TURMERIC; VEGETABLE OIL**

*Although "smoked" does not refer to a specific additive, it represents a process utilizing wood smoke, as "smoke flavoring" does, and therefore the food may contain some cancer-causing benzopyrene chemicals. For this reason, when a food or any of its constituents has been smoked, this has been noted in the additives-of-concern column.

BRANDS	ADDITIVES-OF-CONCERN **BOLD—CONCERN TO ALL** LIGHT—CONCERN TO SOME
BEEF BARLEY; BEEF NOODLE	**MODIFIED FOOD STARCH;** MONOSODIUM GLUTAMATE; **PAPRIKA; TURMERIC**
SWIFT ***SOUP STARTER***	
CHICKEN RICE	**BHA; BHT; COLORING;** GUAR GUM; MONOSODIUM GLUTAMATE; **SODIUM CASEINATE; TURMERIC**
CHICKEN NOODLE	MONOSODIUM GLUTAMATE; **TURMERIC**
SUPERMARKET PRIVATE BRANDS	
A & P	
—ANN PAGE	
NOODLE SOUP MIX	MONOSODIUM GLUTAMATE; **TURMERIC**
ONION	**MODIFIED STARCH;** MONOSODIUM GLUTAMATE
STOP & SHOP	
—STOP & SHOP	
NOODLE SOUP MIX	**BHA; MODIFIED WHEAT STARCH;** MONOSODIUM GLUTAMATE; **TURMERIC (& EXTRACTIVES OF)**
ITEMS IN HEALTH FOOD STORES	
EDWARD & SONS	
MISO-CUP	
ORIGINAL GOLDEN LIGHT	NO ADDITIVES OF CONCERN

BRANDS	**ADDITIVES-OF-CONCERN** **BOLD—CONCERN TO ALL** LIGHT—CONCERN TO SOME
RICH, RED W/ SEAWEED	WAKAME
HAIN NATURALS *SOUP MIX* CHICKEN; CREAM OF MUSHROOM; SPLIT-PEA	MILK SOLIDS (NONFAT)
ONION	WHEY
TOMATO	MILK SOLIDS (NONFAT); WHEY
VEGETABLE	NO ADDITIVES OF CONCERN
HUGLI MINESTRONE SOUP MIX	NO ADDITIVES OF CONCERN
MARUSAN'S *MISO SOUP* RED MISO; WHITE MISO	NO ADDITIVES OF CONCERN

FROZEN SOUP

LA CHOY WON TON	MONOSODIUM GLUTAMATE
ITEMS IN HEALTH FOOD STORES **HEALTH VALLEY** CHINESE VEGETABLE; EGG DROP; WON TON	NO ADDITIVES OF CONCERN

XXIII. VEGETABLE JUICES & VEGETABLES

CANNED BEANS & VEGETABLES

Most of the items in this section do not contain any additives of concern, and these appear first, without an additives-of-concern column.

The items that do contain additives of concern follow, in the usual style.

B IN B MUSHROOM CROWNS; SLICED MUSHROOMS

CONTADINA SLICED BABY TOMATOES; STEWED TOMATOES

DEL MONTE ASPARAGUS SPEARS; ASPARAGUS TIPS; WHOLE BEETS; CUT CARROTS; SLICED CARROTS; WHOLE KERNEL CORN; GREEN BEANS; GREEN LIMA BEANS; FRENCH STYLE GREEN BEANS; ITALIAN BEANS; PEAS & CARROTS; SPINACH; SWEET PEAS; STEWED TOMATOES; TOMATO WEDGES; WAX BEANS

FRESHLIKE VEG-ALL

GREEN GIANT CUT SPEARS ASPARAGUS; NIBLETS GOLDEN CORN; WHITE CORN; FRENCH STYLE GREEN BEANS; KITCHEN SLICED GREEN BEANS; WHOLE GREEN BEANS; MEXICORN; WHOLE MUSHROOMS; LE SUEUR EARLY PEAS; SWEET PEAS

GREENWOOD SLICED PICKLED BEETS; SWEET-SOUR RED CABBAGE

HUNT'S PEAR SHAPED TOMATOES; STEWED TOMATOES; WHOLE TOMATOES

KOUNTY KIST CREAM STYLE CORN; WHOLE KERNEL CORN

LIBBY'S SLICED BEETS; SLICED CARROTS; WHOLE KERNEL CORN; CUT GREEN BEANS; FRENCH STYLE GREEN BEANS; PEAS & CARROTS; SUCCOTASH; SWEET PEAS

PROGRESSO CANNELLINI; CHICK PEAS; FAVA BEANS; KIDNEY BEANS; ITALIAN PEELED TOMATOES

REDPACK CALIFORNIA WHOLE TOMATOES; CRUSHED TOMATOES; ITALIAN STYLE TOMATOES; STEWED TOMATOES; WHOLE TOMATOES

RITTER ASPARAGUS SPEARS

ROYAL PRINCE YAMS

SILVER FLOSS SAUERKRAUT

STEWART'S DARK RED KIDNEY BEANS

STOKELY VAN CAMP'S CUT GREEN BEANS; DARK RED KIDNEY BEANS; LIMA BEANS; PEAS & CARROTS; SAUERKRAUT; CUT WAX BEANS

SUPERMARKET PRIVATE BRANDS

A & P ANN PAGE BUTTER BEANS; SLICED BEETS; SLICED CARROTS; WHOLE KERNEL CORN GOLDEN SWEET; CUT GREEN BEANS; GREEN BEANS FRENCH STYLE; RED KIDNEY BEANS; STEWED TOMATOES; TOMATOES

FIRST NATIONAL FINAST SLICED BEETS; GOLDEN CORN; WHOLE GREEN BEANS; MIXED VEGETABLES; NAVY BEANS; PEAS & CARROTS; SLICED WHITE POTATOES; SAUERKRAUT; SPINACH; MEDIUM SMALL SWEET PEAS; WHOLE TOMATOES

STOP & SHOP ASPARAGUS ALL GREEN SPEARS; SLICED BEETS; SLICED PICKLED BEETS; SLICED

(continues)

STOP & SHOP *(Continued)*

CARROTS; CREAM STYLE CORN; GOLDEN SWEET CORN WHOLE KERNEL; CUT GREEN BEANS; FRENCH STYLE SLICED GREEN BEANS; LIMA BEANS; MIXED VEGETABLES; WHOLE ONIONS; PEAS & CARROTS; EARLY PEAS; WHOLE POTATOES; SAUERKRAUT; SPINACH; PEAR SHAPED PEELED TOMATOES; STEWED TOMATOES; TOMATOES; CUT WAX BEANS; FRENCH STYLE SLICED WAX BEANS

STOP & SHOP SUN GLORY CUT SPEARS ASPARAGUS; SLICED CARROTS; WHOLE KERNEL SWEET CORN; CUT GREEN BEANS; SWEET PEAS; TOMATOES

LUCKY HARVEST DAY PICKLED SLICED BEETS; SLICED BEETS; CREAM STYLE-GOLDEN SWEET CORN; WHOLE KERNEL GOLDEN SWEET CORN; CUT GREEN BEANS; SWEET PEAS; PEELED TOMATOES

LUCKY LADY LEE CUT ALL GREEN ASPARAGUS; SLICED BEETS; BLACKEYE PEAS; BUTTER BEANS; CREAM STYLE-GOLDEN SWEET CORN; WHOLE KERNEL GOLDEN SWEET CORN; GARBANZOS; CUT GREEN BEANS; WHITE HOMINY; KIDNEY BEANS; PIECES & STEMS MUSHROOMS; PINTO BEANS; SLICED WHITE POTATOES; SAUERKRAUT; SPINACH; SWEET PEAS; STEWED TOMATOES; GOLDEN SWEET YAMS

SAFEWAY SCOTCH BUY GOLDEN CREAM STYLE SWEET CORN; CUT GREEN BEANS; JULIENNE (FRENCH STYLE) GREEN BEANS; SWEET PEAS; TOMATOES

SAFEWAY TOWN HOUSE ARTICHOKE HEARTS; ASPARAGUS SPEARS; PICKLED SLICED BEETS; SLICED BEETS; BLACKEYE PEAS; PICKLED CAULIFLOWER; CREAM STYLE SWEET CORN; WHOLE KERNEL SWEET CORN; GREAT NORTHERN BEANS; CUT GREEN BEANS; FRENCH STYLE GREEN BEANS; GOLDEN HOMINY; MILD GIARDINIERA MIXED VEGETABLES; BUTTONS MUSHROOMS; STEMS & PIECES MUSHROOMS; MUSTARD GREENS; WHOLE WHITE POTATOES

WINN DIXIE ASTOR SWEET PEAS

WINN DIXIE THRIFTY MAID ASPARAGUS; MEDIUM WHOLE BEETS; FRESH SHELLED BLACKEYE PEAS; COLLARD GREENS; CREAM STYLE GOLDEN SWEET CORN; WHOLE KERNEL GOLDEN SWEET CORN; GREAT NORTHERN BEANS; FRENCH STYLE GREEN BEANS; GREEN BEANS; RED KIDNEY BEANS; GREEN & WHITE LIMA BEANS; MIXED VEGETABLES; FANCY SLICED BUTTONS MUSHROOMS; NAVY BEANS; GREEN BOILED PEANUTS; LARGE SWEET PEAS; PINTO BEANS; SWEET POTATOES; WHITE POTATOES; SPINACH; YELLOW CUT SQUASH; STEWED TOMATOES; TOMATOES; CHOPPED TURNIP GREENS

ITEMS IN HEALTH FOOD STORES
DEL GAIZO CRUSHED PEELED TOMATOES; PEELED PLUM TOMATOES; PEELED TOMATOES

HAIN SOY BEANS

NA-ZDROWIE CARAWAY SAUERKRAUT

VITARROZ BLACK BEANS; BLACKEYE PEAS; CHICK PEAS; GARBANZOS; GREEN PIGEON PEAS; KIDNEY BEANS; PINK BEANS; PINTO BEANS; SMALL WHITE BEANS

WALNUT ACRES TOMATOES

The following items contain additives of concern.

BRANDS	ADDITIVES-OF-CONCERN BOLD—CONCERN TO ALL LIGHT—CONCERN TO SOME
DEL MONTE CREAM STYLE CORN; ZUCCHINI	**MODIFIED FOOD STARCH**
GREENWOOD HARVARD BEETS	**MODIFIED FOOD STARCH**

BRANDS	ADDITIVES-OF-CONCERN **BOLD—CONCERN TO ALL** LIGHT—CONCERN TO SOME
LIBBY'S CREAM STYLE CORN	**MODIFIED CORN STARCH**
RITTER GOLDEN BUTTER BEANS	COLOR ADDITIVE FD & C YELLOW NO. 5; MONOSODIUM GLUTAMATE
SUPERMARKET PRIVATE BRANDS	
A & P	
ANN PAGE CREAM STYLE CORN	**MODIFIED FOOD STARCH**

CANNED TOMATO & VEGETABLE JUICE*

CAMPBELL'S TOMATO

LIBBY'S TOMATO

RITTER TOMATO; VEG-CREST COCKTAIL

SACRAMENTO TOMATO

V-8 CLAM; (REGULAR); LOW SODIUM; SPICY-HOT

SUPERMARKET PRIVATE BRANDS
A & P ANN PAGE TOMATO

FIRST NATIONAL FINAST TOMATO

LUCKY LADY LEE TOMATO; VEGETABLE COCKTAIL

SAFEWAY SCOTCH BUY TOMATO

—TOWN HOUSE TOMATO; VEGETABLE COCKTAIL

*See note on page 432

WINN DIXIE THRIFTY MAID TOMATO

ITEMS IN HEALTH FOOD STORES
HAIN BEET; CABBAGE; CARROT; CELERY; NATURAL VEGETABLE COCKTAIL; TOMATO

LAKEWOOD BIG TEN VEGETABLE

The following items contain additives of concern.

BRANDS	ADDITIVES-OF-CONCERN **BOLD—CONCERN TO ALL** LIGHT—CONCERN TO SOME
MOTT'S BEEFAMATO; CLAMATO	**ARTIFICIAL COLOR;** MONOSODIUM GLUTAMATE

CANNED TOMATO PASTE, PUREE, SAUCE*

CONTADINA TOMATO PASTE; TOMATO SAUCE

DEL MONTE TOMATO SAUCE

HUNT'S TOMATO PASTE

—*TOMATO SAUCE* PLAIN; W/ MUSHROOMS; W/ ONIONS

PROGRESSO TOMATO PASTE; TOMATO PUREE

SUPERMARKET PRIVATE BRANDS
FIRST NATIONAL EDWARDS TOMATO PASTE; TOMATO PUREE

LUCKY LADY LEE SPANISH STYLE TOMATO SAUCE; TOMATO PASTE; TOMATO SAUCE

SAFEWAY TOWN HOUSE TOMATO PASTE; TOMATO SAUCE

*See note on page 432

WINN DIXIE THRIFTY MAID TOMATO SAUCE SPANISH STYLE

ITEMS IN HEALTH FOOD STORES
DEL GAIZO HEAVY TOMATO PUREE; TOMATO PASTE

HEALTH VALLEY *TOMATO SAUCE* PLAIN; W/ MUSHROOMS & CHEESE*

WALNUT ACRES TOMATO PUREE

The following items contain additives of concern.

BRANDS	ADDITIVES-OF-CONCERN BOLD—CONCERN TO ALL LIGHT—CONCERN TO SOME
HUNT'S *TOMATO SAUCE* HERB; SPECIAL; W/ TOMATO BITS	**MODIFIED FOOD STARCH**

FROZEN FRENCH FRIED POTATOES & VARIATIONS

BIRDS EYE CRINKLE CUTS	**ARTIFICIAL COLOR**
TASTI FRIES; TASTI PUFFS; TINY TATERS	**HYDROGENATED PALM** OR **SOYBEAN OIL**
HEINZ *DEEP FRIES* COUNTRY STYLE DINNER FRIES; CRINKLE CUTS	NO ADDITIVES OF CONCERN

*By law, at this writing, it is not required of a manufacturer to state whether cheeses contain artificial colors, unless the color is FD & C Yellow No. 5 (Tartrazine). Their presence in tomato sauce containing cheese therefore remains an uncertainty, unless it is voluntarily declared on the label that artificial colors have been used or have not. For a more detailed explanation of artificial color in cheese, refer to the beginning of the cheese section of "Dairy Products & Substitutes."

BRANDS	ADDITIVES-OF-CONCERN **BOLD—CONCERN TO ALL** LIGHT—CONCERN TO SOME
ORE IDA COUNTRY STYLE DINNER FRIES; GOLDEN CRINKLES; SHOESTRINGS; SHREDDED HASH BROWNS; SOUTHERN STYLE HASH BROWNS	NO ADDITIVES OF CONCERN
CRISPERS	**BHA**
TATER TOTS	MONOSODIUM GLUTAMATE
SUPERMARKET PRIVATE BRANDS **A & P—A & P** CRINKLE CUT COTTAGE FRIED; FRENCH FRIED; SHOESTRING	NO ADDITIVES OF CONCERN
POTATO MORSELS	**MODIFIED FOOD STARCH**
FIRST NATIONAL —EDWARDS FRENCH FRIED	NO ADDITIVES OF CONCERN
LUCKY—LADY LEE CRINKLE CUT FRENCH FRIED; FRENCH FRIED; HASH BROWN	NO ADDITIVES OF CONCERN

BRANDS	ADDITIVES-OF-CONCERN BOLD—CONCERN TO ALL LIGHT—CONCERN TO SOME
SAFEWAY—BEL-AIR	
FRENCH FRIED; HASH BROWNS; POTATOES O'BRIEN; SHOESTRING; SOUTHERN STYLE HASH BROWN	NO ADDITIVES OF CONCERN
TATER TREATS	**MODIFIED FOOD STARCH;** MONOSODIUM GLUTAMATE
STOP & SHOP —STOP & SHOP	
FRENCH FRIED; OVEN FRIES CRINKLE CUT; SHOESTRING; TATERS POTATO PUFFS	NO ADDITIVES OF CONCERN

FROZEN VEGETABLES (SINGLE, COMBINATIONS) & RICE MIXTURES

By law, at this writing, it is not required of a manufacturer to state whether cheeses contain artificial colors, unless the color is FD & C Yellow No. 5 (Tartrazine). Their presence in frozen vegetables and rice mixtures containing cheese therefore remains an uncertainty, unless it is voluntarily declared on the label that artificial colors have been used or have not. For a more detailed explanation of artificial color in cheese, refer to the beginning of the cheese section of "Dairy Products & Substitutes."

BIRDS EYE	
ARTICHOKE HEARTS; BABY BROCCOLI SPEARS; BABY BRUSSELS SPROUTS; CHOPPED COLLARD GREENS; CUT CORN;	NO ADDITIVES OF CONCERN

(continues)

BRANDS	ADDITIVES-OF-CONCERN **BOLD—CONCERN TO ALL** LIGHT—CONCERN TO SOME
CORN ON THE COB; FORDHOOK LIMA BEANS; CHOPPED MUSTARD GREENS; CUT OKRA; WHOLE ONIONS; TENDER TINY PEAS; COOKED SQUASH; SUMMER SQUASH	NO ADDITIVES OF CONCERN
—AMERICANA RECIPE	
NEW ENGLAND STYLE VEGETABLES	**ARTIFICIAL COLOR; BHA; MODIFIED CORN STARCH;** MONOSODIUM GLUTAMATE
SAN FRANCISCO STYLE VEGETABLES	**ARTIFICIAL COLOR; MODIFIED CORN STARCH**
WISCONSIN COUNTRY STYLE VEGETABLES	**ARTIFICIAL COLOR; BHA;** BUTTERMILK SOLIDS; **MODIFIED CORN STARCH;** MONOSODIUM GLUTAMATE; WHEY
—COMBINATIONS	
BROCCOLI W/ CHEESE SAUCE; CAULIFLOWER W/ CHEESE SAUCE	**ARTIFICIAL COLOR; BHA; CARRAGEENAN;** MONOSODIUM GLUTAMATE; WHEY
FRENCH GREEN BEANS W/ TOASTED ALMONDS	**BHA**
FRENCH GREEN BEANS W/ SLICED MUSHROOMS	NO ADDITIVES OF CONCERN

BRANDS	ADDITIVES-OF-CONCERN BOLD—CONCERN TO ALL LIGHT—CONCERN TO SOME
BIRDS EYE—*COMBINATIONS (Continued)*	
GREEN PEAS W/ SLICED MUSHROOMS; GREEN PEAS & PEARL ONIONS	**MODIFIED CORN STARCH**
SMALL ONIONS W/ CREAM SAUCE; CREAMED SPINACH DOUBLE CHOPPED; MIXED VEGETABLES W/ ONION SAUCE	**ARTIFICIAL COLOR; MODIFIED CORN STARCH;** WHEY
—5 MINUTE	
ASPARAGUS SPEARS; BROCCOLI SPEARS; CAULIFLOWER; CORN; CUT GREEN BEANS; FRENCH GREEN BEANS; ITALIAN GREEN BEANS; BABY LIMA BEANS; PEAS & CARROTS; CHOPPED SPINACH; SUCCOTASH; CUT WAX BEANS; ZUCCHINI SQUASH	NO ADDITIVES OF CONCERN
—INTERNATIONAL RECIPES	
BAVARIAN STYLE BEANS & SPAETZLE; CHINESE STYLE VEGETABLES	**MODIFIED CORN STARCH;** MONOSODIUM GLUTAMATE
DANISH STYLE VEGETABLES	**BHA; MODIFIED CORN STARCH;** MONOSODIUM GLUTAMATE

BRANDS	ADDITIVES-OF-CONCERN BOLD—CONCERN TO ALL LIGHT—CONCERN TO SOME
HAWAIIAN STYLE VEGETABLES; ITALIAN STYLE VEGETABLES; PARISIAN STYLE VEGETABLES	**MODIFIED CORN STARCH**
—INTERNATIONAL RICE RECIPES	
FRENCH STYLE RICE; ITALIAN STYLE RICE	MONOSODIUM GLUTAMATE
SPANISH STYLE RICE	MONOSODIUM GLUTAMATE; **PAPRIKA**
—STIR-FRY VEGETABLES	
CHINESE STYLE; JAPANESE STYLE; MANDARIN STYLE	NO ADDITIVES OF CONCERN
GREEN GIANT	
CREAM STYLE CORN	**MODIFIED CORN STARCH**
NIBBLERS; NIBLET EARS CORN-ON-THE-COB; LITTLE BABY EARLY PEAS; SWEET PEAS	NO ADDITIVES OF CONCERN
—BAKE 'N SERVE	
CAULIFLOWER IN CHEESE SAUCE; CUT BROCCOLI IN CHEESE SAUCE	**ARTIFICIAL COLOR; MODIFIED CORN STARCH**

BRANDS	ADDITIVES-OF-CONCERN BOLD—CONCERN TO ALL LIGHT—CONCERN TO SOME
GREEN GIANT *(Continued)*	
—IN BUTTER SAUCE	
BABY BRUSSELS SPROUTS; CRINKLE CUT CARROTS; NIBLETS CORN; BABY LIMA BEANS; SWEET PEAS; CUT LEAF SPINACH; YOUNG TENDER MIXED VEGETABLES	**AA BUTTER; MODIFIED CORN STARCH**
CUT GREEN BEANS; FRENCH STYLE GREEN BEANS	**AA BUTTER;** MONOSODIUM GLUTAMATE
SLICED POTATOES	**BUTTER; MODIFIED CORN STARCH; TURMERIC**
—IN A FLAVORED CHEESE SAUCE	
CUT BROCCOLI; CAULIFLOWER	**ARTIFICIAL COLORS;** BUTTERMILK SOLIDS; **MODIFIED CORN STARCH;** MONOSODIUM GLUTAMATE; SODIUM ALGINATE; WHEY SOLIDS (MODIFIED)
SMALL ONIONS	**ARTIFICIAL COLOR; MODIFIED CORN STARCH;** MONOSODIUM GLUTAMATE
—LE SUEUR	
BABY EARLY PEAS	**AA BUTTER; MODIFIED CORN STARCH**
BABY PEAS PEARL ONIONS & CARROTS; BABY PEAS PEA PODS & WATER CHESTNUTS	**BUTTER; MODIFIED CORN STARCH; TURMERIC**

BRANDS	ADDITIVES-OF-CONCERN **BOLD—CONCERN TO ALL** LIGHT—CONCERN TO SOME
—ORIENTAL COMBINATIONS	
CHINESE VEGETABLES; JAPANESE VEGETABLES	**ARTIFICIAL COLOR; MODIFIED CORN STARCH; TURMERIC**
HAWAIIAN VEGETABLES	**MODIFIED CORN STARCH; TURMERIC**
—RICE ORIGINALS	
MEDLEY RICE W/ PEAS & MUSHROOMS; PILAF RICE W/ MUSHROOMS & ONIONS	**FERRIC ORTHOPHOSPHATE; MODIFIED CORN STARCH; TURMERIC**
WHITE & WILD LONG GRAIN RICE	**FERRIC ORTHOPHOSPHATE; MODIFIED CORN STARCH;** MONOSODIUM GLUTAMATE
MRS. PAUL'S	
CANDIED SWEET POTATOES; FRIED ONION RINGS	NO ADDITIVES OF CONCERN
OH BOY!	
STUFFED POTATOES W/ NATURAL CHEDDAR CHEESE	**PAPRIKA**

BRANDS	ADDITIVES-OF-CONCERN **BOLD—CONCERN TO ALL** LIGHT—CONCERN TO SOME
ORE IDA CHOPPED ONIONS	NO ADDITIVES OF CONCERN
ONION RINGERS	**MODIFIED FOOD STARCH; OLEORESIN OF PAPRIKA**
PENOBSCOT *BAKED STUFFED POTATOES* CHEESE FLAVOR	**ARTIFICIAL COLOR;** WHEY (DRIED SWEET)
SOUR CREAM & CHIVES FLAVOR	MILK SOLIDS (CULTURED NONFAT DRY); SOUR CREAM SOLIDS
STOUFFER'S *SIDE DISH* BROCCOLI AU GRATIN	NO ADDITIVES OF CONCERN
CORN SOUFFLE; SPINACH SOUFFLE	MONOSODIUM GLUTAMATE
GREEN BEAN MUSHROOM CASSEROLE	**ARTIFICIAL COLOR; BHA; MODIFIED CORN STARCH;** MONOSODIUM GLUTAMATE; **TURMERIC**
POTATOES AU GRATIN	**MODIFIED CORN STARCH;** MONOSODIUM GLUTAMATE
SCALLOPED POTATOES	**MODIFIED CORN STARCH; U.S. CERTIFIED FOOD COLORING**

BRANDS	ADDITIVES-OF-CONCERN BOLD—CONCERN TO ALL LIGHT—CONCERN TO SOME
SUPERMARKET PRIVATE BRANDS A & P —A & P ASPARAGUS SPEARS; BROCCOLI SPEARS; BRUSSELS SPROUTS; WHOLE BABY CARROTS; CAULIFLOWER; CORN ON THE COB; CUT GREEN BEANS; BABY GREEN LIMA BEANS; FORDHOOK LIMA BEANS; MIXED VEGETABLES; PEAS & CARROTS; CHOPPED SPINACH; LEAF SPINACH; STEW VEGETABLES; SWEET PEAS	NO ADDITIVES OF CONCERN
LUCKY —HARVEST DAY BLACKEYE PEAS; BROCCOLI CUTS; BRUSSELS SPROUTS; BABY WHOLE CARROTS; CORN ON THE COB; FRENCH CUT GREEN BEANS; GREEN PEAS; MIXED VEGETABLES; CHOPPED MUSTARD GREENS; CUT OKRA; PEAS & CARROTS	NO ADDITIVES OF CONCERN

BRANDS	ADDITIVES-OF-CONCERN **BOLD—CONCERN TO ALL** LIGHT—CONCERN TO SOME
—LADY LEE BROCCOLI SPEARS; CAULIFLOWER; CORN ON THE COB; CUT CORN; CUT GREEN BEANS; BABY LIMA BEANS; MIXED VEGETABLES; CHOPPED SPINACH; LEAF SPINACH	NO ADDITIVES OF CONCERN
SAFEWAY **—BEL-AIR** 3 BEANS PLUS; BLACKEYE PEAS; COLLARD GREENS; CORN MONTEREY; COUNTRY STYLE VEGETABLES; DICED GREEN BELL PEPPERS; MEXICALI CORN; CUT OKRA; COOKED SQUASH; SUCCOTASH	NO ADDITIVES OF CONCERN
BROCCOLI CUTS W/ CHEESE SAUCE	**ARTIFICIAL COLOR;** FD & C YELLOW NO. 5; **MODIFIED CORN STARCH; POTASSIUM CASEINATE;** WHEY
CHINESE STYLE VEGETABLES; FRENCH CUT GREEN BEANS W/ TOASTED ALMONDS; ITALIAN STYLE VEGETABLES	**MODIFIED FOOD STARCH**

BRANDS	ADDITIVES-OF-CONCERN **BOLD—CONCERN TO ALL** LIGHT—CONCERN TO SOME
FRENCH FRIED ONION RINGS	**ARTIFICIAL COLOR** W/ FD & C YELLOW NO. 5; **MODIFIED FOOD STARCH;** MONOSODIUM GLUTAMATE; **OLEORESIN PAPRIKA**
WHIPPED POTATOES W/ CHEESE	**PAPRIKA;** WHEY
WINTER MIX	**MODIFIED FOOD STARCH;** WHEY (DAIRY)
STOP & SHOP —STOP & SHOP BROCCOLI SPEARS; CHOPPED BROCCOLI; CAULIFLOWER; CORN ON COB; LITTLE EARS; CUT GREEN BEANS; FRENCH CUT GREEN BEANS; GREEN PEAS; CHOPPED ONIONS; PEAS & CARROTS; DICED PEPPERS; CHOPPED SPINACH; COOKED SQUASH; WAX CUT BEANS	NO ADDITIVES OF CONCERN

BRANDS	ADDITIVES-OF-CONCERN BOLD—CONCERN TO ALL LIGHT—CONCERN TO SOME
WINN DIXIE —ASTOR	
CHOPPED BROCCOLI; BRUSSELS SPROUTS; SPECKLED BUTTER BEANS; CAULIFLOWER; SWEET CORN; BABY LIMA BEANS; MIXED VEGETABLES; PEAS & CARROTS; CHOPPED SPINACH; SUCCOTASH; SWEET PEAS	NO ADDITIVES OF CONCERN
ITEMS IN HEALTH FOOD STORES	
HEALTH VALLEY	
BROCCOLI SPEARS; CHOPPED SPINACH; LEAF SPINACH; MIXED VEGETABLES	NO ADDITIVES OF CONCERN
NEWTON ACRES	
BROCCOLI CUTS; BROCCOLI CUTS W/ CAULIFLOWER; BRUSSELS SPROUTS; BUTTERNUT SQUASH; CAULIFLOWER FLORETS; CUT CORN; FRENCH CUT GREEN BEANS; GREEN PEAS; MIXED VEGETABLES; PEAS & CARROTS; SPINACH; STEW VEGETABLES; TURNIPS; WHOLE BABY CARROTS	NO ADDITIVES OF CONCERN

BRANDS	ADDITIVES-OF-CONCERN BOLD—CONCERN TO ALL LIGHT—CONCERN TO SOME

SEAWEED

ITEMS IN HEALTH FOOD STORES

ATLANTIC MARICULTURE DULSE	DULSE
EREWHON	
ARAME	ARAME
HIJIKI	HIJIKI
JAPANESE NORI	NORI
KOMBU	KOMBU

THE DICTIONARY OF FOOD ADDITIVES

WHAT YOU SHOULD KNOW ABOUT A FOOD ADDITIVE

What is it?
Why is it used in food?
What do tests and medical experience tell us about it?*
Is it safe?

The reader will find in this part of the book the facts that address themselves to these questions, when such facts exist. Information from scientific investigations is not always as complete as one would like, or as tidy.

It has been necessary to use a selective procedure in the choice of material that is presented in the pages that follow, as there were hundreds of substances to be dealt with in this single volume. Care, however, has been exercised to report not only the results believed to be the most significant for the determination of safety, but divergencies from these findings as well.

To insure that the reader who wishes it can have access to the more detailed information summarized by the authors, identification of their main sources has been provided at the end of each report. When "NTIS PB" and a number follow the title, it means that the document, identified in this way, can be obtained from National Technical Information Service, 5285 Port Royal Road, Springfield, VA 22161.

ASSESSMENTS OF SAFETY

These safety ratings have been used in the Dictionary.

S—safe for everyone: where the additive has been adequately tested and found to be free of hazard for the consumer. This rating has been used only when the scientific evidence assures reasonable certainty of no harm.

---

*Some of the substances that are used as additives in food also are used as medicines, and their effects on humans, when available and relevant, have been reported in the dictionary section. The findings can provide invaluable information on human tolerances, but it is solely for this purpose that they have been included, not to recommend use in treatment. It is suggested, if anyone has this in mind, to consult a qualified physician.

X—unsafe for everyone: where the scientific reports clearly point to a possible health hazard or risk from the additive for *consumers in general.*

?—uncertain about safety: where the scientific data are too inconclusive or incomplete to warrant a well-informed judgment of safety.

Also combinations of these ratings, such as:

S—for some people; X for others: where the evidence indicates a possible health hazard or risk for a particular segment of consumers, especially heavy consumers of foods containing the additive.

When a combination of safety ratings occurs, the individuals to whom each rating applies are identified. For example:

Albumins: S for most people; X for those allergic to milk or eggs.

Caffeine: S for some people; X for pregnant women, nursing mothers, young children, anyone with a gastrointestinal or cardiovascular ailment.

A caution has not been included in a rating when the adverse effect of an additive applies to a comparatively few people or when it is likely to harm someone probably under medical supervision or on a restricted diet for its avoidance. The iron supplements in fortified foods could be harmful to anyone afflicted with hemochromatosis, a rare, genetically transmitted disorder. Patients suffering from serious kidney ailments should avoid foods containing substantial amounts of aluminum salts. These conditions and others have been noted in the text dealing with the additive when they arise, but are not mentioned in the ratings. Only cautions of wider application are believed to be appropriate in a volume such as this one, which is directed at a general audience.

The authors have concurred with the policy of the Select Committee on GRAS substances stated in its SCOGS reports "that reasoned judgment is expected even in instances where the available information is qualitatively or quantitatively limited"; and ratings of safety have been expressed in this volume in these circumstances in spite of omissions in the data.* Usually the omissions have been identified in the text. The Committee also recognized that on occasion "there are insufficient data upon which to draw a conclusion." With this

---

*An excellent review of the experiences of FASEB/SCOGS in food safety evaluation even when scientific information was very limited can be found in an article entitled "Evaluation of health aspects of GRAS food ingredients: lessons learned and questions unanswered," *Federation Proceedings,* volume 36, pp. 2519–62 (October, 1977).

in mind, as earlier stated, a ?—*uncertain* rating has been provided for this reason.

The reader will find *both additives-of-concern and additives that are not of concern* reviewed in this section. The purpose is to identify each additive so that the consumer will have no doubts, especially when something not previously encountered or noted appears on a food label.

THREE WAYS TO LOCATE WHAT YOU WANT TO KNOW IN THIS DICTIONARY SECTION

Table of Contents. Because it made sense in terms of the way the research has been conducted, and the considerable saving in space, whenever possible, related additives have been dealt with in groups. The various ammonium salts will be found together, as will the glutamates, the phosphates, the vegetable oils, and so on. It has not been difficult to provide ratings of safety when one or more substances in such a group is of concern and others are not. In other cases, such as brominated vegetable oil, mannitol, and others, each additive is reviewed individually. The Table of Contents which follows gives the location of the material arranged in this manner.

To locate a single additive. It may be necessary at times to refer to the Additives Index at the end of the dictionary section in order to find a specific additive. It has not always been possible to present single additives in the dictionary in alphabetical order because related additives are reviewed together. A typical example is Calcium Pantothenate, the form in which Pantothenic Acid is added to food as a nutritional supplement. It is grouped under Pantothenic Acid, one of the vitamins of the vitamin B complex.

To quickly determine whether or not an additive is of concern. You need go no further than the additive index to do this. Each additive-of-concern is identified in the manner described below. If it is of general concern, you'll find two asterisks(**) alongside the additive. If it is of concern to some people, but is viewed here as safe for others, you'll find one asterisk (*) plus a letter symbol alongside. The letter tells you who the "some" people are who are cautioned. If neither asterisks nor letters are present, the additive may be regarded as safe. Examples follow:

Brominated Vegetable Oil** (general concern)
Casein * *A (m)* (*A(m)* indicates caution for anyone allergic to milk)
Citric Acid (safe)

TABLE OF CONTENTS

DICTIONARY

ACETIC ACID

SODIUM ACETATE; SODIUM DIACETATE

Acetic acid, its salt *(sodium acetate),* and *sodium diacetate* (a combination of acetic acid and sodium acetate) are present in small amounts in most plant and animal tissues. Acetic acid is the acid in vinegar, and it is found naturally in substantial amounts in some aged cheeses and wine. It is added to catsup, mayonnaise, and pickles for acidity and taste, and it is in food products such as pickled fruits, vegetables, and meats that are preserved in vinegar. Sodium acetate is used as a preservative, while sodium diacetate is preferred by some food processors as a microbe preventative in baked goods and other products where acetic acid would impart an undesirable flavor.

SAFETY: The amount of acetic acid and the acetates as additives consumed in food in 1975 has been estimated at 80 milligrams daily per person in the U.S., or 1.3 milligrams per kilogram of body weight (kg/bw) for a person weighing 60 kg (132 lbs.). Acetic acid accounted for 93 percent of it.

Aside from what is obtained in food, the body itself produces acetic acid, which it needs as an intermediary in the transformation of ingested substances into other compounds used in the body, such as glucose (see p. 518). A constituent of the gastric juices stimulated in this process is hydrochloric acid, which is likely to remain in the intestines after the acetic acid, which is absorbed more readily. The sequence could lead to damage to mucous membranes in the gastrointestinal tract by the hydrochloric acid.

Highly concentrated acetic acid itself can produce damaging effects due to corrosive action in the digestive tract. This has been experienced by people attempting suicide, or through accidental ingestion. However, the amount thus consumed in a single dose should not be compared with the same amount consumed at lower concentrations, particularly when mixed with other ingredients in the diet over a period of time. For example, normal individuals have long consumed vinegar, which is 5.6 percent acetic acid, without reporting adverse effects.

MAJOR REFERENCE: Evaluation of the health aspects of acetic acid, sodium acetate and sodium diacetate as food ingredients. FASEB/SCOGS Report 82 (NTIS PB 274-670) 1977.

Acetic acid added to drinking water of rats at 390 milligrams per kg/bw, almost 300 times human intake of this additive, adversely affected growth; but did not when half the dosage was administered. Tests indicate that neither acetic acid nor sodium acetate is likely to cause abnormalities in fetuses or newborn, nor does acetic acid affect maternal or fetal survival. Sodium acetate does not exhibit mutagenic activity (gene mutations).

Studies do not appear to have been conducted to determine any long-term effects by these substances, or their possibility as a cause of cancer. Clinical evidence exists that acetic acid can cause allergic reactions in some individuals, which subside following its avoidance. No reports of investigations on sodium diacetate have been located, but since it breaks down in the body to acetic acid and sodium acetate, what is known of these should apply.

ASSESSMENT: Acetic acid is essential to the metabolic processes in the body that transform ingested food constituents into nourishment. In the quantities and concentrations present as additives in food, neither the acid nor the acetates pose a hazard to human health.

RATING: S.

ADIPIC ACID

Adipic acid occurs naturally as a minor component in such food products as beet juice and butter. The commercial additive is produced synthetically. Adipic acid has multiple uses: food processors use it in beverages and candies to control acidity, enhance flavor, and impart tartness; to lighten the texture of baked products; as a gelling agent in imitation jams; and as a preservative that binds chemically with, and so deactivates, metal impurities that can cause rancidity or flavor changes in edible oils, sausages, and other foods.

SAFETY: Based on surveys of usage by food processors conducted by the National Research Council in 1975 and 1976, it was estimated that the daily intake of added adipic acid in the diet of a U.S. individual averaged 41 milligrams, or about 0.7

MAJOR REFERENCE: Evaluation of the health aspects of adipic acid as a food ingredient. FASEB/SCOGS Report 80 (NTIS PB 266-279) 1977.

milligram per kilogram of body weight for a person weighing 60 kg (132 lbs.). In a study of human subjects over a nine-day period using up to 140 times this amount, there were no adverse effects. Long-term experiments with rats fed 700 to over 3500 times the daily human intake (adjusted for body weight) produced no harmful effects. Dosages of adipic acid more than 290 times the daily human intake fed by tube to pregnant rats and mice, and orally to hamsters, caused no ill effects to them or to their offspring; and laboratory tests investigating birth defects and gene mutation did not give reason for concern. Biological analyses indicated that much of the absorbed adipic acid is rapidly excreted in the urine, and the body's processes deal with it without difficulty by the same metabolic routes that are employed for fatty acids (the useful part of fat).

ASSESSMENT: The available evidence demonstrates that adipic acid does not represent a hazard to the public when it is used at levels that are current or that might reasonably be expected in foods in the future.

RATING: S.

ALBUMINS

Egg Albumin (Ovalbumin); Lactalbumin; Lactalbumin Phosphate

Albumins are important constituents in nearly all animal tissues and fluids (including blood serum). They are proteins rich in the essential amino acids which the body is unable to make and must obtain from the diet. *Egg albumin* is obtained from egg whites (which are largely albumin), and *lactalbumin* is derived from whey (the liquid part of milk; see p. 677), of which albumin is a major protein. These are the protein foods that contribute to the excellent nutritive value of eggs and milk.

Lactalbumin phosphate is prepared by adding polyphosphates (see p. 600) to lactalbumin protein. The resulting complex is useful as a partial replacement for milk solids in baked goods, in some gelatin products, and in imitation dairy products. The albumins are used as food additives in diet supplements, and as stabilizers, thickeners, and texturizers in baked goods, breakfast cereals, meat products, candies, fruit drinks, frostings, and sweet sauces.

SAFETY: The albumins used as food additives in 1976 accounted for a dietary intake of less than 24 milligrams per person daily. This is a minuscule contribution (1/3000) to the recommended protein intake of 44 to 56 grams required to meet the protein needs of most people. However, egg or milk protein is the standard for protein quality because of a nearly ideal amino acid makeup. When one of the albumins provides the dietary protein, an optimum growth response or utilization is shown.

Very high protein intakes are considered safe; the amounts in excess of the body's direct needs for protein and their essential amino acids will serve as a source of energy. Some investigators have recommended as much as 260 grams of protein a day under some conditions of physiological stress. Human subjects have consumed 600 grams of protein daily for many weeks without adverse effects other than increased excretion of calcium.

Some people have shown allergic reactions to milk or, to a lesser extent, eggs. The albumin fractions of milk and eggs can cause strong reactions in those allergic to these foods. Children are more likely to be susceptible; the symptoms may resemble hay fever, and include headaches and skin rash.

Two potential hazards that are known for excessively high protein intake are shared by albumins. One relates to the demand placed on the kidney to excrete the nitrogenous products of protein metabolism. This requires considerable water to keep the urea, ammonia, and other end products in solution—thus, an increased volume of urine. The other possible drawback of a very high protein diet is the greatly increased urinary calcium excretion that accompanies it. Calcium loss from the body, even when the diet provided well over twice the recommended calcium intake, has been noted by different investigators when dietary protein exceeded 142 grams daily.

ASSESSMENT: Albumins are excellent and nutritious proteins. They are used as food additives to serve as dietary supplements as well as aids in texture of the food. They add only minimally to the dietary intake of protein, and pose no hazard to consumers who are not allergic to milk or eggs.

RATING: S for most people; X for those allergic to milk or eggs.

ALGAE (SEAWEED) AND EXTRACTIVES

Algae constitute a group of plants that include seaweed and many single-cell marine and freshwater plants. Many species have been used for livestock and human food since before the Christian era. In the Orient, seaweeds are accepted foods and sometimes account for as much as 25 percent of the diet. Various gums that are used as additives in food processing in the U.S. are extracted from species of algae.

They include agar-agar, the alginates, carrageenan and furcelleran, and dulse and kelp. These are evaluated on the following pages.

ALGAE: AGAR-AGAR

Agaroid

Agar-agar is a polysaccharide, a complex carbohydrate consisting of a chemical combination of simple sugars, in this case mainly galactose. It is extracted from several varieties of red algae (seaweed). Agar-agar has the capacity to swell and can form resilient gels; it is used by the food industry as a gelling agent. *Agaroid,* a derivative of agar, serves similar purposes.

SAFETY: Agar-agar has been used for years as a gelling and bulking agent in the diets of experimental animals for various types of feeding studies of other substances. These have included investigations of cancer and gene mutation, in which agar-agar was fed in amounts up to 68,000 times (adjusted for body weight) as great as the 2.6 milligrams estimated to be ingested daily by a U.S. human in 1975, without evidence that it causes adverse effects. It has been used as a laxative for many years in dosages as much as 5000 times as great as that contained in the daily diet. When fed to rats as 30 percent of their diet for 44 weeks, many thousands of times human consumption, agar-agar caused an increase in the weight of the intestine, presumably due to its low digestibility and gelling properties, but the condition did not prevent the normal absorption of nutrients.

One investigation revealed that agar-agar fed to pregnant mice and rabbits at levels 35,000 and 9000 times respectively as great as daily human usage (adjusted for body weight) caused a significant increase in maternal deaths and a decrease in births

MAJOR REFERENCE: Evaluation of the health aspects of agar-agar as a food ingredient. FASEB/SCOGS Report 23 (NTIS PB 265-502) 1974.

by the survivors; and the offspring of mice were retarded in maturation. This did not occur with rats or hamsters, nor did it with mice and rabbits when the dosage was lowered respectively to 7400 and 2600 times human consumption. Taking into consideration the high feeding levels used, one explanation suggested for this effect is that harmful concentrations of certain metals, such as mercury, may be accumulated in agar-agar if the algae used in its manufacture are harvested in waters that are contaminated.

ASSESSMENT: Agar-agar has little effect when added to the diets of laboratory animals, except during pregnancy; and the toxic effects observed in studies of pregnant mice and rabbits only appeared when agar-agar was administered at levels many thousands of times that of human consumption. It has been used safely by man as a laxative in amounts substantially greater than contained in food.

RATING: S.

ALGAE: ALGINATES

Algin; Algin Derivative; Algin Gum; Alginic Acid; Ammonium, Calcium, Potassium, Sodium Alginate; Propylene Glycol Alginate

The alginates are extracted from several species of red and brown algae (seaweed). They are used in dressings, sauces, and sweets to blend ingredients and to prevent their separation, and as a gel and thickener. *Propylene glycol alginate* accounts for half of the total amount of alginates used in food, and *ammonium* and *sodium alginate* for most of the remainder. *Propylene glycol alginate* is preferred as a thickener in foods high in acidity.

SAFETY: A 1976 survey of the use of alginates by the food industry conducted by the National Academy of Sciences-National Research Council indicated an average daily intake by the U.S. consumer of 21 milligrams. Sodium alginate and propylene glycol alginate administered orally to a variety of animal species for periods ranging from several weeks to a

---

MAJOR REFERENCE: Evaluation of the health aspects of alginates as food ingredients. FASEB/SCOGS Report 24 (NTIS PB 265-503) 1974.

year, in amounts greatly exceeding normal human intake (adjusted for body weight) revealed no adverse effects. Six human subjects were given 8 grams of sodium alginate a day for 7 days, approximately 380 times the total amount of alginates currently present in the daily diet, without causing harm; 4 others who received 45 grams of alginic acid a day for the same period experienced only a mild laxative effect.

However, when fed by tube to pregnant mice in dosages 3250 times as great as that in the human diet (adjusted for body weight), propylene glycol alginate caused a significant number of maternal and fetal deaths. The same investigators using identical test procedures determined that propylene glycol by itself did not cause this, an indication that the alginate in the compound most likely was responsible. Another study, this time with pregnant rats and hamsters employing dosages of propylene glycol alginate equivalent to over 2900 times human consumption, determined that it did not cause birth defects.

Investigations have not been carried out with ammonium, calcium, potassium, or sodium alginate to determine whether they can cause defective offspring, gene mutation, or cancer. Only one cancer study of an alginate has been conducted; several injections of alginic acid in mice did not cause cancer.

ASSESSMENT: In sufficiently large amounts, the alginates, as is true of related polysaccharides (carbohydrates containing a union of several simple sugars), may pose some hazard during pregnancy. Two studies of human subjects provide some assurance that immediate adverse effects of any consequence are unlikely; but because of the almost total absence of investigation of the possibility of long-term effects, uncertainties remain unresolved. The evidence at hand does not indicate that the alginates as additives in food are a health hazard, except during pregnancy.

RATING: S for most people; ? for pregnant women.

ALGAE: CARRAGEENAN (IRISH MOSS)

Ammonium Carrageenan; Calcium Carrageenan; Potassium Carrageenan; Sodium Carrageenan

FURCELLERAN

Carrageenan, also called Irish moss, is extracted from a variety of red marine algae. It is composed of ammonium, calcium, potassium, or sodium salts (or combinations of these), and perhaps other salts, and a sulfur-containing polysaccharide (a condensation of a number of simple sugars). As a food additive, it may be identified as the ammonium, or calcium, or potassium, or sodium salt of carrageenan. Two types exist, but only one, undegraded carrageenan, is permitted in food. This is used as an emulsifier (blender), and as a stabilizer that keeps mixtures from separating, and as a gelling agent and thickener. Carrageenan is particularly useful with milk protein, enabling suspension of cocoa or chocolate in milk without the occurrence of settling or thickening.

Furcelleran, which is derived from another variety of red seaweed, is used for similar purposes as an additive in foods.

SAFETY: A survey conducted by the National Academy of Sciences-National Research Council among food processors in 1976, based on their usage, indicated that the daily intake of carrageenan in the diet averaged 15 milligrams per person, or 0.25 milligram per kilogram of body weight (kg/bw) for an individual weighing 60 kilograms (132 pounds). Far less use is made of furcelleran; the daily diet on the average contains 0.05 milligram.

Pregnant mice and rats fed calcium or sodium carrageenan orally or by tube at levels of 600-900 milligrams per kg/bw, somewhat over 2000 times average human consumption (adjusted for body weight), suffered a decrease in the number of live births because of dissolution or death of fetuses; and some of the newborn had immature or retarded skeletal structures or were abnormal. These effects were not observed in hamsters and rabbits.

No adequate feeding studies covering more than half of the life span of an animal species have been conducted, and these are needed to determine long-term consequences. Some information is available from laboratory tests in which calcium carrageenan caused aberrant chromosomes in rat bone marrow. Evidence has been produced that carrageenan can inhibit complement (a crucial catalyst in the body's immunological warning system) and increase the permeability of blood vessels; this could be of significance if a sufficient quantity of carrageenan were absorbed during infectious illness or a dis-

---

MAJOR REFERENCE: Evaluation of the health aspects of carrageenan as a food ingredient. FASEB/SCOGS Report 6 (NTIS PB 266-877) 1973.

turbance of the body's metabolic processes. Generally, however, carrageenan is not absorbed by the body.

Furcelleran has not been tested, but, according to the UN Joint FAO/WHO Expert Committee on Food Additives, it is so similar in chemical structure to carrageenan that the biological data available for carrageenan may be taken to apply to furcelleran.

ASSESSMENT: Based on some of the questions raised from animal experiments and laboratory tests, consumption of carrageenan (and furcelleran, which has a similar chemical structure) may best be avoided during pregnancy until additional studies are conducted with it and other polysaccharides which have had adverse effects on pregnant animals. It should be avoided, on the same basis, during infectious illness or disturbances of the body's metabolic processes. Laboratory tests indicate that carrageenan may cause chromosomal aberrations, and emphasize the desirability of long-term animal experiments to investigate cancer and gene mutation, which are lacking. The UN Joint FAO/WHO Expert Committee on Food Additives apparently does not share these reservations, as it regards up to 500 milligrams per kg/bw of carrageenan as an acceptable level in the daily diet.

RATING (carrageenan and furcelleran): ?; additional studies are needed to resolve uncertainties.

ALGAE: DULSE (RED ALGAE)

Nori

KELP (BROWN ALGAE)

Arame; Hijiki; Kombu; Wakame

Substances derived from red algae (species *Porphyra* and *Rhodymenia palmata*), such as *dulse,* consist mainly of galactose, a simple sugar in collodial form (gelatinlike); while two other sugars, guluronic and mannuronic, are the principal com-

---

MAJOR REFERENCE: Evaluation of the health aspects of certain red and brown algae as food ingredients. FASEB/SCOGS Report 38 (NTIS PB 265-505) 1974.

ponents in collodial compounds that originate from brown algae (species *Laminaria* and *Nereocystis*), such as *kelp*. Some *nori* are *Porphyra* and therefore dulse. *Arame, hijiki, kombu,* and *wakame* are regarded as kelp, or as closely related. As additives, algae may be used as seasonings or flavorings in food, and they provide iodine when used in dietary foods.

SAFETY: Information is not available on the amounts of red and brown algae, dulse and kelp, as such or their products, which are consumed daily by humans in the U.S. In the past this is likely to have been small, for these have been restricted as food ingredients to use as spices, seasonings, and flavorings. Now, however, some people appear to be consuming seaweed as a vegetable, as is done in the Orient where it can amount to a substantial portion of the total diet.

Most of the studies of these substances, other than those used for animals, have been conducted with *Laminaria*. Oral administration has been conducted mainly with ruminants (cud-chewing animals such as sheep, cows, and horses) as supplements in their food, with rats, pigs, and poultry occasionally included. Massive amounts of algae meal or dried seaweed from several species of red and brown algae, at times up to 20 percent of the diet, have not affected growth or productivity of these animals, lactation, or their ability to utilize their food; but caution is advised against quantities much above 15 percent because of iodine and mineral salt content.

A test of two algae ingested daily in the diet of many Japanese determined that 7 to 16 grams (containing 0.3 percent of iodine) of a species of kelp reduced normal thyroid function. But 1.2 to 3.2 grams (0.03 percent iodine content) of a species of dulse did not affect thyroid function. These results can be explained on the basis of the difference in the iodine content of the dosages.

It has been shown that mercury is present in several species of algae, probably due to water pollution. Tests to determine whether dulse or kelp can cause cancer, gene mutations, or abnormal or defective infants, or mortality during pregnancy have not been conducted.

ASSESSMENT: Data are not available on the consumption of dulse and kelp in the U.S. diet; but considering the limitations imposed on their usage as additives, only minute amounts are likely to be present in food ingested by humans in this country.

But the possibility exists that substantial amounts may be present as a food in the diet of some individuals who regard seaweed as a vegetable. Viewed solely as an additive, which is the province of this volume, the finding that mercury may be present in algae would only be of concern, as would the adverse effects on thyroid, should these substances be present at much higher levels as food additives than they appear to be today. On the other hand, the lack of research in several areas, especially during pregnancy where other gums derived from seaweeds such as carrageenan and the alginates have proved questionable, leaves uncertainties that need resolution.

RATING: S for most people; ? during pregnancy.

ALUMINUM COMPOUNDS

Aluminum Ammonium Sulfate; Aluminum Chloride; Aluminum Hydroxide; Aluminum Oleate; Aluminum Palmitate; Aluminum Potassium Sulfate (Alum); Aluminum Sodium Sulfate; Aluminum Sulfate; Sodium Aluminate; Sodium Aluminosilicate; Sodium Aluminum Phosphate; Sodium Calcium Aluminosilicate; Sodium Phosphoaluminate

Aluminum, the most abundant metallic element in the earth's crust, is found naturally in varying amounts in nearly all food and water. Aluminum compounds are added to foods to adjust acidity, to make foods light in texture, to keep processed fruits and vegetables firm, to aid in congealing cheese, and for other purposes. *Sodium aluminum phosphate* constitutes about 90 percent of the aluminum compounds that are used in food; it is a common ingredient in baking powders and self-rising flours.

SAFETY: The daily intake of aluminum as additives in food in 1976, based on a survey conducted by the National Academy of Sciences-National Research Council of usage by the food industry, has been estimated at less than 6 milligrams daily per person in the U.S. Another estimate, which includes aluminum in water, from cooking vessels, etc., suggests that intake can be as high as 100 milligrams daily.

Experiments with a number of animal species fed aluminum compounds greatly in excess of this latter estimate (adjusted

---

MAJOR REFERENCE: Evaluation of the health aspects of aluminum compounds as food ingredients. FASEB/SCOGS Report 43 (NTIS PB 262-655) 1976.

for body weight) indicate that an interaction can occur between aluminum and phosphorus which interferes with the enzyme that incorporates phosphate in the body's metabolic processes. This may cause a decrease in the retention of phosphorus and result in a disturbance of normal bone formation, kidney damage, and interference with the storage of carbohydrates. In one study, a single dose equivalent to 400 times the average amount of aluminum humans may ingest each day in food and water caused a significant decrease in retention of phosphorus in rats.

A study conducted with 11 patients fed relatively small doses of aluminum-containing antacid medicine (but still 170 to 560 times as great as the aluminum intake from food) confirmed the inhibition of phosphorus absorption in the intestine, followed by an increase in calcium loss; and other studies with human subjects bear out this depletion. In some animal experiments, the adverse effects were reduced or controlled by an increase of phosphorus in the diet. The high intake of phosphorus in the American diet may provide a protective effect, especially for someone who consumes large quantities of antacid preparations. But this cannot be assured for specific individuals at all times, particularly for those with kidney disease, who must exercise caution in consuming food containing high levels of aluminum salts which can aggravate their condition.

Evidence from research indicates that these salts do not cause cancer, or birth deformities, or gene mutations.

ASSESSMENT: Aluminum compounds in amounts greatly in excess of human intake have been proven to be hazardous in experiments with animals because they inhibit the retention of phosphorus. Individuals suffering from kidney disease are particularly vulnerable (but they are likely to be under diet control); and anyone regularly taking antacid medication containing aluminum (such as aluminum hydroxide gel) should make certain of sufficient phosphorus in the diet to counteract the effect of the aluminum that is in it.* While the margin of safety between the intake of aluminum compounds by some individuals and the amount that causes adverse effects in animals is narrow, the American diet is sufficiently plentiful in phosphorus to provide protection from aluminum compounds as used in processed foods.

RATING: S.

AMINO ACIDS

Cysteine (Cysteine Hydrochloride); Glycine (Aminoacetic Acid); Lysine (L-Lysine Hydrochloride); Methionine

All proteins are made up of chemical combinations of simpler nitrogen-containing amino acids, which provide the materials needed by the body for replacement and repair of tissue. Several of these amino acids are used in foods, frequently to improve the nutritive value but also for possible contributions to flavor or preservation of the food product. Four will be considered here: cysteine (usually available as the monohydrochloride, which has a molecule of hydrochloric acid attached to the amino acid), glycine, lysine (also usually available commercially as the monohydrochloride), and methionine. (Another amino acid contributing to food flavors, monosodium glutamate, is discussed on page 555).

Cysteine, a sulfur-containing amino acid, is usually present in food proteins as cystine (two molecules of cysteine linked together); cysteine is made by splitting cystine obtained from hair or wool. It is useful as a flavoring ingredient and can improve the effectiveness of certain dough strengtheners or conditioners. *Glycine,* also called aminoacetic acid, is prepared commercially by chemical synthesis. It is an important constituent of the proteins in most foods; it is unusually high in gelatin since it is a major building block in collagen, the connective tissue in the body. This amino acid can improve flavor in beverages that contain saccharin as a sweetener, by masking its aftertaste.

Lysine is usually made commercially by a bacterial fermentation. Most meat and dairy products are rich in lysine, as are legumes such as beans, peas, and soybeans. Lysine is one of the nutritionally essential amino acids; it must be supplied from the diet because the body cannot itself produce it, as it can some amino acids. When added to cereals, which do not contain a sufficient quantity of it, lysine can make the protein more useful in the body's metabolism. *Methionine* is present in eggs in substantial amounts, and in fish and most other animal products. The commercial product, made by chemical synthesis, is also a sulfur-containing, nutritionally essential amino

---

MAJOR REFERENCE: Scientific literature review of amino acids in flavor usage, volume I. FEMA Report to FDA (NTIS PB 265-526) 1977.

acid. As the proteins in legumes such as soybeans tend to be low in methionine, the nutritional value of soy-based infant formulas and other foods can be significantly increased by being fortified with it.

SAFETY: All these amino acids have limited usage as food additives, and all are present as natural constituents and in appreciable amounts in the protein in U.S. diets; in 1972 the average diet per person provided some 101 grams of protein daily, or over 1600 milligrams per kilogram of body weight (kg/bw) for an individual weighing 60 kg (132 lbs). Much of it is from milk and meat, which are rich sources of all these amino acids. The total use of these four amino acid additives by the food industry in 1976 was such that together they provided less than 1 milligram per kg/bw daily to the average diet.

Some of the amino acids needed in the tissue can be synthesized from protein components during the metabolic processes which the human body carries out. A few, including methionine and lysine, cannot be made by humans and thus must be provided by the diet. The National Academy of Sciences-National Research Council has recommended a minimum intake for adults of 12 milligrams per kg/bw per day of lysine. At least 10 milligrams per kg/bw of methionine is needed for adults, and an infant will require up to 49 milligrams per kg/bw daily.

Cysteine has been fed to rats through four generations at a concentration of 0.3 percent of the total diet, or 100-150 milligrams per kg/bw. No effects were seen on litter size, weight, or organ weight, or on examination at autopsy. Generally, as much as 1.5 percent cysteine in the diet has not affected growth of rats, but higher levels did. Cysteine and methionine are closely related sulfur-containing amino acids, and it is known that cysteine can supplement or spare methionine needs when the diet is very low in methionine.

Glycine, aminoacetic acid, has been administered to human adults at daily doses of up to 40 grams and for as long as six months; no adverse effects were seen.

Lysine has been extensively studied to determine its requirement. In the early studies with human adults, an allowance of 1.6 grams per day was suggested; the growing child requires substantially more lysine than the adult.

Methionine is the one amino acid for which a particular form or structure (isomer) is specified when added to an infant food. L-methionine, the form in which the amino acid occurs in nature, is well metabolized, and the D form (also present in DL-methionine) seems to be equally effective for adults. However, the very young infant does not have the full complement of enzyme catalysts to restructure and metabolize some nutrients as effectively as when he is older. One study with infants attempted to establish how much methionine could be safely added to a formula already providing 360 milligrams of methionine. When 180 milligrams of methionine was added daily, growth was superior; but with 360 milligrams additional (a total in the formula of 720 milligrams, or probably about 120 milligrams per kg/bw) some growth depression and extra urine output resulted. Methionine has been used medically in treatment of liver disease, the usual dosage being 3 to 6 grams daily.

ASSESSMENT: Cysteine and glycine are protein constituents that have found uses as flavor additives in certain foods. Two additional amino acids, lysine and methionine, are necessary in the diet because the human body cannot synthesize them. They are used to fortify certain foods deficient in one or the other, thus improving the nutritional quality of the protein. Since they are normal food components, the body regularly absorbs and utilizes each of these amino acids. The small amounts of cysteine, glycine, lysine, and methionine added to processed foods hardly affect the usual dietary intake of these substances, and are far below any possible hazardous levels.

RATING: S.

AMMONIUM SALTS

Ammonium Bicarbonate; Ammonium Carbonate; Ammonium Chloride; Ammonium Hydroxide; Ammonium Isovalerate; Ammonium Phosphate (Mono- and Dibasic); Ammonium Sulfate; Ammonium Sulfide

Ammonia and several ammonium salts (ammonia combined with certain acids) are present naturally in living substances. In man, ammonia plays a vital role in the functioning of a variety of essential processes, including the kidneys and the urinary system, where it participates in the acid-alkali balance. Ammonium salts are added to foods to lighten texture; to help

---

MAJOR REFERENCE: Evaluation of the health aspects of certain ammonium salts as food ingredients. FASEB/SCOGS Report 34 (NTIS PB 254-532) 1974.

achieve greater uniformity and palatability as they increase dryness and extensibility, enabling a better mixture despite variations in the raw food and processing time; and to adjust acidity. A few of the salts are used in small amounts as flavor enhancers.

SAFETY: It has been estimated that, in 1975, 100 milligrams of ammonium salts as additives were contained in the daily diet of U.S. individuals, or 1.7 milligrams per kilogram of body weight (kg/bw) for a person weighing 60 kg (132 lbs.).

Very few animal experiments have been conducted expressly to assess the safety of ammonium salts as ingredients when mixed in food. Some information is available from studies directed at determining their effect on certain vital body processes, and most of these have employed ammonium chloride in pure form or in water rather than in the diet. Investigators using dosages of this compound over 400 times the amount of ammonium salts consumed as additives by humans (adjusted for body weight) have reported kidney damage in animals, probably due to an overaccumulation of acid from the chloride portion. Two studies, one with rats, the other with mice, demonstrated that ammonium chloride inhibited cancer; in another experiment, precancerous changes were observed in rat stomachs. Female rabbits fed ammonium carbonate, chloride, hydroxide, or sulfate did not develop tumors. The weight of evidence appears to indicate that the ammonium salts are not cancer-causing. Studies have not been found that dealt with gene mutation or birth defects.

The healthy liver in normal circumstances readily prevents concentrations of ammonia from rising to harmful levels, but people with substantial liver impairment are not adequately safeguarded and can become seriously ill from it. Ammonium chloride is used medically to correct alkalosis (insufficient acid) and to increase urine; however, humans, some of them patients, fed doses of this compound ranging from 6 to 260 times as great as the amount of ammonium salts consumed in the daily diet experienced a number of adverse effects, such as disturbance of menses, headaches, loss of energy, and acidosis (accumulation of acid). On the other hand, when administered within this dosage range to patients with rheumatoid arthritis, ammonium chloride resulted in a decrease in swelling of joints, relief from pain, and increased mobility.

ASSESSMENT: Research to assess the limits of safety for ammonium salts when present as additives in food has not been adequate. However, findings from animal and human experiments investigating their effect on vital body processes indicate that it is unlikely that the ammonium salts constitute a health hazard, even if the quantity consumed were considerably greater than is present in the daily diet of humans, except to someone seriously ill with a liver impairment. The body requires ammonia for certain essential functions, and the normal liver acts as a safeguard by preventing concentrations of ammonia from rising to an excessive level in the blood, which could be dangerous. In assessing the safety of ammonium salts, a caution for anyone ill with serious liver impairment has not been added, as diets of these people are likely to be under strict control.

RATING: S.

ANIMAL FATS

Beef Fat (Tallow); Butter (Butter Fat); Lard (Pork Fat); Marine (Fish) Oil; Mutton; Poultry Fat, Skin

STEARIC ACID; Calcium Stearate

Beef fat and *tallow* are animal fats usually obtained from cattle, and *lard* is fat rendered from swine. These fats can be converted or hardened by the chemical addition of hydrogen for use in shortening, margarine, and for other purposes in food, and are identified as hydrogenated or partially so, depending on the degree desired. Hydrogenation converts fats to a more solid form, which is more stable and less subject to rancidity and other flavor changes. But it increases the saturation of the fat; the more hydrogenated, the greater the saturation. Hydrogenated lard is also used as a mastic for chewing gum, and lard serves as a component of adhesives used with food packaging materials. *Butter* is used in processed foods as a shortening, and to provide a distinctive flavor. Occasionally *marine* or *fish oils* may be used in a food, frequently after

MAJOR REFERENCES: Evaluation of the health aspects of tallow, hydrogenated tallow, stearic acid, and calcium stearate as food ingredients. FASEB/SCOGS Report 54 (NTIS PB 262-661) 1976; Evaluation of the health aspects of lard and lard oil as they may migrate to foods from packaging materials. FASEB/SCOGS Report 91 (NTIS PB 270-368) 1977; Evaluation of the health aspects of hydrogenated fish oil as a food ingredient. FASEB/SCOGS Report 66 (NTIS PB 262-667) 1976.

partial hydrogenation; and *poultry fat* may be used for its flavor contribution. The fish oils are from menhaden, herring, or tuna; the poultry fat from chicken or turkey. These fats or oils differ from most animal fats because they are relatively rich in polyunsaturated fatty acids; by contrast, butter, tallow, and lard have 4 to 12 times as much saturated fatty acids as polyunsaturated.

Stearic acid is a saturated fatty acid in animal fats and vegetable oils, and is extracted from these substances by food processors for use as a lubricant, blender, and binder; as a foam inhibitor; and as a coating in dry food packaging. It is used in beverages, baked goods, candy, and chewing gum. *Calcium stearate* is a combination of calcium, stearic acid, and palmitic acid (a fatty acid constituent of fat), and is used in food the way stearic acid is.

SAFETY: In 1972 daily U.S. consumption of tallow used in the manufacture of margarine and shortening amounted to 30 grams per person (about an ounce), 4 grams of which was stearic acid, a component of tallow. But this represents only a small fraction of the tallow that is consumed in the daily diet, which is present as the fat in beef. About one-fifth of the fat in hamburger is stearic acid. The use of calcium stearate in food is small, but it tripled between 1960 and 1970, when daily intake amounted to 4 milligrams per capita. In 1973 the quantity of lard used in food totaled 6.6 grams daily per person in the U.S., a decline by half since 1960. In 1975 use of enzyme-modified (lipolyzed) butter fat to enhance flavors provided a daily average of somewhat under 3 milligrams per person in the U.S. Beyond this, no reliable statistics are available for butter, poultry fat, or fish oils, but their uses as food additives obviously would contribute only a small fraction of the total dietary intake from consumption of dairy products, poultry, or fish.

Stearic acid (a completely saturated fat) fed to rats as 3 to 6 percent of their diet caused blood clots and cholesterol deposition in arteries. Beef tallow (which consists of saturated and unsaturated fats) produced less of this effect. In comparison with safflower oil (composed largely of unsaturated fat), beef tallow at a 15 percent level in the diet significantly accelerated blood clotting time in minature pigs. When fed to day-old chicks, tallow improved food utilization or efficiency, but this did not occur when hydrogenated fat or stearic acid was substituted. Butter fat and other animal fats with a high proportion of saturated fatty acids have been shown to elevate blood cholesterol levels when substituting for vegetable oils in the diet.

Poultry fat has considerable amounts of the polyunsaturated fatty acids that are essential dietary constituents. This composition is favorable to lowering blood cholesterol levels and cholesterol deposition in arteries in experimental animals whose diets include saturated fats and cholesterol. The fish oils that are unhydrogenated also are abundant in polyunsaturated fatty acids (though not the essential fatty acids). Experimental studies with rats have shown that lower blood cholesterol levels result when tallow in the diet is accompanied by fish oil; on the other hand, the fish oil is prone to oxygen uptake and rancidity, which can lead to toxic effects.

Long-term studies do not appear to have been conducted on the effects of feeding any of these fats to animals. Nor have tests been located that investigated their possibilities as the causes of gene mutation, fetus or birth abnormalities, or maternal or newborn mortality. Although it has been determined that stearic acid is not a cause of cancer, similar information is not available for various animal fats.

Experiments to determine adverse effects caused by lard have employed dosages ranging from 2 to 25 percent of the diets of laboratory animals, many thousands of times as great as the amount added to a human diet when adjusted for body weight. Mortality increased and the life span was shortened for male mice fed a diet of 24 percent lard, from weaning to death. Female mice fed lard at 2 to 10 percent of their diets through four generations lost considerable weight during lactation, but regained it rapidly after they were separated from litters, whose growth was not affected. The addition of brewer's yeast (see p. 681) to the diet prevented the weight loss, an indication that the large amounts of fat interfered with the ingestion of other food constituents or that the diet lacked some essential constituent.

The incidence of osteoarthritis doubled among male mice fed a diet supplemented with 25 percent of lard, but this did not occur among male mice of another strain with a more rapid growth rate. Oral studies to test whether lard can cause cancer have not been reported. In one instance when it was administered weekly by injection to rats, tumors did occur at injection sites. This is not accepted as evidence of a similar effect when lard is ingested, and did not happen in a number of comparable studies with mice.

ASSESSMENT: The adverse effects observed in experimental animals fed very high levels of lard can be ascribed to excessive fat in the diet rather than to the specific effects of lard. The evidence does indicate that a high degree of saturation of the fat is related to adverse effects on blood clotting, cholesterol deposits in arteries, and somewhat poorer fat digestibility. None of these studies, it must be noted, involved the small quantities of saturated animal fats estimated to be consumed by humans as food additives, which usually are present in exceedingly small amounts, and which account for only a minute fraction of total intake in the human diet. In their own right, saturated fats as additives are unlikely to present a significant hazard for normal people. On the other hand, there is concern over the role of saturated fats in the total diet of people with artery and associated cardiovascular diseases, and in these instances physicians and nutritional scientists recommend curtailment.

The potential health problem that a saturated fat may pose to a consumer will depend on the total amount in the diet, not merely its presence as an additive. The ingredients label can alert one to the presence of a highly saturated fat in a food, although quantities are not given. However, since the ingredients are listed in descending order of their presence in the food, it is possible to estimate when the amount of a given fat may be of concern. Accordingly, a caution will be raised in the Inventory in this volume about the safety of a food when one of the first three listed ingredients (other than water), alone or as part of a shortening blend containing other fats and oils, is any of the animal fats other than poultry or fish, or is stearic acid.

RATING: S for most additive uses; ? if the animal fat (other than poultry or fish) or stearic acid or calcium stearate appears as one of the first three ingredients on a food label.*

---

*The accuracy of this procedure for identifying highly saturated ingredients was tested with fatty acid analyses of over 200 purchased foods of all types contained in the 1980 thesis of Mary Gertrude Enig, conducted in collaboration with the U.S. Department of Agriculture. All the foods listing animal fats on the ingredient label were correctly identified as having excessive saturated fat not balanced by polyunsaturated fats or oils, with the single exception of one margarine.

ASCORBIC ACID (VITAMIN C)

Sodium Ascorbate

ERYTHORBIC ACID (ISOASCORBIC ACID)

Sodium Erythorbate

Ascorbic acid and *sodium ascorbate*, its salt, have multiple uses as food additives. They have value as nutrient supplements because of the vitamin C activity they possess. Along with the closely related *erythorbic acid* and its *sodium erythorbate* salt, these additives have antioxidant properties (prevention of deterioration caused by oxygen), and can help preserve flavor, color, or aroma of foods. They may be used in curing meat products such as bacon to inhibit the tendency of nitrite in curing salts to form nitrosamines following heating (see p. 632). The erythorbates, however, do not possess appreciable vitamin activity and are not regarded as important sources of vitamin C.

Ascorbic acid is found naturally in many plant products, especially leafy vegetables, fruits, and tomatoes; citrus fruits are particularly rich in this vitamin. The ascorbic acid available commercially is synthesized chemically, however. Erythorbic acid is not found in nature, but is a synthetic chemical additive.

SAFETY: The average daily intake per person of the ascorbates as food additives in the diet was estimated in 1970 as totaling 34 milligrams. This represented one-third of the average daily intake from all dietary sources. An estimate made in 1975 indicated that the use of ascorbates as additives in food had increased by over 80 percent, to 62 milligrams. The Recommended Dietary Allowance (RDA) set by the National Academy of Sciences-National Research Council for ascorbic acid is 60 milligrams for adults, or 1 milligram per kilogram of body weight (kg/bw) for a person weighing 60 kg (132 lbs.).

The use of the erythorbates as food additives in the average daily diet in 1970 amounted to 13 milligrams, a little over a third as much as the ascorbates. The use of these, too, has increased some, to 17 milligrams in 1975.

A severe deficiency of ascorbic acid causes scurvy in hu-

MAJOR REFERENCE: Evaluation of the health aspects of ascorbic acid and various ascorbates as food ingredients. FASEB/SCOGS Report 59 (NTIS PB 80-128796) 1979.

mans. Among other roles, the vitamin is required for the synthesis and metabolism of collagen, the protein making up connective tissue, cartilage, or gristle. This explains why the deficiency symptoms of scurvy include failure of cartilage, bone, and teeth to develop normally. Humans, according to the RDA, require about 1 milligram of ascorbic acid per kg/bw daily to maintain their body pools of the vitamin and make up the losses from excretion and metabolism. Erythorbic acid has weak antiscorbutic (scurvy prevention) activity, being about 5 percent as effective as the vitamin itself; however, the two chemicals are about equal in their antioxidant properties, which account for a significant part of their use as food additives.

In short-term studies, no harmful effects were seen in rats fed ascorbic acid at a level of 6500 milligrams per kg/bw. Guinea pigs also tolerated these high levels. Humans have not shown adverse effects after receiving daily supplements of 1 gram of ascorbic acid (some 16 times the average daily consumption of ascorbates as additives) for three months; much larger daily supplements have been taken for a number of weeks, again without apparent harm. Some investigations with experimental animals and humans produced evidence that continued intake of very large amounts of ascorbic acid (3 grams or more daily for humans) may create a dependency because of the overdosage. The rate of metabolism and excretion is accelerated, while concentration of ascorbic acid in tissues remains only slightly higher than normal; and if the dosage is reduced this accelerated metabolism continues, and can result in depletion of the vitamin in the tissues and even a vitamin C deficiency.

Ascorbic acid may significantly improve the absorption of iron in the diet, may depress the absorption of copper, and may prevent adverse effects from some toxic metals such as lead, mercury, or cadmium. There has been speculation that high dosages of ascorbic acid may produce kidney stones. It has been determined that calcium oxalate, the mineral salt causing this condition, increases only negligibly when less than 4 grams of ascorbic acid is ingested daily, which is far greater than the amount contributed to the diet as an additive.

Supplements of 100 milligrams of erythorbic acid daily (six times their presence in the diet) have been ingested safely by adults. Dogs have been fed erythorbic acid for six months or more at levels of 5 to 7 grams daily without toxic effects. There is some evidence that erythorbic acid at high levels can interact and compete with ascorbic acid, reducing uptake of the vitamin and its biological effectiveness. The animal studies with guinea pigs showed this only when erythorbic acid amounted to 2½ to 10 times the ascorbic acid in the diet (the reverse of the current use of these two substances in foods, where erythorbates are present in substantially smaller amounts than ascorbic acid). As much as 300 milligrams of erythorbic acid (5 milligrams per kg/bw) did not deplete ascorbic acid levels in the blood cells of adult humans partially deficient in vitamin C, and there was no indication that erythorbic acid could produce scurvy; indeed, this additive is itself mildly effective as a vitamin C substitute in preventing scurvy.

There are no clear indications that ascorbic acid taken during pregnancy has any adverse effect on survival of the mother or the fetus, or leads to any abnormalities in the offspring. Erythorbic acid and ascorbic acid, however, did cause embryo mortality when injected into the air cells of chick eggs at levels of 40 milligrams per kg/bw. Neither chemical was responsible for any chromosome damage in several types of tests, nor were the sodium salts.

ASSESSMENT: Ascorbic acid (vitamin C) is essential in the diet, and is present as a normal constituent of many fruits and vegetables. Erythorbic acid is an effective antioxidant but has only weak vitamin C activity. Many studies have shown that large amounts of ascorbic acid or sodium ascorbate, as well as erythorbic acid, can be tolerated without harm; the levels used were frequently 100 times the average amount of the substance incorporated as a food additive. No hazard is posed to the consumer from these chemicals.*

RATING: S.

AZODICARBONAMIDE

This chemical has been used since 1962 as a flour-maturing

MAJOR REFERENCE: Studies of the safety of azodicarbonamide as a flour-maturing agent. B. L. Oser, M. Oser, K. Morgareidge, and S. S. Sternberg. *Toxicology and Applied Pharmacology* 7:445 (1965).

*It is not the purpose of this volume to comment on aspects of the use of ascorbic acid (or other substances) other than the effect it has on health as an additive in food. As a consequence, its therapeutic usefulness in high doses, its role as a preventative or cure for various ailments, has not been subject to review or assessment here.

agent, up to 45 parts of azodicarbonamide per million parts (ppm) of flour being permitted by FDA regulations. When liquid is added to it, azodicarbonamide will strengthen the dough.

SAFETY: A survey in 1977 by the National Academy of Sciences-National Research Council determined that the average daily dietary intake per person in the U.S. of azodicarbonamide was 1 milligram.

When flour treated with this chemical is made into a bread dough, during the process the azodicarbonamide reacts chemically, converting rapidly to biurea, a very inert compound with a low solubility, which is mostly excreted in the feces. This reaction does not significantly affect the vitamins or amino acids in the flour. The safety of azodicarbonamide has been tested using mice, rats, and dogs. Mice tolerated doses as much as 6 grams per kilogram of body weight without adverse effect, though some diarrhea was noted.

Rats and dogs consumed a diet in which the principal ingredient was flour treated with this food additive at 100 ppm, ten times the normal usage level. After two years on this diet, no adverse effects were seen in growth, blood composition, microscopic appearance of the cells (no tumor growth), or in reproduction or lactation. This was also true when biurea was added at 1000 times the level expected from conversion of azodicarbonamide in treated doughs. Extremely high levels of biurea (5 percent or more of daily diet, which is many thousands of times above the level usually present in bread treated with azodicarbonamide), fed to rats for a year, were without effect; but dogs showed some deposits of the biurea in the kidney and bladder, due to the very low solubility of this compound.

ASSESSMENT: Azodicarbonamide at low levels is used as an aging or strengthening agent for flour in making bread or rolls. It is readily converted to biurea when the dough is formed. Studies show that no hazard exists when either of these compounds is present in the diet at levels far exceeding the 45 ppm that is permitted to be used in foods.

RATING: S.

BENZOIC ACID

SODIUM BENZOATE (BENZOATE OF SODA)

Benzoic acid occurs naturally in most berries, in prunes, tea, and in spices like cinnamon, ripe cloves, and anise. *Sodium benzoate* is its sodium salt. Both are used in a wide range of processed foods to prevent spoilage by microorganisms.

SAFETY: A survey of these two additives by the food industry in 1975 indicated an average daily intake per person in the U.S. of 48 milligrams.

These substances are rapidly absorbed, then combine with glycine (a component of protein; see p. 475) in the liver, and are excreted without any remaining in the body. The success of this process depends on a healthy functioning liver and a sufficient nutritional supply of glycine. Humans fed 1000 milligrams a day of benzoic acid for 88 days, more than 20 times the average consumption of benzoate additives in food, showed no observable ill effects. At 132 times daily consumption, sodium benzoate employed as a test of liver function caused temporary distress due to gastrointestinal irritation, but did no harm when administered in larger doses as medication to rheumatic patients.

Rats appear to employ body processes and pathways like ours to deal with these substances. Laboratory experiments provide evidence that rats can tolerate many hundreds of times the amount of sodium benzoate usually present in the average diet of a human (adjusted for body weight). A study covering four generations of rats demonstrated that benzoic acid did not cause abnormalities in the newborn. Research investigating cancer provided evidence that sodium benzoate did not cause tumors. Studies dealing with mutation of genes have not been conducted with these additives.

ASSESSMENT: Experiments with humans and rats, along with clinical experience with patients, indicate that in the quantities presently consumed in the daily diet, or that might reasonably be expected in the future, neither benzoic acid nor sodium benzoate offers any hazard to health.

RATING: S.

MAJOR REFERENCE: Evaluation of the health aspects of benzoic acid and sodium benzoate as food ingredients. FASEB/SCOGS Report 7 (NTIS PB 223-837) 1973.

BENZOYL PEROXIDE

This synthetic chemical has been used for many years, principally as a bleaching agent for flour; to a lesser extent it may be used to bleach milk used in manufacture of some cheeses, and to bleach lecithin (see p. 580) used in fats and oils.

SAFETY: A survey conducted by the National Academy of Sciences-National Research Council indicated that food usage of benzoyl peroxide in 1975 was 9 milligrams per person in the U.S. daily diet, or 0.14 milligram per kilogram of body weight (kg/bw) for a person weighing 60 kg (132 lbs.). This is the amount added during food processing, but only a small fraction of the bleach is ingested, as it decomposes to benzoic acid (see p. 487) during processing; most of any trace remaining is converted in the intestine to benzoic acid or to a form that is readily excreted in the urine.

Rats and mice have been fed a diet to which benzoyl peroxide had been added at levels up to 280 milligrams per kg/bw, 2000 times the average human intake. After 104 weeks there were no adverse effects on mortality and no increase in cancer, although there was some reduction in weight gain, perhaps because the bleach can destroy some nutrients such as vitamin E and the yellow carotene pigment precursors of vitamin A. Because carotene (see p. 505) is likely to be destroyed by treatment of milk with benzoyl peroxide in the manufacture of cheese, government regulations require that these losses be compensated for by the addition of supplementary vitamin A. (See p. 665.) Some vitamin C (see p. 483) and vitamin E (see p. 657) are also probably destroyed during bleaching with benzoyl peroxide, but their amounts in flour and milk are too small to have nutritional significance.

From studies with tissues, microorganisms, and mice, it is clear that benzoyl peroxide does not alter the chromosomes; but its effect on the newborn has not been tested. There has been some allergic response to this chemical among workers exposed externally to high levels of benzoyl peroxide, but such sensitivity has not been reported from foods treated with this chemical.

ASSESSMENT: Benzoyl peroxide is used as a bleaching agent in a few foods. It degrades almost wholly to benzoic acid by

---

MAJOR REFERENCE: Evaluation of the health aspects of benzoyl peroxide as a food ingredient. FASEB/SCOGS Report II-2 (NTIS PB 81-127854) 1980.

the time the food is consumed, and benzoic acid is regarded safe as a food ingredient. Certain vitamins can be destroyed by the addition of benzoyl peroxide to food, but where it could be significant, like destruction of vitamin A in milk used in cheese making, government regulations require the addition of the vitamin as a replacement. There appear to be no hazards associated with the use of benzoyl peroxide in foods at current levels or any likely to be used in the future.

RATING: S.

BHA (BUTYLATED HYDROXYANISOLE); BHT (BUTYLATED HYDROXYTOLUENE)

BHA and BHT are synthetic compounds used as preservatives to prevent or delay fats, oils, and fat-containing foods from becoming rancid and developing objectionable tastes and odors. By this means BHA and BHT extend the shelf life of such foods as breakfast cereals, baked goods, vegetable oils, and potato chips.

SAFETY: The average daily intake of BHA in the diet of individuals in the U.S. in 1975 has been estimated at 4.3 milligrams, or less than 0.1 milligram per kilogram of body weight (kg/bw) for a person weighing 60 kg (132 lbs.). For BHT, daily intake amounts to 0.04 milligram per kg/bw; totaling for both is thus a little over 0.1 milligram. The UN Joint FAO/WHO Expert Committee on Food Additives has suggested that intake of both or either should not be more than 0.5 milligram per kg/bw.

Extremely high dosages of BHA and BHT have consistently resulted in considerable enlargement of livers of experimental animals, reflecting a rapid growth of endoplasmic reticulum (the central portion of a cell other than the nucleus), accompanied by a marked increase in the production of microsomal enzymes (catalysts that activate this process). This did not occur when the dosages were reduced to the equivalent of 500 times human consumption. The claim is made that the enlargement of the liver is an adaptive response to an increased demand on this organ and is reversible with the elimination of

---

MAJOR REFERENCES: Evaluation of the health aspects of butylated hydroxyanisole as a food ingredient. FASEB/SCOGS Report 55 (NTIS PB 285-496) 1978; Evaluation of the health aspects of butylated hydroxytoluene as a food ingredient. FASEB/SCOGS Report 2 (NTIS PB 259-917) 1973.

these substances from the diet. However, it has been demonstrated with other compounds that a point can be reached at which adaptation fails and injury begins. The circumstances may arise, then, of further challenge to the liver, not only by BHA and BHT but also by other compounds. In fact, many common drugs and oral contraceptives activate the microsomal enzymes, and the possibility exists of an increase of these enzymes in the intestines, lungs, kidneys, etc. There is evidence that these enzymes can play a role in increasing the vulnerability of tissues to cancer-causing and other toxic substances. BHA and BHT may also stimulate the activity of steroid enzymes and, in this way, may affect the functioning of steroid hormones with adverse effects on reproduction.

Animal species differ in their sensitivity to BHA and BHT. Generally, larger dosages of BHA than of BHT have been needed to produce harmful effects in rodents, dogs, and guinea pigs. An important exception is primates; less of BHA than BHT does injury to monkeys, the significance being that the metabolic processes of monkeys are believed to more closely resemble those in man.

In contrast to these concerns, there are data which indicate that BHA and BHT reduced the occurrence of certain tumors, and they do not have an adverse effect on reproduction or the ability of the fetus to survive. Long-term studies of both additives fed to rats and mice in amounts far in excess of human consumption determined that by themselves they did not cause cancer.

ASSESSMENT: The amount of BHA and BHT that is consumed daily is within the safety levels specified by FAO/WHO, and some data are available indicating that they can reduce the occurrence of tumors and fetal failure. There remain uncertainties concerning their possible role in increasing microsomal enzymes in tissues other than the liver, thereby weakening resistance to cancer-provoking substances or causing hormonal imbalance that may affect reproduction. These possibilities have yet to be investigated, especially in conjunction with such widely used compounds as oral contraceptives and hormonal supplements, each of which may further aggravate BHA's and BHT's effect on the liver.

RATING: Both BHA and BHT, ? (additional studies needed to resolve uncertainties).

BIOTIN

Biotin is one of the B-complex vitamins, water-soluble vitamins that play a vital role as coenzymes* in the body's metabolic processes. Biotin is present in all living cells as a necessary nutrient for growth. It is found in small quantities in most foods, and in larger quantities in liver and other organ meats, some fishes, yeast, egg yolk, peanuts, and dried peas. The body provides a source of biotin because many microorganisms produce it in the intestine.

The biotin that manufacturers add to food is chemically synthesized. Its principal use as a food additive is as a nutrient in soy-based infant formulas and other milk-free formulas for infants and other age groups.

SAFETY: The daily intake of biotin from all food sources will range from 0.1 to 0.3 milligram per person. An infant receiving a fortified formula may receive 0.1 milligram of added biotin per day.

A protein in unheated egg white, avidin, interacts with biotin, binding it so tightly as to render it inactive; in effect, this creates a biotin deficiency known as "egg white injury." The deficiency has been produced experimentally in rats and rhesus monkeys, with symptoms of dermatitis, loss of hair around the eyes, and hind-leg stiffness or paralysis. Human volunteers fed a restricted diet of low biotin content and containing dehydrated egg whites (see p. 465) developed comparable symptoms, which disappeared after injection of as little as 0.15 milligram of biotin. A deficiency of biotin is unlikely to occur in adult humans without the combination of avidin and a diet low in biotin, because the availability of biotin is well in excess of the amount required for normal maintenance and growth. In fact, the body excretes more biotin than it obtains from the diet because of the ability of microorganisms in the gastrointestinal tract to produce it.

Humans have been administered oral doses of 10 milligrams of biotin daily for up to a month, at least a hundred times their

---

MAJOR REFERENCE: Evaluation of the health aspects of biotin as a food ingredient. FASEB/SCOGS Report 92 (NTIS PB 281-421) 1978.

*Coenzymes are linked together with enzymes (the body's protein regulators), which speed up the metabolism of proteins, carbohydrates, and fats, breaking them down to simpler forms usable by the body for energy, or using them in the replacement and building of cells and storage materials.

total dietary intake, without adverse effects. Infants under three months of age suffering from dermatitis, a possible symptom of biotin deficiency, have ingested 2 to 6 milligrams daily for several weeks (20 to 60 times the amount in the usual infant diet), again without adverse reactions and with improvement in the condition. Long-term studies on biotin have not been conducted, nor have there been any to determine whether it causes gene alteration (mutagenicity) or cancer induction (carcinogenicity). One experiment explored the effect of biotin on tumors induced in rats by a known carcinogen, and found it accelerated their growth.

Extremely large doses of biotin were given by injection (not by diet) to rats to determine the effect on reproductive performance. This treatment caused some irregularity in the estrous (fertility) cycle and failure to maintain a normal pregnancy.

ASSESSMENT: Biotin is an essential nutrient for humans, but one where a deficiency is extremely rare. Its use as a food additive is principally as a nutrient supplement in milk-free infant formulas. Even a hundred times the usual amount of biotin added to the formulas has not led to any harmful effects in infants, nor have excessive amounts adversely affected adults. Although adverse effects of biotin on the reproduction changes of rats have been reported, the amounts administered were thousands of times as great as those to which humans conceivably could be exposed. Thus, there is no reason to expect a hazard from this food additive as currently used or as may be expected in the future.

RATING: S.

BROMINATED VEGETABLE OIL (BVO)

Brominated vegetable oil is a combination of bromine (a chemical element, a reddish brown caustic liquid) with a vegetable oil. When bromine is chemically incorporated into the molecule of an unsaturated fat, it substantially increases the relative weight of the oil. The result is that the flavoring oils dissolved

MAJOR REFERENCES: Biochemical and pathological changes in rats fed low dietary levels of brominated cottonseed oil. I. C. Munro et al. *Food and Cosmetics Toxicology* 9:631 (1971); Brominated maize oil. II. Storage of lipid-bound bromine in pigs fed brominated maize oil. I. F. Gaunt et al. *Food and Cosmetics Toxicology* 9:13 (1971).

in the BVO will not rise and separate from the liquid mixture and will not form a ring in the neck of the bottle. It thus "stabilizes" the flavoring oils in the beverage. Used primarily in various citrus soft drinks and fruit-flavored beverages, BVO also provides a cloudy appearance, enabling the drinks to resemble natural fruit juices. Various vegetable oils are used in preparing BVO, including corn, cottonseed, olive, sesame, and soybean oils. (See p. 660.) Presently the FDA permits 15 parts per million of BVO in the finished beverage, pending additional studies concerning its safety.

SAFETY: A survey of the poundage of BVO used by the food industry in 1976, as reported by the National Academy of Sciences-National Research Council, indicated that an average of less than 0.2 milligram per person in the U.S. was present in the daily diet, or 0.03 milligram per kilogram of body weight (kg/bw) for a person weighing 60 kg (132 lbs.).

Although BVO made from various oils has been added to foods for nearly 50 years, toxicology studies during the past decade have raised questions about its safety. In 1969 and 1971 a series of studies reported that BVO from cottonseed oil produced adverse effects in the heart and liver of rats when fed at 2500 milligrams per kg/bw, even when the feeding was for less than a week, and even 400 milligrams per kg/bw resulted in marked reduction in the rate of fatty acid metabolism by the heart tissues. There was enlargement and fat deposition in the liver and kidneys, and some in the heart, because the brominated fatty acid deposited in the tissues was not readily metabolized. At levels of 250 milligrams per kg/bw there were cardiac (heart) lesions, inflammation of the heart muscle, and abnormal increases in thyroid cell growth.

BVO prepared from corn oil and fed to rats and pigs at levels down to 20 milligrams per kg/bw also resulted in deposits of brominated fat in the liver and other tissues. BVO from cottonseed, corn, olive, and sesame oils all caused pathological changes in the hearts of rats fed at 250 milligrams per kg/bw for 15 weeks; some showed these changes when the diet provided 50 milligrams per kg/bw. BVO from sesame or soybean oils fed to pigs at levels of 500 milligrams per kg/bw caused pathological changes, wasting of the testes, reduced growth, and lethargy.

ASSESSMENT: It should be noted that the adverse effects obtained in a variety of animals at levels as low as 20 milligrams per kg/bw were probably hundreds of times as high as the ingestion of BVO by humans, even for heavy users of beverages containing BVO. Nevertheless, the UN Joint FAO/WHO Expert Committee on Food Additives in 1971 considered that the accumulation of brominated fat in the body tissues and the degenerative changes in the hearts of experimental animals suggest problems in safety of BVO. They recommended that BVO not be used as a food additive. The FDA was sufficiently worried about this substance that it deleted it from the GRAS list. (The substance may nevertheless be used lawfully unless the FDA takes further action.) Although many tests were done by the manufacturer of BVO in the early 1970s to establish the safety of BVO in response to the interim permission for its use in foods, the chronic tests and reproduction studies using rats, dogs, and other species were judged to be faulty and unacceptable by the FDA when their results were submitted. The evidence to date has demonstrated that BVO can cause harm to vital organs when administered to experimental animals; it is felt that the technological benefits of BVO do not justify the potential health risks to a heavy consumer of beverages containing brominated vegetable oil.

RATING: X.

CAFFEINE

Caffeine belongs to a group of alkaloids, which are naturally occurring substances in plants. Many of the alkaloids are drugs with known stimulatory effects when ingested; they can also be habit-forming. This is true of caffeine, which is present as a natural constituent found principally in coffee, tea, chocolate, and the kola nut (whose extracts are used in cola drinks). Less than 10 percent of the caffeine in a cola drink is provided by the kola nut extract; the other 90 percent is added, presumably to enhance flavor and stimulation.

Caffeine need not be printed on the labels of coffee, tea, cocoa, or chocolate drinks as it occurs in them naturally. FDA regulations require no label declaration for caffeine on cola or other drinks or on finished foods as long as the caffeine concentration does not exceed 0.02 percent of the product.

MAJOR REFERENCE: Evaluation of the health aspects of caffeine as a food ingredient. FASEB/SCOGS Report 89 (NTIS PB 283-441) 1978.

SAFETY: In the U.S., total exposure to caffeine from all sources daily is estimated as averaging from 140 milligrams for most consumers to 300 milligrams or more for heavy users of beverages and other foods containing it; this would come to 2.3 to 5.0 milligrams per kilogram of body weight (kg/bw) for a person weighing 60 kg (132 lbs.). Approximately one-fourth to one-third of the daily intake of caffeine by adolescents and children comes from the consumption of cola-type beverages. Caffeine intake from all sources for one- to five-year-old cola users was estimated in 1977 as averaging 1.4 milligrams per kg/bw daily, and 1.0 for six-to-11-year-olds. Cola beverages contribute perhaps less than one-tenth of the caffeine intake of adults, who consume more coffee and tea than children do.

Caffeine is retained longer in the body fluids of infants and in pregnant women than in the normal adult. It's distributed into most of the body tissues and into breast milk; it can cross the placenta barrier to the fetus, and, if the nursing mother has been consuming beverages containing this chemical, an infant may have an intake of over 1 milligram per kg/bw. Some children can have an undesirably high consumption of caffeine from cola-type drinks during the period of brain growth and development. It is during this period that the developing nervous system is most sensitive to the effects of all aspects of the environment. In animals and humans, even 2.5 milligrams per kg/bw of caffeine can cause at least temporary effects on the central nervous system, adversely affecting behavior, motor activity, or sleep.

There are suggestions that in humans large doses of caffeine can markedly stimulate gastric secretions, which can cause peptic ulcers. In an FDA laboratory study, pregnant rats were force-fed caffeine in amounts not greatly exceeding the upper limits of human consumption (adjusted for body weight). Preliminary findings indicated that caffeine caused partial or complete absence of the digits of the paws of some of their progeny.

There is no good evidence that caffeine taken in quantities up to 50 milligrams per kg/bw (several times the normal daily intake) has any mutagenic effects (altering chromosomes) or causes cancer. However, results from the administration of larger doses suggest the need for more rigorous studies in these areas.

Because some doubts remain as a consequence of conflicts in findings, further study is also needed on immediate and long-range effects of caffeine stimulation on human behavior and the cardiovascular system.

ASSESSMENT: Caffeine consumption appears to be at a level that can lead to some undesirable effects in certain consumers, especially children from infancy through adolescence. While its use as a food additive contributes only a minor part of the intake of this substance, even the caffeine from cola-type beverages may be sufficient, through the pregnant or nursing mother, to have some effect on the fetus or the infant. A recent experiment with rats provides evidence that caffeine may be a teratogen (cause of birth defects). Although there is not strong evidence pointing to caffeine's contribution to peptic ulcers or heart ailments, physicians do caution susceptible patients to avoid beverages containing caffeine. For other consumers, according to the available evidence, caffeine intake at the present level of consumption is regarded as safe.

RATING: S for some people; X for pregnant women, nursing mothers, young children, anyone with a gastrointestinal or cardiovascular ailment.

CALCIUM PEROXIDE (CALCIUM DIOXIDE, CALCIUM SUPEROXIDE)

This synthetic compound is added to flour which is used in white bread and rolls. It acts as a dough-strengthening agent, making the dough more extensible and more uniform, even when ingredients vary. Its bleaching action may extend shelf life of the baked goods.

SAFETY: The average daily intake per person of calcium peroxide in foods in 1976, according to a survey conducted by the National Academy of Sciences-National Research Council, was calculated as 0.6 milligram.

There appear to be no published data on the biological safety of this additive, alone or in bread or flour treated with calcium peroxide. Because of this, the UN Joint FAO/WHO Expert Committee on Food Additives has set no level for an acceptable intake of calcium peroxide by humans.

When the additive completes its work in the flour, it becomes a simple calcium salt (see p. 498), which is harmless. The following discussion of safety deals with the peroxide part

---

MAJOR REFERENCE: Evaluation of the health aspects of hydrogen peroxide as a food ingredient. FASEB/SCOGS Report 113 (NTIS PB 80-104607) 1979.

of the calcium peroxide molecule, which resembles hydrogen peroxide in its action. During metabolism, the body produces hydrogen peroxide as a by-product of the interaction of certain enzymes (catalysts that accelerate the breakdown of foods) and oxygen; and hydrogen peroxide itself decomposes to oxygen and water in the gastrointestinal tract. Cases of poisoning have been reported in humans who accidentally consumed heavy concentrations of hydrogen peroxide in amounts many thousands of times as great as its presence from additives in food.

Hydrogen peroxide has been studied in many short-term experiments with mice and rats. At dietary levels of up to 30 milligrams per kilogram of body weight (thousands of times human intake), no harmful effects were seen. Higher levels reduced the rate of growth, but pregnant female rats were able to produce normal, healthy litters.

Since hydrogen peroxide can be produced by ionizing radiation (X-rays and gamma rays), its possible role in radiation-induced mutagenesis (gene alteration) has been studied extensively. It has proven to be mutagenic; however, to produce this effect in laboratory animals and tissue required a concentration of hydrogen peroxide ten times the amount produced by radiation, and far greater than the small amount expected from calcium peroxide added to food.

ASSESSMENT: The lack of experiments specifically testing the safety of calcium peroxide does not permit an assessment of any possible hazard from its use in foods. But evidence does exist concerning the mutagenic effects of hydrogen peroxide, a related compound, when used in high concentrations, warranting some caution in the use of calcium peroxide until appropriate studies are conducted.

RATING: ?

CALCIUM SALTS*

Calcium Acetate, Chloride, Gluconate, Hydroxide, Oxide, Phytate

These salts consist of calcium—an important nutrient needed for bones and teeth, as well as for blood coagulation and many metabolic functions in the body—and certain normal constituents present in the diet. The acetate portion of *calcium acetate* is present in acetic acid (see p. 463). The chloride part of *calcium chloride* is a component of sodium chloride (see p. 626). *Calcium gluconate* is calcium and gluconic acid (see p. 553). *Calcium phytate* is calcium and phytic acid, a relatively inert constituent found in many plant foods such as cereals, nuts, legumes, and potatoes. *Calcium oxide* is calcium combined with oxygen. *Calcium hydroxide* is formed by adding water to calcium oxide. *Calcium carbonate* is calcium oxide with the addition of carbon dioxide.

Some of these calcium salts are used in foods as agents to deactivate mineral substances that otherwise could cause undesirable flavor, color, or texture changes in the food; to alter the alkali-acid (pH) balance; or to firm up the texture. Among the large variety of products containing calcium salt additives are baked goods and baking mixes, carbonated fruit beverages, beer and wine, cheese, and processed vegetables. The salts are also used as nutrients or dietary supplements.

SAFETY: In 1975 the average daily intake per person of these added calcium salts, based on reported usage by the food industry, was estimated at about 41 milligrams in total, or somewhat less than 0.7 milligram per kilogram of body weight (kg/bw) for a person weighing 60 kg (132 lbs.). Calcium chloride accounted for 70 percent of this.

The contribution of these six additives toward body calcium needs represented 3 to 5 percent of the 800 to 1200 milligrams of calcium recommended daily for children and adults by the National Academy of Sciences-National Research Council.

MAJOR REFERENCES: Evaluation of the health aspects of certain calcium salts as food ingredients. FASEB/SCOGS Report 45 (NTIS PB 254-539) 1975; Evaluation of the health aspects of calcium oxide and calcium hydroxide as food ingredients. FASEB/SCOGS Report 72 (NTIS PB 254-540) 1975.

*Additional calcium salts are discussed elsewhere: see p. 513 for calcium citrate, p. 503 for calcium carbonate, p. 600 for calcium phosphate, and p. 652 for calcium sulfate.

The safety of these salts relates to the other parts of the compound combined with the calcium. Acetate and gluconate, as acetic acid and gluconic acid, are made by the body regularly in large quantities in its metabolism of carbohydrates. Chloride is an essential nutrient that helps to regulate the blood's acid-alkaline balance and pressure. The oxide and hydroxide readily form calcium carbonate, or chalk, itself a useful nutrient source. These calcium salts thus are substances that the body manufactures or requires in order to meet its needs.

At the high level of about 1500-2000 milligrams per kg/bw of calcium chloride, thousands of times human intake of all of these calcium salts, rabbits experienced an "acidosis" and damage to the stomach lining due to the excessive concentration of the salt solution. However, even at the same high levels, calcium chloride fed to rats for several months had no effect on thyroid size, and microscopic investigation did not reveal any abnormal changes. No adverse effects were seen in the heart, kidney, and liver of rats fed calcium gluconate or calcium chloride at levels of 400 milligrams of calcium per kg/bw. Calcium phytate, at about 300 milligrams per kg/bw, fed to rats as a diet supplement, successfully provided calcium for bone deposition, and the animals remained healthy.

Humans have taken as much as 10 grams of calcium gluconate as a calcium source, and the only deleterious effect was some diarrhea if the salt was taken on an empty stomach. Relevant studies of calcium oxide and hydroxide have not been made. However, these compounds when used in food change from caustic, alkaline materials to simple calcium salts.

No long-term studies appear to have been made on any of these calcium salts, and none on possible effects on cancer or on chromosome damage. Tests indicate that calcium chloride and calcium gluconate do not appear to cause embryo malformation.

ASSESSMENT: Calcium is a nutrient needed in substantial quantities in the diet. The acid components of its salts are normal food constituents and participate in metabolic processes in humans. The alkaline compounds, calcium oxide or hydroxide, change over to calcium salts when incorporated into foods and are then metabolized normally. The use of these various calcium compounds as food additives poses no hazard to the consumer.

RATING: S.

CALCIUM STEAROYL-2-LACTYLATE; SODIUM STEAROYL-2-LACTYLATE

These two additives are prepared by combining lactic acid (see p. 576) and stearic acid (a saturated fatty acid; see p. 479), and converting the product to its calcium or sodium salt by replacing the acidic hydrogen in it with calcium or sodium. The stearoyl lactylates (also referred to as lactylic stearates) are used as conditioners to produce a more stable dough and help ensure good volume for bakery products, baking mixes, pancakes and waffles, gelatins and puddings, and dietetic foods. Stearoyl lactylates are also used as whipping agents for vegetable oil toppings and icings and as emulsifiers to help blend fat and water fractions in products such as coffee cream substitutes and salad dressings.

SAFETY: A survey conducted for the National Academy of Sciences on use of these two additives by the food industry in 1976 determined that, on the average, 26 milligrams of calcium and sodium stearoyl-2-lactylates was present as additives in the daily diet of a U.S. adult, or slightly more than 0.4 milligram per kilogram of body weight (kg/bw) for a person weighing 60 kg (132 lbs.).

Short-term studies have been conducted with rats, but none has been reported for the longer period necessary to observe the possibility of malignancies, effects on the offspring, and so on. Perhaps this is because the stearoyl lactylates are handled in the body in the same manner as equivalent amounts of lactic acid and stearic acid, which are normal ingredients present in the diet and are regularly dealt with by our metabolic processes. The lactylates are readily split by enzymes in the body to yield these two acidic compounds.

In short-term studies with rats, calcium stearoyl lactylate at a level of 2 percent or more in the diet (perhaps 1600 milligrams per kg/bw) caused some reduction in growth over a four- to six-week period, and the liver weight was increased. This dosage is many thousands of times as great as the average human intake. Still higher levels of calcium or sodium stearoyl lactylate in the diet caused increased weights of other organs, including the brain, stomach, spleen, heart, and testes; but the

---

MAJOR REFERENCE: Toxicological evaluation of some food additives including anticaking agents, antimicrobials, antioxidants, emulsifiers and thickening agents. WHO Food Additives Series No. 5 (Geneva, 1974).

histology (microscopic structure) remained normal, with no pathological changes. Kidney weights remained unchanged. With dogs, calcium stearoyl lactylate at levels of some 3000 milligrams per kg/bw in the daily diet (thousands of times as great as average human consumption) allowed normal growth and metabolism over a two-year period, and organs did not change in weight and showed no abnormal microscopic changes.

Changes in inflammation and "granulation" of fat tissues have been observed in studies of rats employing very high levels of these additives in the diet. The changes were determined to be related to excessive intake of stearic acid. Adding unsaturated fats such as corn oil gave a better dietary balance and prevented or reversed the condition.

ASSESSMENT: Calcium and sodium stearoyl lactylates are readily split by the body to stearic acid and lactic acid, which can be metabolized normally. The adverse effects that have been reported occurred in rat studies that employed quantities of these compounds that far exceeded their presence in the human diet. One of these, changes in fatty tissues, appears to be related to a dietary imbalance caused by excessive intake of saturated fatty acids. The UN Joint FAO/WHO Expert Committee on Food Additives indicates that the intake of stearic acid from all sources may need to be taken into account; however, they consider that 20 milligrams per kg/bw of the stearoyl lactylates (thus, up to 1200 milligrams daily for a person weighing 132 pounds) is an acceptable daily intake for humans. As the actual presence of stearoyl lactylates in the U.S. diet is a small fraction of this, a cautionary rating appears to be unnecessary.

RATING: S.

CARAMEL

Caramel color is manufactured for commercial use by controlled heating of various sugars along with small quantities of an acid or a basic (alkaline) salt. Frequently, starch-derived sugars such as dextrose are employed, as are sucrose (table sugar), molasses, malt syrup, and lactose (milk sugar). The

MAJOR REFERENCE: Evaluation of the health aspects of caramel as a food ingredient. FASEB/SCOGS Report 20 (NTIS PB 266-880) 1973.

brown, caramelized color is imparted to many beverages, such as cola and root beer, and to a wide variety of processed foods. Caramel is also used as a flavoring. It is produced for this purpose commercially (or in the home) by heating sugar.

SAFETY: In 1976, the average daily intake of caramel as an additive by persons in the U.S., based on reported usage by the food industry, was 694 milligrams, or 12 milligrams per kilogram of body weight (kg/bw) for a person weighing 60 kg (132 lbs.). Studies with recently weaned rats fed for 90 days at levels 750 times the amount consumed as additives by humans (adjusted for body weight) determined that the only adverse effect experienced was that a greater amount of feed was required to produce a weight gain. Dosages over 4500 times human consumption (adjusted for body weight) fed to dogs for the same period failed to cause any damage to organs or to various body functions.

One human subject consumed up to 100 times the average U.S. intake of added caramel for 20 days without experiencing any adverse effects. In a long-term study, two generations of rats showed no harmful effects from daily feedings equivalent to almost 1000 times human intake, suggesting that caramel will not affect reproduction or lead to cancer. However, investigations specifically directed to determine whether caramel can cause cancer, gene mutation, or abnormalities in fetuses or offspring have not been located.

Some feed supplements for cattle, treated in a manner similar to that used in one of the processes of caramel manufacture (the ammonia process), produced toxic effects due to the presence of 4-methylimidazole, a compound containing nitrogen which has been found to occur in some food-grade caramels, but at levels regarded as insignificant with regard to possible hazard.

ASSESSMENT: Caramel as presently manufactured appears to be safe. Since questions have been raised concerning nitrogen-containing impurities that could be present in caramel produced by the ammonia process, limitation of the presence of these in the specifications for the additive would be desirable. The studies with both animals and humans indicate that caramel poses no hazard to the consumer at levels now consumed or likely to be consumed in future years.

RATING: S.

CARBONATES & BICARBONATES

Calcium Carbonate; Potassium Carbonate; Potassium Bicarbonate; Sodium Bicarbonate (Bicarbonate of Soda); Sodium Sesquicarbonate

Carbonates and bicarbonates are natural constituents of many foods, and are present in the fluids and tissues of the body as a product of its normal metabolic processes, where they play an important role in the control of the acid-alkali balance. The compounds specified above are some of their salts.* They are used as additives in foods to neutralize excess acidity and as leavening agents to lighten or raise dough in bakery products. Calcium carbonate is also considered to be a nutrient and a diet supplement, because it is useful in providing mineral for bone and tooth formation.

SAFETY: These salts as additives in food in the U.S. were estimated as totaling 1013 milligrams daily per person in 1975, or 17 milligrams per kilogram of body weight (kg/bw) for a person weighing 60 kg (132 lbs.). Sodium bicarbonate accounted for more than half, and sodium carbonate and calcium carbonate for most of the remainder. Actual daily intake is less, for when used as leavening agents the added carbonates disappear before the food is consumed.

Few experiments have attempted to determine whether the carbonate compounds are toxic when ingested orally in dosages approximating their intake as additives. *Sodium bicarbonate* injected into rats over a seven-day period at levels averaging 30 times the amount of carbonate salts added in human food, and over 50 times that amount in rabbits, did not cause harm to tissues and organs. However, when fed to dogs at almost 600 times the amount in human diets (adjusted for body weight) for 30 to 114 days, these unusually large doses did result in serious kidney damage and increased mortality due to the increased acidity.

Treatment of patients with large amounts of these salts has been conducted for years, but only rarely have disturbed acid-alkali balances been reported. Imbalance did occur in patients

---

MAJOR REFERENCE: Evaluation of the health aspects of carbonates and bicarbonates as food ingredients. FASEB/SCOGS Report 26 (NTIS PB 254-535) 1975.

*See p. 477 for ammonium carbonate and bicarbonate, and p. 585 for magnesium carbonate.

with gastric or peptic ulcers who were given daily doses of up to 100 grams of sodium bicarbonate by tube for three weeks, the equivalent of 98 times the amount of all these added carbonates in human food. The patients retained large amounts of sodium and developed alkalosis (a condition related to acid-alkali imbalance), but their kidneys were not damaged.

Sodium bicarbonate in laboratory tests proved not to be mutagenic (a cause of gene mutation); nor did it or sodium carbonate cause birth abnormalities in mice or rats.

A one-to-one ratio of calcium and phosphorus is desirable. A marked excess of calcium salts or phosphate salts in the diet can inhibit iron absorption, causing impaired iron utilization and anemia. Female mice were bred after a week on diets supplemented with *calcium carbonate* at 220 to 880 times the human intake of this substance as an additive. At all dosage levels, the number and weight of the first and second litters of newly weaned mice were lowered, and mortality was increased. The highest level caused heart enlargement. Supplementing the maternal diet with iron prevented this, indicating that the effects were really attributable to a mineral imbalance induced by excessive calcium.

In humans, 500 milligrams per kg/bw of calcium carbonate was fed daily to peptic ulcer patients for three weeks, over 145 times the amount ingested as an additive, resulting, in some patients, in an excess of calcium in the blood, accompanied by nausea, weakness, and dizziness.

In laboratory tests *potassium carbonate* proved not to cause gene mutations. Experiments with mice and rats indicate that it does not adversely affect maternal or fetal survival or cause birth abnormalities.

No investigations appear to have been conducted with *sodium sesquicarbonate,* but its biochemical conversion and metabolism in the body is similar to that of sodium carbonate and bicarbonate. Nor have any studies been located that have investigated the cancer-causing possibilities of any of these carbonates.

ASSESSMENT: The findings from animal feeding experiments and therapy with patients are not readily translatable to determine the level at which added carbonate salts in food can be harmful to humans. This is because of the wide discrepancy between the amounts administered and human intake as additives. Large quantities of calcium carbonate can interfere with reproductive performance, but this appears to be traceable to nutritive deficiencies caused by excessive calcium intake, which seem reversible with iron supplementation.

The carbonates are normal products of the body's metabolic processes and are essential for maintenance of its acid-alkali balance. In the quantities currently present in the diet as additives, or that might reasonably be expected in the future, the carbonate salts evaluated here are not regarded as posing any hazard to health.

RATING: S.

CAROTENE

Beta-Carotene

Carotene is a yellow-orange pigment that occurs naturally in many fruits and vegetables and is responsible for much of the yellow, orange, or red coloration of edible plants. Vegetables high in carotene content are parsley, carrots, spinach, turnip and beet greens, broccoli, and watercress. Fruits are less so; however, cantaloupe, peaches, apricots, prunes, and papaya are rich sources. Carotene can be converted by the body to vitamin A (see p. 665). Because the body can convert as much as 50 percent of carotene to this vitamin, nutritionists recommend at least one serving daily of a leafy green or yellow vegetable.

As an additive, carotene often is used in foods as a nutritional supplement, but its principal use is as a food colorant because of its intense and oil-soluble orange-yellow color. While there are a number of carotenes, *beta-carotene,* the only one used, is the important one for man as it possesses the most vitamin A activity. It is produced synthetically for commercial use in foods and it is added to many products such as margarine, cheese, ice cream, cake mixes, orange beverage, and puddings.

SAFETY: The average daily intake of vitamin A and its precursor carotene per person in the U.S. has been estimated at 5100 International Units (IU),* two-thirds of which (about 2 milli-

---

MAJOR REFERENCE: Evaluation of the health aspects of carotenes as food ingredients. FASEB/SCOGS Report 111 (NTIS PB 80-119837) 1979.

*The quantity of vitamin A activity is expressed by nutritionists in International Units (IU). For beta-carotene, 1700 IU are the equivalent of 1 milligram.

grams) comes from carotene present in the diet; 5000 to 6000 IU (3 milligrams) on the average probably would be sufficient for the body's needs. A survey in 1976 found that the carotene added to foods came to 0.67 milligram per person daily, a modest contribution to total intake.

When unusually large doses of carotene are taken, such as an excessive intake of carrots or carrot juice, the storage of carotene in the body can lead to an orange pigmentation of the skin. The condition, termed carotenemia, appears to be harmless, because when such food is removed from the diet, the pigment gradually fades away. Carotene has been used therapeutically to minimize an abnormal sensitivity to light. Doses of up to 180 milligrams of carotene daily for adults and 90 milligrams for children for long periods of time were tolerated well and without adverse symptoms other than yellowish skin coloring. The indications are that carotene taken in large amounts is inefficiently converted to vitamin A (see p. 665); apparently even these large doses of carotene do not lead to hypervitaminosis A, an excessive level of vitamin A in the body which can cause nausea, severe headache, loss of hair, and other toxic symptoms.

Carotene fed at very high levels to laboratory animals did not adversely affect fertility and the normal production of offspring. It did not cause cancer. A high incidence of skeletal abnormalities in fetuses did occur in a single study when pregnant rats were fed thousands of times the amount of added carotene contained in the human diet. The observations were difficult to interpret and as yet have not been confirmed.

ASSESSMENT: Carotene is present in a large variety of colored fruits and vegetables, where it serves as a source of vitamin A when metabolized by the body. Doses administered to humans far greater than the amount normally added to foods have been proved to be nontoxic. Carotene as a food additive poses no hazard to the consumer at current levels or at levels that may be expected in the future.

RATING: S.

CASEIN

AMMONIUM, CALCIUM, MAGNESIUM, POTASSIUM, SODIUM CASEINATE

Casein, the major protein in milk and milk products, has been a component in man's diet for centuries. The casein added to food is prepared from skim milk by processes that accelerate the formation of the casein curd and wash and dry it. The caseinates listed above are produced by dissolving casein in the desired alkaline solution, then spray or roller drying with the appropriate compound.

These substances are used for different purposes in food; some are added to serve as binders and extenders in imitation sausage, soups, and stews; as clarifying agents in wine; certain ones are permitted in specified frozen desserts; and calcium caseinate qualifies as a dietary supplement.

SAFETY: It is estimated that in 1970 the daily consumption of added casein and caseinates in food averaged 200 milligrams per person in the U.S. Sodium caseinate, the most widely used, accounted for two-thirds of this. About 100 times this amount of casein is consumed in the daily diet as a natural component of milk, cheese, and other dairy products.

The heating of casein, along with the alkali-treating process, results in the formation of some lysinoalanine (LAL). In a number of feeding studies with rats, LAL has caused kidney damage when present in the diet at levels of 100 parts per million (0.01 percent). Sensitivity to LAL appears to differ among animal species; when fed to mice, hamsters, rabbits, quail, dogs, and monkeys, LAL did no harm, possibly because of differences in metabolism. LAL has been detected in samplings of casein, calcium caseinate, and sodium caseinate used in food, at levels ranging up to 0.6 percent, although in some instances none at all was present.

Clinical sensitivity to cow's milk occurs in a small percentage of children. One study of subjects allergic to milk showed that 60 percent of them reacted allergically when they ingested casein. Sensitivity may increase or spread when added casein interacts during digestion with pepsin, the enzyme catalyst in gastric juice, or with other ingredients in processed foods.

MAJOR REFERENCE: Evaluation of the health aspects of casein and caseinates as food ingredients. FASEB/SCOGS Report 96 (NTIS PB 301-401) 1979.

Fortunately, only a small number of infants and children who suffer from this affliction carry it beyond age six.

The occurrence of nitrite (see p. 631) in spray-dried soy protein suggests that it may be present in spray-dried caseinates, which are manufactured by a similar process, although data do not exist to confirm this. Tests to determine whether casein or caseinates can cause birth defects or gene mutations have not been conducted, but the presence of LAL apparently does not produce abnormalities in the offspring of experimental animals.

ASSESSMENT: Casein as a natural protein component in cow's milk does not represent a hazard to health except to the few who are allergic to it. While its addition to food as an additive amounts to only a small fraction of its total presence in the diet of U.S. humans, some of the processes by means of which it is extracted and converted to caseinate can form lysinoalanine (LAL), a substance which has been found to cause kidney damage in experiments with rats, though not to several other species of animals, including subhuman primates, which is reassuring. For those allergic to milk, the possibility exists that casein as an additive can cause at least mild sensitive reactions.

RATING: Casein S for most people; X for anyone allergic to cow's milk. Caseinates ? because of uncertainties about the safety of LAL in the human diet.

CELLULOSE DERIVATIVES

Hydroxypropyl Cellulose; Hydroxypropylmethyl Cellulose; Methyl Cellulose; Methyl Ethyl Cellulose; Pure and Unregenerated Cellulose (Including Microcrystalline Cellulose); Sodium Carboxymethyl Cellulose (Carboxymethyl Cellulose, Cellulose Gum)

Cellulose is a natural fibrous carbohydrate present in the cell walls of green plants; it provides most of their structural strength. The cellulose used in food additives is obtained from wood pulp and cotton lint and is converted by chemical synthesis into forms or derivatives suitable for incorporation into

---

MAJOR REFERENCE: Evaluation of the health aspects of cellulose and certain cellulose derivatives as food ingredients. FASEB/SCOGS Report 25 (NTIS PB 274-667) 1974.

foods, or for use as surfacing in food packaging materials. The six cellulose derivatives listed above are permitted in food products and are assessed here for their safety. Three more that are allowed solely in packaging (and need not be listed on labels) are not covered here: carboxymethyl cellulose, cellulose acetate, and ethyl cellulose. It is unlikely that any of these could migrate to food in sufficient quantity to be of consequence; one, carboxymethyl cellulose, converts to sodium carboxymethyl cellulose (which is covered in this report).

Cellulose compounds are used in foods as thickeners. They add bulk, act as stabilizers that prevent separation and control texture, aid in blending of ingredients, help convert liquids to granular form or smooth-spreading gels, and prevent caking. They are used in such sweets as candy, ice cream, fillings, icings, and jellies, and they provide satisfying "body" to diet foods and breads by adding volume while increasing the "dietary fiber" content.

SAFETY: The amount of cellulose derivatives added to food in 1976, based on reported use by the food industry, totaled 40 milligrams per person per day, or 0.67 milligram per kilogram of body weight (kg/bw) for a human weighing 60 kg (132 lbs.). It has been suggested, since cellulose is contained naturally in many foods (cereals, vegetables, fruits), that the total amount of cellulose fiber in the daily diet may be 100 to 200 times the quantity added to processed foods.

The evidence from many metabolic studies indicates that ingested cellulose derivatives are not digestible, pass rapidly through the intestinal tracts of rats and man, and are excreted almost intact with little likelihood of being absorbed and stored in the body's tissues. It is not surprising under the circumstances that a diet consisting of 30 percent *microcrystalline cellulose* fed to rats for 72 weeks did not affect their appearance, behavior, or survival rate, although it did cause lower body weight in females and in some organs. The identical diet fed to three generations of rats lowered the reproduction rate, although it did not result in deformities in the offspring. The investigators attributed the adverse effects on reproduction to nutritional deficiencies caused by the high proportion of cellulose in the diet rather than to the derivative itself. Humans, when fed 30 grams of microcrystalline cellulose daily—more than 700 times the added cellulose in the average diet—for six weeks, did not experience any adverse effects on body tissues and organs.

Methyl cellulose, fed to a variety of animal species in

amounts far exceeding the added cellulose in the human diet for periods up to 95 days, did not affect growth rate, body weight gain, or behavior; nor did the animals suffer other toxic effects, tumor growths, or undesirable pathological changes, even after two years on diets consisting of 5 percent of this additive. Six normal humans taking up to 12 grams of methyl cellulose daily for a week or more, and 30 patients taking half again as much for as long as eight months, reported relief from constipation, and the continued use did not produce evidence of harm.

The survival rate during pregnancy was not affected in mice fed daily doses of methyl cellulose by tube up to 345 milligrams per kg/bw (over 100,000 times the average human consumption of added methyl cellulose, adjusted for body weight). Fertility and fetal survival were unaffected, and the incidence of abnormal young did not differ from that of the control group. However, when the dosage was raised to 1600 milligrams, it caused a significant increase in the mortality of dams, fewer fetuses survived, and these were smaller and retarded in maturation, although this did not occur with rats or rabbits.

Hydroxypropylmethyl cellulose, which is prepared from methyl cellulose, when fed to rats at 10 percent of their diet for three months, did not cause harm except for slight growth retardation. A dog ingested 25 grams daily for a month without adverse effects; at 50 grams daily (25,000 times its presence in the human diet) the substance caused anemia. Studies of effects when it is administered during pregnancy do not appear to have been conducted.

Sodium carboxymethyl cellulose, when fed to a variety of experimental animals at 20 percent of the diet, or up to 1 gram per kg/bw daily, for six months or longer, did not demonstrate ill effects. It has been used as a laxative in a study of 250 adult humans over a three-year period, given 2 to 18 grams twice daily, without harm. A reproduction study covering three generations of rats placed on diets containing 1 gram of sodium carboxymethyl cellulose per kg/bw did not find any undue effect on weight gain or body tissues or organs, or other evidences of hazard.

ASSESSMENT: Little or no breakdown and absorption of the cellulose derivatives considered in this review occurs in animal and human digestive tracts. Large amounts appear to have little effect other than providing "dietary fiber" bulk and thereby reducing the nutritive value of the diet, and possibly exerting a mild laxative effect. The increase in mortality of dams and retardation of unborn and developing young observed when extremely high dosages of methyl cellulose were administered to pregnant mice did not occur at lower dosages that were still substantially greater than the presence of cellulose derivatives in the human diet. Data are not available for hydroxypropyl cellulose or methyl ethyl cellulose, and until appropriate research is conducted on these a caution is indicated.

RATING: S for cellulose derivatives other than hydroxypropyl cellulose and methyl ethyl cellulose; for these ? (because of lack of information).

CHEWING-GUM BASE

The Food and Drugs section of the Code of Federal Regulations for chewing-gum base specifies 18 masticatory substances of vegetable origin consisting of coagulated or concentrated latex (frequently chicle), 8 synthetic masticatory materials, 13 plasticizing materials (softeners), a synthetic and a natural resin, and 5 chemicals used as antioxidants and for other preserving needs. These are permitted to be used separately or in combinations as a chewing-gum base. Some are reviewed elsewhere in this book. In addition, any food additive designated as GRAS* (many reviewed in this book) may also be used for this purpose, and these number in the hundreds. The regulation requires only that "chewing-gum base," if used, be listed on the label, but that the substance (or substances) comprising it need not be identified. It serves no purpose to provide assessments here of each of these, since there is no way of determining which one (or ones) have been used in a particular gum; and while some of the substances used for this purpose are viewed as of health concern when present in food which is ingested, it is doubtful that much gum base is eaten or swallowed, or even if it is, that much of the substances comprising it would "migrate" out of the digestive tract and into the bloodstream.

MAJOR REFERENCE: Code of Federal Regulations, Food & Drugs, *21*, Part 172.615, revised April 1, 1979.

*The Food Additives Amendments of 1958 exempted from FDA approval of safety substances that had been added to food prior to this legislation, which, based on the knowledge and experience of experts, were "generally recognized as safe." These additives are designated as GRAS.

CHOLINE BITARTRATE; CHOLINE CHLORIDE

These two choline salts are chemically synthesized for use as food additives. Choline is universally found in plant and animal products because it is a component of the fatty material, lecithin (see p. 580), in cell membranes. Egg yolk, meat, fish, milk, cereals, and legumes are particularly rich in choline. The average daily mixed diet may contain 150 milligrams of choline. Choline is added to milk products or infant formulas as a nutrient or dietary supplement to bring them up to the choline level normally found in milk.

SAFETY: Most of the choline salts used will be consumed by infants in formulas. Infants less than six months old on milk-free formulas will receive 70 to 80 milligrams of added choline chloride daily (15 milligrams per kilogram of body weight, kg/bw); when milk-based formulas are used, choline bitartrate intake will amount to about 30 milligrams per kg/bw. Older children and adults consuming choline as a supplement or on special diets will average less than this amount.

Choline helps the body's metabolism to prevent excessive fat deposition in the liver, and as a constituent of lecithin it is useful in transport of fat throughout the body. It is not an essential ingredient in the diet, like a vitamin, since it can be made within an animal or human if the diet contains adequate protein.

Rats and mice receiving 500 to 1000 milligrams choline chloride per kg/bw in the diet showed normal growth. Some growth depression resulted from higher amounts. However, no significant tissue changes due to the choline were found. No studies have been reported on any effects of choline on cancer, gene mutation, or embryo development during pregnancy; or on any long-term effects.

ASSESSMENT: Choline is an important constituent in metabolic functions in the body, including fat transport. However, its nutritional significance for humans still needs to be clarified. Data on possible harmful effects are scarce but, as noted by the UN Joint FAO/WHO Expert Committee on Food Addi-

---

MAJOR REFERENCE: Evaluation of the health aspects of choline chloride and choline bitartrate as food ingredients. FASEB/SCOGS Report 42 (NTIS PB 262-654) 1976.

tives, it appears to be without adverse effect when taken orally. Present evidence indicates that choline bitartrate and choline chloride as additives in foods pose no hazard even to the infant consumer.

RATING: S.

CITRIC ACID AND CITRATES

Ammonium Citrate; Calcium Citrate; Isopropyl Citrate; Mono-, Di-, Tripotassium Citrate; Mono-, Di-, Trisodium Citrate; Stearyl Citrate; Triethyl Citrate

Citric acid and its salts (ammonium, calcium, potassium, and sodium citrates) are natural constituents of plants and animals. The salts readily dissolve in water, releasing the free acid. Other derivatives of citric acid that are used as food additives are the isopropyl, stearyl, and triethyl citrates, which chemically are esters. (An ester is a compound formed from an acid and an alcohol by the removal of water.)

The acid and its salts are widely distributed in foodstuffs and are in especially high concentrations in citrus fruits and products. Citric acid is the dominant organic acid in apricots, many berries, pineapple, and tomatoes. By contrast, the esters occur naturally in foods only in extremely low quantities.

These substances have multiple uses as food additives. Citric acid and some of the salts are good sequestrants, collecting and deactivating metal contaminants, and thus may increase the effectiveness of preservatives used to maintain freshness and prevent rancidity. As flavor enhancers, citrates are used to impart tartness and to control acidity in foods and beverages. Calcium citrate is used as a firming agent in canned vegetables and as a nutrient in baby foods. The citrate esters are useful because of their solubility in fatty portions of foods such as margarines; triethyl citrate in particular performs functions as an additive somewhat similar to the citrate salts.

SAFETY: The use of citrates as food additives adds a relatively small part of the total consumed in human diets. The per capita intake in 1970 was estimated at approximately 500 milligrams. A resurvey in 1975 indicated an increase to more than 750

MAJOR REFERENCE: Evaluation of the health aspects of citric acid and citrates as food ingredients. FASEB/SCOGS Report 84 (NTIS PB 280-954) 1977.

milligrams in the daily diet of the average U.S. adult. This is the equivalent of the citrate intake from 3 ounces of orange juice.

It is well established that citrates participate in body metabolism as key intermediates in the process of deriving energy from carbohydrates, proteins, and fats, and can serve as energy-producing nutrients themselves. The esters, like the salts, are digested and metabolized normally. Understandably, citric acid and its salts and esters have very low levels of toxicity.

In adult human subjects, ammonium citrate added to the diet has been demonstrated useful as a nitrogen source and has a sparing effect on the protein requirement. Long-term studies with rats have shown that citric acid, even at 150 times the added amount found in human diets (adjusted for body weight), had no effect on survival or on the various organs and tissues. The citrate esters showed no adverse effects in rats in two-year feeding studies at even higher dosage levels. Because of its ability to bind calcium, citric acid may interfere with excess calcium absorption if the diet is deficient in phosphorus. Citric acid, its salts, and triethyl citrate neither alter the development of the fetus nor produce chromosome alterations. (Similar tests have not been conducted with the other esters.)

ASSESSMENT: Citric acid, its salts, and its esters are metabolized normally by the body. They are normal constituents of many foods, and are present naturally at far higher levels than the amount added to food in processed products. These compounds appear to pose no hazard to the consumer in amounts likely to be present in the diet.

RATING: S.

COCOA PROCESSED WITH ALKALI (DUTCHED)

DIOCTYL SODIUM SULFOSUCCINATE

Cocoa products may be processed from the cacao bean through heating with various mild alkalies, such as sodium, ammonium, or potassium bicarbonate, carbonate, or with the oxide or hydroxide. Magnesium carbonate or oxide also may be used. This alkali treatment is called the Dutch process.

Powdered cocoa is a hard-to-wet food; for some uses, a dispersing and solubilizing chemical, dioctyl sodium sulfosuccinate (a synthetic compound), is added to it (and other dry drink mixes) to serve as a wetting agent to make it easier to blend the dry powder with liquids.

SAFETY: The effects of the various means of processing or dispersing of cocoa come from either the alkali or the wetting agent. The alkalies used in the Dutch process are discussed and evaluated S on pages 477, 503, and 604.

Dioctyl sodium sulfosuccinate (DSS) as a dispersing agent in cocoa is not permitted to exceed 0.4 percent by weight. This compound has been studied in a few experiments with rats. Three successive generations received up to 1 percent of their diet as DSS. For the first mating, measures of fertility and gestation remained high. The ability of the young to survive and lactation by the mother were somewhat depressed in subsequent matings, but still similar to those of control animals. However, the mean weight of the young decreased with increased amounts of DSS in the diets of mothers. No significant changes due to the chemical showed up on autopsy. Another group of rats, which consumed these diets for two years, displayed no gross pathological changes or changes in the various organs and tissues.

Monkeys administered 125 milligrams per kilogram of body weight (kg/bw) of DSS by tube into the stomach for 24 weeks experienced gastrointestinal irritation, but autopsy did not reveal any organ abnormalities. Dogs given up to 0.25 milligram per kg/bw of DSS in their diets for the same period had no adverse effects; but higher levels caused gastrointestinal irrita-

---

MAJOR REFERENCE: Toxicological evaluation of some food colours, enzymes, flavour enhancers, thickening agents, and certain other food additives. WHO Food Additives Series No. 6 (Geneva, 1975).

tion. The high level of 500 milligrams of DSS per kg/bw fed by tube to rabbits caused severe diarrhea, loss of appetite, and death.

For many years DSS has been used as a bowel softener during chronic constipation for infants, children, and adults, involving doses up to 100 milligrams per day. Patch tests on humans show DSS to be nonirritating and not an allergic compound. Laboratory tests have not been conducted to assess whether DSS can induce cancer or gene mutation.

ASSESSMENT: The alkalies used in the Dutch process of cocoa demonstrate no hazard to the consumer. The additive dioctyl sodium sulfosuccinate, however, has been tested only minimally, and even with rats some suggestions of depressing effects on lactation and on the very young were noted. It also has caused gastrointestinal irritation in monkeys and dogs. More complete long-term studies are needed to properly evaluate possible hazard to the consumer.

RATING: S for cocoa processed with alkali; ? for dioctyl sodium sulfosuccinate.

COPPER SALTS

Basic Copper Carbonate (Copper Carbonate and Copper Hydroxide); Copper (Cupric) Gluconate; Copper (Cupric) Sulfate; Cuprous Iodide

Copper is a mineral trace element that is essential for man and other animals, and for most plants. Trace elements are necessary for the activity of various enzymes, hormones, and vitamins. Humans depend on obtaining copper almost entirely from food, water at times making a contribution. Shellfish, liver, nuts, wheat germ, legumes, and cocoa are rich sources of copper.

Basic copper carbonate, a combination of copper carbonate and copper hydroxide, and *copper (cupric) gluconate* are added to food as nutrients and as diet supplements. *Copper (cupric) sulfate* is used as a supplement in special dietary foods and in infant formulas. *Cuprous iodide* when present in table

MAJOR REFERENCE: Evaluation of the health aspects of copper gluconate as a food ingredient and copper sulfate as it may migrate to foods from packaging materials. FASEB/SCOGS Report 98 (NTIS PB 301-400) 1979.

salt provides iodine. The copper compounds are also used to clarify and stabilize wines and as preservatives in packaging materials that contact foods.

SAFETY: Most estimates of the total copper intake of an average adult for a single day's diet range from 2 to 4 milligrams, or 0.03 to 0.06 milligram per kilogram of body weight (kg/bw) for a person weighing 60 kg (132 lbs.). The National Academy of Sciences-National Research Council's Recommended Dietary Allowances advise a daily intake of 2 to 3 milligrams of copper for adults. A satisfactory balance in the body stores of the normal adult can be maintained on an intake of 0.03 milligram per kg/bw of copper per day, and somewhat larger amounts for infants and children.

The contribution of copper to the diet by copper salts used as additives is trivial compared to what is naturally present in food that is eaten. It was estimated that in 1975-76 only 0.05 milligram of copper gluconate and 0.02 milligram of copper sulfate were consumed daily by the average U.S. adult, and only a fraction of these weights consists of copper. Similar information for basic copper carbonate is not available, but its use in food is believed to be even less; and when last reported, cuprous iodide was not being used as an iodizing agent.

True copper deficiency is relatively rare in man because of the widespread distribution of copper in the ecosystem. However, copper deficiency has been reported in infants who are severely malnourished or who suffer from a rare genetic disease. Some scientists, on the other hand, believe that the usual copper intake is somewhat less than it should be. Copper intoxication also is rare, as man's intestinal capacity for absorption of copper that is ingested is limited, and much of it remains unabsorbed and is excreted. But cases of copper poisoning have been reported: people ingesting 5 to 32 milligrams of copper from cocktails mixed in a copper-lined container exhibited weakness, abdominal cramps, dizziness, and headache. A woman administered 15 milligrams per kg/bw of copper sulfate as an emetic, several thousand times the average daily intake of copper as an additive, died.

Adverse effects in experiments with animals were observed only when the dosages of copper salts that were administered far exceeded human consumption. Sheep appear to be particularly sensitive to copper salts; when fed 30 milligrams of copper sulfate per kg/bw daily for 26 to 73 days (some 30,000 times human consumption of copper salts), they suffered injury to liver, kidneys, and heart. Yet twice the amount produced no ill effect on ponies, and an even greater intake did not harm pigs. Rats fed diets containing 53 milligrams per kg/bw of copper in the form of copper gluconate or copper sulfate, thousands of times as much as the copper intake by humans from their total diet, did not suffer adverse effects in comparison with controls.

Microbial test-tube experiments indicated that copper gluconate, copper sulfate, and cuprous iodide will not cause gene mutations. Nor did copper gluconate or copper sulfate prove to be carcinogenic (cause of cancer) when administered by mouth. These tests were not conducted for cuprous iodide. Copper gluconate produced birth defects when injected into the egg in chicken embryos, but did not produce the same effects in mice or rats when given by stomach tube to pregnant animals. Copper sulfate was toxic to embryos and caused defective births when injected in large amounts in pregnant hamsters.

Research on basic copper carbonate has not been located.

ASSESSMENT: Copper is an essential trace element for man. The customary adult diet provides adequate copper to prevent a deficiency, as it is present in many foods. As the body can absorb only a fraction of the intake, excreting the rest, copper intoxication is rare. The amount contributed by copper salts in the average diet is negligible.

Although in humans adverse effects from copper have been reported, they have occurred only from ingestion of amounts far exceeding normal consumption. This is confirmed by the large quantity needed to cause harm in experiments with a variety of animal species. At the levels at which copper salts are present as additives in food, or that might reasonably be expected in the future, they do not pose a hazard.

RATING: S.

CORN SWEETENERS

Corn Syrup (Glucose Syrup); Dextrose (Corn Sugar, Glucose); Fructose (Fruit Sugar, Levulose); High-Fructose Corn Syrup; Invert Sugar; Invert Syrup; Maltodextrin

These carbohydrates are discussed together because they are interrelated in composition and in many properties. When corn starch is partially split chemically by heating in the presence of an acid (hydrolysis), *corn syrups* with varying proportions of dextrins (partially hydrolyzed starch; see p. 521) and free dextrose are obtained. Complete splitting by hydrolysis of the starch can lead to the simple sugar *dextrose* or glucose, or its syrup. *Maltodextrins* are manufactured by a similar procedure except that the hydrolysis is not as complete.

Glucose syrup may also be treated with an enzyme (a protein catalyst) that can convert glucose to its close relative, *fructose*, which is sweeter; such converted syrups are termed *high-fructose corn syrups*. They may closely approximate the composition of an invert syrup, which also contains equal parts of dextrose and fructose. *Invert sugar* or *invert syrup* is prepared by the splitting of sucrose (or common table sugar; see p. 648).

All these additives are used in foods as sweeteners. Dextrose has about three-fourths the sweetness of sucrose (cane or beet sugar), while invert sugar and fructose are somewhat sweeter than sucrose.

SAFETY: The presence of corn sweeteners in the daily diet of a person in the U.S. in 1976, based on usage reported by food manufacturers, was estimated at 18 grams of corn syrup, 22 to 25 milligrams each of dextrose and fructose, and close to 300 milligrams of invert sugar. High-fructose corn syrup has been replacing an appreciable amount of sucrose previously used in processed food as a sweetener.

Glucose and fructose are normal constituents of the body. Blood sugar is glucose. Fructose is largely converted to glucose when metabolized in the body. Corn syrup is readily broken down by digestive juices, and the resulting glucose is then absorbed and utilized as an energy source.

Studies have shown that high levels of fructose sugars in the diet, which may come from fructose itself or from sucrose, invert sugar, or high-fructose corn syrup, can increase the blood triglyceride (neutral fat) level in humans, though it does not have this effect on cholesterol levels. These studies involved some 30 times the average intake, and the triglyceride fraction in serum lipids is not a prime consideration in risk of coronary heart disease.

Studies have shown that corn syrup and corn sugar (dextrose) are free of allergenic properties, even for patients who are sensitive to corn starch. There are no confirmed reports of

---

MAJOR REFERENCE: Evaluation of the health aspects of corn sugar (dextrose), corn syrup, and invert sugar as food ingredients. FASEB/SCOGS Report 50 (NTIS PB 262-659) 1976.

cancer-producing responses to these sweeteners, and no known studies of effects on the developing embryo or genetic effects.

Sugars (and other carbohydrates) can be a serious hazard for some diabetics who are unable to produce a sufficient supply of insulin and cannot transform the glucose in sweeteners into energy; instead, glucose rises in the blood. The principal health concern for people is dental caries (cavities). All of these sugar products are readily fermentable and can support caries-producing organisms in the mouth. Sweet foods containing these additives may contribute to dental health problems, but more likely factors are the frequency and timing of eating, whether food remains in contact with the teeth, and dental hygiene habits.

ASSESSMENT: Dextrose, fructose, corn syrup, and invert sugar in the diet are all readily absorbed and utilized as energy sources by humans. Diabetics are an exception. Because of a metabolic disorder which interferes with utilization of sugar, they should avoid excessive amounts of it. A caution for them to avoid the substances under review here is not believed necessary, as they probably are, or should be, under medical supervision regarding their intake of all carbohydrates. There is no known hazard for nondiabetics at the present rate of consumption of these sweeteners as additives in the U.S. diet, other than their contribution to dental caries.*

RATING: S.

---

*Glucose, corn syrup, and related sweeteners have not been rated as hazardous because of their effect on cavities. While they play a role in tooth decay, they do so only in combination with other factors, such as improper dental hygiene, or between-meal snacks which contain fermentable carbohydrates, or water that is not fluoridated.

The rating procedure followed here does not consider an additive hazardous if it is harmful only when abused by the consumer, as almost anything can be. However, the sugar content in some dry breakfast cereals and instant breakfast bars and powders represents a sizable percentage of their total content. Because these percentages are not readily available, and because children consume much of these foods, they can be regarded as of concern to health. As a caution we have provided the percentage of sugar content in many of the brands in these categories, in the inventory section.

DEXTRIN

Dextrins are carbohydrates containing many molecules of glucose* chemically linked together, and are prepared commercially by dry-heating starch. This process changes some of its physical properties, including an increase in water solubility. Usually corn starch is the raw material, but potato starch, tapioca, and other starch sources may be used. The annual production and import of dextrins for direct food uses has been relatively stable for many years. In 1971 it was estimated at 30 million pounds, enough to provide a daily intake of 180 milligrams per person. Because of their water-holding properties, dextrins are used as food additives in baked goods, as thickeners in gravies and sauces, as coatings to prevent migration of oils from products containing nuts or from flavors in dry mixes. They are also employed as sugar substitutes.

SAFETY: The dextrins are only slightly poorer in digestibility than their parent starches. They too must be split to their constituent glucose units through digestive enzymes; the glucose is then absorbed and metabolized normally. Short-term and long-term studies with rats have not shown any adverse effects even where dextrin was a significant component of the diet (many thousandfold that of average human consumption, when adjusted for body weight).

There are no scientific studies on any effects of dextrin on such responses as allergy, cancer, embryo abnormalities, and genetic alterations.

ASSESSMENT: Dextrins behave in the body much like the starches from which they are derived. No toxic effects have been noted. Dextrins appear to present no hazard to the public at current levels in the diet or levels likely to be met in the future.

RATING: S.

MAJOR REFERENCE: Evaluation of the health aspects of dextrin and corn dextrin as food ingredients. FASEB/SCOGS Report 75 (NTIS PB 254-538) 1975.

*Glucose, also called dextrose, is a simple sugar found in plants and animals and is a source of energy in living organisms. See p. 518.

DIACETYL

STARTER CULTURE; STARTER DISTILLATE (BUTTER STARTER DISTILLATE)

When parts of milk are treated or cultured with selected harmless bacteria (*starter cultures* or bacterial starters), a mixture of flavor compounds is formed. The culture that results is distilled with steam to capture the flavor materials. The resulting *starter distillate,* also referred to as *butter starter distillate,* contains a large number of chemicals, but *diacetyl* is the major flavor component, comprising 80 to 90 percent of the mixture. The flavor chemicals in starter distillate account for less than 5 percent of the distillate, the remainder being water. Some 75 chemicals may be present, but obviously in very small amounts, since only a few hundredths of a percent of distillate will be incorporated into a food. Diacetyl, which occurs naturally in some fruits, berries, and cheese, usually is synthesized chemically rather than produced by natural bacterial fermentation. It is used alone as a flavoring ingredient in margarines, hard and chewy candies, and gum; it has a buttery odor and flavor. Starter distillate is also used in margarines, and to enhance the flavor of baked goods, fats and oils, dairy products and their analogs, beverages, and other processed foods.

SAFETY: The average daily consumption of starter distillate was 10 milligrams per person in 1978, or 0.25 milligram with the water removed. Use of diacetyl as a food additive, including its presence in starter distillate, was 0.3 milligram per person. The other starter distillate flavor components as a group contributed about 0.05 milligram to the daily diet.

The principal study on safety of the additive was to determine the amount of diacetyl that would cause any adverse effects in rats. Dosages of 30, 90, and 540 milligrams per kilogram of body weight (kg/bw) of the chemical were administered daily by stomach tube. After 90 days, some effects on blood and on organ weights were noted in animals receiving 540 milligrams per kg/bw, but no adverse effects were observed in those receiving 90. This amount is several thousand times the average dietary intake by humans when adjusted for body weight.

MAJOR REFERENCE: Evaluation of the health aspects of starter distillate and diacetyl as food ingredients. FASEB/SCOGS Report 94 (NTIS PB 80-178668) 1980.

Studies of possible chromosome alteration indicate lack of such activity from diacetyl or starter distillate. Starter distillate fed to pregnant rats, mice, hamsters, and rabbits did not harm either the fetus or the mother. The possibility that either of these compounds may cause cancer has not been investigated.

ASSESSMENT: Diacetyl accounts for 80 percent or more of the flavor ingredients in starter distillate. Less than a milligram is present in the average daily diet in the U.S. Several thousand times this amount has been administered to rats without adverse effects. The remaining components in starter distillate together contribute only hundredths of a milligram to the daily diet, any one of them representing a small fraction of this minute amount. While additional long-term studies on starter distillate of known composition and of diacetyl would be desirable, there is no reason at present to suspect any hazard to the consumer from the addition of either when used to enhance flavors of processed foods.

RATING: S.

DISODIUM 5′-RIBONUCLEOTIDES (RIBOTIDES)

Disodium 5′-Inosinate (IMP); Disodium 5′-Guanylate (GMP)

Disodium 5′-inosinate (referred to as *IMP*) and *disodium 5′-guanylate (GMP)* are prepared from ribonucleic acid (RNA) of yeast, or by a fermentation and partial chemical synthesis. RNA occurs in all cells, where it is responsible for the transfer of the genetic code and for protein synthesis, so it is understandable that the products derived from it occur widely in nature; meat, fish, and mushrooms are rich sources. IMP and GMP originally were produced in Japan from dried fish; they are principal flavor-enhancing components in this food.

The IMP and GMP ribonucleotides have the property of enhancing and improving food flavors without adding flavor of their own. Even at low concentrations, IMP and GMP help bring out "meaty" or "brothy" flavors in soups and bouillons, intensify the flavor of processed meat and fish, and can add to the "fresh" flavor of many canned products and mixes.

MAJOR REFERENCE: Toxicological evaluation of some food colours, enzymes, flavour enhancers, thickening agents, and certain other food additives. WHO Food Additives Series No. 6 (Geneva, 1975).

SAFETY: In 1976, usage of IMP and GMP as additives, according to a survey conducted by the National Academy of Sciences-National Research Council among food manufacturers, totaled approximately 0.5 milligram in the daily diet of the average U.S. adult, the intake being about equally divided between the two additives. This represented only a minuscule part of the nucleotide present as a natural ingredient in food in U.S. diets, where 2500 milligrams has been estimated as the average daily intake per person.

While IMP and GMP in the body are partially derived from the diet, they probably largely come from synthesis within the body, where they may be incorporated into various nitrogen-containing components of tissue, nucleic acids and genetic constituents, converted to the important energy mediator ATP in muscles, or broken down and metabolized to the excretory product uric acid.

Healthy humans have taken 2500 milligrams of IMP daily for a week with no signs of toxic effects, although serum and urinary uric acid levels increased sharply. Short-term and long-term diet studies have been made using mice, rats, and dogs. In rats, after 90 days of eating 1000 milligrams per kilogram of body weight (kg/bw) of IMP daily (equivalent to a human intake of 60 grams for a person weighing 60 kilograms), no adverse effects were observable on weight gain, organ size, or tissue and cellular structure. Similar negative findings were reported for animals receiving as much as 2 percent of these ribonucleotides in the diet (approximately 1000 milligrams per kg/bw daily) for up to two years.

Even at 8 percent of the diet fed to rats for a year, IMP did not cause toxicity, other than some calcification in the kidney due, it was reported, to a change in the concentration of the urine rather than the specific additive itself. Dogs also showed no significant adverse effects after two years on a diet containing 2 percent of a mixture of IMP and GMP (approximately 500 to 900 milligrams per kg/bw). IMP fed to dogs for two years at 2000 milligrams per kg/bw daily, more than double the amount in the previous study, again did not cause harm.

Neither of the additives has adverse effects on reproduction or on the offspring; nor do they produce malformed fetuses in mice, rats, monkeys, rabbits, or chicks.

ASSESSMENT: The safety of IMP and GMP has been demonstrated in many tests. The sole reservation is related to the metabolism of these and similar nitrogen-containing substances in the diet to uric acid. While this is normal and without complications in most people, those inflicted with gout accumulate an excess of uric acid which is deposited around their joints, causing a painful swelling and inflammation. The minuscule contribution of added IMP and GMP to the daily diet hardly warrants a caution to avoid these as additives in food. Usually people with gout are under diet restrictions and avoid foods rich in nucleotides such as organ meats, duck, and other "rich" foods, and 0.5 milligram is not likely to be of any consequence.

RATING: S.

EDTA (ETHYLENEDIAMINE TETRAACETIC ACID)

Calcium Disodium EDTA; Disodium EDTA

These two salts of ethylenediamine tetraacetic acid (EDTA) are capable of tightly binding with mineral elements present in foods (removing them from effective action), such as copper and iron. These metal contaminants may cause oxidation, rancidity, induce off-colors or off-flavors, and lead to texture changes. The EDTA salts thus may improve the stability of food. They are sometimes found in fruit drinks and beer, processed fruits, vegetables, vegetable juices, and margarines, salad dressings, mayonnaise, and condiments.

SAFETY: A survey conducted in 1976 for the National Academy of Sciences indicated that the average daily diet per person in the U.S. contained 1.3 milligrams of these EDTA salts, based on poundage of the additives used in processed foods. Only a small percentage of the EDTA is absorbed from normal diets containing one of its salts, and even this amount is rapidly excreted in the urine. At a level of 0.5 percent of the diet of dogs and rats for a period of two years, calcium disodium EDTA showed no toxic effects. This was true for four generations of offspring of rats receiving up to many thousands of times the amount present in the average human diet. When disodium EDTA was fed to rats in a two-year study at 5

MAJOR REFERENCE: Toxicological evaluation of some food additives including anticaking agents, antimicrobials, antioxidants, emulsifiers and thickening agents. WHO Food Additives Series No. 5 (Geneva, 1974).

percent of the diet—approximately 2500 milligrams per kilogram of body weight (kg/bw)—the only adverse symptom was diarrhea.

Disodium EDTA fed to pregnant rats at 3 percent of the diet (1500 milligrams per kg/bw) caused a reduction in litter size and the newborn were malformed. It is noteworthy that this did not occur if the zinc in the diet was raised. Since zinc deficiency is known to cause abnormalities in the newborn, the adverse effect noted above was ascribed to a deficiency due to the excess EDTA binding zinc in the tissues.

There are studies indicating that calcium disodium EDTA may cause an allergic reaction in some people, but this was after topical (surface) applications of pharmaceutical preparations containing the EDTA salt. This substance has proven to be useful medically in the treatment of metal poisoning and prevention of blood clotting; these clinical applications have demonstrated its safety for humans. Gross and microscopic findings in long-term studies with animals have uniformly been negative, indicating that the EDTA salts do not induce cancer.

The UN Joint FAO/WHO Expert Committee on Food Additives considers that 2.5 milligrams per kg/bw, or 150 milligrams for a person weighing 60 kg (132 lbs.), is an acceptable daily intake of these additives.

ASSESSMENT: The salts of EDTA are useful food additives because of their ability to bind and remove mineral contaminants that lower food quality and stability. Animal studies have demonstrated the safety of calcium disodium EDTA and disodium EDTA at feeding levels far higher than their presence in the human diet; and clinical applications substantiate that they are safe in humans. No health hazard to the consumer is posed by these additives even at levels in foods that may be expected in the future.

RATING: S.

ENZYMES

PROTEOLYTIC ENZYMES (PROTEASES, PROTEINASES)

Animal: Pepsin; Rennet (Rennin)

Microbial (Bacterial or Fungal): Fungal Protease; Fungal Enzyme derived from *Aspergillus (Aspergillus Oryzae);* Microbial Rennet

Plant: Bromelain (Bromelin); Ficin; Papain

CARBOHYDRASES

Animal: Alpha-Amylase

Microbial (Bacterial or Fungal): Alpha-Amylase; Glucoamylase (Amyloglucosidase)

Plant: Alpha-Amylase; Beta-Amylase

PHOSPHORYLASES

Enzymes are proteins and are present in all living matter. Most of them act as catalysts that accelerate the metabolic processes in which proteins, fats, and carbohydrates are broken down into simpler forms needed for the building and replacement of cells, and for energy required for essential activity. The human body contains many hundreds of varieties of enzymes; usually each produces only a single chemical change, and in a specific substance.

Man has known for centuries about the usefulness of enzymatic reactions in fermentation of yeast in beer and wine and of malted barley during the making of bread. Since the early part of this century food producers have made use of enzymes in the manufacture of cheese, baked goods, beer, and wine. Their enzyme sources have been *rennet* from mucosal tissues of young calves, *pepsin* from the stomach of pigs, *papain* from papaya fruit, *bromelain* from pineapple, *ficin* from figs, and *amylase* from malted barley. As it became known that various microorganisms (bacteria and fungi) could produce enzymes similar in their actions to those derived from animals and plants, and demand increased, production from these sources progressed rapidly. Microbial enzymes are less costly to produce and more readily available in the volume that food processors require.

MAJOR REFERENCES: Evaluation of the health aspects of rennet as a food ingredient. FASEB/SCOGS Report 76 (NTIS PB 274-668) 1977; Evaluation of the health aspects of papain as a food ingredient. FASEB/SCOGS Report 77 (NTIS PB 274-174) 1977; Toxicological evaluation of some food colours, enzymes, flavour enhancers, thickening agents, and certain other food additives. WHO Food Additives Series No. 6 (Geneva, 1975).

Three groups of enzymes are listed above. *Proteolytic enzymes,* also referred to as proteases or proteinases, are used when the catalytic action required is the splitting of the bonds or breakdown of certain proteins; *carbohydrases* are specific for starches or other carbohydrates; while *phosphorylases* are specific for inserting phosphorus (phosphate) into a molecule.

Individual enzymes are used in many ways to improve the quality of finished food. Papain and the other *plant proteases* are well-known meat tenderizers. They are also useful in splitting down large molecules in beer that otherwise would separate out and cause a haze when beer is chilled, and in the production of protein hydrolyzates (see p. 613). *Microbial proteases* have similar food uses, and may be used to modify the dough in cracker manufacture. *Fungal proteases* have been used for centuries in making soy sauce and in producing oriental foods. Animal and microbial rennet and pepsin, because of their milk-clotting activity, are of particular importance in cheese manufacture. Rennet, an extract which has been used for centuries in cheesemaking, contains the enzyme rennin, a catalyst which coagulates the protein in milk. Rennet is also used in frozen dairy desserts and mixes, puddings, gelatins, and fillings. Until recently it was obtained from the lining of stomachs of unweaned calves; a similar preparation called bovine rennet comes from the stomachs of older animals. An increase in the demand for cheese and a decrease in slaughtered calves led to the development of rennet substitutes. Pepsin, an enzyme from gastric juices, obtained from pigs, is used as an extender of rennet; microbial proteases may also be used as extenders.

The presence and balance of *alpha-* and *beta-amylases* are of significance in flour milling and baking. An important use of the amylases is in the production of sweet syrups from starch. FDA regulations permit addition of "a harmless preparation of enzymes of animal or plant origin capable of aiding in the curing or development of flavor" of many types of cheeses. Sometimes the specific enzyme doesn't appear on the ingredient label because the food—examples include various cheeses—has been "standardized" by FDA regulation. Thus a permitted "safe and suitable" microbial milk-clotting enzyme need not be separately mentioned on a label for cheese, or may be designated as "enzymes."

SAFETY: Enzymes extracted from animals and plants have been in use extensively for a long time, and questions have not arisen concerning the possibility of any hazard in their use in food processing. Little difference in chemical structure exists between them and microbial enzymes from bacterial and fungal sources; with few exceptions, all enzymes consist of a long, linear string of amino acids characteristic of many proteins. Because the absence of hazard has been assumed, few independent studies of bacterial and fungal enzymes have been published. Virtually all the research has been conducted by manufacturers petitioning the FDA for GRAS (generally recognized as safe) status, which would absolve them of the need for further proof of safety or for other use in foods. Generally, these studies have shown in animal experiments that large doses of purified microbial enzyme preparations are not toxic.

There is no information on the extent to which some of the enzymes are used as food additives, which limits knowledge of consumer exposure to them. It is certain to be less than the amount added to food during manufacture since often an enzyme is no longer present at the time the food is consumed. Much of the milk-clotting enzyme remains with the whey, and not with the curd from which cheese is made. Enzymes are readily deactivated by heat; thus if the food is pasteurized, baked, or otherwise heated after an enzyme treatment, enzyme activity will have been destroyed and the small amount of the added enzyme will behave merely as a food protein and be digested and metabolized like any other protein in the diet.

Amylases. A few studies of these enzymes have been reported in petitions by manufacturers to the FDA for GRAS status. Rats administered 3.5 to 7 grams orally per kilogram of body weight (kg/bw) of glucoamylase for 90 days showed no adverse effects. A single dose of 4 grams per kg/bw was fed by tube to ten mice without harm. No research has been located that employed alpha- or beta-amylase orally, though these enzymes are widely distributed in plants used as foods.

Bromelain is derived from the pineapple plant; it has been used for certain medical treatments, and this has enabled evaluation of effects of oral doses on humans. In separate studies, a total of 216 patients with inflammations, edema, bruises, or "black eye" purplish discolorations were given 2 to 8 bromelain tablets for two to ten days; generally, these conditions showed improvement. No side effects attributable to bromelain were reported. Doses of up to 10 grams of bromelain per kg/bw have been given orally to mice and rats without harm. Dogs given 750 milligrams per kg/bw of this substance in their daily diet for six months did not experience any toxic effects.

Tests conducted with rats receiving 1.5 grams of bromelain per kg/bw, as well as on their offspring, demonstrated this enzyme to be free of cancer-producing or teratogenic (deformed fetus) effects. Nor does it produce allergic reactions.

Ficin is obtained from the latex of the fig. Unfortunately, there is very little information concerning the safety or toxicity of this enzyme in experimental animals or humans, especially when the additive is a component of the diet rather than being injected. In 1959 a patent was issued on the addition of ficin or papain to poultry feed, which increased the weight of the birds over a seven-to-nine-week period. Amounts up to 10 grams of ficin or 40 grams of papain proved to be effective, the beneficial growth suggesting lack of toxicity.

Papain. The average intake of this enzyme in the U.S. is small, about 1 milligram per person in 1976. However, it is possible that some individuals who make frequent use of meat tenderizers in the home, or of condiments, seasonings, and gravies containing this enzyme, may consume as much as 25 milligrams daily, or 0.4 milligram per kg/bw. Preparations containing the pure enzyme have been studied in terms of possible usefulness as digestive aids or agents capable of controlling parasites in the digestive tract. Papain at high levels of 200-600 milligrams per kg/bw have reduced inflammation and pain in paws of experimental animals, and no adverse effects were seen. In rats and dogs, papain has been shown to increase the digestibility of protein in the meal. Secretions from the pancreas are generally needed for proper digestive action; dogs after removal of the pancreas had their digestive function restored by papain. In sheep, the enzyme proved effective in destroying the worms and eggs of parasites in the intestine. Humans have been successfully treated for roundworms by doses of 200 milligrams of papain per kg/bw, with no adverse effects in the subjects. However, it has been shown that even 45 milligrams of papain taken orally can somewhat reduce the clotting time of the blood.

Papain has not proved a safe method of digesting away meat that has lodged in the throat; where this has been attempted, using large doses of over a gram of the enzyme preparation, the lining of the throat has been damaged because it too was being digested by the enzyme.

If inhaled, papain can cause an allergic reaction; workers processing the enzyme have developed asthma. One investigator has concluded that papain is an antigen (a substance which, besides causing a specific allergic response, can broaden the range of sensitivity), and believes that allergic sensitization may possibly occur from ingestion. Routine allergy skin tests of 330 subjects found 7 (2 percent) who reacted to papain, an indication that not many are sensitive to it.

There appear to be no adverse effects of papain on maternal or fetal survival when administered orally to pregnant mice and rats. Studies of its possible cause of cancer apparently have not been made.

Pepsin, a normal constituent of the body, is the principal digestive enzyme in gastric juice for both humans and animals. It is usually derived from the stomachs of hogs when used as an additive. Pepsin has medicinal uses, including use as a digestive aid, particularly when stomach secretions are inadequate. A usual dosage for humans is 500 milligrams.

Phosphorylase. Research on the safety of this enzyme has not been located.

Fungal protease derived from *Aspergillus* (a genus of fungi) has had minimal short-term studies for toxicity. Rats fed for three months on a diet containing 7 grams per kg/bw daily showed no toxic symptoms and no microscopic changes in tissues. The enzyme has been given intravenously to dissolve blockages in the artery of the thigh or knee, 150 to 1050 milligrams of the fungal protease being administered during one to 11 days. Of nine patients thus treated, reopening of the artery was effected in four cases. A secondary effect of the treatment was local pain. The UN Joint FAO/WHO Expert Committee on Food Additives has pointed out that a product of metabolism of *Aspergillus* has been suspected of cancer-producing properties, and notes the need for broader long-term studies to investigate this matter.

Rennet. In 1975, a survey of the poundage of rennet added to foods by the industry as reported to the National Academy of Sciences-National Research Council indicated a daily intake per person in the U.S. of a little over 3 milligrams. The major source of rennet in the diet is from the consumption of cheese; about 40 percent of the milk coagulants used is rennet or a rennet-pepsin blend.

Few studies of rennet or rennin exist. One, an investigation of the effect of 1 gram of rennin on the digestion of milk which was administered by tube to human patients on three to five alternate days, found it had no effect on digestion, nor did it cause any harm. Improvements in weight gain and diet tolerance were noted among 130 hospitalized infants given cow's milk curdled with a rennin preparation.

Ulcers occurred in intestines exposed directly to solutions containing several proteolytic enzymes (including rennin and pepsin). This is unlikely to occur from these substances in the normal human diet, since they are ingested in low concentrations which are embedded in substantial amounts of bulk food (like cheese), and would be rapidly deactivated by digestion.

Laboratory tests to determine whether rennet can cause birth defects proved negative, but no tests as yet have been conducted to determine whether it can cause cancer or gene mutations. Nor are there any feeding experiments with animals available.

ASSESSMENT: Many of the enzymes used in food processing are extracted from edible plant and animal tissues, and have been in use by man for a considerable period without evidence of causing harm. Most frequently, they are destroyed (inactivated) by heat during processing or food cookery. Experimental studies of these, as well as clinical use with humans, confirm their safety. Enzymes of microbial origin are similar in chemical structure to those of animal origin; they are proteins which the body is accustomed to metabolize in a normal way. Research on these has been sparse, but the findings that do exist indicate lack of hazard. A caution is noted, however, about *Aspergillus,* a fungus source for some amylases and proteases. A suspicion exists that it may produce a carcinogen (cancer-causing substance) during metabolism, and further research is indicated. The FDA requires that when alpha-amylase obtained from *Aspergillus oryzae* is used in flour or other products, it must be declared in the list of ingredients by that name.

RATING: S for enzymes of animal, plant, and microbial origins. Exception: ? for enzymes derived from *Aspergillus.*

FOLIC ACID

Folacin

Folic acid is one of the vitamins of the vitamin B complex. It is needed for forming heme, the iron-containing pigment attached to the protein in hemoglobin, which is the oxygen-carrying constituent of red blood cells, and for nucleic acid,

MAJOR REFERENCE: A conspectus of research on folacin requirements of man. M. S. Rodriguez. *Journal of Nutrition* 108:1893 (1978).

which is essential to the growth and reproduction of the body's cells. Folic acid also participates with other vitamins (B_{12} and C) in the processes that break down or alter amino acids and proteins.

This vitamin occurs widely in nature; good sources are liver, leafy vegetables, eggs, and whole grain cereals. When found in foods, it frequently is as *folacin,* folic acid combined with additional molecules of glutamic acid (see p. 555), an amino acid. In this form it is less readily available to the body than free folic acid—a synthetic compound when used as an additive—which contains only one glutamic acid molecule. Folic acid is added as a nutrient in foods like breakfast cereals, frozen fruit juice, baby foods, and a variety of dietetic products.

SAFETY: A survey among food manufacturers, conducted by the National Academy of Sciences-National Research Council, determined that in 1976 the daily diet of an average U.S. adult contained 0.25 milligram of added folic acid. It is unlikely that this amount actually was ingested, as the vitamin is liable to destruction during cooking.

The Food and Nutrition Board of the National Academy of Sciences-National Research Council has proposed a Recommended Dietary Allowance for total dietary folacin of 50 micrograms (0.05 milligram) for small children, 400 micrograms (0.4 milligram) for most adults, and 800 micrograms (0.8 milligram) for pregnant or lactating women. They note that when the source is pure folic acid, the daily intake may need to be only a fourth as much, because folic acid is more readily absorbed and utilized than many of the combined forms of the vitamin occurring in foods.

One of the primary results of folic acid deficiency is megaloblastic anemia, where abnormal red blood cells with large nuclei appear in the blood circulation. This condition is also a characteristic of pernicious anemia resulting from a vitamin B_{12} (see p. 671) deficiency. Folic acid can bring about a temporary remission or alleviation of symptoms of the anemia in vitamin B_{12} deficiency. Thus one of the concerns about extra folic acid in foods or vitamin preparations is that it can mask some of the complications of the nervous system which can result from a vitamin B_{12} deficiency. Nevertheless, megaloblastic anemia is more likely to be caused by a folic acid deficiency than by inadequate vitamin B_{12}.

Folic acid is regarded as nontoxic. In earlier studies, no

adverse effects were seen in adults who were given the large doses of 400 milligrams of folic acid daily for five months. In 1970 a report, which was not confirmed, claimed that 15 milligrams of folic acid daily brought about mental changes and other adverse effects in healthy subjects after a month.

There are some apparent interactions of folic acid metabolism and some drugs. Aspirin may change the distribution of the folic acid in the body tissues. Both methotrexate (a folic acid inhibitor used in acute leukemia) and oral contraceptives can alter folic acid metabolism, but the possible effect on the dietary requirement is not clear. Alcohol can affect the body's use of dietary folacin; the Recommended Dietary Allowance is intended to cover such increased needs of the vitamin. Generally, the effect of drugs is likely to increase the need for folic acid.

ASSESSMENT: Folic acid is an essential vitamin; inadequate intake can cause a serious anemia. Its use as a food additive is limited by the Food and Drug Administration regulations to assure an intake of no more than the daily recommended allowance of the vitamin. In the quantities present as a nutrient in some fortified foods, folic acid poses no problems or hazard to the consumer.

RATING: S.

FOOD COLORS

Artificial colors are dyes and pigments that are synthesized from coal tar and petroleum. *U.S. certified colors (FD & C colors)* are colors that have met government specifications for composition and purity. Approval of a color for use in food

MAJOR REFERENCES: FOOD COLORS—Food colors. National Academy of Sciences-National Research Council Food Protection Committee (Washington, D.C., 1971); Handbook of food additives, 2nd ed. T. E. Furia, ed. (Cleveland: CRC Press, 1972); UN Joint FAO/WHO Expert Committee on Food Additives Reports 38B, 1966; 40 ABC, 1967; 46A, 1969; 48A, 1971; 54A, 1975. FOOD COLORS AND HYPERACTIVITY—G. T. Augustine and H. Levitan. *Science* 207:1489 (1980); C. K. Connors et al. *Pediatrics* 58:154 (1976); P. S. Cook and J. M. Woodhill. *Medical Journal of Australia* 2:85 (1976); Why your child is hyperactive. B. F. Feingold (New York: Random House, 1975); J. P. Harley et al. *Contemporary Nutrition* 3:No. 4 (April 1978), and *Pediatrics* 61:818, 62:975 (1978); S. Palmer et al. *Clinical Pediatrics* 14:956 (1975); L. K. Salzman. *Medical Journal of Australia* 2:248 (1976); J. A. Swanson and M. Kinsbourne. *Science* 207:1485 (1980).

requires documentation of safety based on research findings that are satisfactory to the FDA, guided by laws. Unfortunately, the judgment of this agency at times has been based on too meager evidence and is open to question. Thus a number of colors have been removed from the lists as evidence has come in of toxic effects. *Natural colors* are extracted from pigment naturally occurring in plants, animals, small organisms, and minerals; some of these can also be produced synthetically.

The obvious purpose of color additives is to make food look as acceptable and desirable as possible. Because of consumer expectation of what a food should look like, any marked deviation is likely to arouse suspicion that the product is inferior and to discourage sales. This expectation is reinforced by food grading and regulatory quality standards that take color into consideration. Besides some variation in the food to begin with, food can change color during manufacture and storage; dyes and pigments frequently are needed to achieve the desired and uniform hue, and for the color to remain stable afterward. By the same means, regrettably, foods can be made to look as if they contain ingredients that, in fact, they do not. A color rarely adds nutritive value to food; of the colors used in food, only the carotene pigments (see p. 505) and riboflavin (see p. 668) significantly contribute to nutrition. Most color additives are used in beverages, but they are also put into candy and confections, cereals, ice cream, butter and cheese, sausage casings and meats, baked foods, snack foods, gravies, jams and jellies, nuts, salad dressings, and much more.

ARTIFICIAL COLORS

Citrus Red No. 2; Orange B; FD & C Red No. 3 (Erythrosine); FD & C Red No. 40 (Allura AC); FD & C Yellow No. 5 (Tartrazine); FD & C Yellow No. 6; FD & C Blue No. 1; FD & C Blue No. 2; FD & C Green No. 3

SAFETY: There are two major aspects of concern regarding the health implications of these food additives. One relates to their possible effects on behavior of children, the other to their toxicology and experimental testing for safety.

Food Colors and Hyperactivity. A connection between diet and hyperactivity (hyperkinesis) in the child has been postulated and publicized by Dr. Benjamin Feingold, stating the belief that food additives such as artificial food colors and flavors, along with foods containing "salicylatelike" natural compounds* and medicines that contain aspirin, are responsible for many behavioral disturbances in some growing children. These may show up as shortened attention span, an easier distractibility, and various degrees of compulsive behavior or overactivity.

This provocative theory, implicating many food additives, has caused a flurry of experiments with children. Although there is now some scientific information on the effect of artificial colors in the diet of the hyperactive child, there are no final answers. Artificial flavors could not be tested because they number in the hundreds and because the children used in the experiment probably would know by the taste whether they were receiving the placebo (inactive substance) or the flavor.

Two types of investigations have evolved. In one, a group of hyperactive children are fed the Feingold diet (which omits foods that contain artificial colors and flavors, foods that contain salicylic acid, and certain preservatives), while another group are fed a normal diet which contains these foods. After a number of weeks, those fed the Feingold diet are shifted to the normal diet for a similar period, while those initially fed the normal diet are switched to the Feingold diet. Objective scientific tests are performed, and parents and teachers also subjectively evaluate the children's behavior in both conditions. Studies conducted in this manner at the universities of Pittsburgh and Wisconsin came up with similar findings; by parents' ratings, a minority of the children showed improvement (a quarter of the hyperactive children in the former study, a third in the latter one) when changed from the normal diet to the Feingold diet; teacher ratings showed much fewer differences. However, no behavioral change occurred when the shift was made from the Feingold diet to the normal diet.

A second procedure employed the Feingold diet throughout the experiment, and at intervals added to it a dose of artificial colors (a blend of eight FD & C certified colors) in a cracker, capsule, or soft drink. The dosage of artificial colors varied from 26 to 150 milligrams on the day of administration, the latter amount corresponding, according to FDA estimates, to the daily intake of the highest 10 percent of child consumers of these substances. Tests of learning performance, standardized scales for measurement of behavior, and other measures were

---

*These include fruits (apples, apricots, oranges, peaches, prunes, raisins, and many berries), vegetables (cucumbers, tomatoes), and flavorings (cloves, oil of wintergreen) that contain salicylic acid.

conducted to assess the effect of the addition of artificial color to the diet. When dosages of less than 100 milligrams were used, very few children appeared to be adversely affected; in one study, two of 22 children showed a response to 35 milligrams of artificial color (estimated as a daily average intake of these additives). When the artificial colors were upped to 100 milligrams or more in a Canadian study, the learning performance of 17 out of 20 hyperactive children deteriorated, though not to a considerable extent, but their social behavior did not seem to have been affected.

Two studies have been conducted in Australia. One used children who had shown allergic-type sensitivity to salicylates and artificial colors and flavors. When the rating of the mother was used to assess the diet effect, 93 percent indicated some improved behavior on the Feingold diet; but the average score on "overactivity" only slightly improved, from 5.8 to 4.6, which may not be significant by statistical testing. The other study used a parent questionnaire after the children had been placed on the diet recommended by Dr. Feingold, but adapted to Australian food habits; most of the children reportedly showed substantial improvement in behavior. A comparative study was made of the food consumption and dietary habits in the U.S. of hyperactive versus more normal children. Here no significant difference in the presence of food additives was found in the diets. It is possible that the hyperactive child may be more susceptible to certain food additives than other children.

An animal experiment conducted at the University of Maryland studied the effect of FD & C Red No. 3 (which is permitted in food) on the nerve impulses leading to a frog's muscle, and the findings may provide an explanation of the manner in which a food color might contribute to hyperactive behavior. In the experiment this food color was able independently to increase the frequency of the transmission of nerve impulses, an indication that it was able to affect nerve cells with the capability of altering behavior.

Individual Artificial Colors (U.S. Certified Colors). Nine artificial colors are permitted as additives in food. Two are restricted, each to a single product. The UN Joint FAO/WHO Expert Committee on Food Additives has cautioned that one of these is a health hazard, and the other is similar to Amaranth (FD & C No. 2), which has been banned.

Citrus Red No. 2 is restricted to coloring orange skins not used for processing. It has induced cancer in animals.

Orange B is restricted to casings and surfaces of frankfurters and sausages; it is similar in chemical structure to Amaranth, banned because of research linking it to cancer. The FDA in 1978 proposed that Orange B be banned because of a cancer-causing contaminant appearing during its manufacture. The sole manufacturer has discontinued production.

Some evidence exists that two other artificial colors may be harmful, but clear evidence is lacking. *FD & C Red No. 3* (Erythrosine) has demonstrated adverse effects on blood and may also cause gene mutation. FAO/WHO considers up to 2 milligrams per kilogram of body weight (kg/bw) as an acceptable daily intake, but has asked for metabolic studies with humans. *FD & C Red No. 40* (Allura AC) has been imputed by some to induce cancer in animals. A working group from the National Cancer Institute and the FDA, in a reappraisal of the data in 1978, concluded that evidence was not provided that it causes cancer.

A fifth color, *FD & C Yellow No. 5* (Tartrazine), has been found to cause allergic reactions, usually minor, but serious on occasion. The FDA has issued a regulation which requires it to be listed on labels of food that contain it after July 1, 1981 (but July 1, 1982, for ice cream and frozen custard). Most people allergic to it are also allergic to aspirin. It is used in candy, desserts, cereals, and dairy products.

No evidence of hazard has come to light concerning the four artificial colors that remain, but FAO/WHO is critical of the adequacy of the research that has been conducted on some of these. They are *FD & C Blue No. 1; FD & C Blue No. 2; FD & C Green No. 3;* and *FD & C Yellow No. 6.*

ASSESSMENT: Since food manufacturers are not required to, and usually do not, list each artificial color they use in a product, for the purposes of evaluation of safety the color of the product must be considered a clue to the artificial color used. On this basis, if the color is blue, green, or yellow it is likely to be one of the four colors listed immediately above, which according to present knowledge are safe. The one exception to this color judgment is FD & C Yellow No. 5, which can be dealt with separately because it must now be identified on the label. It causes allergic reactions in some people.

If the product is colored red, orange, or violet, a questionable artificial color additive probably is involved. There is no way at present to avoid the uncertain or the potentially hazardous ones except by not purchasing brands of foods of these hues that list artificial color(s) among their ingredients.

An issue of concern regarding the safety not only of artificial colors, but also of artificial food flavors and some natural components in foods, is a possibility of their connection with behavioral disturbances in growing children. The research to date on the relationship between food additives in the diet and hyperactivity of some children has not provided clear-cut answers. Many parents have observed benefits in the child's behavior when the diet is changed to eliminate additives; this is not clearly apparent when standardized, objective measures are employed.

RATING: If food is yellow, blue or green: S for adults; ? for children because of uncertainties about contribution to hyperactivity. If food is red, orange, or violet: ? for everyone. If FD & C Yellow No. 5 (Tartrazine) is listed: S for most adults; X for anyone susceptible to allergic reactions, especially if intolerant to aspirin; ? for children because of uncertainties about contribution to hyperactivity.

NATURAL COLORS

Annatto (Bixin); Beet Red (Dehydrated or Powdered Beets); Beta-Apo 8′-Carotenal; Beta-Carotene; Canthaxanthine; Caramel Color; Carrot Oil; Cochineal and Carmine; Ferrous Gluconate; Fruit Juice; Grape Skin Extract (Enocianina); Paprika; Paprika Oleoresin; Riboflavin; Saffron; Titanium Dioxide; Toasted Defatted Cottonseed Flour; Turmeric; Turmeric Oleoresin; Vegetable Juice

SAFETY: The substances above may appear as individual items on labels, or may just be identified as natural color(s). The FDA's exemption from further investigation of safety for these substances causes a problem for assessment of hazard, as at times research has been inadequate or nonexistent. The groupings below make an attempt at guidance. A number of these substances are also used as flavorings, and a few are used as vitamin sources. Most of those in the "safe" group can be produced synthetically. When a synthetic color is used in a food, it is regarded as an artificial color by the FDA, and in most products must be identified on the label as artificial coloring. On occasion, "artificial color (beta-carotene)," or another compound in the parentheses, may be found on the list of ingredients in order to meet this requirement and to specify the substance actually used.

The safety of the following natural colors is supported by research or clinical experience.

*Beta-carotene** and *Beta-apo 8'-carotenal* occur naturally in vegetables and citrus fruits and are a source of vitamin A (see p. 665). They impart orange and yellow colors to food.

Canthaxanthine is found in edible mushrooms, crustaceans, trout and salmon, and tropical birds. It produces a pink to red color when used in foods. FAO/WHO considers up to 25 milligrams per kilogram of body weight (kg/bw) as an acceptable intake.

Caramel color (see p. 501) provides a tan or brown color. The substances used to produce it are various carbohydrates (such as table sugar, corn sugar, or molasses) heated together with small amounts of acids, bases, or malts, and using a variety of temperature and pressure conditions.

Ferrous gluconate (see p. 573) is present in the body, and its components are essential for the body's chemical processes. As a color additive, it is used to provide a greenish yellow coloring.

Riboflavin (vitamin B_2; see p. 668) exists in plants and animals and as a coloring adds yellow with a greenish fluorescence.

Titanium dioxide is a white pigment which is present in minerals; and, as it is very insoluble, it is rapidly excreted. Studies in several species, including man, have shown neither significant absorption nor tissue storage following ingestion, nor did the pigment cause toxic effects.

A second group of natural colors are probably safe: research is incomplete, but further study is unwarranted.

Annatto (bixin) is extracted from the seeds of a tropical tree *(Bixa orellano L.)*. Research so far on this yellow pigment reports no adverse effects. FAO/WHO has established a temporary "acceptable daily intake" of 1.25 milligrams per kg/bw, but is withholding final judgment pending the completion of metabolic studies.

Beet red (dehydrated or powdered beets), a normal ingredient in the diet, is unlikely to be harmful. Nevertheless, research has been inadequate, and metabolic and long-term studies have been requested by FAO/WHO.

A third group of natural colors are also probably safe: research is nonexistent, but they are components of food in the normal diet. Included are *carrot oil; fruit juice; grape skin*

---

*This substance is also used for other purposes as a food additive. See p. 505.

extract; toasted defatted cottonseed flour; and vegetable juice.

A fourth group should be regarded with caution: there is some possibility of harm.

Cochineal is a red color derived from an insect found in the Canary Islands and South America, and *carmine* is the pigment that is extracted. A few short-term studies of carminic acid (the active agent in carmine) injected into veins or in the abdominal cavities of laboratory animals revealed an abnormal effect on spleen tissue. Research is unavailable on long-term effects, reproduction, and metabolism.

Paprika, a sweet orange-red pepper, contains capsaicin, which when injected in cats and mice has slowed heartbeat, caused abnormally low blood pressure, and stopped breathing. Administered by tube, it reduced body temperature and raised acid secretion because of irritation. Rats fed chili, which contained paprika, as 10 percent of their diet developed liver tumors. Paprika is used as well as a spicy flavoring, and the amount necessary to cause harm probably would make the food unpalatable. *Paprika oleoresin* is the fraction that is extracted by a percolation process, and is more concentrated, stronger in color, and less abrasive.

Turmeric is an herb whose coloring agent is curcumin, which gives a yellow color. Limited research on turmeric employing a single dosage level did not disclose adverse effects, but curcumin did affect the body liquids and livers of rats. *Turmeric oleoresin* is the active fraction extracted by a percolation process, and thus is more concentrated. FAO/WHO considers that adequate short-term studies indicate safety, but that long-term ones are needed to establish the safety level of turmeric in food. For curcumin the FDA has requested research on metabolic and long-term effects, on reproduction, and on the developing organism.

One natural color, *saffron,* does not fit in any of these groups, as further information is needed in order to provide a safety rating. It is extracted from the seed-bearing organ of a Near East crocus, and crocin is the substance in it that provides the orange-red powder used in food. FAO/WHO reports that available data are inadequate for assessing the possibility of harmful effects.

ASSESSMENT: An evaluation of hazard for a natural or uncertified food color can be provided for a specific substance if adequate information concerning it exists and if it is identified on the label. However, when only "natural color(s)" or "uncertified color(s)" are mentioned, this is not possible. The ratings that follow must reflect this limitation.

RATING: S for annatto (bixin), beet red (dehydrated or powdered beets), beta-apo 8′-carotenal, beta-carotene, canthaxanthine, caramel color, carrot oil, ferrous gluconate, fruit juice, grape skin extract (enocianina), riboflavin, titanium dioxide, and vegetable juice; ? for cochineal and carmine, paprika and paprika oleoresin, saffron, and turmeric and turmeric oleoresin (uncertainties remain, although the amount used in food is unlikely to cause harm).

FOOD FLAVORS

More flavor additives are used in foods (perhaps 1700 flavoring agents) than all other food additives combined. Some are derived from natural ingredients, while others are synthetic chemicals. Most often, complicated combinations of them are required to achieve the desired flavor, which the flavor chemist usually cannot create using a single chemical or ingredient, especially if a natural flavor is to be simulated. Because it is not required by law or of much help to the average consumer, only rarely are the individual chemical components that constitute the flavoring identified on the brand's label. The formulas are regarded as trade secrets and need only be specified in general terms like "artificial flavors" or "imitation flavors" (similar to artificial) or "natural flavors," and even this is not required for some products.

Natural flavors are often processed in ways that concentrate and enhance them, enabling the manufacturer to provide a better distribution and effect in the food. *Essential oil,* for example, is obtained from plants and usually retains its original taste and smell, but is as much as 100 times as concentrated. *Oleoresin* is usually the extractive of a spice and is more concentrated than the original material. *Extracts* are derived from certain fruits and berries, but they may be weak. Further

---

MAJOR REFERENCES: Evaluation of the health aspects as a food ingredient of caprylic acid. FASEB/SCOGS Report 29 (NTIS PB 254-530) 1975; . . . of dill. Report 22 (NTIS PB 234-906) 1973; . . . of garlic and oil of garlic. Report 17 (NTIS PB 223-838) 1973; . . . of mustard and oil of mustard. Report 16 (NTIS PB 254-528) 1975; . . . of nutmeg, mace and their essential oils. Report 18 (NTIS PB 266-878) 1973; . . . of oil of cloves. Report 19 (NTIS PB 238-792) 1973; Handbook of Food Additives, 2d ed. (Cleveland: CRC Press) 1972.

strength can be obtained by combining them with other natural flavors. An extract must consist of at least 51 percent of the original fruit's flavor to be identified as its extract.

Artificial flavors may consist of synthetic chemicals alone, or may combine them with natural substances. If a single artificial ingredient is contained in a flavoring, it must be labeled as an artificial flavoring. Occasionally a single ingredient is used as a flavoring; an example is vanillin or ethyl vanillin (see p. 659).

Flavor additives are used to achieve or assure an acceptable, desirable, or uniform flavor in the product. The flavor of food can deteriorate when it is subjected to the varying conditions imposed by processing, packaging, and storage over a period of time. Often the original ingredients themselves may have varied in flavor quality. To achieve a desirable and uniform flavor that meets the consumer's expectations, flavors are added to some food products to modify any undesirable changes, mask disagreeable ones, or even to wholly re-create the taste and odor of the food. Foods in which these flavor additives are found frequently are beverages, ice cream, cereals, candy, baked goods, meats, icings and toppings, gelatins, jellies, syrups, sauces, seasoning, margarine, and shortening; flavor additives are essential for simulated, tailor-made products such as artificial bacon bits, which are made from soybean protein.

SAFETY: The Food Additives Amendment of the Food, Drug, and Cosmetic Act, which initiated federal regulations in 1958 on safety-in-use of additives, permitted continuing use of food additives such as flavorings in existence at the time, provided that they qualified on the basis of experts' experience in the past, or of scientific data already at hand. Neither measure proved to be a very effective screen; normal use at best might reveal immediate acute reactions, but hardly any insidious but traceable long-term effects, and the research available was inadequate by today's standards. In effect, the vast majority of flavors went unchallenged. Since then laboratory studies have uncovered a few dangerous offenders; for example, safrole, a flavoring that had been used for years in root beer, can induce cancer. It no longer is permitted as a flavor additive. Coumarin, once present in imitation vanilla extract, is now banned because large amounts can cause hemorrhaging. The FDA has been aware of the inadequacy of the more permissive initial rulings, and in its own studies of some substances has found a few that could do serious harm to vital organs, cause malignancies, and increase fatal consequences. But only recently has there been a concerted effort by the agency to review the adequacy of safety information on many flavor ingredients. Flavorings that have come into existence since 1958 are required to have their safety determined by scientific procedures.

Since the 1958 Food Additives Amendment does not require the identification of the individual chemicals that comprise an added flavoring, it poses an insoluble problem for our assessment of safety. A typical artificial flavor may contain as many as a dozen or more chemicals, with no means of determining which ones of these are among the FDA list of 800 to 900 permitted synthetic flavoring substances.

The fact that "natural flavors" (no other identification) are added is no assurance of safety either. Natural flavors often contain the same chemicals as the artificial flavors that imitate them. A host of edible plants and animal products contain small amounts of natural components which can be toxic. If they were to be added to foods rather than introduced by nature, they would be prohibited by the FDA. (See Nutmeg, p. 548.) The National Academy of Sciences in a publication on toxicants occurring naturally in food flavors has noted that there are only a few of them; however, a concentration of some natural flavors, such as in essential oils, oleoresins, and extracts, in sufficient amounts can do harm.

It is argued that disclosure of the composition of food flavorings is not needed since only an extremely minute amount of each compound in a flavoring is used. (More would make the food unpalatable, a self-limiting safeguard.) Low dosages clearly lessen the hazard; while gram quantities of some chemicals and ingredients used in food flavors are required to cause serious illness or fatality, the daily intake of an individual flavor ingredient in the U.S. diet is likely to be only a small fraction of this amount. However, an important exception should be noted; the amount sufficient to cause cancer, if a substance should have this capability, remains an unknown.

The authors regret that an evaluation of safety is not possible here for flavors when their sole identification on a label is grouping as artificial, imitation, or natural flavors. Nor is it possible to assess the validity of the claim that artificial flavors can contribute to the hyperactivity of some children, because, unlike artificial colors, no research has been conducted to determine its truth.

Individual flavors at times are identified on labels, usually when used alone; most of these are reviewed elsewhere in this volume. The others are dealt with below.

ASSESSMENT: When unspecified flavors are grouped as artificial, imitation, or natural flavors, an assessment of safety is not possible.

See elsewhere in this volume for assessments of the following individual flavors.

Safe: acetic acid, adipic acid, caramel, citric acid, corn sweeteners (dextrose, fructose, corn syrup, invert sugar), formic acid and ethyl formate, fumaric acid, lactic acid, licorice, malic acid, malt, maltol and ethyl maltol, succinic acid, sucrose (cane or beet sugar), tannic acid, vanillin and ethyl vanillin.

Safe for some, not for others: caffeine, quinine.

Not safe or questionable: saccharin, smoke flavoring, xylitol.

Other individual flavors are assessed below:

Caprylic acid, a fatty acid (a component of fat) and a natural constituent in many foods, is nutritionally utilizable by man and animals. Less than 0.02 milligram was present in the daily diet of the average U.S. adult in 1976. Feeding experiments with rats using dosages approximating several hundred thousand times that amount (adjusted for body weight) did not cause injury.

RATING: S.

Cassia oil and extract are prepared from cassia, a variety of an aromatic Chinese cinnamon bark. It has a pungent flavor and is used to flavor liqueurs, baked goods, meats, confections, condiments, and beverages. The value of cassia oil depends on its content of cinnamaldehyde; it may contain 80 percent or more of this compound. Cassia oil has been used as a colic to help cleanse and remove excess gas from the intestinal tract. The use of cassia oil or extracts in 1976 as reported by the food industry indicated an average daily intake per person in the U.S. of just under 1 milligram. Cassia oil and cinnamaldehyde can cause inflammation and irritation of the intestinal lining if present in large amounts; they have a low order of toxicity, and have gained conditional acceptance as flavoring substances by the UN Joint FAO/WHO Expert Committee on Food Additives.

RATING: S.

Dill oil, an essential oil, is obtained by steam distillation of the freshly cut stalks, leaves, or seeds of dill, an herb. Daily consumption in the U.S. in 1970 averaged about 1 milligram per person. The most plentiful constituent, carvone, present to the extent of 60 percent of the oil, can cause toxic responses, but only when present in the diet of rats at thousands of times human consumption (adjusted for body weight).

RATING: S.

Ethyl acetate occurs naturally in many fruits, and is the principal volatile ester in pineapple flavor, where it is present along with closely related esters including *ethyl propionate* and *ethyl butyrate*. It is used as a flavor modifier in baked goods, milk products, frozen dairy desserts, jams, candy, gelatins, beverages, and chewing gum. In 1976 the usage of ethyl acetate in foods averaged a little over 5 milligrams per person in the daily diet. Ethyl acetate is considered relatively innocuous; FAO/WHO considers that there is adequate toxicological data to give an unconditional acceptance to use of ethyl acetate and ethyl butyrate as flavoring substances. The chemically related ester *ethyl heptanoate* (ethyl heptoate) also has conditional acceptance by FAO/WHO.

RATING: S.

Ethyl methyl phenylglycidate is used as a flavor agent in baked goods, frozen dairy desserts, candy, gelatins and puddings, beverages, and chewing gum. Its use by the food industry in 1976 amounted to an average daily intake per person in the U.S. of only 0.2 milligram. This chemical has been shown to produce adverse neurological effects in experimental animals, and more studies, with rats, are in progress.

RATING: ?.

Extractives of fenugreek: Fenugreek is a leguminous Asian herb with aromatic seeds; the seeds have been used externally and internally as a softening and soothing agent for inflammation. Extractives of fenugreek are used in curry powders and in some artificial vanilla flavorings, candies, frozen dairy desserts, sausages, baked goods, gelatins, and toppings. In 1976 use of these extractives in the daily diet averaged 2 milligrams per person. The limited information on its use by humans does not suggest any adverse effects.

RATING: S.

Garlic and *oil of garlic* are obtained from *Allium*, a genus of the lily family which includes onions, leeks, shallots, and chives. Garlic oil is obtained by steam distillation of fresh garlic, but garlic yields very little of the oil; it takes almost 500 milligrams of garlic to produce 1 milligram of garlic oil. The long history of use of garlic in food, and animal feeding studies (which are limited), reveal no credible adverse biological effects at concentrations many thousands of times as great as the 1 to 5 milligrams of garlic and garlic oil contained in the daily diet of the average U.S. adult in 1970.

RATING: S.

Ionone is an intermediate compound in the chemical synthesis of vitamin A (see p. 665). It has the drawback of being able to cause allergic reactions; susceptible individuals should avoid products containing ionone.

RATING: S for most people; X for anyone susceptible to allergies.

Kola nut extractives: The seeds of the kola nut may be extracted to give a flavoring ingredient used in cola-type beverages. While kola nut extractives contain some caffeine (see p. 494), this does not pose a hazard, as the amount in the processed extract is small and contributes less than a tenth of the caffeine in cola drinks.

RATING: S.

Mustard and *mustard oil:* The brown and yellow mustards commonly used in the U.S. are derived from two *Brassica* species that are quite different in the major constituents of their essential oils. The characteristic flavor of brown mustard, described as "horseradish bite," comes from allyl isothiocyanate. The distilled, commonly used mustard oil consists of more than 90 percent allyl isothiocyanate. The active flavor constituent of yellow mustard apparently is quite different; other constituents of the seed and added spice are responsible.

Daily consumption of these mustards and their oils, based on industry usage in 1970, totaled 305 milligrams per person, about 94 percent of it being the yellow variety. The available information from research findings indicates that the major constituents of these mustards require dosages far exceeding their human consumption to cause harm to experimental animals.

RATING: S.

Nutmeg, mace, and their essential oils, and mace oleoresin: Nutmeg comes from the ripe seed and mace from the dried shell that contains the seed of trees of the *Myristica* species cultivated in the East and West Indies. Oil of nutmeg and oil of mace are the essential oils obtained by steam distillation of nutmeg and mace, respectively. Mace oleoresin is a butterlike product obtained by pressing; 73 percent of it is the fat trimyristin, and about 12 percent is essential oil. It has been estimated, based on usage for food purposes reported by manufacturers in 1970, that the average daily intake per person in the U.S. was 11 milligrams of nutmeg and 3 milligrams of mace.

Nutmeg can have a modifying effect on mental activity. Single oral doses of 10 to 15 grams may produce acute intoxication. In doses of 5 grams or more, nutmeg can produce euphoria and hallucination, followed by abdominal pain, nausea, giddiness, drowsiness, and stupor; rapid heartbeat and respiration, effects on vision, and fever may also occur. A constituent in nutmeg, safrole (it is present in the East Indian variety but not the West Indian), is believed to be a weak hepatocarcinogen (cause of liver cancer). Safrole itself is prohibited as an additive.

The amount of nutmeg required to elicit its psychoactive effect is over 450 times as great as the amount contained in the daily diet of the average U.S. adult, and for this reason may not warrant caution in ingesting food containing it. However, the presence of safrole, a possible cause of liver cancer, in East Indian nutmeg does merit concern.

RATING: X.

Oil of clove, also called clove bud oil, clove stem oil, and clove leaf oil, is the essential oil obtained by steam distillation of these products of the clove tree. Two other clove products are used in food, *clove bud extract* (obtained by solvent extraction from clove buds) and *clove bud oleoresin*. It is estimated, based on the average annual import of cloves and stems and clove oils, that the average intake of these flavorings totals 23 milligrams per person daily. The available research has been conducted with eugenol, the chief constituent of clove oil (70 to 90 percent of clove bud oil consists of eugenol). Only when administered at far greater levels than those occurring in foods did eugenol produce irritation in the gastrointestinal tracts of laboratory animals.

RATING: S.

FORMIC ACID

ETHYL FORMATE

Formic acid is a fatty acid, one of several that function in the body as intermediaries in metabolic processes that transform ingested substances into useful compounds. Formic acid acts with components of proteins and is incorporated into DNA and RNA, constituents that carry and transmit the genetic code. The acid occurs naturally in honey, some fruits and berries, coffee, rum, wine, and milk and cheese. *Ethyl formate*, an ester of formic acid, is a component in certain plant oils, fruits, honey, and wine. As additives, both are used principally to enhance flavors or as flavorings themselves.

SAFETY: The average intake per person in 1970 of added formic acid and ethyl formate has been estimated at 1 milligram per kilogram of body weight (kg/bw). The UN Joint FAO/WHO Expert Committee on Food Additives has conditionally proposed an acceptable intake from additives of five times this amount.

The tolerance of the body for these substances is high. 160 milligrams of formic acid per kg/bw, at least 160 times human consumption, administered orally to rats did not harm them. Nor did it harm human subjects who over a four-week period ingested eight times the amount they would have normally in their diet. Calcium formate (not used in food, but containing formic acid) in dosages 150 to 200 times human consumption,

---

MAJOR REFERENCE: Evaluation of the health aspects of formic acid, sodium formate and ethyl formate as food ingredients. FASEB/SCOGS Report 71 (NTIS PB 266-282) 1977.

adjusted for body weight, fed in drinking water to rats through five successive generations, had no adverse effect on mortality rate, fertility, or fetal development. The amount administered was doubled for two years, again without adverse effect.

Human deaths have been recorded after accidental or intentional overdoses of 50 grams or more. But considering the quantities present as additives in food, such a finding is not regarded as relevant.

Results of in vitro (test-tube) experiments investigating gene mutation activity of formic acid are in conflict. Some have indicated it to be moderately mutagenic, while others have not. The possibility of formic acid or ethyl formate as a cause of cancer does appear to have been studied.

ASSESSMENT: Formic acid and its ester ethyl formate are natural constituents in a number of foods. Formic acid is a normal intermediary in the metabolic processes of the body. Ingestion of it by animals and man far exceeding human consumption as an additive provides evidence that at present levels in food, or at levels likely in the future, it does not pose a hazard to health.

RATING: S.

FUMARIC ACID

This compound is a normal constituent of the body, since it is one of the acids produced in tissues during metabolism of carbohydrates. It has been found in blood, brain tissue, kidney, liver, muscle, and bones. As fumaric acid is essential in all plants and animals, it is naturally present in foods in the normal diet. For the quantities required for commercial use as an additive, it is produced synthetically by chemicals or by bacterial fermentation.

Fumaric acid is used in foods to impart an acid flavor, as a flavor enhancer, and to extend the shelf life of powdered food products such as beverages, puddings, and gelatin desserts, because it absorbs moisture very slowly.

SAFETY: A survey conducted by the National Academy of Sciences-National Research Council on usage of fumaric acid

---

MAJOR REFERENCE: Toxicological evaluation of some food colours, enzymes, flavour enhancers, thickening agents, and certain other food additives. WHO Food Additives Series No. 6 (Geneva, 1975).

as an additive in foods in 1976 indicated an average daily intake per person of 31 milligrams. This amounts to about 0.5 milligram per kilogram of body weight (kg/bw) for a person weighing 60 kg (132 lbs.).

Fumaric acid has been fed to rats and to guinea pigs for a year or two at levels several hundred times the average human intake (adjusted for body weight) with no adverse effects being observed. Indeed, rabbits have been fed for 150 days at a rate of 1500 milligrams per kg/bw daily without harm to appetite, body weight gain, blood counts, mortality rate, or tissue structure. Some 75 human patients have taken fumaric acid at daily doses of 500 milligrams (8 milligrams per kg/bw) for a year, again with no toxic effects. This is not surprising, since fumaric acid is regularly converted to citric acid and other intermediates in the body's metabolism of carbohydrates. At unusually high levels (oral doses of 5 to 30 grams of the sodium salt of fumaric acid) a laxative effect has been observed.

The UN Joint FAO/WHO Expert Committee on Food Additives considers 6 milligrams per kg/bw an acceptable and safe daily intake for humans.

ASSESSMENT: Fumaric acid is a regular constituent in body tissues and is found in the normal metabolism of carbohydrates by humans. At levels hundreds of times the average intake of the food additive, no adverse effects have been seen in experimental animals or humans. At levels now used in foods or expected to be used in the future, fumaric acid appears without hazard.

RATING: S.

GELATIN

Gelatin is extracted from collagen, the main protein component in the connective tissue of the animal body. Collagen occurs to some extent in all tissues and organs, and is concentrated in skin, skeletal bones, and tendons that attach muscles to the skeleton. Two types of gelatin are produced commercially: one converts collagen in pig skins by an acid process, while the other uses cattle hides and bones and an alkaline or lime procedure.

MAJOR REFERENCE: Evaluation of the health aspects of gelatin as a food ingredient. FASEB/SCOGS Report 58 (NTIS PB 254-527) 1975.

Gelatin functions as a thickener and a stabilizer (prevents separation) in food. It is found most often in gelatin desserts, meat products, consommés, candies, bakery and dairy products, marshmallows, and ice cream.

SAFETY: In the U.S. in 1972 the average daily intake of gelatin was estimated as 262 milligrams per person, about 4 milligrams per kilogram of body weight (kg/bw) for a human weighing 60 kg (132 lbs.).

A good deal of the research on gelatin, which has been directed at discovering its nutritional properties rather than its toxicity, has demonstrated its low nutritional value. Although gelatin is derived from a protein, it lacks tryptophan, which is necessary for human metabolism, and it is deficient in several other biologically essential amino acids (components of proteins). Rats fed a diet containing 35 grams per kg/bw of gelatin daily, supplemented with some but not all of its amino acid deficiencies, suffered retarded growth, and half of the animals died within 48 days. Thus gelatin is a poor-quality protein which, without adequate supplementation, will not sustain life.

Allergic reactions to gelatin derived from bone have been reported in human patients sensitive to beef, but the same patients did not repeat this response to gelatin originating from a pork source. Among allergic individuals, 1 in 150 tested gave positive skin reactions to gelatin, but only 1 in 500 produced clinical symptoms, an indication that an allergic reaction is likely to occur only rarely.

Tests do not appear to have been conducted investigating the possibilities of gelatin as a cause of birth defects or gene mutations. A number of studies provide evidence that it does not cause tumors in mice.

ASSESSMENT: Gelatin is derived from collagen, a natural ingredient in commonly consumed foods of animal origin. There is no evidence that it is harmful to humans when ingested, except for a rare allergic response. It lacks one essential amino acid, tryptophan, and is deficient in several others. While by itself it would be insufficient for maintaining health, gelatin is unlikely to be used as the sole source of food by humans, and considering its current level of use in food, or levels that might reasonably be expected in the future, it appears to be without hazard.

RATING: S.

GLUCONIC ACID

MAGNESIUM, POTASSIUM, SODIUM, ZINC GLUCONATE

A number of the gluconates—mineral salts of *gluconic acid*—are used in a variety of ways in nutrition and in food processing. Easily soluble in water and readily utilized by the body, these food additives provide an excellent way in which essential minerals that they contain may be introduced as nutrients or dietary supplements.* *Magnesium, potassium,* and *sodium gluconate* act as buffering agents in soda water that help retain carbonation. The gluconates may also be used to neutralize some mineral elements in foods such as gelatins and puddings, helping to maintain the consistency and appearance of the product.

SAFETY: The daily intake of sodium and zinc gluconate per person is 0.25 milligram, estimated on total poundage reported as used by the food industry in 1976. No usage figures for magnesium and potassium gluconates were reported at that time, indicating that these salts were used in minimal amounts.

Gluconate is a normal product in the metabolism of glucose in mammals. The daily production of gluconate during metabolism in the body is about 450 milligrams per kilogram of body weight for a person weighing 60 kg (132 lbs.). This level is so much higher than the amount of gluconate supplied by the diet that the amounts added to foods are not likely to be of significance.

The information available from acute (high-dosage) toxicity studies that have used a variety of animals and various gluconates indicates that any adverse effects observed are to be ascribed to the mineral portion of the salt and not to the gluconate part. Evidence from clinical medicine supports the usefulness of *zinc gluconate* administered in substantial doses to patients for such disturbances as skin inflammation and leukemia; the dosages were well tolerated.

MAJOR REFERENCE: Evaluation of the health aspects of gluconates as food ingredients. FASEB/SCOGS Report 78 (NTIS PB 288-675) 1978; Potassium gluconate, supplemental review and evaluation. FASEB/SCOGS Report II-18 (NTIS PB 81-12786) 1980.

*This review and evaluation is limited to the gluconates of magnesium, potassium, sodium, and zinc. Calcium, copper, iron, and manganese gluconate, and glucono-delta-lactone, are covered elsewhere in this volume.

Tests have shown that sodium and zinc gluconates do not produce gene mutations, but no studies have been reported in this area for either magnesium or potassium gluconate. None of the gluconates reviewed here appears to have been investigated for possibilities as causes of cancer. Tests using one species (chicks) gave no evidence that zinc gluconate could cause birth abnormalities.

ASSESSMENT: These gluconate salts are useful as nutritional supplements, since their high solubility allows rapid absorption of their mineral constituents. The body's normal metabolic processes produce gluconic acid from glucose, in amounts many times as great as are likely to be consumed from food additives. The minerals in these salts appear to bear the responsibility for any adverse effects that may occur from extremely high intakes. At the present low level of use as additives, or levels that may be expected in the future, there is no evidence of hazard from the gluconic salts in review here.

RATING: S.

GLUCONO-DELTA-LACTONE

Glucono-delta-lactone is a form of the sugar-acid gluconic acid (see p. 553) which is obtained by the removal of the elements of water from the acid molecule; in water, glucono-delta-lactone readily reverts to gluconic acid. Humans (and other mammals) produce gluconic acid as an intermediate in the metabolic processes that break down the simple sugar glucose, and other carbohydrates, into sources of energy. The acid is a natural constituent in many foods because of its presence in living cells and blood. Glucono-delta-lactone is used as an additive when a dry acid is required, increasing the acidity in foods like jelly powders and soft-drink mixes; it is used also as a leavening agent, improving the characteristics of a dough.

SAFETY: The total amount of glucono-delta-lactone estimated to be added to foods averaged slightly over 3 milligrams in the daily diet of U.S. adults in 1975.

MAJOR REFERENCES: Toxicological evaluation of some food colours, enzymes, flour enhancers, thickening agents, and certain other food additives. WHO Food Additives Series No. 6 (Geneva, 1975); Evaluation of the health aspects of glucono-delta-lactone as a food ingredient. FASEB/SCOGS Report II-11 (NTIS PB 82-108663) 1981.

Human patients have been given doses of 5 to 25 grams of glucono-delta-lactone daily, several thousand times its presence as a food additive, with no change in urinary constituents and no discernible effects other than some diarrhea.

Rats have been fed glucono-delta-lactone at a level of 0.4 percent of the diet for 29 months, with no differences being noted compared with control animals receiving no added glucono-delta-lactone. Fed during pregnancy, this compound had no effect on maternal or fetal survival or on abnormalities in offspring in mice, rats, hamsters, or rabbits. In the long-term experiment with rats, glucono-delta-lactone showed no evidence of causing cancer.

ASSESSMENT: The dietary intake of glucono-delta-lactone as an additive represents a rather minute fraction compared to the body's exposure to gluconic acid during metabolism of carbohydrates. According to experimental and clinical evidence, glucono-delta-lactone does not present a hazard to the consumer as a food additive at levels currently in use or levels likely to be used in the future.

RATING: S.

GLUTAMATES

Glutamic Acid; Glutamic Acid Hydrochloride; Monoammonium, Monopotassium, Monosodium Glutamate (MSG)

Glutamic acid is one of the amino acid compounds that form proteins; it is present naturally in appreciable concentrations in fish, vegetables, cereals and grains, cow's milk, and meats. On the average, 20 percent of food proteins consist of glutamic acid. The *acid,* its *hydrochloride,* and its ammonium, potassium, and sodium salts are produced in commercial quantities by fermentation of glucose or by extraction from hydrolyzates (products obtained by a chemical splitting involving the addition of water) of wheat, corn, soybean, and sugar beet proteins. The glutamates are added to foods to improve or enhance flavor, particularly to high-protein foods. *Monopotassium* and *monoammonium glutamate* are also used as components of sodium-free salt substitutes. *Monosodium glutamate*

MAJOR REFERENCE: Evaluation of the health aspects of certain glutamates as food ingredients. FASEB/SCOGS Report 37a (NTIS PB 283-475) 1978, Report 37a Supplement (NTIS PB 80-178635) 1980.

(MSG), a component found in seasoning salts, accounts for 99 percent of the glutamates used as food additives.

SAFETY: It has been estimated, based on usage reported by the food industry, that the average daily intake of MSG as an additive in food in 1976 was approximately 170 milligrams per person (other glutamates may have contributed an additional 1 or 2 milligrams), or slightly more than 3 milligrams per kilogram of body weight (kg/bw) for a person weighing 60 kg (132 lbs.). The intake of naturally occurring glutamic acid from foods is almost 70 times as great, the daily diet contributing 200 milligrams per kg/bw.

Glutamic acid concentrates in the brain, and the mature brain appears to be protected by mechanisms that maintain a steady level of brain glutamate. While it is possible to overload these mechanisms, this occurs only at very high levels of glutamic acid intake, and the presence of other foods in the diet appears to restrict its spread and modify the effect. However, anyone sensitive to sugar beets, corn, or wheat may suffer an allergic reaction if MSG is added, since it is derived from these. If food containing large amounts of MSG is consumed on an empty stomach, the "Chinese restaurant syndrome" of burning sensations, facial and chest pressure, and headache will be experienced by some people.

For infants and very young children, the adverse effects of high glutamate levels can be more serious. Several investigators have demonstrated that glutamates caused damage in the central nervous system in a number of animal species during the first ten days of life, such as lesions in the retina of the eye and the hypothalamus of the brain. While in most of these studies the dosages were administered by injection and involved levels more than 600 times human dietary intake (adjusted for body weight), in one experiment 160 times such intake force-fed to 10-to-12-day-old mice also produced brain lesions in half of the animals. When the dosage was halved, this did not occur. In mice or rats, a brain barrier develops by the twelfth day, reducing the hazard. These adverse effects have not been observed by a number of other researchers. Significant decreases in learning performance have been observed in rats fed high dosages of MSG; however, clinical studies have not convincingly demonstrated that this extends to intelligence in humans.

Data from animal experiments suggest that the blood-brain protective barrier in adults may be weakened by acute hypertension and illnesses affecting the vascular system, brain edema (excessive fluid), eye inflammation, and eye surgery. Damage from these illnesses may be increased by the entrance of glutamic acid.

Glutamates administered to pregnant animals do not cause birth defects, or adversely affect growth or development in the newborn; nor do they alter genes or cause cancer. In one experiment a glutamate inhibited growth of malignant tumors.

ASSESSMENT: Glutamic acid, its salts, and its hydrochloride should not be added to infant foods (the practice has been discontinued by manufacturers). Moderation in intake of foods containing these substances is advisable for younger children. MSG might best be avoided by anyone sensitive to sugar beets, corn, or wheat, and particularly on an empty stomach. It would be prudent for anyone afflicted with vascular illness, brain edema, or eye inflammation, undergoing eye surgery, or suffering from acute hypertension to restrict intake of glutamates. With these exceptions, it is believed that these substances offer no health hazard at their present levels as additives in food.

RATING: S for some people; X for infants and very young children, persons with vascular and eye ailments, and persons allergic to corn, wheat, or sugar beets.

GLUTEN (CORN OR WHEAT)

Vital Gluten

Gluten is the principal protein component of cereal grains. Wheat and corn gluten used as food additives are prepared from flours by washing out the starch, leaving a doughlike gluten residue which is then dried. Wheat and corn gluten are mixtures of proteins. One part of wheat gluten helps trap gas bubbles during yeast fermentation, while another protein component provides elasticity to the dough. Corn gluten has a different protein mixture and is not used in baking. Instead, it is added to extend the protein in a food. As a nutritional

---

MAJOR REFERENCES: Nutrition in preventive medicine. G. H. Beaton and J. M. Bengoa, eds. WHO Monograph Series No. 62 (Geneva, 1976); Evaluation of the health aspects of wheat gluten, corn gluten, and zein as food ingredients. FASEB/SCOGS Report II-12 (NTIS PB 82–108671) 1981.

supplement, gluten is used in protein-fortified cereals. When gluten has been dried without altering the protein by heat (prepared in this way it is called *vital gluten*), it improves the texture in baked goods.

SAFETY: Gluten is a useful protein source, but is deficient in the nutritionally essential amino acid lysine (see p. 475). However, the U.S. diet is high in proteins, especially animal protein, and almost always will provide adequate lysine to balance out the body's needs.

The sole concern about the safety of gluten in the diet is gluten sensitivity in some individuals; about 1 person in 3000 in the U.S. is believed to have this malabsorption disease. Its cause is not known, but may be of genetic origin. In such individuals, gluten may irritate the lining of the intestine and interfere with the normal absorption of nutrients in the diet. The symptoms at times can be severe. There may be distress, diarrhea, weakness, damage to the small intestine, and weight loss, particularly in infants. The condition has been called celiac sprue (abdominal malabsorption), gluten-sensitive enteropathy, idiopathic steatorrhea, and nontropical sprue. The only successful treatment is to go onto a gluten-free diet, which usually means elimination of cereals, especially wheat and rye, since these grains contain gluten; corn seems to be acceptable in not having this toxicity, however.

ASSESSMENT: Gluten is the edible protein of grains, and is useful as a diet supplement; wheat gluten also is used as a dough-strengthener in baked goods. A few people have a gluten sensitivity and cannot adequately digest this protein. For them, use of wheat gluten as an added food ingredient poses a hazard due to the distress and diarrhea associated with this celiac disease.

RATING: S for most people; X for wheat gluten for those with a gluten sensitivity (celiac sprue).

GLYCERIDES

SIMPLE GLYCERIDES: Monoglycerides (Glyceryl Monostearate, Monostearin, Monoglyceryl Stearate); Diglycerides; Triglycerides

CHEMICALLY-MODIFIED GLYCERIDES: Acetylated Glycerides; Glyceryl Triacetate (Triacetin), Diacetyl Tartaric Esters of Mono- and Diglycerides
Ethoxylated Mono- and Diglycerides (Polyglycerates; Polyoxyethylene Stearates)
Glyceryl-Lacto Esters of Fatty Acids (Glyceryl Lacto-Palmitate, Lactopalmitate)
Lactylated Fatty Acid Esters of Glycerol and Propylene Glycol (Lacto Esters of Propylene Glycol)
Oxystearin
Polyglycerol Esters of Fatty Acids
Succinylated Mono- and Diglycerides, Succistearin

Glycerin or glycerol (see p. 563), a type of alcohol and a component of fat, can be combined chemically with various acids, including fatty acids, to form glyceryl esters, which are called glycerides. There are three types of the more simple, natural glycerides: monoglycerides, diglycerides, and triglycerides, depending on the number of alcohol groups (hydroxyl groups) that are combined in the molecule.

Many natural or simple glycerides occur in foods, such as vegetable oils (see p. 660), animal fats (see p. 479; these are all triglycerides), and lecithin (see p. 580). Mono- and diglycerides are formed in the body as the first step in digestion of edible fats and oils. They have been added to food for over 60 years, and are used to maintain softness in bakery products. *Monostearin,* a monoglyceride, has only one fatty acid, stearic acid, attached to glycerol.

Various chemically modified glycerides are now synthesized to serve as emulsifiers (to help blend oil and water mixtures, such as shortening), as crystallization inhibitors in fatty food products (to prevent clouding when food is chilled), and to help dissolve antioxidant additives (which inhibit the undesirable changes caused by oxygen, such as rancidity). Sometimes acids in addition to fatty acids are incorporated into the

---

MAJOR REFERENCE: Evaluation of the health aspects of glycerin and glycerides as food ingredients. FASEB/SCOGS Report 30 (NTIS PB 254-536) 1975.

glyceryl ester. Acetic acid (see p. 463), lactic acid (see p. 576), succinic acid (see p. 648), and tartaric acid (see p. 655) may be used; a mixture of related compounds usually results.

When acetic acid is incorporated, an *acetylated glyceride* (acetoglyceride) may be formed. *Glyceryl triacetate* (triacetin, a triglyceride ester with acetic acid, the ingredient of vinegar substituting for the fatty acid of a fat) may be used as a flavoring agent.

Ethoxylated mono- and *diglycerides* (sometimes referred to as polyglycerates or polyoxyethylene stearates) are manufactured by reacting an edible glyceride with ethylene oxide, a gas often used to sterilize biological preparations. The resulting emulsifier is used in bakery products, toppings and icings, frozen desserts, and coffee cream substitutes.

Lactic acid incorporated into the glyceride (lactylated, giving *glyceryl-lacto esters of fatty acids*) provides an additive useful as an emulsifier in baked goods. Another emulsifier used in baked goods, identified on food labels as *lactylated fatty acid esters of glycerol and propylene glycol* (or lacto esters of propylene glycol), includes lactic acid and propylene glycol (see p. 611) in the modified glyceride additive.

Oxystearin is a glyceride combined with oxygen that is prepared from hydrogenated soybean or cottonseed oil. It is a cloud inhibitor in salad oils.

Polyglycerol esters of fatty acids are prepared from a variety of vegetable oils or fatty acids, and also from tallow. They are made up of chemical combinations of glycerol that may involve as many as ten glycerol molecules linked together. They may be used as food emulsifiers, or as cloud inhibitors in salad oils.

When succinic acid replaces one or more fatty acids in a fat, *succinylated mono-* and *diglycerides* are formed. (A glyceride that includes the term "succinylated" indicates the presence of this acid.) The resulting additive may be used as an emulsifier or as a dough conditioner in baked products. In the case of the emulsifier *succistearin,* propylene glycol, fully hydrogenated vegetable oil, and succinic anhydride (a version of succinic acid) are used in the manufacture, incorporating succinic acid in various glycerin and propylene glycol esters of the fatty acids.

SAFETY: The daily diet of simple as well as chemically modified glycerides as additives in food in the diet, based on reported usage by food manufacturers in 1976, has been estimated at somewhat over 600 milligrams per person, or 10 milligrams per kilogram of body weight (kg/bw) for a person weighing 60 kg (132 lbs.). The modified glycerides represented less than 10 percent of the total, the principal ones used being ethoxylated mono- and diglycerides and the glyceryl-lacto esters of fatty acids, each accounting for about a third of these chemically altered glyceride additives. Most of the consumer exposure to these additives thus is in the form of the mono- or diglycerides, which are natural constituents obtained from fats during digestion and absorption of fatty foods in humans. As additives they are readily used and metabolized by the body, serving as an energy source for the body, just as do animal and vegetable fats and oils in the diet.

Monoglycerides of saturated fatty acids are more poorly absorbed than the more unsaturated fatty acids. Generally, however, the diet will include enough fats containing oleic acid (having some unsaturated linkages) and polyunsaturated fatty acids to help bring the saturated fatty acid into solution, increasing the absorption and assuring availability to the body of an additive such as monostearin.

The high degree of saturation of the fatty acid is of concern only in its presumed role in human heart disease. A high-fat diet, especially when the fat contains considerable amounts of saturated fatty acids, is considered by many authorities as a risk factor in arteriosclerosis and heart disease, based on population studies and experimental studies with both animals and humans. The fatty foods of the diet obviously contribute most of the fatty acids; food additives such as monostearin add a tiny amount to the total fat intake, which may amount to over 150 grams daily.

When *triacetin* (glyceryl triacetate) was fed to rats at unusually high levels (at 55 percent of the diet for two months, and for nearly two years at a level of slightly over 3 percent of the diet, some 1500 milligrams per kg/bw), no differences in growth from that of control animals were observed, and no toxic effects were seen. When *acetylated glycerides* or *diacetyl tartaric acid esters of mono- and diglycerides* made up 20 percent of the diet of rats (10 grams per kg/bw) over a two-year period, no adverse effects were seen on growth, survival, or tissue abnormalities, if there was adequate vitamin E in the diet; the same lack of effect was noted in dogs over a 25-month period.

Two *ethoxylated monoglycerides* (polyoxyethylene stearates, or polyglycerates) have been examined for safety in the diet. In humans, as much as 6 grams daily (several hundred times the usual dietary intake) for up to two months had no effect; only small amounts of it are absorbed. Similar findings of lack of effect were seen in studies of the *glyceryl-lacto esters of fatty acids* added to the diet of experimental animals.

Ninety-day studies on the safety of *lacto esters of propylene glycol* (propylene glycol lactostearate) have used rats and dogs as experimental animals. No significant abnormalities were noted in the studies when the additive constituted 10 percent of the diet, an enormously high level when compared with use in human foods.

A two-year feeding study with *oxystearin* at dietary levels up to 7½ grams per kg/bw (hundreds of thousands of times the usual human intake of oxystearin) again resulted in normal growth of the animals and no toxic effects, with the exception of an observation of some tumors in the testes, which the investigators doubted were related to the oxystearin fed; the UN Joint FAO/WHO Expert Committee on Food Additives questions the validity of such an excessive level of feeding.

Polyglycerol esters of fatty acids have been tested with mice, rats, and dogs. A two-year study with mice (receiving amounts much larger than those ingested by humans) showed that the substance does not induce cancer or other harmful effects. Rats fed at levels as high as 5 grams per kg/bw (thousands of times the usual human intake of polyglycerol esters) showed no adverse effects beyond a slight enlargement of the liver at the highest dosage. Dogs eating the additive for 90 days at 5 grams per kg/bw had no abnormalities in any of many examinations that were made.

Succistearin at the level of 10 percent of the diet for rats (5 grams per kg/bw) provided no evidence of toxicity or harm.

There appear to be no studies on whether any of these glycerides can cause allergy, malformation of the fetus, or chromosome damage.

ASSESSMENT: The mono-, di-, and triglycerides used as food additives are handled by the body in the same manner as the food fats. They will add to the caloric level of the food, and in some cases will add to the saturated fatty acid intake. Long-term studies at levels many hundreds of times as high as exposure through diets of consumers have demonstrated, with a single exception, that the glyceride additives are probably free from hazard other than the small contribution they make to the normal daily intake of saturated fatty acids. Since these additives represent only a minute fraction of the total intake of saturated fat in the human diet, they pose little additional risk and do not represent a significant hazard for people with heart ailments.

A possible exception to the otherwise risk-free modified glycerides is oxystearin; the only adverse effect noted for it was the presence of some tumors after rats had been fed for two years with the additive at 7.5 grams per kg/bw (equivalent to 450 grams daily for a human weighing 60 kilograms). Despite the extremely high level fed, caution is suggested regarding intake of oxystearin until more detailed research becomes available.

RATING: For oxystearin, ? pending clarification of tumor effects; for all other glycerides or modified glycerides, S.

GLYCERIN (GLYCEROL)

Glycerin (or glycerol), an alcohol, is a natural constituent of all fats; about 10 percent by weight of animal and vegetable fats consists of it. Glycerin is a slightly sweet food additive that has a variety of uses. It readily absorbs moisture and thus serves to help retain moistness of a food. As a processing aid, it serves as a crystallization modifier and a plasticizer to maintain consistent texture in candy creams. It may be found in marshmallows, various candies, baked goods, some meat products, and many other foods. For commercial use by food manufacturers, it is produced in a number of ways, among them chemical synthesis, bacterial fermentation of sugar, and as a by-product of soap manufacture.

SAFETY: A survey of food usage by processors in 1976, conducted by the National Academy of Sciences-National Research Council, established that the average daily dietary intake in the U.S. was 106 milligrams per person, or close to 2 milligrams per kilogram of body weight (kg/bw) for a person weighing 60 kg (132 lbs.).

The body is accustomed to dealing with glycerin usefully. It forms glycerin from ingested carbohydrates, from glycogen (the body's carbohydrate reserve of energy), and during the breakdown of fats. Along with the fatty acids, glycerin aids in the metabolic processes that build and reconstitute cells.

MAJOR REFERENCE: Evaluation of the health aspects of glycerin and glycerides as food ingredients. FASEB/SCOGS Report 30 (NTIS PB 254-536) 1975.

Glycerin has proven useful medically in the treatment of humans suffering from cerebral pressure. Oral administration of 1.5 grams per kg/bw (some 800 times the presence of this substance as an additive in the diet) for four days resulted in improvement, without toxic effects. Dosages of up to 2 grams per kg/bw have lowered intraocular pressure in patients afflicted with glaucoma, and also in healthy subjects.

Long-term studies with rats and dogs fed glycerin at levels of up to 5 grams per kg/bw showed no adverse effects from the chemical. Similarly, glycerin did not affect reproductive capabilities, growth, maternal or fetal survival, or result in malformations of the offspring. One investigation conducted through seven generations of rats reared on a diet providing 15 grams per kg/bw of this compound found even this massive dosage to be without influence on growth and reproduction.

Research has not been conducted to determine whether glycerin can induce cancer or gene mutations. Glycerin does not appear to cause allergic reactions in humans.

ASSESSMENT: Glycerin is a normal constituent of the body, accounting for some 10 percent of the body fats or dietary fat. Many studies with this material conducted with humans and animals, and employing dosages far in excess of its consumption as an additive, demonstrate it to be free from hazard to the consumer.

RATING: S.

GLYCEROL ESTERS OF WOOD ROSIN (TALL OIL ROSIN ESTERS)

ESTER GUM; GLYCERYL ABIETATE; SOFTENERS

Rosin is obtained from the wood of pine trees. When the acid fraction of rosin is chemically combined with the alcohol groups of glycerol (glycerin, see p. 563), *glycerol esters of wood rosin* are produced. The rosin may be obtained from chips of pine wood in paper manufacturing; its acid fraction when combined with glycerol is called *tall oil rosin esters*. These rosin esters are a very complex mixture and usually are purified by treating with steam. Abietic acid is one of the

MAJOR REFERENCE: Evaluation of certain food additives. WHO Technical Report Series No. 557 (Geneva, 1974).

components of pine rosin; its ester is *glyceryl abietate*. As food additives, sometimes called *ester gum,* they are used in beverages to modify the tendency of citrus oils to separate, or as cloud crystal aids or inhibitors; for serving as a *softener* in chewing gum to impart plasticity to chewing-gum base materials;* as an emulsifier or blender; and as a flavor agent. Frozen desserts and gelatins make use of them.

SAFETY: In a 1976 survey of the use of these additives by the food industry, it was estimated that on the average approximately 130 milligrams of these glycerol esters of rosin were contained in food in the daily diet of a person in the U.S. Most of this is in chewing gum, which usually is not ingested and thus not truly part of the diet. The esters of wood rosin are essentially insoluble in water and are likely to be excreted intact.

There apparently have been no published studies on the safety of these materials in foods. The composition of the rosin is not controlled, and is known to vary depending on the starting material, species of pine trees used, and manufacturing process for preparing the rosin acids.

ASSESSMENT: A considerable portion of the use made of glycerol esters of wood rosin as an additive is as a softener in chewing gum, which usually is not part of the diet. They also are insoluble, and there is little likelihood of absorption by the body of these esters. Nevertheless, the lack of toxicity studies prevents any basis for rating the safety of the rosin esters. Long-term studies to characterize these additives for any possible effects on cancer, reproduction, or other metabolic changes are needed.

RATING: ? (inadequate data on safety are available).

---

*See p. 511. There are softeners used as chewing-gum base materials other than the rosin esters.

GUAR GUM

Guar gum is extracted from the seed of the guar plant, a legume resembling the soybean plant. India and Pakistan are major producers. The gum is a complex sugar, a condensation of the simple sugars mannose (found in many plants) and galactose (a constituent of milk sugar). It absorbs cold water readily, forming thick, semifluid mixtures. This property makes guar gum very useful in the food industry to stabilize the consistency of ice cream and as a texture modifier or thickening agent in various food products.

SAFETY: The intake of guar gum in food in the U.S. in 1975, calculated from figures reported on weight used in food, averaged 50 milligrams per person per day, or 0.8 milligram per kilogram of body weight (kg/bw) for a person weighing 60 kg (132 lbs.).

No apparent adverse effects were found in studies with monkeys fed guar gum at levels 250 times as high as the estimated daily human intake (adjusted for body weight); rats were free of any harmful effects, even when consuming guar gum at several thousand times human intake. Tests using several animal species have shown that guar gum does not cause physical defects in the embryo during pregnancy. In vitro (laboratory test-tube) investigations indicate that it apparently does not produce gene mutation or chromosome damage, though some cell division effects were seen in one test at high levels. Force-feeding relatively high dosages (about 1000 times the estimated daily human intake) to pregnant mice did result in the loss of some animals. While human consumption of guar gum is unlikely to approach this amount, a greater mortality rate has occurred in a variety of pregnant animals when fed very large doses of other vegetable gums (carrageenan, gum arabic, gum tragacanth, locust bean gum, and others); this suggests the advisability of conducting additional feeding studies to help explain this maternal toxicity. No evidence of cancer-producing or allergenic properties of guar gum has been reported.

The UN Joint FAO/WHO Expert Committee on Food Additives considers the acceptable daily intake of guar gum for man as ranging up to 125 milligrams per kg/bw. This amount is about 150 times the U.S. average daily intake.

MAJOR REFERENCE: Evaluation of the health aspects of guar gum as a food ingredient. FASEB/SCOGS Report 13 (NTIS PB 223-836) 1973.

ASSESSMENT: Long-term feeding studies are needed, but the available information indicates that guar gum is not hazardous to human health at the present consumption level. However, when fed at high levels it caused some mortality in pregnant mice, and similar findings have occurred with other vegetable gums, suggesting caution in its use by pregnant women pending further investigation.

RATING: S for most people; ? for pregnant women.

GUM ARABIC (ACACIA GUM)

Gum arabic is a vegetable gum obtained from the discharge of a number of species of acacia, a Middle Eastern tree. The U.S. supply comes mostly from the *Acacia senegal* in the Sudan. Gum arabic is a complex polysaccharide, a carbohydrate consisting of several simple sugars. It contains calcium, magnesium, and potassium as well and can be almost completely dissolved in water—an unusual characteristic for a gum—making it useful in a range of concentrations and ways for food processors. As an additive, gum arabic enables mixtures of ingredients to blend together successfully, prevents separation, and can improve ''body feel'' of a food and act as a thickener.

SAFETY: The daily intake of gum arabic in food by U.S. individuals in 1975 averaged less than 50 milligrams per person. A study of hospital patients determined that even when administered intravenously at least 180 times this amount was required to cause harm. Under normal conditions, gum arabic breaks down into simple sugars in the body and is completely digested by animals and, in all likelihood, by man.

Investigations conducted among a number of animal species during pregnancy did not reveal that gum arabic caused defects in the newborn; but among rabbits it did result in the death of the majority of the mothers at a dosage over 1000 times the average daily human intake (adjusted for body weight). Laboratory tests failed to disclose gene mutation properties, and short-term studies of rats and mice revealed no evidence that this substance can cause cancer. However, gum arabic is a proven cause of allergic reactions in animals. Human sensitivity has been reported among people who work with it, and this

---

MAJOR REFERENCE: Evaluation of the health aspects of gum arabic as a food ingredient. FASEB/SCOGS Report 1 (NTIS PB 234-904) 1973.

effect has been confirmed in research among patients prone to allergies.

ASSESSMENT: Gum arabic appears to be an antigen, a substance capable of stimulating a reaction in a specific antibody of the body's immunological warning system and resulting in an allergic response, such as an attack of asthma or a rash. As an antigen, it may spread its effect to other closely related antibodies, increasing the severity of the attack or broadening the range of allergic sensitivity. The extent to which this occurs has not been determined. People prone to allergies will be well advised to avoid gum arabic.

Other polysaccharides have caused fatalities among pregnant animals when fed at very high levels, and similar findings among rabbits fed gum arabic merit a caution about its safety for women during pregnancy. Further research is needed. Aside from these areas, the evidence indicates that this substance is not hazardous to human health in the quantities presently in food, or even if these quantities substantially increase.

RATING: S for most people; X for anyone susceptible to allergies; ? for pregnant women (additional studies are needed to resolve uncertainties).

GUM GHATTI

Gum ghatti is the dried sap that oozes from taps in a tree native to India and Sri Lanka. This gum is a complex carbohydrate containing a number of simple sugars; its exact chemical structure has not been determined. The gum is used in the food industry only to a limited extent, primarily in frozen dairy products and nonalcoholic beverages as a stabilizer for oil and water emulsions.

SAFETY: The intake of gum ghatti in food in the U.S. in 1970 averaged slightly less than 0.05 milligram per person per day.

Minimal biological and toxicological information is available on gum ghatti in animals or humans. Laboratory tests on rats and mice, as well as on human and animal cells, have shown that gum ghatti does not produce gene mutation. Experiments

---

MAJOR REFERENCE: Evaluation of the health aspects of gum ghatti as a food ingredient. FASEB/SCOGS Report 12 (NTIS PB 223-841) 1973.

with four species of pregnant animals confirm that this substance does not cause physical defects in the embryo. However, it has been noted that force-feeding pregnant rats an extremely high dose of 1700 milligrams per kilogram of body weight (kg/bw), equivalent to 2 million times the daily estimated human intake, resulted in the loss of some of the animals. Similar findings did not occur with hamsters or mice, nor did they in rats when the dosage was reduced to 370 milligrams. There were losses among pregnant rabbits fed at a lower dose level (33 milligrams per kg/bw), which still is the equivalent of 180,000 times the estimated daily human intake.

No evidence that gum ghatti has cancer-producing or allergy-producing properties has been reported.

ASSESSMENT: The very limited information available on gum ghatti presents no evidence to indicate that this substance is hazardous to human health at current levels of consumption. The sole adverse effect was with pregnant rats and rabbits, but this occurred only when force-fed at levels 180,000 times as great as the presence of gum ghatti in human diets.

RATING: S.

GUM TRAGACANTH

Gum tragacanth, a vegetable gum, is the dried discharge obtained from several species of *Astragalus*, a wild shrub found in the Middle East. A complex mixture of sugars and sugar acids that contains calcium, magnesium, and potassium salts, gum tragacanth swells in cold water to produce very viscous solutions. It is used as a stabilizer or thickening agent in a wide variety of food products.

SAFETY: The intake of gum tragacanth in food in the U.S. in 1975 averaged a little under 4 milligrams per person per day. Very few reports have been published on the biological activity of this substance.

Gum tragacanth can induce an allergic response in sensitive people by ingestion, contact, or inhalation. With respect to incidence or severity of these reactions, it resembles many allergens commonly encountered in the diet. Cases of sensitiv-

MAJOR REFERENCE: Evaluation of the health aspects of gum tragacanth as a food ingredient. FASEB/SCOGS Report 4 (NTIS PB 223-835) 1973.

ity to gum tragacanth have been reported. Seven times the average daily consumption of 4 milligrams administered for one week caused severe symptoms in susceptible people. Other vegetable gums that may cause an allergic response are arabic (acacia) and sterculia.

A study published in 1972, using several species of animals, reported that gum tragacanth did not cause physical defects in the developing embryo. However, feeding very high dosages (adjusted for weight differences, equivalent to 2200 to 18,000 times the estimated daily human intake) did result in the loss of a significant number of pregnant rats and rabbits. This observation suggests the advisability of conducting additional feeding studies with pregnant animals that would include other dosage levels equivalent to and exceeding the current estimated daily human intake of gum tragacanth.

No reports of studies of gene mutation or cancer-producing properties of gum tragacanth have been found thus far, although there is evidence that it can inhibit some tumors in mice.

ASSESSMENT: Since gum tragacanth can cause an allergic response, persons sensitive to such allergens should avoid this substance. While the dosages of this substance that caused fatalities in pregnant animals were far in excess of human consumption, similar findings employing other polysaccharides suggest caution in its use by pregnant women pending further investigation.

Excluding these areas, the evidence indicates that gum tragacanth is not hazardous to human health at the present consumption level.

RATING: S for most people; ? for pregnant women and for anyone with allergic reactions.

INOSITOL

Inositol occurs naturally in plant and animal tissues, where it is one of the constituents of phosphorus-containing fatty substances essential for maintenance of life. The organ meats of animals and cereals are rich sources of inositol. It is not con-

---

MAJOR REFERENCE: Evaluation of the health aspects of inositol as a food ingredient. FASEB/SCOGS Report 51 (NTIS PB 262-660) 1976.

sidered to be a vitamin (a substance which the body needs, cannot make, and must obtain from food), because man is able to synthesize it from other substances. When inositol is added to foods, it generally is as a nutrient for milk-free infant formulas or special dietary foods.

SAFETY: The information on daily human intake is confined to infants, and only to those 10 percent who are on milk-free infant formulas. These are infants under six months of age, and their added intake of inositol averages 65 milligrams daily. This is within the same range as the normal inositol intake received by babies from cow's milk, and about a fourth of the intake from breast feeding. Adults average an intake of 1 gram of inositol daily from the normal foods in their diet.

Inositol has some capability to facilitate the distribution of fat throughout the body, and helps in metabolism to prevent excessive fat deposition in the liver. Added intakes up to 2 grams daily for several weeks produced no harmful effects in humans. A variety of tests have shown that inositol does not cause cancer, abnormalities in the newborn, or gene alterations.

ASSESSMENT: Inositol is widely distributed in foods and is readily synthesized in humans. It participates in fat metabolism, but its role in nutrition is not fully understood. The rationale for adding inositol to milk-free infant foods is the assumption that the greater intake ensures against possible deficiency of this substance during early growth and development, when the need might be maximum and the body's ability to synthesize it might not be fully developed. It has shown no adverse effects even when appreciable amounts have been taken by adults. There is no likelihood of any hazard from its use in foods.

RATING: S.

IODINE SALTS*

Calcium Iodate; Potassium Iodate; Potassium Iodide

Iodine is found naturally in some drinking waters and in various plants, but especially in seafoods; by contrast, freshwater fish are rather poor sources of this element. Iodine is a nutrient essential for production of thyroxine in the body, which serves to monitor or regulate the body's metabolism. Because the food and water in many parts of the country are deficient in this nutrient, a situation that can lead to goiter, *iodine salts* are added to some foods to supplement human diets. Iodized salt is the major fortified product; it contains *potassium iodide*. In bread manufacture, *calcium* or *potassium iodate* may be used as a dough conditioner to improve texture; generally the iodates are converted to iodide salts during the baking process.

SAFETY: A survey conducted by the National Academy of Sciences-National Research Council (NAS-NRC) to determine the intake in the diet of added potassium iodide, based on reported usage by food processors in 1976, indicated it to be 395 micrograms (0.395 milligram) daily, or 302 micrograms calculated as iodine. The iodates used as food additives in bakery products would be in addition to this. While the recommended daily intake of iodine of 150 micrograms proposed for optimum health by NAS-NRC is considerably lower, this group considers 1000 micrograms of iodine in the daily diet to be safe.

A deficiency of iodine will cause changes in the thyroid gland leading to goiter. An excess of dietary iodine also can cause adverse effects, including thyroid enlargement, but inhibition of iodine uptake by the thyroid gland in humans occurs only with doses of potassium iodide at least 100 times as high as the average dietary intake. With experimental animals, toxic effects have been seen only when iodine intake was many hundred times human intake, adjusted for body weight differences; at these high iodine levels, occasional effects on lactation, body weight and appetite, blood components, inflammation of the gastrointestinal tract, and mortality among the newborn have been seen in various studies.

MAJOR REFERENCE: Evaluation of the health aspects of potassium iodide, potassium iodate, and calcium iodate as food ingredients. FASEB/SCOGS Report 39 (NTIS PB 254-533) 1975.

*See p. 516 for cuprous iodide.

Potassium iodide supplementation has no apparent effect on thyroid cancer, and shows no adverse effect on the chromosomes.

ASSESSMENT: Iodine is essential in the diet, and is frequently added to some foods because many diets otherwise would be deficient. The iodine-containing salts that are used as food additives or in seasoning salts more than meet human requirements; their toxic effects are evident only after an intake hundreds of times as high as normal consumption. These additives pose no hazard to the consumer at current levels in the diet.

RATING: S.

IRON

Electrolytic Iron; Reduced or Elemental Iron

IRON SALTS

Ferric Ammonium Citrate; Ferric Phosphate (Iron Phosphate, Ferric Orthophosphate); Ferric Pyrophosphate; Ferric Sodium Pyrophosphate (Sodium Iron Pyrophosphate); Ferrous Fumarate; Ferrous Gluconate; Ferrous Lactate; Ferrous Sulphate

Iron is an essential mineral element. A deficiency of iron leads to anemia. Iron occurs widely in foods, especially in organ meats such as liver, red meats, poultry, and leafy vegetables. Nevertheless, iron deficiency anemia is extensive, and iron fortification of some foods is recommended by nutritionists. Women of childbearing age are especially in need of iron; their recommended dietary intake is 18 milligrams daily.

The principal foods to which iron or iron salts (compounds resulting from interaction of iron with an acid) have been added are enriched cereal products and some beverages, including milk. In addition, some iron salts may have special uses as food additives; ferrous gluconate is used for coloring ripe olives.

Iron may occur in two chemical forms in its salts—ferrous (iron with two chemical linkages available for forming a salt) and ferric iron (the more stable form, with three linkages available).

MAJOR REFERENCE: Evaluation of the health aspects of iron and iron salts as food ingredients. FASEB/SCOGS Report 35 (NTIS PB 80-178676) 1980.

SAFETY: A survey of the reported use of iron salts as food additives conducted in 1976 by the National Academy of Sciences-National Research Council indicated an average daily intake per person in the U.S. of 11 milligrams.

The form of iron used in food enrichment affects its usefulness as a nutrient for humans. There is great variability in the solubility and the body's ability to absorb the various iron compounds that are used. Iron powder (reduced or elemental iron) and the iron phosphates, for example, are so insoluble that they are poorly absorbed. By contrast, the ferrous salts are quite readily absorbed and thus have higher biological availability in replenishing the body's stores. The iron in heme (a part of hemoglobin, and the major form in which iron occurs in red meats) is the most readily useful form of iron in the diet, although it is not used as a food additive. However, either heme or ascorbic acid (vitamin C) in the diet can appreciably raise the absorption of iron from foods that are eaten at the same time.

The excessive accumulation of iron in the body can lead to a toxic clinical condition called hemochromatosis, which is due to a faulty metabolism occurring in only a small part of the population. Feeding studies with animals using diets containing iron in amounts of 200 to 1000 milligrams per kilogram of body weight daily (1000 to 5000 times as high as average human intake) have failed to reproduce this condition.

Elemental iron has been shown to be most effective in maintaining normal blood hemoglobin when the particle size of the iron powder is extremely fine. Even massive doses (up to 10 grams) have been fed to animals and humans without apparent harm; it is the least toxic form of iron compounds used in foods.

Ferrous fumarate is widely used as an iron supplement in medication, but apparently has very limited use as a food additive. It is well absorbed and utilized by humans, and has been recommended for use in infant formulas. High doses caused less gastric irritation than ferrous sulfate and ferrous gluconate.

Ferrous gluconate also has high biological availability. Patients have been given this iron salt at levels of up to 180 milligrams iron daily, with some individuals showing gastrointestinal side effects (common to excessive doses of any of the iron salts). Since the body normally produces large amounts of gluconate (see p. 553), this should not in itself pose any hazard. The additive has shown chromosome alteration activity in some tests but not in others.

Ferrous lactate dissolves readily and is absorbed quite efficiently by the body. It did not affect the developing embryo when injected into chick eggs. However, there are no long-term studies on this compound, and the one limited test of its effect on cancer when injected suggests need for a more thorough study to discover whether it might cause tumors when present in the diet.

Ferrous sulfate has been quite thoroughly investigated, since it is the recognized standard in comparing iron compounds for their anemia prevention usefulness. Adults have taken 300 milligrams three times daily for years with no ill effects; however, higher doses are to be avoided, since an excess of any soluble iron salt may be toxic. Ferrous sulfate has been shown to be free from any adverse effects on fetal development, and most studies indicate that it does not damage chromosomes or cause tumors.

There is more limited information on which to assess the safety of ferric salts as food additives. While experimental studies indicate the relative biological availability of the iron (its ability to be absorbed and used in metabolism), there are few studies with animals to examine any possible long-term hazards.

Ferric ammonium citrate has limited use as a food additive, principally in dairy products, since it is one of the few iron salts that are soluble and do not induce off-flavors in such foods. It is less useful for hemoglobin regeneration in anemia than the ferrous salts. In treating patients with anemia, dosages equivalent to 400 milligrams of iron have been administered daily with good tolerance.

Ferric phosphate (ferric orthophosphate) and *ferric sodium pyrophosphate* have been used in the past as a major source of iron in fortified cereals because of their chemical inertness. Unfortunately this inertness also means very poor absorption by the body. Both are used in foods much less today. Neither chemical caused gene alteration in a variety of tests, and ferric sodium pyrophosphate induced no abnormal fetal growth when administered to pregnant animals.

Ferric pyrophosphate has only limited use as a food additive. It, too, is relatively insoluble and thus is poorly absorbed; it has low biological availability for replenishing the blood cells. It does not cause chromosome damage. Long-term studies of its effect on animals or humans have not been reported.

ASSESSMENT: The addition of some form of iron to selected foods is sometimes necessary to prevent anemia from an iron deficiency, since many consumers, and especially women, get less than recommended amounts in their usual diets. For nearly all people, the body mechanisms prevent accumulation of too much iron; for a very few with a metabolic defect, excessive stores may arise from dietary iron and lead to a hemachromatosis toxicity. Ferrous salts are preferred additives (when compared to iron powder or ferric salts) because of their greater biological availability in red-blood-cell regeneration. There is only sparse experimental evidence of the safety of many of these forms of iron, particularly in long-term studies or studies of cancer-induction. It is possible to conclude that elemental iron powders (reduced iron), ferrous fumarate, ferrous gluconate, or ferrous sulfate pose no hazard to the consumer at levels currently used in foods. In view of the very poor biological availability of the ferric salts used as food additives, they may not be acceptable ingredients in food fortification.

RATING:* S for iron and most ferrous iron salts; ? for ferrous lactate (more studies needed) and ferric iron salts (ineffective for fortification).

LACTIC ACID

CALCIUM LACTATE

Lactic acid is widely distributed in living cells, and is contained in blood. The body produces lactic acid during certain metabolic processes, primarily during the breakdown of carbohydrates into simpler compounds. The acid occurs naturally in many foods. For the quantities required in commercial food processing, lactic acid can be produced by chemical synthesis or from a bacterial fermentation of a carbohydrate such as corn sugar. To form *calcium lactate,* the acid is treated with calcium carbonate (chalk).

Calcium lactate has several food uses. By providing calcium, it can help firm the texture of some processed foods; it also is used to improve the properties of baked products and dry milk powders, and to inhibit discoloration in processed

MAJOR REFERENCE: Evaluation of the health aspects of lactic acid and calcium lactate as food ingredients. FASEB/SCOGS Report 116 (NTIS PB 283-713) 1978.

*Iron salts are not additionally rated hazardous for individuals known to have hemachromatosis, since diets of these people are likely to be under strict control.

fruits and vegetables. Lactic acid is used to impart flavor and tartness to some desserts and carbonated juices. It provides acidity, thus inhibiting spoilage by fermentation in some processed foods, including cheeses and Spanish olives. It conditions dough and stabilizes certain wines.

SAFETY: Average daily intake has been estimated at 11 milligrams for lactic acid and less than 1 milligram for calcium lactate, based on use reported by the food industry in 1975. Both substances are readily absorbed by the body and either converted back to sugar or utilized as energy sources in metabolism. The normal adult may make and convert as much as 140 grams of lactate daily in the course of carbohydrate metabolism.

A single dose of 10 grams of calcium lactate caused vomiting, diarrhea, and abdominal distress in humans, but no such violent reactions occurred with a 5-gram dose. (Such doses have been used to supply calcium for medical reasons.) Infants have been fed formulas acidified with lactic acid to reduce curd tension (this no longer is done in the U.S.). When the added lactic acid consisted of the L and D forms present in the usual food additives, premature infants usually showed a disturbed acid-base metabolism, a condition which could inhibit growth of certain gastrointestinal microorganisms in the infant. This was not observed when the formula contained only the L form normally produced in the body's metabolism. It should be noted that the daily intake of lactic acid in these cases was at least 2000 times the amount used as additives in the average U.S. diet.

Lactic acid and calcium lactate have been shown to be devoid of gene-alteration effects.

ASSESSMENT: The additional lactic acid provided by its use as a food additive is probably less than 0.1 percent of the lactate produced and metabolized normally in the body. This poses no hazard to the consumer beyond infancy. The UN Joint FAO/WHO Expert Committee on Food Additives has recommended that lactic acid and calcium lactate should not be added to formulas for infants less than three months of age, since there is evidence that high dosages as additives may cause health problems with young infants. These additives are not used in infant formulas in the U.S.

RATING: S.

LACTOBACILLUS CULTURE (LACTIC CULTURE, CHEESE CULTURE, VIABLE YOGURT CULTURE)

The *Lactobacillus* microorganism occurs widely in nature. It enables milk to sour (lactic acid—see p. 576—has been formed from the milk sugar), and shredded cabbage to ferment and form sauerkraut. Since the organism is killed by heating, for instance in pasteurization, *Lactobacillus cultures* (lactic cultures) are sometimes added for acidity during food processing. For example, if pasteurized milk is used to make cheese, the FDA states that it may be "subjected to the action of harmless lactic acid bacteria, present in such milk or added thereto" in order to make food products such as blue cheese or cheddar cheese. For some products, such as cottage cheese, the use of these bacterial cultures may appear on the ingredient label as "cultured" or "made from cultured skim milk"; for others, there may be reference to *"cheese culture"* or *"viable yogurt culture."*

SAFETY: Because this group of microorganisms is so widespread, and is present in the gastrointestinal tract as well as in unprocessed foods, direct tests of possible effects on health are rare. There are population studies that have related longevity of peasants in Bulgaria to their consumption of milk soured with *Lactobacillus bulgaricus*. Many articles in medical journals have recommended cultured dairy foods, such as yogurt, to help gastrointestinal disorders. Infants have had some relief from diarrhea when fed either yogurt or milk containing *Lactobacillus acidophilus*, the culture used to make "acidophilus buttermilk."

ASSESSMENT: The lactic acid-producing organisms used in preparing certain foods are harmless and ubiquitous. Use of these cultures in processed foods poses no hazard to the consumer.

RATING: S.

MAJOR REFERENCE: Cultured dairy foods. *Dairy Council Digest* 43:No. 4 (July-August 1972).

LACTOSE

Lactose, or milk sugar, is a major carbohydrate constituent of milk and occurs naturally in all dairy products; human milk contains 7 percent lactose, and cow's milk approximately 5 percent. Lactose is a sugar which, when split, will yield a molecule of glucose and one of galactose. It has only about a sixth the sweetness of sucrose (cane or beet sugar). It is used in foods as a carrier of other flavors, aromas, and color, and can contribute to the texture, flavor, and toasting qualities of baked goods.

SAFETY: About 29 grams of lactose is contained in the daily diet of the average consumer in the U.S., but only a tiny fraction, less than 1 milligram, was contributed to this intake by the lactose used as a food additive in 1976. A breast-fed infant consumes 50 grams daily, or 35 grams if fed cow's milk. As much as a fifth of ice cream consists of lactose, and over 50 percent of dry skim milk.

In most people, lactose is split into its constituent sugars by an enzyme secreted in the intestines; only then can it be absorbed and utilized by the body. This enzyme, lactase, is at its maximum during the early years of childhood, but begins to decrease after weaning. Among adolescents or adults, some individuals do not secrete adequate amounts of lactase. This leads to "lactose intolerance," characterized by a bloated feeling, cramps, gassiness, and a watery diarrhea, due to the bacterial fermentation of the undigested lactose in the lower intestine. Lactose intolerance varies among individuals, and even among races. It is most frequent among Africans and Orientals. It is believed present in 70 percent of U.S. blacks, but only 10 to 15 percent of U.S. whites appear to be afflicted. The symptoms are not to be confused with the allergic reaction of those with "milk intolerance"; lactose-intolerant individuals usually can consume a glass or two of milk daily (containing perhaps 10 grams of lactose) with no difficulty, since some residual lactase activity is usually present. When lactose is accompanied by protein and other food components present in a mixed diet, tolerance for it by susceptible individuals is increased, and this holds true when the lactose is fermented, as it is in buttermilk and yogurt.

Galactose, one of the constituent sugars of lactose, or lactose itself can cause cataracts in the eyes of rats fed excessively large quantities (over 30 percent of the diet). In rats, inability to efficiently metabolize such large quantities of galactose apparently is a cause of this cataract development. In humans, a rare "inborn error of metabolism" or genetic defect (galactosemia) can lead to cataract formation when galactose or lactose is ingested, since these people do not have the right enzymes in the liver to properly metabolize the sugar. With this exception, lactose has not been shown to induce cataracts in humans.

Lactose is known to improve the absorption of some essential minerals in the diet, especially calcium. No reports were found to assess whether lactose has any adverse effect on reproduction, or whether it can cause chromosome damage, or cancer.

ASSESSMENT: Lactose is the principal carbohydrate of milk, the earliest food for infants. Its presence in food is not hazardous except for the individuals unable to fully metabolize high amounts of lactose in the diet. The intestinal distress of lactose-intolerant individuals may arise from consumption of dairy products, but is unlikely to occur from the minute contribution to the total diet of the lactose used as a food additive.

RATING: S.

LECITHIN (SOY LECITHIN)

HYDROXYLATED LECITHIN

The *lecithin* that is added to food by manufacturers consists of a complex mixture of fatty substances derived from the processing of soybeans, for the most part, and to a lesser extent from corn and eggs. The main constituents of lecithin are choline (see p. 512), phosphoric acid (see p. 600), glycerin (see p. 563), and fatty acids (which, in combination with glycerin, form fats). None of them is regarded as a health hazard. They are present in all living organisms as chief components of all cell membranes and also in bile and blood. *Hydroxylated lecithin*, which has been modified by reacting with hydrogen peroxide or benzoyl peroxide, acetic or lactic acid, and sodium hydroxide, disperses more easily in water and is superior in its emulsifying (blending) properties.

MAJOR REFERENCE: Evaluation of the health aspects of lecithin as a food ingredient. FASEB/SCOGS Report 106 (NTIS PB 301-405) 1979.

Lecithin as an additive is used principally as an emulsifier and stabilizer of components in products like oils and margarines, frozen desserts, chocolate, and baked goods. It serves also as an antioxidant (one of its functions in living organisms), preventing destruction of fats by oxygen, which otherwise would cause rancidity, objectionable odors, and destruction of flavor.

SAFETY: The UN Joint FAO/WHO Expert Committee on Food Additives has estimated that the average daily diet contains between 1 and 5 grams of lecithin. Based on reported usage by food manufacturers in 1970, its presence as an additive averaged 96 milligrams daily, or 2 to 10 percent of its total presence in the diet.

A two-year feeding study of rats fed soy lecithin in dosages 15 to 80 times as great (in proportion to their body weight) as the amount consumed by humans in their total diets did not result in any adverse effects accountable to lecithin. An unconfirmed experiment conducted with mice, investigating separately the effects of lecithin diet and a cholesterol diet, reported a high incidence of brain tumors in both. No such result occurred in two rat studies.

Human volunteers ingesting 20 grams or more daily for 6 to 12 weeks did not experience harm.

In a test to determine the advisability of adding lecithin to bacon, in which conditions simulated smokehouse temperatures, a nitrosamine known to cause gene alterations was reportedly formed by the reaction of lecithin with sodium nitrite (see p. 631). Tests of lecithin by itself indicated that it is not mutagenic. Experiments with pregnant mice and rats determined that lecithin had no adverse effect on fertility, or maternal or fetal survival, and does not cause deformed offspring. Chick embryos showed no abnormalities after treatment with benzoyl peroxide-bleached lecithin.

One rat study with hydroxylated lecithin has been located. For a year rats were fed dosages comparable to thousands of times its presence in the average diet of U.S. humans, without ill effects. Studies are available of animals fed compounds which could correspond to the action of hydrogen peroxide or benzoyl peroxide on unsaturated fatty acids. They indicate that neither bleaching agent acting on fatty acids causes cancer, and that the products are toxic only in amounts thousands of times as great as the presence of hydroxylated lecithin or bleached lecithin in food.

ASSESSMENT: Lecithin is a component in membranes, blood, and other parts of the body. It is a natural constituent in foods consumed in the average diet, since it is present in all living plants and animals. This natural lecithin accounts for 90 to 98 percent of human intake of this substance, only a fraction of the total being added by food processors. Humans have ingested amounts considerably in excess of what is contained in their food without difficulty, and animal feeding studies support the conclusion that there is no cause for concern. The one investigation that reported the occurrence of brain tumors in mice was not confirmed in two other studies. The evidence at hand on bleached or hydroxylated lecithin treated with hydrogen peroxide or benzoyl peroxide indicates that neither will introduce a hazard when employed as an additive.

RATING: S.

LICORICE (GLYCYRRHIZIN)

AMMONIATED GLYCYRRHIZIN

Licorice is an extract prepared commercially from the roots and root stems of a shrub, *Glycyrrhizin glabra L.*, which is found in moderate and semitropical regions of Europe and Asia. Its biologically active component, glycyrrhizin, which constitutes about 20 percent of the extract, is a compound of sugars and a complex acid. *Ammoniated glycyrrhizin*, obtained from the licorice root by a hot-water process involving sulfuric acid, and then by neutralization by dilute ammonia, is 50 times as sweet as sucrose (cane or beet sugar), and can greatly enhance flavor. In foods, licorice is used as a spice and seasoning, as well as a flavoring. Also, it has long been valued as a medicinal remedy. Ninety percent of licorice production is used in tobacco products.

SAFETY: The amount of licorice present as an additive in food has been estimated at 3 milligrams daily in the diet of a U.S. adult in 1976, based on a survey of usage reported by the food industry conducted by the National Academy of Sciences-National Research Council; this is 0.05 milligram per kilogram

---

MAJOR REFERENCE: Evaluation of the health aspects of licorice, glycyrrhiza and ammoniated glycyrrhizin as food ingredients. FASEB/SCOGS Report 28 (NTIS PB 254-529) 1975.

of body weight (kg/bw) for a human weighing 60 kg (132 lbs.).

Ammoniated glycyrrhizin is only slightly absorbed in the body, with the remainder, for the most part, excreted in the feces. It (like licorice), when fed to or injected in a variety of animal species, caused suppression of urine. This occurred in rats fed 125 milligrams per kg/bw, about 2500 times average human consumption (adjusted for body weight), while 160 milligrams of glycyrrhizin caused a 25 percent rise in blood pressure.

On the other hand, a smaller amount, 100 milligrams per kg/bw, showed antiarthritic and anti-inflammatory effects in rats. Ammoniated glycyrrhizin in tests conducted with different animals did not adversely affect maternal or fetus survival or cause birth defects or gene mutations. Studies to determine possible cancer-causing properties have not been located.

Observations of the effect of licorice in humans record disparate findings. Individuals who overindulged in licorice candy, some ingesting as much as 35 to 75 grams in a day (12,000 to 25,000 times the amount in the average diet), experienced elevated blood pressure, hypertension with unpleasant cardiac sensations, severe muscle and nerve discomfort, and many related symptoms. A controlled experiment with ten people, to whom 20 to 45 grams of licorice extract were administered daily for periods up to three weeks, resulted in decreases in hemoglobin and serum protein and a considerable rise in blood and pulse pressure. Four grams of ammonium glycyrrhizin fed for five to ten days to the same group caused inhibition of hormone output of the pituitary-adrenal system. On a positive note, 100 grams of licorice extract mixed in water and given three times daily to 45 patients with gastric ulcers resulted in the disappearance of the ulcers in nearly two-thirds of the cases. This treatment, however, was not as effective for patients with duodenal ulcers.

ASSESSMENT: While licorice and licorice derivatives elicit a variety of adverse effects in humans as well as in laboratory animals, these are at levels thousands of times as great as likely to occur in usual diets. The substances provide some remedial benefits for arthritic inflammation and peptic ulcers. At the present level of licorice consumption in food as an additive, the evidence does not indicate a health hazard; but overindulgence, particularly in licorice candy, is inadvisable.

RATING: S.

LOCUST BEAN GUM (CAROB BEAN GUM, CAROB SEED GUM)

Locust bean gum, also called *carob bean gum* or *carob seed gum,* is extracted from the seed of the carob tree, an evergreen widely cultivated in the Mediterranean area. The gum, a carbohydrate, is a compound that contains D-mannose (a simple sugar found in many plants), and D-galactose (a component of milk sugar). It is used to blend ingredients and to prevent separation in foods such as ice creams, sauces, and salad dressings. It also acts as a binder in sausages and will improve texture.

SAFETY: Research on the possibility of adverse effects from locust bean gum has not been adequate. Feeding studies exceeding half the life span of any animal species have not been conducted, and these are required to determine the likelihood of long-term consequences. Studies covering shorter periods produced evidence that this additive depressed growth in chicks, but not in rats. The relevance of this finding to human beings is doubtful, as the dosages employed were thousands of times as great (adjusted for body weight) as the 17 milligrams per person estimated as present in the U.S. daily diet in 1976. Information on the absorption, digestion, metabolism, and excretion of locust bean gum is scanty. A single dosage amounting to over 800 times the daily human intake was followed through the intestinal tracts of eight adults by means of X ray, and stools were examined, with no evidence of interference with normal digestion.

Test-tube experiments in laboratories using living matter such as rat bone marrow and human lung cells found no evidence of gene mutation properties, nor did the feeding of locust bean gum by tube in massive doses to four species of pregnant animals result in abnormalities in their newborn. However, administered in amounts more than 4000 times human consumption (adjusted for body weight), the gum did result in a significant number of maternal deaths among rabbits and mice, although this effect did not occur with doses lowered to 600 times (for rabbits) and 900 times (for mice) the amount consumed by humans.

The evidence at hand does not indicate that this substance can cause cancer or allergic activity.

MAJOR REFERENCE: Evaluation of the health aspects of carob bean gum as a food ingredient. FASEB/SCOGS Report 3 (NTIS PB 221-952) 1972.

ASSESSMENT: While the available evidence does not suggest that locust bean gum offers a hazard at current levels of consumption, further research is needed, including long-term feeding studies and ones with pregnant animals, to determine whether its increase in use in food could pose a health hazard. The high incidence of maternal deaths in two animal species when fed locust bean gum in amounts far greater than it is likely that humans will ever consume, has been repeated in identical tests with a number of substances which, like locust bean gum, contain a condensation of simple sugars. Meanwhile, it is viewed as wise to avoid this additive during pregnancy until the animal deaths are satisfactorily explained.

RATING: S for most people; ? during pregnancy, as additional studies are needed to resolve uncertainties.

MAGNESIUM SALTS*

Magnesium Carbonate; Magnesium Chloride; Magnesium Hydroxide (Milk of Magnesia); Magnesium Oxide; Magnesium Phosphate; Magnesium Stearate; Magnesium Sulfate (Epsom Salts)

Magnesium is an essential nutrient needed in human diets. It is necessary for many of the body's processes, including the production and transfer of energy, fat and protein synthesis, contractability in muscle, excitability of nerves, and enzyme activity. An adult body may contain about 24 grams of magnesium, much of it in bone.

Salts of magnesium find a variety of uses as general purpose food additives. They may serve as binders and firming agents, as anticaking agents, as alkalies to adjust the acidity of foods, as flavor enhancers and color retention agents, and as nutrients or dietary supplements.

SAFETY: The average American diet has been estimated to contain 300 milligrams of magnesium daily, whereas 7 to 10 milligrams per kilogram of body weight (kg/bw) are recommended (420 to 600 milligrams for a person weighing 60 kg, or 132 lbs.), an indication that average U.S. consumption is not sufficient. The magnesium in the additives in food in the daily

---

MAJOR REFERENCE: Evaluation of the health aspects of magnesium salts as food ingredients. FASEB/SCOGS Report 60 (NTIS PB 265-509) 1977.

*See p. 622 for magnesium silicate and p. 553 for magnesium gluconate.

diet of an average U.S. individual amounted to only approximately 2 milligrams in 1976, according to a survey of usage by food processors conducted by the National Academy of Sciences-National Research Council.

Very large doses of magnesium sulfate may cause toxic symptoms and kidney problems, but only at levels several thousand times the normal intake. Magnesium salts have been beneficial in minimizing deposits of cholesterol and other deposits in coronary arteries (rabbits) and kidney stones (humans).

Studies of possible effects of magnesium salts on cancer do not provide a clear picture. One study suggests that high levels of magnesium (320 milligrams per kg/bw) may increase the effect of a known carcinogen, the chemical urethan. A second study, in contrast, showed that a twentieth of this dosage led to a marked reduction in tumors induced by two carcinogenic benzanthracene compounds. High levels of magnesium sulfate given by injection to female rats before and during pregnancy had adverse effects on their newborn, but these levels were thousands of times normal human intake, and also were not taken orally as foods are.

ASSESSMENT: Magnesium is an essential nutrient in the diet. The contribution of magnesium salts as food additives is so small that they rarely will bring the dietary intake even up to recommended levels. The few observed toxic effects from magnesium salts are at levels far beyond the intake from foods. Magnesium salts as added to foods appear to pose no hazard to the consumer, either now or at levels likely to be found in the future.

RATING: S.

MALIC ACID

Malic acid occurs naturally in a wide variety of fruits and vegetables. It is the major acid in rhubarb and in many fruits such as apples, bananas, cherries, pears, plums, and many berries. In the normal metabolism of carbohydrates in the human body, malic acid is formed as one of the key intermediates in a series of energy-supplying reactions. Malic acid is

---

MAJOR REFERENCE: Evaluation of the health aspects of malic acid as a food ingredient. FASEB/SCOGS Report 56 (NTIS PB 262-662) 1976.

used in foods as a flavoring agent as well as to acidify the product, especially by imparting a tart taste for sweets and fruit-flavored foods such as jellies, preserves, some candies, and sherbets.

SAFETY: The average daily intake of malic acid added to processed foods has been estimated at 112 milligrams per person (1975 data), or less than 2 milligrams per kilogram body weight (kg/bw). The malic acid added to food is all in the form of the natural L-isomer normally found in nature. Usual daily food consumption provides up to 3 grams of malic acid from natural sources, 27 times as much as from the food additive.

Because of its key role in metabolism of carbohydrates and organic acids in the body, L-malic acid has been studied thoroughly. Another form of malic acid, the D-isomer, apparently is not used in metabolism by rabbits and dogs, being excreted unchanged. Malic acid has a very low toxicity when ingested. No significant effects were seen in dogs or rats over a two-year period when they were fed as much as 200 milligrams (rats) and 1400 milligrams (dogs) per kg/bw of the additive in the daily ration. These levels are 100 to 700 times the intake for humans. No effects of malic acid on reproduction were observed when it was fed to rats at 20 times the usual human intake (adjusted for body weight). Similarly, malic acid was not found to cause abnormal fetal growth when fed to experimental animals or injected into eggs. Some concern has been expressed by the UN Joint FAO/WHO Expert Committee on Food Additives that D-malic acid might be toxic in early infancy, since the enzyme responsible for conversion of this substance is relatively deficient in very young infants. Fortunately, D-malic acid, which normally is not found in nature, no longer is added to infant foods.

ASSESSMENT: Malic acid is normally produced by the body and is a common constituent of many foods used in human diets. The many studies with experimental animals demonstrate that malic acid as a food additive poses no hazard to the public at current levels of consumption or levels that may be expected in the future.

RATING: S.

MALT (DIASTATIC, NONDIASTATIC)

Malt Extract; Malt Syrup

Malt is a product obtained from germinated barley. *Malt* (or nondiastatic malt) *syrup,* a thick concentrate, is extracted from the malt with water, and the dried *malt extract,* a powder, is obtained by drying the syrup. Malt products are used to flavor meat and poultry products and a variety of other foods and beverages, including vanilla ice cream, flavored milk, sour cream, chocolate syrup, candy, cough drops, condiments and dressings, and breakfast cereals. Malt syrup may be used in preparation of caramel coloring. Because it contains active enzymes (proteins that can hasten a chemical reaction) which split or hydrolyze starch, malt (or *diastatic malt*) is used in bread and cereal products and in beer and whiskey production. (*Nondiastatic malt* does not contain these enzymes.)

SAFETY: Derivatives of malt have been used in foods for many centuries. In a 1976 survey of the use of malt extracts by the food industry, the average intake in the U.S. per person was estimated as about 68 milligrams, or slightly over 1 milligram per kilogram of body weight (kg/bw) daily.

Many of the substances present in malt extract and malt syrup may be used as food additives. Among those assessed elsewhere in this dictionary are dextrins, glucose, fructose, starch, sucrose, various fatty acid components of animal fats and vegetable oils, mineral salts (calcium, iron, magnesium, phosphorus, potassium, silicon), and several vitamins (biotin, niacin, pantothenic acid, riboflavin, thiamin). When used as food additives, these individual compounds in malt have not been found to cause harm, providing support for the suggestion that this is likely to be true of the malt products under review.

Few studies on malt syrup or extract have evaluated the substances for short- or long-term toxicity, or for the possibility that they may cause cancer. However, malt extracts have been used in human diets throughout historical times with no evidence that they have adverse effects. Tests of malt extract have determined that it did not alter chromosomes, and, when

---

MAJOR REFERENCE: Evaluation of the health aspects of malt syrup and malt extract as food ingredients. FASEB/SCOGS Report II-13 (NTIS PB 81-121402) 1980.

fed to rats, actually improved growth and produced no adverse effects. Malt syrup did not induce abnormalities in the offspring when introduced into chicken eggs at a dosage of 200 milligrams per kg/bw. Infrequent cases of allergic reactions to malt have been reported; only two reports of allergy (in children) have been cited in medical literature.

Humans have consumed this product for a month to improve constipation, with no undesirable side effects. Again, no harmful effects were seen when athletes took 100 grams of malt extract (approximately 1.5 grams per kg/bw) daily for six days.

ASSESSMENT: Malt extract and syrup, which are derived from barley, are used in many foods for the associated flavor and texture changes they induce. The few controlled studies on their safety are augmented by the many studies on individual components and the centuries of use by humans with no indication of hazard. Apparently the instances of anyone being allergic to malt products are extremely rare and thus pose no hazard.

RATING: S.

MALTOL; ETHYL MALTOL

Maltol, a natural flavor that occurs in the bark of larch trees, pine needles, chicory, and wood tars and oils, is also found in many heated and roasted foods such as coffee, cocoa, bread, and milk products. *Ethyl maltol* is a synthetic compound not present naturally in unprocessed foods. Both substances are often used as flavorings and flavor enhancers in baked goods, gelatin desserts, frozen dairy products, soft drinks, and other carbohydrate-rich or sugary foods. They bring out sweetness in a food and thus permit a reduction in the sugar content while maintaining the desired degree of sweetness. They also can impart a fresh-baked or browned odor to bakery products, and act as synthetic berry and citrus fruit flavorings.

SAFETY: Flavors and flavor enhancers are added to foods in very small amounts because their intense flavor in larger amounts may be unpalatable. As a consequence they are con-

---

MAJOR REFERENCE: Toxicological evaluation of some food colours, enzymes, flavour enhancers, thickening agents, and certain other food additives. WHO Food Additives Series No. 6 (Geneva, 1975).

sumed only in minute quantities. The average daily intake per person in the U.S. in 1970 has been estimated as 0.4 milligram of maltol and 0.3 milligram for ethyl maltol as additives in foods. Combined, this amounts to about 0.01 milligram per kilogram of body weight (kg/bw) for a person weighing 60 kg (132 lbs.).

In short-term studies, rats and dogs were fed ethyl maltol for 90 days at levels of up to 500 milligrams per kg/bw, many thousands of times human intake when adjusted for body size. No abnormalities or other effects were observed other than a mild anemia and some vomiting at the highest level of 500 milligrams. Maltol in the diet was somewhat more toxic, and the 500 milligrams per kg/bw dose proved excessive and caused tissue damage and even death, although this did not occur at 250 milligrams per kg/bw. Long-term studies, where ethyl maltol was fed daily to rats and dogs for as long as two years, showed that at 200 milligrams per kg/bw, the flavor enhancer was without adverse effect. The animals were mated to investigate any effects on fertility, survival and size of the offspring, and development of abnormalities of the fetus, and there were none. No adequate long-term feeding studies using maltol appear to have been made.

Neither of these additives produces any allergic reaction or sensitization. No studies directed toward possible cancer-producing properties have been conducted.

ASSESSMENT: Maltol and ethyl maltol are used as ingredients to accentuate natural flavors and as flavorings in foods. Both additives have been without hazard at levels in the diet many thousands of times the average intake by humans. The UN Joint FAO/WHO Expert Committee on Food Additives has indicated that up to 2 milligrams per kg/bw (or 120 milligrams for a person weighing 132 pounds) is an acceptable human intake of ethyl maltol, which is well over 2000 times present average consumption of both compounds. The low level of these additives used in processed foods indicates that harm to the consumer is unlikely from their use, now or in the future.

RATING: S.

MANGANOUS SALTS

Manganous Chloride; Manganous Glycerophosphate; Manganous Hypophosphite; Manganous Sulfate

Manganese, a mineral element, is nutritionally essential for man. It participates as an activator of enzyme systems in metabolism and is necessary in the normal development of bones and the nervous system, and in sex-hormone production. Manganese occurs in many foods of plant and animal origin and is especially abundant in nuts and whole grains. Any of the salts *manganous chloride, manganous glycerophosphate, manganous hypophosphite,* and *manganous sulfate* may be added as a nutrient or diet supplement to foods such as baked goods and baking mixes, infant formulas, and dairy product substitutes.

SAFETY: The average daily adult intake of manganese from the amounts occurring naturally in foods is estimated to range from 2 to 9 milligrams. In 1975, approximately 0.2 milligram of manganous sulfate was added to foods, and a much smaller amount of manganous chloride (almost entirely in infant formulas). The Food and Nutrition Board of the National Academy of Sciences-National Research Council has recommended that the daily manganese intake for an adult be in the range of 2.5 to 5 milligrams. The varied nature of U.S. diets indicates that a deficiency of this mineral is unlikely to occur with any frequency in the U.S.

In experimental animals, a deficiency of manganese in the diet impaired bone formation and produced diabeteslike symptoms. When extremely large doses (thousands of times human intake) of manganous chloride or manganous sulfate were given to rats, rabbits, and farm animals, they developed anemia because of an interaction of manganese and iron in the body. Liver damage has been observed in hamsters and rats when the salt is fed at these high levels.

Manganous sulfate fed to rabbits in drinking water for several months, again in amounts thousands of times as high as its presence as an additive in the diet, caused transient paralysis in hind paws and some effects on the nerves. Several cases of poisoning of humans have occurred from drinking well water

---

MAJOR REFERENCE: Evaluation of the health aspects of manganous salts as food ingredients. FASEB/SCOGS Report 67 (NTIS PB 301-404) 1979.

contaminated with manganese, with similar neurological effects. Large dosages of manganous sulfate fed for four weeks to rats adversely affected formation of blood cells.

No adverse effects have been seen from manganous sulfate fed to pregnant animals when studied for possible abnormal fetal growth. Both manganous salts have been found to cause chromosome damage in some tests, but not in all. Long-term feeding studies to determine whether they cause cancer have not been made.

ASSESSMENT: Manganese is an essential mineral in the human diet. It has been demonstrated that a deficiency can have serious effects. It has also been shown that amounts administered far in excess of human intake have been extremely harmful; and disputed findings exist about whether the salts can cause chromosomal alterations. Considering the amounts added to foods, a minute fraction of the total dietary intake of manganese, these salts are hardly likely to be a hazard to health; they are used as nutrients in fortifying foods that otherwise would be low in manganese and thus are likely to be of benefit.

RATING: S.

MANNITOL

Mannitol is prepared commercially by the chemical addition of hydrogen to glucose (corn sugar). It is found naturally in such plant foods as beets, celery, and olives. Mannitol has about half the sweetness of sucrose (cane sugar), and is used in some sugarless dietary foods. Because this substance does not readily take up moisture, it is useful in powdered products, such as the dusting on chewing gum. It also can help blend ingredients and improve texture. It is present in amounts as high as 20 percent in chewing gum and 32.5 percent in soft candy. It may be used in breakfast cereals and frostings.

SAFETY: The average daily intake of mannitol, based on reported use by food processors in 1975, was estimated at about 36 milligrams per person. Mannitol is only moderately utilized by the body. Adult humans have ingested up to 100 grams of

---

MAJOR REFERENCE: Evaluation of the health aspects of mannitol as a food ingredient. FASEB/SCOGS Report 10 (NTIS PB 221-953) 1973.

mannitol in one dose, with two-thirds of it being absorbed and either excreted in the urine or metabolized to more readily useful substances such as sugar and other carbohydrates. Mannitol may have an energy value of about 2 kilocalories per gram. (The energy value of sugar is about 4 kilocalories per gram.)

Mannitol shows a laxative effect at lower total intakes (10 to 20 grams) than does the closely related compound sorbitol (which requires 50 grams). Short-term studies with humans and experimental animals have shown mannitol to have very low toxicity and to have no adverse effect on the fetus when added to the diet of pregnant animals at levels several thousand times the average intake for humans (adjusted for body weight). There are no reported long-term animal feeding studies (extending more than half the life spans of the species), and a lack of experimental data prevents assessment of any carcinogenic or mutagenic effects of mannitol, or of its effects on reproduction.

ASSESSMENT: The available evidence reveals no short-term adverse consequences in a variety of animal species or in man when mannitol is fed in amounts exceeding those currently consumed in the U.S. diet, and it has been used as a food additive for three decades without known adverse effects. The absence of information to determine whether mannitol is free of cancer-producing or chromosome-damaging properties or can affect reproduction is of concern. Mannitol exerts a laxative effect at levels well above the probable average adult intake. If diets are high in mannitol, it is possible that infants and children less than two years of age could consume amounts close to those capable of causing a laxative effect. Current evidence indicates that the adult consumer has no hazard from current levels of mannitol in the diet, or ones likely to be encountered in the future.

RATING: S.

NIACIN

Nicotinic Acid; Nicotinamide (Niacinamide)

Niacin is a vitamin of the B-complex which prevents pellagra. It is a nutrient that is essential for many of the body's crucial functions: it participates as a coenzyme in metabolic processes that break down foods for their utilization as energy and also for fat synthesis in the body. It is needed to maintain the body's protection from infection, to avoid certain changes in the nervous system, to improve circulation, and to aid in the formation of sex hormones. *Nicotinic acid* is the active substance in niacin. It is converted to the physiologically active *nicotinamide,* also referred to as *niacinamide.*

Niacin normally has to be obtained by humans from their diets, although the body can make the vitamin from an excess of the essential amino acid tryptophan. However, 60 milligrams of tryptophan are required to produce the equivalent of 1 milligram of niacin. The recommended daily intake of niacin to prevent a deficiency is 6.6 milligrams per 1000 calories in the diet for the adult, with not less ingested than 13 milligrams—somewhat less for children or infants, and more for pregnant and lactating women. These levels are normally exceeded because lean meat, poultry, cereals, milk, legumes, and other high-protein foods contain not only tryptophan but appreciable amounts of niacin. As a food additive, niacin is used solely for nutritional purposes, and FDA regulations require it to be added to enrich foods such as bakery, cereal, and pasta products.

SAFETY: A nationwide nutritional survey in 1974 determined that the total niacin/niacinamide intake of adults averaged 20 milligrams daily (about 0.33 milligram per kilogram of body weight, kg/bw). Less than half of this probably came from the vitamin being added to the food.

Humans have taken doses of this vitamin as large as 10 grams daily, for periods of several years, often to reduce elevated blood cholesterol levels or to help in schizophrenia. When niacin by itself is fed, a flushing of the skin is common; the symptoms include redness of the face and neck, a sensation of warmth, some sweating, and occasional nausea. In

---

MAJOR REFERENCE: Evaluation of the health aspects of niacin and niacinamide as food ingredients. FASEB/SCOGS Report 108 (NTIS PB 80-112030) 1979.

addition to flushing reactions, abnormal liver function has been observed in tests where gram quantities of niacin were taken. Liver function returned to normal once the increased niacin intake was discontinued, but there have been reports of liver disease and jaundice after administration of ¾ to 3 grams daily of niacin. Many coronary patients receiving 3 grams of niacin daily developed abnormal skin pigmentation, scaliness, rash, and inflammatory diseases of the skin.

Laboratory animals fed diets containing 1 to 2 grams per kg/bw per day have demonstrated growth depression in some studies, but not in all. Fatty livers may occur at a level of 1 gram of niacin per kg/bw, reflecting an induced choline deficiency. The addition of choline (see p. 512), one of the components of lecithin (see p. 580) in various fats, prevents this.

There are no animal studies on the effects of large doses of niacin or niacinamide covering several generations, or reports on possible effects on normal embryo growth or on chromosome damage. Niacinamide does not appear to cause cancer. It did not alter the effect of a known chemical carcinogen applied to the skin of mice, but it did promote the appearance of tumors induced by another carcinogen in rats.

ASSESSMENT: Niacin is a vitamin that is essential for humans and is added for fortification or enrichment of certain foods. When large doses (more than 100 times the amount in the average U.S. diet) are administered to patients, particularly to reduce high blood cholesterol concentrations, undesirable side effects frequently are experienced. Generally these are temporary. Greater dosages (when adjusted for body weight) have produced similar effects in laboratory animals. The quantity of niacin present naturally and as an additive in the diet of individuals in the U.S. does not pose a health hazard, but rather the reverse, for it is a necessity for good health.

RATING: S.

PANTOTHENIC ACID

CALCIUM PANTOTHENATE

Pantothenic acid, one of the vitamins of the vitamin B complex, is a necessity in human diets. It is a constituent of coenzyme A, an essential enzyme factor involved in metabolism of fats, proteins, and carbohydrates. It also participates in a number of other vital body functions, among them the production of cortisone and other adrenal hormones responsible for the health of nerves and skin. This vitamin is naturally present in many foods; rich sources are liver, meats, whole-grain cereals, legumes, and many fresh vegetables. When added to some processed foods, it is as a nutritional or dietary supplement, almost always in the form of *calcium pantothenate.*

SAFETY: The daily per capita consumption of pantothenates in the average U.S. diet from all food sources is estimated at 5 to 19 milligrams. Based on poundage used by the food industry, the amount of calcium pantothenate added to foods in 1976 amounted to 0.3 milligram per person in the daily diet, a minute fraction of the total intake of this vitamin. The Food and Nutrition Board of the National Academy of Sciences has stated that a daily intake of 4 to 7 milligrams is probably adequate for adults, with a higher intake suggested for pregnant and lactating women. It is known that the vitamin will readily pass through the placenta and be taken up by the fetus.

Adult patients suffering from a disease characterized by superficial inflammation of the skin have ingested oral dosages of 1 gram or more daily for several months with improvement in their condition and no evidence of toxic effects. Excess amounts of the vitamin taken orally are rapidly excreted in the urine.

Experimental animals (mice, rats, dogs, monkeys) have not suffered adverse effects over a period of six months or longer from daily intakes of calcium pantothenate many thousands of times normal human consumption. Nor have investigations produced evidence of harmful effect on the normal development of the fetus, on reproduction, or on alteration of chromosomes.

MAJOR REFERENCE: Evaluation of the health aspects of calcium and sodium pantothenate and d-pantothenyl alcohol as food ingredients. FASEB/SCOGS Report 93 (NTIS PB 288-672) 1978.

ASSESSMENT: Pantothenic acid is an essential vitamin needed in the daily diet. Its use as a food additive provides only a small fraction of what is needed daily by humans and provided by naturally occurring food sources. There is no evidence, either from clinical treatment of humans or experiments with animals, that this vitamin used as an additive to supplement the diet poses any hazard to the consumer.

RATING: S.

PARABENS

Methyl Paraben; Propyl Paraben

Methyl and *propyl paraben* are esters of *paraben* (para-hydroxybenzoic acid). Neither of them occurs in nature; they are synthetic compounds produced for food, cosmetic, and pharmaceutical purposes. In food, these parabens function as preservatives that prevent microbial activity, particularly the growth of yeasts and molds. The parabens are closely related to benzoic acid (see p. 487) and its salt sodium benzoate and when used in combination with them extend their effective range of antimicrobial activity to foods high in pH (high in alkalinity, low in acidity). Methyl and propyl paraben are used in some baked goods such as fruit cakes, sweet rolls, and cookies, in sugar substitutes and in products that use them—for example, artificially sweetened jams and jellies and low-calorie foods and beverages, in fats and oils, and in frozen dairy desserts and many other milk products.

SAFETY: A survey conducted by the National Academy of Sciences-National Research Council, based on usage by food processors in 1976, determined that the daily diet of the average U.S. adult contained only 0.1 milligram of methyl and propyl paraben. Far more extensive use is made of benzoic acid and sodium benzoate by the food industry for similar purposes.

Experiments with a variety of animal species indicate that even when administered in their diets in amounts thousands of times human consumption, these esters of paraben are harmless. Dogs fed 1000 milligrams per kilogram of body weight

---

MAJOR REFERENCE: Evaluation of the health aspects of methyl paraben and propyl paraben as food ingredients. FASEB/SCOGS Report 8 (NTIS PB 221-950) 1973.

(kg/bw) six days a week for one year were unaffected. Evidence of toxicity did occur when dosages of methyl paraben were doubled, and those of propyl paraben were tripled.

Rabbits fed 500 milligrams per kg/bw per day for six days of either compound showed no ill effects, but these did appear when the dosages were increased to 3000 milligrams. 500 milligrams per kg/bw in animals is the equivalent of over 300,000 times human consumption when adjusted for body weight.

Rats fed up to 1200 milligrams per kg/bw daily of methyl or propyl paraben for almost two years were unaffected. In another experiment, a decrease in growth rate was experienced by rats at a level of 1500 milligrams per kg/bw of propyl paraben for a year and a half. A human volunteer who ingested 2000 milligrams of methyl paraben daily for a month was not adversely affected, nor was another volunteer who ingested the same amount of propyl paraben each day for the same period.

Methyl paraben did not cause birth defects in offspring of mice and rats fed 550 milligrams per kg/bw daily during pregnancy, and in hamsters fed 300 milligrams. Studies to determine whether these paraben esters can cause cancer when taken orally have not been conducted.

ASSESSMENT: The available information reveals that methyl and propyl paraben do not cause harmful consequences in various species of animals or humans when ingested in amounts greatly exceeding the minute quantity currently present in the diet of the average U.S. human, or likely to be so in the future.

RATING: S.

PECTIN

Amidated Low-Ester Pectin; Low-Ester Pectin; High-Ester Pectin

Pectin is present in most plants, where it provides a cementlike strength to cell walls. Fruits and vegetables are highest in pectin content. The main sources for production of this substance for the food industry are citrus peels and apple pomace

---

MAJOR REFERENCE: Evaluation of the health aspects of pectin and pectinates as food ingredients. FASEB/SCOGS Report 81 (NTIS PB 274-477) 1977.

(the residue from apple pressings). Pectin is a complex polysaccharide, a carbohydrate that consists of a number of simple sugars and sugar-acids.

Pectin is added to foods for its gelling, thickening, and blending properties and to prevent separation of ingredients. It is useful in ice creams and ices; in processed fruits and juices; in fruit jellies, jams, and preserves; and in soft candies. The presence of sugar is usually required to make pectin gel, but its molecular structure can be altered to enable it to gel in products with low-sugar content. These are termed *low-ester pectins* (or *amidated low-ester pectins,* when ammonia is employed). *High-ester pectins* require sugar.

SAFETY: It has been estimated, based on a survey of usage by food processors in 1976 conducted by the National Academy of Sciences-National Research Council, that 23 milligrams of pectin as additives are consumed daily in the diet of an average individual in the U.S., or 0.4 milligram per kilogram of body weight (kg/bw) for a person weighing 60 kg (132 lbs.). Less than a fifth of this is low-ester pectin. The UN Joint FAO/WHO Expert Committee on Food Additives considers pectins and their salts to be normal constituents of the human diet and places a limitation on acceptable daily intake only on amidated low-ester pectin, their suggested limitation being 25 milligrams per kg/bw, or over 350 times the average consumption of all low-ester pectins.

Extensive studies of pectins have demonstrated that they are decomposed by organisms in the intestinal tract and, for the most part, are excreted in the feces. They do not appear to enter into the metabolic processes, and they are not absorbed into tissues to any extent. Thus, unlike some carbohydrates, pectins do not serve as a source for the body's energy.

Animal studies have failed to disclose adverse effects when these compounds, including amidated pectins, are fed in amounts far greater than their estimated human intake as additives. Amidated pectin administered in diets of pregnant rats did not cause birth defects in their newborn, or adversely affect maternal health, fertility, or fetuses. However, pectins have yet to be investigated as possible causes of cancer and gene mutation.

A study conducted on 24 men provided evidence that pectin can lower blood cholesterol level somewhat. Medically, it is used in combination with other ingredients for treatment of diarrhea.

ASSESSMENT: Pectin is a natural constituent in many edible plants, and, as such, is consumed in the normal diet in quantities far in excess of the amount that is added to foods. Animal feeding studies confirm that pectins do not present a hazard even in quantities far exceeding their consumption as additives by humans, and, since little if any is absorbed in the body's tissues, it appears unlikely for pectins to be of health concern.

RATING: S.

PHOSPHATES*

Ammonium, Calcium, Potassium, Sodium Phosphate; Phosphoric Acid; Sodium Hexametaphosphate; Sodium Polyphosphate; Sodium Pyrophosphate

A large number of phosphates (which are phosphorus-containing chemicals) are used as food additives. They are prepared commercially from phosphoric acid. In foods they are used as flavoring agents, as nutritional supplements, to keep mixtures of ingredients from separating, to change or control the degree of acidity or alkalinity, and for other purposes. Many of the phosphates occur as natural constituents of both plants and animals, since phosphorus is an essential nutrient in the diet; phosphates are found in high concentrations in muscle and organ meats, cereals, legumes, nuts, cheese, and eggs.

MAJOR REFERENCE: Evaluation of the health aspects of phosphates as food ingredients. FASEB/SCOGS Report 32 (NTIS PB 262-651) 1976.

*Many phosphates may appear on food labels, and food processors have different ways of naming them. In forming phosphates, one to three of the acid groups of phosphoric acid may be combined with a base, or alkali, rather than with acidic hydrogen. Thus in the case of sodium phosphate, there can be monosodium (or monobasic sodium, or sodium acid, or monosodium acid) phosphate, disodium (dibasic sodium) phosphate, or trisodium (tribasic sodium) phosphate as permissible food additives. The phosphates listed above provide the primary terms and can vary according to the base, or alkali, and the number of phosphoric acid units as well as the different ways of identifying each one. When two phosphoric acid units are chemically linked together, a pyrophosphate results, with four acid groups available on it; a salt of this may be a disodium pyrophosphate, or a tetrasodium pyrophosphate (sometimes referred to merely as tetrasodium phosphate). Polyphosphates (metaphosphates) generally occur with linkages of four or more phosphoric acid units; a hexametaphosphate, for example, would have six such phosphoric acid units, and eight acidic groups on which mineral salts such as sodium can replace the acidic hydrogen.

SAFETY: A survey of the use of phosphates by food manufacturers in 1976, conducted by the National Academy of Sciences-National Research Council, determined that the daily diet of the average individual in the U.S. contained 210 milligrams of added phosphate, or 3.5 milligrams per kilogram of body weight (kg/bw) for a person weighing 60 kg (132 lbs.). As phosphorus is necessary for life, 800 milligrams per day are recommended in the diet for an adult. Generally, however, this is met by the phosphorus present naturally in food.

The safety of phosphates depends on their amount in relation to calcium in the diet; a calcium-phosphorus ratio of at least one to one is desirable in humans. Appreciably raising the level of phosphate without an accompanying increase in calcium may have undesirable consequences; it can result in some loss of calcium from bones or teeth and in damage such as calcification in the kidneys.

Rats on a diet containing 1000 milligrams of added phosphorus per kg/bw as phosphoric acid, sodium or potassium phosphate, or sodium pyrophosphate (285 times the average additive intake by humans) showed some kidney damage after several weeks. Appreciably higher levels of phosphate caused gradual bone decalcification. In long-term studies with rats, 630 milligrams of phosphorus per kg/bw added as sodium tripolyphosphate or sodium phosphate led to some growth retardation, anemia, and kidney damage, and thigh bones were reduced in size. The level at which phosphates did not cause harm when added to the laboratory diet of rats was 500 milligrams phosphorus per kg/bw.

Brief studies with humans consuming 450 to 600 milligrams of calcium and at least 2000 milligrams of phosphorus daily did not disclose an adverse effect on calcium retention. However, in another investigation, 1000 milligrams of added phosphorus resulted among adult humans in a marked increase in serum parathyroid hormones (which influence calcium and phosphorus metabolism and bone formation) and a slight decrease in serum calcium, which could lead to adverse effects on bones and kidneys.

A large number of studies have demonstrated the lack of effect of added phosphate on either the developing fetus or on change in the chromosomes. Extremely high levels of phosphate additives did not cause an increase in the incidence of tumors in rats, but long-term experiments specifically designed to test for ability to cause cancer have not been conducted.

ASSESSMENT: Phosphorus is an essential dietary constituent that is closely interrelated with calcium in its effect; the calcium-phosphorus ratio should not vary substantially from one to one. Despite some uncertainties about the amount of consumer exposure to phosphates in the diet in relation to calcium intake, phosphate additives appear to pose no hazard when used at current levels. Nutritionists consider that the ratio of calcium to phosphorus in the usual diets of man would be more favorable if calcium were higher, but phosphorus levels generally appear adequate. The very high levels of added phosphate that can lead to some deterioration in bones and teeth, or cause kidney disturbances, are unlikely from customary food intakes.

RATING: S.

POTASSIUM BROMATE

BROMATED FLOUR

Potassium bromate is a chemical that has been used for 60 years as a conditioner or maturing agent in flour. It reacts with and changes some undesirable flour constituents and in this way helps improve baking quality and produce loaves that have better volume and keeping quality. *Bromated flour* is flour that contains added potassium bromate.

SAFETY: The daily intake of potassium bromate as an additive in food averaged about one milligram in the diet of a U.S. adult in 1976, according to a survey conducted by the National Academy of Sciences-National Research Council. Potassium bromate converts completely to bromide when the dough is mixed and the product is baked, if the concentration in the flour does not exceed 75 parts per million (ppm), the limit permitted by the FDA. A pound loaf of bread contributes about 20 milligrams of potassium to the diet. Potassium bromide has been used therapeutically in humans, and doses as high as 15 milligrams per kilogram of body weight (900 milligrams for a 130-pound person) have been administered without adverse effects. Many foods have a natural bromide content, ranging up to 10 ppm.

MAJOR REFERENCE: Specifications for the identity and purity of food additives and their toxicological evaluation: emulsifiers, stabilizers, bleaching and maturing agents. WHO Technical Report Series No. 281 (Geneva, 1964).

Some 20 years ago studies were made using rats, dogs, mice, and monkeys to determine any possible effect of bromated flour in the diet. Both flour containing potassium bromate (in concentrations up to 627 ppm) and bread from flour containing potassium bromate (in concentrations up to 200 ppm) were used, and at times the bread or flour constituted 84 percent of the total diet of the animals. The rat studies covered up to five generations, and those of mice over eight generations. No adverse effects were noted in any of these, or in short-term studies with dogs and monkeys. Reproductive performance of rodents also was normal.

Recent studies conducted with rats for two years and mice for 80 weeks have examined the possibility of long-term effects on, for example, cancer rate and survival rate, of bread-based diets when the bread was made from flour containing up to the maximum limit (75 ppm) permitted by FDA. No adverse effects were observed.

The treatment of flour with potassium bromate at a concentration of 45 ppm does not affect its nutritive value, since it does not cause a decrease in its content of thiamin, riboflavin, or niacin. Flour treated with this chemical at a concentration of 25 ppm does not show any greater decrease in tocopherol content (35 to 50 percent) than untreated flour when stored for 12 months.

The UN Joint FAO/WHO Expert Committee on Food Additives has estimated that up to 20 ppm of potassium bromate in flour, the average level used, is unconditionally acceptable as presenting no significant hazard, and 20 to 75 ppm of potassium bromate is conditionally acceptable for special purposes, such as certain biscuit flours.

ASSESSMENT: Potassium bromate is used as a food additive to improve certain breads, rolls, buns, and pasta. It has been without adverse effect in feeding studies of a variety of animals. Bromate converts to bromide in the baking process, and bromide has been used therapeutically with humans in concentrations 100 times as great as the total intake of bromate in the daily diet. The low level permitted in flours and breads poses no hazard to the consumer.

RATING: S.

POTASSIUM CHLORIDE; POTASSIUM HYDROXIDE

Natural deposits of mineral sylvinite, crystalline masses like rock salt, are a commercial source of *potassium chloride,* which occurs naturally in substantial quantities in foods in the daily diet: in dairy products; meat, fish, and poultry; cereals, grains, and potatoes; and in lesser amounts in fruits, vegetables, and beverages. Potassium is essential to animals including man for a number of the body's vital functions, among them the regulation of the acid-base balance, for it is a principal base in tissues and blood. It also functions as an intermediary in the metabolic processes that transform carbohydrates into glycogen for storage of energy in the liver and muscles and as activator of transmission of nerve impulses. And potassium provides a protective effect against the hypertensive action of high salt intake.

Potassium chloride is used as an aid to fermentation in brewing. Food processors add it as a flavoring agent and flavor enhancer, and as a nutrient. Medicinally, it is administered orally or intravenously for potassium depletion caused by treatment of kidney, liver or heart failure, hypertension, and other cardiac ailments. *Potassium hydroxide* is an alkali used as an agent to neutralize acids in food products, including cocoa (see p. 515) and instant coffee and tea.

SAFETY: The average diet of a U.S. adult contains 4 to 8 grams of potassium chloride daily. In a survey of food manufacturers in 1975, it was determined that about 20 milligrams of potassium chloride and 16 milligrams of potassium hydroxide per person were being added to foods. The National Academy of Sciences-National Research Council in 1980 suggested that between 1875 and 5625 milligrams of potassium is desirable to meet an adult's daily nutritional needs.

Potassium hydroxide during processing reacts with the acids in the foods, and changes to potassium chloride or another potassium salt. Serious toxic reactions by man to potassium chloride have occurred rarely, and only when it was adminis-

---

MAJOR REFERENCES: Evaluation of the health aspects of potassium chloride and sodium chloride as food ingredients. FASEB/SCOGS Report 102 (NTIS PB 298-139) 1979; Evaluation of the health aspects of sodium hydroxide and potassium hydroxide as food ingredients. FASEB/SCOGS Report 85 (NTIS PB 265-507) 1977.

tered for medical reasons. It is difficult to administer excessive amounts of potassium salts to healthy people without causing nausea and elimination by vomiting. Elimination of excess potassium may be impaired by diseases of the kidney, heart, and liver, and special precautions are indicated here to avoid overdosage. However, oral dosages of up to 10 grams of potassium chloride daily, when administered to patients with kidney impairment, did not cause adverse effects, leading the investigators to conclude that even in these instances the intestinal absorption of potassium and its mode of distribution in the body tended to prevent high concentrations in the blood.

Occasional occurrence of ulcers has been observed in patients receiving potassium chloride tablets; in most cases the potassium chloride had been incorporated in a thiazide drug prescribed for control of hypertension. It occurred only in a small percentage of the patients, 1 in 35,000. Rhesus monkeys were administered similar tablets, with and without thiazide. Intestinal ulcers developed in those receiving the potassium chloride (equivalent to 1 to 2 grams for a human), whether or not it contained thiazide.

In test-tube experiments, neither potassium hydroxide nor potassium chloride proved to be a cause of gene mutations. Tests conducted on pregnant mice and rats did not disclose any discernible adverse effects on fertility or on maternal or fetal survival; nor did it result in any malformations of their offspring.

ASSESSMENT: Potassium is a mineral that is essential for many of the body's metabolic and chemical processes. The body appears well equipped to dispose of excessive oral intake without difficulty. Ulcers have occurred rarely in patients administered potassium chloride for treatment of hypertension, but the low frequency as well as the minuscule amounts of potassium chloride used as an additive in food—perhaps 0.25 percent of the amount naturally present in food in the average diet—does not warrant concern about its contribution as a health hazard.

RATING: S.

PROPELLANT GASES

Carbon Dioxide; Chloropentafluorethane; Isobutane; Nitrogen; Nitrous Oxide; Propane

These additives are relatively inert or chemically nonreacting gases. They are used to aerate and dispense foamed or sprayed food preparations from pressurized or aerosol containers. They may be used in dairy products such as whipped cream, vegetable fat toppings, and dairy product substitutes. Some, such as nitrogen, also may be used to displace air or oxygen in a food package such as canned coffee, to prevent oxidation or chemical deterioration of the food. Carbon dioxide is the gas used in preparing carbonated or sparkling soft drinks, where it also imparts a sharp flavor to the beverage because it forms a weak acid when dissolved in water.

Carbon dioxide and *nitrogen* are important components of the air that we breathe. (Carbon dioxide in solid form is "dry ice.") *Chloropentafluorethane* is related to chemicals developed for use as refrigerants, the fluorinated hydrocarbons. Their use is being limited because of environmental concerns that their presence may reduce the protective ozone layer in the upper atmosphere. *Isobutane* and *propane* are present in natural gas and petroleum; propane is a major ingredient of bottled gas fuel. The atmosphere contains *nitrous oxide,* a gas which occurs from bacterial action on ammonium or nitrate salts in the soil. It is the most widely used anesthetic in the U.S., one of low potency that is used for the relief of pain without loss of consciousness. It is sometimes referred to as "laughing gas."

SAFETY: Consumer exposure to any of these gases from their presence in food products is minimal. The gases are relatively unreactive with the food and are designed to be released to the atmosphere when the food product is dispensed. Thus the amount used in preparing processed foods is no indication of the exposure of the user. Obviously, the principal exposure would be by inhalation, since little of the gas will remain in the

---

MAJOR REFERENCES: Evaluation of the health aspects of butane, helium, nitrogen, nitrous oxide, and propane as food ingredients. FASEB/SCOGS Report 112 (NTIS PB 275-750) 1979; Evaluation of the health aspects of carbon dioxide as a food ingredient. FASEB/SCOGS Report 117 (NTIS PB 80-104615) 1979.

product—though the solubility of carbon dioxide means it is still present in a beverage when it is drunk. People drinking many bottles of carbonated beverages daily may ingest gram quantities of carbon dioxide.

Carbon dioxide is the major respiratory product or end product when the body metabolizes food to produce energy. Even with little physical activity, a person may produce and excrete (largely through the lungs) several hundred grams of carbon dioxide each day. The blood in the veins contains about 55 to 60 milliliters of the gas per 100 milliliters of blood; an average carbonated drink may contain several times this concentration, much of which is dispersed to the air after the pressure is released. Humans have been exposed in a submarine for six weeks to air containing 1.5 percent carbon dioxide (the air we normally breathe contains 0.03 percent), with an initial acidosis (increase in the acidity of body tissues) that later was compensated for by the body. The acid-base balance returned to normal and no other lasting effects were noted. Carbon dioxide has had some adverse effects on reproduction and fetal malformation and has prevented successful pregnancies in some experimental animals, but only after exposure to levels far higher than any obtained from foods or beverages.

Chloropentafluorethane is judged relatively nontoxic in the Underwriters Laboratory ratings, 1 part per 1000 being allowable when inhaled. Increased fluorination of the hydrocarbon usually decreases its pharmacological action so that the effect of this highly-fluorinated gas on metabolism is minimized. Chronic inhalation of 20 percent of chloropentafluorethane has no effect on rats, guinea pigs, dogs, and cats. It produced no central nervous system or behavioral effects when inhaled at a concentration of 60 percent.

Isobutane exposure to humans at levels far higher than can be expected from its use in foods was studied for a two-week period. No adverse effects were noted from these high levels of inhalation.

Nitrogen, which makes up nearly four-fifths of the air, is also present as a dissolved gas in body tissues and blood. The only known effects from it are a feeling of euphoria and decrease in motor performance when retained nitrogen has been markedly increased by pressure, as in deep-sea diving.

Nitrous oxide can produce a light-headed feeling if one inhales 2 to 3 grams over a period of several minutes. For general anesthesia in dentistry or surgery, two-thirds of the gas inhaled may be nitrous oxide, and many hundreds of grams may be inhaled. Some short-term effects on blood pressure and heart rate have been observed in humans, but the exposure was thousands of times what could be derived from the gas used as a propellant in foods. Nurses exposed to nitrous oxide in operating rooms apparently suffered no chromosome damage. A 1980 study indicated that this gas can cause damage to the fetus when pregnant rats are exposed to it.

Exposure of mice or monkeys to 20 percent concentrations of *propane* did not affect heart rhythms or blood pressure. Propane has been inhaled by humans for up to eight hours per day for one to two weeks, and at a level as high as 100 parts per million in air, with no adverse effects. Because of its nontoxicity, industrial hygienists have set a threshold limit of propane in the air of workspace at 1000 parts per million.

ASSESSMENT: Several gases, selected in part because of their chemical inertness, have been used as propellants in aerosol-type containers to expel food products. In addition, carbon dioxide is used in carbonated beverages. Nearly all the gas will be released to the atmosphere when the food is dispensed, and only a tiny fraction will be exposed to the consumer. Each gas is considered relatively nontoxic and has been shown to be free of adverse effects when inhaled at concentrations far higher than could be expected from its use as a food additive. The present or anticipated usage in foods of carbon dioxide, chloropentafluorethane, isobutane, nitrogen, nitrous oxide, and propane appears to pose no hazard to the consumer.

RATING: S.

PROPIONIC ACID

CALCIUM PROPIONATE; SODIUM PROPIONATE

Propionic acid, along with its mineral salts *calcium propionate* and *sodium propionate,* is a natural constituent in dairy products, such as butter and Swiss cheese. These substances also function as products of metabolism in the body, participating as intermediaries during the processes that break down ingested food into usable, accessible forms. They are usually

MAJOR REFERENCE: Evaluation of the health aspects of propionates as food ingredients. FASEB/SCOGS Report 79 (NTIS PB 80-104599) 1979.

produced by chemical synthesis for food processors, who use them as additives in food to inhibit mold growth and as preservatives in some cheeses, and in bread and other baked goods.

SAFETY: A survey by the National Academy of Sciences-National Research Council, based on usage of the propionates as food additives by food processors in 1976, indicated an average of 24 milligrams per person added to the daily diet, about 90 percent as calcium propionate and less than 1 percent as propionic acid. This combined intake would be about 0.4 milligram per kilogram of body weight (kg/bw) for a person weighing 60 kg (132 lbs.).

Rats have been fed sodium or calcium propionate at levels of 1 to 3 percent of the diet (up to 1200 milligrams per kg/bw) for several weeks with no effect on growth. Administered orally to rats in even larger amounts and for a longer period (4000 milligrams per kg/bw for one year), sodium propionate caused growth depression for the first few weeks, but resulted in no other adverse effects. Some stomach lesions did occur in rats fed 5 grams of propionic acid per kg/bw daily for 110 days, many thousands of times human consumption of all added propionates—but without evidence of any malignancy. As much as 6 grams of sodium propionate taken orally by an adult human for a number of days caused no adverse effects, only a faintly alkaline urine.

When pregnant hamsters, rats, and mice consumed calcium propionate at levels up to 400 milligrams per kg/bw, it did not affect survival of the mother or young, or cause abnormalities in their offspring. Neither calcium nor sodium propionate was found to cause chromosome damage in a number of laboratory tests.

ASSESSMENT: The propionates are effective inhibitors of fungi and some bacteria, and thus are particularly useful in baked goods and cheese. They occur naturally in dairy products, and as such, are handled without difficulty metabolically. As metabolites themselves, they facilitate this process. The feeding studies demonstrate that there is no hazard to the consumer from calcium propionate, sodium propionate, or propionic acid at levels currently used in foods or levels that may be expected in the future.

RATING: S.

PROPYL GALLATE

Propyl gallate, a synthetic chemical compound, is one of several that are added to foods containing fats and oils. It prevents rancidity and the development of objectionable tastes and odors caused by the reaction of fatty ingredients to oxygen. These antioxidants are frequently used in combinations, such as BHA and BHT (see p. 489) and/or propyl gallate, as they become more effective together and less of them is required in the food. They act as "chain breakers" by blocking or retarding deterioration of fats under the usual conditions of processing, storage, and use of foods. Propyl gallate is found in such items as shortenings and vegetable oils, meats, candies and gum, some snack foods, baked goods, nuts, and frozen dairy products.

SAFETY: The daily intake of propyl gallate in the diet of the average individual in the U.S., based on reported usage by food manufacturers in 1975, was 1 milligram. This amounts to 0.02 milligram per kilogram of body weight (kg/bw) for a person weighing 60 kg (132 lbs.), which is well under the 0.2 milligram per kg/bw regarded unconditionally as a safe and acceptable daily intake by the UN Joint FAO/WHO Expert Committee on Food Additives.

Interpretation of some of the research on propyl gallate is difficult, since it often has been studied in mixtures with other antioxidants. However, feeding studies with propyl gallate alone have been conducted with a number of animal species (rat, mouse, guinea pig, dog), and have established 100 milligrams per kg/bw as the level at which it has no adverse effect on them. This is more than 5000 times its presence in the daily diet of U.S. humans (adjusted for body weight).

Fed at five times this amount (500 milligrams per kg/bw) to pregnant rats, propyl gallate reduced fertility, but did not do so when the dosage was reduced to 202 milligrams per kg/bw. In another experiment, excessively high levels of propyl gallate fed to rats for one to two years caused some growth retardation and kidney damage.

A man ingested 500 milligrams of propyl gallate daily for six consecutive days. Examination of his urine failed to reveal any presence of blood constituents (such as albumin), abnormal sedimentation, or evidence of kidney damage.

MAJOR REFERENCE: Evaluation of the health aspects of propyl gallate as a food ingredient. FASEB/SCOGS Report 11 (NTIS PB 223-840) 1973.

Tests have yet to be conducted to determine whether this compound can cause cancer or alteration of genes.

ASSESSMENT: The "no-adverse-effect" level of propyl gallate fed to experimental animals has been established at several thousand times its presence in the daily diet of the average adult. Although adverse effects have been reported at materially higher dosages, these are not regarded as relevant considering the minute quantities (in comparison) of propyl gallate present at current levels in food, or at levels that might reasonably be expected in the future. The available information indicates that this compound as an additive in food does not constitute a hazard to the health of the consumer.

RATING: S.

PROPYLENE GLYCOL

PROPYLENE GLYCOL MONOSTEARATE (PROPYLENE GLYCOL MONO- AND DIESTERS)

The *propylene glycol* used in food processing is derived from propylene, a gaseous by-product in petroleum refining, or from glycerol, the alcohol component in fats. *Propylene glycol monostearate*, a mixture of propylene glycol mono- and diesters of stearic and palmitic acids (see p. 479), is the product of the chemical interaction between propylene glycol and a hydrogenated vegetable oil (an oil chemically bonded with hydrogen; see p. 660). Propylene glycol monoester contains one molecule of the fatty acid from the vegetable oil; the diester has two. Another food additive, propylene glycol alginate, is discussed under alginates (see p. 468).

Food manufacturers find propylene glycol useful in blending ingredients, and in increasing their flexibility and spreadability. It is soluble in both watery and dry mixtures and readily absorbs water. Food processors employ it in confections, ice creams, beverages, baked goods, and some meat products. Propylene glycol monostearate is used to improve texture, softness, and to preserve the quality of several foods, including baked goods, puddings, and toppings.

MAJOR REFERENCE: Evaluation of the health aspects of propylene glycol and propylene glycol monostearate as food ingredients. FASEB/SCOGS Report 27 (NTIS PB 265-504) 1974.

SAFETY: The daily intake per person of the propylene compounds in the U.S., based on a survey conducted by the National Research Council-National Academy of Sciences of actual poundage used by food processors in 1976, averaged 51 milligrams, almost all of it propylene glycol monostearate. This amounted to slightly less than 1 milligram per kilogram of body weight (kg/bw) for a person weighing 60 kg (132 lbs.). The UN Joint FAO/WHO Expert Committee on Food Additives has indicated that an acceptable daily intake for man is 25 milligrams per kg/bw, many times the amount normally present in the diet of the average U.S. adult.

During digestion, propylene glycol mono- and diesters are split into fatty acid plus the propylene glycol. These substances are absorbed in the body, where the propylene glycol is converted (by the same metabolic processes that handle carbohydrates) into glucose, which is the chief source of energy for living organisms. Propylene glycol can be ingested in substantial quantities by experimental animals for long periods of time, without adverse effects. Dogs have tolerated the equivalent of 2000 milligrams per kg/bw (over 200 times estimated human consumption). A long-term study with rats showed that up to 2500 milligrams per kg/bw had no deleterious effect on reproduction through three generations. Investigations employing a variety of animal species provided evidence that propylene glycol does not cause cancer, nor does it adversely affect maternal or fetal survival.

Some investigators, but not all, have found that at extremely high doses, 6000 milligrams per kg/bw or more, propylene glycol can cause kidney damage. However, considering the amount normally consumed by humans, this finding hardly indicates that the substance is a threat.

ASSESSMENT: Propylene glycol and propylene glycol monostearate are metabolized and used by the body like carbohydrates. Experimental evidence indicates that propylene glycol can be ingested in substantial quantities over long periods by laboratory animals far in excess of man's present consumption without causing harm. These additives do not pose a hazard at levels now current in foods, or likely to be used in them in the future.

RATING: S.

PROTEIN HYDROLYZATES

Autolyzed Yeast Extract; Hydrolyzed Casein (Hydrolyzed Milk Protein); Hydrolyzed Cereal Solids; Hydrolyzed Plant Protein (HPP) and Hydrolyzed Vegetable Protein (HVP); Soy Sauce (Fermented Soy Sauce, Shoyu, Tamari); Hydrolyzed Soy Sauce

Protein hydrolyzates are mixtures of naturally occurring amino acids, the chief constituents of proteins. Their composition varies according to the source materials from which they are derived, and they are extracted from these by a variety of chemical and manufacturing procedures. *Hydrolyzed plant protein* (HPP) and *hydrolyzed vegetable protein* (HVP), interchangeable terms, are obtained either by hydrolysis (chemical splitting involving the use of water) of soybean and peanut meals or of crude protein recovered from the wet milling of grains such as wheat and corn. At times they are identified on labels as *hydrolyzed cereal solids*. Soybeans are the base of most manufactured HPP and HVP.

Autolyzed yeast extract, a concentration of the soluble components of hydrolyzed brewer's or baker's yeast (a by-product of brewing), provides a potent source of B-vitamin complex in addition to the nitrogen-containing materials derived from the yeast protein. A starting mixture of soybeans or soy grits and wheat is the base of *fermented soy sauce*. The Japanese have produced such sauces for hundreds of years. *Hydrolyzed soy sauce* is produced in the same manner and from the same material as HPP and HVP. *Hydrolyzed casein,* used as a nutritional supplement and amino acid source in infant formulas, is prepared from casein, the principal protein in milk, by use of an enzyme (a catalyst) to hydrolyze the protein.

When hydrolysis is brought about by an acid rather than by an enzyme or natural distintegration, the final product after neutralizing with alkali is likely to have a high content of salt. This is true of HPP and HVP, and hydrolyzed soy sauce. Fermented soy sauce will also be high in salt content, since the fermentation is carried out in the presence of up to 18 percent salt.

MAJOR REFERENCES: Evaluation of the health aspects of certain protein hydrolyzates as food ingredients. FASEB/SCOGS Report 37b (NTIS PB 283-440) 1978; Supplemental review and evaluation. FASEB/SCOGS Report 37b Supplement (NTIS PB 80-178643) 1980.

The major uses of protein hydrolyzates (such as hydrolyzed cereal solids) are as flavor enhancers and sources of "meat-like" flavor when added to foods like soup mixes, gravies, and chili. Soy sauce is used solely as a flavor ingredient. Some protein hydrolyzates are also included as nutritional supplements in special diet products; for example, those used in rapid weight reduction and, specifically, hydrolyzed casein for infants with health problems.

SAFETY: In 1976, an estimated 313 milligrams of hydrolyzed proteins was consumed daily on the average by U.S. individuals in processed foods and in sauces used by restaurants and other retailers, or 5 milligrams per kilogram of body weight (kg/bw) for a person weighing 60 kg (132 lbs.).

Protein and its amino acid components are essential nutrients and energy sources in the diet, and are routinely metabolized by the body. Thus it is not surprising that animal feeding studies experimenting with a variety of hydrolyzates, and employing amounts far exceeding average human consumption, did not provide evidence for concern at the levels currently present in the human diet.

However, the components of protein hydrolyzates contain a substantial presence of glutamic acid, ranging from 5 to 25 percent depending on the original source material; and some concern does exist about glutamic acid's possible effect on the central nervous system and the brain of infants, and on adults afflicted with vascular and brain-related ailments. Brain lesions in ten-day-old mice occurred after the injection of doses of hydrolyzed casein 300 times average human intake (adjusted for body weight). Similar findings with young mice have been reported by two other investigators using monosodium glutamate equivalent to that contained in 2 grams per kg/bw of a protein hydrolyzate, some 400 times human intake. It has been pointed out that hydrolyzed casein has been used for decades in feeding infants, with no reports of any abnormalities. (For health hazards that may arise from the consumption of glutamic acid, see p. 555.)

A major problem associated with the addition of an amino acid mixture from hydrolyzed proteins as a supplement to diet is the possibility of producing an imbalance of amino acids. The efficiency with which proteins are utilized is dependent on the amino acids contained in the mixture. Experiments with young rats have demonstrated that an unbalanced mixture, which could come from an improperly selected diet, can depress food intake and retard growth. The U.S. Public Health Service has had a special task force investigating reports of deaths associated with rapid reduction diets consisting solely or primarily of protein hydrolyzates.

Long-term studies of animals fed protein hydrolyzates such as acid-hydrolyzed soy protein or wheat gluten have shown that they do not affect reproduction, maternal or fetal survival, or the normal development of offspring. Nor do they produce pathological changes or tumors.

ASSESSMENT: With the exception of enzymatically hydrolyzed casein, protein hydrolyzates are used exclusively as flavor enhancers. This, together with their high salt content, restricts their consumption as food additives to about 3 milligrams per kg/bw. Casein hydrolyzates may also be used as a nutrient supplement and thus can be a more significant part of the diet. In digesting protein, the body regularly metabolizes protein hydrolyzates, but the reservation that experimental studies have raised is the potential hazard from an imbalance of the constituent amino acids or an excess of glutamic acid. Studies associated with the administration of hydrolyzed casein (about 20 percent of which can be glutamic acid) to newborn mice that resulted in brain lesions were by injection, but more recent research has established 400 milligrams per kg/bw as the minimum oral intake of glutamic acid required to cause brain lesions immediately after birth (shortly thereafter, the minimum required to cause an effect becomes much higher). The other possible health hazard is the use of hydrolyzed casein exclusively or as the main part of the diet; this is not advised until the deaths associated with the "liquid protein diet" are otherwise explained.

RATING: S for all protein hydrolyzates except hydrolyzed casein; for hydrolyzed casein, S for some people, ? for infants, X for individuals on weight-reducing diets without adequate supplementation.

QUININE

Quinine Hydrochloride; Quinine Sulfate

The hydrochloride or sulfate salts of quinine are used to impart a refreshing bitter flavor to beverages, especially tonic water. Use in carbonated beverages is limited to a maximum of 83 parts per million, equivalent to about 24 milligrams per 10-fluid-ounce bottle. Quinine is an alkaloid* extracted from the bark of the *Cinchona* tree, and for several hundred years has been a therapeutic agent for malaria.

SAFETY: In 1976 a survey of the usage of quinine salts as an additive, based on reports by the food industry, indicated an average daily intake for individuals consuming products containing these quinine salts of 0.6 milligram, or a daily intake of 0.01 milligram per kilogram of body weight (kg/bw) on the average for a consumer of these products weighing 60 kg (132 lbs.). A gin-and-tonic highball may provide 13 to 20 milligrams of quinine. Medical use in controlling malaria may call for daily use of over 1 gram of quinine, 50 times this amount.

Quinine does not accumulate in the body. It usually disappears from the blood circulation in less than 24 hours, since it and the products obtained from its breakdown metabolically are excreted in the urine. Although repeated use of doses of 1 gram or more of quinine can cause adverse or toxic effects in humans, the only symptoms reported from use of quinine salts in carbonated beverages is an allergic type of hypersensitivity. In susceptible people, temporary small hemorrhages beneath the skin may cause purplish blotches to appear.

Hearing loss and effects on equilibrum have been observed in guinea pigs consuming quinine hydrochloride daily, at 67 milligrams per kg/bw or more, for several months. (This is many hundreds of times the usual human consumption, adjusted for body weight.) The fetuses of pregnant rabbits have also shown hearing-nerve damage when the mother received approximately 125 milligrams per kg/bw of quinine sulfate daily for ten days. There are studies with monkeys and humans suggesting that they do not show such effects. It should be

---

MAJOR REFERENCE: Scientific literature review of quinine salts in flavor usage. FEMA Report to FDA (NTIS PB 296-017) 1979.

*Alkaloids are bitter substances of vegetable origin with a nitrogen base, such as caffeine, morphine, nicotine, quinine, and strychnine, which often have a powerful effect on animals and humans.

noted, however, that among the toxic effects of large doses of quinine in humans is the temporary impairment of hearing, and there are claims associating deafness of offspring with quinine usage.

Quinine did not cause malformation of the offspring when fed to pregnant rats or monkeys. When quinine sulfate was injected into the vaginal tissue of mice twice weekly for 40 weeks, no evidence of cancers or tumors in the vaginal area or elsewhere was found.

ASSESSMENT: Quinine salts are used as flavor ingredients in beverages, notably tonics. Quinine has been used therapeutically in areas where malaria is present; its use as a food additive involves substantially lower levels of intake. Some evidence that hearing may be impaired from high intakes of quinine, and that the fetus may also be subject to toxic effect, suggests that pregnant women should avoid quinine. Obviously, the very few people who show an unusual sensitivity, manifested by a flushing caused by temporary hemorrhages, should also avoid beverages containing quinine.

RATING: S for most people; X for pregnant women and for hypersensitive individuals.

SACCHARIN

Sodium Saccharin

The one noncaloric sweetener most commonly used today* and approved for use in dietetic foods is saccharin, usually as the sodium salt, which is more water-soluble. Saccharin is several hundred times as sweet as ordinary sugar. It has a bitter aftertaste, which usually is masked by the addition of the amino acid glycine, a protein component. Saccharin is widely used as an additive to provide sweetness in low-calorie soft

MAJOR REFERENCES: Artificial sweeteners and human bladder cancer. R. N. Hoover and P. H. Strasser. *Lancet* (April 19, 1980), p. 837; Artificial sweetener use and bladder cancer: a case-control study. E. Wynder and S. Stellman. *Science* 207:1214 (1980); Artificial sweeteners and cancer of the lower urinary tract. A. Morrison and J. Buring. *New England Journal of Medicine* (March 6, 1980).

*Aspartame, a chemical combination of two amino acids, aspartic acid and phenylalanine, was approved in July 1981 for use as a low-calorie sweetener in cold cereals, powdered beverages, puddings, gelatins, chewing gum, dessert toppings, and instant coffee and tea.

drinks (not to exceed 12 milligrams per fluid ounce), dietetic ice creams, and various other low-calorie processed foods (not to exceed 30 milligrams per serving), and as a replacement for table sugar. It is a synthetic sweetener which has been used for calorie reduction in foods throughout this century, and, since it does not convert to glucose in the body, diabetics use it instead of sugar.

SAFETY: The National Academy of Sciences-National Research Council (NAS-NRC) has estimated that saccharin consumption in 1977-78 by users of low-calorie or dietetic foods and beverages (roughly a third of all consumers) averaged 30 milligrams daily. By far the greatest amount is consumed in diet soft drinks; some consumers averaged as many as five bottles daily, containing a total of some 365 milligrams of saccharin. For a person weighing 60 kg (132 lbs.), this would amount to 6 milligrams per kilogram of body weight (kg/bw).

Saccharin has been the subject of a seemingly endless series of safety scrutinies. President Theodore Roosevelt had a group of scientists review it in 1912; NAS-NRC reviewed toxicity data on saccharin in 1955, 1968, 1974, 1978, and 1979. Additional reviews by the federal government have come from the Food and Drug Administration (FDA), the National Cancer Institute, and the U.S. Congress Office of Technology Assessment.

In two studies, one conducted by the FDA, there was an indication of a higher incidence of bladder cancer among rats consuming saccharin, but whether saccharin or the impurities it contained was the cause remained uncertain. In 1977 researchers for Canada's Health Protection Branch (similar to our FDA), who had been investigating this matter for 25 years, produced findings substantiating that saccharin without impurities was the sole culprit. The levels used in the initial studies in Canada were 5 percent saccharin in the rat diet, or approximately 2500 milligrams per kg/bw. This is many hundred times the upper level of human consumption, but such an amount is not uncommon in tests of possible cancer effect of a chemical when using a necessarily limited number of experimental animals.*

---

*Nobody knows with any assurance the level at which a known carcinogen (cancer-causing substance), or a substance suspected of being one, causes the malignancy. The type of cancer under investigation may occur in only one of a thousand people exposed to the substance. To test it experimentally while

Since the initial report in 1977, additional studies have confirmed that some bladder tumors may develop in male rats fed saccharin throughout their lives, especially if their mothers, during pregnancy, ate a similar diet. Some evidence exists that saccharin is also a cocarcinogen, promoting the cancer-causing effects of other carcinogens.

The findings led to a proposal by the FDA to ban use of saccharin as a food additive, since the 1958 Delaney Clause in the Food and Drug Act bans use of any chemical in food at any level if the chemical is found to induce cancer in man or animals. The widespread opposition to such a ban among the public, health professionals, and legislators led to the Saccharin Study and Labeling Law, which came into effect in November 1977, prohibiting the FDA from banning this additive for eighteen months; in August 1979, the moratorium was extended to June 30, 1981; and on expiration, the moratorium was extended for an additional two years.

The saccharin moratorium had been recommended by the American Medical Association, the American Society of Internal Medicine, the saccharin committee of the National Academy of Sciences, the American Diabetes Association, and the American Society of Bariatric Physicians. But there is opposition to a "unilateral modification of present laws which would exempt saccharin from complying with specific regulations."*

That saccharin is a "weak carcinogen" seems evident. That the dosages used were unusually huge is also recognized; indeed, the findings of a tumor increase were only observed at a dosage of 5 percent of total diet or more. The linkage between such studies and probable risks to humans is uncertain.

---

using low levels of the chemical would require groups of 50,000 animals. Instead, many scientists believe detection is possible by employing large doses administered to a few hundred animals.

The evidence has not supported the contention that any substance can cause cancer, if the dosage administered is sufficiently large. One hundred and twenty chemicals, including pesticides, many of which were suspected of being able to cause malignancies, were tested in the same way as saccharin. The findings were reported in 1969 in the *Journal of the National Cancer Institute:* only 11 of these chemicals caused cancers. It appears likely that the substance must be a carcinogen to begin with, and that the dosage by itself, however large or small, is not the responsible agent. And while it is not certain that all substances causing cancer in rats will also do so in humans, it is known that of 30 which cause cancer in man, 29 have produced cancer in rats.

*The saccharin question re-examined: an A.D.A. statement. *Journal of the American Dietetic Association* (May 1979), pp. 574-581.

One study in Canada did suggest a connection, but for males only. However, at least six studies of various population groups (epidemiologic studies), which included diabetic patients who are large users of saccharin, have been conducted and failed to give statistical evidence of any association between bladder cancer in humans and intake of saccharin in the diet. Three of these studies were reported early in 1980. One was conducted by epidemiologists of the National Cancer Institute and involved 9000 people, about a third of whom were bladder cancer patients. There was little or no increased risk of bladder cancer for average users of saccharin. The researchers inferred a somewhat greater risk among those consuming eight or more diet soft drinks and tabletop artificial sweeteners daily, but this was based on only seven cases of 9000 people studied.

A second population survey by the American Health Foundation focused on 367 bladder cancer patients, comparing their usage of artificial sweeteners with 367 others from a control population of 5597 patients with no bladder cancer. These investigators found no indication of increased cancer with saccharin intake, no response to increasing dosages or duration, and no evidence that the artificial sweeteners promoted the tumor-producing effects of smoking.

The third large-scale population study was made by scientists at Harvard University. More than half of the 1128 people studied had a bladder tumor. This cancer bore no relationship to a history of use of dietetic beverages or of sugar substitutes. Again, increasing frequency or duration of use did not appear to be associated with greater relative risk of bladder cancer.

Saccharin appears not to cause malformations of the fetus, and does not affect reproduction or normal growth.

ASSESSMENT: To many, the scientific facts on saccharin are based on dosages given at such excessive levels that it is easy to belittle any danger to a human eating a diet even where saccharin is present in appreciable amounts, as in consumption of many diet soft drinks daily. Yet the concern that saccharin in the diet may pose an unnecessary risk to some consumers is less easily dismissed. At high levels, saccharin has caused bladder cancer in rats. The risk that it could bring about a similar result in humans seems minimal, based on population studies. Nevertheless, that there is some risk suggests that overriding benefits are not likely to fully offset any potential hazards. Some diabetics who need to drastically restrict carbohydrate intake may find the risk worth taking. Overweight but sweet-toothed persons truly needing to restrict calories despite large consumption of beverages may concur. For the public in general, even the small risk from saccharin in food suggests that this food additive should be avoided.

RATING: ? for persons on medically restricted low-calorie diets; X for all others.

SHELLAC

Confectioner's Glaze

Shellac, the only commercial resin secreted by an insect* (the other resins occur in plants), is harvested principally in India and Thailand. It is a familiar material for finishing furniture because of its protective, glossy, hard finish. The shellac used in food ("food-grade" shellac) is produced by refining and bleaching regular shellac. Refined food-grade shellac is used as a food glaze, especially in coating candy *(confectioner's glaze)* and some fruits and vegetables, such as citrus and avocados, and ice-cream cones and fruit cakes.

SAFETY: The bulk of food-grade shellac is on skins of citrus fruit and avocados that are peeled off and discarded; this shellac is not likely to be ingested. The remainder, which has very limited use in food, contributes on the average approximately 0.25 milligram to the daily diet of a U.S. adult.

There are no studies on the biological effects in humans or in experimental animals from ingestion of shellac, although its food use is "generally recognized as safe" by FDA. It has been tested in laboratory tests for chromosome damage and been found free of such activity.

ASSESSMENT: Because there are no studies on which to base an evaluation of the safety of shellac in food use, no meaningful assessment of its safety is possible.

RATING: ?

MAJOR REFERENCE: Evaluation of the health aspects of shellac and shellac wax as food ingredients. FASEB/SCOGS Report II-19 1980.

**Kerria lacca*, a scale insect which lives on twigs of various trees.

SILICATES

Calcium Silicate (Calcium Trisilicate); Magnesium Silicate (Magnesium Trisilicate); Methyl Polysilicone (Dimethyl Polysiloxane, Methyl Silicone); Phenylmethyl Cyclosiloxane (Cyclophenyl Methylsilicone); Silicon Dioxide (Silica, Silica Aerogel); Sodium Aluminosilicate (Aluminum Sodium Silicate, Sodium Silicoaluminate); Sodium Calcium Aluminosilicate; Sodium Silicate; Talc

Silicates are compounds of silica, a principal constituent of rocks and sand, and other minerals. They are present in practically all natural waters (city water may contain 7 milligrams per quart), plants, animals, and humans. Silicon in trace amounts is an essential mineral element for humans; it is believed to participate in bone calcification, and it may be a component of the body's connective tissues.

As additives, the silicates contribute only a minor portion of the total intake of silica in the normal diet, because many foods and liquids naturally contain substantial amounts. The compounds listed above are usually employed in foods for only a few purposes; several are used for preventing salt and dry mixes from caking; methyl polysilicone and silicon dioxide are used to reduce foam and reduce sticking; talc provides a base for chewing gum and a coating for rice.

SAFETY:* Estimates of the amount of silicates as additives in the daily diet of U.S. adults, based on a survey conducted by the National Academy of Sciences-National Research Council of usage by food processors in 1976, are available for silicon dioxide (60 milligrams); talc (25); sodium aluminum silicate (12); calcium silicate (3); dimethyl polysiloxane (2); and magnesium silicate (1)—for a total of 103 milligrams, or less than 2 milligrams per kilogram of body weight (kg/bw) for a person weighing 60 kg (132 lbs.).

The ability of the body to absorb silicates depends on their solubility in water. The silicates that are used as direct food

---

MAJOR REFERENCES: Evaluation of the health aspects of silicates as food ingredients. FASEB/SCOGS Report 61 (NTIS PB 301-402) 1979; Evaluation of the health aspects of methylpolysilicones as food ingredients. FASEB/SCOGS Report II-14 (NTIS PB 81-229239) 1981.

*For safety findings on sodium aluminosilicate and sodium calcium aluminosilicate, see also p. 473.

additives are essentially insoluble, and are not likely to be absorbed; instead, they pass through the body inert and are excreted. Studies of the effects of feeding various silicon compounds to laboratory animals have generally shown them not to be harmful under the test conditions, but some adverse effects have been recorded:

Magnesium trisilicate at extremely high levels in the diets of young dogs resulted in kidney damage. Contrary to these results, the substance has been administered without serious harm to patients as an antacid in the treatment of peptic ulcers and related illnesses, some patients taking several grams daily for a number of years.

Silicon dioxide fed at 6 milligrams per kg/bw in one experiment caused kidney damage in guinea pigs, but did not in other experiments when dogs and rats were used. It is possible that this compound is more noxious for one species of animal than another.

Experiments with pregnant animals indicated that neither silicon dioxide, *sodium silicoaluminate,* nor *calcium silicate* caused birth defects, and laboratory tests determined that they did not induce mutations or other genetic changes.

Talc may contain asbestos fibers, but the FDA requires that when it is used in food it be free of this substance. At this writing, no practical means exists for determining absence of asbestos. Inhalation of talcum powder has resulted in fatalities, and injections of crushed drug tablets containing talc have caused serious illness. Evidence exists of inflammatory tissue reaction caused by contact with talc dust from surgical gloves and from its intentional use to induce lesions in the treatment of lung diseases. But these effects have not been found when talc has been administered orally; and laboratory tests indicate that it does not cause mutations, birth defects, or genetic changes.

Biologic effects and safety data are not available for *sodium calcium aluminosilicate,* but its toxicity should not differ from closely related compounds for which there are data that indicate their safety.

Several short-term feeding studies using rats and dogs have shown that *methyl polysilicone* does not adversely affect their health when doses of up to 10 grams per kg/bw were administered. Monkeys fed as much as 60 grams daily, five days a week for eight months, did not demonstrate abnormalities in behavior, blood, body weight, or urine, but did exhibit occasional diarrhea. A life-span study with mice given 5.8 grams per kg/bw of methyl polysilicone in their daily diets found it caused no adverse health effects, nor were any observed in rats fed silicone through three generations. The dosages employed in the experiments cited above were many thousands of times as great as the 2 milligrams of methyl polysilicone present in the daily diet of the average U.S. adult. This compound has been used therapeutically in man at dosages of up to 200 milligrams for excess gas in the digestive tract. It has been shown to be free of properties that can lead to cancer, malformed offspring, or chromosome (gene) alterations.

Methyl polysilicone is a high-molecular-weight (large-molecule) compound. A variation that in part contains small-molecule silicon polymers has caused some damage to livers of dogs fed 3 grams daily per kg/bw for six months, and to kidneys of rabbits, an effect not seen in mice and rats. It was identified in these experiments as Dow-Corning Antifoam A. When small molecules are present, they may be absorbed in limited amounts and then may accumulate in tissues. *Phenylmethyl cyclosiloxane* (which includes the phenyl group as well as small molecules, with cyclic structure rather than linear) caused testicle atrophy and reduction in sperm in a variety of animals, including monkeys who developed this condition when given as little as 50 milligrams per kg/bw by mouth.

ASSESSMENT: Except for talc and phenylmethyl cyclosiloxane, the evidence indicates that the silicates can be regarded as safe when used as additives in food at levels now current or that reasonably can be expected in the future. Silicates added in this manner represent only a minute portion of total intake by humans, because of their presence in most natural foods. When talc is used in food, uncertainty remains until a means is devised of assuring the absence of asbestos fibers; phenylmethyl cyclosiloxanes have caused damage to reproductive capacities, livers, and kidneys in a number of experimental animals.

RATING: S for silicates other than talc and phenylmethyl cyclosiloxane; ? for talc until absence of asbestos fibers can be determined; X for phenylmethyl cyclosiloxane.

SMOKE FLAVORING (LIQUID SMOKE, CHAR-SMOKE FLAVOR)

These solutions are condensed fractions or extracts of wood smoke that has been trapped from wood burned with a limited amount of air and then further treated to remove some of the tars. Hickory and maple are preferred woods. Smoke flavoring is used in meats, cheese, barbecue sauces, baked beans, pizza, fabricated snack foods and vegetables, and other food products. Smoked flavorings have an advantage over conventional, direct smoking of foods (meat, poultry, fish) in that most of the resinous tar materials present in the smoke, which can contain some cancer-producing benzopyrene chemicals, have been removed in manufacturing.

SAFETY: In 1978 the food usage of smoke-flavoring solutions indicated a daily consumption on the average of about 30 milligrams per person, or 0.5 milligram per kilogram of body weight (kg/bw) for a person weighing 60 kg (132 lbs.).

In a study of approximately three months' duration, rats consuming meals containing up to 2 grams per kg/bw of two liquid smoke preparations, an amount 4000 times as great as average human intake, showed no significant abnormalities. In a study of similar duration conducted in Poland, pigs fed up to 300 milligrams per kg/bw of a Polish wood-smoke extract in their daily diet did not develop abnormalities, and results of blood and urine tests were in the normal range.

The majority of long-term toxicity studies on smoked products have been primarily concerned with the presence of benzopyrene chemicals, suspected carcinogens which are associated with the tars and resinous materials developing from wood smoke. This concern has been substantiated by investigations in which a significant number of experimental animals fed meats smoked directly over wood fire developed malignancies. The smoked flavorings reviewed here, while derived from wood smoke, employed processing methods that appear to have made them essentially free of benzopyrene. Tests have indicated that remaining traces, if any, are likely to be less than 0.5 parts per billion. The only study of sufficient duration to determine whether a hazard remains, a two-year experiment

---

MAJOR REFERENCE: Evaluation of the health aspects of smoke flavoring solutions and smoked yeast flavoring as food ingredients. FASEB/SCOGS Report II-7 1980.

on rats fed sausage containing a Polish smoke extract estimated to be the equivalent of 100 times the amount eaten by the average Polish consumer (adjusted for body weight), found that it did not cause a higher incidence of tumors among the experimental animals who ingested it than among the controls who did not. However, the Polish extract differs from those available in the U.S. in its components.

Smoke-flavoring products have proved to be free of chromosome-altering properties in several types of tests.

ASSESSMENT: The composition of smoke flavoring varies, depending on the kind of wood used, combustion conditions, and method of entrapment and extraction of the smoke and purification of the extract. Although the procedures used commercially remove nearly all benzopyrene chemicals, there is inadequate evidence from long-term studies with experimental animals to assess the absolute safety in the food supply of liquid smoke as prepared and used in the U.S. Clearly, liquid smoke is less hazardous to a consumer than the simple smoking of foods or charcoal broiling of meats. But while the existing evidence suggests no hazard from consuming products containing smoke flavoring, the unknowns and uncertainties call for further research, and especially long-term studies, to properly assess safety of this additive.

RATING: ?

SODIUM CHLORIDE

Sodium chloride is common table salt. It is abundant in nature and is found in many natural waters and in underground deposits. Commercial quantities for use in food are obtained by mining, by evaporation from natural brines, and from seawater. The food industry finds it useful as a seasoning, preservative, and curing agent; in formulating and processing; as a nutritional supplement; and as a dough conditioner. Solutions of sodium chloride are used in medicine for replacement of fluid following trauma or operations, usually in intravenous preparations, and as tablets for rapid replacement of body salt loss.

MAJOR REFERENCE: Evaluation of the health aspects of potassium chloride and sodium chloride as food ingredients. FASEB/SCOGS Report 102 (NTIS PB 298-139) 1979.

SAFETY: The diet of the U.S. adult, on the average, contains 10 to 12 grams of sodium chloride each day. While salt is essential to the body, the minimum requirement is substantially less than 1 gram; this amount is already exceeded by the 3 grams that are naturally present in the foods we eat. Four to 6 grams are added to foods by manufacturers, baked goods and meat products accounting for more than half, making it difficult to restrict salt intake. Salting foods by the consumer is responsible for the remainder of the salt in the daily diet.

Investigations of many of the chronic effects of ingesting sodium chloride in amounts far exceeding requirements have been focused on its role in high blood pressure. The U.S. Health and Nutrition Examination Survey has estimated that 23 million persons 12 to 74 years of age suffer from hypertension. Clinical and epidemiological studies suggest a relationship between salt intake and the onset of hypertension. A low sodium intake is characteristic of populations that do not exhibit much if any hypertension; while comparable populations with high sodium intake experience a higher incidence.

A critical determinant appears to be a genetic predisposition. Data on 1000 New York City residents, 563 normotensive (normal blood pressure) individuals and 437 hypertensive (who did not know it), revealed little difference in sodium intake, except that higher intakes were found more frequently among the "normals." A separate study comparing 717 hypertensive and 819 normotensive patients, however, found a significant correlation between family history of high blood pressure and hypertension in the patients. Consistent excess consumption of sodium chloride seems to play a primary role in the prevalence of hypertension among "responsive" individuals, and a number of clinical studies confirm the therapeutic effectiveness of low-salt intake for this condition.

Animal experimentation with strains of mice and rats bred either to be resistant or susceptible to salt toxicity impressively demonstrates the significance of heredity. Both resistant and susceptible mice were given the same dosages of sodium chloride in their drinking water, comparable to thousands of times that of human intake. All the susceptible strain died from salt toxicity within three months, while a significant number of the resistant variety survived for more than a year. Two strains of rats, differing genetically in their response to chronic ingestion of excess salt, were studied for its effect on systolic (period of heart contraction) blood pressure. The sensitive strain developed hypertension, while the resistant strain did not. Neither strain developed high blood pressure on a normal diet.

A National Academy of Sciences committee has expressed concern about the capacity of an infant to excrete sodium chloride daily in excess of 23 to 58 milligrams per kilogram of body weight. The committee found no nutritional justification for the addition of salt to the normal infant's diet, since commonly used unsalted foods supply more than does human breast milk, and by four months of age most infants are receiving cow's milk, which supplies three times as much sodium as human milk.

ASSESSMENT: The amount of sodium chloride in the daily diet of the average U.S. individual is many times in excess of a human's requirements. (However, extra salt—and water—may be needed where there is salt loss by sweating, diarrhea, or vomiting.) A more than sufficient amount usually is present naturally in food before what is added by the food manufacturer and by consumer salting. While this excess is not likely to be harmful for many people, it does represent a risk to the estimated 23 million who exhibit tendencies to develop high blood pressure. The addition of salt to the foods of most infants is not warranted nutritionally, and may be beyond their disposal capacities.

RATING: S for many people; X for anyone with high blood pressure, or with family history of this tendency, or for normal infants in their prepared foods.

SODIUM FERROCYANIDE (YELLOW PRUSSIATE OF SODA)

Sodium ferrocyanide is an effective anticaking agent. It is used in small amounts in table salt to prevent the formation of clumps and keep it free-flowing by causing the salt to form into rough crystals during crystallization. The additive is produced synthetically by heating sodium carbonate and iron together with organic materials. FDA regulations permit a maximum of 13 parts of sodium ferrocyanide per million parts of salt (sodium chloride; see p. 626). As salt is added to many pro-

---

MAJOR REFERENCE: Monograph on ferrocyanide salts. Informatics, Inc., Report to FDA (NTIS PB 289-591) 1978.

cessed foods, sodium ferrocyanide may be present in a variety of products, such as breads, breakfast cereals, natural cheeses, meat products, and salad dressings.

SAFETY: The average daily diet in the U.S., based on reported usage in food in 1976 by manufacturers, contained 0.6 milligram of sodium ferrocyanide per person.

The cyanide part of sodium ferrocyanide is a deadly poison, but when a strong chemical bond between iron and the cyanide part of the molecule is formed, the toxic action is neutralized, and sodium ferrocyanide shows a low toxicity. There was no evidence of urinary disturbance in infants given 0.1 percent of sodium ferrocyanide administered intravenously, or of harm in kidney function tests in which 550 milligrams, over 800 times the presence of this chemical in the diet, was injected into adults. Indeed, as much as 6 grams of sodium ferrocyanide has been injected into humans to study excretion problems, the only adverse finding being the presence of blood albumin and granulation in the urine, which disappeared in two weeks.

There are no long-term studies to assess toxicity of sodium ferrocyanide, but 13-week studies have included rats and dogs. Rats fed 25 milligrams of the additive per kilogram of body weight, 2500 times the average human consumption when adjusted for body weight, did not experience any adverse effects. However, at ten times this dosage there was evidence of minimal damage or inflammation in the kidney tubules. Dogs were not harmed when fed this compound at a level of 0.1 percent of their diet, an amount thousands of times as high as is present in human diets.

Tests with bacteria showed potassium ferrocyanide to be free of chromosome alteration effects; sodium ferrocyanide should be similar.

ASSESSMENT: Sodium ferrocyanide has a very low toxicity, and its use solely as an anticaking agent in salt limits consumer exposure to minimal amounts. The UN Joint FAO/WHO Expert Committee on Food Additives considers 1.5 milligrams daily an acceptable and safe intake for a 132-pound human (2½ times the amount in the U.S. diet). There is no evidence of hazard to the consumer from the present or probable future usage of sodium ferrocyanide as a food additive.

RATING: S.

SODIUM LAURYL SULFATE

This additive is a mixture prepared from coconut oil fatty acids (components of its fat), chiefly lauric acid, which are chemically converted to fatty alcohols and then combined with sulfuric acid and made into sodium salts. Sodium lauryl sulfate is a surface-active agent (one that modifies the surface properties of liquid food components because of detergent properties); it acts as a cleanser of fresh fruits and vegetables and improves whipping or emulsion formation with egg whites or gelatin. It also is used as a finishing agent in hard and soft candies, and as a wetting agent in dry beverage mixes containing fumaric acid.

SAFETY: The presence of sodium lauryl sulfate as an additive in food, according to 1976 usage reported by food processors, amounted to less than 0.2 milligram daily in the average diet of a U.S. adult.

Many studies of the possible toxicity of sodium lauryl sulfate have been conducted during the past 40 years. When the compound was added in amounts of 0.1 percent in the drinking water of rats, it did not produce any harmful effects, but above this level it did cause some depressed growth and gastrointestinal irritation. An intake of 0.1 percent approximates 130 milligrams per kilogram of body weight (kg/bw) daily. In a 132-pound person it is the equivalent of well over 7 grams per day, many thousands of times its presence in the daily diet. Other studies have confirmed that levels of this chemical in the diet of experimental animals providing over 100 milligrams per kg/bw of sodium lauryl sulfate daily are without adverse effect.

Sodium lauryl sulfate has been used therapeutically in human patients. Such use has demonstrated that even gram quantities do not produce toxic effects. Studies of this additive as a possible cause of cancer or gene mutation, or of harmful effects on reproduction, have not been found.

ASSESSMENT: Sodium lauryl sulfate added to the diet of experimental animals to provide an intake of 100 milligrams per kg/bw has had no apparent adverse effect, nor have gram quantities used medicinally in humans. Any hazard to the

---

MAJOR REFERENCE: Toxicity of sodium lauryl sulphate, sodium lauryl ethoxysulphate and corresponding surfactants derived from synthetic alcohols. A. I. T. Walker, V. K. H. Brown, L. W. Ferrigan, R. G. Pickering, and D. A. Williams. *Food and Cosmetics Toxicology* 5:763 (1967).

consumer is unlikely from the minute quantity of this additive presently in processed foods, or likely to be expected in the future.

RATING: S.

SODIUM NITRATE, POTASSIUM NITRATE; SODIUM NITRITE

Nitrate and nitrite are closely alike in chemical composition, but nitrite has less oxygen in the molecule and is less stable when exposed to air. Nitrate can convert to nitrite by the loss of oxygen. Nitrates are present in tap water and in many foods, in some measure because of the widespread use of nitrogen fertilizers. Spinach, celery, other leafy vegetables, and their juices contain substantial quantities. About 80 percent of the human dietary exposure to nitrites comes from nitrates in drinking water and in foods that have not had any added nitrate or nitrite; about 20 percent comes from cured food products.

The nitrate in food before or during the digestive process can degrade to nitrite by enzymatic or bacterial action. Nitrate is a regular constituent of saliva and also can be converted into nitrite, entering the stomach in amounts estimated at as much as 10 times the quantity actually present in cured meats and other foods in the diet. Further formation of nitrite in the intestines raises it to levels many times as great as the nitrite added to foods, and probably thousands of times as great as the nitrite remaining in processed foods at the time they are consumed.

For decades bacon, ham, corned beef, frankfurters, sausages, and fish products have been prepared by curing with sodium and potassium nitrate and sodium nitrite (always in combination with sodium chloride, or table salt; see p. 626). These two additives contribute to the characteristic flavor, produce a pink color in the meat, and serve as meat preservatives, greatly extending the shelf life of the product. Nitrite has the property of inhibiting the botulinus microorganism, thus preventing development of botulism toxin, a deadly poison. Many years ago it was discovered that nitrate was effective

---

MAJOR REFERENCE: Toxicological evaluation of some food additives including anticaking agents, antimicrobials, emulsifiers and thickening agents. WHO Food Additives Series No. 5 (Geneva, 1974).

only after it was converted to nitrite by bacterial action; today sodium nitrite is used directly in meat curing.

SAFETY: A survey conducted for the National Academy of Sciences-National Research Council determined the total poundage in 1976 of sodium nitrate and nitrite used in food processing. These figures would suggest an average daily intake per person of approximately 11 milligrams, most of it added to food as sodium nitrite (though it is recognized that much of the additive will be further altered during processing and storage and thus end up as nitrate when consumed). In comparison, a person's exposure to salivary nitrite has been estimated at 15 milligrams daily; and an additional 90 milligrams are produced in the intestine. Calculated in terms of body weight, the intake of nitrate-nitrite used as food additives would be less than 0.2 milligram per kilogram of body weight (kg/bw) for a person weighing 60 kg (132 lbs.).

There are two major and opposing factors in considering possible hazards to the consumer through use of these additives. Botulinus toxin is a potent and deadly food poisoning agent. It has been found that at least 150 to 200 parts per million of nitrite are needed to prevent growth of the botulinus organism, which is not eliminated from cured meats because they are not sterilized by a high heat treatment. The other side of the coin is that nitrite can, under certain conditions such as the frying of bacon, chemically combine with some nitrogen-containing chemicals in foods (or in the body) to form nitrosamines; some nitrosamines are potent carcinogenic (cancer-causing) materials.

Sodium nitrate is readily absorbed and excreted when taken in the diet. It is, in certain circumstances, converted to nitrite (containing less oxygen in the molecule) by organisms in the digestive tract; this has been seen especially in infants less than six months old. The nitrite can react with the hemoglobin in the blood and cause a potentially fatal condition where the blood is not effective as a carrier of oxygen. The young infant has less acid production in the stomach and this favors bacterial conversion of nitrate to nitrite. Where a child has imperfect digestion (dyspepsia), even 0.05 percent of nitrate in tap water can be a real hazard, whereas healthy babies may easily tolerate 21 milligrams per kg/bw daily for a year with no adverse effect.

However, the greater concern lies with the property of nitrites to combine with certain substances (amines) to form carcinogenic nitrosamines. Some nitrosamines can cause cancer in experimental animals even at the low level of 2 parts of nitrosamine per million parts of diet (0.0002 percent, probably equivalent to 0.2 milligrams per kg/bw daily). Studies have shown that tumors in rats and mice may be formed following the simultaneous administration of an amine (present in most foods) and sodium nitrite in the diet. Commercial processing and home cooking of foods containing nitrite, before consumption, may give rise to nitrosamine formation, though this does not always occur and even if it does, the levels remain at the very minute concentration of a few parts per billion in the food. Recent studies have shown that nitrosamine formation in cured meat products, even after frying, may be greatly reduced or eliminated by an excess of ascorbic acid (vitamin C; see p. 483) or alpha-tocopherol (vitamin E; see p. 657).

In 1978, preliminary experimental findings suggested that there may be a low level of carcinogenicity from nitrite itself. However, government scientists and independent pathologists dispute this, finding on review that the higher incidence of lymphomas (malignant tumors) found in the experimental animals, compared with the controls not receiving nitrite, was the result of a rare type of cancer not likely to be caused by nitrite. With these eliminated, the occurrence of malignancies did not differ between the experimental and control animals, in effect eliminating the evidence that nitrite can cause cancer in its own right.

Long-term studies with rats showed some growth depression over a two-year period when sodium nitrate was 5 percent of the diet, but no demonstrable effect at 1 percent (500 milligrams per kg/bw daily). Fertility or reproductive performance of guinea pigs was poorer when nitrate was 0.3 percent of the drinking water, but no other adverse effects were seen. Sodium nitrite did not affect fertility, but when pregnant rats or guinea pigs consumed 0.3 to 0.5 percent of sodium nitrite in the water or diet, the offspring grew more slowly and had higher death rates, though no malformed young resulted. The dosages administered in these experiments were at least 2000 times as great as human intake of these compounds as additives.

ASSESSMENT: Sodium or potassium nitrate and sodium nitrite are used in curing meats, and some fish and poultry products. The nitrate may be converted to the nitrite, the effective chemical in preserving the meat and in controlling development of botulinus toxin. Under some circumstances, the nitrite may chemically combine with some nitrogen-containing substances during processing, cooking, or during metabolism to form cancer-causing nitrosamines. Long-term studies with experimental animals indicate that sodium nitrate and nitrite have some adverse effects on the offspring when consumed during pregnancy. It also is evident that the young infant is more susceptible than adults to problems from these additives; clearly, they should not be added to foods intended for the very young. The use of these chemicals is restricted by FDA to the minimum levels necessary for blocking development of the botulinus microorganism—a trade-off with the possibility of increasing exposure to nitrosamines.

RATING: ? for most people; X for infants and pregnant women.

SODIUM STEARYL FUMARATE

This is a synthetic chemical, the sodium salt of the acid resulting from the reactions when combining stearyl alcohol and fumaric acid (see p. 550). Both of the latter occur widely in nature and in foods, stearyl alcohol in some oils as in herring and whale, and fumaric acid in animal and plant tissues. But their combination as stearyl fumarate is not a normal food constituent. The additive is used in foods as a dough improver to give greater strength during food processing, to give better volume and improved texture to yeast-leavened baked goods, and as a stabilizing or conditioning agent that facilitates processing of dehydrated potatoes, starch-thickened foods, and dry cereals.

SAFETY: A survey of the use of sodium stearyl fumarate in 1976 by food processors showed only a minimal use of this additive; less than 0.02 milligram appeared in the average daily diet of the U.S. consumer. The calcium and sodium stearoyl lactylates (see p. 500), additives that provide similar benefits in food processing, are used far more by the industry.

The body's metabolic processes deal with the components of sodium stearyl fumarate without difficulty. The additive was rapidly metabolized by rats fed 300 milligrams of the chemical

---

MAJOR REFERENCE: The absorption and metabolism of orally administered tritium labeled sodium stearyl fumarate in the rat and dog. *Journal of Agricultural and Food Chemistry* 18:872 (1970).

per kilogram of body weight daily for 90 days. Apparently during digestion the stearyl fumarate is split into its original stearyl alcohol and fumaric acid components, and the stearyl alcohol combines with oxygen in the body to form stearic acid (see p. 479), a source of energy along with the other fatty acids. Fumaric acid is essential in tissues and, in fact, the body produces it in quantity during the metabolism of carbohydrates.

ASSESSMENT: Sodium stearyl fumarate is used as a food additive to improve the texture and handling properties of some foods, especially baked goods. The additive is split by digestive enzymes to its constituent stearyl alcohol and fumaric acid, both of which are present in a variety of foods and are easily handled in the body. It poses no hazard to the consumer.

RATING: S.

SORBIC ACID

POTASSIUM SORBATE

Sorbic acid and its salt *potassium sorbate* are made commercially by chemical synthesis. These compounds are useful preservatives which inhibit yeast and mold growth as well as some bacteria, being most effective when the food product is somewhat on the acid side. They may be used in cheeses, wine, chocolate syrups, margarine, and fruit-juice drinks.

SAFETY: The use of sorbates in foods indicated an average daily intake per person of 33 milligrams in 1975, or 0.6 milligram per kilogram of body weight (kg/bw) for a person weighing 60 kg (132 lbs.). The UN Joint FAO/WHO Expert Committee on Food Additives has estimated that even 45 times this amount would be an acceptable daily intake.

Sorbic acid is chemically related to a fatty acid, caproic acid (which is present in butter, coconut oil, and other food fats). Sorbic acid and caproic acid are metabolized and used as a source of energy by the body in the same manner. Studies with

---

MAJOR REFERENCE: Evaluation of the health aspects of sorbic acid and its salts as food ingredients. FASEB/SCOGS Report 57 (NTIS PB 262-663) 1976.

experimental animals have shown that rats can tolerate 6 grams of sorbic acid per kg/bw (10,000 times the average human intake) for four months without effect on reproductive performance but with a slight enlargement of the liver. Feeding rats sorbic acid at 4000 times human intake (adjusted for body weight) for 1000 days did not affect growth, reproduction, or survival, and there were no abnormalities in the various organs and no increase in tumors. Potassium sorbate has been shown to be negative in tests for embryo abnormalities and chromosome alteration.

ASSESSMENT: Sorbic acid and potassium sorbate are metabolized in the normal manner for fatty acids. They produce no evidence of hazard to the consumer even at levels of consumption much higher than is to be expected in the diet.

RATING: S.

SORBITAN DERIVATIVES

Polysorbate 60 (Polyoxyethylene-20-Sorbitan Monostearate); Polysorbate 65; Polysorbate 80; Sorbitan Monostearate

Sorbitan derivatives are obtained from sorbitol (see p. 638), a simple sugar-alcohol, which is modified by chemical dehydration. Extensive use is made in processed foods of four of the sorbitan derivatives. *Polysorbate 60* consists of chemically combined stearic and palmitic acids (fatty acids that are constituents of fats; see p. 479) and sorbitol, together with its dehydrated form, and condensed with 20 parts of ethylene oxide, a toxic gas frequently used as a sterilizing agent. *Polysorbate 65* differs in that it combines three molecules of stearic acid rather than a single molecule (monostearate). *Polysorbate 80* contains oleic acid (also a fatty acid) in place of stearic acid. *Sorbitan monostearate* chemically combines sorbitol with edible stearic and palmitic acid mixtures, an initial step in manufacture of polysorbate 60. Frequently the sorbitan derivatives are used in combination with mono- and diglycerides (see p. 559) and with one another, since through selection of the proper emulsifier system, significantly better aeration may be obtained, increasing volume and improving grain and texture.
Sorbitan derivatives are used in foods or in flavor composi-

MAJOR REFERENCE: Scientific literature review of sorbitan derivatives in flavor usage. FEMA Report to FDA (NTIS PB 296-016) 1979.

tions as emulsifiers or dispersing agents that blend oil and water components. The polysorbates are water-soluble, and sorbitan monostearate is oil-soluble. A wide range of products employ them: shortenings, confections, dressings, baked goods, dairy products including frozen desserts, beverages, coffee whiteners, meats and fish, and others.

SAFETY: A survey conducted by the National Academy of Sciences-National Research Council, based on 1976 usage reported by food processors, determined that the average daily diet of the U.S. adult contained 15 milligrams of polysorbate 60, 1 of polysorbate 65, 5 of polysorbate 80, and 6 of sorbitan monostearate, or 27 milligrams in total. An individual weighing 60 kg (132 lbs.) ingested on the average slightly less than 0.5 milligram daily per kilogram of body weight (kg/bw) of these sorbitan derivatives.

When ingested, the polysorbates are handled similarly by the body. The fatty acids portion is readily separated during digestion and metabolized normally, since these acids are common fat constituents. A small portion of the sorbitol also will be separated and metabolized, but most of it along with the polyethylene portion is not absorbed, and in humans is excreted.

Over the past 30 years, extensive studies on these substances, using mice, rats, hamsters, dogs, and monkeys as well as humans, have shown that at levels of 2 percent of the diet (200 to 1500 milligrams per kg/bw, depending on the species), or even more, the sorbitan derivatives will not cause harm. Such levels are many hundreds of times the average human intake of the compounds. Human infants have been given 4 grams daily of polysorbate 60 for over a month, and adults 6 grams daily, without ill effect. Humans have been fed 15 grams of polysorbate 80 daily for a month, again with no signs of any toxicity. When sorbitan monostearate was fed to infants at 1 gram per day, or to adults at 6 grams daily (approximately 100 milligrams per kg/bw), there were no adverse effects.

Studies with rats fed polysorbate 60 at 10 grams per kg/bw over most of the life span have failed to show any histological tissue changes, indicating lack of cancerous effect, and no effect on reproduction, lactation, or the offspring. Similar findings were noted with polysorbate 80 and with sorbitan monostearate.

ASSESSMENT: The sorbitan derivatives, the polysorbates and sorbitan monostearate, find important uses as emulsifying agents in foods. Dosages of these substances hundreds of times as great as are contained in the adult diet have been administered to humans without harm. They obviously are free of hazard to the consumer at their current levels in foods, or at levels far above these amounts.

RATING: S.

SORBITOL

Sorbitol is a sweet-tasting compound made by chemical addition of hydrogen to the simple sugar glucose (corn sugar). It is found as a normal constituent in many fruits and berries. Sorbitol has about half the sweetness of sucrose (cane sugar). Sorbitol also functions as a crystallization modifier to control hardening in soft sugar-based confections, and it serves to help maintain moisture, plasticity, or viscosity in certain foods. It is used in sugar-free candies and chewing gum for diabetics because its slow absorption into the bloodstream leads to little rise in blood sugar in the body. Sorbitol is not truly a sugar; it does not promote dental cavities and thus finds use in some chewing gums.

SAFETY: The 1975 estimate of the average intake of sorbitol per person was 231 milligrams, a little under 4 milligrams per kilogram body weight (kg/bw) for a person weighing 60 kg (132 lbs.).

Sorbitol is metabolized like sugars; the body converts it to fructose (fruit sugar), which is then utilized in normal energy-producing steps. Humans have consumed 10 grams (167 milligrams per kg/bw) of sorbitol daily for a month without any harm. Fifty grams acted on adults as a laxative, but not 25 grams. Infants and children consuming 500 milligrams per kg/bw have had diarrhea but no other effects. Studies throughout the life span of rats showed no evidence of adverse effects on growth, reproduction, or lactation when fed at 5 grams per kg/bw daily. There were no tissue abnormalities in the organs, suggesting lack of any carcinogenic effect, and no gene-altering response was noted. Similarly, no malformed offspring were seen when pregnant hamsters, rats, and mice received 1200 to 1600 milligrams per kg/bw daily for five to ten days.

MAJOR REFERENCE: Evaluation of the health aspects of sorbitol as a food ingredient. FASEB/SCOGS Report 9 (NTIS PB 221-951) 1973.

ASSESSMENT: Sorbitol has been used in foods by humans for many decades, with no indication that such use has had adverse effects. It can act as a laxative at levels that are considerably above normal intake. The substance is readily metabolized by the body, and as a food additive appears to pose no hazard to the consumer at current levels in the diet, or at levels that may be expected in future years.

RATING: S.

SOY PROTEIN ISOLATE (SOY PROTEIN CONCENTRATE)

Textured Vegetable Protein (TVP, Textured Soy Protein)

WHEY PROTEIN CONCENTRATE

Soybeans constitute a major agricultural crop in the U.S. that, in the past, has been grown primarily for edible oil and animal feed. Increasingly in recent years, soybean flakes, the residue after the extraction of the oil, have been further processed to separate *soy protein isolate*, a defatted protein which food manufacturers have found useful in a number of foods for human consumption. (A similar product is obtained from whey:* *whey protein concentrate*.) An alkaline extraction procedure is applied to the flakes to produce a liquor, which is then neutralized by an acid. The liquor is further processed by filtering or centrifugal force to obtain a concentrated protein isolate solution. Currently the practice is to spray-dry the solution in equipment heated by direct-fire burners. *Textured vegetable protein* (TVP) is produced by a spinning process or cooking under high pressure, which makes it fibrous, giving it a texture that better simulates meat.

Soy protein isolates are employed to provide the protein in commercially prepared milk-free formulas for the estimated 10 percent of the infants in the U.S. who cannot digest milk. As spun fiber, they represent 20 percent or more of the content of fabricated meat substitutes. A wide range of manufactured food products contain substantial amounts, among them snack

---

MAJOR REFERENCE: Evaluation of the health aspects of soy protein isolates as food ingredients. FASEB/SCOGS Report 101 (NTIS PB 300-717) 1979.

*For whey, the liquid portion of milk after separation from casein, see p. 677.

foods, gravies and sauces, seasonings and flavors, breakfast cereals, and dairy products like frozen desserts.

SAFETY: It was estimated in 1970 that the per capita daily intake in the U.S. of soy protein isolates was 150 milligrams, or 2.5 milligrams per kilogram of body weight (kg/bw) for a person weighing 60 kg (132 lbs.). Considering increasing use as replacements for animal proteins, this intake is likely to have increased materially by now. Infants who receive formulas in which the protein is supplied by these isolates may be consuming well over 1000 times the per capita amount when adjusted for body weight.

The nutritional and biologic effects of soy protein isolates differ somewhat from those of other proteins. Because of the alkali-processing procedures employed in their extraction, there is a loss of certain nutritionally essential amino acids, and the formation of lysinoalanine (LAL) as a component of the protein molecules. LAL interferes with the body's ability to metabolize certain nutrients. If these isolates were the sole source of protein in the diet, phosphorus would be utilized poorly, certain minerals (especially zinc) would be insufficiently available, and the requirements would be increased for vitamins E, K, D, and B_{12}. It is likely, however, that when the protein isolate is added to food it will be supplemented by sulfur-bearing amino acids like methionine, accompanied by the needed minerals and vitamins. The protein quality of soy isolate formulas for infants has been found to be very high and similar to milk.

A number of investigators have demonstrated that high levels of alkali-modified soy protein isolate when present as the sole source in diets of rats can cause cytomegalic inclusion disease (growth of large, partially lifeless cells) in kidneys. An LAL-induced nutritional deficiency is believed responsible. In rat diets, lesser levels of LAL than were contained in these experiments failed to produce this effect. Sensitivity to LAL appears to differ among animal species. It did not harm mice, hamsters, rabbits, quail, and rhesus monkeys, nor have these symptoms been reported in humans. LAL has been detected at low levels in samplings of soy protein isolates used in food, including the spun fiber variety employed in meat substitutes.

Soy protein isolates may contain up to 50 ppm (parts per million) of nitrite. The nitrite appears to be formed during spray drying when the product comes into contact with combustion gases. It is estimated as contributing 0.04 milligram per kg/bw in the daily diets of maximum consumers such as vegetarians who eat substitutes prepared from spun protein isolates, and 0.03 milligram per kg/bw daily to infants subsisting on formulas based on these proteins. Ingestion by others of nitrite from these protein substitutes should be materially less, since they are less likely to intentionally select them.

Nitrite can react with other nitrogen-containing compounds in foods, drugs, and other substances to produce nitrosamines, which have been shown to cause cancer in animals (see p. 631).

Soy protein isolate when fed at high levels to pregnant rats did not adversely affect their offspring. Human infants who received all their protein from soy protein isolate formulas for six months did not differ from others who subsisted on milk-based formulas. The same was true of adults who consumed their protein as soy protein isolate for 24 weeks. Tests to determine whether soy protein isolate can cause cancer have not been located.

ASSESSMENT: Consumption of unsupplemented soy protein isolate as a sole protein source in a human's diet could contribute to nutritional deficiencies and serious illness, but this is unlikely to happen. Whenever the substance is added to food, it usually is supplemented with needed amino acids, minerals and vitamins, and other and adequate proteins, and many studies with humans have confirmed it to be safe in these circumstances.

The adverse effect of lysinoalanine (LAL) on rat kidneys required far greater amounts than the levels detected in soy protein isolates that are used in food; lesser amounts, still far in excess of current human intake, failed to cause harm. Adverse effects did not occur in other animal species even at greater dosages, nor have they been reported in humans. Thus the low levels of LAL present in soy protein isolates are not regarded at present to be of concern to health.

The amount of nitrite contributed to the diet is minimal compared to the total intake from all sources of food and the nitrite that is produced in the body during digestion. About 10 percent of infants cannot tolerate milk and depend on soy protein isolate-based formulas for their protein, and the substantial benefits gained warrant whatever slight risk may be involved. Studies on the safety of whey protein concentrate have not been located, but because of close similarity to lactalbumin (p. 465) the findings for that additive will be applicable.

Since the concentrate usually is prepared by a heat treatment, there is minimal likelihood of allergy from its use.

RATING: S.

STANNOUS CHLORIDE

This compound, sometimes called tin salt, is obtained by the action of hydrochloric acid on tin. Tin is widely distributed in nature and is present in foods like fish and to a lesser extent in fresh vegetables. Humans accumulate tin in differing degrees in bone, liver, heart, stomach, muscles, and blood. It is reported to be nutritionally essential for growth in rats, but there is no direct evidence that this is true for man.

Stannous chloride is permitted in food as a chemical preservative, and also for color retention. It is used in processed vegetables such as asparagus, wax beans, and sauerkraut and also in processed fruits and nonalcoholic beverages.

SAFETY: It has been estimated that in 1976, based on industry's reported usage, 0.25 milligram of stannous chloride was added to food consumed in the diet of the average U.S. adult. An analysis of the amount of tin in a one-day institutional diet for a person determined that it contained 3.6 milligrams of tin, which provides a perspective of the relative contributions from food and from additives.

A study of anemia in rats determined that the no-adverse-effect level of tin salts was 22 milligrams per kilogram of body weight (kg/bw) if the diet contained sufficient iron. This is well over 350 times the amount found in the institutional diet reported above, when adjusted for body weight. Rats and mice receiving 5 parts per million of stannous chloride in their drinking water over their life span did not suffer any toxic effects, nor did it affect their growth rate or longevity.

The few reported observations concerning stannous chloride and elemental tin as possible causes of cancer have been negative, with the exception of one study where three malignant tumors were found in 30 mice in a feeding experiment employing a diet containing 2 percent sodium chlorostannate,

---

MAJOR REFERENCE: Evaluation of the health aspects of stannous chloride as a food ingredient. FASEB/SCOGS Report 31 (NTIS PB 254-531) 1974.

a compound containing tin. However, the investigators regarded this as probably without significance because of the small numbers involved. Tumors did not occur when the sodium chlorostannate was reduced to 1 percent. Tin, in fact, may deter cancer; fewer malignancies occurred among mice fed 0.5 percent of tin as sodium chlorostannate or sodium stannous oleate than among controls that received neither substance. Unlike some metals which caused cancerous tumors when implanted under the skin of rats, tinfoil did not.

Stannous chloride fed by tube to pregnant mice, rats, and hamsters in dosages up to 50 milligrams per kg/bw did not affect fertility or maternal or fetal survival. Tests in laboratories indicate that it is unlikely to cause defective young.

ASSESSMENT: Feeding studies of stannous chloride conducted among a number of animal species, and including observations on cancer, maternal and fetal survival and health, at dosages far greater than the amounts present in the daily diet of humans, indicate that this compound is not harmful.

RATING: S.

STARCH

GELATINIZED STARCH; MODIFIED STARCH

Starches from various sources may be used as food ingredients. They may come from tapioca, potatoes, or several of the cereals, notably corn, wheat, and rice. Starch is a carbohydrate polymer—a condensation of many glucose molecules (a sugar; see p. 518) into long chains. It is produced commercially by steeping and grinding the seed or tuber of starchy plants to produce a wet, thin mixture, or slurry. Sulfur dioxide (see p. 650) is added to help separate the protein from the starch granules and to improve the color, and the unmodified starch is settled out and separated. When starch and water are heated, the granules swell and burst; the result is a *gelatinized starch,* which is much easier to disperse in water and which readily forms a thick gel. The term *"modified starch"* does not refer

MAJOR REFERENCE: Evaluation of the health aspects of starch and modified starches as food ingredients. FASEB/SCOGS Report 115 (NTIS PB 80-128804) 1979.

to this physical change, but rather to a chemical modification, which may involve bleaching and oxidation (combining with oxygen), partial splitting of the molecules with the aid of acids, or cross-linking or bridging (combining) of the starch chains with various substances to produce starch acetate, starch succinates (see p. 648), starch phosphate, and other substances. The various starch sources and the physical and chemical modifications provide the food processor with starches with many different properties in terms of clarity, tolerance of acidic conditions, permanency of gel, and even blandness of flavor.

Starches are used in foods as thickening and gelling agents, to increase viscosity or thickness of a solution, to help keep ingredients from separating, to prevent caking of foods such as powdered sugar or baking powder, and even as dusting powders to prevent sticking of a food such as bread dough.

SAFETY: Starch is a major component of cereals and many vegetables. The average U.S. diet provides about 180 grams per person daily. By contrast, the use of unmodified starch as a food additive contributed less than 1 gram per person daily in 1971. About an equal amount of chemically modified starches was added to the food supply, a daily consumption averaging about 17 milligrams of modified starch per kilogram of body weight (kg/bw) per person. A resurvey of the food industry in 1976 indicated about the same.

The use of modified starches in infant foods has received special attention. In 1977 a food consumption survey found that somewhat less than two-thirds of infant foods contained modified starch. The survey indicated an overall daily average per infant of about 3 grams, perhaps 400 milligrams per kg/bw of modified starch. The maximum daily intake for infants up to three months of age was 3.1 grams, and at eight months was 15.8 grams.

The source of the starch and the type of modification rarely are identified on food labels, since this is not required by the FDA; occasionally the starch source is noted. It is known that most of the starch used comes from corn. Five forms of modified starch account for most of the usage in foods: bleached starch, acetylated distarch adipate, distarch phosphate, acetylated distarch phosphate, and hydroxypropyl distarch phosphate. The latter three forms are the ones commonly used in baby foods.

Starch is a food, and as such is digested, metabolized, and

used as an energy source, as are most carbohydrates. Even in infants, who have lower amounts of the digestive enzymes during the first few months, the digestibility of the different unmodified starches is complete. The starch is split by the enzymes to its constituent glucose molecules, and these are readily absorbed and metabolized. Essentially all of the starch present in the diet is gelatinized by cooking before being eaten. Some raw starches, especially ungelatinized potato starch, are more difficult for the enzymes to digest and have led to lower weight gains in experimental animals, but no other adverse effects were seen. Some humans have shown a compulsive eating of raw starch, as much as 2 pounds of laundry starch being ingested daily; they frequently are obese and anemic.

Perhaps two dozen different types of modified starches have been studied with various kinds of experiments designed to assess their safety. A few have been studied with short-term tests involving humans (showing no adverse effect when fed at 1 gram per kg/bw, some 60 times the average daily intake of modified starch in processed foods), pigs, and dogs. Most of the studies used rats and included a number of two-year feeding tests in multigeneration experiments. Some short-term tests involved diets incorporating the modified starch at 4 grams per kg/bw, but others ranged as high as 100 grams per kg/bw.

None of the animal studies showed any adverse effects of the modified starch on reproduction, the offspring, or on tumor development. With a single exception, digestibility and metabolism seemed normal. Only four effects of any significance were noted in all of these studies. Some diarrhea was observed for a very few of the modified starches; these instances were at feeding levels of 20 grams per kg/bw or higher. A few modified starches resulted in a slightly lower rate of growth when present in the diet at a level of 15 to 60 grams per kg/bw. While most of the starches were readily and completely digested, hydroxypropyl starch was less completely digested by rats. Finally, there was some evidence of greater calcium deposition in the kidney tubules when rats were fed high levels of several of the modified starches.

ASSESSMENT: Starch is present as a major carbohydrate and calorie source in the diet. All of the evidence confirms the safety of unmodified or gelatinized starch added to processed foods. Chemically modified starches come from a variety of food starch sources and are treated with many different chemicals to accentuate a desirable physical property of the additive. Some diarrhea, some slower growth, and some calcium deposition in kidney tubules have occurred with a few of these modified starches. It is uncertain whether these effects have any significant bearing on safety, and they have resulted from feeding at levels of 20 grams per kg/bw or more; the total modified starch intake in human diets would appear to average only about 17 milligrams per kg/bw daily, and this is distributed among a number of forms of modified starch rather than a single type. The poor digestibility of one modified starch, hydroxypropyl starch, causes some possible concern; however, this modified starch is not at present used in baby foods.

No modified starch that has been tested has shown any adverse effects on fertility, and none appears to have caused cancer, allergic sensitivity, abnormal offspring, or altered genes. While there are no suggestions of any adverse symptoms at the moderate levels of modified starches present in processed foods, there are some unanswered questions about whether any could pose even a slight hazard to the consumer. Several have not been specifically studied in long-term feeding tests, or for such effects as cancer or teratogenicity; the significance of the occasional calcium deposition in the kidney remains questionable.

RATING: S for unmodified or gelatinized starch; ? for modified starches (as further long-term studies are needed to resolve questions of possible hazard).

STERCULIA GUM (GUM KADAYA, GUM KARAYA, INDIA GUM, INDIAN TRAGACANTH)

Sterculia gum (also referred to by the other names above) is the dried discharge, obtained by drilling or tapping, of various species of *Sterculia,* a tree native to central and eastern India, and also found in Africa, Australia, China, and Indochina. The gum is a complex carbohydrate (a condensation of a number of simple sugars); on aging or heating it may release a high acetyl content (acetic acid such as is found in vinegar, see p. 463).

MAJOR REFERENCE: Evaluation of the health aspects of sterculia gum as a food ingredient. FASEB/SCOGS Report 5 (NTIS PB 234-905) 1973.

Sterculia gum absorbs water readily, forming viscous, semi-fluid mixtures at low concentrations, and is used in milk and frozen dairy products, meat products, soft candy, and nonalcoholic beverages to blend ingredients and keep them from separating.

SAFETY: The intake of sterculia gum as an additive in the daily diet of a U.S. individual, based on reported usage by the food industry in 1975, averaged less than 2 milligrams. Research and clinical experience reported on the biological effects of this substance are not extensive, but do permit a number of observations. Allergic reactions to sterculia gum have been documented in humans, both by ingestion and surface contact, with symptoms such as hay fever, asthma, dermatitis, and gastrointestinal distress, and caution has been expressed about its indiscriminate use as a laxative.

When fed to rats at 3 grams daily for a week, a dosage 100,000 times as great as human intake (adjusted for body weight), these animals appeared to be bloated and their intestinal weights were substantially greater than those of the controls. An even larger quantity, 5 grams, was fed to dogs for 30 days, and while their feces showed increased bulk and moisture, no irritating effect was observed. The laxative effect of sterculia gum was studied by oral administration of about 7 grams daily to 89 human subjects over a four-week period. Because of its water-absorbing qualities, the gum increased the bulk and moisture of the stools, but the investigators considered it to be a useful and harmless laxative.

Tests conducted with pregnant mice, rats, and hamsters fed 6000 to 34,000 times sterculia gum's presence in the human diet (adjusted for body weight) have shown that it does not cause physical defects in the embryo. However, it has been reported that the feeding of dosages equivalent to 29,000 times human intake did result in the death of a significant number of pregnant mice (but not rats or hamsters).

According to findings of laboratory tests, sterculia gum does not produce gene mutation. Studies have not been conducted to determine whether it can cause cancer.

ASSESSMENT: Since sterculia gum can cause an allergic response, people sensitive to such allergens should avoid this substance. The fatalities among pregnant mice when force-fed sterculia gum occurred at levels so far above human intake that a health hazard is unlikely.

RATING: S for most people; X for anyone who is hyperallergic.

SUCCINIC ACID

Succinic acid is present in meats, cheese, and many vegetables such as asparagus, beets, broccoli, and rhubarb (which have distinct flavors that may be related to it), since it is a key compound in the metabolic conversion of carbohydrates in plants and animals. It is used as an additive to foods to impart a distinct acid taste and is usually manufactured for this purpose by chemical addition of hydrogen to synthetic maleic or fumaric acid (see p. 550).

SAFETY: The daily intake of succinic acid added to foods in 1976 was less than 0.025 milligram per person. By contrast, up to 50 grams have been given daily in studies of diabetic patients. In normal animals or humans, succinic acid when ingested is converted to glucose for energy or stored as glycogen in the body for future use. Studies have shown that succinic acid does not adversely affect normal embryo development. It has not been investigated as a possible cause of cancer or genetic changes.

ASSESSMENT: Succinic acid occurs naturally and is present in foods, and in the body, in far greater amounts than what is added to processed foods. It is tolerated without hazard in amounts thousands of times those used in foods or likely to be used in the future.

RATING: S.

MAJOR REFERENCE: Evaluation of the health aspects of succinic acid as a food ingredient. FASEB/SCOGS Report 53 (NTIS PB 254-541) 1975.

SUCROSE (CANE OR BEET SUGAR)

Sucrose is common table sugar. A carbohydrate (like starch and cellulose), it consists of two simple sugars, glucose and fructose (see p. 518). Sugar beets and sugar cane are the sources for sucrose used by food processors, and it is found in abun-

---

MAJOR REFERENCE: Evaluation of the health aspects of sucrose as a food ingredient. FASEB/SCOGS Report 69 (NTIS PB 262-668) 1976.

dance in many other plants. As an additive, it is used as a sweetener in foods and beverages.

SAFETY: In 1975 refined sucrose accounted for approximately 89 of the 120 pounds of sweeteners used annually per person, which means an average daily consumption of this sugar of 110 grams per person, or a quarter pound.

Sucrose is split by enzymes in the digestive tract to its constituent sugars, which are then absorbed and readily metabolized and used as sources of energy. High levels of sucrose in the diet can increase the plasma triglyceride (neutral fat*) levels of human subjects, but this appears to be transitory. The more common levels of sucrose in the diet of normal individuals do not have any greater effect on blood lipids than do other carbohydrates, such as starch (see p. 643). While elevation of plasma triglycerides has been associated with increased susceptibility to coronary artery disease, the kind and amount of fat in the diet, which can raise the serum cholesterol level, is regarded as of greater significance. Carbohydrates consumed in the amounts contained in the normal diet are unlikely to be of importance here.

Sucrose is also linked by some with risk of diabetes, but the available evidence denies such a direct relationship. Since diabetes is a disorder characterized by the inability to properly metabolize glucose, carbohydrates in the diet have been suspect. However, all information at hand indicates that the cause is really calorie intake, regardless of source. Obesity can induce diabetes in genetically susceptible people, and being overweight has at times been linked with sucrose intake. But obesity occurs when more calories are consumed than expended, and sucrose in the food supply accounts for only about 15 percent of total calorie intake.

Sucrose as a replacement for starch in the diet has been found to affect the life span of some strains of animals susceptible to kidney disease. Although this may not apply to humans, these studies suggest that persons with kidney problems may take the precaution of avoiding excessive sucrose intake. Animal studies have shown that sucrose does not induce cancer or gene alteration, and has a very low toxicity.

Dental caries (cavities) is associated with most fermentable carbohydrates in the diet; it is most likely to be a problem

---

*The way in which lipids (constituents of cells and a source of body fuel) are stored, as in body fat.

when sweet foods that tend to be retained on the teeth are eaten frequently, and especially between meals. Sucrose often is used in sweet snack foods (such as sticky candies) and thus certainly contributes to dental health problems, particularly if oral hygiene (cleaning the teeth) is poor and the water consumed is not fluoridated.

ASSESSMENT: Sucrose is widely used to provide sweetness in food preparations and beverages. That this contributes to tooth decay is well documented. Too much sugar in the diet clearly can pose a hazard to diabetics, who cannot efficiently use the glucose as a source of energy. In addition, experimental evidence suggests that excessive sucrose may prove to be harmful to some individuals with kidney ailments. However, both diabetics and people with kidney ailments are likely to be under strict dietary controls and a caution in rating sucrose in food does not seem necessary.

RATING: S.*

SULFITING AGENTS

Potassium Bisulfite; Potassium Metabisulfite; Sodium Bisulfite; Sodium Metabisulfite; Sodium Sulfite; Sulfur Dioxide

Sulfites are sulfur-containing chemicals that can release sulfur dioxide. They are effective as sanitary agents for food containers and fermentation equipment. They are also used as preservatives to reduce or prevent spoilage by bacteria, to minimize browning and other discoloration of food during processing, storage, and distribution, and as inhibitors of undesir-

---

MAJOR REFERENCE: Evaluation of the health aspects of sulfiting agents as food ingredients. FASEB/SCOGS Report 15 (NTIS PB 265-508) 1977.

*Sucrose has not been rated here as hazardous because of its effect on cavities. While it does have a role in tooth decay, it does so only in combination with other factors, such as improper dental hygiene or in-between-meal snacks which contain fermentable carbohydrates or water that is not fluoridated.

The rating procedure followed here does not consider a substance hazardous if it is harmful only when it is abused by the consumer, as almost anything can be. However, the sugar content of some dry breakfast cereals and instant breakfast bars and powders is a sizable percentage of total content. Because these percentages are not readily available and because children consume much of these foods, sucrose can be regarded as of concern to health. As a caution, we have provided the percentage of sugar content in many of the brands in these categories that are listed in the inventory section of this book.

able microorganisms during fermentation. Sulfites are used in dehydration, freezing, and brining of fruits and vegetables; in fruit juices and purees, syrups, and condiments; and in winemaking.

SAFETY: Sulfur dioxide to some extent evaporates or transforms to sulfate (which is harmless) during processing and subsequent storage, and any subsequent preparation, such as cooking, at home. The amount remaining in food before it is eaten is likely to be considerably less than the quantity added originally, and when it is finally ingested, an enzyme (sulfite oxidase) transforms it rapidly to sulfate. (A rare hereditary deficiency of this enzyme in the liver has been reported in humans.)

The usual basis for calculating the margin of safety for daily human consumption of a substance is the level that caused no ill effects in animal experimentation. This level varies for sulfur dioxide, its lowest being 30 milligrams per kilogram of body weight (kg/bw). An expert panel in 1975 estimated the daily intake per person as 0.2 milligram per kg/bw for most people and not over 2.0 milligrams for excessive users of sulfited foods and beverages. This is 1/150 of the animal safety level for the bulk of consumers, but for excessive users the ratio is 1/15; note that frequently 1/100 is regarded as the desired margin of safety.

Sulfites can destroy thiamin (vitamin B_1), and they are not permitted by the FDA in meats or other foods that are known to be major sources of this vitamin. Sulfites are unlikely to cause sufficient destruction of thiamin to threaten a deficiency because they are present in only a fraction of the mixed foods eaten in the course of a day. Large dosages (70 milligrams per kg/bw) of sulfites have resulted in gastrointestinal irritation, evidenced by abdominal pains and vomiting in animals and humans. In an experiment, rats fed with sodium sulfite for over a year suffered a deficiency in vitamin E, but only when extremely large doses (500 milligrams per kg/bw) were used.

In a number of test-tube experiments sulfites caused mutations in microorganisms by altering the nucleic acids which store and transfer the genetic code. There is no evidence of this effect in studies conducted with living bodies, and it seems reasonable to assume that the rapid destruction of sulfur dioxide by the enzyme sulfite oxidase provides protection. Investigations indicate that the sulfites do not adversely affect reproduction or offspring or cause cancer.

When evaluating human exposure to sulfiting agents in food, it merits consideration that inhaling air polluted with sulfur from coal or petroleum products can add an additional burden of sulfur dioxide. It is not possible to estimate the amount of the chemical that is being inhaled.

ASSESSMENT: The sulfiting agents are rapidly transformed by oxygen to harmless sulfate in the body and are not likely to present a hazard to humans at the levels and manner in which they are currently used as additives in food and beverages, except for the very few who may be afflicted with a deficiency of the liver enzyme sulfite oxidase. In the event of a significant increase in the use of these substances, this judgment would require reassessment, particularly for individuals who are excessive in their use of foods and beverages high in sulfur content.

RATING: S.

SULFURIC ACID

AMMONIUM, CALCIUM, POTASSIUM, SODIUM SULFATE

Sulfuric acid, which becomes a sulfate when added to food, and its salts *(ammonium, calcium, potassium,* and *sodium sulfate)* are used in food in a variety of ways. Calcium sulfate, besides qualifying as a nutrient supplement (calcium is essential to life), can act as a firming agent in tomato products and canned vegetables and as a dough conditioner to give desirable texture characteristics in bakery products and flours. Sulfuric acid may also be useful in a limited number of foods as an acidifier (to provide tartness and control acid-alkali balance).

SAFETY: The daily dietary intake of sulfuric acid and its sulfates as additives approximated 140 milligrams per person in 1976, according to a survey conducted by the National Academy of Sciences-National Research Council of usage by food processors. Calcium sulfate and sulfuric acid accounted for nearly all. Additionally, most foods normally contain sulfates among their mineral constituents. And when the body metabolizes protein, sulfate is formed from the sulfur which most proteins contain. Sulfate is incorporated into mucins (the

---

MAJOR REFERENCE: Evaluation of the health aspects of sulfuric acid and sulfates as food ingredients. FASEB/SCOGS Report 33 (NTIS PB 262-652) 1975.

slime of mucous membranes) and plays a role in detoxifying some products of metabolism that might otherwise be harmful in the body or more difficult to excrete.

From various studies with animals and humans, it is clear that the sulfates do not have adverse effects until the level is very much greater than the usual exposure in the daily diet. No tumors were found in mice or rabbits administered 300 to 600 times (respectively) the daily exposure of humans (adjusted for body weight). There appear to be no investigations of specific effects such as chromosome damage, birth defects, or allergy response to sulfates.

ASSESSMENT: Since sulfates are normally found in most foods and are the final products of the body's metabolism of sulfur-containing proteins, the body is regularly called on to handle these materials. The available evidence indicates that as additives, these sulfates pose no hazard to the consumer at levels presently used or likely to be expected in the future.

RATING: S.

TANNIC ACID

Tannin is naturally present in a wide distribution of plants; extracts of it are found in wine, tea, and coffee. The tannic acids permitted in food processing differ from other tannic acids in their tannin sources and chemical characteristics and in the effects they have on the body. Only food-grade tannic acids require evaluation here. These are usually derived from a powder found in nutgalls, growths that form on twigs of species of hardwoods such as oak, usually in temperate climates of western Asia and southern Europe, or from seed pods of Peruvian, Polynesian, or Australian palms and ferns. Tannic acid adds a desirable astringent taste to butter, caramel, fruit, maple, and nut flavorings. Its ability to filter out proteins makes it useful as a clarifier in the wine and brewing industry.

SAFETY: Based on reported usage in industry, per capita consumption of added tannic acid in the U.S. in 1976 was estimated at 9 milligrams daily, less than 0.2 milligram per kilogram of body weight (kg/bw) for a person weighing 60 kg (132 lbs.). It is questionable whether anything like this amount

---

MAJOR REFERENCE: Evaluation of the health aspects of tannic acid as a food ingredient. FASEB/SCOGS Report 48 (NTIS PB 274-669) 1977.

is actually consumed. When tannic acid is used as a filtering agent, and most of the acid probably is used in this way, good manufacturing practice requires its removal.

The extent and nature of absorption of tannic acid have not been established for man. In experimental animals, before absorption the acid has caused damage to mucous membranes of the stomach and intestines, but only when large, concentrated doses are fed by tube into empty stomachs or when exposure of the membranes to tannic acid is artificially prolonged. The method of administration apparently affects the toxicity of tannic acid: 1000 milligrams per kg/bw taken orally by rats did not disturb their liver function or do damage to the intestinal tract, whereas 60 milligrams per kg/bw injected into the abdominal cavity did damage their livers. The latter dosage is still 400 times human consumption (adjusted for body weight).

Long-term feeding studies reviewed by the UN Joint FAO/WHO Expert Committee on Food Additives indicate that tannic acid taken orally will not produce tumors or cancer. One study in which this substance was administered to rats by injection reported the development of liver tumors which were suggestive of malignancy; but other studies contest this finding.

Laboratory tests indicate that tannic acid does not cause gene mutations, nor does it adversely affect maternal or fetal survival, or cause birth abnormalities.

ASSESSMENT: The total intake in the U.S. diet of tannic acid as an additive is likely to be small. While food-grade tannic acid in concentrated doses prior to absorption can cause damage to the mucous membranes of the gastrointestinal tract, this effect is unlikely from the minute amounts (100 parts per million) of this substance when present in food. The adverse effect on livers of rats, resulting from injection of doses of tannic acid 400 times human consumption, cannot be regarded as relevant to human safety because of the amount and the method of administration as well as evidence that when taken orally, a far greater dosage did not cause harm.

RATING: S.

TARTARIC ACID

POTASSIUM ACID TARTRATE (CREAM OF TARTAR; POTASSIUM BITARTRATE)

Tartaric acid is a normal constituent of grapes and wines, fruits, coffee, and even sugar cane juice. *Potassium acid tartrate* is one of its salts. For commercial purposes, these are obtained from the waste products of wine manufacture. Both substances are added to augment fruit flavors in beverages and candies. Tartaric acid is used as a stabilizing agent in some foods to prevent discoloration or flavor changes that occur from rancidity. As an ingredient in baking powders, potassium acid tartrate (cream of tartar) prevents fermentation in baked goods.

SAFETY: As food additives, the average consumption of tartaric acid and potassium acid tartrate combined has been estimated at 2 milligrams per person in the U.S. in 1976, or 0.03 milligram per kilogram of body weight (kg/bw) for a person weighing 60 kg (132 lbs.), according to a survey conducted by the National Academy of Sciences-National Research Council of usage by food processors.

There were no ill effects in rabbits fed a daily diet containing 2300 milligrams per kg/bw for 60 to 150 days, nor did rats suffer measurable adverse changes after a two-year feeding of a diet containing 1200 milligrams per kg/bw daily. Humans have been fed dosages ranging from 3500 to 11,500 milligrams, the former amount for as long as nine consecutive days, without injury. When tartrates were ingested by humans, it was found that they can be absorbed but may be only minimally metabolized by the body; they are either excreted in the urine or destroyed by bacteria in the intestinal tract.

Experiments on a variety of animal species failed to disclose any indication that tartaric acid could cause birth defects, nor did laboratory tests provide evidence of gene mutation.

ASSESSMENT: Many studies with humans and with experimental animals have demonstrated that tartaric acid and potassium acid tartrate pose no hazard to the public when used at current levels or amounts that may be expected in future years.

RATING: S.

MAJOR REFERENCE: Evaluation of the health aspects of tartaric acid and tartrates as food ingredients. FASEB/SCOGS Report 107 (NTIS PB 301-403) 1979.

TBHQ (TERTIARY BUTYLHYDROQUINONE)

TBHQ is a chemical used as an antioxidant to prevent uptake of oxygen which can cause deteriorating flavors and odors (rancidity) in oils, fatty foods, or even low-fat products incorporating some unsaturated fat. It may be used in combination with BHA or BHT (see p. 489), and its chemical structure resembles that of BHA. If a combination is used, the total antioxidant is still limited to no more than 0.02 percent of the food product. TBHQ has proved to be very effective in polyunsaturated vegetable oils such as safflower, soybean, and cottonseed oils.

SAFETY: The 1976 survey of the food industry usage conducted by the National Academy of Sciences-National Research Council indicated that the average daily intake per person of TBHQ in foods was 0.5 milligram, less than 0.01 milligram per kilogram of body weight (kg/bw) for a person weighing 60 kg (132 lbs.). Heavy users of foods containing it may consume five times this amount.

A number of short- and long-term studies of the safety of TBHQ have been made on rats and dogs. When dogs were fed for two years on diets containing 0.5 percent of TBHQ (200 milligrams per kg/bw), all evidence indicated no effect on behavior, appearance, growth, biochemical studies of blood and urine, organ weights, gross pathology, or microscopic structure of the cells. The only effect of this high dosage was a slight change in some of the blood picture, principally a slightly lower red-blood-cell count. There was no toxicological effect at the lower level of 75 milligrams per kg/bw, equivalent to thousands of times the presence of TBHQ in the daily diet of U.S. humans.

A 20-month study with rats, again with a diet of 0.5 percent of TBHQ (250 milligrams per kg/bw, or 25,000 times the average intake by humans) disclosed no effects of the compound. There was no evidence of any significant storage of TBHQ in the tissues of the body. The animals were carried through three successive generations, and very detailed studies were made. Reproduction efficiency and litter size were normal, but some increase in early mortality of the offspring was noted, though

---

MAJOR REFERENCE: Toxicological evaluation of some food colours, thickening agents, and certain other substances. WHO Food Additives Series No. 8 (Geneva, 1975).

there was no increase in any abnormalities. TBHQ did not appear to cause birth defects.

ASSESSMENT: TBHQ is effective as an antioxidant preventing flavor changes in food fats. Feeding studies with dogs and rats have demonstrated its safety when TBHQ is included at levels thousands of times as great as its presence in the human diet. The UN Joint FAO/WHO Expert Committee on Food Additives considers 0.5 milligram per kg/bw safe and acceptable as a daily intake for humans (50 times the amount actually in the U.S. diet). There appears to be no hazard to the consumer from use of TBHQ as a food-preserving chemical, even at levels that may be expected in the future.

RATING: S.

TOCOPHEROLS (VITAMIN E)

Alpha-Tocopherol; Alpha-Tocopherol Acetate

The tocopherols are present naturally in a wide range of plant and animal tissue; they are either produced synthetically or isolated from cereal and vegetable oils for use in food. *Alpha-tocopherol* contains the most potent type of vitamin E, which is needed for normal muscular development and organic processes. It also prevents destruction in the body by oxygen of some essential fatty substances (required for cell repair and replacement and for immediate energy), including vitamin A and certain hormones. As additives in food, the tocopherols act as antioxidants, preventing or retarding flavor deterioration and rancidity caused by oxygen. Because vitamin E is an essential nutrient, they also are used in food fortification and as a vitamin supplement. Synthetic *alpha-tocopherol acetate* is the usual form of vitamin E used.

SAFETY: The daily intake of tocopherols contained in food in the diet of U.S. individuals was estimated as averaging 7 to 9 milligrams, much of it present naturally. About 3.5 milligrams were added to food in 1975. Not all the vitamin E is available for absorption in the body at the time it is eaten, as some is

MAJOR REFERENCE: Evaluation of the health aspects of the tocopherols and α-tocopherol acetate as food ingredients. FASEB/SCOGS Report 36 (NTIS PB 262-653) 1976.

destroyed in cooking and even more during commercial processing and storage. The UN Joint FAO/WHO Expert Committee on Food Additives, basing its judgment on human clinical experience, concluded that an acceptable daily intake (ADI) of alpha-tocopherol for man should not be more than 2 milligrams per kilogram of body weight. For an adult weighing 60 kilograms (132 lbs.), this would be 120 milligrams, or many times as great as the daily consumption reported above.

Investigators working with animals document adverse effects on growth, development, and metabolism caused by the administration of vitamin E orally or ingested in the diet. But this happened only when the levels tested far exceeded human intake, and the deviations were eliminated when dosing with this vitamin was stopped. A variety of animal species can tolerate oral dosages 100 times the FAO/WHO ADI for humans (adjusted for body weight). Hypervitaminosis E (an excess of this vitamin), which can affect the liver, heart, and reproductive cycle, is only a possibility when over 400 milligrams per day are ingested by an individual over an extended period of time, and the evidence is not convincing that it will occur even then. But neither have benefits been demonstrated, as some claim, from the addition of large amounts of vitamin E to the diet. Research on the possibility of tocopherols causing birth defects, gene mutations, or cancer has not revealed such alterations.

ASSESSMENT: Alpha-tocopherol is a prime source of vitamin E, an essential constituent for maintenance of a number of the body's normal biological and organic functions. As an additive, it contributes possibly a tenth of the total tocopherol content ingested in the daily diet, for it is also present naturally in cereals, vegetables, and other foods. Experimental and clinical evidence indicates that in quantities present in the diet, both naturally and added, alpha-tocopherol is not harmful and actually is needed. Any hazard from it appears possible only in the event of excessive doses taken over long periods.

RATING: S.

VANILLIN

ETHYL VANILLIN

Vanillin, the component in the vanilla bean that provides the aroma and flavor, is naturally present in many foods. Other than in vanilla bean extracts, a synthetic chemical substitute, *ethyl vanillin,* may be used, since its flavor is many times stronger than that of vanillin. When natural vanilla extracts are fortified with additional vanillin or ethyl vanillin, they are labeled artificial or imitation. Vanillin and ethyl vanillin are used as flavoring agents in a wide range of products, which include ice cream, candy, soft drinks, gelatin desserts, toppings and frostings, butter, margarine, and chocolate products.

SAFETY: Use of the two flavor ingredients by the U.S. food industry in 1970 indicated an average daily intake per person of 11 milligrams of vanillin and a little under 3 milligrams of ethyl vanillin. Together, they total less than 0.2 milligram daily per kilogram of body weight (kg/bw) in the diet of a person weighing 60 kg (132 lbs.).

Humans and experimental animals normally metabolize vanillin by converting most of it to vanillic acid, by combining it with oxygen or reducing it to an alcohol and eliminating both in the urine. One human subject consumed 100 milligrams of vanillin, and during the next 24 hours excreted 94 percent of it as vanillic acid. Metabolic changes of ethyl vanillin do not appear to have been reported.

Vanillin added to the diet of rats for three months at 500 milligrams per kg/bw was reported by one research group to produce some "mild toxic symptoms." This level is comparable to over 2000 times the usual human intake; lower levels of 150 milligrams per kg/bw did not produce these effects at all. Other studies have reported feeding rats dosages of vanillin at 14,000 times human intake (adjusted for body weight) for one to two years without evidence of harm.

Again, while one group of investigators found that ethyl vanillin in the diet of rats at 64 milligrams per kg/bw caused some growth retardation and tissue changes after two months (still well over 1000 times human intake), others have fed ethyl vanillin to rats for one to two years at levels up to 60,000 times

---

MAJOR REFERENCE: Scientific literature review of vanillin and derivatives in flavor usage. FEMA Report to FDA (NTIS PB 285-495) 1978.

the average per capita consumption of this chemical by humans and reported no adverse effects.

Studies do not appear to have been conducted that evaluate the effects of these two additives on reproduction, or the genes or chromosomes, or as a possible cause of cancer.

ASSESSMENT: Vanillin and its synthetic substitute ethyl vanillin are popular flavor ingredients used in a variety of foods. Available data indicate that dietary intakes far above usual human consumption do not cause adverse effects in experimental animals. Current information suggests no hazard to the consumer from vanillin or ethyl vanillin as food additives.

RATING: S.

VEGETABLE OILS

Hydrogenated, Partially Hydrogenated, Unhydrogenated Coconut, Corn, Cottonseed, Olive, Palm, Palm Kernel, Peanut, Rapeseed, Safflower (High Linoleic, High Oleic), Sheanut, Soybean, Sunflower Oils

Many of the vegetable oils, which are fats, are used directly in foods such as margarine, shortening, various cooking and salad oils, and mayonnaise. Most are highly unsaturated fats, initially in liquid rather than semisolid form. Coconut and palm kernel oils are exceptions in that they contain mainly saturated fatty acids, yet retain the character of oils. A vegetable oil can be converted, or hardened, by the chemical addition of hydrogen to the oil, and called partially hydrogenated or hydrogenated. When fully hydrogenated, the oil is converted to a semisolid fat, making it more stable and less subject to rancidity or other flavor changes. Coconut or palm kernel oil when hydrogenated can produce fats that substitute for cocoa butter in some foods.

The most common of the partially hydrogenated vegetable oils used in foods, soybean oil, is widely used in salad dress-

---

MAJOR REFERENCES: Evaluation of the health aspects of coconut oil, peanut oil, and oleic acid as they may migrate to food from packaging materials, and linoleic acid as a food ingredient. FASEB/SCOGS Report 65 (NTIS PB 274-475) 1977; Evaluation of the health aspects of hydrogenated soybean oil as a food ingredient. FASEB/SCOGS Report 70 (NTIS PB 266-280) 1977.

ings, shortenings, and margarines. The oil is usually extracted from soybeans with hexane, a solvent from petroleum. It is then purified, and hydrogen is chemically incorporated into some (but not all) of the polyunsaturated fatty acid molecules;* this improves the flavor and stability of the oil and produces some texture changes such as viscosity. Hydrogenation changes these fatty acids, increasing saturation and altering some of their components into ''unnatural'' arrangements, which may affect their nutritional value and biological effect.

Soybean oil usually is only partially hydrogenated, the extent depending on its intended use. Less liquid and more plastic compositions of soybean oil needed for shortenings, for example, can be obtained by hydrogenating to a greater degree (which increases saturation); and the hardened product may also be blended with liquid vegetable oils to get a desired consistency and fatty acid makeup, especially when a higher content of polyunsaturated fatty acids is sought.

Other processed or treated oils may include any of the common vegetable oils, notably coconut, corn, cottonseed, palm, palm kernel, peanut, rape, safflower, and sunflower oils. They may be found as additives in food products such as crackers, cookies, margarines, frozen yogurt pies, and potato chips. A less common oil is sheanut oil. It comes from a tropical African tree seed; its fatty acid makeup is largely equal parts of oleic and stearic acids,† and only small amounts of polyunsaturated fatty acids, a composition of fatty acids resembling some shortenings.

Safflower oil is somewhat different in that plant breeders have separated the plant into two varieties: one with an oil high in polyunsaturated linoleic acid, about three-fourths of the fatty acids being linoleic; and another that is high in oleic acid, about three-fourths of the fatty acids being oleic acid, and only 14 percent being linoleic acid. In composition, high-oleic safflower oil resembles olive oil (rather than the polyunsaturated vegetable oils), which contains approximately 73 percent oleic acid and 8 percent polyunsaturated fatty acids and is relatively low in saturated fatty acids. Both types of safflower oil are used as cooking and salad oils. The high-linoleic oil also is used

---

*A fat or oil is made up of various fatty acids chemically linked with glycerin (see p. 563).

†Stearic acid is fully saturated—a fully hydrogenated fatty acid. Oleic acid has some unsaturated (monosaturated) linkages, and will convert to stearic acid if hydrogenated.

in polyunsaturated margarines. Olive oil is usually not hydrogenated before its use in foods.

Rapeseed oil as a food additive is fully hydrogenated and bleached. It can serve as a stabilizer and thickener or as an emulsifier in shortenings.

SAFETY: Food use of soybean oil has increased from an average of about 19 pounds per person in 1964 to 29 pounds in 1974. About half of this was probably partially hydrogenated soybean oil, which thus would account for a daily consumption of 19 grams per person. Coconut oil consumption in 1970 amounted to an average daily intake of slightly over 2 grams per person; palm kernel oil intake came to 0.5 gram per person, and peanut oil to about 1 gram.

Surveys of populations have demonstrated a relationship between intake of saturated fat and blood cholesterol level, which is regarded as a risk factor in coronary heart disease. Saturated fats in the diet may raise the cholesterol level in the blood. While partial hydrogenation does cause saturation of some of the polyunsaturated fat in vegetable oils, it represents only a fraction of the total. The saturated fat content in commercial shortening made with partially hydrogenated soybean oil ranges from 15 to 40 percent, and is 13 to 20 percent in soybean oil margarines. By contrast, butter contains over 65 percent saturated fatty acids.

Polyunsaturated fats, substituting for saturated fats in the diet, can lower elevated blood cholesterol levels, and in this way may reduce the risk of coronary heart attack. It has been shown that partially hydrogenated soybean oil, when substituted for substances with higher saturated fat content, also can lower these levels because of the unsaturated fatty acids they retain. While this is true for the majority of the vegetable oils, some, such as coconut oil and palm kernel oil, do not have appreciable amounts of polyunsaturated fatty acids and thus will not have their protective effect.

There are studies in humans showing that coconut oil in the diet may raise the serum cholesterol level, which could add to the risk of heart disease if the diet included a high intake of such an oil for a prolonged period. Olive oil appears to have little effect on cholesterol levels, probably because it has few of the cholesterol-elevating saturated fatty acids, but also few of the protective polyunsaturated fatty acids.

Many of the biological studies have focused on the "unnatural" forms of the fatty acids produced by the partial hydrogenation of unsaturated vegetable oil. These acids have somewhat different physical properties, but they are absorbed and readily digested and will appear in the fat stores in the body in a similar manner. The natural polyunsaturated linoleic acid is an essential fatty acid, one which the body cannot make itself and must obtain from the diet. It is needed for healthy tissues and cell membranes, regulation of cholesterol metabolism, and production of certain hormones.

The bulk of the linoleic acid present in the diet is in the natural form, which retains these biological capabilities. However, some forms (isomers) of linoleic acid produced through hydrogenation lose this essential fatty acid property, but when metabolized still retain their energy value for the body. When incorporated into the lipid (fats, waxes, etc.) component of the membranes in various cells they may somewhat alter the membrane properties, but the significance of this remains uncertain.

Feeding studies with rats receiving 54 percent of the diet as partially hydrogenated soybean oil for several months showed no abnormal effects when a variety of physical and metabolic measures were examined. This was also true in long-term studies followed through 60 generations. The tests showed no adverse effect on fertility and reproduction, nor did they show abnormal embryo growth, or alteration of the chromosomes, or cancer development.

One study on pregnant rats receiving 20 percent high-linoleic safflower oil in their diet found fewer completed gestations (completions of pregnancy), poorer lactation, and smaller brains in the offspring when compared with rats on a commercial ration. The study needs to be confirmed.

Rapeseed sometimes contains erucic acid, an unusual fatty acid that is toxic. Selective breeding has eliminated this compound in some sources of rapeseed oil; however, the oil used as a food additive is always completely hydrogenated to chemically eliminate any residue of erucic acid and to ensure its safety in foods.

Coconut oil has been studied; it does not induce allergies and does not enhance the ability of a known carcinogen to produce cancer. The refining procedures used in preparing the oil for food uses should remove any cancer-causing contaminants that may arise from smoke-drying of coconut meats.

Besides energy value and essential fatty acids, the other nutrient commonly found in a vegetable oil is alpha-tocopherol, or vitamin E (see p. 657). Coconut and palm kernel oils are low in this vitamin, but the other common vegetable oils contain from 11 to 45 milligrams per 100 grams. Most of the vitamin remains after the hydrogenation processing and incorporation into food products.

ASSESSMENT: The practice of partially hydrogenating a vegetable oil for various food uses converts some of the fatty acids to forms not normally present. In all but coconut and palm kernel oils, the polyunsaturated "essential fatty acid" content remains high, however, and the caloric value is unchanged. The polyunsaturated fatty acids that are present have a cholesterol-lowering effect when fed as a replacement for saturated fats or carbohydrates in the diet. No hazard to the consumer is posed by use of partially hydrogenated vegetable oils in the diet, other than coconut, palm kernel, and rapeseed oils, or if the vegetable oils are fully hydrogenated. These may pose some problems. Evidence indicates that a high degree of saturation of fat or oil is related to adverse effects on blood clotting, cholesterol deposits in arteries, and somewhat poorer fat digestibility.

The potential health problem that a saturated fat may pose to a consumer will depend on the amount consumed in the diet, not merely its presence in the food. The ingredient label can alert one to the presence of a highly saturated fat, but quantities are not given. However, since the ingredients are listed in descending order of their presence in the food, it is possible to estimate when the amount of a given oil may be of concern. Accordingly, a caution is raised in the Inventory of this volume about the safety of a food where one of the first three listed ingredients (other than water), alone or as part of a shortening blend containing other vegetable oils, is coconut oil, palm kernel oil, rapeseed oil, or when "hydrogenated" rather than "partially hydrogenated" precedes the named fat or oil ingredient; these are the highly saturated vegetable oils used in foods.*

---

*The accuracy of this procedure for identifying highly saturated ingredients was tested with laboratory analyses of fatty acids in over 200 purchased foods of all types contained in a 1980 thesis by Mary Gertrude Enig, conducted in collaboration with the USDA. In only five of the 200 foods would this rating procedure have been in error. Four foods having appreciable amounts of saturated fats or oils would have been missed, and one food would have been cited incorrectly as having an excess of highly saturated fats. This figure does not include two foods that were mislabeled, or peanut butter, which has been excluded from the procedure as it naturally contains a considerable amount of unsaturated oil.

RATING: S for all vegetable oils except coconut oil, palm kernel oil, rapeseed oil, hydrogenated oils; for these three oils, and for any oil labeled "hydrogenated" rather than "partially hydrogenated," ? if it appears as part of one of the first three ingredients on a food label.

VITAMIN A

Vitamin A Acetate; Vitamin A Palmitate

Vitamin A is essential for bone growth, normal eyesight, and protection against impaired cell membranes. It is a complex substance called retinol, and its chemical combination with acetic acid *(vitamin A acetate)* or palmitic acid *(vitamin A palmitate)* provides the compounds used as additives in food fortification. The active form of the chemical has been synthesized, and this is the product used in foods or dietary supplements.

Vitamin A, as distinct from its "provitamin," carotene (see p. 505), from which the body is able to form the vitamin, is found naturally in animal products such as cheese, eggs, cream, butter, oysters, and particularly in liver. It may be added as a nutritional supplement in breakfast cereals, milk, margarine, baby formulas, beverages, and other foods.

SAFETY: Vitamin A commonly has been expressed in units of activity rather than weight. One milligram of vitamin A palmitate equals 1820 International Units (IU) of activity; 1 milligram of vitamin A acetate equals 2940 IU. A survey of the vitamin A added to fortify foods in the diet from 1971 to 1974 indicated that these additives would provide an average daily intake per person of about 800 IU. Based on nationwide food consumption studies, the total dietary intake of vitamin A from all sources is probably 5000 IU, just meeting the Recommended Dietary Allowance to maintain good nutritional health for an adult.

Any excess of vitamin A is stored in the liver. Studies in the U.S. and Canada have indicated that human liver stores of vitamin A are minimal; but where dietary intake is appreciable, as it is in some foods such as the polar bear liver, which

---

MAJOR REFERENCE: Evaluation of the health aspects of vitamin A, vitamin A acetate, and vitamin A palmitate as food ingredients. FASEB/SCOGS Report 118 (NTIS PB 80-178650) 1980.

contains as much as 1 gram of vitamin A palmitate in 4 ounces, acute poisoning has occurred in humans. There is also danger from excessive intake of vitamin A, and even 50,000 IU daily in an adult, and less for a child, can lead to severe headaches, nausea, irritability, weakness, pain, hair loss, and other toxicity symptoms. The highest daily safe level appears to be about 700 IU per kilogram of body weight, or 42,000 IU for a person weighing 60 kg (132 lbs.). This intake is highly unlikely from the vitamin A present naturally or as an additive in most foods.

High levels of vitamin A (usually over 100 times the average human intake from food) have produced some adverse effects on reproduction among laboratory animals, and have caused congenital defects in offspring. The vitamin does not cause chromosome damage. There have been no studies to determine whether vitamin A can cause cancer; however, there is some evidence that it may reduce the risk of cancer deliberately induced by some chemical agents.

ASSESSMENT: Vitamin A and its acetate and palmitate compounds provide an important vitamin essential for humans. This vitamin is toxic at high levels, but these amounts are many times as high as would be supplied by foods. The fortification of foods with vitamin A derivatives appears to pose no hazard to the consumer at current levels or levels likely to be encountered in the future.

RATING: S.

VITAMIN B_1 (THIAMIN)

Thiamin Hydrochloride; Thiamin Mononitrate

Vitamin B_1, or thiamin, is widely distributed in plant and animal tissues, especially in pork products, liver, cereal grains, and legumes. It is essential for tissue growth and maintenance, and for many of the metabolic reactions in the body, in particular for converting carbohydrates to energy. Practically all the thiamin that is added to food is produced synthetically in two forms: *thiamin hydrochloride*, which is very soluble in water, and *thiamin mononitrate*, which is only moderately soluble in

---

MAJOR REFERENCE: Evaluation of the health aspects of thiamin, thiamin hydrochloride and thiamin mononitrate as food ingredients. FASEB/SCOGS Report 109 (NTIS PB 288-674) 1978.

water but is more stable than the hydrochloride and is preferred by the food industry for the enrichment of flour mixes. These compounds are added to various foods such as baked goods, cereals, and pasta products as nutritive and dietary supplements, since the milling of wheat (which lightens it and produces a finer flour texture) removes fractions of the wheat which contain a good deal of this vitamin.

SAFETY: The daily intake per person in the U.S. of added vitamin B_1 was estimated at 2 milligrams in 1975, based on reported usage by the food industry; 0.33 milligram of this was as thiamin hydrochloride. The Food and Nutrition Board of the National Academy of Sciences-National Research Council has suggested a Recommended Dietary Allowance (RDA) of 0.5 milligram of vitamin B_1 per 1000 calories of food intake (up to 1.5 milligrams for an adult male), but not less than 1 milligram for anyone consuming less than 2000 calories. A survey in 1971-74 determined that the mean intake in the U.S. was 0.64 milligram per 1000 calories, and that all population groups, according to age, sex, race, and income, exceeded the RDA.

Extreme deficiency of thiamin leads to the severe nerve and muscular disease beriberi. No comparable clinical condition in humans is associated with an excess of the vitamin, since it is readily excreted, and oral doses of several grams daily would be required for toxic symptoms to develop. There are infrequent cases of allergy to thiamin due to exposure during pharmaceutical handling and packaging of the vitamin, or to its use as a drug.

Thiamin hydrochloride or thiamin mononitrate fed to rats or mice at levels near 1000 times normal human intake (adjusted for body weight differences) over several generations failed to affect fertility, lactation, growth, or reproductive performance. Conflicting findings have been reported on the effect of thiamin on cancer development induced by chemical carcinogens; in some cases it retarded growth, in others accelerated it, and in another had no discernible effect. It did not cause malformations of the fetus in experiments with mice and rats, and had no adverse effects on chromosomes or genes in laboratory tests.

ASSESSMENT: Vitamin B_1 is essential for good nutrition, and is added to foods to assure an adequate intake. It is free of adverse effects at levels hundreds of times normal intake. This vitamin used as a food additive poses no health hazard to consumers even at levels that might be expected in future use.

RATING: S.

VITAMIN B_2

Riboflavin; Riboflavin-5′-Phosphate; Sodium Riboflavin Phosphate (Disodium Riboflavin Phosphate)

Riboflavin (vitamin B_2) is found in minute amounts in practically all animal and plant tissues and cells. Its phosphate ester, *riboflavin-5′-phosphate,* is more soluble in water, and is the form in which the vitamin is found in nature and stored in the body. Vitamin B_2 is a component of a group of important enzymes (catalysts) that enable utilization of oxygen in cell respiration and in the metabolism of foods into usable forms. An adequate supply is necessary for healthy skin and hair and good vision. Milk, liver and other organ meats, leafy vegetables, eggs, and yeast are the best sources, but little of the vitamin is present in many foods, and supplementation may be desirable by means of the synthetic riboflavin phosphate and its sodium salt *(sodium riboflavin phosphate),* produced for commercial use as a nutrient. It is added for this reason to such products as macaroni, noodles, bread, and beverages. The vitamin may be lost when exposed to light, or when cooking water is discarded. As riboflavin is yellow to orange-yellow in color, it may be used as a food coloring as well as an enrichment or fortification.

SAFETY: The daily intake of vitamin B_2 added to foods in 1975 has been estimated at a little over 1 milligram per person, almost wholly in the form of riboflavin. Possibly four times as much is consumed in vitamin preparations. The Recommended Dietary Allowance suggested by the National Academy of Sciences-National Research Council is 0.6 milligram per 1000 calories, or up to 1.7 milligrams for young adult men; women need additional intakes during pregnancy and lactation. A survey that attempted to assess the nutritional status of the U.S. population found that this amount was

---

MAJOR REFERENCE: Evaluation of the health aspects of riboflavin and riboflavin-5′-phosphate as food ingredients. FASEB/SCOGS Report 114 (NTIS PB 301-406) 1979.

exceeded in the diet of every age, sex, race, and income group; the average was 0.96 milligram per 1000 calories or, translated to individuals, a daily intake of almost 2 milligrams of vitamin B_2 from all food sources, including fortified foods.

A deficiency of vitamin B_2 leads to metabolic impairments and clinical changes, including a type of skin eczema and inflammation, defects in the cornea of the eye, and subnormal growth. Large doses of riboflavin can be tolerated by the body. Even 10 grams per kilogram of body weight taken orally produced no toxic effects in rats. Humans have been given riboflavin in doses of 4 grams daily for various medical conditions, again with no adverse effects.

Studies with rats followed over several generations indicate that riboflavin in substantial amounts has no adverse effect on fertility or reproductive performance. On the other hand, a deficiency is known to cause severe malformation of offspring. The influence of this vitamin on experimentally induced cancer in mice and rats appears uncertain: a deficiency of riboflavin in the diet in two instances retarded cancerous growth, in another it accelerated it. In one case of deficiency where the growth had been retarded, supplementation reversed the effect. This variability may be related to the chemical that initially caused the cancer. Riboflavin does not alter genes.

ASSESSMENT: Vitamin B_2 (riboflavin) is essential in the human diet. It is relatively nontoxic, and doses thousands of times normal intake have proved harmless to humans and experimental animals. No health hazard is indicated from the addition of this vitamin to foods at current levels or any that might be expected in the future.

RATING: S.

VITAMIN B_6

Pyridoxine; Pyridoxine Hydrochloride

Pyridoxine and two derivatives, pyridoxal and pyridoxamine, are collectively called vitamin B_6, which is essential to humans and must be obtained from the diet. It is present naturally in foods mostly as pyridoxal, and less so as pyridoxamine. Good

---

MAJOR REFERENCE: Evaluation of the health aspects of pyridoxine (vitamin B_6) and pyridoxine hydrochloride as food ingredients. FASEB/SCOGS Report 100 (NTIS PB 275-340) 1977.

sources for it include eggs, yeast, liver, kidney, meats, poultry, fish, whole grains, and legumes. When vitamin B_6 is added to food, it is in the form of a synthetic compound, *pyridoxine hydrochloride*. Vitamin B_6 plays a vital role as a coenzyme in combination with more than 60 enzymes (see p. 527) in the metabolic processes that break down ingested food into usable forms in the body, and it is particularly important in the metabolism of amino acids and proteins. It is needed in the formation of hemoglobin in the red blood cells. Pyridoxine hydrochloride is added as a nutrient or diet supplement in prepared baby foods, breakfast cereals, baked goods and mixes, milk and milk products, and dairy product analogs.

SAFETY: The Recommended Dietary Allowance (RDA) for vitamin B_6 suggested by the Food and Nutrition Board of the National Academy of Sciences-National Research Council is 2.0 to 2.2 milligrams per day for normal adults, and 2.5 to 2.6 milligrams during pregnancy or lactation; higher amounts are not considered necessary for women taking contraceptives. Intakes recommended for infants and adolescents range up to 2 milligrams daily. The estimated daily intake of vitamin B_6 as a food additive in 1975, based on usage reported by the food industry, was 0.6 milligram per person, about a fourth of the RDA. A U.S. Department of Agriculture survey conducted in 1977-78 estimated that the total dietary intake of vitamin B_6 for females was only 60 to 65 percent of the RDA; the mean dietary intake for men older than 65 years was 78 percent of the RDA.

Humans have ingested as much as 100 milligrams of pyridoxine hydrochloride, equivalent to some 170 times the estimated daily intake as a food additive, without adverse effects. Patients suffering from inherited disorders known to require greater amounts of vitamin B_6 have been given large doses (100 to 1500 milligrams daily) for periods of up to three or four years; these intakes did not cause harmful reactions.

Repeated intramuscular administration of a large amount of pyridoxine hydrochloride to a pregnant woman resulted in a pyridoxine dependency in the infant, manifested by convulsions and the death of the infant. Other cases have not been reported, but studies have been conducted with pregnant rats to determine the effect on the newborn of large doses during pregnancy. None of these have produced such an effect, nor did pyridoxine or pyridoxine hydrochloride affect infant growth or development, or reproductive performance by mothers. In one experiment the dosage employed was the equivalent of over 3000 times human intake of added pyridoxine (adjusted for body weight).

Laboratory tests of this vitamin indicate that it does not cause birth abnormalities. Studies to determine whether it has cancer-producing properties have not been conducted.

ASSESSMENT: Pyridoxine is an essential vitamin and is naturally present in a wide variety of foods. With a recommended dietary intake of 2 milligrams per day for adults, the daily average intake of pyridoxine hydrochloride resulting from its addition to foods may amount to no more than 10 percent of total intake, which frequently is less than desired. The evidence indicates that vitamin B_6 (pyridoxine or pyridoxine hydrochloride) poses no hazard to the public when used as a food additive at levels now current or that might reasonably be expected in the future.

RATING: S.

VITAMIN B_{12}

Cobalamin; Cyanocobalamin

Vitamin B_{12}, which is found in organ meats (liver, brain, kidney), as well as in oysters, clams, and egg yolk in relatively substantial amounts, is the active factor that is clinically effective in the treatment of pernicious anemia. All forms contain the trace mineral cobalt. The form in which it is usually present in these natural sources (all are animal products), *cobalamin,* has an unstable linkage with the cobalt; when vitamin B_{12} is added to processed foods, another more stable form, *cyanocobalamin,* in which cyanide is linked with the cobalt, is produced from the fermentation of microorganisms. Cobalamin is the vitamin minus the cyanide group. Vitamin B_{12} is added to a limited number of food products as a nutrient or dietary supplement. Among them are breakfast cereals, baby-food baked products and prepared formulas, rice and pasta dishes, milk products, and some snack foods.

MAJOR REFERENCE: Evaluation of the health aspects of vitamin B_{12} as a food ingredient. FASEB/SCOGS Report 104 (NTIS PB 289-922) 1978.

SAFETY: Based on use of vitamin B_{12} for fortification by food processors, the daily intake per person in 1975 was estimated as 39 micrograms (millionths of a gram). Vitamin B_{12} is essential in the physiologic effectiveness of folic acid (see p. 532) and in cell functioning, especially in the metabolic conversions related to nerve tissue, bone marrow, and red-blood-cell formation. It should be noted that this vitamin is one of the most biologically active known; the Food and Nutrition Board of the National Academy of Sciences-National Research Council recommends only 3 micrograms as being needed in the daily diet to meet all needs of the normal, healthy adult to prevent the anemia caused by a vitamin B_{12} deficiency.

Vitamin B_{12} in huge doses, as much as 100 milligrams, has been taken orally by patients with pernicious anemia, without harmful effects. There are no reports of any sensitivity to taking vitamin B_{12} orally, although allergy may arise from injections. Large doses of the vitamin fed to female rats did not affect reproduction and had no ill effects on the offspring, nor did they cause any abnormalities. Various studies have reported that developing cancers arising from other causes may be enhanced by the vitamin, but no studies have been conducted to determine whether the vitamin can itself cause cancer or alter genes.

ASSESSMENT: Vitamin B_{12} is essential in the metabolic processes of the body related to cell functioning; an insufficiency in the diet or failure to absorb it can result in pernicious anemia. Very large doses administered to humans have proved to be free of hazard. Thus the addition of vitamin B_{12} to foods is considered safe at present levels, or even at higher levels in the future.

RATING: S.

VITAMIN D (CALCIFEROL)

Vitamin D_2 (Ergocalciferol); Vitamin D_3 (Cholecalciferol)

Vitamin D is needed for calcium absorption and normal bone growth; its absence will lead to rickets. It occurs naturally in some foods, such as liver, eggs, and fish oils (like codfish oil). However, the limited food sources have led to fortification of a few products, particularly those used by growing children; they include milk, infant formulas, margarines, and cereals.

Two forms of vitamin D are used as additives in fortifying foods. *Vitamin D_2 (ergocalciferol)* is produced by ultraviolet irradiation of a compound of very similar chemical structure obtained from yeast. *Vitamin D_3 (cholecalciferol)* is the form of the vitamin produced through activation of the compound 7-dehydrocholesterol by sunlight, which normally occurs in humans through skin exposed to sun.

SAFETY: The quantity of vitamin D is reported as International Units (IU).* The recommended intake per day is 400 IU for children, adolescents, and pregnant and lactating women (since these individuals are not likely to meet their vitamin D needs through exposure to sunlight). Dietary requirement for normal healthy adults is less as some vitamin D is supplied by sunlight radiation. Estimates have been made on vitamin D intake from supplements and foods. They indicate that a baby may be receiving 800 IU daily from food and vitamin supplements and, in total, not more than 1600 IU (160 to 300 IU per kilogram of body weight, kg/bw). An eight-year-old's intake may be 800 IU from food together with supplements and up to 2900 IU in total (30 to 100 IU per kg/bw). The data on which the estimates are based are questionable and need improvement.

For its use in calcium metabolism, vitamin D must first be transformed by the liver and the kidneys into potent hormonelike regulatory products. Sometimes kidney failure may prevent this and thus lead to bone diseases.

While too little vitamin D can cause rickets or other disturbances in calcium metabolism, there is a real danger from

---

MAJOR REFERENCE: Evaluation of the health aspects of vitamin D, vitamin D_2 and vitamin D_3 as food ingredients. FASEB/SCOGS Report 95 (NTIS PB 293-099) 1978.

*An IU is 1/40 of a microgram, which is a millionth of a gram.

prolonged and excessive intake of this vitamin. Reduced kidney function along with calcium deposits in soft tissues is frequently seen. Behavioral disturbances may result from vitamin D intakes of even 1000 to 3000 IU per kg/bw if this is continued for very long periods of time. There are some suggestions that prolonged intake of more than 1250 IU daily per person may lead to greater risk of heart disease.

Vitamin D fed to pregnant rats and rabbits in dosages some thousands of times as great as likely human consumption may have provided a clue to the role an overdose of this substance may play in infantile hypercalcemia, a disorder which in mild form can slightly retard growth, but which when severe will prevent a baby from thriving, impair kidney function, and possibly cause mental retardation. The findings from these animal experiments indicate that large doses of vitamin D taken during pregnancy pass through the placenta barrier to the fetus, with effects on offspring that are comparable with infantile hypercalcemia. An accompanying symptom of this ailment in humans is a serious vascular disorder affecting the aorta (the main artery), and this too appeared in infant rabbits.

Anticonvulsant drugs taken regularly can inhibit the benefits of vitamin D, producing effects similar to vitamin D deficiency. Children can develop rickets; adults may experience below-normal blood calcium levels or bone softening.

The evidence indicates that large amounts of vitamin D have not caused cancer in experimental animals. Research relating to its effects on chromosome or gene alteration appears not to have been conducted.

ASSESSMENT: Vitamin D is an essential nutrient; its use in fortified foods has largely eliminated rickets in the U.S. The few foods with added vitamin D will assure that the daily requirement is met, and current levels of fortification make it unlikely that excessive intakes that can be harmful will come from the diet. However, many vitamin supplements and fish liver oils contain this vitamin, and undesirably high intakes can occur if these substances are used indiscriminately. Since the margin of safety is small between recommended intakes and toxic effects associated with higher intake levels, caution is advised on use of supplements containing this vitamin. Anyone taking anticonvulsant drugs should be alert to the possibility of an interaction between some of these and vitamin D, which can cause a vitamin deficiency.

Present food fortification practices will not pose any hazard to the consumer from dietary sources.

RATING: S.

VITAMIN K

Menadione (Vitamin K_3); Menaquinone (Vitamin K_2); Phylloquinone (Vitamin K_1, Phytonadione)

Vitamin K consists of a group of substances that are needed in the blood-clotting systems of higher animals. Three types are relevant to the dietary needs of humans: *vitamin* K_1 is a natural component of green plants, such as carrot tops and leafy vegetables (spinach, kale, broccoli, cabbage); *vitamin* K_2 is produced by various bacteria, including those in the intestine, and is present in beef liver and various tissues of chickens, rats, and other animals; and *vitamin* K_3, a simpler form which is produced synthetically, can be made into water-soluble forms which offer the advantage of being absorbable in the intestine without using bile, which vitamins K_1 and K_2 require. Vitamin K's function as a food additive at present is as a nutritional supplement in prepared foods for small infants. It is used medicinally for a number of illnesses related to blood conditions and side effects caused in their treatment.

SAFETY: The Food and Nutrition Board of the National Academy of Sciences-National Research Council in its 1980 revision of Recommended Dietary Allowances included an "estimated safe and adequate daily dietary intake" for vitamin K. For infants up to six months of age, it is 12 micrograms (millionths of a gram), gradually rising with age to an intake of 70 to 140 micrograms for adults.

Estimates of the average daily intake of vitamin K from natural sources are 300 to 500 micrograms. Vitamin K deficiency is rarely found. However, supplementation may be required for the newborn infant who often has low levels and no appreciable stores of blood-clotting factors, for which this vitamin is needed. Until the intestinal bacteria to synthesize it in the body are established, an infant may not be able to

---

MAJOR REFERENCE: The vitamins, volume 3. R. S. Harris and W. H. Sebrell, Jr., eds. (New York: Academic Press, 1971).

produce the prothrombin and other coagulation factors needed to prevent hemorrhage (abnormal bleeding).

In the form of menadione, vitamin K given to premature infants and pregnant women can easily rise to excessive levels, causing a toxicity characterized by anemia, flushing, and sweating. Phylloquinone does not have this undesirable property, and is the preferred form of vitamin K, unless there is evidence of malabsorption. There are studies showing that 2 milligrams of vitamin K_1 may be adequate and safe given orally to newborn infants, and may be adequate to prevent hemorrhagic disease in the newborn.

In people taking antibiotic drugs, bacterial growth in the digestive tract may be suppressed to the point where more vitamin K may be needed. Similarly, where there is liver disease or poor absorption because of inadequate bile secretion, a deficiency may occur even on an adequate diet.

Patients may take anticoagulant drugs to prevent blood clots that can cause heart attacks. Many of the anticoagulants are vitamin K antagonists, and vitamin K_1 may be used to maintain a balance against too little capacity of the blood to coagulate because of an excess of the anticoagulant drug. Doses of as much as 72 milligrams of menadione have been given intravenously following overdosages of oral anticoagulants; but far smaller dosages are usual, even in emergency cases, and vitamin K_1 is the form used.

ASSESSMENT: Usual dietary habits, supplemented by bacterial synthesis in the intestinal tract, assure an adequate intake of vitamin K for nearly everyone. Newborn infants, those with poor absorption or inadequate bile secretions, and people receiving antibiotics or anticoagulants may be exceptions. Vitamin K as a food additive is aimed at the needs of infants, and there is no reason to believe that it will be a hazard to these consumers from its presently limited use as a nutritional supplement in special foods.

RATING: S.

WHEY

DELACTOSED WHEY; DEMINERALIZED WHEY

When the principal protein of milk, casein, is separated from it (as in the manufacture of cheese), the remaining liquid portion is called *whey*. Some whey is processed to obtain lactose, or milk sugar (see p. 579); it also is a source of the valuable protein lactalbumin (see p. 465), which is rich in animo acids essential for the building, replacement, and repair of tissues. Dried whey solids are nearly three-fourths lactose, contain about 13 percent lactalbumin, and are rich in mineral elements such as potassium, sodium, phosphorus, and calcium.

Whey solids are used in more than 100 processed foods, which include ice cream, baked goods, confections, imitation dairy products, milk products such as eggnog, and breakfast cereals. Whey solids can serve as a binder in sausage products and meat loaves. Sometimes the whey may be treated to remove either the mineral salts *(demineralized whey)* or the lactose sugar *(delactosed whey)*.

SAFETY: A survey of food processors in 1977 indicated that the average daily diet included 2.2 grams of whey per person. Whey, a normal part of milk (an important food in the diet) contributes to the energy requirements as well as providing a very nutritious protein and many essential minerals for the body's needs. The National Academy of Sciences-National Research Council recommends a daily intake of 44 to 56 grams of protein for adults; whey as a food additive will contribute only a few percentage points of this.

The only question about the safety of whey as an additive in the diet relates to its extremely high content of the sugar lactose. Many people have an intolerance or inability to digest this sugar because they do not have the necessary enzymes to break it down and make possible its absorption and use by the body (see p. 579).

ASSESSMENT: Whey is a nutritious food and contributes needed protein and energy for the body. For those who are lactose-intolerant, whey may pose some problems of discomfort and diarrhea if excessive amounts are included in the diet; the average daily intake of whey as an additive would contribute an amount of lactose equivalent to a little over 1 ounce of skim milk. No other hazards are likely from including whey in processed foods.

RATING: S for delactosed whey; S for whey for most individuals; X for those allergic to milk and those with recognized lactose intolerance.

XANTHAN GUM

This additive is a complex carbohydrate-containing gum composed of sugar and sugar-acid units. It is produced from a microorganism by controlled fermentation of dextrose (see p. 518). When dissolved in water it results in a very viscous or gummy solution, even at low concentrations. This property makes it useful in a wide variety of foods as a stabilizer or thickener, as an emulsifier to keep water and oily components from separating, and as a suspending agent. It is used as a food additive in low-calorie products to simulate the viscosity and texture of sugar or oil, and to replace the starch normally used in such foods as puddings and pie fillings.

SAFETY: A survey by the National Academy of Sciences-National Research Council, based on usage reported by food manufacturers in 1976, determined that the daily diet of the average person in the U.S. contained 8 milligrams of xanthan gum, or 0.14 milligram per kilogram of body weight (kg/bw) for an individual weighing 60 kg (132 lbs.).

As is common in vegetable and microbial gums used as food additives, xanthan gum is not digested by the body and is mostly excreted unchanged. A long-term study using both rats and dogs, covering two years of feeding up to 1 gram of xanthan gum per kg/bw, well over 1000 times human consumption, established that this substance is harmless. Compared with the control animals whose diets did not contain this gum, there were no differences in survival, weight gain, organ weight, blood components, blood pressure or heart rate, microscopic tissue structure, or tumor incidence. The rats were studied over three generations, and the high level of the gum in the diet had no effect on parental or offspring survival, repro-

---

MAJOR REFERENCE: Toxicological evaluation of some food colours, enzymes, flavour enhancers, thickening agents, and certain other food additives. WHO Food Additive Series No. 6 (Geneva, 1975).

ductive performance, litter size or condition, or birth weight of the young.

Xanthan gum did not produce sensitization or irritation in tests for possible allergic effect. With rats, a diet containing 15 percent of the gum did not cause diarrhea; with dogs, some diarrhea was seen when the animals received 1 gram per kg/bw daily, and softer stools with 0.5 gram per kg/bw.

ASSESSMENT: Xanthan gum is used as a thickener and suspending agent in foods. This gum is essentially inert and poses no hazard even at very high levels in the diet. Like other gums that hold considerable amounts of water, it may cause diarrhea, but only at high dosages. The UN Joint FAO/WHO Expert Committee on Food Additives considers up to 10 milligrams per kg/bw as a safe and acceptable daily intake for humans, which is 75 times its presence in the U.S. diet.

RATING: S.

XYLITOL

Xylitol is not a true sugar, but rather a carbohydrate alcohol that is used as a synthetic sweetener in place of sucrose (cane or beet sugar; see p. 648) in certain dietary foods and "sugar-free" chewing gums. Although it has the same caloric value as sugar, xylitol is metabolized differently and thus has been used in diets for diabetics. Xylitol occurs naturally in many berries, fruits, and mushrooms. Commercially it is produced from "wood sugar," or xylose, which is abundant in wood and in plants. Finland has been the major producer of xylitol for use as a food additive.

SAFETY: Xylitol is one of the normal products in carbohydrate metabolism; the body itself produces 5 to 15 grams daily as an intermediate to aid in the conversion of carbohydrates into energy and its storage form, glycogen. Xylitol has been useful for diabetics because, although it does not increase blood sugar levels as much as do normal sugars in the diet, it is well metabolized and can be used as a source of energy by humans, even when a few hundred grams are consumed daily. It also has been found useful in reducing dental caries (cavi-

---

MAJOR REFERENCE: Dietary sugars in health and disease. II. Xylitol. FASEB/LSRO Report to FDA (NTIS PB 285-494) 1978.

ties) because the caries-producing bacteria in the mouth do not grow on and ferment xylitol to produce undesirable acids, as they do with sugar.

When xylitol was administered orally to rats in daily amounts of as much as 30 percent of the diet (equivalent to 30 grams per kilogram of body weight, kg/bw) for a period of 12 weeks, it did not adversely affect growth, reproduction, or the function or microscopic structure of major organs. Long-term studies in which three generations of rats were given 100 milligrams of xylitol per kg/bw daily during a period of two years showed that this additive did not adversely affect reproduction or fertility; nor did it cause cancers or pathological changes in any tissue. Preliminary findings are available from long-term animal feeding trials under way in England, in which significantly greater quantities of xylitol were administered than in the preceding study. Male mice fed daily diets for two years, 10 to 20 percent of which consisted of xylitol (approximately 8 to 17 grams per kg/bw), suffered bladder damage associated with abnormal concentration of mineral salts. Female mice, and rats and dogs fed similar diets for extended periods did not experience this effect. However, at the 20 percent level rats (but not dogs) developed adrenal tumors, while dogs at both the 10 and 20 percent levels exhibited an increase in liver weight caused by cell enlargement.

Evidence from animal tests and laboratory microbial studies indicates that xylitol neither causes birth defects nor alters genes.

Because animal experiments have shown that cataracts can be induced by feeding high-xylose diets (xylitol is formed from xylose), a question arises whether xylitol can produce a similar effect. There is no such evidence; in fact, it is unlikely that it can, as absorbed xylitol is removed from the blood as it is metabolized in the liver; and even if it weren't and high levels remained, the cells of the eye are known to be resistant to the diffusion that would be necessary to cause this effect.

Humans have taken xylitol at levels in the diet of up to 220 grams daily—3.7 grams per kg/bw for a person weighing 60 kg (132 lbs.)—in a three-week study of tolerance of this chemical; no significant adverse effects were observed, though loose stools were noted. Male and female volunteers have ingested 53 grams of xylitol per day over a two-year period without harm. In addition, normal children were born to these subjects during the period.

Xylitol has been fed intravenously to people with such

symptoms as kidney failure. In a few instances, where dosage levels were quite high, adverse changes were noted (including some kidney, liver, and brain disturbances). In Australia some deaths occurred in patients receiving this treatment. The most common effect of high doses of xylitol (several grams per kg/bw) is a transient diarrhea. Xylitol is known to be more slowly absorbed than sugars and thus tends to hold water and produce a watery stool. This has been seen in rats, monkeys, and humans.

ASSESSMENT: Xylitol provides calories but does not behave the way most carbohydrates do in raising blood sugar levels. In addition to its use in dietary foods, it has been used in sugar-free gum, which appears to be effective in reducing cavities in the teeth. Until recently, research indicated that xylitol in the diet had no adverse effect other than a possible mild diarrhea. However, the discovery that xylitol has caused tumors and organ injury in some animals administered high dosages in long-term feeding studies has caused concern. There are also the disturbing hazardous effects observed in humans receiving intravenous feeding of high levels of xylitol as an energy source. Xylitol's status as a permissible additive in food is currently under review by the FDA, and manufacturers in the U.S. have voluntarily ceased using it for the present. Until additional research can assure its safety in foods, uncertainties remain regarding whether this food additive may pose a hazard to the consumer.

RATING: ?

YEASTS*

Baker's Yeast; Brewer's Yeast; Dried Yeast; Smoked Yeast; Torula Yeast

Yeast, a type of fungus, is produced or grown by the fermentation of carbohydrates. The yeast used in food may be *baker's yeast* (a strain of *Saccharomyces cerevisiae* used in breadmaking and producing the leavening effect of copious amounts of gaseous carbon dioxide); *brewer's yeast* (a different strain

---

MAJOR REFERENCE: Single Cell Protein, II. S. R. Tannenbaum and D. I. Wang, eds. (Cambridge, Mass.: M.I.T. Press, 1975).

*For autolyzed yeast, a hydrolyzed brewer's yeast, see p. 613.

which produces greater amounts of alcohol in fermenting sugar, but is not effective in leavening), which is obtained as a by-product from the fermentation of beer made from cereal and hops (after removal of the bitter material derived from hops); or *torula yeast* (*Candida* species), which is obtained from cultures grown on molasses, the carbohydrate residues of papermaking from wood pulp, or more recently, petroleum. *Dried yeast* consists of the dry cells of any suitable yeast fungi, usually from brewer's yeast. It is high in protein (45 percent), and is rich in many of the B vitamins. It is also high in nucleic acids, and this has limited use of yeast as a major protein source. *Smoked yeast* is used as a flavoring agent in soups, cheese spreads, crackers, and snack foods; it is prepared by exposing dried yeast to wood smoke.

Yeasts are useful in foods as dough conditioners and leavening agents in baked goods; as a fermenting aid, particularly for alcoholic beverages; in formulating flavors in soup mixes, gravies, and other foods; and in providing nutrients.

SAFETY: In 1975 yeast used in food processing averaged 545 milligrams per person in the daily diet. Dried yeast approximated a tenth of the total. Smoked yeast flavoring had an average daily consumption of 4 milligrams per person in 1978.

In earlier years, yeast was used as a dietary source of vitamins. Today pure vitamins are available at much lower cost, so the use of yeast as a nutrient is primarily for its protein value. A high-lysine baker's yeast has been suggested as a protein supplement to improve the nutritional quality of cereal foods, which tend to be limited in lysin (see p. 475). Yeast also has enhanced the nutritional benefit to humans of several kinds of formulation of vegetable protein mixtures. The usefulness of yeast as a diet supplement has been demonstrated many times during the past decades; at levels up to 10 percent of yeast in the diet, weight gain has increased and the nutritive value of the dietary protein has improved. Many thousands of tons of yeast were used as meat substitutes and to extend meat, and in army rations in Germany, Russia, and Japan during World War II.

In humans, the nucleic acids in yeast are converted to uric acid when metabolized in the body. A large excess of uric acid can cause gout, a painful inflammation of the toes and joints. A safe intake of nucleic acid is about 2 grams per day. Since the daily intake of yeasts in the diet totals less than 0.5 gram, a harmful excess of uric acid from this source is unlikely unless yeast is consumed as a major source of protein in the diet, perhaps 20 grams or more, and this is not the way yeast is used as a food additive.

Clinical studies with human subjects indicate that an intake of 20 grams of yeast may result in nausea and diarrhea. At these high levels of consumption, there can be a sensitization to yeast.

In the 1970s there was interest in growing torula yeast on petroleum rather than using carbohydrate sources. The safety of this practice has been examined primarily because petroleum products may contain small amounts of cancer-inducing chemicals. Yeast grown on petroleum hydrocarbons has been dried and fed to rats to provide 30 percent of the protein; in 90-day studies, there were no significant effects of these yeasts on appearance, behavior, growth, food intake, blood components (including blood uric acid, though rats can metabolize uric acid and degrade it further, in contrast to humans), or on various pathological measures (including microscopic examination of the tissues and organs for precancerous changes) as compared with animals on a casein (see p. 507) diet. Proteins prepared from such yeasts have been fed to rats as the sole source of protein (20 percent of the diet). During the 100-day study there was no effect on deaths of the animals or on their general condition and behavior, but there was some occurrence of calcium deposits in the kidney. The level of feeding in this study would be equivalent to well over a thousand times the average human intake, adjusted for body weight.

A study has been conducted in which mice were given an injection of some 30,000 cancer cells. The mice were then tested for effects of feeding a yeast preparation as a food supplement. The tumor growth over the next four weeks was reduced, apparently because the yeast in the diet antagonized the establishment and early growth of the cancer. Yeasts grown on petroleum fractions have also been tested to see what effect they might have on tumor growth. In one test, rats were treated with a cancer-inducing chemical and fed yeast at a level of 17 to 27 percent of the diet (up to 80 percent of the protein) for seven months. The yeast did not influence growth or food consumption, nor did it affect the cancer development or incidence in the treated rats.

ASSESSMENT: Yeasts are useful nutrient supplements. They have been used for centuries and are indispensable for certain fermentation processes, such as making bread or brewing. No safety problem appears to come from growing yeast on either carbohydrate by-products or on petroleum. The use of yeast as a food additive poses no hazard to the consumer at levels now used or likely to be used in foods in the future. However, smoked yeast has not been adequately tested for safety, and there are reasons for concern about possible health hazards from the wood smoking (see p. 625).

RATING: S for all yeasts except smoked yeast; ? for smoked yeast.

ZINC SALTS

Zinc Acetate; Zinc Carbonate; Zinc Chloride; Zinc Gluconate; Zinc Hydrosulfite; Zinc Oxide; Zinc Stearate; Zinc Sulfate

Zinc is an essential element required in the diet of man; it is present in every cell, and is a component of enzymes, the specialized proteins in cells that act on substances in the body which initiate the chemical changes involved in metabolism. It is believed to be vital also for the transport of vitamin A from the liver, where it is mostly stored. Manifestation of inadequate intake of zinc in humans includes stunted growth and delayed sexual maturation.

In food, zinc is found chiefly in meats and cereals; liver, oysters, and eggs are good sources; vegetables, fruits, and milk less so. A number of zinc salts are permitted in food; 75 percent of the amount used is zinc oxide. The salts are used chiefly as nutritional supplements and are found for the most part in infant foods and ready-to-eat cereals.

SAFETY: Reported use of zinc salts in 1976 as a food additive in the U.S. diet averaged slightly more than 1 milligram per person daily; this represents only a fraction of the total intake because of the zinc content present naturally in foods. It has been estimated that the consumption of zinc in the daily diet of an adult is 5 to 22 milligrams. The Food and Nutrition Board advises a daily allowance of 3 milligrams for infants, 5 for children, 15 for adults, 20 for pregnant women, and 25 during lactation.

A wide margin exists between present human intake levels of zinc salts and levels that can produce adverse effects. Feed-

---

MAJOR REFERENCE: Evaluation of the health aspects of certain zinc salts as food ingredients. FASEB/SCOGS Report 21 (NTIS PB 266-879) 1977.

ing tests with a number of experimental animal species have shown that the salts caused no harm below 100 milligrams per kilogram of body weight, 250 times the maximum estimate of average human consumption adjusted for body weight. A few investigations of zinc sulfate have been conducted with man, without evidence of toxicity at dosages of up to 660 milligrams daily for as long as three months. One human fatality attributed to zinc sulfate has been reported following the accidental consumption of 30 grams (30,000 milligrams).

The most important effect of ingesting excess zinc is the appearance of a type of anemia in which there is a decrease in hemoglobin (the oxygen-carrying pigment in red blood cells), probably caused by interference with the body's utilization of iron and copper. Supplementation of these minerals in the diet can reverse the condition.

Studies performed through several generations of mice employing a variety of zinc salts did not show adverse effects on fertility, fetus health and development, or maternal or fetal enzymatic activities. Nor did oral administration of zinc sulfate, in quantities well in excess of human consumption, to three species of animals cause discernible harm to maternal survival or result in defective offspring.

Experiments with rats fed several zinc salts over three generations failed to produce evidence of cancer. In the early 1960s two studies of mice given zinc chloride in drinking water did report occurrence of cancer. However, control animals (mice exposed to the same conditions except for the zinc chloride) were not employed, nor were other relevant data made available to enable assessment of the validity of the findings. Another study with mice, using zinc sulfate in the same manner, did not show this result. Experienced investigators and laboratories specializing in experimental cancer have concluded, after reviewing the scientific literature, that zinc salts taken orally are not a cancer hazard.

ASSESSMENT: Zinc is an essential component for human life which plays a vital role in the body's metabolic processes. The Food and Nutrition Board of the National Academy of Sciences-National Research Council has suggested the fortification of cereal grain products at a level of 10 milligrams of zinc per pound, to help assure the adequacy of this mineral in the diet. A review of the evidence indicates that taken orally, zinc salts are not a cause of cancer.

RATING: S.

ADDITIVES INDEX

IDENTIFYING LEGEND FOR ADDITIVES-OF-CONCERN

**	Additives-of-concern to everyone
*	Additives-of-concern to some people only, and further defined for easy reference in the following manner:
***A**	Anyone hyperallergic
***A (c)**	Anyone allergic to corn, wheat, sugar beets
***A (e)**	Anyone allergic to eggs
***A (g)**	Anyone sensitive to gluten
***A (l)**	Anyone intolerant of lactose
***A (m)**	Anyone allergic to milk
***C (h)**	Children, especially hyperactive ones
***C (y)**	Young children
***CV**	Anyone with a cardiovascular ailment
***E**	Anyone with an eye ailment
***GI**	Anyone with a gastrointestinal ailment
***H**	Anyone with high blood pressure (hypertension)
***I**	Infants
***N**	Nursing mothers
***P**	Pregnant women
***W**	Anyone on a weight-reducing diet

APPENDIX 1

GENERAL TERMS IN LISTS OF INGREDIENTS WHICH MAY OR MAY NOT INCLUDE ADDITIVES-OF-CONCERN

These general terms will be found in the additives-of-concern column alongside an item in the Inventory of Brands when they appear in the list of ingredients on its label. It is not possible to determine whether these contain additives regarded in this volume as warranting a caution.

There are 13 of these general terms contained in the accompanying table. In each case, listed below it, are the ingredients they can be referring to, divided into those of concern and those that are not. All are reviewed elsewhere in this book.

ADDITIVES-OF-CONCERN	NOT ADDITIVES-OF-CONCERN
ANIMAL FATS	
Beef fat (tallow); butter (butter fat); lard (pork fat); mutton (fat); stearic acid; calcium stearate	Marine (fish) oil; poultry fat and skin
CELLULOSE DERIVATIVES	
Hydroxypropyl cellulose; methyl ethyl cellulose	Cellulose derivatives *other than* hydroxypropyl cellulose: methyl ethyl cellulose.
COLORING, FOOD COLORS	
Artificial color; certified color; FD&C colors; cochineal and carmine; paprika, turmeric, and their oleoresins; saffron	Natural color *other than* cochineal and carmine, paprika, turmeric, and their oleoresins; saffron.

NATURAL COLORS, VEGETABLE COLORS	
Cochineal and carmine; paprika, turmeric, and their oleoresins; saffron	Natural color *other than* cochineal and carmine; paprika, turmeric and their oleoresins; saffron
SEAWEED	
Alginates; carrageenan and furcelleran; dulse and kelp	Agar-agar
SHORTENING, VEGETABLE OILS	
Coconut oil; hydrogenated vegetable oils; palm kernel oil; rapeseed oil	Non- and partially hydrogenated vegetable oils *other than* coconut, palm kernel, and rapeseed oils
SOFTENERS, STABILIZERS, THICKENERS, VEGETABLE GUMS	
Alginates; carrageenan and furcelleran; dulse and kelp; glycerol esters of wood rosin; gum arabic; gum tragacanth; guar gum; hydroxypropyl cellulose; locust bean gum; methyl ethyl cellulose; modified starch	Agar-agar; cellulose derivatives *other than* hydroxypropyl cellulose, methyl ethyl cellulose; unmodified or gelatinized starch; xanthan gum

SUBSTANCES DERIVED FROM MILK* AND FLOUR THAT MAY CONTAIN INGREDIENTS REGARDED AS ADDITIVES-OF-CONCERN

A number of substances prepared from milk may contain ingredients which, if specified as such on a food label, would be viewed here as additives-of-concern.

	Ingredients of Concern
Buttermilk Solids Milk Derivatives Milk Protein Milk Solids Sour Milk Solids Sour Cream Solids	All may contain casein, lactalbumin, or whey.

A similar caution applies to High Protein Flour, which may contain added albumin, casein, or gluten.

These products prepared from milk and flour, when they appear on a food item's ingredients list, have been placed alongside the item in the additives-of-concern column. The ingredients of concern listed above are reviewed elsewhere in this volume.

*Milk itself is considered a food, not an additive. It is not included as an additive-of-concern in this book, although some people may have a milk intolerance.

APPENDIX 2

A COMPARISON IN RATINGS OF SAFETY OF FOOD ADDITIVES BETWEEN SCOGS AND THE FOOD ADDITIVES BOOK

For those food additives which were separately rated by both the Select Committee on GRAS Substances (SCOGS) and the authors, the data used were identical. They were contained in the reports issued by SCOGS.

The SCOGS final rating of additives had to conform to the requirements of the 1958 Food Additives Amendment of the Food, Drug, and Cosmetic Act. This stipulated that "credible evidence of, or reasonable grounds to suspect, adverse biological effects had to be present in whatever information was available before the pronouncement of a potential health hazard was to be advanced."* Upon completion of the initial information base to a given GRAS substance or a group of related substances, and later when tentative conclusions had been made, these were made available to the public by announcements in the *Federal Register*, and public hearings were scheduled for anyone desiring an opportunity to provide information or to express an opinion.† The effect, of these requirements and procedures on the SCOGS' final judgments imposed the same standards as would be required of the FDA if it were to challenge the safety of a GRAS substance as an ingredient in food.

The Food Additives Book (TFAB), which is directed to the food consumer, often found it more suitable for this purpose to base its judgments on information supplied in the SCOGS reports even when the data did not fully satisfy the standards of evidence demanded by federal legislation to support an action to ban a substance.

Because the information that was available often was far less complete than normally would be desirable, the Select Committee found it necessary to establish five ratings, two for degrees of safety, two for hazard, and one when data were insufficient or totally absent:

---

*Evaluation of health aspects of GRAS food ingredients. *Federation Proceedings,* volume 36, p. 2534 (1977)

†Ibid, p. 2531.

I There is no evidence at hand to suspect a hazard to the public when used at current levels, or levels that might reasonably be expected in the future.

II Identical with "I" except that evidence of safety was not sufficient in the event of a significant increase in current usage.

III Uncertainties exist about safety that require additional studies for their resolution.

IV Evidence of adverse effects exists.

V Data at hand are insufficient to evaluate safety.

By contrast, *TFAB*'s rating system made provision for three categories of safety:

S Safe for everyone.

? Uncertain about safety.

X Unsafe for everyone.

It also employed combinations of these ratings, such as S for some people, ? and/or X for others (who would be identified).

These disparities in categories of safety, as a consequence, make for difficulty in comparing the degree of correspondence between SCOGS and *TFAB* in their judgments of safety of additives. Despite this, a comparison has been attempted by means of combining some of the ratings in order to achieve greater comparability.

SCOGS Rating Categories		*TFAB*'s *Rating Categories*
I	equivalent to	S
II	equivalent to	All combinations that include S, S/?, S/X, S/?/X
III & IV	equivalent to	?, X, ?/X

V has been omitted as safety ratings were not possible for these additives because of insufficient information.

In these rating categories, SCOGS I and *TFAB* S are essentially identical; additives allocated to these groups have been judged to be safe as ingredients in food without qualification. In the ratings suggesting hazard, SCOGS III and IV are regarded here as similar to *TFAB*'s ? and X and ?/X combinations.

The relationship of SCOGS II and the various combinations of *TFAB*'s ratings that include S is not as clear cut. What is similar is that SCOGS II rating expresses less certainty of the safety of these additives than those in its I category; and the same is true of *TFAB*'s S combinations compared with its unqualified S ratings. The S combinations caution some consumers of the possibility of a hazard.

The table which follows contains a comparison of 279 additives rated for safety by both SCOGS* and *TFAB*, based on the joined categories outlined above.

TFAB Categories	*SCOGS Categories*			
	I	II	III & IV	Total
S	195	32	0	227
S/?, S/X, S/?/X	3	16	2	21
?, ?/X, X	6	8	17	31
Total	204	56	19	279

Given the different requirements and objectives of SCOGS and *TFAB*, it is not surprising that differences exist in their ratings of the same additives, although it should be noted that there is considerable correspondence, as the table below reveals. Also of interest is that when SCOGS and *TFAB* are in disagreement, SCOGS arrives at a more severe rating in twice the number of instances as *TFAB*.

Extent of Correspondence
and
Direction of Severity of Rating
in Instances of Disagreement

	TFAB less severe	*TFAB* & SCOGS in Correspondence	*TFAB* more severe
S	32	195	0
S Combinations	2	16	3
?, X, ?/X	0	17	14
Total	34	228	17

*SCOGS ratings were obtained from Final Report FDA 223-75-2004. *Evaluation of GRAS Monographs,* FASEB Life Sciences Research Office, April 30, 1980.

FOODS INDEX

Metals

Metalloids

Nonmetals

10 8B	11 1B	12 2B	13 3A	14 4A	15 5A	16 6A	17 7A	18 8A
								2 **He** 4.00 helium
			5 **B** 10.81 boron	6 **C** 12.01 carbon	7 **N** 14.01 nitrogen	8 **O** 16.00 oxygen	9 **F** 19.00 fluorine	10 **Ne** 20.18 neon
			13 **Al** 26.98 aluminum	14 **Si** 28.09 silicon	15 **P** 30.97 phosphorus	16 **S** 32.07 sulfur	17 **Cl** 35.45 chlorine	18 **Ar** 39.95 argon
28 **Ni** 58.69 nickel	29 **Cu** 63.55 copper	30 **Zn** 65.39 zinc	31 **Ga** 69:72 gallium	32 **Ge** 72.61 germanium	33 **As** 74.92 arsenic	34 **Se** 78.96 selenium	35 **Br** 79.90 bromine	36 **Kr** 83.80 krypton
46 **Pd** 106.42 palladium	47 **Ag** 107.87 silver	48 **Cd** 112.41 cadmium	49 **In** 114.82 indium	50 **Sn** 118.71 tin	51 **Sb** 121.75 antimony	52 **Te** 127.60 tellurium	53 **I** 126.90 iodine	54 **Xe** 131.29 xenon
78 **Pt** 195.08 platinum	79 **Au** 196.97 gold	80 **Hg** 200.59 mercury	81 **Tl** 204.38 thallium	82 **Pb** 207.2 lead	83 **Bi** 208.98 bismuth	84 **Po** (209) polonium	85 **At** (210) astatine	86 **Rn** (222) radon
110 **Ds** (281) darmstadtium	111 **Rg** (280) roentgenium	112 **Cn** (285)	113 — (284)	114 — (289)	115 — (288)	116 — (292)	117 ** (292)	118 — (294)

64 **Gd** 157.25 gadolinium	65 **Tb** 158.93 terbium	66 **Dy** 162.50 dysprosium	67 **Ho** 164.93 holmium	68 **Er** 167.26 erbium	69 **Tm** 168.93 thulium	70 **Yb** 173.04 ytterbium	71 **Lu** 174.97 lutetium
96 **Cm** (247) curium	97 **Bk** (247) berkelium	98 **Cf** (251) californium	99 **Es** (252) einsteinium	100 **Fm** (257) fermium	101 **Md** (258) mendelevium	102 **No** (259) nobelium	103 **Lr** (260) lawrencium

**Discovered in 2010, element 117 is currently under review by IUPAC.

PEARSON ALWAYS LEARNING

Nivaldo J. Tro

Introductory Chemistry

Custom Edition for Foothill College

Taken from:
Introductory Chemistry, Fourth Edition
by Nivaldo J. Tro

Cover Art: Courtesy of Photodisc/Getty Images.

Taken from:

Introductory Chemistry, Fourth Edition
by Nivaldo J. Tro

Published by Prentice Hall
Upper Saddle River, New Jersey 07458

This special edition published in cooperation with Pearson Learning Solutions.

Pearson Learning Solutions, 501 Boylston Street, Suite 900, Boston, MA 02116
A Pearson Education Company
www.pearsoned.com

Printed in the United States of America

1 2 3 4 5 6 7 8 9 10 V0ZN 16 15 14 13 12 11

000200010270769235

AD

ISBN 10: 1-256-34287-4
ISBN 13: 978-1-256-34287-8

To Annie

ABOUT THE AUTHOR

Niva Tro, *chairman of the Chemistry Department at Westmont College in Santa Barbara, California, has been a faculty member at the college since 1990. He received his B.A. degree in chemistry from Westmont College in 1985 and earned a Ph.D. from Stanford University in 1989, after which he performed postdoctoral research at the University of California at Berkeley. Honored as Westmont's outstanding teacher of the year in 1994, 2001, and 2008, he was also named the college's outstanding researcher of the year in 1996.*

Professor Tro lives in Santa Barbara with his wife, Ann, and their four children, Michael, Alicia, Kyle, and Kaden. For leisure, he enjoys reading, writing, snowboarding, biking, and other outdoor activities with his family.

BRIEF CONTENTS

CONTENTS

6 Chemical Composition 165

7 Chemical Reactions 205

8 Quantities in Chemical Reactions 249

11 Gases 359

12 Liquids, Solids, and Intermolecular Forces 411

Problem-Solving Procedures

To the Student

This book is for *you*, and every text feature has you in mind. I have two main goals for you in this course: to see chemistry as you never have before, and to develop the problem-solving skills you need to succeed in chemistry.

I want you to experience chemistry in a new way. Each chapter of this book is written to show you that chemistry is not just something that happens in a laboratory; chemistry surrounds you at every moment. I have worked with several outstanding artists to develop photographs and art that will help you visualize the molecular world. From the opening example to the closing chapter, you will *see* chemistry. I hope that when you finish this course, you think differently about your world because you understand the molecular interactions that underlie everything around you.

I also want you to develop problem-solving skills. No one succeeds in chemistry—or in life, really—without the ability to solve problems. I can't give you a formula for problem solving, but I can give you strategies that will help you develop the *chemical intuition* you need to understand chemical reasoning.

Look for several recurring structures throughout this book designed to help you master problem solving. The most important ones are (1) a four-step process (Sort, Strategize, Solve, and Check) designed to help you learn how to solve problems; (2) the solution map, a visual aid that helps you navigate your way through a problem; (3) the two-column Examples, in which the left column explains in clear and simple language the purpose of each step of the solution shown in the right column; and (4) the three-column Examples, which describe a problem-solving procedure while demonstrating how it is applied to two different Examples. In addition, since students have specifically asked me to provide connections between Examples and end-of-chapter problems, I have added a For More Practice feature at the end of worked Examples that will guide you to the end-of-chapter problems that will provide more opportunity to practice the skill(s) covered in the Example.

Lastly, know that chemistry is *not* reserved only for those with some superhuman intelligence level. With the right amount of effort and some clear guidance, anyone can master chemistry, including you.

Sincerely,

Nivaldo J. Tro
tro@westmont.edu

To the Instructor

I thank all of you who have used any of the first three editions of *Introductory Chemistry*—you have made this book the most widely selling book in its market, and for that I am extremely grateful. The preparation of the fourth edition has enabled me to continue to refine the book to meet its fundamental purpose: teaching chemical skills in the context of relevance.

Introductory Chemistry is designed for a one-semester, college-level, introductory or preparatory chemistry course. Students taking this course need to develop problem-solving skills—but they also must see *why* these skills are important to them and to their world. *Introductory Chemistry* extends chemistry from the laboratory to the student's world. It motivates students to learn chemistry by demonstrating how it plays out in their daily lives.

This is a visual book. Today's students often learn by seeing, so wherever possible, I have used images to help communicate the subject. In developing chemical principles, for example, I worked with several artists to develop multipart images that show the connection between everyday processes visible to the eye and the molecular interactions responsible for those processes. This art has been further refined and improved in the fourth edition, making the visual impact sharper and more targeted to student learning. For example, I have implemented a hierarchical method of labeling in many of the images: the white-boxed labels are the most important, the tan-tint boxes are second most important, and unboxed labels are the third most important. This allows me to treat related labels and annotations within an image in the same way, so that the relationships between them are immediately evident. My goal is to create an art program that teaches, and that presents complex information clearly and concisely. Many of the illustrations showing molecular depictions of a real-world object or process have three parts: macroscopic (what we can see with our eyes); molecular and atomic (space-filling models that depict what the molecules and atoms are doing); and symbolic (how chemists represent the molecular and atomic world). The goal is for the student to begin to see the connections between the macroscopic world, the molecular world, and the representation of the molecular world with symbols and formulas.

In the fourth edition, I have also refined the problem-solving pedagogy to include four steps: Sort, Strategize, Solve, and Check. The *solution map*, which has been part of this book since the beginning, is now part of the *Strategize* step. This four-step procedure is meant to guide students as they learn chemical problem-solving. Extensive flowcharts are also incorporated throughout the book, allowing students to visualize the organization of chemical ideas and concepts. The color scheme used in both the solution maps and the flowcharts is designed to have pedagogical value. More specifically, the solution maps utilize the colors of the visible spectrum—always in the same order, from violet to red.

Throughout the worked Examples in this book, I use a *two- or three-column* layout in which students learn a general procedure for solving problems of a particular type as they see this procedure applied to one or two worked Examples. In this format, the *explanation* of how to solve a problem is placed directly beside the actual steps in the *solution* of the problem. Many of you have said that you use a similar technique in lecture and office hours. Since students have specifically asked for connections between Examples and end-of-chapter problems, I include a For More Practice feature at the end of each worked Example that lists the review examples and end-of-chapter problems that provide more opportunity to practice the skill(s) covered in the Example.

A successful new feature in the second edition was the Conceptual Checkpoints, a series of short questions that students can use to test their mastery of key concepts as they read through a chapter. Emphasizing understanding rather than calculation, they are designed to be easy to answer if the student has grasped the essential concept but difficult if he or she has not. Your positive remarks on this new feature prompted me to continue adding more of these to the fourth edition, including questions that highlight visualization of the molecular world.

PREFACE

New to This Edition

- **A student-friendly, step-by-step problem-solving approach is presented throughout** (fully introduced and explained in Chapter 2): The format for the majority of the worked examples in the book has been changed to involve four steps: Sort, Strategize, Solve, and Check. "Relationships Used" have been identified and new "Check" step content has been added to most worked examples in the book.
- **In all chapters, figure labels now follow a consistent hierarchy**. Three types of labels appear on the art. The most important are in white shadow boxes; the second most important, in tinted boxes (with no border); and the third appear unboxed.
- **Page numbers have been added to chapter-opening outlines** in all chapters.
- **Approximately 25% more Conceptual Checkpoints** have been added throughout the text.
- **All figures and figure captions have been carefully examined, and images and labels have been replaced or revised when needed** to improve the teaching focus of the art program.
- **Every end-of-chapter question has been carefully reviewed** by the author and editor and revised and/or replaced when necessary.
- **Reading quizzes for every chapter in MasteringChemistry®.**

Some significant improvements have been made to key content areas as well. These include:

- Section 2.6: *Problem Solving and Unit Conversion* is a new section that introduces and explains the new general problem-solving method used throughout the worked Examples in this edition. Problems are organized into Sort, Strategize, Solve, and Check steps. The new category of "Relationships Used" is called out in the Strategize step of many of the worked examples. New "Check" material has also been added.
- Section 2.10 has been revised in conjunction with Section 2.6 *Problem Solving and Unit Conversion* and is now titled *Numerical Problem-Solving Overview*.
- Updated or revised chapter-opening art in Chapters 3, 5, 6, 10, and 17.
- Conversion factor for K to Celsius changed from 273° to 273.15° throughout.
- Introduction to Section 3.8 *Energy* revised to more effectively introduce the concept of work, the law of conservation of energy, and the different forms of energy.
- Time-sensitive data, such as the graph regarding global temperature in Figure 8.2, and the data in Figures 14.20 *Acid rain in the United States* and 14.22 *Emissions of* SO_2 *from 1980 to 2009*, have been updated throughout.
- Section 5.3: *Chemical Formulas: How to Represent Compounds* has been revised to include the different ways of representing compounds (molecular formulas, structural formulas, ball-and-stick models, and space-filling models.) A new color key for space-filling models has been added to this section.
- Section 5.7: *Naming Ionic Compounds* has been revised. The terms "Type I" and "Type II" ionic compounds have been eliminated, and the subsections and worked Examples dealing with naming binary ionic compounds have been renamed and revised.

- A new solubility flowchart has been added to Section 7.5: *Aqueous Solutions and Solubility: Compounds Dissolved in Water*.
- Every end-of-chapter question has been carefully reviewed and revised or replaced when necessary.

MasteringChemistry is the most effective and widely used online tutorial, homework and assessment system for chemistry. It helps instructors maximize class time with customizable, easy-to-assign, and automatically graded assessments that motivate students to learn outside of class and arrive prepared for lecture. These assessments can easily be customized and personalized by instructors to suit their individual teaching style. The powerful gradebook provides unique insight into student and class performance even before the first test. As a result, instructors can spend class time where students need it most.

I hope the changes in the fourth edition support you in your mission of teaching students chemistry. Ours is a worthwhile cause, even though it requires constant effort. Please feel free to e-mail me with any questions or comments you might have. I look forward to hearing from you as you use this book in your course.

Sincerely,

Nivaldo J. Tro
tro@westmont.edu

The design and features of this text have been conceived to work together as an integrated whole with a single purpose: to help students understand chemical principles and to master problem-solving skills in a context of relevance. Students must be able not only to grasp chemical concepts and solve chemical problems, but also to understand how those concepts and problem-solving skills are relevant to their other courses, their eventual career paths, and their daily lives.

Teaching Principles

The development of basic chemical principles—such as those of atomic structure, chemical bonding, chemical reactions, and the gas laws—is one of the main goals of this text. Students must acquire a firm grasp of these principles in order to succeed in the general chemistry sequence or the chemistry courses that support the allied health curriculum. To that end, the book integrates qualitative and quantitative material and proceeds from concrete concepts to more abstract ones.

ORGANIZATION OF THE TEXT

The main divergence in topic ordering among instructors teaching introductory and preparatory chemistry courses is the placement of electronic structure and chemical bonding. Should these topics come early, at the point where models for the atom are being discussed? Or should they come later, after the student has been exposed to chemical compounds and chemical reactions? Early placement gives students a theoretical framework within which they can understand compounds and reactions. However, it also presents students with abstract models before they understand why they are necessary. I have chosen a later placement for the following reasons:

1. **A later placement provides greater flexibility.** An instructor who wants to cover atomic theory and bonding earlier can simply cover Chapters 9 and 10 after Chapter 4. However, if atomic theory and bonding were placed earlier, it would be more difficult for the instructor to skip these chapters and come back to them later.
2. **A later placement allows earlier coverage of topics that students can more easily visualize.** Coverage of abstract topics too early in a course can lose some students. Chemical compounds and chemical reactions are more tangible than atomic orbitals, and the relevance of these is easier to demonstrate to the beginning student.
3. **A later placement gives students a reason to learn an abstract theory.** Once students learn about compounds and reactions, they are more easily motivated to learn a theory that explains them in terms of underlying causes.
4. **A later placement follows the scientific method.** In science, we normally make observations, form laws, and then build models or theories that explain our observations and laws. A later placement follows this ordering.

Nonetheless, I know that every course is unique and that each instructor chooses to cover topics in his or her own way. Consequently, I have written each chapter for maximum flexibility in topic ordering. In addition, the book is offered in two formats. The full version, *Introductory Chemistry*, contains 19 chapters, including organic chemistry and biochemistry. The shorter version, *Introductory Chemistry Essentials*, contains 17 chapters and omits these topics.

Print and Media Resources

FOR THE INSTRUCTOR

MasteringChemistry (*http://www.masteringchemistry.com*)
MasteringChemistry is the best adaptive-learning online homework and tutorial system. Instructors can create online assignments for their students by choosing from a wide range of items, including end-of-chapter problems and research-enhanced tutorials. Assignments are automatically graded with up-to-date diagnostic information, helping instructors pinpoint where students struggle either individually or as a class as whole.

Instructor Resource and Full Solutions Manual (0-321-73019-4) Prepared by Mark Ott of Jackson Community College, and Matthew Johll of Illinois Valley Community College. This manual features lecture outlines with presentation suggestions, teaching tips, suggested in-class demonstrations, and topics for classroom discussion. It also contains full solutions to all the end-of-chapter problems from the text.

Printed Testbank (0-321-73009-7) Prepared by Michael Hauser of St. Louis Community College. This printed test bank includes more than 1500 questions. A computerized version of the test item file is available on the Instructor's Resource DVD and can be downloaded from the Instructor Resource Center.

Instructor Resource DVD (0-321-73007-0) This resource provides an integrated collection of resources to help instructors make efficient and effective use of their time. This package features the following:

- All the art from the text, including figures and tables in JPG and PDF formats; movies; animations; Interactive Molecules; and the Instructor's Resource Manual files.
- Four PowerPoint™ presentations: (1) a lecture outline presentation for each chapter, (2) all the art from the text, (3) the worked Examples from the text, and (4) CRS (Classroom Response System) questions.
- The TestGen, a computerized version of the Test Item File that allows you to create and tailor exams to your needs.

FOR THE STUDENT

Pearson eText: The integration of Pearson eText within MasteringChemistry gives students, with new books, easy access to the electronic text when they are logged into MasteringChemistry. Pearson eText pages look exactly like the printed text, offering powerful new functionality for students and instructors. Users can create notes, highlight text in different colors, create bookmarks, zoom, view in single-page or two-page view, etc.

Study Guide (0-321-73010-0) by Donna Friedman, St. Louis Community College—Florissant Valley. Each chapter contains an overview, chapter objectives, a chapter review, as well as practice problems for each major concept in the text. This is followed by two or three self-tests with answers located at the end of each chapter so students can check their work.

Student Solution Manual (0-321-73018-6) by Matthew Johll of Illinois Valley Community College. This book provides solutions only to those problems that have a short answer in the text's Answers section (problems numbered in blue in the text).

Acknowledgments

This book has been a group effort, and there are many people whose help has meant a great deal to me. First and foremost, I would like to thank my editor, Terry Haugen, who came on board during this edition. Terry is a good thinker who knows the needs of both students and professors. Thanks, Terry, for your guidance on and commitment to this revision. As always, I am grateful to Paul Corey, the president of the Science Division at Pearson, for his unwavering support.

New to this edition, but not to working with me, is Erin Mulligan, a development editor whose friendship and guidance I continue to cherish. Thanks, Erin, for all your outstanding help and advice. I cannot thank my project editor Jennifer Hart enough. Jennifer, you are always there to guide me, to keep me on task, and to take care of whatever needs to be done. I am so grateful. I would also like to thank Erin Gardner, my marketing manager whose creativity in describing and promoting the book is without equal. Thanks also to Brian Buckley and the MasteringChemistry team who continue to provide and promote the best online homework system on the planet.

I also appreciate the expertise and professionalism of my copy editor, Betty Pessagno, as well as the skill and diligence of Francesca Monaco and her colleagues at Prepare. I am a picky author, and they always accommodated my seemingly endless requests. Thank you, Francesca. Thanks as well to my project manager Shari Toron, managing editor Gina Cheselka, senior technical art specialist Connie Long, and the rest of the Pearson-Prentice Hall team—they are part of a first-class operation. This text has benefited immeasurably from their talents and hard work. I owe a special debt of gratitude to Quade Paul, who continues to make my ideas come alive in his chapter-opener and cover art.

I am grateful for the support of my colleagues Allan Nishimura, David Marten, Stephen Contakes, Kristi Lazar, Carrie Hill, and Heidi Henes-Vanbergen, who have supported me in my department while I worked on this book. I am particularly grateful to Allan, who started me on this whole chemistry business—he remains an inspiration in my life. I am also grateful to Brittany Hammer, who helped me with manuscript preparation, and to Andrew Schwemmer, Ryan Fields, and Michael Tro who helped to review end-of-chapter problems for accuracy.

I am grateful to those who have given so much to me personally while writing this book. First on that list is my wife, Ann. Her patience and love for me are beyond description. I also thank my children, Michael, Ali, Kyle, and Kaden, whose smiling faces and love of life always inspire me. I come from a large Cuban family, whose closeness and support most people would envy. Thanks to my parents, Nivaldo and Sara; my siblings, Sarita, Mary, and Jorge; my siblings-in-law, Jeff, Nachy, Karen, and John; my nephews and nieces, Germain, Danny, Lisette, Sara, and Kenny. These are the people with whom I celebrate life.

Lastly, I am indebted to the many reviewers, listed next, whose ideas are scattered throughout this book. They have corrected me, inspired me, and sharpened my thinking on how best to teach this subject we call chemistry. I deeply appreciate their commitment to this project.

Reviewers of the 4th Edition

Jeffrey Allison,
Austin Community College

Mikhail V. Barybin,
The University of Kansas

Lara Baxley,
California Polytechnic State University

Kelly Beefus,
Annoka-Ramsey Community College

Joseph Bergman,
Illinois Central College

Simon Bott,
University of Houston

Maria Cecilia D. de Mesa,
Baylor University

Guy Dadson,
Fullerton College

Brian G. Dixon,
Massachusetts Maritime Academy

Timothy Dudley,
Villanova University

Jeannine Eddleton,
Virginia Tech

Ron Erickson,
University of Iowa

Donna Friedman,
St. Louis Community College—Florissant Valley

Luther D. Giddings,
Salt Lake Community College

Marcus Giotto,
Quinsigamond Community College

Melodie Graber,
Oakton Community College

Maru Grant,
Ohlone College

Jerod Gross,
Roanoke Benson High School

Tammy S. Gummersheimer,
Schenectady County Community College

Tamara E. Hanna,
Texas Tech

Michael A. Hauser,
St. Louis Community College

Bruce E. Hodson,
Baylor University

Donald R. Jones,
Lincoln Land Community College

Martha R. Kellner,
Westminster College

Farkhondeh Khalili,
Massachusetts Bay Community College

Margaret Kiminsky,
Monroe Community College

Rebecca Krystyniak,
Saint Cloud State

Chuck Laland,
Black Hawk College

Richard Lavallee,
Santa Monica College

Laurie Leblanc,
Cuyamaca College

Vicki MacMurdo,
Anoka Ramsey Community College

Carmela Magliocchi Brynes,
MiraCosta College

Jack F. McKenna,
St. Cloud State University

Virginia Miller,
Montgomery College

Meg Osterby,
Western Technical College

John Petty,
University of South Alabama

Jason Serin,
Glendale Community College

Youngju Sohn,
Florida Institute of Technology

Clarissa Sorenson-Unruh,
Central New Mexico Community College

Vidyullata C. Waghulde,
St. Louis Community—Meramec

4TH EDITION ACCURACY REVIEWERS

Steven Socol,
McHenry Community College

David Vanderlinden,
Des Moines Area Community College

FOCUS GROUP PARTICIPANTS

Carmela Byrnes,
Miracosta College

Tammy Gummersheimer,
Schenectady County Community College

Tamara Hanna,
Texas Tech University

Nancy Lee,
MiraCosta College

Geoff Mitchell,
Washington International School

Jie Song,
Univeristy of Michigan, Flint

Reviewers of the 3rd Edition

Benjamin Arrowood
Ohio University

Joe Bergman
Illinois Central College

Timothy Dudley
Villanova University

Sharlene J. Dzugan
University of Cumberlands

Thomas Dzugan
University of Cumberlands

Donna G. Friedman
St. Louis Community College

Erick Fuoco
Daley College

Melodie A. Graber
Oakton Community College

Michael A. Hauser
St Louis Community College, Meramec Campus

Martha R. Joseph
Westminster College

Timothy Kreider
University of Medicine & Dentistry of New Jersey

Laurie Leblanc
Grossmont College

Carol A. Martinez
Central New Mexico Community College

Kresimir Rupnik
Louisiana State University

Kathleen Thrush Shaginaw
Particular Solutions, Inc.

Pong (David) Shieh
Wharton College

Mary Sohn
Florida Tech

Kurt Allen Teets
Okaloosa-Walton College

John Thurston
University of Iowa

Anthony P. Toste
Missouri State University

Carrie Woodcock
Eastern Michigan University

Reviewers of the 2nd Edition

David S. Ballantine, Jr.
Northern Illinois University

Colin Bateman
Brevard Community College

Michele Berkey
San Juan College

Steven R. Boone
Central Missouri State University

Morris Bramlett
University of Arkansas—Monticello

Bryan E. Breyfogle
Southwest Missouri State University

Frank Carey
Wharton County Junior College

Robbey C. Culp
Fresno City College

Michelle Driessen
University of Minnesota—Minneapolis

Donna G. Friedman
St. Louis Community College—Florissant Valley

Crystal Gambino
Manatee Community College

Steve Gunther
Albuquerque Technical Vocational Institute

Michael Hauser
St. Louis Community College—Meramec

Newton P. Hillard, Jr.
Eastern New Mexico University

Carl A. Hoeger
University of California—San Diego

Donna K. Howell
Angelo State University

Nichole Jackson
Odessa College

T. G. Jackson
University of South Alabama

Donald R. Jones
Lincoln Land Community College

Kirk Kawagoe
Fresno City College

Roy Kennedy
Massachusetts Bay Community College

Blake Key
Northwestern Michigan College

Rebecca A. Krystyniak
St. Cloud State University

Laurie LeBlanc
Cuyamaca College

Ronald C. Marks
Warner Southern College

Carol A. Martinez
Albuquerque Technical Vocational Institute

Charles Michael McCallum
University of the Pacific

Robin McCann
Shippensburg University

Victor Ryzhov
Northern Illinois University

Theodore Sakano
Rockland Community College

Deborah G. Simon
Santa Fe Community College

Mary Sohn
Florida Institute of Technology

Peter-John Stanskas
San Bernardino Valley College

James G. Tarter
College of Southern Idaho

Ruth M. Topich
Virginia Commonwealth University

Eric L. Trump
Emporia State University

Mary Urban
College of Lake County

Richard Watt
University of New Mexico

Lynne Zeman
Kirkwood Community College

Reviewers of the 1st Edition

Lori Allen
University of Wisconsin—Parkside

Laura Andersson
Big Bend Community College

Danny R. Bedgood
Arizona State University

Christine V. Bilicki
Pasadena City College

Warren Bosch
Elgin Community College

Bryan E. Breyfogle
Southwest Missouri State University

Carl J. Carrano
Southwest Texas State University

Donald C. Davis
College of Lake County

Donna G. Friedman
St. Louis Community College at Florissant Valley

Leslie Wo-Mei Fung
Loyola University of Chicago

Dwayne Gergens
San Diego Mesa College

George Goth
Skyline College

Jan Gryko
Jacksonville State University

Roy Kennedy
Massachusetts Bay Community College

C. Michael McCallum
University of the Pacific

Kathy Mitchell
St. Petersburg Junior College

Bill Nickels
Schoolcraft College

Bob Perkins
Kwantlen University College

Mark Porter
Texas Tech University

Caryn Prudenté
University of Southern Maine

Connie M. Roberts
Henderson State University

Rill Ann Reuter
Winona State University

Jeffery A. Schneider
SUNY—Oswego

Kim D. Summerhays
University of San Francisco

Ronald H. Takata
Honolulu Community College

Calvin D. Tormanen
Central Michigan University

Eric L. Trump
Emporia State University

A GUIDE TO USING THIS TEXT

Drawing from Professor Tro's experience in the classroom with his own students, ***Introductory Chemistry,* Fourth Edition** brings chemistry out of the laboratory and into the world—helping you learn chemistry by showing you how it is manifested in our daily lives. Clear, specific examples are woven throughout this text to tell the story of chemistry. The **Fourth Edition** is also available with MasteringChemistry®, the premier online homework and assessment tool.

NEW! A CONSISTENT STRATEGY FOR SOLVING PROBLEMS

helps you develop the skills you need to succeed in your chemistry course. A new student-friendly, step-by-step problem-solving approach adds four steps to many of the worked examples (Sort, Strategize, Solve, and Check).

Solution Maps

Many of the Examples use a unique visual approach in the Strategize Step, where you'll be shown how to draw a solution map for a problem.

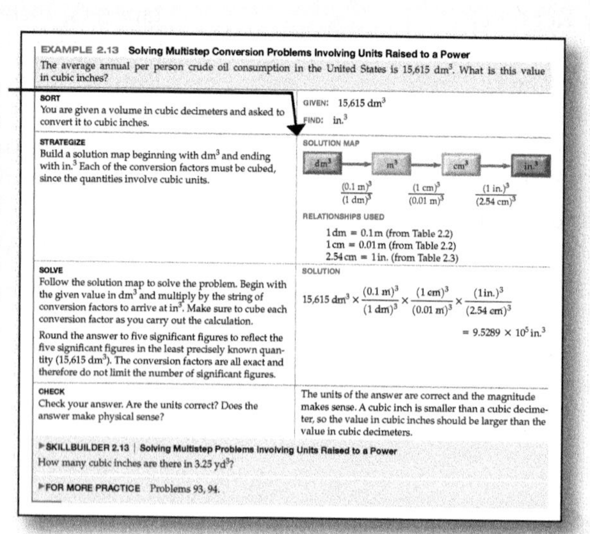

EXAMPLE 2.13 Solving Multistep Conversion Problems Involving Units Raised to a Power

The average annual per person crude oil consumption in the United States is 15,615 dm^3. What is this value in cubic inches?

SORT You are given a volume in cubic decimeters and asked to convert it to cubic inches.	GIVEN: 15,615 dm^3 FIND: $in.^3$
STRATEGIZE Build a solution map beginning with dm^3 and ending with $in.^3$ Each of the conversion factors must be cubed, since the quantities involve cubic units.	SOLUTION MAP $dm^3 \rightarrow m^3 \rightarrow cm^3 \rightarrow in.^3$ $\frac{(0.1\ m)^3}{(1\ dm)^3}$ $\frac{(1\ cm)^3}{(0.01\ m)^3}$ $\frac{(1\ in.)^3}{(2.54\ cm)^3}$ RELATIONSHIPS USED 1 dm = 0.1 m (from Table 2.2) 1 cm = 0.01 m (from Table 2.2) 2.54 cm = 1 in. (from Table 2.3)
SOLVE Follow the solution map to solve the problem. Begin with the given value in dm^3 and multiply by the string of conversion factors to arrive at in^3. Make sure to cube each conversion factor as you carry out the calculation. Round the answer to five significant figures to reflect the five significant figures in the least precisely known quantity (15,615 dm^3). The conversion factors are all exact and therefore do not limit the number of significant figures.	SOLUTION $15{,}615\ dm^3 \times \frac{(0.1\ m)^3}{(1\ dm)^3} \times \frac{(1\ cm)^3}{(0.01\ m)^3} \times \frac{(1 in.)^3}{(2.54\ cm)^3}$ $= 9.5289 \times 10^5\ in.^3$
CHECK Check your answer. Are the units correct? Does the answer make physical sense?	The units of the answer are correct and the magnitude makes sense. A cubic inch is smaller than a cubic decimeter, so the value in cubic inches should be larger than the value in cubic decimeters.

▸**SKILLBUILDER 2.13 | Solving Multistep Problems Involving Units Raised to a Power**

How many cubic inches are there in 3.25 yd^3?

▸**FOR MORE PRACTICE** Problems 93, 94.

Two-Column Examples

All but the simplest examples are presented in a unique two-column format.

- The left column explains the purpose of each step, while the right column shows how the step is executed.
- This format will help you think about the reason for each step in the solution and to fit the steps together.

Writing Formulas for Ionic Compounds	EXAMPLE 5.5 Write a formula for the ionic compound that forms from aluminum and oxygen.	EXAMPLE 5.6 Write a formula for the ionic compound that forms from magnesium and oxygen.
1. Write the symbol for the metal and its charge followed by the symbol of the nonmetal and its charge. For many elements, you can determine these charges from their group number in the periodic table (refer to Figure 4.14).	SOLUTION Al^{3+} O^{2-}	SOLUTION Mg^{2+} O^{2-}
2. Make the magnitude of the charge on each ion (without the sign) become the subscript for the other ion.	Al^{3+} O^{2-} Al_2O_3	Mg^{2+} O^{2-} Mg_2O_2
3. If possible, reduce the subscripts to give a ratio with the smallest whole numbers.	In this case, the numbers cannot be reduced any further; the correct formula is Al_2O_3.	To reduce the subscripts, divide both subscripts by 2. $Mg_2O_2 \div 2 = MgO$
4. Check to make sure that the sum of the charges of the cations exactly cancels the sum of the charges of the anions.	Cations: 2(3+) = 6+ Anions: 3(2−) = 6− The charges cancel.	Cations: 2+ Anions: 2− The charges cancel.
	▸**SKILLBUILDER 5.5** Write a formula for the compound formed from strontium and chlorine.	▸**SKILLBUILDER 5.6** Write a formula for the compound formed from aluminum and nitrogen. ▸**FOR MORE PRACTICE** Example 5.21; Problems 53, 54, 55, 56.

Three-Column Examples

Procedures for solving particular types of problems are presented in a unique three-column format.

- The first column outlines the problem-solving procedure and explains the reasoning that underlies each step.
- The second and third columns show two similar but slightly different examples to solve this problem.
- Seeing the method applied to solve two related problems helps you understand the general procedure in a way that no single example could convey.

Skillbuilder Exercises

Every worked example is followed by at least one similar (but un-worked) Skillbuilder exercise.

For More Practice

These follow every worked example, linking you to in-chapter examples and end-of-chapter problems that give you a chance to practice the skills in each worked example.

CONCEPTUAL UNDERSTANDING completes the picture.

In every chemistry course you take, success requires more than problem-solving skills. Real understanding of concepts will help you see why these skills are important to you and to your world.

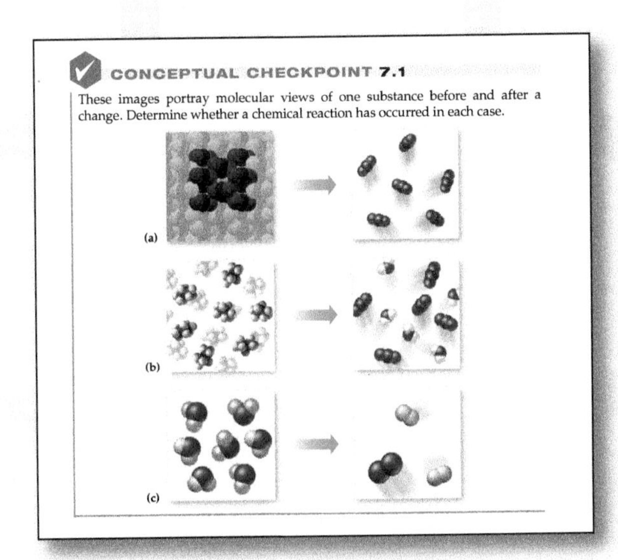

CONCEPTUAL CHECKPOINT 7.1

These images portray molecular views of one substance before and after a change. Determine whether a chemical reaction has occurred in each case.

(a)

(b)

(c)

Conceptual Checkpoints

These conceptual questions enhance understanding of chemical principles, encourage you to stop and think about the ideas just presented, and provide a tool to assess your own progress. Answers and explanations are given at the end of each chapter. There are approximately 25% more Conceptual Checkpoints in the Fourth Edition.

Chapter Review

Consistent review material at the end of each chapter helps reinforce what you've learned.

CHEMICAL PRINCIPLES	RELEVANCE
Formula Mass: The formula mass of a compound is the sum of the atomic masses of all the atoms in the chemical formula for the compound. Like atomic mass for elements, formula mass characterizes the average mass of a molecule or formula unit.	**Formula Mass:** Besides being the characteristic mass of a molecule or formula unit, formula mass is important in many calculations involving the composition of compounds and quantities in chemical reactions.

CHEMICAL SKILLS	EXAMPLES
Constant Composition of Compounds (Section 5.2) The law of constant composition states that all samples of a given compound should have the same ratio of their constituent elements.	**EXAMPLE 5.16 Constant Composition of Compounds** Two samples said to be carbon disulfide (CS_2) are decomposed into their constituent elements. One sample produced 8.08 g S and 1.51 g C, while the other produced 31.3 g S and 3.85 g C. Are these results consistent with the law of constant composition?
To determine whether experimental data are consistent with the law of constant composition, compute the ratios of the masses of each element in all samples. When computing these ratios, it is most convenient to put the larger number in the numerator (top) and the smaller one in the denominator (bottom); that way, the ratio is greater than 1. If the ratios are the same, then the data are consistent with the law of constant composition.	SOLUTION **Sample 1** $\frac{\text{Mass S}}{\text{Mass C}} = \frac{8.08\text{ g}}{1.51\text{ g}} = 5.35$ **Sample 2** $\frac{\text{Mass S}}{\text{Mass C}} = \frac{31.3\text{ g}}{3.85\text{ g}} = 8.13$ These results are not consistent with the law of constant composition, so the information that the two samples are the same substance must therefore be in error.

Chemical Principles

The left column summarizes the key principles that you should take away from the chapter, and the right column tells why each topic is important for you to understand.

Chemical Skills

The left column describes the key skills you should gain after reading the chapter, and the right column contains a worked example illustrating that skill.

HIGHLIGHT PROBLEMS

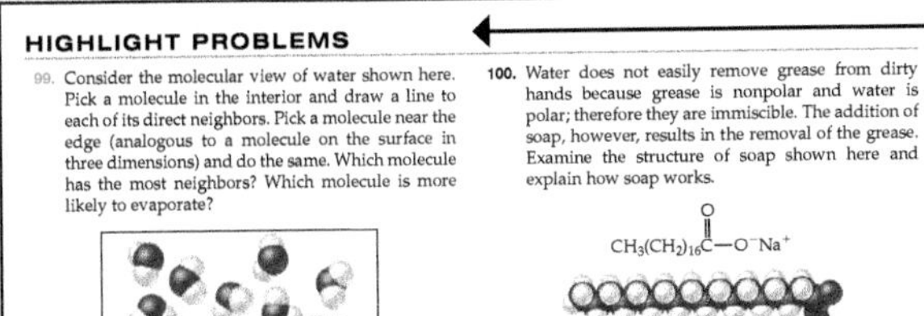

99. Consider the molecular view of water shown here. Pick a molecule in the interior and draw a line to each of its direct neighbors. Pick a molecule near the edge (analogous to a molecule on the surface in three dimensions) and do the same. Which molecule has the most neighbors? Which molecule is more likely to evaporate?

100. Water does not easily remove grease from dirty hands because grease is nonpolar and water is polar; therefore they are immiscible. The addition of soap, however, results in the removal of the grease. Examine the structure of soap shown here and explain how soap works.

$CH_3(CH_2)_{16}C(=O)-O^-Na^+$

Nonpolar tail

Polar head

Sodium stearate
a soap

Highlight Problems

These are set within a context that will be of particular interest to students because of its timeliness, familiarity, or relevance to an important issue.

Additional End-of-Chapter Features

- Key Terms
- Review Questions
- Problems by Topic
- Cumulative Problems
- Conceptual Problems

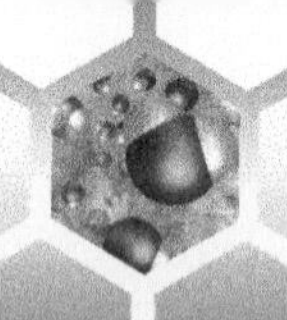

VISUALIZING CHEMISTRY
CREATES DEEPER UNDERSTANDING

BY CONNECTING the macroscopic and microscopic worlds, visualizing concepts brings chemistry to life and creates a deeper understanding that will serve you throughout the course.

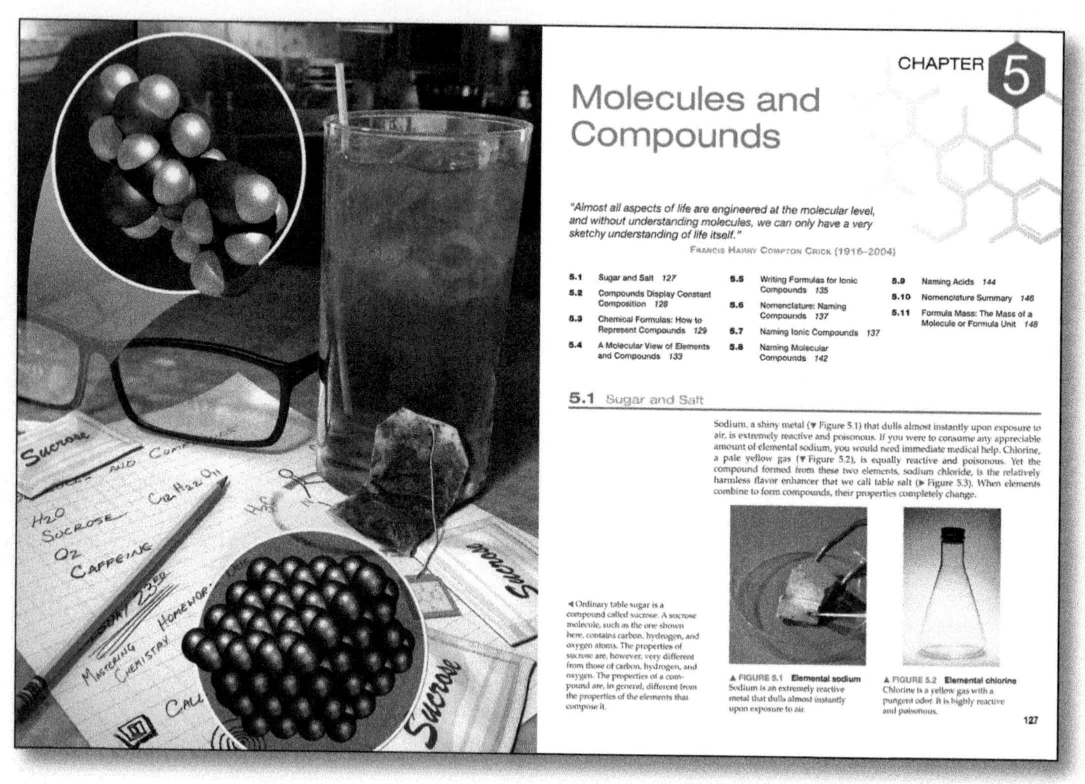

CHAPTER 5

Molecules and Compounds

"Almost all aspects of life are engineered at the molecular level, and without understanding molecules, we can only have a very sketchy understanding of life itself."

FRANCIS HARRY COMPTON CRICK (1916–2004)

5.1 Sugar and Salt

Sodium, a shiny metal (▼ Figure 5.1) that dulls almost instantly upon exposure to air, is extremely reactive and poisonous. If you were to consume any appreciable amount of elemental sodium, you would need immediate medical help. Chlorine, a pale yellow gas (▼ Figure 5.2), is equally reactive and poisonous. Yet the compound formed from these two elements, sodium chloride, is the relatively harmless flavor enhancer that we call table salt (▶ Figure 5.3). When elements combine to form compounds, their properties completely change.

◀ Ordinary table sugar is a compound called sucrose. A sucrose molecule, such as the one shown here, contains carbon, hydrogen, and oxygen atoms. The properties of sucrose are, however, very different from those of carbon, hydrogen, and oxygen. The properties of a compound are, in general, different from the properties of the elements that compose it.

▲ FIGURE 5.1 **Elemental sodium** Sodium is an extremely reactive metal that dulls almost instantly upon exposure to air.

▲ FIGURE 5.2 **Elemental chlorine** Chlorine is a yellow gas with a pungent odor. It is highly reactive and poisonous.

127

Chapter Openers

Every chapter opens by describing an everyday situation or practical application that demonstrates the importance of the material covered in that chapter. Each chapter-opening image combines macroscopic and molecular views that bring the content to life.

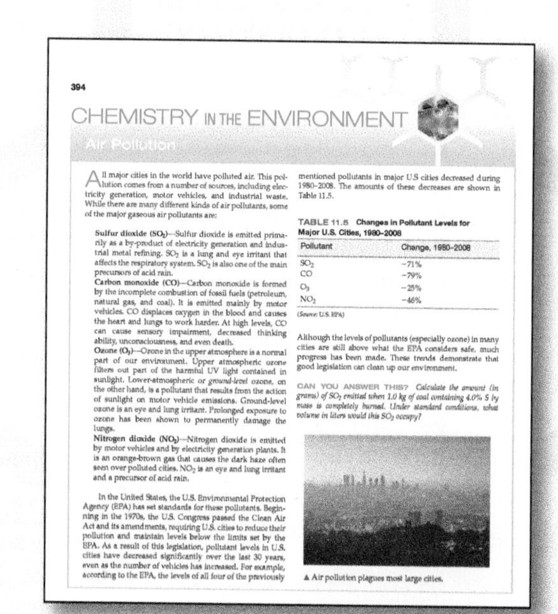

394

CHEMISTRY IN THE ENVIRONMENT

Air Pollution

All major cities in the world have polluted air. This pollution comes from a number of sources, including electricity generation, motor vehicles, and industrial waste. While there are many different kinds of air pollutants, some of the major gaseous air pollutants are:

Sulfur dioxide (SO_2)—Sulfur dioxide is emitted primarily as a by-product of electricity generation and industrial metal refining. SO_2 is a lung and eye irritant that affects the respiratory system. SO_2 is also one of the main precursors of acid rain.

Carbon monoxide (CO)—Carbon monoxide is formed by the incomplete combustion of fossil fuels (petroleum, natural gas, and coal). It is emitted mainly by motor vehicles. CO displaces oxygen in the blood and causes the heart and lungs to work harder. At high levels, CO can cause sensory impairment, decreased thinking ability, unconsciousness, and even death.

Ozone (O_3)—Ozone in the upper atmosphere is a normal part of our environment. Upper atmospheric ozone filters out part of the harmful UV light contained in sunlight. Lower-atmospheric or *ground-level* ozone, on the other hand, is a pollutant that results from the action of sunlight on motor vehicle emissions. Ground-level ozone is an eye and lung irritant. Prolonged exposure to ozone has been shown to permanently damage the lungs.

Nitrogen dioxide (NO_2)—Nitrogen dioxide is emitted by motor vehicles and by electricity generation plants. It is an orange-brown gas that causes the dark haze often seen over polluted cities. NO_2 is an eye and lung irritant and a precursor of acid rain.

In the United States, the U.S. Environmental Protection Agency (EPA) has set standards for these pollutants. Beginning in the 1970s, the U.S. Congress passed the Clean Air Act and its amendments, requiring U.S. cities to reduce their pollution and maintain levels below the limits set by the EPA. As a result of this legislation, pollutant levels in U.S. cities have decreased significantly over the last 30 years, even as the number of vehicles has increased. For example, according to the EPA, the levels of all four of the previously mentioned pollutants in major U.S cities decreased during 1980-2008. The amounts of these decreases are shown in Table 11.5.

TABLE 11.5 **Changes in Pollutant Levels for Major U.S. Cities, 1980-2008**

Pollutant	Change, 1980-2008
SO_2	−71%
CO	−79%
O_3	−25%
NO_2	−46%

(*Source*: U.S. EPA)

Although the levels of pollutants (especially ozone) in many cities are still above what the EPA considers safe, much progress has been made. These trends demonstrate that good legislation can clean up our environment.

CAN YOU ANSWER THIS? *Calculate the amount (in grams) of SO_2 emitted when 1.0 kg of coal containing 4.0% S by mass is completely burned. Under standard conditions, what volume in liters would this SO_2 occupy?*

▲ Air pollution plagues most large cities.

Interest Boxes

Four different types of interest boxes apply chemistry to everyday events and topics.

- **Chemistry in the Environment** boxes discuss environmental issues that are closely tied to chemistry, such as the reactions involved in ozone depletion.
- **Everyday Chemistry** boxes demonstrate the importance of chemistry in everyday situations, such as bleaching your hair.
- **Chemistry in the Media** boxes discuss chemical topics that have been in the news recently, such as the controversy over oxygenated fuels.
- **Chemistry and Health** boxes focus on personal health and fitness topics, as well as biomedical topics.

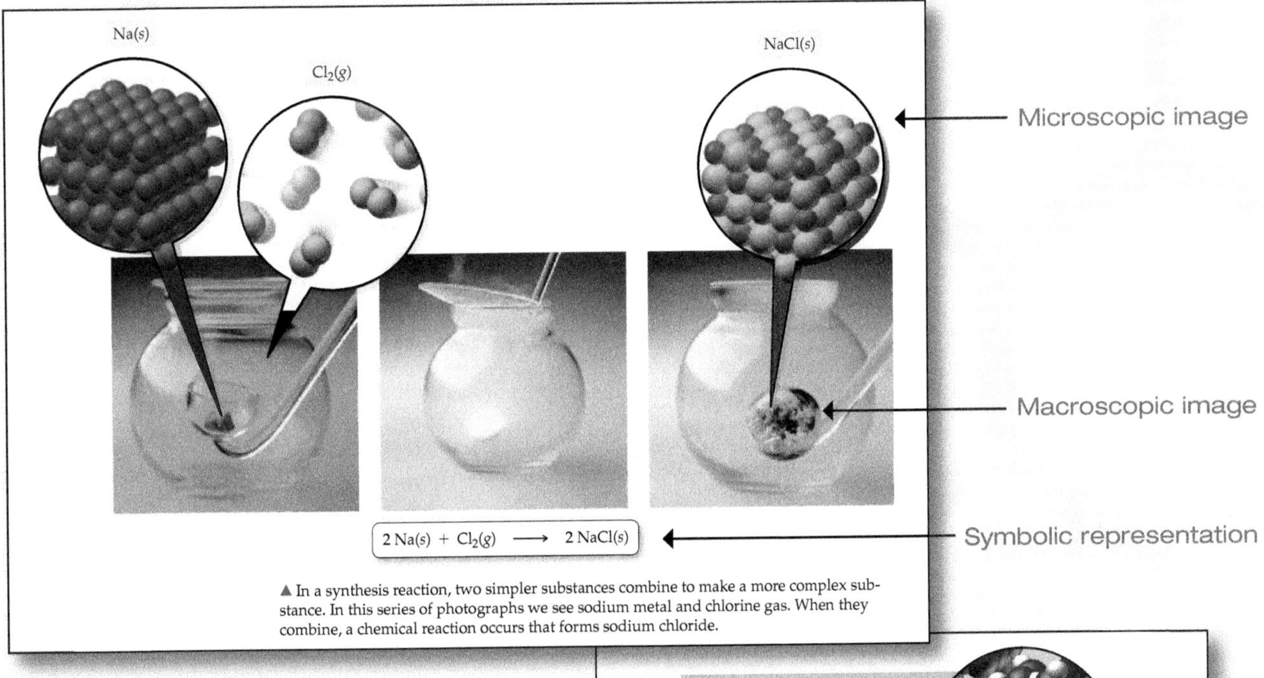

▲ In a synthesis reaction, two simpler substances combine to make a more complex substance. In this series of photographs we see sodium metal and chlorine gas. When they combine, a chemical reaction occurs that forms sodium chloride.

Macroscopic to Microscopic Art

Many illustrations have three parts:

- **a macroscopic image** (what you can see with your eyes)
- **a microscopic image** (what the molecules are doing)
- **a symbolic representation** (how chemists represent the process with symbols and equations)

The goal is for you to connect what you see and experience with the molecules responsible, and with the way chemists represent those molecules.

▲ FIGURE 12.3 **Solids have a definite shape** In a solid such as ice, the molecules are fixed in place. However, they vibrate about fixed points.

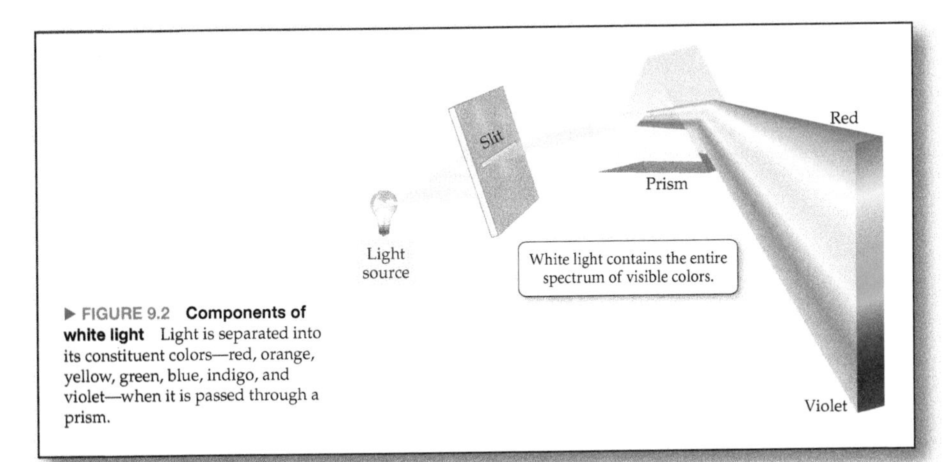

▶ FIGURE 9.2 **Components of white light** Light is separated into its constituent colors—red, orange, yellow, green, blue, indigo, and violet—when it is passed through a prism.

Labeling Figures

NEW! to the **Fourth Edition** is a consistent hierarchy for labeling figures. Up to three types of labels appear on the art: the most important in white shadow boxes; the second most important, in tinted boxes with no border; and the third, unboxed. This new feature helps you to efficiently navigate the figure, and to grasp its main points.

MASTERINGCHEMISTRY®
EXTENDS LEARNING BEYOND THE CLASSROOM

MasteringChemistry® is the most effective and widely used online tutorial, homework and assessment system for chemistry. It helps instructors maximize class time with customizable, easy-to-assign, and automatically graded assessments that motivate students to learn outside of class and arrive prepared for lecture. These assessments can easily be customized and personalized by instructors to suit their individual teaching style. To learn more visit: www.masteringchemistry.com

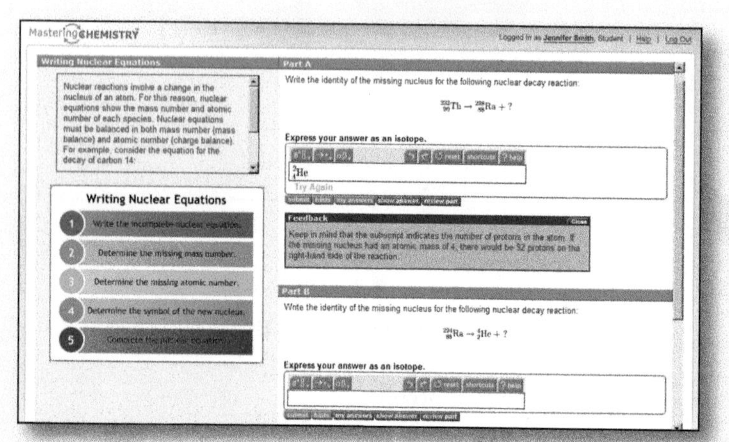

Student Tutorials

MasteringChemistry is the only system to provide instantaneous feedback specific to the most-common wrong answers. Students can submit an answer and receive immediate, error-specific feedback. Simpler sub-problems—"hints"—are provided upon request.

Gradebook

Every assignment is automatically graded. Shades of red highlight vulnerable students and challenging assignments.

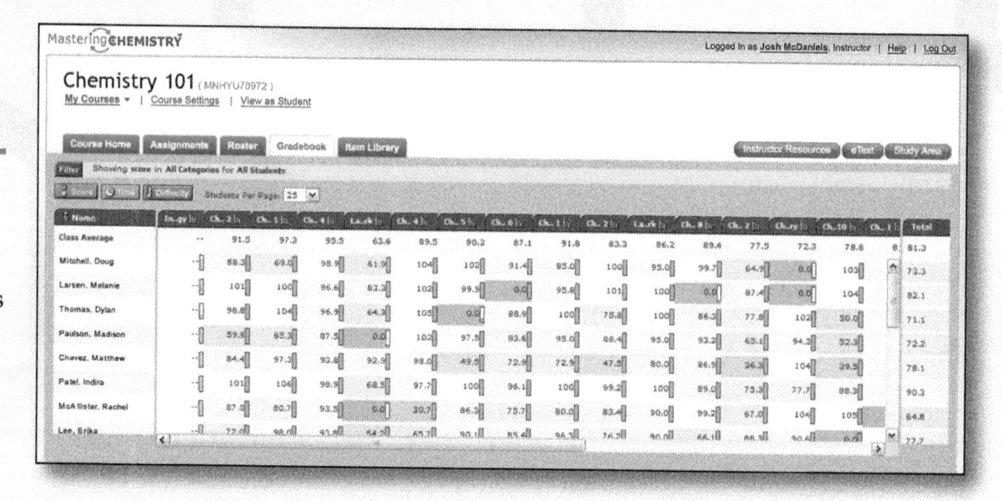

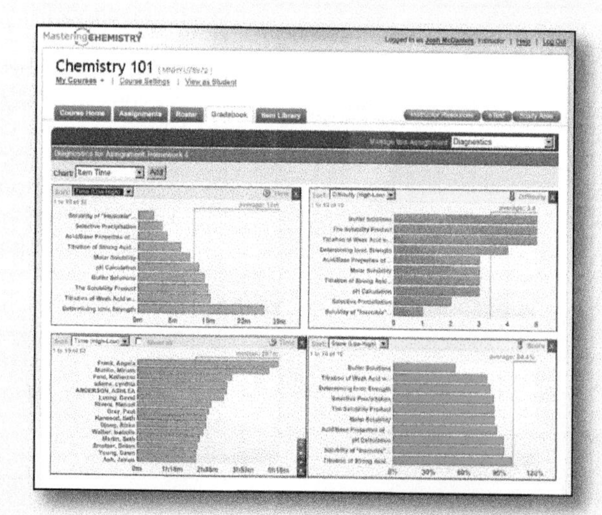

Gradebook Diagnostic

This screen provides your favorite diagnostics. With a single click, charts summarize the most difficult problems, vulnerable students, grade distribution, and even score improvement over the course.

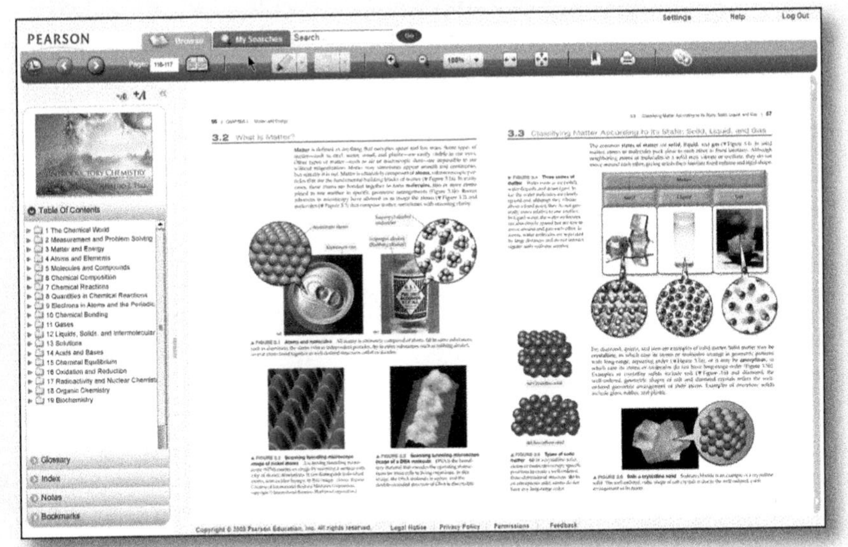

Pearson eText

Pearson eText provides access to the text when and wherever students have access to the Internet. eText pages look exactly like the printed text, offering powerful new functionality. Users can create notes, highlight text in different colors, create bookmarks, zoom, click hyperlinked words and phrases to view definitions, view as single or two-pages. eText also links to associated media files, enabling students to view an animation as they read the text. Pearson eText offers a full-text search and the ability to save and export notes.

NEW! Visualizations

These new tutorials, including PhET simulations, enable students to make connections between real-life phenomena and the underlying chemistry that explains such phenomena. The tutorials increase students' understanding of chemistry and clearly illustrate cause-and-effect relationships.

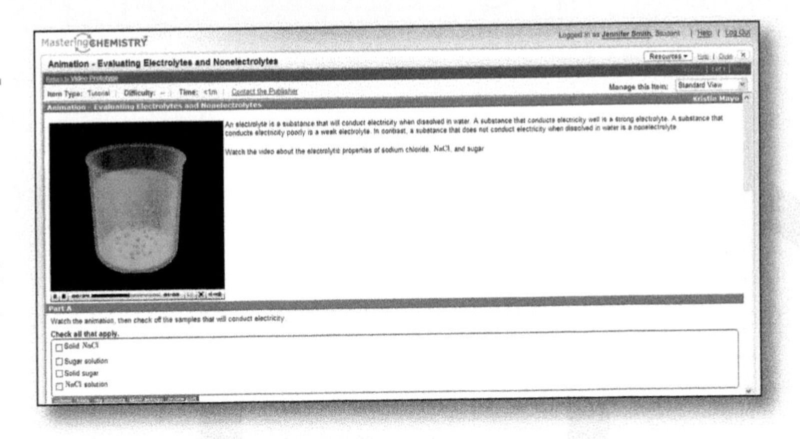

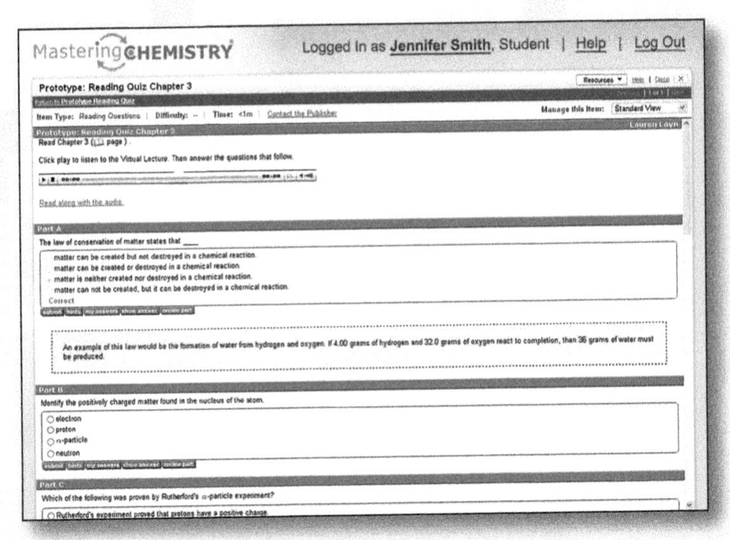

Reading Quizzes

Chapter-specific quizzes and activities focus on important, hard-to-grasp chemistry concepts.

CHAPTER 1

The Chemical World

"Imagination is more important than knowledge."

ALBERT EINSTEIN (1879–1955)

1.1 Soda Pop Fizz

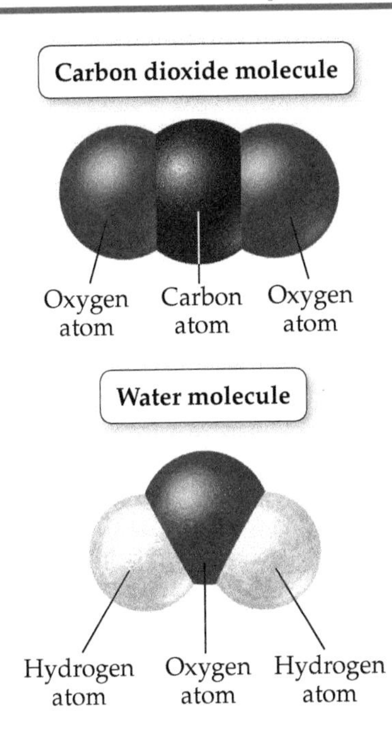

◀ Soda pop is a mixture of carbon dioxide and water and a few other substances that contribute flavor and color. When soda pop is poured into a glass, some of the carbon dioxide molecules come out of the mixture, producing the familiar fizz.

Open a can of soda pop and you hear the familiar "chchchch" of pressure release. Take a sip and you feel the carbon dioxide bubbles on your tongue. Shake the can before you open it and you will be sprayed with the bubbly liquid. A can of soda pop, like most familiar items in our daily lives, is a chemical mixture. Soda pop consists primarily of sugar, water, and carbon dioxide. It is the unique combination of these substances that gives soda pop its properties. Have you every wondered why soda pop tastes sweet? To understand why, you need to understand sugar and solutions of sugar with water. We will learn about solutions in Chapter 13. Have you every wondered why soda fizzes when you open it? To understand the reason, you need to understand gases and their ability to dissolve in liquids and how that ability changes with changing pressure. We will learn about gases in Chapter 11. And if you want to know how drinking too much soda pop makes you gain weight, you need to understand energy and the production of energy by chemical reactions. We will discuss energy in Chapter 3 and chemical reactions in Chapter 7. You need not go any farther than your own home and your own everyday experiences to encounter chemical questions. Chemicals compose virtually everything in our world: the soda; this book; your pencil; indeed, even your own body.

Chemists are particularly interested in the connections between the properties of substances and the properties of the particles that compose them. For example, why does soda pop fizz? Like all common substances, soda pop is ultimately composed of tiny particles called *atoms*. Atoms are so small that a single drop of soda pop contains about one billion trillion of them. In soda pop, as in many substances, these atoms are bound together to form several different types of *molecules*. The molecules important to fizzing are carbon dioxide and water. Carbon dioxide molecules consist of three atoms—one carbon and two oxygen atoms—held together in a straight line by chemical bonds. Water molecules also consist of three atoms—one oxygen and two hydrogen atoms—bonded together, but rather than being straight like carbon dioxide, the water molecule is bent.

▶ Virtually everything around you is composed of chemicals.

We will explore the nature of atoms, molecules, and chemical bonds more fully in later chapters. For now, think of atoms and molecules as tiny particles that compose all common matter, and chemical bonds as the attachments that hold atoms together.

The details of how atoms bond together to form a molecule—straight, bent, or some other shape—as well as the type of atoms in the molecule, determine *everything* about the substance that the molecule composes. The characteristics of water molecules make water a liquid at room temperature. The characteristics of carbon dioxide molecules make carbon dioxide a gas at room temperature. The characteristics of sugar molecules allow them to interact with our taste buds to produce the sensation of sweetness.

The makers of soda pop use *pressure* (the result of collisions between gaseous molecules and the surfaces around them) to force gaseous carbon dioxide molecules to mix with liquid water molecules. As long as the can of soda is sealed, the carbon dioxide molecules remain mixed with the water molecules, held there by pressure. When the can is opened, the pressure is released and carbon dioxide molecules escape out of the soda mixture (▼ Figure 1.1). As they do, they create bubbles—the familiar fizz of soda pop.

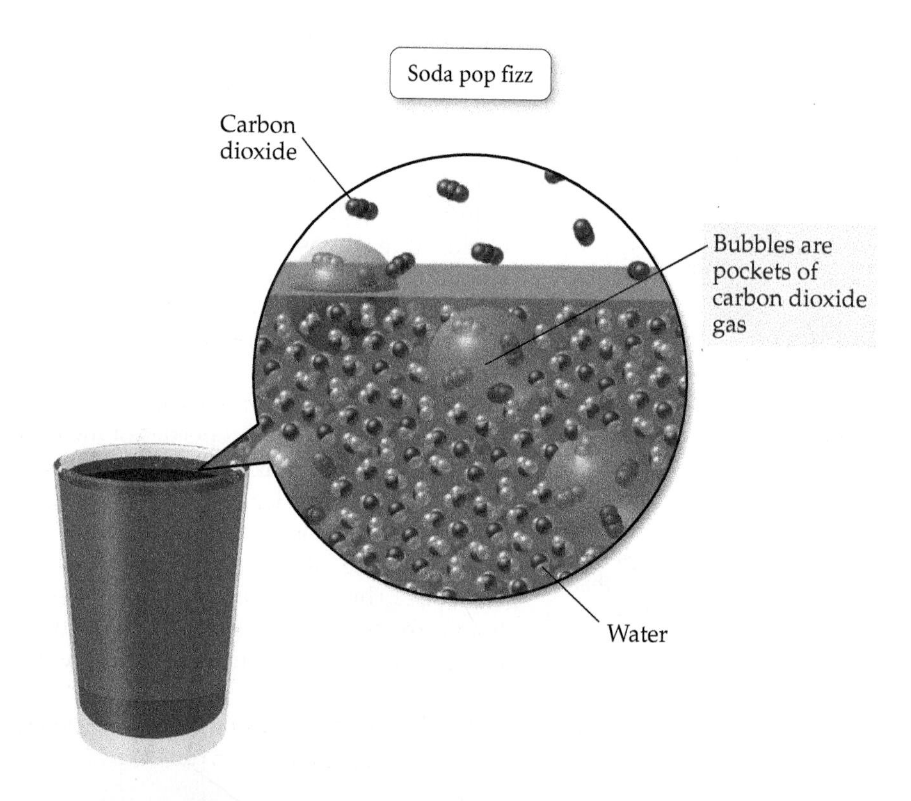

▶ **FIGURE 1.1 Where the fizz comes from** Bubbles in soda pop are pockets of carbon dioxide gas molecules escaping out of the liquid water.

▶ The public often has a very narrow view of chemicals, thinking of them only as dangerous poisons or pollutants.

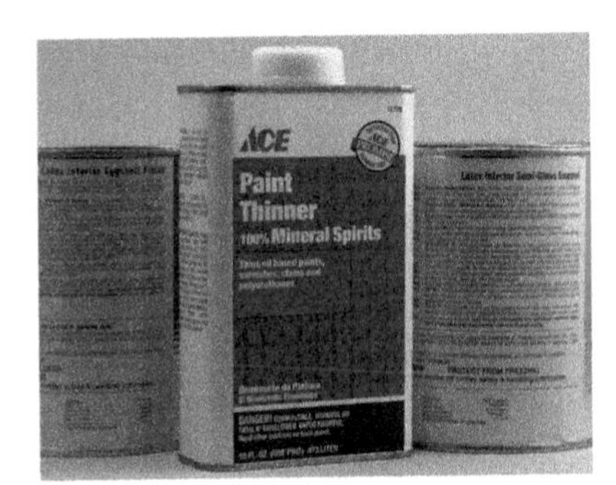

1.2 Chemicals Compose Ordinary Things

▲ Chemists are interested in knowing why ordinary things, such as water, are the way they are. When a chemist sees a pitcher of water, she thinks of the molecules that compose the liquid and how those molecules determine its properties.

Is soda pop composed of chemicals? Yes. In fact, there is nothing you can hold or touch that is *not* made of chemicals. When most people think of chemicals, however, they envision a can of paint thinner in their garage, or they recall a headline about a river polluted by industrial waste. But chemicals compose more than just these things—they compose ordinary things, too. Chemicals compose the air we breathe and the water we drink. They compose toothpaste, Tylenol, and toilet paper. Chemicals make up virtually everything we come into contact with. Chemistry explains the properties and behavior of chemicals, in the broadest sense, by helping us understand the molecules that compose them.

As you experience the world around you, molecules are interacting to create your experience. Imagine watching a sunset. Molecules are involved in every step. Molecules in air interact with light from the sun, scattering away the blue and green light and leaving the red and orange light to create the color you see. Molecules in your eyes absorb that light and as a result are altered in a way that sends a signal to your brain. Molecules in your brain then interpret the signal to produce images and emotions. This whole process—mediated by molecules—creates the experience of seeing a sunset.

Chemists are interested in why ordinary substances are the way they are. Why is water a liquid at room temperature? Why is salt a solid? Why does soda fizz? Why is a sunset red? Throughout this book, you will learn the answers to these questions and many others. *You will learn the connections between the behavior of matter and the behavior of the particles that compose it.*

1.3 All Things Are Made of Atoms and Molecules

▲ Richard Feynman (1918–1988), Nobel Prize–winning physicist and popular professor at California Institute of Technology.

Professor Richard Feynman, in a lecture to first-year physics students at the California Institute of Technology, said that the most important idea in all human knowledge is that *all things are made of atoms.* Since atoms are usually bound together to form molecules, however, a chemist might add the concept of *molecules* to Feynman's bold assertion. This simple idea—that all things are made of atoms and molecules—explains much about our world and our experience of it. Atoms and molecules determine how matter behaves—if they were different, matter would be different. The nature of water molecules, for example, determines how water behaves. The nature of sugar molecules determines how sugar behaves, and the molecules that compose humans determine much about how our bodies behave.

There is a direct connection between the world of atoms and molecules and the world you and I experience every day. Chemists explore this connection. They seek to understand it. A good, simple definition of **chemistry** is *the science that tries to understand how matter behaves by studying how atoms and molecules behave.*

Chemistry—The science that seeks to understand what matter does by studying what atoms and molecules do.

1.4 The Scientific Method: How Chemists Think

Chemists use the **scientific method**—a way of learning that emphasizes observation and experimentation—to understand the world. The scientific method stands in contrast to ancient Greek philosophies that emphasized *reason* as the way to understand the world. Although the scientific method is not a rigid procedure that automatically leads to a definitive answer, it does have key characteristics that distinguish it from other ways of acquiring knowledge. These key characteristics include observation, the formulation of hypotheses, the testing of hypotheses by experiment, and the formulation of laws and theories.

The first step in acquiring scientific knowledge (▼ Figure 1.2) is often the **observation** or measurement of some aspect of nature. Some observations are simple, requiring nothing more than the naked eye. Other observations rely on the use of sensitive instrumentation. Occasionally, an important observation happens entirely by chance. Alexander Fleming, for example, discovered penicillin when he observed a bacteria-free circle around a certain mold that had accidentally grown on his culture plate. Regardless of how the observation occurs, it usually involves the measurement or description of some aspect of the physical world. For example, Antoine Lavoisier (1743–1794), a French chemist who studied combustion, burned substances in closed containers. He carefully measured the mass of each container and its contents before and after burning the substance inside, noting that there was no change in the mass during combustion. Lavoisier made an *observation* about the physical world.

Combustion means burning. The mass of an object is a measure of the quantity of matter within it.

Observations often lead scientists to formulate a **hypothesis**, a tentative interpretation or explanation of the observations. Lavoisier explained his observations on combustion by hypothesizing that the process involved the combination of a substance with a component of air. A good hypothesis is *falsifiable*, which means that further testing has the potential to prove it wrong. Hypotheses are tested by **experiments**, highly controlled observations designed to validate or invalidate hypotheses. The results of an experiment may confirm a hypothesis or show it to be mistaken in some way. In the latter case, the hypothesis may have to be modified, or even discarded and replaced by an alternative. Either way, the new or revised hypothesis must also be tested through further experimentation.

Sometimes a number of similar observations lead to the development of a **scientific law**, a brief statement that synthesizes past observations and predicts future ones. For example, based on his observations of combustion, Lavoisier developed the **law of conservation of mass**, which states, "In a chemical reaction matter is neither created nor destroyed." This statement grew out of Lavoisier's observations, and it predicted the outcome of similar experiments on *any* chemical reaction. Laws are also subject to experiments, which can prove them wrong or validate them.

Scientific theories are also called *models*.

One or more well-established hypotheses may form the basis for a scientific **theory**. Theories provide a broader and deeper explanation for observations and laws. They are models of the way nature is, and they often predict behavior that

▼ FIGURE 1.2 The scientific method.

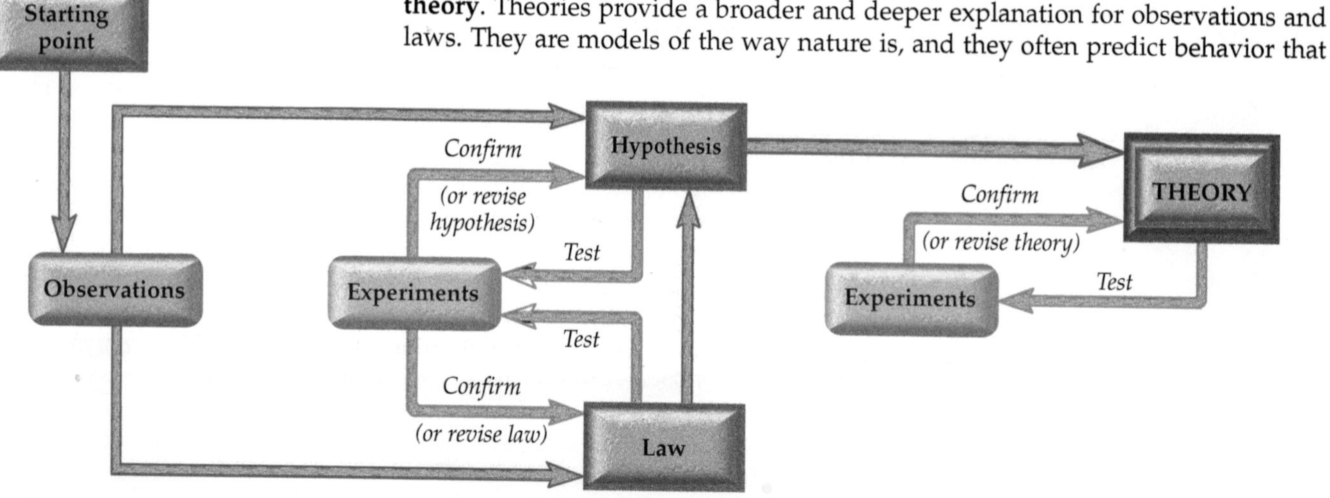

▲ (Left) Painting of the French chemist Antoine Lavoisier and his wife, Marie, who helped him in his work by illustrating his experiments, recording results, and translating scientific articles from English. (*Source:* Jacques Louis David (French, 1748–1825). "Antoine-Laurent Lavoisier (1743–1794) and His Wife (Marie-Anne-Pierrette Paulze, 1758–1836)," 1788, oil on canvas, H. 102-1/4 in. W. 76-5/8 in. (259.7 × 194.6cm). The Metropolitan Museum of Art, Purchase, Mr. and Mrs. Charles Wrightsman Gift, in honor of Everett Fahy, 1977. (1977.10) Image copyright © The Metropolitan Museum of Art.) (Right) John Dalton, the English chemist who formulated the atomic theory.

extends well beyond the observations and laws on which they are founded. A good example of a theory is the **atomic theory** of John Dalton (1766–1844). Dalton explained the law of conservation of mass, as well as other laws and observations, by proposing that all matter was composed of small, indestructible particles called atoms. Dalton's theory was a model of the physical world—it went beyond the laws and observations of the time to explain these laws and observations.

Theories are also tested and validated by experiments. Notice that the scientific method begins with observation, and then laws, hypotheses, and theories are developed based on those observations. Experiments, which are carefully controlled observations, are then used to determine the validity of laws, hypotheses, or theories. If a law, hypothesis, or theory is inconsistent with the findings of an experiment, it must be revised and new experiments must be conducted to test the revisions. Over time, poor theories are eliminated and good theories—those consistent with experiments—remain. Established theories with strong experimental support are the most powerful pieces of scientific knowledge. People unfamiliar with science sometimes say, "That is just a theory," as if theories were mere speculations. However, well-tested theories are as close to truth as we get in science. For example, the idea that all matter is made of atoms is "just a theory," but it is a theory with 200 years of experimental evidence to support it, including the recent imaging of atoms themselves (◀ Figure 1.3). Established theories should not be taken lightly—they are the pinnacle of scientific understanding.

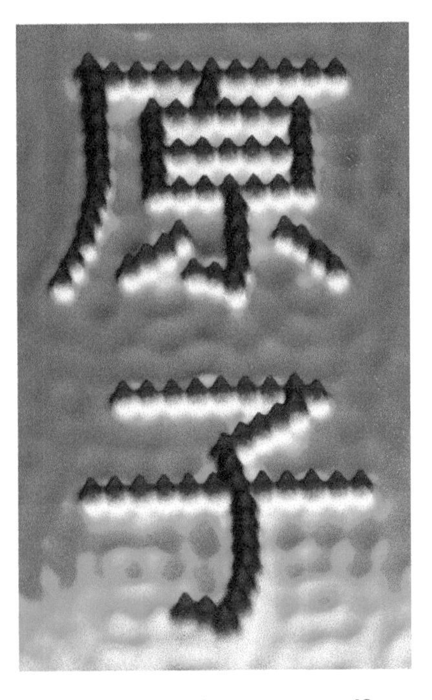

▲ **FIGURE 1.3 Are atoms real?** The atomic theory has 200 years of experimental evidence to support it, including recent images, such as this one, of atoms themselves. This image shows the Kanji characters for "atom" written with individual iron atoms on top of a copper surface.

CONCEPTUAL CHECKPOINT 1.1

Which statement most resembles a scientific theory?

(a) When the pressure on a sample of oxygen gas is increased 10%, the volume of the gas decreases by 10%.

(b) The volume of a gas is inversely proportional to its pressure.

(c) A gas is composed of small particles in constant motion.

(d) A gas sample has a mass of 15.8 grams and a volume of 10.5 liters.

Note: The answers to all Conceptual Checkpoints appear at the end of the chapter.

EVERYDAY CHEMISTRY

Combustion and the Scientific Method

Early chemical theories attempted to explain common phenomena such as combustion. Why did things burn? What was happening to a substance when it burned? Could something that was burned be unburned? Early chemists burned different substances and made observations to try to answer these questions. They observed that substances would stop burning if placed in a closed container. They found that many metals would burn to form a white powder that they called a *calx* (now we know that these white powders are oxides of the metal) and that the metal could be recovered from the calx, or unburned, by combining the calx with charcoal and heating it.

Chemists in the first part of the eighteenth century formed a theory about combustion to explain these observations. In this theory, combustion involved a fundamental substance that they called *phlogiston*. This substance was present in anything that burned and was released during combustion. Flammable objects were flammable because they contained phlogiston. When things burned in a closed container, they didn't burn for very long because the space within the container became saturated with phlogiston. When things burned in the open, they continued to burn until all of the phlogiston within them was gone. This theory also explained how metals that had burned could be unburned. Charcoal was a phlogiston-rich material—they knew this because it burned so well—and when it was combined with a calx, which was a metal that had been emptied of its phlogiston, it transferred some of its phlogiston into the calx, converting it back into the unburned form of the metal. The phlogiston theory was consistent with all of the observations of the time and was widely accepted as valid.

Like any theory, the phlogiston theory was tested continually by experiment. One set of experiments, conducted in the mid-eighteenth century by Louis-Bernard Guyton de Morveau (1737–1816), consisted of weighing metals before and after burning them. In every case the metals *gained* weight when they were burned. This observation was inconsistent with the phlogiston theory, which predicted that they should *lose* weight because phlogiston was supposed to be lost during combustion. Clearly, the phlogiston theory needed modification.

The first modification proposed that phlogiston was a very light substance so that it actually "buoyed up" the materials that contained it. Thus when phlogiston was released, the material became heavier. Such a modification seemed to fit the observations but also seemed far-fetched. Antoine Lavoisier developed a more likely explanation by devising a completely new theory of combustion. Lavoisier proposed that, when a substance burned, it actually took something *out* of the air, and when it unburned, it released something back into the air. Lavoisier said that burning objects *fixed* (attached or bonded) the air and that the *fixed* air was released during unburning. In a confirming experiment (▼ Figure 1.4), Lavoisier roasted a mixture of calx and charcoal with the aid of sunlight focused by a giant burning lens, and found that a huge volume of "fixed air" was released in the process. The scientific method had worked. The phlogiston theory was proven wrong, and a new theory of combustion took its place—a theory that, with a few refinements, is still valid today.

CAN YOU ANSWER THIS? *What is the difference between a law and a theory? How does the example of the phlogiston theory demonstrate this difference?*

▶ **FIGURE 1.4 Focusing on combustion** The great burning lens belonging to the Academy of Sciences. Lavoisier used a similar lens in 1777 to show that a mixture of *calx* (metal oxide) and charcoal released a large volume of *fixed air* when heated.

1.5 A Beginning Chemist: How to Succeed

▲ To succeed as a scientist, you must have the curiosity of a child.

You are a beginning chemist. This may be your first chemistry course, but it is probably not your last. To succeed as a beginning chemist, keep the following ideas in mind. First, chemistry requires curiosity and imagination. If you are content knowing that the sky is blue, but don't care *why* it is blue, then you may have to rediscover your curiosity. I say "rediscover" because even children—or better said, *especially* children—have this kind of curiosity. To succeed as a chemist, you must have the curiosity and imagination of a child—*you must want to know the why of things.*

Second, chemistry requires calculation. Throughout this course, you will be asked to calculate answers and quantify information. *Quantification* involves measurement as part of observation—it is one of the most important tools in science. Quantification allows you to go beyond merely saying that this object is hot and that one is cold or that this one is large and that one is small. It allows you to specify the difference precisely. For example, two samples of water may feel equally hot to your hand, but when you measure their temperatures, you may find that one is 40 °C and the other is 44 °C. Even small differences can be important in a calculation or experiment, so assigning numbers to observations and manipulating those numbers become very important in chemistry.

Lastly, chemistry requires commitment. To succeed in this course, you must commit yourself to learning chemistry. Roald Hoffman, winner of the 1981 Nobel Prize for chemistry, said,

> I like the idea that human beings can do anything they want to. They need to be trained sometimes. They need a teacher to awaken the intelligence within them. But to be a chemist requires no special talent, I'm glad to say. Anyone can do it, with hard work.

Professor Hoffman is right. The key to success in this course is hard work—that requires commitment. You must do your work regularly and carefully. If you do, you will succeed, and you will be rewarded by seeing a whole new world—the world of molecules and atoms. This world exists beneath the surface of nearly everything you encounter. I welcome you to this world and consider it a privilege, together with your professor, to be your guide.

CHAPTER IN REVIEW

CHEMICAL PRINCIPLES

Matter and Molecules: Chemists are interested in all matter, even ordinary matter such as water or air. You don't need to go to a chemical storeroom to find chemical questions. Chemicals are all around you. Chemistry is the science that tries to understand what matter does by understanding what molecules do.

RELEVANCE

Matter and Molecules: Chemists want to understand matter for several reasons. First, chemists are simply curious—they want to know why. Why are some substances reactive and others not? Why are some substances gases, some liquids, and others solids? Chemists are also practical; they want to understand matter so that they can control it and produce substances that are useful to society and to humankind.

The Scientific Method: Chemists employ the scientific method, which makes use of observations, hypotheses, laws, theories, and experiments. Observations involve measuring or observing some aspect of nature. Hypotheses are tentative interpretations of the observations. Laws summarize the results of a large number of observations, and theories are models that explain and give the underlying causes for observations and laws. Hypotheses, laws, and theories must be tested and validated by experiment. If they are not confirmed, they are revised and tested through further experimentation.

The Scientific Method: The scientific method is a way to understand the world. Since the inception of the scientific method, knowledge about the natural world has grown rapidly. The application of the scientific method has produced technologies that have raised living standards throughout the world with advances such as increased food production, rapid transportation, unparalleled access to information, and longer life spans.

Success as a Beginning Chemist: To succeed as a beginning chemist, you must be curious and imaginative, be willing to do calculations, and be committed to learning the material.

Success as a Beginning Chemist: Understanding chemistry will give you a deeper appreciation for the world in which you live, and if you choose science as a career, it will be a foundation upon which you will continue to build.

KEY TERMS

atomic theory **[1.4]**
chemistry **[1.3]**
experiment **[1.4]**
hypothesis **[1.4]**
law of conservation of mass **[1.4]**
observation **[1.4]**
scientific law **[1.4]**
scientific method **[1.4]**
theory **[1.4]**

EXERCISES

QUESTIONS

Answers to all questions numbered in blue appear in the Answers section at the back of the book.

1. Why does soda fizz?
2. What are chemicals? Give some examples.
3. What do chemists try to do? How do they understand the natural world?
4. What is meant by the statement, "Matter does what molecules do"? Give an example.
5. Define *chemistry*.
6. How is chemistry connected to everyday life? How is chemistry relevant outside the chemistry laboratory?
7. Explain the scientific method.
8. Give an example from this chapter of the scientific method at work.
9. What is the difference between a law and a theory?
10. What is the difference between a hypothesis and a theory?
11. What is wrong with the statement, "It is just a theory"?
12. What is the law of conservation of mass, and who discovered it?
13. What is the atomic theory, and who formulated it?
14. What are three things you need to do to succeed in this course?

PROBLEMS

Note: The exercises in the Problems section are paired, and the answers to the odd-numbered exercises (numbered in blue) appear in the Answers section at the back of the book.

15. Examine the opening figure of this chapter. Use the information in Section 1.1 to identify the two molecules sitting next to the cola glass and identify each of the atoms within each molecule.
16. Examine Figure 1.1 and, from a molecular point of view, explain why soda pop fizzes. What molecules are inside the bubbles in a glass of soda pop?

17. Classify each statement as an observation, a law, or a theory.

(a) When a metal is burned in a closed container, the sum of the masses of the container and its contents do not change.

(b) Matter is made of atoms.

(c) Matter is conserved in chemical reactions.

(d) When wood is burned in a closed container, its mass does not change.

18. Classify each statement as an observation, a law, or a theory.

(a) The star closest to Earth is moving away from Earth at high speed.

(b) A body in motion stays in motion unless acted upon by a force.

(c) The universe began as a cosmic explosion called the Big Bang.

(d) A stone dropped from an altitude of 450 m falls to the ground in 9.6 s.

19. A student prepares several samples of the same gas and measures their mass and volume. The results are tabulated as follows. Formulate a tentative law from the measurements.

Mass of Gas (in grams)	Volume of Gas (in L)
22.5	1.60
35.8	2.55
70.2	5.00
98.5	7.01

20. A student measures the volume of a gas sample at several different temperatures. The results are tabulated as follows. Formulate a tentative law from the measurements.

Temperature of Gas (in Kelvin)	Volume of Gas (in L)
298	4.55
315	4.81
325	4.96
335	5.11

21. A chemist in an imaginary universe does an experiment that attempts to correlate the size of an atom with its chemical reactivity. The results are tabulated as follows.

Size of Atom	Chemical Reactivity
small	low
medium	intermediate
large	high

(a) Formulate a law from this data.

(b) Formulate a theory to explain the law.

22. A chemist decomposes several samples of water into hydrogen and oxygen and weighs (or more correctly "measures the mass of") the hydrogen and the oxygen obtained. The results are tabulated as follows.

Sample Number	Grams of Hydrogen	Grams of Oxygen
1	1.5	12
2	2	16
3	2.5	20

(a) Summarize these observations in a short statement.

Next, the chemist decomposes several samples of carbon dioxide into carbon and oxygen. The results are tabulated as follows.

Sample Number	Grams of Carbon	Grams of Oxygen
1	0.5	1.3
2	1.0	2.7
3	1.5	4.0

(b) Summarize these observations in a short statement.

(c) Formulate a law from the observations in **(a)** and **(b)**.

(d) Formulate a theory that might explain your law in **(c)**.

▶ANSWERS TO CONCEPTUAL CHECKPOINTS

1.1 (c) Answers **(a)** and **(d)** are observations. Answer **(b)** is a scientific law. Answer **(c)** is the only answer that proposes a *model* for what a gas is like.

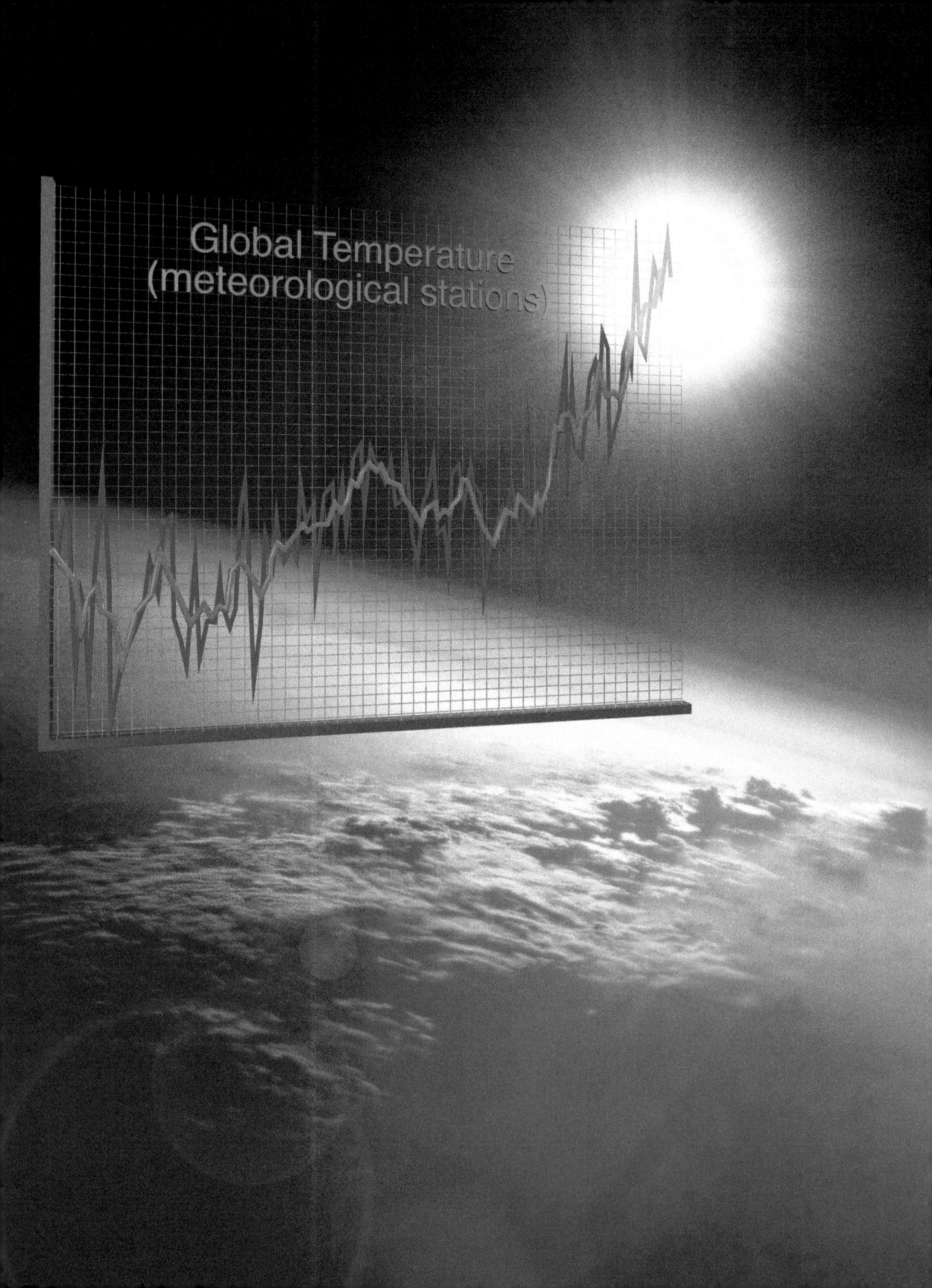

Global Temperature
(meteorological stations)

CHAPTER 2

Measurement and Problem Solving

"The important thing in science is not so much to obtain new facts as to discover new ways of thinking about them."

SIR WILLIAM LAWRENCE BRAGG (1890–1971)

2.1 Measuring Global Temperatures

Global warming has become a household term. Average global temperatures affect things from agriculture to weather and ocean levels. The media report that global temperatures are increasing. These reports are based on the work of scientists who—after analyzing records from thousands of temperature-measuring stations around the world—concluded that average global temperatures have risen by 0.6 °C in the last century.

A unit is a standard, agreed-on quantity by which other quantities are measured.

Notice how the scientists reported their results. What if they had reported a temperature increase of simply 0.6 without any *units*? The result would be unclear. Units are extremely important in reporting and working with scientific measurements, and they must always be included. Suppose that the scientists had included additional zeros in their results—for example, 0.60 °C or 0.600 °C—or that they had reported the number their computer displayed after averaging many measurements, something like 0.58759824 °C. Would these convey the same information? Not really. Scientists agree to a standard way of reporting measured quantities in which the number of reported digits reflects the precision in the measurement—more digits, more precision; fewer digits, less precision. Numbers are usually written so that the uncertainty is indicated by the last reported digit. For example, by reporting a temperature increase of 0.6 °C, the scientists mean 0.6 ± 0.1 °C ($\pm$ means plus or minus). The temperature rise could be as much as 0.7 °C or as little as 0.5 °C, but it is not 1.0 °C. The degree of certainty in this particular measurement is critical, influencing political decisions that directly affect people's lives.

◀ The graph in this image displays average global temperatures (relative to the mean) over the past 100 years.

2.2 Scientific Notation: Writing Large and Small Numbers

▲ Lasers such as this one can measure time periods as short as 1×10^{-15} s.

Science has constantly pushed the boundaries of the very large and the very small. We can, for example, now measure time periods as short as 0.000000000000001 seconds and distances as great as 14,000,000,000 light-years. Because the many zeros in these numbers are cumbersome to write, scientists use **scientific notation** to write them more compactly. In scientific notation, 0.000000000000001 is 1×10^{-15}, and 14,000,000,000 is 1.4×10^{10}. A number written in scientific notation consists of a **decimal part,** a number that is usually between 1 and 10, and an **exponential part,** 10 raised to an **exponent,** n.

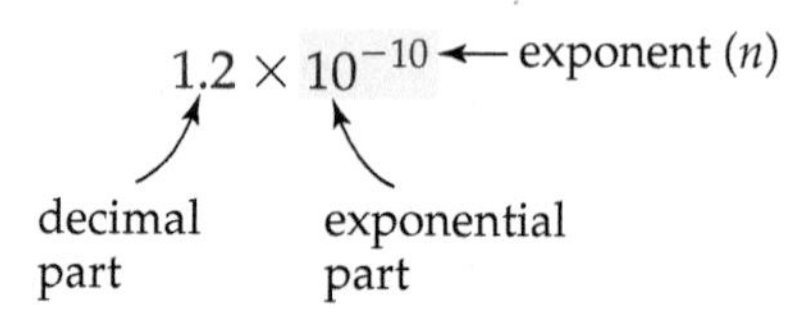

A positive exponent means 1 multiplied by 10 n times.

$$10^0 = 1$$
$$10^1 = 1 \times 10 = 10$$
$$10^2 = 1 \times 10 \times 10 = 100$$
$$10^3 = 1 \times 10 \times 10 \times 10 = 1000$$

A negative exponent ($-n$) means 1 divided by 10 n times.

$$10^{-1} = \frac{1}{10} = 0.1$$
$$10^{-2} = \frac{1}{10 \times 10} = 0.01$$
$$10^{-3} = \frac{1}{10 \times 10 \times 10} = 0.001$$

To convert a number to scientific notation, move the decimal point (either to the left or to the right, as needed) to obtain a number between 1 and 10 and then multiply that number (the decimal part) by 10 raised to the power that reflects the movement of the decimal point. For example, to write 5983 in scientific notation, move the decimal point to the left three places to get 5.983 (a number between 1 and 10) and then multiply the decimal part by 1000 to compensate for moving the decimal point.

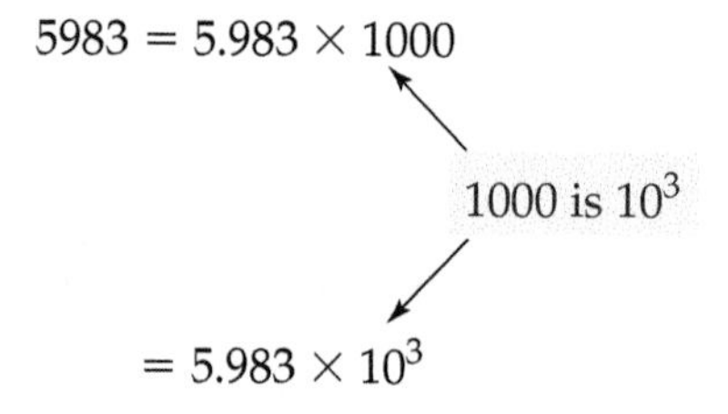

You can do this in one step by counting how many places you move the decimal point to obtain a number between 1 and 10 and then writing the decimal part multiplied by 10 raised to the number of places you moved the decimal point.

$$5983 = 5.983 \times 10^3$$

3 2 1

If the decimal point is moved to the left, as in the previous example, the exponent is positive. If the decimal is moved to the right, the exponent is negative.

$$0.00034 = 3.4 \times 10^{-4}$$

1234

To express a number in scientific notation:

1. Move the decimal point to obtain a number between 1 and 10.
2. Write the result from Step 1 multiplied by 10 raised to the number of places you moved the decimal point.
   - The exponent is positive if you moved the decimal point to the left.
   - The exponent is negative if you moved the decimal point to the right.

EXAMPLE 2.1 Scientific Notation

The 2010 U.S. population was estimated to be 308,255,000 people. Express this number in scientific notation.

To obtain a number between 1 and 10, move the decimal point to the left 8 decimal places; the exponent is 8. Since you move the decimal point to the left, the sign of the exponent is positive.

SOLUTION

$$308{,}255{,}000 \text{ people} = 3.08255 \times 10^{8} \text{ people}$$

▶SKILLBUILDER 2.1 | Scientific Notation

The total U.S national debt in 2010 was approximately $12,102,000,000,000. Express this number in scientific notation.

Note: The answers to all Skillbuilders appear at the end of the chapter.

▶FOR MORE PRACTICE Example 2.18; Problems 31, 32.

EXAMPLE 2.2 Scientific Notation

The radius of a carbon atom is approximately 0.000000000070 m. Express this number in scientific notation.

To obtain a number between 1 and 10, move the decimal point to the right 11 decimal places; therefore, the exponent is 11. Since the decimal point was moved to the right, the sign of the exponent is negative.

SOLUTION

$$0.000000000070 \text{ m} = 7.0 \times 10^{-11} \text{ m}$$

▶SKILLBUILDER 2.2 | Scientific Notation

Express the number 0.000038 in scientific notation.

▶FOR MORE PRACTICE Problems 33, 34.

CONCEPTUAL CHECKPOINT 2.1

The radius of a dust speck is 4.5×10^{-3} mm. What is the correct value of this number in decimal notation (i.e., express the number without using scientific notation)?

(a) 4500 mm

(b) 0.045 mm

(c) 0.0045 mm

(d) 0.00045 mm

Note: The answers to all Conceptual Checkpoints appear at the end of the chapter.

2.3 Significant Figures: Writing Numbers to Reflect Precision

▲ Since pennies come in whole numbers, 7 pennies means 7.00000… pennies. This is an exact number and therefore never limits significant figures in calculations.

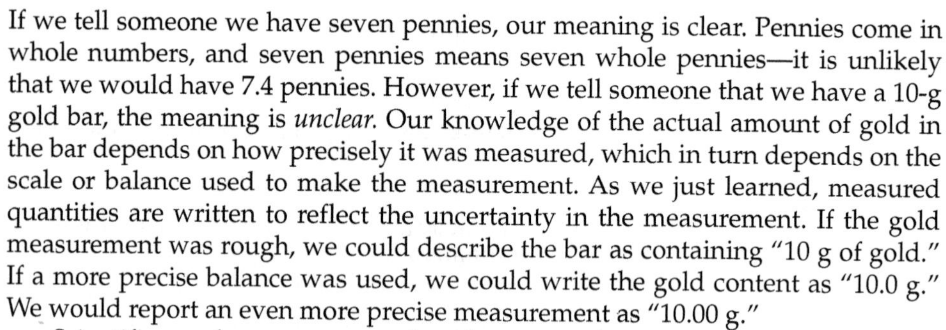

If we tell someone we have seven pennies, our meaning is clear. Pennies come in whole numbers, and seven pennies means seven whole pennies—it is unlikely that we would have 7.4 pennies. However, if we tell someone that we have a 10-g gold bar, the meaning is *unclear.* Our knowledge of the actual amount of gold in the bar depends on how precisely it was measured, which in turn depends on the scale or balance used to make the measurement. As we just learned, measured quantities are written to reflect the uncertainty in the measurement. If the gold measurement was rough, we could describe the bar as containing "10 g of gold." If a more precise balance was used, we could write the gold content as "10.0 g." We would report an even more precise measurement as "10.00 g."

Scientific numbers are reported so that every digit is certain except the last, which is estimated. For example, suppose a reported measurement is:

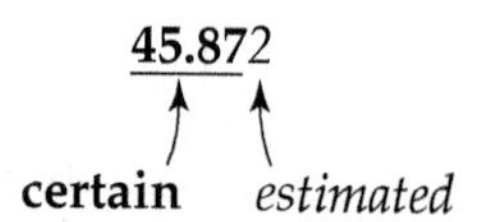

The first four digits are certain; the last digit is estimated.

Suppose that we weigh an object on a balance with marks at every 1 g, and the pointer is between the 1-g mark and the 2-g mark (▼ Figure 2.1) but much closer to the 1-g mark. To record the measurement, we mentally divide the space between the 1- and 2-g marks into 10 equal spaces and estimate the position of the pointer. In this case, the pointer indicates about 1.2 g. We then write the measurement as 1.2 g, indicating that we are sure of the "1" but have estimated the ".2."

▲ Our knowledge of the amount of gold in a 10-g gold bar depends on how precisely it was measured.

If we measure the same object using a balance with marks every tenth of a gram, we need to write the result with more digits. For example, suppose that on this more precise balance the pointer is between the 1.2-g mark and the 1.3-g mark (▼ Figure 2.2). We again divide the space between the two marks into 10 equal spaces and estimate the third digit. In the case of the nut shown in Figure 2.2, we report 1.26 g. Digital balances usually have readouts that report the mass to the correct number of digits.

▲ **FIGURE 2.1 Estimating tenths of a gram** This balance has markings every 1 g, so we estimate to the tenths place. To estimate between markings, mentally divide the space into 10 equal spaces and estimate the last digit. This reading is 1.2 g.

▲ **FIGURE 2.2 Estimating hundredths of a gram** Since this scale has markings every 0.1 g, we estimate to the hundredths place. The correct reading is 1.26 g.

EXAMPLE 2.3 Reporting the Right Number of Digits

The bathroom scale in ▼ Figure 2.3 has markings at every 1 lb. Report the reading to the correct number of digits.

▲ **FIGURE 2.3 Reading a bathroom scale**

SOLUTION

Since the pointer is between the 147- and 148-lb markings, mentally divide the space between the markings into 10 equal spaces and estimate the next digit. In this case, the result should be reported as:

147.7 lb

What if you estimated a little differently and wrote 147.6 lb? In general, one unit of difference in the last digit is acceptable because the last digit is estimated and different people might estimate it slightly differently. However, if you wrote 147.2 lb, you would clearly be wrong.

▶**SKILLBUILDER 2.3 | Reporting the Right Number of Digits**

A thermometer is used to measure the temperature of a backyard hot tub, and the reading is shown in ▼ Figure 2.4. Write the temperature reading to the correct number of digits.

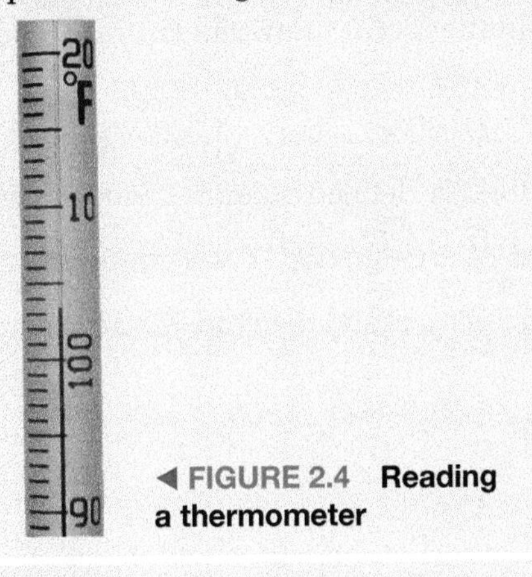

◀ **FIGURE 2.4 Reading a thermometer**

▶**FOR MORE PRACTICE** Example 2.19; Problems 41, 42.

COUNTING SIGNIFICANT FIGURES

The non–place-holding digits in a measurement are **significant figures** (or **significant digits**) and, as we have seen, represent the precision of a measured quantity. The greater the number of significant figures, the greater the precision of the measurement. We can determine the number of significant figures in a written number fairly easily; however, if the number contains zeros, we must distinguish between the zeros that are significant and those that simply mark the decimal place. In the number 0.002, for example, the leading zeros simply mark the decimal place; they *do not* add to the precision of the measurement. In the number 0.00200, the trailing zeros *do* add to the precision of the measurement.

To determine the number of significant figures in a number, follow these rules:

1. All nonzero digits are significant.

   1.05 0.0110

2. Interior zeros (zeros between two numbers) are significant.

   4.0208 50.1

3. Trailing zeros (zeros to the right of a nonzero number) that fall after a decimal point are significant.

   5.10 3.00

4. Trailing zeros that fall before a decimal point are significant.

   50.00   1700.24

When a number is expressed in scientific notation, all trailing zeros are significant.

5. Leading zeros (zeros to the left of the first nonzero number) are not significant. They only serve to locate the decimal point.

   For example, the number 0.0005 has only one significant digit.

6. **Trailing** zeros at the end of a number, but before an *implied* decimal point, are ambiguous and should be avoided by using scientific notation.

   For example, it is unclear if the number 350 has two or three significant figures. We can avoid confusion by writing the number as 3.5×10^2 to indicate two significant figures or as 3.50×10^2 to indicate three.

Some books put a decimal point after one or more trailing zeros if the zeros are to be considered significant. We avoid that practice in this book, but you should be aware of it.

EXACT NUMBERS

Exact numbers have an unlimited number of significant figures. Exact numbers originate from three sources:

- Exact counting of discrete objects. For example, 3 atoms means 3.00000...atoms.
- *Defined quantities*, such as the number of centimeters in 1 m. Because 100 cm is defined as 1 m,

$$100\,\text{cm} = 1\,\text{m means } 100.00000\ldots\,\text{cm} = 1.0000000\ldots\,\text{m}$$

  Note that some conversion factors are defined quantities whereas others are not.

- Integral numbers that are part of an equation. For example, in the equation, $radius = \frac{diameter}{2}$, the number 2 is exact and therefore has an unlimited number of significant figures.

EXAMPLE 2.4 Determining the Number of Significant Figures in a Number

How many significant figures are in each number?

(a) 0.0035
(b) 1.080
(c) 2371
(d) 2.97×10^5
(e) 1 dozen = 12
(f) 100.00
(g) 100,000

	SOLUTION
The 3 and the 5 are significant (rule 1). The leading zeros only mark the decimal place and are not significant (rule 5).	(a) 0.0035 two significant figures
The interior zero is significant (rule 2), and the trailing zero is significant (rule 3). The 1 and the 8 are also significant (rule 1).	(b) 1.080 four significant figures
All digits are significant (rule 1).	(c) 2371 four significant figures
All digits in the decimal part are significant (rule 1).	(d) 2.97×10^5 three significant figures
Defined numbers are exact and therefore have an unlimited number of significant figures.	(e) 1 dozen = 12 unlimited significant figures
The 1 is significant (rule 1), and the trailing zeros before the decimal point are significant (rule 4). The trailing zeros after the decimal point are also significant (rule 3).	(f) 100.00 five significant figures
This number is ambiguous. Write as 1×10^5 to indicate one significant figure or as 1.00000×10^5 to indicate six significant figures.	(g) 100,000 ambiguous

▶SKILLBUILDER 2.4 | Determining the Number of Significant Figures in a Number

How many significant figures are in each number?

(a) 58.31
(b) 0.00250
(c) 2.7×10^3
(d) 1 cm = 0.01 m
(e) 0.500
(f) 2100

▶FOR MORE PRACTICE Example 2.20; Problems 43, 44, 45, 46, 47, 48.

CONCEPTUAL CHECKPOINT 2.2

A researcher reports that the Spirit rover on the surface of Mars recently measured the temperature to be −25.49 °F. What is the actual temperature?

(a) between −25.490 °F and −25.499 °F
(b) between −25.48 °F and −25.50 °F
(c) between −25.4 °F and −25.5 °F
(d) exactly −25.49 °F

2.4 Significant Figures in Calculations

When we use measured quantities in calculations, the results of the calculation must reflect the precision of the measured quantities. We should not lose or gain precision during mathematical operations.

MULTIPLICATION AND DIVISION

In multiplication or division, the result carries the same number of significant figures as the factor with the fewest significant figures.

For example:

$$\underset{\text{(3 sig. figures)}}{5.02} \times \underset{\text{(5 sig. figures)}}{89.665} \times \underset{\text{(2 sig. figures)}}{0.10} = 45.0118 = \underset{\text{(2 sig. figures)}}{45}$$

The intermediate result (in blue) is rounded to two significant figures to reflect the least precisely known factor (0.10), which has two significant figures.

In division, we follow the same rule.

$$\underset{\text{(4 sig. figures)}}{5.892} \div \underset{\text{(3 sig. figures)}}{6.10} = 0.96590 = \underset{\text{(3 sig. figures)}}{0.966}$$

The intermediate result (in blue) is rounded to three significant figures to reflect the least precisely known factor (6.10), which has three significant figures.

ROUNDING

When we round to the correct number of significant figures:

> we round down if the last (or leftmost) digit dropped is 4 or less;
> we round up if the last (or leftmost) digit dropped is 5 or more.

CHEMISTRY IN THE MEDIA

The COBE Satellite and Very Precise Measurements That Illuminate Our Cosmic Past

Since the earliest times, humans have wondered about the origins of our planet. Science has slowly probed this question and has developed theories for how the universe and the Earth began. The most accepted theory today about the origin of the universe is the Big Bang theory. According to the Big Bang theory, the universe began in a tremendous expansion about 13.7 billion years ago and has been expanding ever since. A measurable prediction of this theory is the presence of a remnant "background radiation" from the expansion of the universe. That remnant is characteristic of the current temperature of the universe. When the Big Bang occurred, the temperature of the universe was very hot and the associated radiation very bright. Today, 13.7 billion years later, the temperature of the universe is very cold and the background radiation very faint.

In the early 1960s, Robert H. Dicke, P. J. E. Peebles, and their coworkers at Princeton University began to build a device to measure this background radiation and thus take a direct look into the cosmological past and provide evidence for the Big Bang theory. At about the same time, quite by accident, Arno Penzias and Robert Wilson of Bell Telephone Laboratories measured excess radio noise on one of their communications satellites. As it turned out, this noise was the background radiation that the Princeton scientists were looking for. The two groups published papers together in 1965 reporting their findings along with the corresponding current temperature of the universe, about 3 degrees above absolute zero, or 3 K. We will define temperature measurement scales in Chapter 3. For now, know that 3 K is an extremely low temperature (460 degrees below zero on the Fahrenheit scale).

In 1989, the Cosmic Background Explorer (COBE) satellite was developed by NASA's Goddard Space Flight Center to measure the background radiation more precisely. The COBE satellite determined that the background radiation corresponded to a universe with a temperature of 2.735 K. (Notice the difference in significant figures from the previous measurement.) It went on to measure tiny fluctuations in the background radiation that amount to temperature differences of 1 part in 100,000. These fluctuations, though small, are an important prediction of the Big Bang theory. Scientists announced that the COBE satellite had produced the strongest evidence yet for the Big Bang theory of the creation of the universe. This is the way that science works. Measurement, and precision in measurement, are important to understanding the world—so important that we dedicate most of this chapter just to the concept of measurement.

CAN YOU ANSWER THIS? *How many significant figures are there in each of the preceding temperature measurements (3 K, 2.735 K)?*

▲ The COBE Satellite, launched in 1989 to measure background radiation. Background radiation is a remnant of the Big Bang—the expansion that is believed to have formed the universe.

Consider rounding each of these numbers to two significant figures.

2.33 rounds to 2.3
2.37 rounds to 2.4
2.34 rounds to 2.3
2.35 rounds to 2.4

We use only the *last (or leftmost) digit being dropped* to decide in which direction to round—we ignore all digits to the right of it. For example, to round 2.349 to two significant figures, only the 4 in the hundredths place (2.349) determines which direction to round—the 9 is irrelevant.

2.349 rounds to 2.3

For calculations involving multiple steps, we round only the final answer—we do not round off between steps. This prevents small rounding errors from affecting the final answer.

EXAMPLE 2.5 Significant Figures in Multiplication and Division

Perform each calculation to the correct number of significant figures.

(a) 1.01 × 0.12 × 53.51 ÷ 96
(b) 56.55 × 0.920 ÷ 34.2585

	SOLUTION
Round the intermediate result (in blue) to two significant figures to reflect the two significant figures in the least precisely known quantities (0.12 and 96).	**(a)** 1.01 × 0.12 × 53.51 ÷ 96 = 0.067556 = 0.068
Round the intermediate result (in blue) to three significant figures to reflect the three significant figures in the least precisely known quantity (0.920).	**(b)** 56.55 × 0.920 ÷ 34.2585 = 1.51863 = 1.52

▶SKILLBUILDER 2.5 | Significant Figures in Multiplication and Division

Perform each calculation to the correct number of significant figures.

(a) 1.10 × 0.512 × 1.301 × 0.005 ÷ 3.4
(b) 4.562 × 3.99870 ÷ 89.5

▶FOR MORE PRACTICE Examples 2.21, 2.22; Problems 57, 58, 59, 60.

ADDITION AND SUBTRACTION

In addition or subtraction, the result carries the same number of decimal places as the quantity carrying the fewest decimal places.

For example:

$$\begin{array}{r} 5.74 \\ 0.823 \\ +2.651 \\ \hline 9.214 \end{array} = 9.21$$

It is sometimes helpful to draw a vertical line directly to the right of the number with the fewest decimal places. The line shows the number of decimal places that should be in the answer.

We round the intermediate answer (in blue) to two decimal places because the quantity with the fewest decimal places (5.74) has two decimal places.

For subtraction, we follow the same rule. For example:

$$\begin{array}{r} 4.8 \\ -3.965 \\ \hline 0.835 \end{array} = 0.8$$

We round the intermediate answer (in blue) to one decimal place because the quantity with the fewest decimal places (4.8) has one decimal place. Remember: *For multiplication and division, the quantity with the fewest* ***significant figures*** *determines the number of significant figures in the answer. For addition and subtraction, the quantity with the fewest* ***decimal places*** *determines the number of decimal places in* *the answer.* In multiplication and division we focus on significant figures, but in addition and subtraction we focus on decimal places. When a problem involves addition and subtraction, the answer may have a different number of significant figures than the initial quantities. For example:

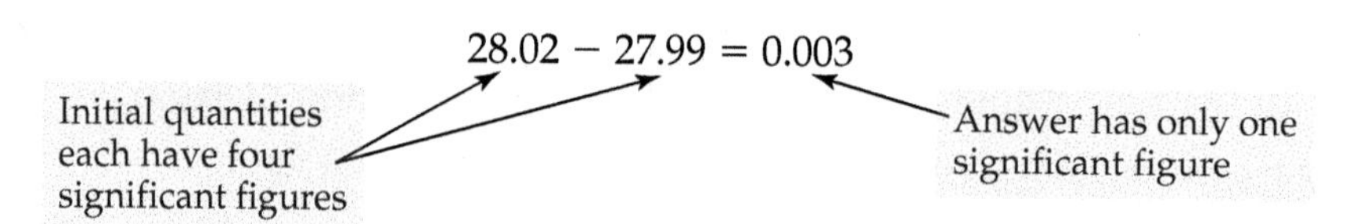
28.02 − 27.99 = 0.003
Initial quantities each have four significant figures
Answer has only one significant figure

The answer has only one significant figure, even though the initial quantities each had four significant figures.

EXAMPLE 2.6 Significant Figures in Addition and Subtraction

Perform the calculations to the correct number of significant figures.

(a)
$$\begin{array}{r} 0.987 \\ +125.1 \\ -1.22 \\ \hline \end{array}$$

(b)
$$\begin{array}{r} 0.765 \\ -3.449 \\ -5.98 \\ \hline \end{array}$$

SOLUTION

Round the intermediate answer (in blue) to one decimal place to reflect the quantity with the fewest decimal places (125.1). Notice that 125.1 is not the quantity with the fewest significant figures—it has four while the other quantities only have three—but because it has the fewest decimal places, it determines the number of decimal places in the answer.

(a)
$$\begin{array}{r} 0.987 \\ +125.1 \\ -1.22 \\ \hline 124.867 \end{array} = 124.9$$

Round the intermediate answer (in blue) to two decimal places to reflect the quantity with the fewest decimal places (5.98).

(b)
$$\begin{array}{r} 0.765 \\ -3.449 \\ -5.98 \\ \hline -8.664 \end{array} = -8.66$$

▶SKILLBUILDER 2.6 | Significant Figures in Addition and Subtraction

Perform the calculations to the correct number of significant figures.

(a)
$$\begin{array}{r} 2.18 \\ +5.621 \\ +1.5870 \\ -1.8 \\ \hline \end{array}$$

(b)
$$\begin{array}{r} 7.876 \\ -0.56 \\ +123.792 \\ \hline \end{array}$$

▶FOR MORE PRACTICE Example 2.23; Problems 61, 62, 63, 64.

CALCULATIONS INVOLVING BOTH MULTIPLICATION/DIVISION AND ADDITION/SUBTRACTION

In calculations involving both multiplication/division and addition/subtraction, we do the steps in parentheses first; determine the correct number of significant figures in the intermediate answer; then do the remaining steps.

For example:

$$3.489 \times (5.67 - 2.3)$$

We complete the subtraction step first.

$$5.67 - 2.3 = 3.37$$

We use the subtraction rule to determine that the intermediate answer (3.37) has only one significant decimal place. To avoid small errors, it is best not to round at this point; instead, we underline the least significant figure as a reminder.

$$= 3.489 \times 3.\underline{3}7$$

We then do the multiplication step.

$$3.489 \times 3.\underline{3}7 = 11.758 = 12$$

We use the multiplication rule to determine that the intermediate answer (11.758) rounds to two significant figures (12) because it is limited by the two significant figures in $3.\underline{3}7$.

EXAMPLE 2.7 Significant Figures in Calculations Involving Both Multiplication/Division and Addition/Subtraction

Perform the calculations to the correct number of significant figures.

(a) $6.78 \times 5.903 \times (5.489 - 5.01)$

(b) $19.667 - (5.4 \times 0.916)$

SOLUTION

Do the step in parentheses first. Use the subtraction rule to mark 0.479 to two decimal places since 5.01, the number in the parentheses with the least number of decimal places, has two.

Then perform the multiplication and round the answer to two significant figures since the number with the least number of significant figures has two.

(a) $6.78 \times 5.903 \times (5.489 - 5.01)$

$= 6.78 \times 5.903 \times (0.479)$

$= 6.78 \times 5.903 \times 0.4\underline{7}9$

$6.78 \times 5.903 \times 0.4\underline{7}90 = 19.1707$

$= 19$

Do the step in parentheses first. The number with the least number of significant figures within the parentheses (5.4) has two, so mark the answer to two significant figures.

Then perform the subtraction and round the answer to one decimal place since the number with the least number of decimal places has one.

(b) $19.667 - (5.\underline{4} \times 0.916)$

$= 19.667 - (4.9464)$

$= 19.667 - 4.\underline{9}464$

$19.667 - 4.\underline{9}464 = 14.7206$

$= 14.7$

▶SKILLBUILDER 2.7 | Significant Figures in Calculations Involving Both Multiplication/Division and Addition/Subtraction

Perform each calculation to the correct number of significant figures.

(a) $3.897 \times (782.3 - 451.88)$

(b) $(4.58 \div 1.239) - 0.578$

▶FOR MORE PRACTICE Example 2.24; Problems 65, 66, 67, 68.

CONCEPTUAL CHECKPOINT 2.3

Which calculation would have its result reported to the *greater* number of significant figures?

(a) 3 + (15/12)

(b) (3 + 15)/12

2.5 The Basic Units of Measurement

By themselves, numbers have limited meaning. Read this sentence: When my son was 7 he walked 3, and when he was 4 he threw his baseball 8 and said his school was 5 away. The sentence is confusing because we don't know what the numbers mean—the **units** are missing. The meaning becomes clear, however, when we add the missing units to the numbers: When my son was 7 *months old* he walked 3 *steps*, and when he was 4 *years old* he threw his baseball 8 *feet* and said his school was 5 *minutes* away. Units make all the difference. In chemistry, units are critical. Never write a number by itself; always use its associated units—otherwise your work will be as confusing as the initial sentence.

The two most common unit systems are the **English system,** used in the United States, and the **metric system,** used in most of the rest of the world. The English system uses units such as inches, yards, and pounds, while the metric system uses centimeters, meters, and kilograms. The most convenient system for science measurements is based on the metric system and is called the **International System** of units or **SI units.** SI units are a set of standard units agreed on by scientists throughout the world.

The abbreviation *SI* comes from the French *le Système International.*

THE STANDARD UNITS

TABLE 2.1 Important SI Standard Units

Quantity	Unit	Symbol
Length	meter	m
Mass	kilogram	kg
Time	second	s
Temperature*	kelvin	K

*Temperature units are discussed in Chapter 3.

Table 2.1 lists the standard units in the SI system. They include the **meter (m)** as the standard unit of length; the **kilogram (kg)** as the standard unit of mass; and the **second (s)** as the standard unit of time. Each of these standard units is precisely defined. The meter is defined as the distance light travels in a certain period of

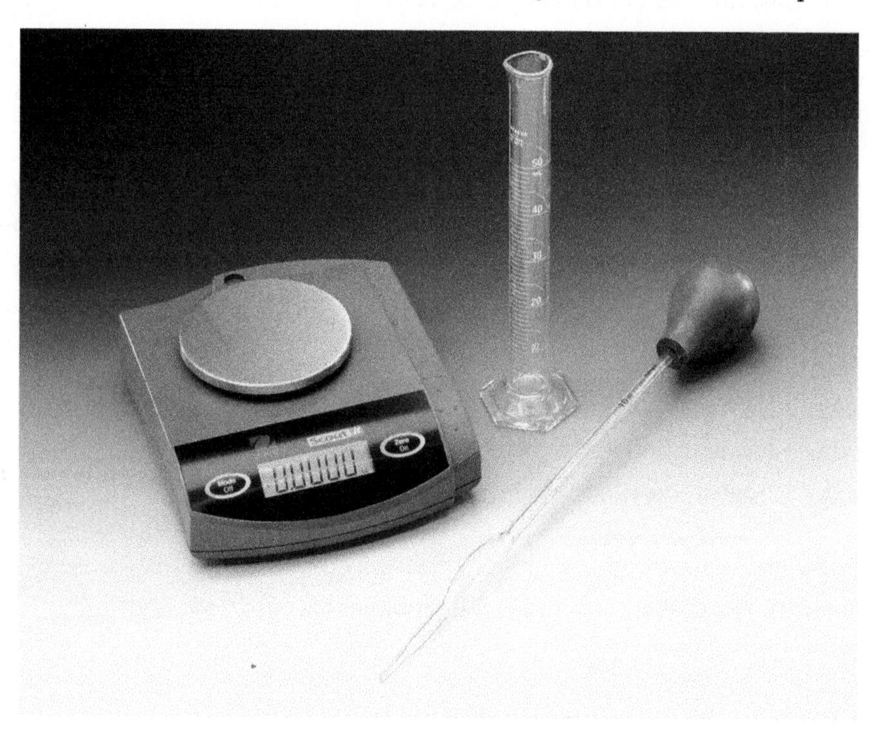

▶ Science uses instruments to make measurements. Every instrument is calibrated in a particular unit without which the measurements would be meaningless.

▲ **FIGURE 2.5 The standard of length** The definition of a meter, established by international agreement in 1983, is the distance that light travels in vacuum in 1/299,792,458 s. Question: Why is such a precise standard necessary?

▲ **FIGURE 2.6 The standard of mass** A duplicate of the international standard kilogram, called kilogram 20, is kept at the National Institute of Standards and Technology near Washington, DC.

▲ **FIGURE 2.7 The standard of time** The second is defined, using an atomic clock, as the duration of 9,192,631,770 periods of the radiation emitted from a certain transition in a cesium-133 atom.

time: 1/299,792,458 s (▲ Figure 2.5). (The speed of light is 3.0×10^8 m/s.) The kilogram is defined as the mass of a block of metal kept at the International Bureau of Weights and Measures at Sèvres, France (▲ Figure 2.6). The second is defined using an atomic standard (▲ Figure 2.7).

A nickel (5 cents) has a mass of about 5 grams.

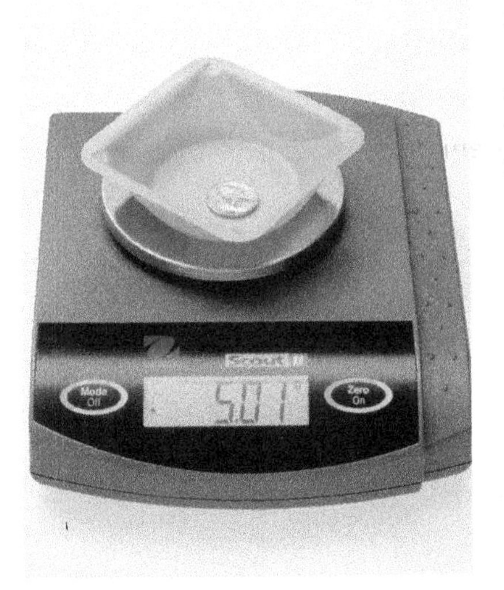

Most people are familiar with the SI standard unit of time, the second. However, if you live in the United States, you may be less familiar with the meter and the kilogram. The meter is slightly longer than a yard (a yard is 36 in. while a meter is 39.37 in.). A 100-yd football field measures only 91.4 m.

The kilogram is a measure of mass, which is different from weight. The **mass** of an object is a measure of the quantity of matter within it, whereas the weight of an object is a measure of the gravitational pull on that matter. Consequently, weight depends on gravity while mass does not. If you were to weigh yourself on Mars, for example, the lower gravity would pull you toward the scale less than Earth's gravity would, resulting in a lower weight. A 150-lb person on Earth weighs only 57 lb on Mars. However, the person's mass, the quantity of matter in his or her body, remains the same. A kilogram of mass is the equivalent of 2.205 lb of weight on Earth, so if we express mass in kilograms, a 150-lb person on Earth has a mass of approximately 68 kg. A second common unit of mass is the gram (g), defined as follows:

$$1000\,\text{g} = 10^3\,\text{g} = 1\,\text{kg}$$

PREFIX MULTIPLIERS

The SI system employs **prefix multipliers** (Table 2.2) with the standard units. These multipliers change the value of the unit by powers of 10. For example, the kilometer (km) has the prefix *kilo-*, meaning 1000 or 10^3. Therefore:

$$1\,\text{km} = 1000\,\text{m} = 10^3\,\text{m}$$

Similarly, the millisecond (ms) has the prefix *milli-*, meaning 0.001 or 10^{-3}.

$$1\,\text{ms} = 0.001\,\text{s} = 10^{-3}\,\text{s}$$

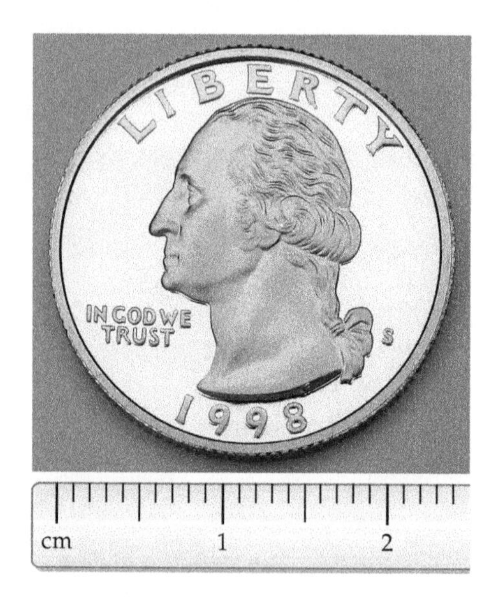

▲ The diameter of a quarter is about 2.4 cm. **Question:** Why would you *not* use meters to make this measurement?

TABLE 2.2 SI Prefix Multipliers

Prefix	Symbol	Multiplier	
tera-	T	1,000,000,000,000	(10^{12})
giga-	G	1,000,000,000	(10^{9})
mega-	M	1,000,000	(10^{6})
kilo-	k	1,000	(10^{3})
deci-	d	0.1	(10^{-1})
centi-	c	0.01	(10^{-2})
milli-	m	0.001	(10^{-3})
micro-	μ	0.000001	(10^{-6})
nano-	n	0.000000001	(10^{-9})
pico-	p	0.000000000001	(10^{-12})
femto-	f	0.000000000000001	(10^{-15})

The prefix multipliers allow us to express a wide range of measurements in units that are similar in size to the quantity we are measuring. You should choose the prefix multiplier that is most convenient for a particular measurement. For example, to measure the diameter of a quarter, use centimeters because a quarter has a diameter of about 2.4 cm. A centimeter is a common metric unit and is about equivalent to the width of a pinky finger (2.54 cm = 1 in.). The millimeter could also work to express the diameter of the quarter; then the quarter would measure 24 mm. The kilometer, however, would not work as well since, in that unit, the quarter's diameter is 0.000024 km. Pick a unit similar in size to (or smaller than) the quantity you are measuring. Consider expressing the length of a short chemical bond, about 1.2×10^{-10} m. Which prefix multiplier should you use? The most convenient one is probably the picometer (pico = 10^{-12}). Chemical bonds measure about 120 pm.

TABLE 2.3 Some Common Units and Their Equivalents

Length
1 kilometer (km) = 0.6214 mile (mi)
1 meter (m) = 39.37 inches (in.)
= 1.094 yards (yd)
1 foot (ft) = 30.48 centimeters (cm)
1 inch (in.) = 2.54 centimeters (cm) (exact)
Mass
1 kilogram (kg) = 2.205 pounds (lb)
1 pound (lb) = 453.59 grams (g)
1 ounce (oz) = 28.35 grams (g)
Volume
1 liter (L) = 1000 milliliters (mL)
= 1000 cubic centimeters (cm^3)
1 liter (L) = 1.057 quarts (qt)
1 U.S. gallon (gal) = 3.785 liters (L)

CONCEPTUAL CHECKPOINT 2.4

What would be the most convenient unit to express the dimensions of a polio virus, which is about 2.8×10^{-8} m in diameter?

(a) Mm

(b) mm

(c) μm

(d) nm

DERIVED UNITS

A derived unit is formed from other units. For example, many units of **volume,** a measure of space, are derived units. Any unit of length, when cubed (raised to the third power), becomes a unit of volume. Therefore, cubic meters (m^3), cubic centimeters (cm^3), and cubic millimeters (mm^3) are all units of volume. In these units, a three-bedroom house has a volume of about 630 m^3, a can of soda pop has a volume of about 350 cm^3, and a rice grain has a volume of about 3 mm^3. We also use the **liter (L)** and milliliter (mL) to express volume (although these are not derived units). A gallon is equal to 3.785 L. A milliliter is equivalent to 1 cm^3. Table 2.3 lists some common units and their equivalents.

2.6 Problem Solving and Unit Conversions

Problem solving is one of the most important skills you will acquire in this course. Not only will this skill help you succeed in chemistry, but it will help you to learn how to think critically, which is important in every area of knowledge. My daughter, a freshman in high school, recently came to me for help on an algebra problem. The statement of the problem went something like this:

> Sam and Sara live 11 miles apart. Sam leaves his house traveling at 6 miles per hour toward Sara's house. Sara leaves her house traveling at 3 miles per hour toward Sam's house. How much time until Sam and Sara meet?

Solving the problem requires setting up the equation $11 - 6t = 3t$. Although my daughter could solve this equation for t quite easily, getting to the equation from the problem statement was another matter—that process requires *critical thinking*. You can't succeed in chemistry—or in life, really—without developing critical thinking skills. Learning how to solve chemical problems will help you develop these kinds of skills.

Although no simple formula applies to every problem, you can learn problem-solving strategies and begin to develop some chemical intuition. Many of the problems you will solve in this course can be thought of as *unit conversion problems*, where you are given one or more quantities and asked to convert them into different units. Other problems require the use of *specific equations* to get to the information you are trying to find. In the sections that follow, we examine strategies to help you solve both of these types of problems. Of course, many problems contain both conversions and equations, requiring the combination of these strategies, and some problems may require an altogether different approach but the basic tools you learn here can be applied to those problems as well.

CONVERTING BETWEEN UNITS

Using units as a guide to solving problems is called dimensional analysis.

Units are critical in calculations. Knowing how to work with and manipulate units in calculations is a very important part of problem solving. In calculations, units help determine correctness. Units should always be included in calculations, and we can think of many calculations as converting from one unit to another. Units are multiplied, divided, and canceled like any other algebraic quantity.

Remember:

1. Always write every number with its associated unit. Never ignore units; they are critical.
2. Always include units in your calculations, dividing them and multiplying them as if they were algebraic quantities. Do not let units magically appear or disappear in calculations. Units must flow logically from beginning to end.

Consider converting 17.6 in. to centimeters. We know from Table 2.3 that 1 in. = 2.54 cm. To determine how many centimeters are in 17.6 in., we perform the conversion:

$$17.6\ \cancel{\text{in.}} \times \frac{2.54\ \text{cm}}{1\ \cancel{\text{in.}}} = 44.7\ \text{cm}$$

The unit *in.* cancels and we are left with *cm* as our final unit. The quantity $\frac{2.54\ \text{cm}}{1\ \text{in.}}$ is a **conversion factor** between *in.* and *cm*—it is a quotient with *cm* on top and *in.* on bottom.

For most conversion problems, we are given a quantity in some unit and asked to convert the quantity to another unit. These calculations take the form:

$$\text{information given} \times \text{conversion factor(s)} = \text{information sought}$$

$$\cancel{\text{given unit}} \times \frac{\text{desired unit}}{\cancel{\text{given unit}}} = \text{desired unit}$$

Conversion factors are constructed from any two quantities known to be equivalent. In our example, $2.54\,\text{cm} = 1\,\text{in.}$, so we construct the conversion factor by dividing both sides of the equality by 1 in. and canceling the units.

$$2.54\ \text{cm} = 1\ \text{in.}$$

$$\frac{2.54\ \text{cm}}{1\ \text{in.}} = \frac{1\ \cancel{\text{in.}}}{1\ \cancel{\text{in.}}}$$

$$\frac{2.54\ \text{cm}}{1\ \text{in.}} = 1$$

The quantity $\frac{2.54\ \text{cm}}{1\ \text{in.}}$ is equal to 1 and can be used to convert between inches and centimeters.

What if we want to perform the conversion the other way, from centimeters to inches? If we try to use the same conversion factor, the units do not cancel correctly.

$$44.7\,\text{cm} \times \frac{2.54\ \text{cm}}{1\ \text{in.}} = \frac{114\ \text{cm}^2}{\text{in.}}$$

The units in the answer, as well as the value of the answer, are incorrect. The unit $\text{cm}^2/\text{in.}$ is not correct, and, based on our knowledge that centimeters are smaller than inches, we know that 44.7 cm cannot be equivalent to 114 in. In solving problems, always check if the final units are correct, and consider whether or not the magnitude of the answer makes sense. In this case, our mistake was in how we used the conversion factor. We must invert it.

$$44.7\ \cancel{\text{cm}} \times \frac{1\ \text{in.}}{2.54\ \cancel{\text{cm}}} = 17.6\ \text{in.}$$

Conversion factors can be inverted because they are equal to 1 and the inverse of 1 is 1.

$$\frac{1}{1} = 1$$

Therefore,

$$\frac{2.54\ \text{cm}}{1\ \text{in.}} = 1 = \frac{1\ \text{in.}}{2.54\ \text{cm}}$$

We can diagram conversions using a **solution map.** A solution map is a visual outline that shows the strategic route required to solve a problem. For unit conversion, the solution map focuses on units and how to convert from one unit to another. The solution map for converting from inches to centimeters is:

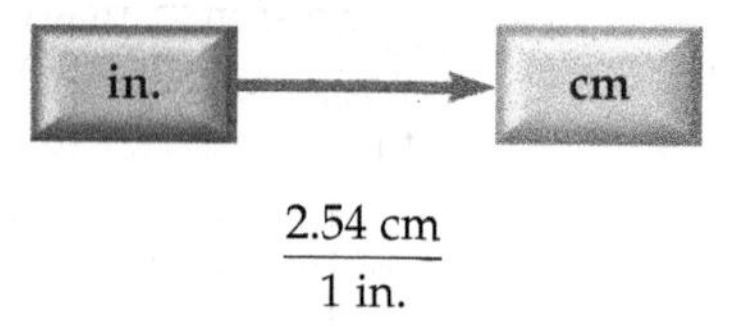

$$\frac{2.54\ \text{cm}}{1\ \text{in.}}$$

The solution map for converting from centimeters to inches is:

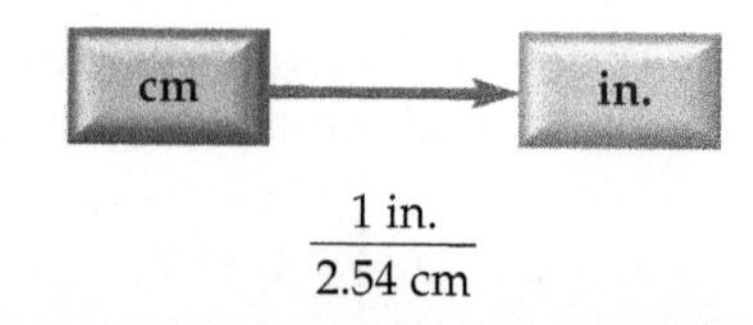

$$\frac{1\ \text{in.}}{2.54\ \text{cm}}$$

Each arrow in a solution map for a unit conversion has an associated conversion factor with the units of the previous step in the denominator and the units of the following step in the numerator. For one-step problems such as these, the solution map is only moderately helpful, but for multistep problems, it becomes a powerful way to develop a problem-solving strategy. In the section that follows, you will learn how to incorporate solution maps into an overall problem-solving strategy.

GENERAL PROBLEM-SOLVING STRATEGY

In this book, we use a standard problem-solving procedure that can be adapted to many of the problems encountered in chemistry and beyond. Solving any problem essentially requires you to assess the information given in the problem and devise a way to get to the information asked for. In other words, you need to

- Identify the starting point (the ***given*** information).
- Identify the end point (what you must ***find***).
- Devise a way to get from the starting point to the end point using what is given as well as what you already know or can look up. You can use a *solution map* to diagram the steps required to get from the starting point to the end point.

In graphic form, we can represent this progression as

Given ⟶ **Solution Map** ⟶ **Find**

One of the main difficulties beginning students have when trying to solve problems in general chemistry is not knowing where to start. Although no problem-solving procedure is applicable to all problems, the following four-step procedure can be helpful in working through many of the numerical problems you will encounter in this book.

1. **Sort.** Begin by sorting the information in the problem. *Given* information is the basic data provided by the problem—often one or more numbers with their associated units. The given information is the starting point for the problem. *Find* indicates what the problem is asking you to find (the end point of the problem).
2. **Strategize.** This is usually the hardest part of solving a problem. In this step, you must create a solution map—the series of steps that will get you from the given information to the information you are trying to find. You have already seen solution maps for simple unit conversion problems. Each arrow in a solution map represents a computational step. On the left side of the arrow is the quantity (or quantities) you had before the step; on the right side of the arrow is the quantity (or quantities) you will have after the step; and below the arrow is the information you need to get from one to the other—the relationship between the quantities.

   Often such relationships will take the form of conversion factors or equations. These may be given in the problem, in which case you will have written them down under "Given" in Step 1. Usually, however, you will need other information—which may include physical constants, formulas, or conversion factors—to help get you from what you are given to what you must find. You may recall this information from what you have learned or you can look it up in the chapters or tables within the book.

   In some cases, you may get stuck at the strategize step. If you cannot figure out how to get from the given information to the information you are asked to find, you might try working backwards. For example, you may want to look at the units of the quantity you are trying to find and look for conversion factors to get to the units of the given quantity. You may even try a combination of strategies; work forward, backward, or some of both. If you persist, you will develop a strategy to solve the problem.

3. **Solve.** This is the easiest part of solving a problem. Once you set up the problem properly and devise a solution map, you follow the map to solve the problem. Carry out mathematical operations (paying attention to the rules for significant figures in calculations) and cancel units as needed.
4. **Check.** This is the step most often overlooked by beginning students. Experienced problem solvers always ask, Does this answer make physical sense? Are the units correct? Is the number of significant figures correct? When solving multistep problems, errors easily creep into the solution. You can catch most of these errors by simply checking the answer. For example, suppose you are calculating the number of atoms in a gold coin and end up with an answer of 1.1×10^{-6} atoms. Could the gold coin really be composed of one-millionth of one atom?

In Examples 2.8 and 2.9, you will find this problem-solving procedure applied to unit conversion problems. The procedure is summarized in the left column, and two examples of applying the procedure are shown in the middle and right columns. This three-column format is used in selected examples throughout this text. It allows you to see how a particular procedure can be applied to two different problems. Work through one problem first (from top to bottom) and then examine how the same procedure is applied to the other problem. Recognizing the commonalities and differences between problems is a key part of problem solving.

PROBLEM-SOLVING PROCEDURE	**EXAMPLE 2.8** **Unit Conversion** Convert 7.8 km to miles.	**EXAMPLE 2.9** **Unit Conversion** Convert 0.825 m to millimeters.
SORT Begin by sorting the information in the problem into *given* and *find*.	**GIVEN:** 7.8 km **FIND:** mi	**GIVEN:** 0.825 m **FIND:** mm
STRATEGIZE Draw a *solution map* for the problem. Begin with the *given* quantity and symbolize each step with an arrow. Below the arrow, write the conversion factor for that step. The solution map ends at the *find* quantity. (In these examples, the relationships used in the conversions are below the solution map.)	**SOLUTION MAP** km → mi $\frac{0.6214\text{ mi}}{1\text{ km}}$ **RELATIONSHIPS USED** $1\text{ km} = 0.6214\text{ mi}$ (This conversion factor is from Table 2.3.)	**SOLUTION MAP** m → mm $\frac{1\text{ mm}}{10^{-3}\text{ m}}$ **RELATIONSHIPS USED** $1\text{ mm} = 10^{-3}\text{ m}$ (This conversion factor is from Table 2.2.)
SOLVE Follow the *solution map* to solve the problem. Begin with the *given* quantity and its units. Multiply by the appropriate conversion factor, canceling units to arrive at the *find* quantity.	**SOLUTION** $7.8\text{ km} \times \frac{0.6214\text{ mi}}{1\text{ km}} = 4.84692\text{ mi}$ $4.84692\text{ mi} = 4.8\text{ mi}$	**SOLUTION** $0.825\text{ m} \times \frac{1\text{ mm}}{10^{-3}\text{ m}} = 825\text{ mm}$ $825\text{ mm} = 825\text{ mm}$
Round the answer to the correct number of significant figures. (If possible, obtain conversion factors to enough significant figures so that they do not limit the number of significant figures in the answer.)	Round the answer to two significant figures, since the quantity given has two significant figures.	Leave the answer with three significant figures, since the quantity given has three significant figures and the conversion factor is a definition and therefore does not limit the number of significant figures in the answer.

CHECK
Check your answer. Are the units correct? Does the answer make physical sense?

The units, mi, are correct. The magnitude of the answer is reasonable. A mile is longer than a kilometer, so the value in miles should be smaller than the value in kilometers.

The units, mm, are correct and the magnitude is reasonable. A millimeter is shorter than a meter, so the value in millimeters should be larger than the value in meters.

▶SKILLBUILDER 2.8
Unit Conversion

Convert 56.0 cm to inches.

▶FOR MORE PRACTICE Example 2.25; Problems 73, 74, 75, 76.

▶SKILLBUILDER 2.9
Unit Conversion

Convert 5678 m to kilometers.

▶FOR MORE PRACTICE Problems 69, 70, 71, 72.

CONCEPTUAL CHECKPOINT 2.5

Which conversion factor would you use to convert a distance in meters to kilometers?

(a) $\dfrac{1\,\text{m}}{10^3\,\text{km}}$

(b) $\dfrac{10^3\,\text{m}}{1\,\text{km}}$

(c) $\dfrac{1\,\text{km}}{10^3\,\text{m}}$

(d) $\dfrac{10^3\,\text{km}}{1\,\text{m}}$

2.7 Solving Multistep Unit Conversion Problems

When solving multistep unit conversion problems, we follow the preceding procedure, but we add more steps to the solution map. Each step in the solution map should have a conversion factor with the units of the previous step in the denominator and the units of the following step in the numerator. For example, suppose we want to convert 194 cm to feet. The solution map begins with cm, and we use the relationship 2.54 cm = 1 in to convert to in. We then use the relationship 12 in. = 1 ft to convert to ft.

SOLUTION MAP

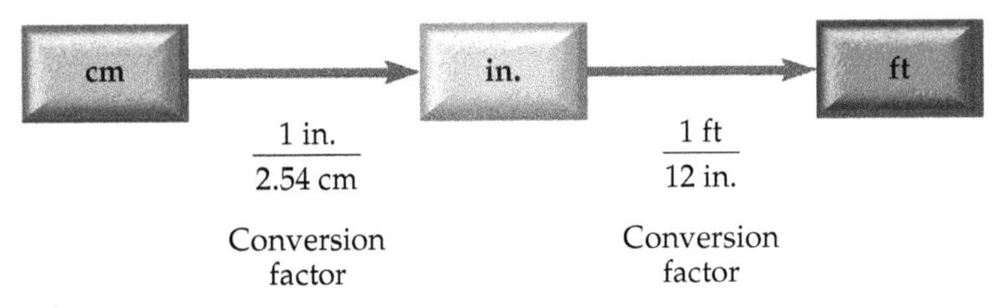

Once the solution map is complete, we follow it to solve the problem.

SOLUTION

$$194\,\text{cm} \times \frac{1\,\text{in.}}{2.54\,\text{cm}} \times \frac{1\,\text{ft}}{12\,\text{in.}} = 6.3648\,\text{ft}$$

Since 1 foot is defined as 12 in., it does not limit significant figures.

We then round to the correct number of significant figures—in this case, three (from 194 cm, which has three significant figures).

$$6.3648 \text{ ft} = 6.36 \text{ ft}$$

Finally, we check the answer. The units of the answer, feet, are the correct ones, and the magnitude seems about right. Since a foot is larger than a centimeter, it is reasonable that the value in feet is smaller than the value in centimeters.

EXAMPLE 2.10 Solving Multistep Unit Conversion Problems

A recipe for making creamy pasta sauce calls for 0.75 L of cream. Your measuring cup measures only in cups. How many cups of cream should you use? (4 cups = 1 quart)

SORT Begin by sorting the information in the problem into given and find.	**GIVEN:** 0.75 L **FIND:** cups
STRATEGIZE Draw a solution map for the problem. Begin with the *given* quantity and symbolize each step with an arrow. Below the arrow, write the conversion factor for that step. The solution map ends at the find quantity.	**SOLUTION MAP** 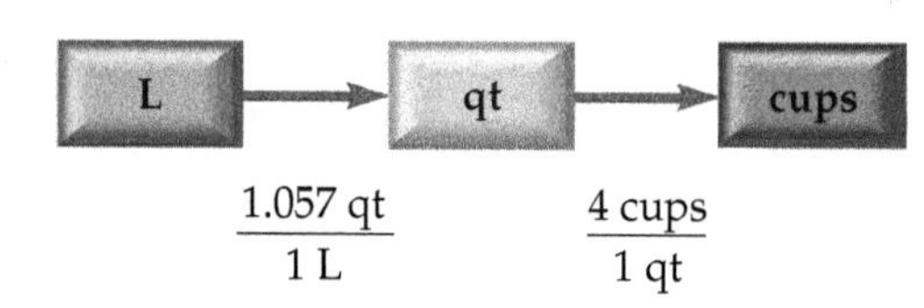 $\frac{1.057 \text{ qt}}{1 \text{ L}}$ $\frac{4 \text{ cups}}{1 \text{ qt}}$ **RELATIONSHIPS USED** 1.057 qt = 1 L (from Table 2.3.) 4 cups = 1 qt (given in problem statement)
SOLVE Follow the solution map to solve the problem. Begin with 0.75 L and multiply by the appropriate conversion factor, canceling units to arrive at qt. Then, use the second conversion factor to arrive at cups. Round the answer to the correct number of significant figures. In this case, round the answer to two significant figures, since the quantity given has two significant figures.	**SOLUTION** $0.75 \text{ L} \times \frac{1.057 \text{ qt}}{1 \text{ L}} \times \frac{4 \text{ cups}}{1 \text{ qt}} = 3.171 \text{ cups}$ $3.171 \text{ cups} = 3.2 \text{ cups}$
CHECK Check your answer. Are the units correct? Does the answer make physical sense?	The answer has the right units (cups) and seems reasonable. A cup is smaller than a liter, so the value in cups should be larger than the value in liters.

▶SKILLBUILDER 2.10 | Solving Multistep Unit Conversion Problems

A recipe calls for 1.2 cups of oil. How many liters of oil is this?

▶FOR MORE PRACTICE Problems 85, 86.

EXAMPLE 2.11 Solving Multistep Unit Conversion Problems

One lap of a running track measures 255 m. To run 10.0 km, how many laps should you run?

SORT Begin by sorting the information in the problem into given and find. You are given a distance in km and asked to find the distance in laps. You are also given the quantity 255 m per lap, which is a conversion factor between m and laps.	**GIVEN:** 10.0 km 255 m = 1 lap **FIND:** number of laps

STRATEGIZE

Build the solution map beginning with km and ending at laps. Focus on the units.

SOLUTION MAP

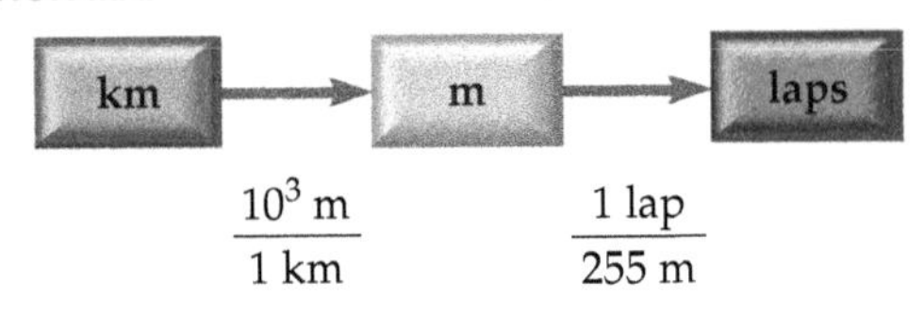

RELATIONSHIPS USED

1 km = 10^3 m (from Table 2.2)
1 lap = 255 m (given in problem)

SOLVE

Follow the solution map to solve the problem. Begin with 10.0 km and multiply by the appropriate conversion factor, canceling units to arrive at m. Then, use the second conversion factor to arrive at laps. Round the intermediate answer (in blue) to three significant figures because it is limited by the three significant figures in the given quantity, 10.0 km.

SOLUTION

$$10.0\ \cancel{\text{km}} \times \frac{10^3\ \cancel{\text{m}}}{1\ \cancel{\text{km}}} \times \frac{1\ \text{lap}}{255\ \cancel{\text{m}}} = 39.216\ \text{laps} = 39.2\ \text{laps}$$

CHECK

Check your answer. Are the units correct? Does the answer make physical sense?

The units of the answer are correct, and the value of the answer makes sense: If a lap is 255 m, there are about 4 laps to each km (1000 m), so it seems reasonable that you would have to run about 40 laps to cover 10 km.

▶**SKILLBUILDER 2.11 | Solving Multistep Unit Conversion Problems**

A running track measures 1056 ft per lap. To run 15.0 km, how many laps should you run? (1 mi = 5280 ft)

▶**SKILLBUILDER PLUS**

An island is 5.72 nautical mi from the coast. How far is the island in meters? (1 nautical mi = 1.151 mi)

▶**FOR MORE PRACTICE** Problems 83, 84.

2.8 Units Raised to a Power

The unit cm^3 is often abbreviated as cc.

When converting quantities with units raised to a power, such as cubic centimeters (cm^3), *the conversion factor must also be raised to that power.* For example, suppose we want to convert the size of a motorcycle engine reported as 1255 cm^3 to cubic inches. We know that

$$2.54\ \text{cm} = 1\ \text{in.}$$

Most tables of conversion factors do not include conversions between cubic units, but we can derive them from the conversion factors for the basic units. We cube both sides of the preceding equality to obtain the proper conversion factor.

2.54 cm = 1 in. is an exact conversion factor. After cubing, we retain five significant figures so that the conversion factor does not limit the four significant figures of our original quantity (1255 cm^3).

$$(2.54\ \text{cm})^3 = (1\ \text{in.})^3$$
$$(2.54)^3\ \text{cm}^3 = 1^3\ \text{in.}^3$$
$$16.387\ \text{cm}^3 = 1\ \text{in.}^3$$

We can do the same thing in fractional form.

$$\frac{1\ \text{in.}}{2.54\ \text{cm}} = \frac{(1\ \text{in.})^3}{(2.54\ \text{cm})^3} = \frac{1\ \text{in.}^3}{16.387\ \text{cm}^3}$$

We then proceed with the conversion in the usual manner.

CHEMISTRY AND HEALTH

Drug Dosage

The unit of choice in specifying drug dosage is the milligram (mg). Pick up a bottle of aspirin, Tylenol, or any other common drug, and the label tells you the number of milligrams of the active ingredient contained in each tablet, as well as the number of tablets to take per dose. The following table shows the mass of the active ingredient per pill in several common pain relievers, all reported in milligrams. The remainder of each tablet is composed of inactive ingredients such as cellulose (or fiber) and starch.

The recommended adult dose for many of these pain relievers is one or two tablets every 4 to 8 hours (depending on the specific pain reliever). Notice that the extra-strength version of each pain reliever just contains a higher dose of the same compound found in the regular-strength version. For the pain relievers listed, three regular-strength tablets are the equivalent of two extra-strength tablets (and probably cost less).

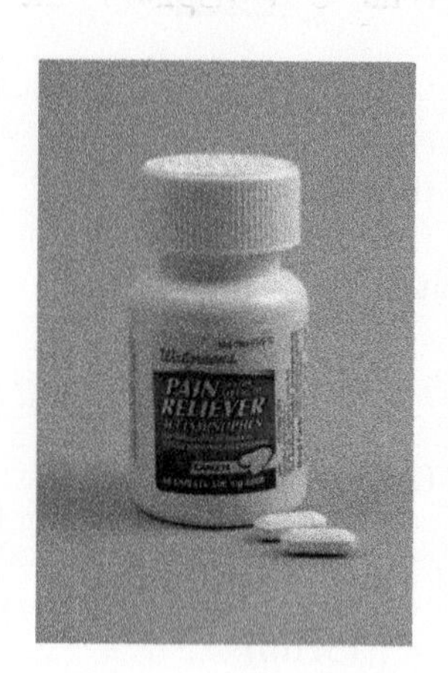

The dosages given in the table are fairly standard for each drug, regardless of the brand. When you look on your drugstore shelf, you will find many different brands of regular-strength ibuprofen, some sold under the generic name and others sold under their brand names (such as Advil). However, if you look closely at the labels, you will find that they all contain the same thing: 200 mg of the compound ibuprofen. There is no difference in the compound or in the amount of the compound. Yet these pain relievers will most likely all have different prices. Choose the least expensive. Why pay more for the same thing?

CAN YOU ANSWER THIS? *Convert each of the doses in the table to ounces. Why are drug dosages not listed in ounces?*

Drug Mass per Pill for Common Pain Relievers

Pain Reliever	Mass of Active Ingredient per Pill
Aspirin	325 mg
Aspirin, extra strength	500 mg
Ibuprofen (Advil)	200 mg
Ibuprofen, extra strength	300 mg
Acetaminophen (Tylenol)	325 mg
Acetaminophen, extra strength	500 mg

SOLUTION MAP

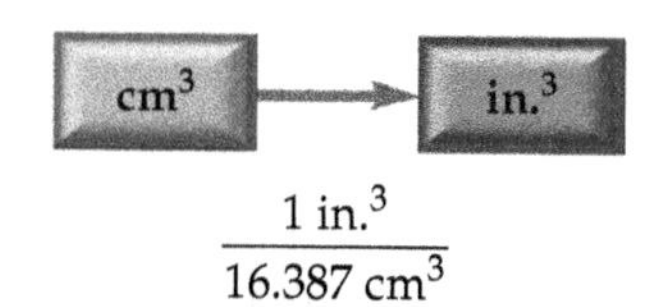

$$\frac{1 \text{ in.}^3}{16.387 \text{ cm}^3}$$

SOLUTION

$$1255 \text{ cm}^3 \times \frac{1 \text{ in.}^3}{16.387 \text{ cm}^3} = 76.5851 \text{ in.}^3 = 76.59 \text{ in.}^3$$

EXAMPLE 2.12 Converting Quantities Involving Units Raised to a Power

A circle has an area of 2659 cm^2. What is its area in square meters?

SORT

You are given an area in square centimeters and asked to convert the area to square meters.

GIVEN: 2659 cm^2

FIND: m^2

STRATEGIZE

Build a solution map beginning with cm^2 and ending with m^2. Remember that you must square the conversion factor.

SOLUTION MAP

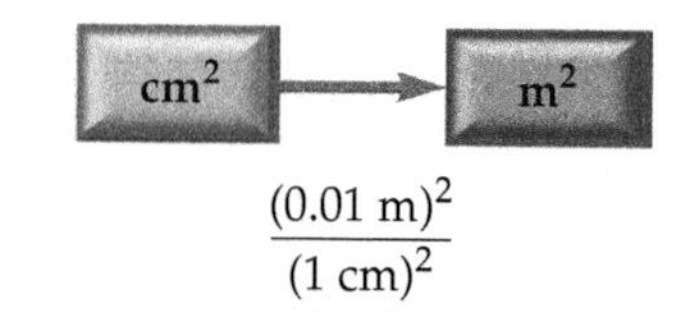

$$\frac{(0.01 \text{ m})^2}{(1 \text{ cm})^2}$$

RELATIONSHIPS USED

1 cm = 0.01 m (from Table 2.2)

SOLVE Follow the solution map to solve the problem. Square the conversion factor (both the units and the number) as you carry out the calculation. Round the answer to four significant figures to reflect the four significant figures in the given quantity. The conversion factor is exact and therefore does not limit the number of significant figures.	**SOLUTION** $2659\,\text{cm}^2 \times \dfrac{(0.01\,\text{m})^2}{(1\,\text{cm})^2} = 2659\,\text{cm}^2 \times \dfrac{10^{-4}\,\text{m}^2}{1\,\text{cm}^2} = 0.265900\,\text{m}^2 = 0.2659\,\text{m}^2$
CHECK Check your answer. Are the units correct? Does the answer make physical sense?	The units of the answer are correct, and the magnitude makes physical sense. A square meter is much larger than a square centimeter, so the value in square meters should be much smaller than the value in square centimeters.

▶SKILLBUILDER 2.12 | Converting Quantities Involving Units Raised to a Power

An automobile engine has a displacement (a measure of the size of the engine) of 289.7 in.^{3} What is its displacement in cubic centimeters?

▶FOR MORE PRACTICE Example 2.26; Problems 87, 88, 89, 90, 91, 92.

EXAMPLE 2.13 Solving Multistep Conversion Problems Involving Units Raised to a Power

The average annual per person crude oil consumption in the United States is 15,615 dm^3. What is this value in cubic inches?

SORT
You are given a volume in cubic decimeters and asked to convert it to cubic inches.

GIVEN: 15,615 dm^3

FIND: in.^{3}

STRATEGIZE
Build a solution map beginning with dm^3 and ending with in.^{3} Each of the conversion factors must be cubed, since the quantities involve cubic units.

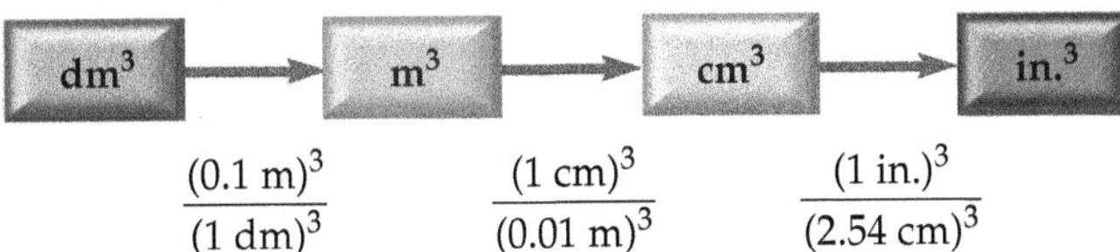

$$\frac{(0.1\,\text{m})^3}{(1\,\text{dm})^3} \qquad \frac{(1\,\text{cm})^3}{(0.01\,\text{m})^3} \qquad \frac{(1\,\text{in.})^3}{(2.54\,\text{cm})^3}$$

RELATIONSHIPS USED

1 dm = 0.1 m (from Table 2.2)
1 cm = 0.01 m (from Table 2.2)
2.54 cm = 1 in. (from Table 2.3)

SOLVE
Follow the solution map to solve the problem. Begin with the given value in dm^3 and multiply by the string of conversion factors to arrive at in^3. Make sure to cube each conversion factor as you carry out the calculation.

Round the answer to five significant figures to reflect the five significant figures in the least precisely known quantity (15,615 dm^3). The conversion factors are all exact and therefore do not limit the number of significant figures.

SOLUTION

$$15{,}615\,\text{dm}^3 \times \frac{(0.1\,\text{m})^3}{(1\,\text{dm})^3} \times \frac{(1\,\text{cm})^3}{(0.01\,\text{m})^3} \times \frac{(1\,\text{in.})^3}{(2.54\,\text{cm})^3} = 9.5289 \times 10^5\,\text{in.}^3$$

CHECK
Check your answer. Are the units correct? Does the answer make physical sense?

The units of the answer are correct and the magnitude makes sense. A cubic inch is smaller than a cubic decimeter, so the value in cubic inches should be larger than the value in cubic decimeters.

▶SKILLBUILDER 2.13 | Solving Multistep Problems Involving Units Raised to a Power

How many cubic inches are there in 3.25 yd^3?

▶FOR MORE PRACTICE Problems 93, 94.

CONCEPTUAL CHECKPOINT 2.6

You know that there are 3 ft in a yard. How many cubic feet are there in a cubic yard?

(a) 3

(b) 6

(c) 9

(d) 27

2.9 Density

▲ Top-end bicycle frames are made of titanium because of titanium's low density and high relative strength. Titanium has a density of 4.50 g/cm^3, while iron, for example, has a density of 7.86 g/cm^3.

Why do some people pay more than $3000 for a bicycle made of titanium? A steel frame would be just as strong for a fraction of the cost. The difference between the two bikes is their mass—the titanium bike is lighter. For a given volume of metal, titanium has less mass than steel. We describe this property by saying that titanium is *less dense* than steel. The **density** of a substance is the ratio of its mass to its volume.

$$\text{Density} = \frac{\text{Mass}}{\text{Volume}} \quad \text{or} \quad d = \frac{m}{V}$$

Density is a fundamental property of substances that differs from one substance to another. The units of density are those of mass divided by those of volume, most conveniently expressed in grams per cubic centimeter (g/cm^3) or grams per milliliter (g/mL). See Table 2.4 for a list of the densities of some common substances. Aluminum is among the least dense structural metals with a density of 2.70 g/cm^3, while platinum is among the densest with a density of 21.4 g/cm^3. Titanium has a density of 4.50 g/cm^3.

TABLE 2.4 Densities of Some Common Substances

Substance	Density (g/cm^3)
Charcoal, oak	0.57
Ethanol	0.789
Ice	0.92
Water	1.0
Glass	2.6
Aluminum	2.7
Titanium	4.50
Iron	7.86
Copper	8.96
Lead	11.4
Gold	19.3
Platinum	21.4

Remember that cubic centimeters and milliliters are equivalent units.

CALCULATING DENSITY

We calculate the density of a substance by dividing the mass of a given amount of the substance by its volume. For example, a sample of liquid has a volume of 22.5 mL and a mass of 27.2 g. To find its density, we use the equation $d = m/V$.

$$d = \frac{m}{V} = \frac{27.2\text{ g}}{22.5\text{ mL}} = 1.21\text{ g/mL}$$

We can use a solution map for solving problems involving equations, but the solution map will take a slightly different form than for pure conversion problems. In a problem involving an equation, the solution map shows how the *equation* takes you from the *given* quantities to the *find* quantity. The solution map for this problem is:

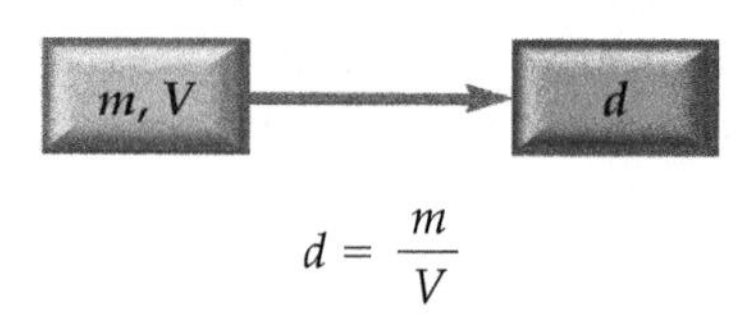

$$d = \frac{m}{V}$$

The solution map illustrates how the values of m and V, when substituted into the equation $d = \frac{m}{V}$ give the desired result, d.

EXAMPLE 2.14 Calculating Density

A jeweler offers to sell a ring to a woman and tells her that it is made of platinum. Noting that the ring felt a little light, the woman decides to perform a test to determine the ring's density. She places the ring on a balance and finds that it has a mass of 5.84 g. She also finds that the ring *displaces* 0.556 cm^3 of water. Is the ring made of platinum? The density of platinum is 21.4 g/cm^3. (The displacement of water is a common way to measure the volume of irregularly shaped objects. To say that an object *displaces* 0.556 cm^3 of water means that when the object is submerged in a container of water filled to the brim, 0.556 cm^3 of water overflows. Therefore, the volume of the object is 0.556 cm^3.)

SORT
You are given the mass and volume of the ring and asked to find the density.

GIVEN: $m = 5.84$ g

$V = 0.556\ cm^3$

FIND: density in g/cm^3

STRATEGIZE
If the ring is platinum, its density should match that of platinum. Build a solution map that represents how you get from the given quantities (mass and volume) to the find quantity (density). Unlike in conversion problems, where you write a conversion factor beneath the arrow, here you write the equation for density beneath the arrow.

SOLUTION MAP

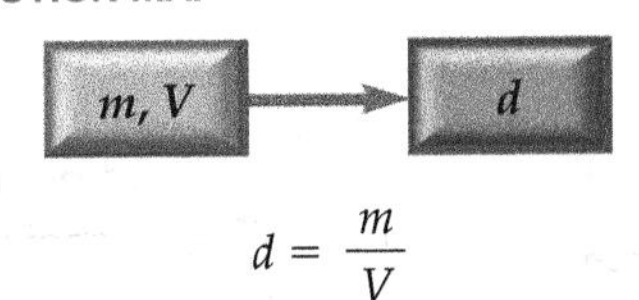

$$d = \frac{m}{V}$$

RELATIONSHIPS USED

$$d = \frac{m}{V} \quad \text{(equation for density)}$$

SOLVE
Follow the solution map. Substitute the given values into the density equation and compute the density.

Round the answer to three significant figures to reflect the three significant figures in the given quantities.

SOLUTION

$$d = \frac{m}{V} = \frac{5.84\ \text{g}}{0.556\ \text{cm}^3} = 10.5\ \text{g/cm}^3$$

The density of the ring is much too low to be platinum; therefore the ring is a fake.

CHECK
Check your answer. Are the units correct? Does the answer make physical sense?

The units of the answer are correct, and the magnitude seems reasonable to be an actual density. As you can see from Table 2.4, the densities of liquids and solids range from below 1 g/cm^3 to just over 20 g/cm^3.

▶SKILLBUILDER 2.14 | Calculating Density

The woman takes the ring back to the jewelry shop, where she is met with endless apologies. They accidentally had made the ring out of silver rather than platinum. They give her a new ring that they promise is platinum. This time when she checks the density, she finds the mass of the ring to be 9.67 g and its volume to be 0.452 cm^3. Is this ring genuine?

▶FOR MORE PRACTICE Example 2.27; Problems 95, 96, 97, 98, 99, 100.

DENSITY AS A CONVERSION FACTOR

We can use the density of a substance as a conversion factor between the mass of the substance and its volume. For example, suppose we need 68.4 g of a liquid with a density of 1.32 g/cm^3 and want to measure the correct amount with a graduated cylinder (a piece of laboratory glassware used to measure volume). How much volume should we measure?

We start with the mass of the liquid and use the density as a conversion factor to convert mass to volume. However, we must use the inverted density expression 1 cm^3/1.32 g because we want g, the unit we are converting from, to be on the bottom (in the denominator) and cm^3, the unit we are converting to, on the top (in the numerator). Our solution map takes this form:

CHEMISTRY AND HEALTH

Density, Cholesterol, and Heart Disease

Cholesterol is fatty substance found in animal-derived foods such as beef, eggs, fish, poultry, and milk products. Cholesterol is used by the body for several purposes. However, excessive amounts in the blood—which can be caused by both genetic factors and diet—may result in the deposition of cholesterol in arterial walls, leading to a condition called atherosclerosis, or blocking of the arteries. These blockages are dangerous because they inhibit blood flow to important organs, causing heart attacks and strokes. The risk of stroke and heart attack increases with increasing blood cholesterol levels (Table 2.5). Cholesterol is carried in the bloodstream by a class of substances known as lipoproteins. Lipoproteins are often separated and classified according to their density.

The main carriers of blood cholesterol are low-density lipoproteins (LDLs). LDLs, also called bad cholesterol, have a density of 1.04 g/cm^3. They are bad because they tend to deposit cholesterol on arterial walls, increasing the risk of stroke and heart attack. Cholesterol is also carried by high-density lipoproteins (HDLs). HDLs, also called good cholesterol, have a density of 1.13 g/cm^3. HDLs transport cholesterol to the liver for processing and excretion and therefore have a tendency to reduce cholesterol on arterial walls. Too low a level of HDLs (below 35 mg/100 mL) is considered a risk factor for heart disease. Exercise, along with a diet low in saturated fats, is believed to raise HDL levels in the blood while lowering LDL levels.

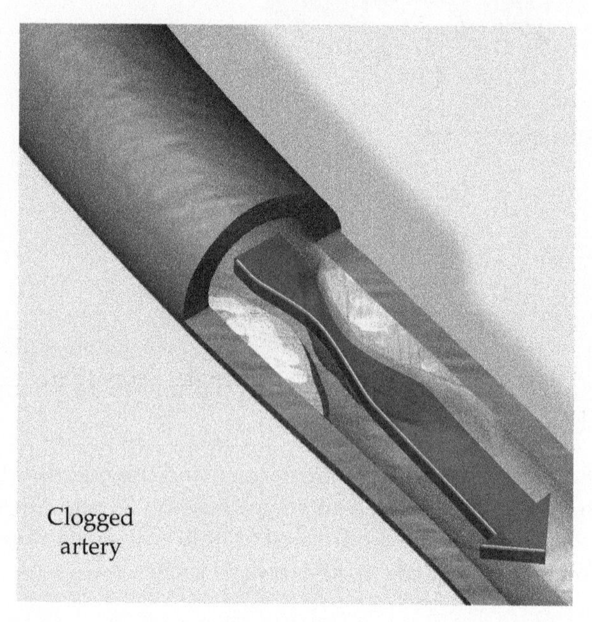

▲ Too many low-density lipoproteins in the blood can lead to the blocking of arteries.

CAN YOU ANSWER THIS? *What mass of low-density lipoprotein is contained in a cylinder that is 1.25 cm long and 0.50 cm in diameter? (The volume of a cylinder, V, is given by* $V = \pi r^2 \ell$*, where r is the radius of the cylinder and* ℓ *is its length.)*

TABLE 2.5 Risk of Stroke and Heart Attack vs. Blood Cholesterol Level

Risk Level	Total Blood Cholesterol (mg/100 mL)	LDL (mg/100 mL)
low	<200	<130
borderline	200–239	130–159
high	240+	160+

SOLUTION MAP

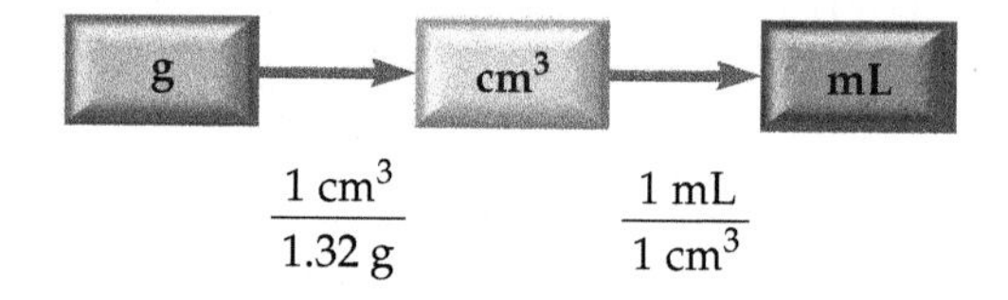

$$\frac{1\ cm^3}{1.32\ g} \qquad \frac{1\ mL}{1\ cm^3}$$

SOLUTION

$$68.4\ \cancel{g} \times \frac{1\ \cancel{cm^3}}{1.32\ \cancel{g}} \times \frac{1\ mL}{1\ \cancel{cm^3}} = 51.8\ mL$$

We must measure 51.8 mL to obtain 68.4 g of the liquid.

EXAMPLE 2.15 Density as a Conversion Factor

The gasoline in an automobile gas tank has a mass of 60.0 kg and a density of $0.752\ g/cm^3$. What is its volume in cm^3?

SORT You are given the mass in kilograms and asked to find the volume in cubic centimeters. Density is the conversion factor between mass and volume.	**GIVEN:** 60.0 kg Density $= 0.752\ g/cm^3$ **FIND:** volume in cm^3
STRATEGIZE Build the solution map starting with kg and ending with cm^3. Use the density (inverted) to convert from g to cm^3.	**SOLUTION MAP** 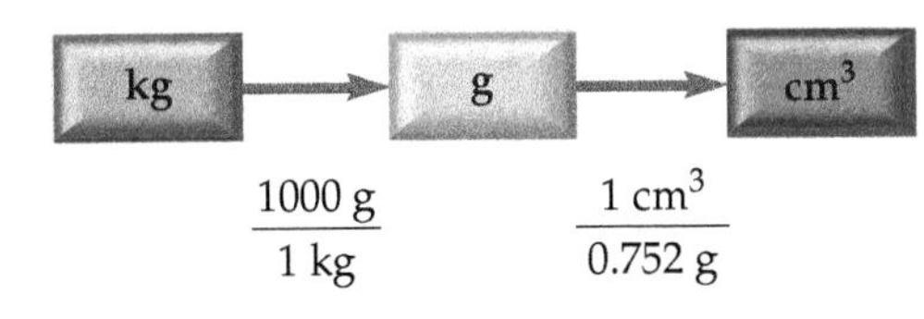 $\frac{1000\ g}{1\ kg}$ $\frac{1\ cm^3}{0.752\ g}$ **RELATIONSHIPS USED** $0.752\ g/cm^3$ (given in problem) $1000\ g = 1\ kg$ (from Table 2.2)
SOLVE Follow the solution map to solve the problem. Round the answer to three significant figures to reflect the three significant figures in the given quantities.	**SOLUTION** $60.0\ \text{kg} \times \frac{1000\ \text{g}}{1\ \text{kg}} \times \frac{1\ \text{cm}^3}{0.752\ \text{g}} = 7.98 \times 10^4\ \text{cm}^3$
CHECK Check your answer. Are the units correct? Does the answer make physical sense?	The units of the answer are those of volume, so they are correct. The magnitude seems reasonable because the density is somewhat less than $1\ g/cm^3$; therefore the volume of 60.0 kg should be somewhat more than $60.0 \times 10^3\ cm^3$.

▶SKILLBUILDER 2.15 | Density as a Conversion Factor

A drop of acetone (nail polish remover) has a mass of 35 mg and a density of $0.788\ g/cm^3$. What is its volume in cubic centimeters?

▶SKILLBUILDER PLUS

A steel cylinder has a volume of $246\ cm^3$ and a density of $7.93\ g/cm^3$. What is its mass in kilograms?

▶FOR MORE PRACTICE Example 2.28; Problems 101, 102.

2.10 Numerical Problem-Solving Overview

In this chapter, you have seen a few examples of how to solve numerical problems. In Section 2.6, we developed a procedure to solve simple unit conversion problems. We then learned how to modify that procedure to work with multistep unit conversion problems and problems involving an equation. We will now summarize and generalize these procedures and apply them to two additional examples. As we did in Section 2.6, we provide the general procedure for solving numerical problems in the left column and the application of the procedure to two examples in the center and right columns.

SOLVING NUMERICAL PROBLEMS

EXAMPLE 2.16 — Unit Conversion

A 23.5-kg sample of ethanol is needed for a large-scale reaction. What volume in liters of ethanol should be used? The density of ethanol is 0.789 g/cm^3.

EXAMPLE 2.17 — Unit Conversion with Equation

A 55.9-kg person displaces 57.2 L of water when submerged in a water tank. What is the density of the person in grams per cubic centimeter?

SORT

- Scan the problem for one or more numbers and their associated units. This number (or numbers) is (are) the starting point(s) of the calculation. Write them down as given.
- Scan the problem to determine what you are asked to find. Sometimes the units of this quantity are implied; other times they are specified. Write down the quantity and/or units you are asked to find.

Example 2.16

GIVEN: 23.5 kg ethanol

$$\text{density} = 0.789 \text{ g/cm}^3$$

FIND: volume in L

Example 2.17

GIVEN: $m = 55.9 \text{ kg}$

$$V = 57.2 \text{ L}$$

FIND: density in g/cm^3

STRATEGIZE

- For problems involving only conversions, focus on units. The solution map shows how to get from the units in the given quantity to the units in the quantity you are asked to find.
- For problems involving equations, focus on the equation. The solution map shows how the equation takes you from the given quantity (or quantities) to the quantity you are asked to find.
- Some problems may involve both unit conversions and equations, in which case the solution map employs both of the above points.

Example 2.16

SOLUTION MAP

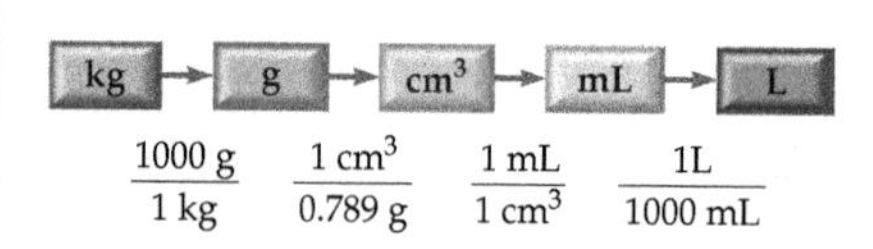

RELATIONSHIPS USED

$$0.789 \text{ g/cm}^3 \text{ (given in problem)}$$

$$1000 \text{ g} = 1 \text{ kg (Table 2.2)}$$

$$1000 \text{ mL} = 1 \text{ L (Table 2.2)}$$

$$1 \text{ mL} = 1 \text{ cm}^3 \text{ (Table 2.3)}$$

Example 2.17

SOLUTION MAP

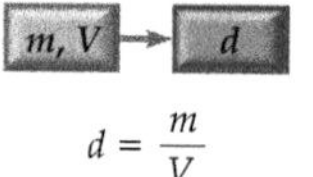

RELATIONSHIPS USED

$$d = \frac{m}{V} \text{ (definition of density)}$$

SOLVE

- For problems involving only conversions, begin with the given quantity and its units. Multiply by the appropriate conversion factor(s), canceling units, to arrive at the quantity you are asked to find.

Example 2.16

SOLUTION

$$23.5 \cancel{\text{kg}} \times \frac{1000 \cancel{\text{g}}}{1 \cancel{\text{kg}}} \times \frac{1 \cancel{\text{cm}^3}}{0.789 \cancel{\text{g}}} \times \frac{1 \cancel{\text{mL}}}{1 \cancel{\text{cm}^3}} \times \frac{1 \text{ L}}{1000 \cancel{\text{mL}}} = 29.7845 \text{ L}$$

$$29.7845 \text{ L} = 29.8 \text{ L}$$

Example 2.17

The equation is already solved for the find quantity. Convert mass from kilograms to grams.

$$m = 55.9 \cancel{\text{kg}} \times \frac{1000 \text{ g}}{1 \cancel{\text{kg}}}$$

$$= 5.59 \times 10^4 \text{ g}$$

- For problems involving equations, solve the equation to arrive at the quantity you are asked to find. (Use algebra to rearrange the equation so that the quantity you are asked to find is isolated on one side.) Gather each of the quantities that must go into the equation in the correct units. (Convert to the correct units using additional solution maps if necessary.) Finally, substitute the numerical values and their units into the equation and compute the answer.
- Round the answer to the correct number of significant figures. Use the significant-figure rules from Sections 2.3 and 2.4.

Convert volume from liters to cubic centimeters.

$$V = 57.2\ \cancel{L} \times \frac{1000\ \cancel{mL}}{1\ \cancel{L}} \times \frac{1\ cm^3}{1\ \cancel{mL}}$$

$$= 57.2 \times 10^3\ cm^3$$

Compute density.

$$d = \frac{m}{V} = \frac{55.9 \times 10^3}{57.2 \times 10^3\ cm^3}$$

$$= 0.9772727\ \frac{g}{cm^3}$$

$$= 0.977\ \frac{g}{cm^3}$$

CHECK

- Does the magnitude of the answer make physical sense? Are the units correct?

The units are correct (L) and the magnitude is reasonable. Since the density is less than 1 g/cm^3, the computed volume (29.8 L) should be greater than the mass (23.5 kg).

The units are correct. Since the mass in kilograms and the volume in liters were very close to each other in magnitude, it makes sense that the density is close to 1 g/cm^3.

▶SKILLBUILDER 2.16

Unit Conversion

A pure gold metal bar displaces 0.82 L of water. What is its mass in kilograms? (The density of gold is 19.3 g/cm^3.)

▶FOR MORE PRACTICE Problems 103, 109, 110, 111, 112.

▶SKILLBUILDER 2.17

Unit Conversion with Equation

A gold-colored pebble is found in a stream. Its mass is 23.2 mg, and its volume is 1.20 mm^3. What is its density in grams per cubic centimeter? Is it gold? (The density of gold = 19.3 g/cm^3.)

▶FOR MORE PRACTICE Problems 104, 105, 106.

CHAPTER IN REVIEW

CHEMICAL PRINCIPLES

Uncertainty: Scientists report measured quantities so that the number of digits reflects the certainty in the measurement. Write measured quantities so that every digit is certain except the last, which is estimated.

RELEVANCE

Uncertainty: Measurement is a hallmark of science, and the precision of a measurement must be communicated with the measurement so that others know how reliable the measurement is. When you write or manipulate measured quantities, you must show and retain the precision with which the original measurement was made.

Units: Measured quantities usually have units associated with them. The SI unit for length is the meter; for mass, the kilogram; and for time, the second. Prefix multipliers such as *kilo-* or *milli-* are often used in combination with these basic units. The SI units of volume are units of length raised to the third power; liters or milliliters are often used as well.

Units: The units in a measured quantity communicate what the quantity actually is. Without an agreed-on system of units, scientists could not communicate their measurements. Units are also important in calculations, and the tracking of units throughout a calculation is essential.

Density: The density of a substance is its mass divided by its volume, $d = m/V$, and is usually reported in units of grams per cubic centimeter or grams per milliliter. Density is a fundamental property of all substances and generally differs from one substance to another.

Density: The density of substances is an important consideration in choosing materials from which to make things. Airplanes, for example, are made of low-density materials, while bridges are made of higher-density materials. Density is important as a conversion factor between mass and volume and vice versa.

CHEMICAL SKILLS

Scientific Notation (Section 2.2)

To express a number in scientific notation:

- Move the decimal point to obtain a number between 1 and 10.
- Write the decimal part multiplied by 10 raised to the number of places you moved the decimal point.
- The exponent is positive if you moved the decimal point to the left and negative if you moved the decimal point to the right.

Reporting Measured Quantities to the Right Number of Digits (Section 2.3)

Report measured quantities so that every digit is certain except the last, which is estimated.

EXAMPLES

EXAMPLE 2.18 Scientific Notation

Express the number 45,000,000 in scientific notation.

45,000,000

7 6 5 4 3 2 1

4.5×10^7

EXAMPLE 2.19 Reporting Measured Quantities to the Right Number of Digits

Record the volume of liquid in the graduated cylinder to the correct number of digits. Laboratory glassware is calibrated (and should therefore be read) from the bottom of the meniscus (see figure).

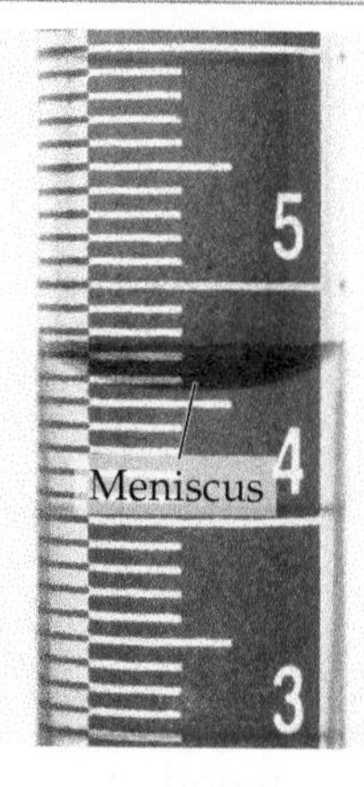

Since the graduated cylinder has markings every 0.1 mL, the measurement should be recorded to the nearest 0.01 mL. In this case, that is 4.57 mL.

Counting Significant Digits (Section 2.3)

The following digits should always be counted as significant:

- nonzero digits
- interior zeros
- trailing zeros after a decimal point
- trailing zeros before a decimal point but after a nonzero number

The following digits should never be counted as significant:

- zeros to the left of the first nonzero number

The following digits are ambiguous and should be avoided by using scientific notation:

- zeros at the end of a number, but before a decimal point

EXAMPLE 2.20 Counting Significant Digits

How many significant figures are in the following numbers?

1.0050	five significant figures
0.00870	three significant figures
100.085	six significant digits
5400	It is not possible to tell in its current form.

In order for us to know, the number needs to be written as 5.4×10^3, 5.40×10^3, or 5.400×10^3, depending on the number of significant figures intended.

Rounding (Section 2.4)

When rounding numbers to the correct number of significant figures, round down if the last digit dropped is 4 or less; round up if the last digit dropped is 5 or more.

EXAMPLE 2.21 Rounding

Round 6.442 and 6.456 to two significant figures each.

6.442 rounds to 6.4
6.456 rounds to 6.5

Significant Figures in Multiplication and Division (Section 2.4)

The result of a multiplication or division should carry the same number of significant figures as the factor with the least number of significant figures.

EXAMPLE 2.22 Significant Figures in Multiplication and Division

Perform the following calculation and report the answer to the correct number of significant figures.

$$8.54 \times 3.589 \div 4.2$$
$$= 7.2976$$
$$= 7.3$$

Round the final result to two significant figures to reflect the two significant figures in the factor with the least number of significant figures (4.2).

Significant Figures in Addition and Subtraction (Section 2.4)

The result of an addition or subtraction should carry the same number of decimal places as the quantity carrying the least number of decimal places.

EXAMPLE 2.23 Significant Figures in Addition and Subtraction

Perform the following operation and report the answer to the correct number of significant figures.

$$\begin{array}{r} 3.098 \\ 0.67 \\ -0.9452 \\ \hline 2.8228 \end{array} = 2.82$$

Round the final result to two decimal places to reflect the two decimal places in the quantity with the least number of decimal places (0.67).

Significant Figures in Calculations Involving Both Addition/Subtraction and Multiplication/Division (Section 2.4)

In calculations involving both addition/subtraction and multiplication/division, do the steps in parentheses first, keeping track of how many significant figures are in the answer by underlining the least significant figure, then proceeding with the remaining steps. Do not round off until the very end.

EXAMPLE 2.24 Significant Figures in Calculations Involving Both Addition/Subtraction and Multiplication/Division

Perform the following operation and report the answer to the correct number of significant figures.

$$8.16 \times (5.4323 - 5.411)$$
$$= 8.16 \times 0.02\underline{1}3$$
$$= 0.1738 = 0.17$$

Unit Conversion (Sections 2.6, 2.7)

Solve unit conversion problems by following these steps.

1. **Sort** Write down the given quantity and its units and the quantity you are asked to find and its units.
2. **Strategize** Draw a solution map showing how to get from the given quantity to the quantity you are asked to find.
3. **Solve** Follow the solution map. Starting with the given quantity and its units, multiply by the appropriate conversion factor(s), canceling units, to arrive at the quantity to find in the desired units. Round the final answer to the correct number of significant figures.
4. **Check** Are the units correct? Does the answer make physical sense?

EXAMPLE 2.25 Unit Conversion

Convert 108 ft to meters.

GIVEN: 108 ft

FIND: m

SOLUTION MAP

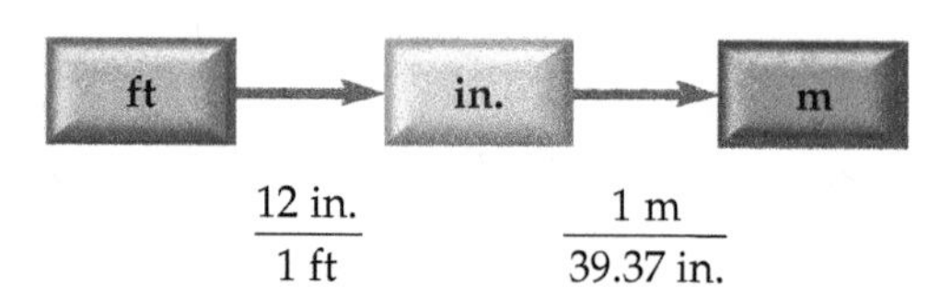

$$\frac{12 \text{ in.}}{1 \text{ ft}} \qquad \frac{1 \text{ m}}{39.37 \text{ in.}}$$

RELATIONSHIPS USED

$$1 \text{ m} = 39.37 \text{ in.} \quad \text{(Table 2.3)}$$
$$1 \text{ ft} = 12 \text{ in.} \quad \text{(by definition)}$$

SOLUTION

$$108 \text{ ft} \times \frac{12 \text{ in.}}{1 \text{ ft}} \times \frac{1 \text{ m}}{39.37 \text{ in.}}$$
$$= 32.918 \text{ m}$$
$$= 32.9 \text{ m}$$

The answer has the right units (meters), and it makes sense; since a meter is longer than a foot, the number of meters should be less than the number of feet.

Unit Conversion Involving Units Raised to a Power (Section 2.8)

When working problems involving units raised to a power, raise the conversion factors to the same power.

1. **Sort** Write down the given quantity and its units and the quantity you are asked to find and its units.
2. **Strategize** Draw a solution map showing how to get from the given quantity to the quantity you are asked to find. Since the units are squared, you must square the conversion factor.

EXAMPLE 2.26 Unit Conversion Involving Units Raised to a Power

How many square meters are in 1.0 km^2?

GIVEN: 1.0 km^2

FIND: m^2

SOLUTION MAP

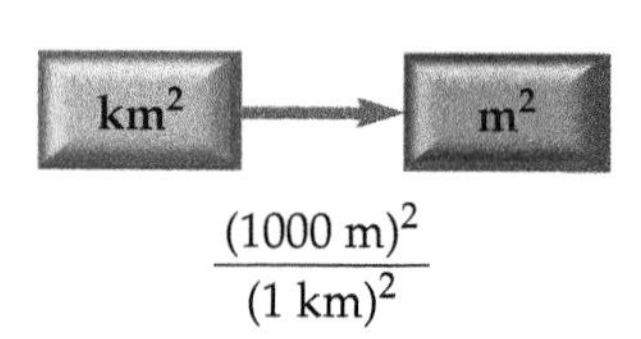

$$\frac{(1000 \text{ m})^2}{(1 \text{ km})^2}$$

RELATIONSHIPS USED

$$1 \text{ km} = 1000 \text{ m} \quad \text{(Table 2.2)}$$

3. **Solve** Follow the solution map. Starting with the given quantity and its units, multiply by the appropriate conversion factor(s), canceling units, to arrive at the quantity you are asked to find in the desired units. Don't forget to square the conversion factor for squared units.
4. **Check** Are the units correct? Does the answer make physical sense?

SOLUTION

$$1.0\,\text{km}^2 \times \frac{(1000\,\text{m})^2}{(1\,\text{km})^2}$$
$$= 1.0\ \text{km}^2 \times \frac{1 \times 10^6\,\text{m}^2}{1\ \text{km}^2}$$
$$= 1.0 \times 10^6\,\text{m}^2$$

The units are correct. The answer makes physical sense; a square meter is much smaller than a square kilometer, so the number of square meters should be much larger than the number of square kilometers.

Calculating Density (Section 2.10)

The density of an object or substance is its mass divided by its volume.

$$d = \frac{m}{V}$$

1. **Sort** Write down the given quantity and its units and the quantity you are asked to find and its units.
2. **Strategize** Draw a solution map showing how to get from the given quantity to the quantity you are asked to find. Use the definition of density as the equation that takes you from the mass and the volume to the density.
3. **Solve** Substitute the correct values into the equation for density.
4. **Check** Are the units correct? Does the answer make physical sense?

EXAMPLE 2.27 Calculating Density

An object has a mass of 23.4 g and displaces 5.7 mL of water. Determine its density in grams per milliliter.

GIVEN:

$$m = 23.4\ \text{g}$$
$$V = 5.7\ \text{mL}$$

FIND: density in g/mL

SOLUTION MAP

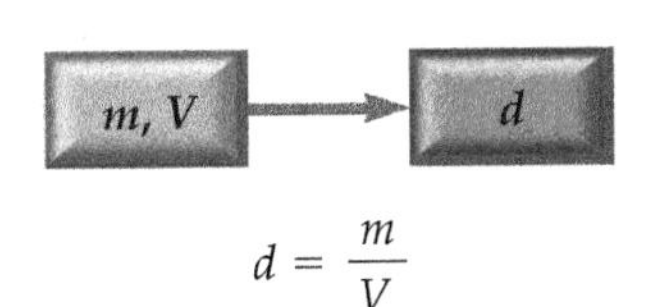

$$d = \frac{m}{V}$$

RELATIONSHIPS USED

$$d = \frac{m}{V}\ \text{(definition of density)}$$

SOLUTION

$$d = \frac{m}{V}$$
$$= \frac{23.4\,\text{g}}{5.7\,\text{mL}}$$
$$= 4.11\,\text{g/mL}$$
$$= 4.1\ \text{g/mL}$$

The units (g/mL) are units of density. The answer is in the range of values for the densities of liquids and solids (see Table 2.4).

Density as a Conversion Factor (Section 2.10)
Density can be used as a conversion factor from mass to volume or from volume to mass. To convert between volume and mass, use density directly. To convert between mass and volume, invert the density.

1. **Sort** Write down the given quantity and its units and the quantity you are asked to find and its units.
2. **Strategize** Draw a solution map showing how to get from the given quantity to the quantity you are asked to find. Use the inverse of the density to convert from g to mL.
3. **Solve** Begin with given quantity and multiply by the appropriate conversion factors to arrive at the quantity you are asked to find. Round to the correct number of significant figures.
4. **Check** Are the units correct? Does the answer make physical sense?

EXAMPLE 2.28 Density as a Conversion Factor

What is the volume in liters of 321 g of a liquid with a density of 0.84 g/mL?

GIVEN: 321 g

FIND: volume in L

SOLUTION MAP

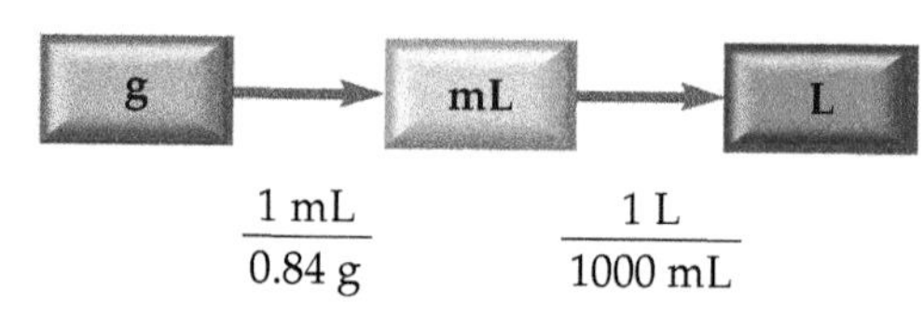

$$\frac{1\text{ mL}}{0.84\text{ g}} \qquad \frac{1\text{ L}}{1000\text{ mL}}$$

RELATIONSHIPS USED

0.84 g/mL (given in the problem)
1 L = 1000 mL (Table 2.2)

SOLUTION

$$321\text{ g} \times \frac{1\text{ mL}}{0.84\text{ g}} \times \frac{1\text{ L}}{1000\text{ mL}} = 0.382\text{ L} = 0.38\text{ L}$$

The answer is in the correct units. The magnitude seems right because the density is slightly less than 1; therefore the volume (382 mL) should be slightly greater than the mass (321 g).

KEY TERMS

conversion factor **[2.6]**
decimal part **[2.2]**
density **[2.9]**
English system **[2.5]**
exponent **[2.2]**
exponential part **[2.2]**
International System **[2.5]**
kilogram (kg) **[2.5]**
liter (L) **[2.5]**
mass **[2.5]**
meter (m) **[2.5]**
metric system **[2.5]**
prefix multipliers **[2.5]**
scientific notation **[2.2]**
second (s) **[2.5]**
SI units **[2.5]**
significant figures (digits) **[2.3]**
solution map **[2.6]**
units **[2.5]**
volume **[2.5]**

EXERCISES

QUESTIONS

Answers to all questions numbered in blue appear in the Answers section at the back of the book.

1. Why is it important to report units with scientific measurements?
2. Why are the number of digits reported in scientific measurements important?
3. Why is scientific notation useful?
4. If a measured quantity is written correctly, which digits are certain? Which are uncertain?
5. Explain when zeros count as significant digits and when they do not.
6. How many significant digits are there in exact numbers? What kinds of numbers are exact?
7. What limits the number of significant digits in a calculation involving only multiplication and division?
8. What limits the number of significant digits in a calculation involving only addition and subtraction?
9. How are significant figures determined in calculations involving both addition/subtraction and multiplication/division?
10. What are the rules for rounding numbers?
11. What are the basic SI units of length, mass, and time?
12. List the common units of volume.
13. Suppose you are trying to measure the diameter of a Frisbee. What unit and prefix multiplier should you use?
14. What is the difference between mass and weight?

15. Obtain a metric ruler and measure these objects to the correct number of significant figures.
(a) quarter (diameter)
(b) dime (diameter)
(c) notebook paper (width)
(d) this book (width)

16. Obtain a stopwatch and measure each time to the correct number of significant figures.
(a) time between your heartbeats
(b) time it takes you to do the next problem
(c) time between your breaths

17. Explain why units are important in calculations.

18. How are units treated in a calculation?

19. What is a conversion factor?

20. Why is the fundamental value of a quantity not changed when the quantity is multiplied by a conversion factor?

21. Write the conversion factor that converts a measurement in inches to feet. How would the conversion factor change for converting a measurement in feet to inches?

22. Write conversion factors for each:
(a) miles to kilometers
(b) kilometers to miles
(c) gallons to liters
(d) liters to gallons

23. This book outlines a four-step problem-solving strategy. Describe each step and its significance.
(a) Sort
(b) Strategize
(c) Solve
(d) Check

24. Experienced problem solvers always consider both the value and units of their answer to a problem. Why?

25. Draw a solution map to convert a measurement in grams to pounds.

26. Draw a solution map to convert a measurement in milliliters to gallons.

27. Draw a solution map to convert a measurement in meters to feet.

28. Draw a solution map to convert a measurement in ounces to grams. (1 lb = 16 oz)

29. What is density? Explain why density can work as a conversion factor. Between what quantities does it convert?

30. Explain how you would calculate the density of a substance. Include a solution map in your explanation.

PROBLEMS

Note: The exercises in the Problems section are paired, and the answers to the odd-numbered exercises (numbered in blue) appear in the Answers section at the back of the book.

SCIENTIFIC NOTATION

31. Express each number in scientific notation.
(a) 36,756,000 (population of California)
(b) 1,288,000 (population of Hawaii)
(c) 19,490,000 (population of New York)
(d) 532,000 (population of Wyoming)

32. Express each number in scientific notation.
(a) 6,796,000,000 (population of the world)
(b) 1,338,000,000 (population of China)
(c) 11,451,000 (population of Cuba)
(d) 4,203,000 (population of Ireland)

33. Express each number in scientific notation.
(a) 0.00000000007461 m (length of a hydrogen–hydrogen chemical bond)
(b) 0.0000158 mi (number of miles in an inch)
(c) 0.000000632 m (wavelength of red light)
(d) 0.000015 m (diameter of a human hair)

34. Express each number in scientific notation.
(a) 0.000000001 s (time it takes light to travel 1 ft)
(b) 0.143 s (time it takes light to travel around the world)
(c) 0.000000000001 s (time it takes a chemical bond to undergo one vibration)
(d) 0.000001 m (approximate size of a dust particle)

35. Express each number in decimal notation (i.e., express the number without using scientific notation).
(a) 6.022×10^{23} (number of carbon atoms in 12.01 g of carbon)
(b) 1.6×10^{-19} C (charge of a proton in coulombs)
(c) 2.99×10^{8} m/s (speed of light)
(d) 3.44×10^{2} m/s (speed of sound)

36. Express each number in decimal notation (i.e., express the number without using scientific notation).
(a) 450×10^{-19} m (wavelength of blue light)
(b) 13.7×10^{9} years (approximate age of the universe)
(c) 5×10^{9} years (approximate age of Earth)
(d) 4.7×10^{1} years (approximate age of this author)

37. Express each number in decimal notation (i.e., express the number without using scientific notation).
(a) 3.22×10^{7}
(b) 7.2×10^{-3}
(c) 1.18×10^{11}
(d) 9.43×10^{-6}

38. Express each number in decimal notation. (i.e., express the number without using scientific notation)
(a) 1.30×10^{6}
(b) 1.1×10^{-4}
(c) 1.9×10^{2}
(d) 7.41×10^{-10}

39. Complete the table.

Decimal Notation	Scientific Notation
2,000,000,000	______
______	1.211×10^{9}
0.000874	______
______	3.2×10^{11}

40. Complete the table.

Decimal Notation	Scientific Notation
______	4.2×10^{-3}
315,171,000	______
______	1.8×10^{-11}
1,232,000	______

SIGNIFICANT FIGURES

41. Read each instrument to the correct number of significant figures. Laboratory glassware should always be read from the bottom of the *meniscus* (the curved surface at the top of the liquid column).

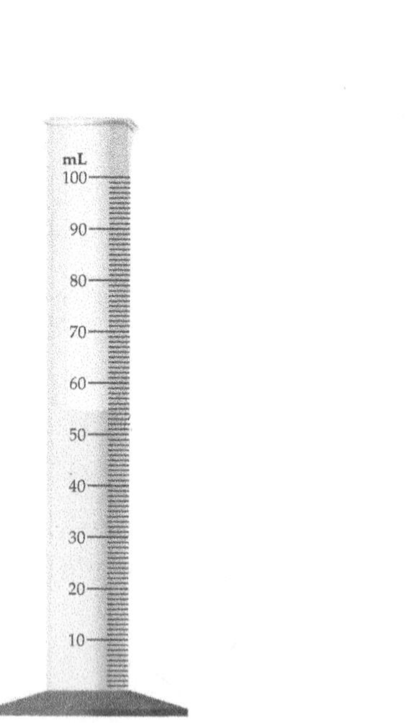

(a)

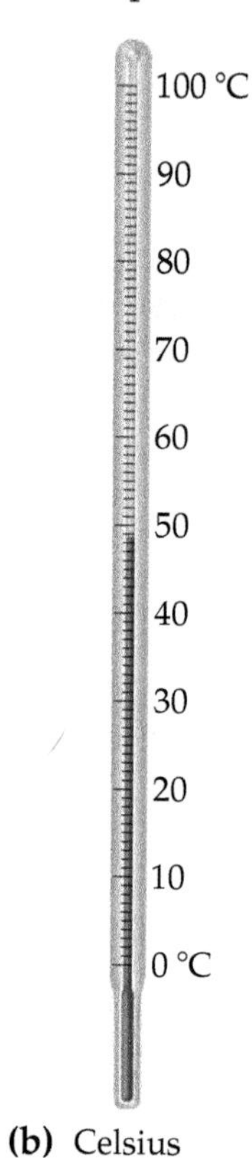

(b) Celsius

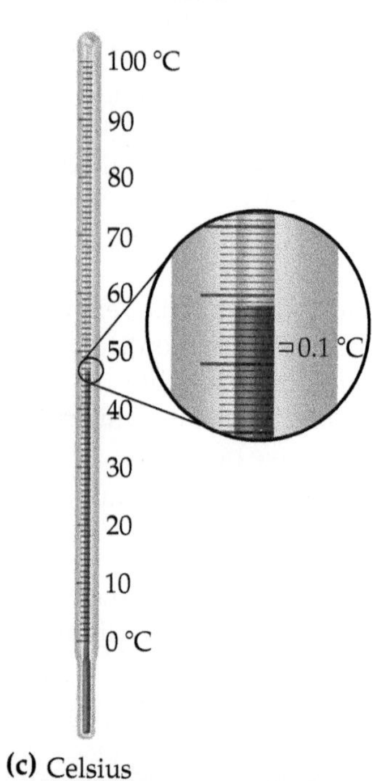

(c) Celsius

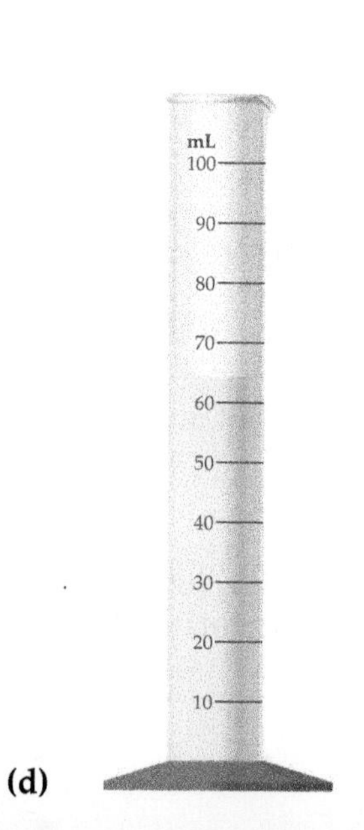

(d)

42. Read each instrument to the correct number of significant figures. Laboratory glassware should always be read from the bottom of the meniscus (the curved surface at the top of the liquid column).

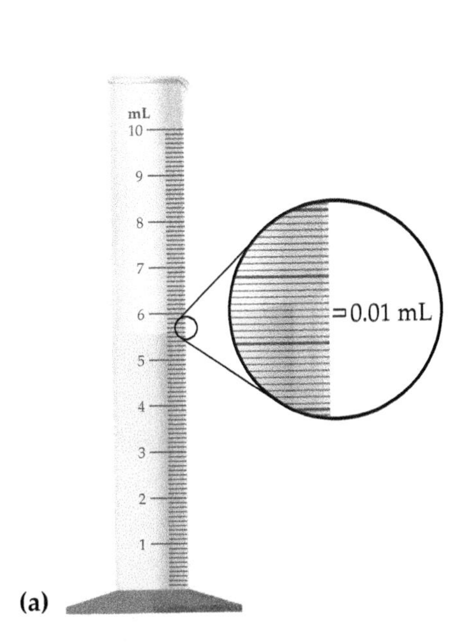

(a)

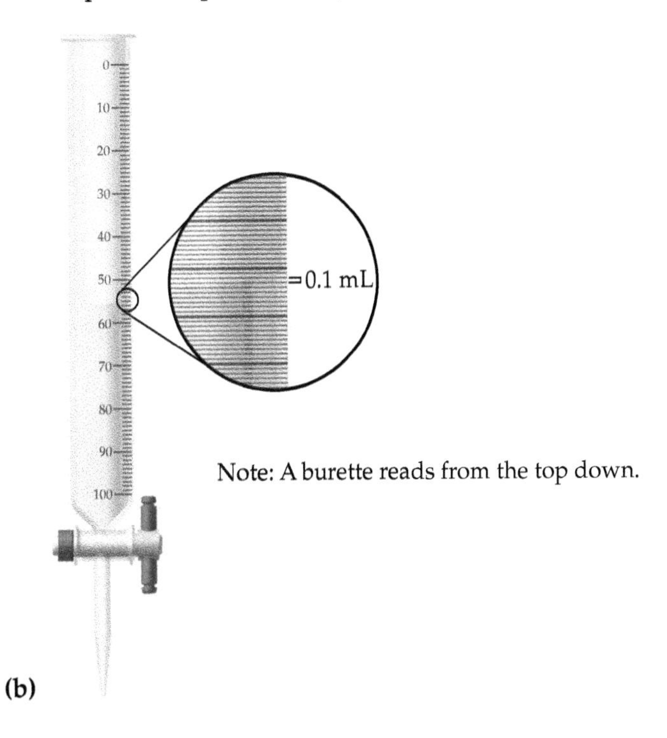

(b)

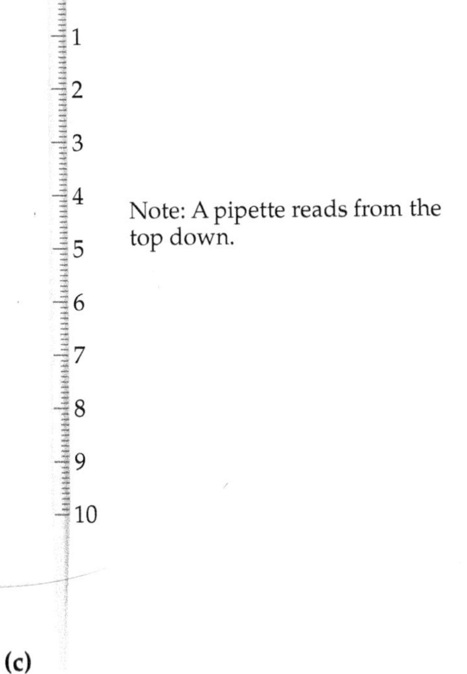

(c)

Note: Digital balances normally display mass to the correct number of significant figures for that

(d) particular balance.

43. For each measured quantity, underline the zeros that are significant and draw an X through the zeros that are not.

(a) 0.005050 m
(b) 0.0000000000000060 s
(c) 220,103 kg
(d) 0.00108 in.

44. For each measured quantity, underline the zeros that are significant and draw an X through the zeros that are not.

(a) 0.00010320 s
(b) 1,322,600,324 kg
(c) 0.0001240 in.
(d) 0.02061 m

45. How many significant figures are in each measured quantity?
(a) 0.001125 m
(b) 0.1125 m
(c) 1.12500×10^4 m
(d) 11205 m

46. How many significant figures are in each measured quantity?
(a) 13001 kg
(b) 13111 kg
(c) 1.30×10^4 kg
(d) 0.00013 kg

47. Determine whether each of the entries in the table is correct. Correct the entries that are wrong.

Quantity	Significant Figures
(a) 895675 m	6
(b) 0.000869 kg	6
(c) 0.5672100 s	5
(d) 6.022×10^{23} atoms	4

48. Determine whether each of the entries in the table is correct. Correct the entries that are wrong.

Quantity	Significant Figures
(a) 24 days	2
(b) 5.6×10^{-12} s	3
(c) 3.14 m	3
(d) 0.00383 g	5

ROUNDING

49. Round each number to four significant figures.
(a) 255.98612
(b) 0.0004893222
(c) 2.900856×10^{-4}
(d) 2,231,479

50. Round each number to three significant figures.
(a) 10,776.522
(b) 4.999902×10^6
(c) 1.3499999995
(d) 0.0000344988

51. Round each number to two significant figures.
(a) 2.34
(b) 2.35
(c) 2.349
(d) 2.359

52. Round each number to three significant figures.
(a) 65.74
(b) 65.749
(c) 65.75
(d) 65.750

53. Each number was supposed to be rounded to three significant figures. Find the ones that were incorrectly rounded and correct them.
(a) 42.3492 to 42.4
(b) 56.9971 to 57.0
(c) 231.904 to 232
(d) 0.04555 to 0.046

54. Each number was supposed to be rounded to two significant figures. Find the ones that were incorrectly rounded and correct them.
(a) 1.249×10^3 to 1.3×10^3
(b) 3.999×10^2 to 40
(c) 56.21 to 56.2
(d) 0.009964 to 0.010

55. Round the number on the left to the number of significant figures indicated as shown by the example in the first row. (Use scientific notation as needed to avoid ambiguity.)

Number	Rounded to 4 Significant Figures	Rounded to 2 Significant Figures	Rounded to 1 Significant Figure
1.45815	1.458	1.5	1
8.32466			
84.57225			
132.5512			

56. Round the number on the left to the number of significant figures indicated as shown by the example in the first row. (Use scientific notation as needed to avoid ambiguity.)

Number	Rounded to 4 Significant Figures	Rounded to 2 Significant Figures	Rounded to 1 Significant Figure
94.52118	94.52	95	9×10^1
105.4545			
0.455981			
0.009999991			

SIGNIFICANT FIGURES IN CALCULATIONS

57. Perform each calculation to the correct number of significant figures.
(a) $4.5 \times 0.03060 \times 0.391$
(b) $5.55 \div 8.97$
(c) $(7.890 \times 10^{12}) \div (6.7 \times 10^4)$
(d) $67.8 \times 9.8 \div 100.04$

58. Perform each calculation to the correct number of significant figures.
(a) $89.3 \times 77.0 \times 0.08$
(b) $(5.01 \times 10^5) \div (7.8 \times 10^2)$
(c) $4.005 \times 74 \times 0.007$
(d) $453 \div 2.031$

59. Determine whether the answer to each calculation has the correct number of significant figures. If not, correct it.
(a) $34.00 \times 567 \div 4.564 = 4.2239 \times 10^3$
(b) $79.3 \div 0.004 \times 35.4 = 7 \times 10^5$
(c) $89.763 \div 22.4581 = 3.997$
(d) $(4.32 \times 10^{12}) \div (3.1 \times 10^{-4}) = 1.4 \times 10^{16}$

60. Determine whether the answer to each calculation has the correct number of significant figures. If not, correct it.
(a) $45.3254 \times 89.00205 = 4034.05$
(b) $0.00740 \times 45.0901 = 0.334$
(c) $49857 \div 904875 = 0.05510$
(d) $0.009090 \times 6007.2 = 54.605$

61. Perform each calculation to the correct number of significant figures.
(a) $87.6 + 9.888 + 2.3 + 10.77$
(b) $43.7 - 2.341$
(c) $89.6 + 98.33 - 4.674$
(d) $6.99 - 5.772$

62. Perform each calculation to the correct number of significant figures.
(a) $1459.3 + 9.77 + 4.32$
(b) $0.004 + 0.09879$
(c) $432 + 7.3 - 28.523$
(d) $2.4 + 1.777$

63. Determine whether the answer to each calculation has the correct number of significant figures. If not, correct it.
(a) $(3.8 \times 10^5) - (8.45 \times 10^5) = -4.7 \times 10^5$
(b) $0.00456 + 1.0936 = 1.10$
(c) $8475.45 - 34.899 = 8440.55$
(d) $908.87 - 905.34095 = 3.5291$

64. Determine whether the answer to each calculation has the correct number of significant figures. If not, correct it.
(a) $78.9 + 890.43 - 23 = 9.5 \times 10^2$
(b) $9354 - 3489.56 + 34.3 = 5898.74$
(c) $0.00407 + 0.0943 = 0.0984$
(d) $0.00896 - 0.007 = 0.00196$

65. Perform each calculation to the correct number of significant figures.
(a) $(78.4 - 44.889) \div 0.0087$
(b) $(34.6784 \times 5.38) + 445.56$
(c) $(78.7 \times 10^5 \div 88.529) + 356.99$
(d) $(892 \div 986.7) + 5.44$

66. Perform each calculation to the correct number of significant figures.
(a) $(1.7 \times 10^6 \div 2.63 \times 10^5) + 7.33$
(b) $(568.99 - 232.1) \div 5.3$
(c) $(9443 + 45 - 9.9) \times 8.1 \times 10^6$
(d) $(3.14 \times 2.4367) - 2.34$

67. Determine whether the answer to each calculation has the correct number of significant figures. If not, correct it.
(a) $(78.56 - 9.44) \times 45.6 = 3152$
(b) $(8.9 \times 10^5 \div 2.348 \times 10^2) + 121 = 3.9 \times 10^3$
(c) $(45.8 \div 3.2) - 12.3 = 2$
(d) $(4.5 \times 10^3 - 1.53 \times 10^3) \div 34.5 = 86$

68. Determine whether the answer to each calculation has the correct number of significant figures. If not, correct it.
(a) $(908.4 - 3.4) \div 3.52 \times 10^4 = 0.026$
(b) $(1206.7 - 0.904) \times 89 = 1.07 \times 10^5$
(c) $(876.90 + 98.1) \div 56.998 = 17.11$
(d) $(455 \div 407859) + 1.00098 = 1.00210$

UNIT CONVERSION

69. Perform each conversion within the metric system.
(a) 3.55 kg to grams
(b) 8944 mm to meters
(c) 4598 mg to kilograms
(d) 0.0187 L to milliliters

70. Perform each conversion within the metric system.
(a) 155.5 cm to meters
(b) 2491.6 g to kilograms
(c) 248 cm to millimeters
(d) 6781 mL to liters

71. Perform each conversion within the metric system.
(a) 5.88 dL to liters
(b) 3.41×10^{-5} g to micrograms
(c) 1.01×10^{-8} s to nanoseconds
(d) 2.19 pm to meters

72. Perform each conversion within the metric system.
(a) 1.08 Mm to kilometers
(b) 4.88 fs to picoseconds
(c) 7.39×10^{11} m to gigameters
(d) 1.15×10^{-10} m to picometers

73. Perform each conversion between the English and metric systems.
(a) 22.5 in. to centimeters
(b) 126 ft to meters
(c) 825 yd to kilometers
(d) 2.4 in. to millimeters

74. Perform each conversion between the English and metric systems.
(a) 78.3 in. to centimeters
(b) 445 yd to meters
(c) 336 ft to centimeters
(d) 45.3 in. to millimeters

75. Perform each conversion between the metric and English systems.
(a) 40.0 cm to inches
(b) 27.8 m to feet
(c) 10.0 km to miles
(d) 3845 kg to pounds

76. Perform each conversion between the metric and English systems.
(a) 254 cm to inches
(b) 89 mm to inches
(c) 7.5 L to quarts
(d) 122 kg to pounds

77. Complete the table:

m	km	Mm	Gm	Tm
5.08×10^8 m	____	508 Mm	____	____
____	____	27,976 Mm	____	____
____	____	____	____	1.77 Tm
____	1.5×10^5 km	____	____	____
____	____	____	423 Gm	____

78. Complete the table:

s	ms	μs	ns	ps
1.31×10^{-4} s	____	131 μs	____	____
____	____	____	____	12.6 ps
____	____	____	155 ns	____
____	1.99×10^{-3} ms	____	____	____
____	____	8.66×10^{-5} μs	____	____

79. Convert 2.255×10^{10} g to each unit:
(a) kg
(b) Mg
(c) mg
(d) metric tons (1 metric ton = 1000 kg)

80. Convert 1.88×10^{-6} g to each unit.
(a) mg
(b) cg
(c) ng
(d) μg

81. A student loses 3.3 lb in one month. How many grams did he lose?

82. A student gains 1.9 lb in two weeks. How many grams did he gain?

83. A runner wants to run 10.0 km. She knows that her running pace is 7.5 mi/h. How many minutes must she run? *Hint:* Use 7.5 mi/h as a conversion factor between distance and time.

84. A cyclist rides at an average speed of 24 mi/h. If she wants to bike 195 km, how long (in hours) must she ride?

85. A recipe calls for 5.0 qt of milk. What is this quantity in cubic centimeters?

86. A gas can holds 2.0 gal of gasoline. What is this quantity in cubic centimeters?

UNITS RAISED TO A POWER

87. Fill in the blanks.
(a) 1.0 km^2 = ____ m^2
(b) 1.0 cm^3 = ____ m^3
(c) 1.0 mm^3 = ____ m^3

88. Fill in the blanks.
(a) 1.0 ft^2 = ____ $in.^2$
(b) 1.0 yd^2 = ____ ft^2
(c) 1.0 m^2 = ____ yd^2

89. The hydrogen atom has a volume of approximately 6.2×10^{-31} m^3. What is this volume in each unit?
(a) cubic picometers
(b) cubic nanometers
(c) cubic angstroms (1 angstrom = 10^{-10} m)

90. Earth has a surface area of 197 million square miles. What is its area in each unit?
(a) square kilometers
(b) square megameters
(c) square decimeters

91. A modest-sized house has an area of 215 m^2. What is its area in each unit?
(a) km^2
(b) dm^2
(c) cm^2

92. A classroom has a volume of 285 m^3. What is its volume in each unit?
(a) km^3
(b) dm^3
(c) cm^3

93. Total U.S. farmland occupies 954 million acres. How many square miles is this?
(1 acre = 43,560 ft^2; 1 mi = 5280 ft)

94. The average U.S. farm occupies 435 acres. How many square miles is this?
(1 acre = 43,560 ft^2; 1 mi = 5280 ft)

DENSITY

95. A sample of an unknown metal has a mass of 35.4 g and a volume of 3.11 cm^3. Calculate its density and identify the metal by comparison to Table 2.4.

96. A new penny has a mass of 2.49 g and a volume of 0.349 cm^3. Is the penny pure copper?

97. Glycerol is a syrupy liquid often used in cosmetics and soaps. A 2.50-L sample of pure glycerol has a mass of 3.15×10^3 g. What is the density of glycerol in grams per cubic centimeter?

98. An aluminum engine block has a volume of 4.77 L and a mass of 12.88 kg. What is the density of the aluminum in grams per cubic centimeter?

99. A supposedly gold tooth crown is tested to determine its density. It displaces 10.7 mL of water and has a mass of 206 g. Could the crown be made of gold?

100. A vase is said to be solid platinum. It displaces 18.65 mL of water and has a mass of 157 g. Could the vase be solid platinum?

101. Ethylene glycol (antifreeze) has a density of 1.11 g/cm^3.
   (a) What is the mass in grams of 387 mL of this liquid?
   (b) What is the volume in liters of 3.46 kg of this liquid?

102. Acetone (fingernail-polish remover) has a density of 0.7857 g/cm^3.
   (a) What is the mass in grams of 17.56 mL of acetone?
   (b) What is the volume in milliliters of 7.22 g of acetone?

CUMULATIVE PROBLEMS

103. A thief uses a bag of sand to replace a gold statue that sits on a weight-sensitive, alarmed pedestal. The bag of sand and the statue have exactly the same volume, 1.75 L. (Assume that the mass of the bag is negligible.)
   (a) Calculate the mass of each object. (density of gold $= 19.3\,g/cm^3$; density of sand $= 3.00\,g/cm^3$)
   (b) Did the thief set off the alarm? Explain.

104. One of the particles that composes an atom is the proton. A proton has a radius of approximately 1.0×10^{-13} cm and a mass of 1.7×10^{-24} g. Determine the density of a proton.

$$\left(\text{volume of a sphere} = \frac{4}{3}\pi r^3;\ \pi = 3.14\right)$$

105. A block of metal has a volume of 13.4 $in.^3$ and weighs 5.14 lb. What is its density in grams per cubic centimeter?

106. A log is either oak or pine. It displaces 2.7 gal of water and weighs 19.8 lb. Is the log oak or pine? (density of oak $= 0.9\,g/cm^3$; density of pine $= 0.4\,g/cm^3$)

107. The density of aluminum is 2.7 g/cm^3. What is its density in kilograms per cubic meter?

108. The density of platinum is 21.4 g/cm^3. What is its density in pounds per cubic inch?

109. A typical backyard swimming pool holds 150 yd^3 of water. What is the mass in pounds of the water?

110. An iceberg has a volume of 8975 ft^3. What is the mass in kilograms of the iceberg?

111. The mass of fuel in an airplane must be carefully accounted for before takeoff. If a 747 contains 155,211 L of fuel, what is the mass of the fuel in kilograms? Assume the density of the fuel to be 0.768 g/cm^3.

112. A backpacker carries 2.5 L of white gas as fuel for her stove. How many pounds does the fuel add to her load? Assume the density of white gas to be 0.79 g/cm^3.

113. Honda produces a hybrid electric car called the Honda Insight. The Insight has both a gasoline-powered engine and an electric motor and has an EPA gas mileage rating of 43 miles per gallon on the highway. What is the Insight's rating in kilometers per liter?

114. You rent a car in Germany with a gas mileage rating of 12.8 km/L. What is its rating in miles per gallon?

115. A car has a mileage rating of 38 miles per gallon of gasoline. How many miles can the car travel on 76.5 liters of gasoline?

116. A hybrid SUV consumes fuel at a rate of 12.8 km/L. How many miles can the car travel on 22.5 gallons of gasoline?

117. Block A of an unknown metal has a volume of 125 cm^3. Block B of a different metal has a volume of 145 cm^3. If block A has a greater mass than block B, what can be said of the relative densities of the two metals? (Assume that both blocks are solid.)

118. Block A of an unknown metal has a volume of 125 cm^3. Block B of a different metal has a volume of 105 cm^3. If block A has a greater mass than block B, what can be said of the relative densities of the two metals? (Assume that both blocks are solid.)

119. The masses and volumes of two cylinders are measured. The mass of cylinder 1 is 1.35 times the mass of cylinder 2. The volume of cylinder 1 is 0.792 times the volume of cylinder 2. If the density of cylinder 1 is 3.85 g/cm^3, what is the density of cylinder 2?

120. A bag contains a mixture of copper and lead BBs. The average density of the BBs is 9.87 g/cm^3. Assuming that the copper and lead are pure, determine the relative amounts of each kind of BB.

HIGHLIGHT PROBLEMS

121. In 1999, NASA lost a $94 million orbiter because one group of engineers used metric units in their calculations while another group used English units. Consequently, the orbiter descended too far into the Martian atmosphere and burned up. Suppose that the orbiter was to have established orbit at 155 km and that one group of engineers specified this distance as 1.55×10^5 m. Suppose further that a second group of engineers programmed the orbiter to go to 1.55×10^5 ft. What was the difference in kilometers between the two altitudes? How low did the probe go?

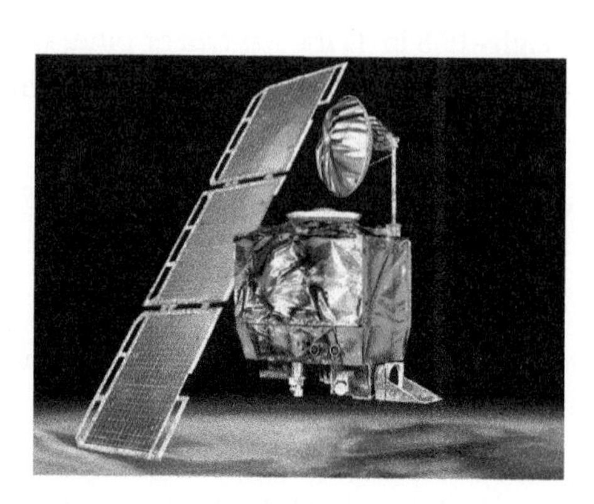

▲ The $94 million Mars Climate Orbiter was lost in the Martian atmosphere in 1999 because two groups of engineers failed to communicate to each other the units that they used in their calculations.

122. A NASA satellite showed that in 2009 the ozone hole over Antarctica had a maximum surface area of 24.1 million km^2. The largest ozone hole on record occurred in 2006 and had a surface area of 29.6 million km^2. Calculate the difference in diameter (in meters) between the ozone hole in 2009 and in 2006.

▲ A layer of ozone gas (a form of oxygen) in the upper atmosphere protects Earth from harmful ultraviolet radiation in sunlight. Human-made chemicals react with the ozone and deplete it, especially over the Antarctic at certain times of the year (the so-called ozone hole). The region of low ozone concentration in 2006 (represented here by the dark purple color) was the largest on record.

123. In 1999, scientists discovered a new class of black holes with masses 100 to 10,000 times the mass of our sun, but occupying less space than our moon. Suppose that one of these black holes has a mass of 1×10^3 suns and a radius equal to one-half the radius of our moon. What is its density in grams per cubic centimeter? The mass of the sun is 2.0×10^{30} kg, and the radius of the moon is 2.16×10^3 mi. (Volume of a sphere $= \frac{4}{3}\pi r^3$.)

124. A titanium bicycle frame contains the same amount of titanium as a titanium cube measuring 6.8 cm on a side. Use the density of titanium to calculate the mass in kilograms of titanium in the frame. What would be the mass of a similar frame composed of iron?

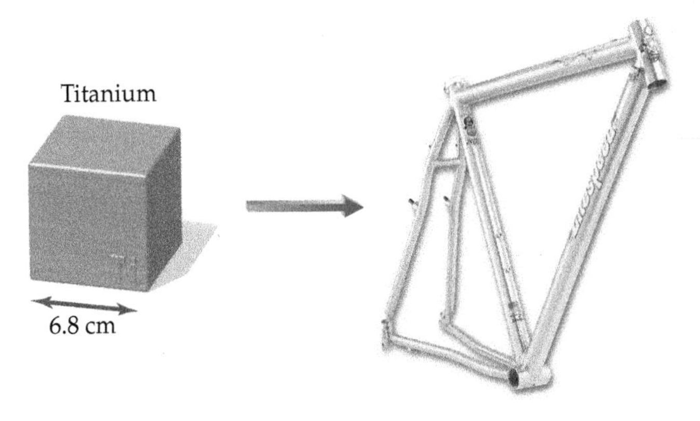

▲ A titanium bicycle frame contains the same amount of titanium as a titanium cube measuring 6.8 cm on a side.

▸ANSWERS TO SKILLBUILDER EXERCISES

Skillbuilder 2.1 1.2102×10^{13}

Skillbuilder 2.2 3.8×10^{-5}

Skillbuilder 2.3 103.4 °F

Skillbuilder 2.4
(a) four significant figures
(b) three significant figures
(c) two significant figures
(d) unlimited significant figures
(e) three significant figures
(f) ambiguous

Skillbuilder 2.5
(a) 0.001 or 1×10^{-3}
(b) 0.204

Skillbuilder 2.6
(a) 7.6
(b) 131.11

Skillbuilder 2.7
(a) 1288
(b) 3.12

Skillbuilder 2.8 22.0 in.

Skillbuilder 2.9 5.678 km

Skillbuilder 2.10 0.28 L

Skillbuilder 2.11 46.6 laps

Skillbuilder Plus, p. 31 1.06×10^4 m

Skillbuilder 2.12 4747 cm^3

Skillbuilder 2.13 1.52×10^5 $in.^3$

Skillbuilder 2.14 Yes, the density is 21.4 g/cm^3 and matches that of platinum.

Skillbuilder 2.15 4.4×10^{-2} cm^3

Skillbuilder Plus, p. 37 1.95 kg

Skillbuilder 2.16 16 kg

Skillbuilder 2.17 $d = 19.3 g/cm^3$; yes, the density is consistent with that of gold.

▸ANSWERS TO CONCEPTUAL CHECKPOINTS

2.1 (c) Multiplying by 10^{-3} is equivalent to moving the decimal point three places to the left.

2.2 (b) The last digit is considered to be uncertain by ±1.

2.3 (b) The result of the calculation in **(a)** would be reported as 4; the result of the calculation in **(b)** would be reported as 1.5.

2.4 (d) The diameter would be expressed as 28 nm.

2.5 (c) Kilometers must appear in the numerator and meters in the denominator, and the conversion factor in **(d)** is incorrect ($10^3 km \neq 1 m$).

2.6 (d) $(3 ft) \times (3 ft) \times (3 ft) = 27 ft^3$

CHAPTER 3

Matter and Energy

"Thus, the task is, not so much to see what no one has yet seen; but to think what nobody has yet thought, about that which everybody sees."

ERWIN SCHRÖDINGER (1887–1961)

3.1 In Your Room

Look around the room you are in—what do you see? You might see your desk, your bed, or a glass of water. Maybe you have a window and can see trees, grass, or mountains. You can certainly see this book and possibly the table it sits on. What are these things made of? They are all made of *matter*, which we will define more carefully shortly. For now, know that all you see is matter—your desk, your bed, the glass of water, the trees, the mountains, and this book. Some of what you don't see is matter as well. For example, you are constantly breathing air, which is also matter, into and out of your lungs. You feel the matter in air when you feel wind on your skin. Virtually everything is made of matter.

◀ Everything that you can see in this room is made of matter. As students of chemistry, we are interested in how the differences between different kinds of matter are related to the differences between the molecules and atoms that compose the matter. The molecular structures shown here are water molecules on the left and carbon atoms in graphite on the right.

Think about the differences between different kinds of matter. Air is different from water, and water is different from wood. One of our first tasks as we learn about matter is to identify the similarities and differences among different kinds of matter. How are sugar and salt similar? How are air and water different? Why are they different? Why is a mixture of sugar and water similar to a mixture of salt and water but different from a mixture of sand and water? As students of chemistry, we are particularly interested in the similarities and differences between various kinds of matter and how these reflect the similarities and differences between their component atoms and molecules. We strive to understand the connection between the macroscopic world and the molecular one.

3.2 What Is Matter?

Matter is defined as anything that occupies space and has mass. Some types of matter—such as steel, water, wood, and plastic—are easily visible to our eyes. Other types of matter—such as air or microscopic dust—are impossible to see without magnification. Matter may sometimes appear smooth and continuous, but actually it is not. Matter is ultimately composed of **atoms**, submicroscopic particles that are the fundamental building blocks of matter (▼ Figure 3.1a). In many cases, these atoms are bonded together to form **molecules**, two or more atoms joined to one another in specific geometric arrangements (Figure 3.1b). Recent advances in microscopy have allowed us to image the atoms (▼ Figure 3.2) and molecules (▼ Figure 3.3) that compose matter, sometimes with stunning clarity.

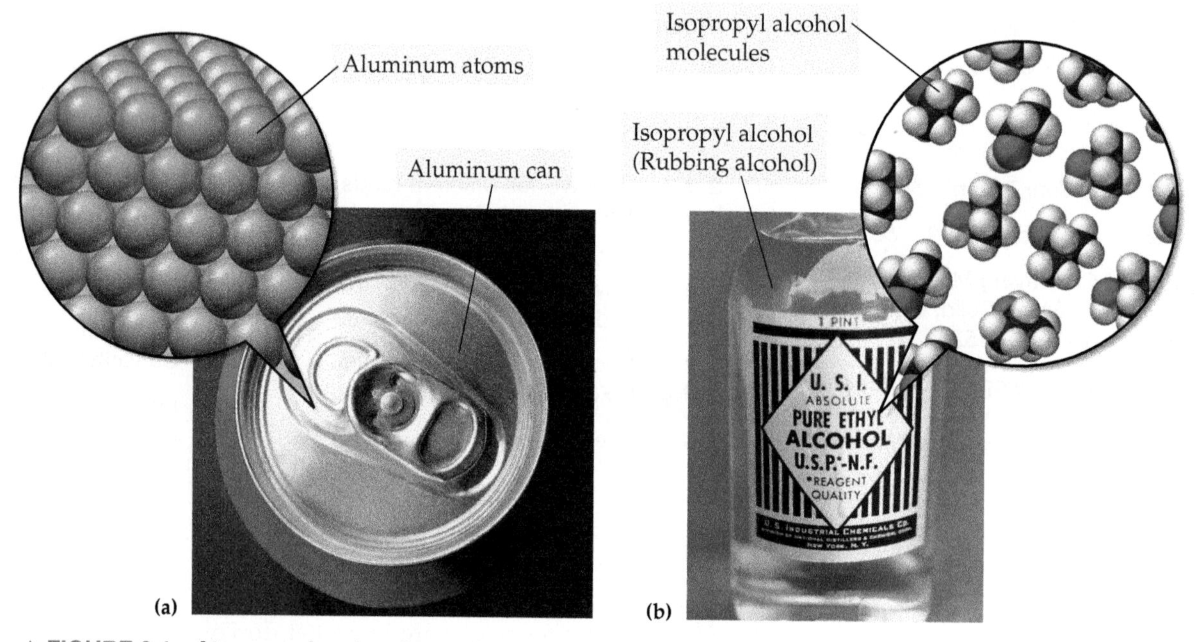

▲ FIGURE 3.1 **Atoms and molecules** All matter is ultimately composed of atoms. **(a)** In some substances, such as aluminum, the atoms exist as independent particles. **(b)** In other substances, such as rubbing alcohol, several atoms bond together in well-defined structures called molecules.

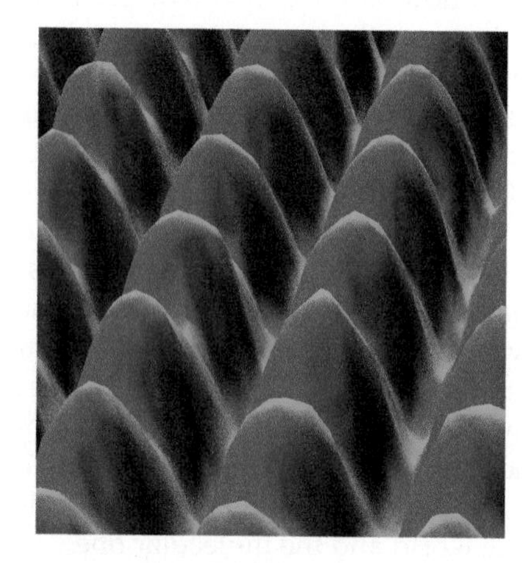

▲ FIGURE 3.2 **Scanning tunneling microscope image of nickel atoms** A scanning tunneling microscope (STM) creates an image by scanning a surface with a tip of atomic dimensions. It can distinguish individual atoms, seen as blue bumps, in this image. (*Source:* Reprint Courtesy of International Business Machines Corporation, copyright © International Business Machines Corporation.)

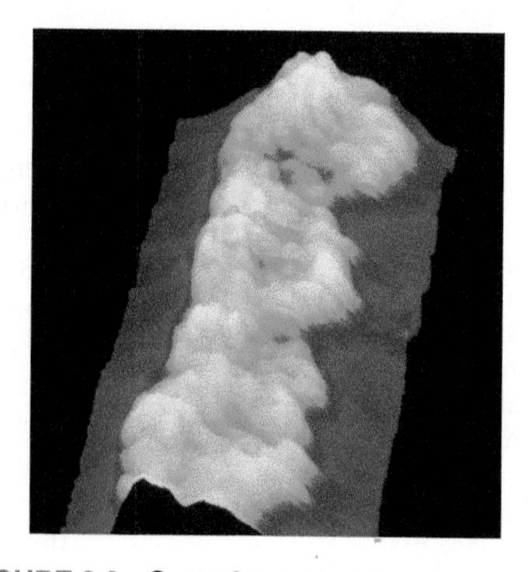

▲ FIGURE 3.3 **Scanning tunneling microscope image of a DNA molecule** DNA is the hereditary material that encodes the operating instructions for most cells in living organisms. In this image, the DNA molecule is yellow, and the double-stranded structure of DNA is discernible.

3.3 Classifying Matter According to Its State: Solid, Liquid, and Gas

The common **states of matter** are **solid**, **liquid**, and **gas** (▼ Figure 3.4). In solid matter, atoms or molecules pack close to each other in fixed locations. Although neighboring atoms or molecules in a solid may vibrate or oscillate, they do not move around each other, giving solids their familiar fixed volume and rigid shape.

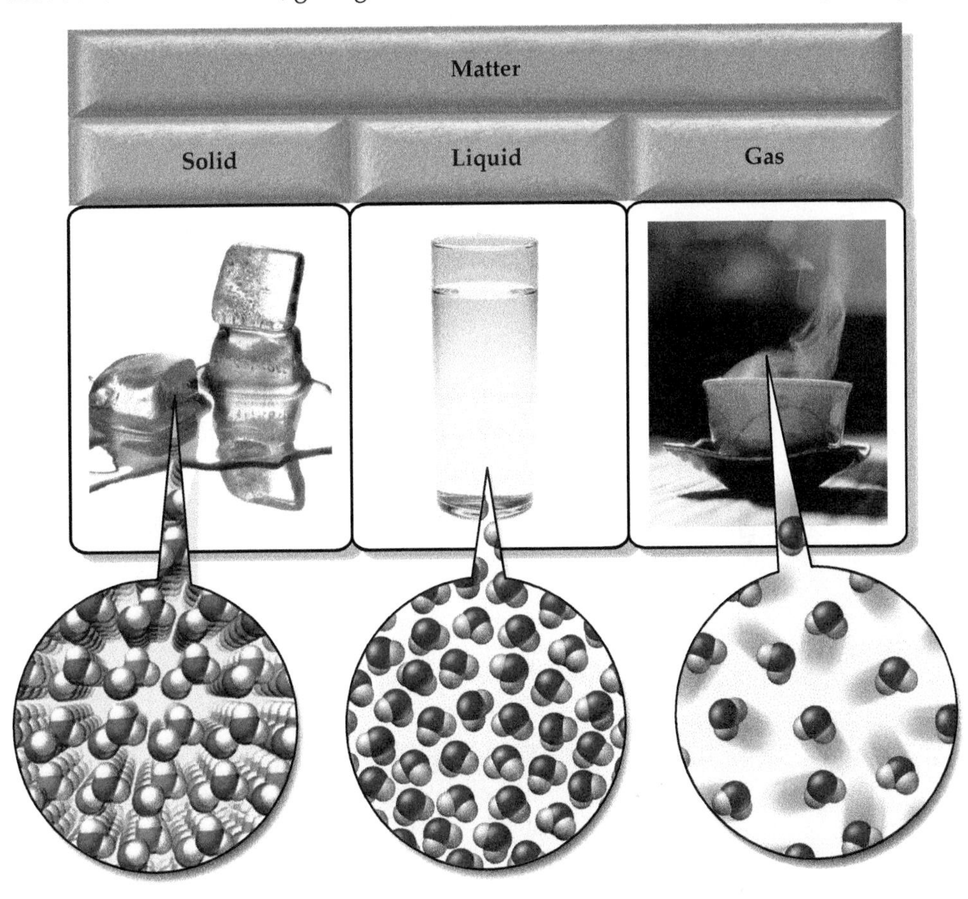

▶ **FIGURE 3.4 Three states of matter** Water exists as ice (solid), water (liquid), and steam (gas). In ice, the water molecules are closely spaced and, although they vibrate about a fixed point, they do not generally move relative to one another. In liquid water, the water molecules are also closely spaced but are free to move around and past each other. In steam, water molecules are separated by large distances and do not interact significantly with one another.

Ice, diamond, quartz, and iron are examples of solid matter. Solid matter may be **crystalline**, in which case its atoms or molecules arrange in geometric patterns with long-range, repeating order (◀ Figure 3.5a), or it may be **amorphous**, in which case its atoms or molecules do not have long-range order (Figure 3.5b). Examples of *crystalline* solids include salt (▼ Figure 3.6) and diamond; the well-ordered, geometric shapes of salt and diamond crystals reflect the well-ordered geometric arrangement of their atoms. Examples of *amorphous* solids include glass, rubber, and plastic.

(a) Crystalline solid

(b) Amorphous solid

▲ **FIGURE 3.5 Types of solid matter** **(a)** In a crystalline solid, atoms or molecules occupy specific positions to create a well-ordered, three-dimensional structure. **(b)** In an amorphous solid, atoms do not have any long-range order.

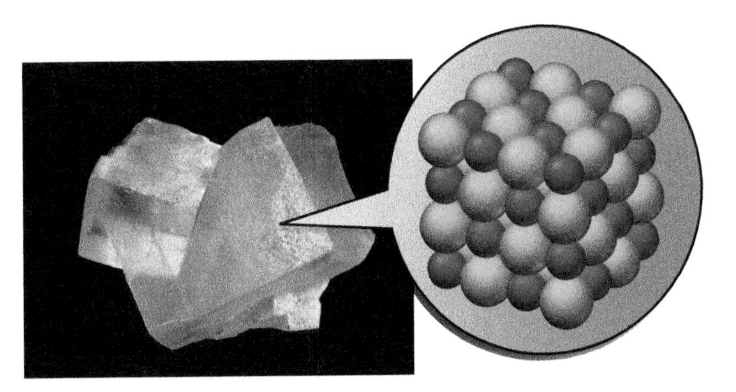

▲ **FIGURE 3.6 Salt: a crystalline solid** Sodium chloride is an example of a crystalline solid. The well-ordered, cubic shape of salt crystals is due to the well-ordered, cubic arrangement of its atoms.

Solid—not compressible

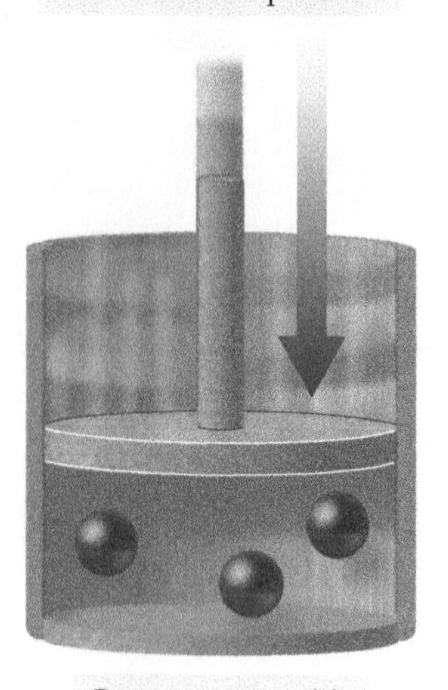
Gas—compressible

In liquid matter, atoms or molecules are close to each other (about as close as molecules in a solid) but are free to move around and by each other. Like solids, liquids have a fixed volume because their atoms or molecules are in close contact. Unlike solids, however, liquids assume the shape of their container because the atoms or molecules are free to move relative to one another. Water, gasoline, alcohol, and mercury are all examples of liquid matter.

In gaseous matter, atoms or molecules are separated by large distances and are free to move relative to one another. Since the atoms or molecules that compose gases are not in contact with one another, gases are **compressible** (◀ Figure 3.7). When you inflate a bicycle tire, for example, you push more atoms and molecules into the same space, compressing them and making the tire harder. Gases always assume the shape and volume of their containers. Oxygen, helium, and carbon dioxide are all good examples of gases. Table 3.1 summarizes the properties of solids, liquids, and gases.

TABLE 3.1 Properties of Liquids, Solids, and Gases

State	Atomic/Molecular Motion	Atomic/Molecular Spacing	Shape	Volume	Compressibility
Solid	Oscillation/ vibration about fixed point	Close together	Definite	Definite	Incompressible
Liquid	Free to move relative to one another	Close together	Indefinite	Definite	Incompressible
Gas	Free to move relative to one another	Far apart	Indefinite	Indefinite	Compressible

◀ **FIGURE 3.7 Gases are compressible** Since the atoms or molecules that compose gases are not in contact with one another, gases can be compressed.

3.4 Classifying Matter According to Its Composition: Elements, Compounds, and Mixtures

In addition to classifying matter according to its state, we can classify it according to its composition (▶ Figure 3.8). Matter may be either a **pure substance**, composed of only one type of atom or molecule, or a **mixture**, composed of two or more different types of atoms or molecules combined in variable proportions.

Pure substances are composed of only one type of atom or molecule. Helium and water are both pure substances. The atoms that compose helium are all helium atoms, and the molecules that compose water are all water molecules—no other atoms or molecules are mixed in.

Pure substances can themselves be divided into two types: elements and compounds. Copper is an example of an **element**, a substance that cannot be broken down into simpler substances. The graphite in pencils is also an element—carbon. No chemical transformation can decompose graphite into simpler substances; it is pure carbon. All known elements are listed in the periodic table in the inside front cover of this book and in alphabetical order on the inside back cover of this book.

A compound is composed of different atoms that are chemically united (bonded). A mixture is composed of different substances that are not chemically united, but simply mixed together.

A pure substance can also be a **compound**, a substance composed of two or more elements in fixed definite proportions. Compounds are more common than pure elements because most elements are chemically reactive and combine with other elements to form compounds. Water, table salt, and sugar are examples of compounds; they can all be decomposed into simpler substances. If you heat sugar on a pan over a flame, you decompose it into several substances including carbon

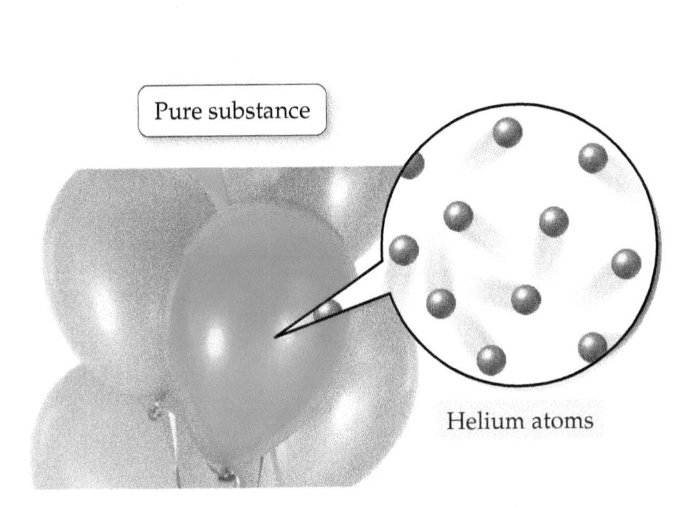

▲ Helium is a pure substance composed only of helium atoms.

▲ Water is a pure substance composed only of water molecules.

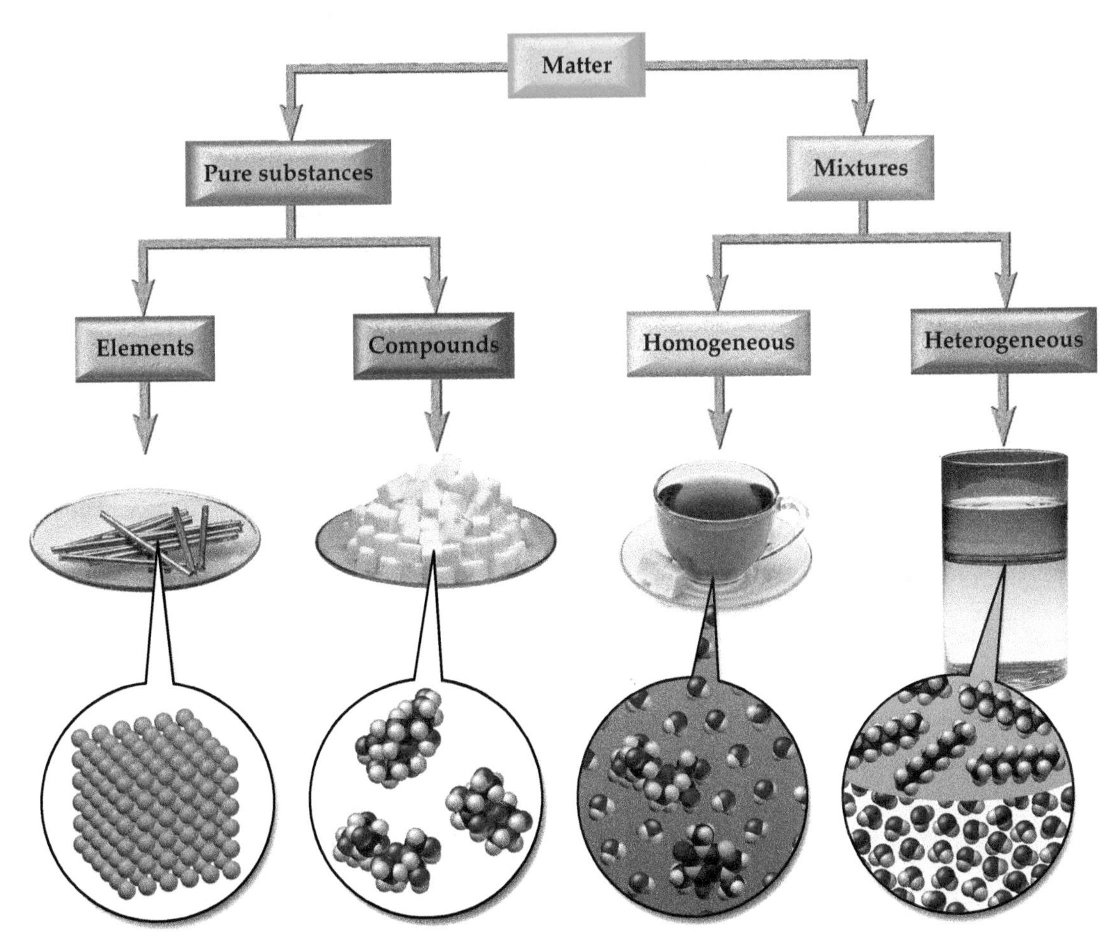

▲ **FIGURE 3.8 Classification of matter** Matter may be a pure substance or a mixture. A pure substance may be either an element (such as copper) or a compound (such as sugar), and a mixture may be either homogeneous (such as sweetened tea) or heterogeneous (such as hydrocarbon and water).

(an element) and gaseous water (a different compound). The black substance left on your pan after burning contains the carbon; the water escapes into the air as steam.

The majority of matter that we encounter is in the form of mixtures. Apple juice, a flame, salad dressing, and soil are all examples of mixtures; they each contain several substances mixed together in proportions that vary from one sample to another. Other common mixtures include air, seawater, and brass. Air is a mixture composed primarily of nitrogen and oxygen gas, seawater is a mixture composed primarily of salt and water, and brass is a mixture composed of copper and zinc. Each of these mixtures can have different proportions of its constituent components. For example, metallurgists vary the relative amounts of copper and zinc in brass to tailor the metal's properties to its intended use—the higher the zinc content relative to the copper content, the more brittle the brass.

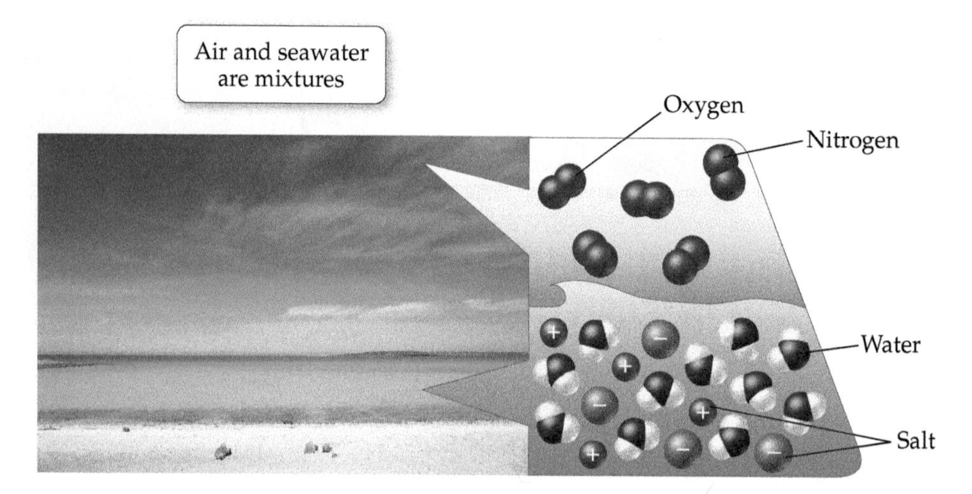

▶ Air and seawater are examples of mixtures. Air contains primarily nitrogen and oxygen. Seawater contains primarily salt and water.

Mixtures can be classified according to how uniformly the substances within them mix. In a **heterogeneous mixture**, such as oil and water, the composition varies from one region to another. In a **homogeneous mixture**, such as salt water or sweetened tea, the composition is the same throughout. Homogeneous mixtures have uniform compositions because the atoms or molecules that compose them mix uniformly. Remember that the properties of matter are determined by the atoms or molecules that compose it.

To summarize, as shown in Figure 3.8:

- Matter may be a pure substance, or it may be a mixture.
- A pure substance may be either an element or a compound.
- A mixture may be either homogeneous or heterogeneous.
- Mixtures may be composed of two or more elements, two or more compounds, or a combination of both.

EXAMPLE 3.1 Classifying Matter

Classify each type of matter as a pure substance or a mixture. If it is a pure substance, classify it as an element or a compound; if it is a mixture, classify it as homogeneous or heterogeneous.

(a) a lead weight
(b) seawater
(c) distilled water
(d) Italian salad dressing

SOLUTION

Begin by examining the alphabetical listing of pure elements inside the back cover of this text. If the substance appears in that table, it is a pure substance and an element. If it is not in the table but is a pure substance, then it is a compound.

If the substance is not a pure substance, then it is a mixture. Refer to your everyday experience with each mixture to determine if it is homogeneous or heterogeneous.

(a) Lead is listed in the table of elements. It is a pure substance and an element.
(b) Seawater is composed of several substances, including salt and water; it is a mixture. It has a uniform composition, so it is a homogeneous mixture.
(c) Distilled water is not listed in the table of elements, but it is a pure substance (water); therefore, it is a compound.
(d) Italian salad dressing contains a number of substances and is therefore a mixture. It usually separates into at least two distinct regions with different composition and is therefore a heterogeneous mixture.

▶SKILLBUILDER 3.1 | Classifying Matter

Classify each type of matter as a pure substance or a mixture. If it is a pure substance, classify it as an element or a compound. If it is a mixture, classify it as homogeneous or heterogeneous.

(a) mercury in a thermometer
(b) exhaled air
(c) minestrone soup
(d) sugar

▶FOR MORE PRACTICE Example 3.12; Problems 31, 32, 33, 34, 35, 36.

Note: The answers to all Skillbuilders appear at the end of the chapter.

3.5 How We Tell Different Kinds of Matter Apart: Physical and Chemical Properties

The characteristics that distinguish one substance from another are called **properties**. Different substances have unique properties that characterize them and distinguish them from other substances. For example, we can distinguish water from alcohol based on their different smells, or we can distinguish gold from silver based on their different colors.

In chemistry, we categorize properties into two different types: physical and chemical. A **physical property** is one that a substance displays without changing its composition. A **chemical property** is one that a substance displays only through changing its composition. For example, the characteristic odor of gasoline is a physical property—gasoline does not change its composition when it exhibits its odor. On the other hand, the flammability of gasoline is a chemical property—gasoline does change its composition when it burns.

The atomic or molecular composition of a substance does not change when the substance displays its physical properties. For example, the boiling point of water—a physical property—is 100 °C. When water boils, it changes from a liquid to a gas, but the gas is still water (◀ Figure 3.9).

◀ **FIGURE 3.9 A physical property** The boiling point of water is a physical property, and boiling is a physical change. When water boils, it turns into a gas, but the water molecules are the same in both the liquid water and the gaseous steam.

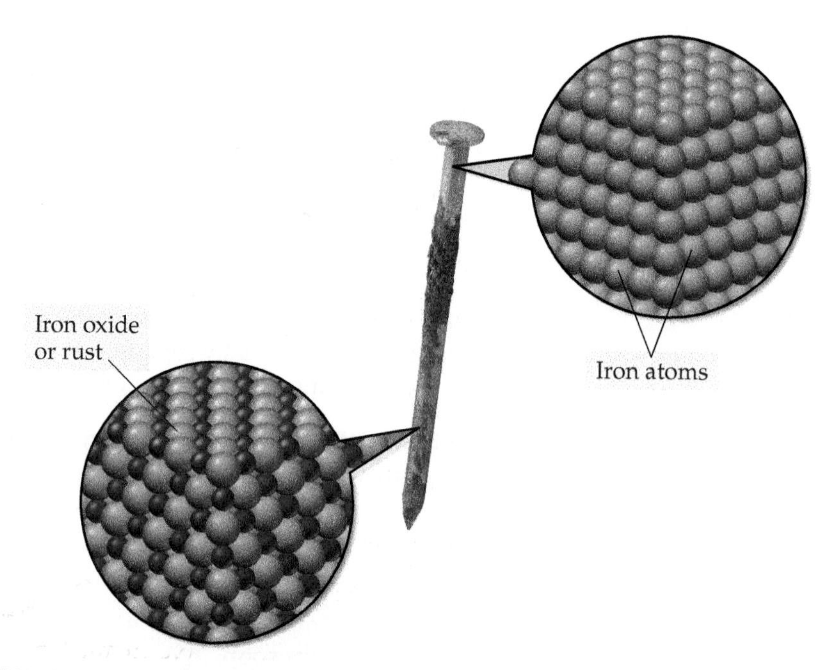

▲ **FIGURE 3.10 A chemical property** The susceptibility of iron to rusting is a chemical property, and rusting is a chemical change. When iron rusts, it turns from iron to iron oxide.

On the other hand, the susceptibility of iron to rust is a chemical property—iron must change into iron oxide to display this property (▲ Figure 3.10). Physical properties include odor, taste, color, appearance, melting point, boiling point, and density. Chemical properties include corrosiveness, flammability, acidity, and toxicity.

EXAMPLE 3.2 Physical and Chemical Properties

Determine whether each property is physical or chemical.

(a) the tendency of copper to turn green when exposed to air Chemical
(b) the tendency of automobile paint to dull over time chemical
(c) the tendency of gasoline to evaporate quickly when spilled Physical
(d) the low mass (for a given volume) of aluminum relative to other metals Physical

SOLUTION

(a) Copper turns green because it reacts with gases in air to form compounds; this is a chemical property.
(b) Automobile paint dulls over time because it can fade (decompose) due to sunlight or it can react with oxygen in air. In either case, this is a chemical property.
(c) Gasoline evaporates quickly because it has a low boiling point; this is a physical property.
(d) Aluminum's low mass (for a given volume) relative to other metals is due to its low density; this is a physical property.

▶**SKILLBUILDER 3.2 | Physical and Chemical Properties**

Determine whether each property is physical or chemical.

(a) the explosiveness of hydrogen gas Chemical
(b) the bronze color of copper Physical
(c) the shiny appearance of silver Physical
(d) the ability of dry ice to sublime (change from solid directly to vapor) Physical

▶**FOR MORE PRACTICE** Example 3.13; Problems 37, 38, 39, 40.

3.6 How Matter Changes: Physical and Chemical Changes

Every day, we witness changes in matter: Ice melts, iron rusts, and fruit ripens, for example. What happens to the atoms and molecules that make up these substances during the change? The answer depends on the kind of change. In a **physical change**, matter changes its appearance but not its composition. For example, when ice melts, it looks different—water looks different from ice—but its composition is the same. Solid ice and liquid water are both composed of water molecules, so melting is a physical change. Similarly, when glass shatters, it looks different, but its composition remains the same—it is still glass. Again, this is a physical change. On the other hand, in a **chemical change**, matter *does* change its composition. For example, copper turns green upon continued exposure to air because it reacts with gases in air to form new compounds. This is a chemical change. Matter undergoes a chemical change when it undergoes a **chemical reaction**. In a chemical reaction, the substances present before the chemical change are called **reactants**, and the substances present after the change are called **products**:

$$\text{Reactants} \xrightarrow[\text{Change}]{\text{Chemical}} \text{Products}$$

We cover chemical reactions in much more detail in Chapter 7.

The differences between physical and chemical changes are not always apparent. Only chemical examination of the substances before and after the change can verify whether the change is physical or chemical. For many cases, however, we can identify chemical and physical changes based on what we know about the changes. Changes in state, such as melting or boiling, or changes that involve merely appearance, such as those produced by cutting or crushing, are always physical changes. Changes involving chemical reactions—often evidenced by heat exchange or color changes—are always chemical changes.

State changes—transformations from one state of matter (such as solid or liquid) to another—are always physical changes.

The main difference between chemical and physical changes is related to the changes at the molecular and atomic level. In physical changes, the atoms that compose the matter *do not* change their fundamental associations, even though the matter may change its appearance. In chemical changes, atoms do change their fundamental associations, resulting in matter with a new identity. *A physical change results in a different form of the same substance, while a chemical change results in a completely new substance.*

Consider physical and chemical changes in liquid butane, the substance used to fuel butane lighters. In many lighters, you can see the liquid butane through the plastic case of the lighter. If you push the fuel button on the lighter without turning the flint, some of the liquid butane *vaporizes* (changes from liquid to gas). If you listen carefully you can usually hear hissing as the gaseous butane leaks out (◀ Figure 3.11). Since the liquid butane and the gaseous butane are both composed of butane molecules, the change is physical. On the other hand, if you push the button *and* turn the flint to create a spark, a chemical change occurs. The butane molecules react with oxygen molecules in air to form new molecules, carbon dioxide and water (◀ Figure 3.12). The change is chemical because the molecular composition changes upon burning.

▼ **FIGURE 3.11 Vaporization: a physical change** If you push the button on a lighter without turning the flint, some of the liquid butane vaporizes to gaseous butane. Since the liquid butane and the gaseous butane are both composed of butane molecules, this is a physical change.

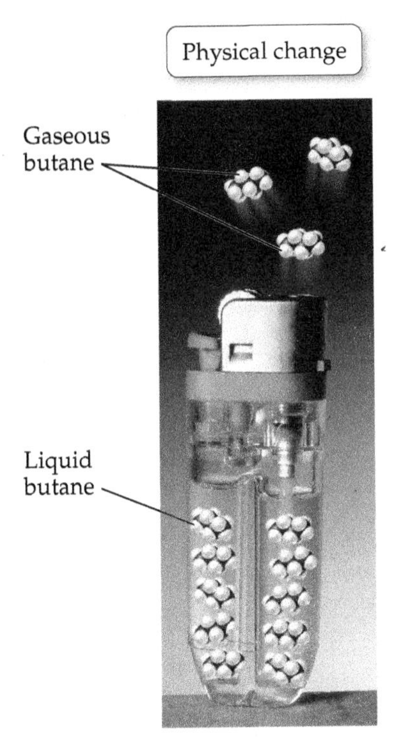

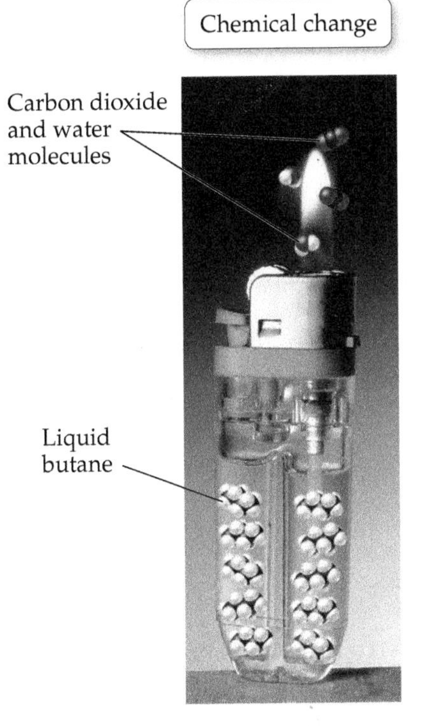

◀ **FIGURE 3.12 Burning: a chemical change** If you push the button *and* turn the flint to create a spark, you produce a flame. The butane molecules react with oxygen molecules in air to form new molecules, carbon dioxide and water. This is a chemical change.

EXAMPLE 3.3 Physical and Chemical Changes

Determine whether each change is physical or chemical.

(a) the rusting of iron
(b) the evaporation of fingernail-polish remover (acetone) from the skin
(c) the burning of coal
(d) the fading of a carpet upon repeated exposure to sunlight

SOLUTION

(a) Iron rusts because it reacts with oxygen in air to form iron oxide; therefore, this is a chemical change.
(b) When fingernail-polish remover (acetone) evaporates, it changes from liquid to gas, but it remains acetone; therefore, this is a physical change.
(c) Coal burns because it reacts with oxygen in air to form carbon dioxide; this is a chemical change.
(d) A carpet fades on repeated exposure to sunlight because the molecules that give the carpet its color are decomposed by sunlight; this is a chemical change.

▶SKILLBUILDER 3.3 | Physical and Chemical Changes

Determine whether each change is physical or chemical.

(a) copper metal forming a blue solution when it is dropped into colorless nitric acid
(b) a train flattening a penny placed on a railroad track
(c) ice melting into liquid water
(d) a match igniting a firework

▶FOR MORE PRACTICE Example 3.14; Problems 41, 42, 43, 44.

CONCEPTUAL CHECKPOINT 3.1

In this figure liquid water is being vaporized into steam.

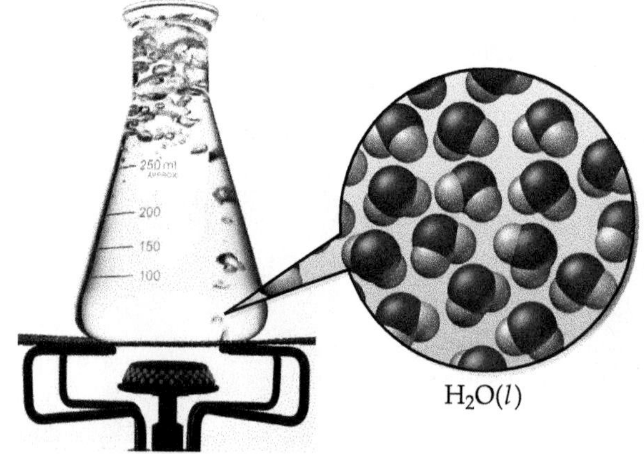

Which diagram best represents the molecules in the steam?

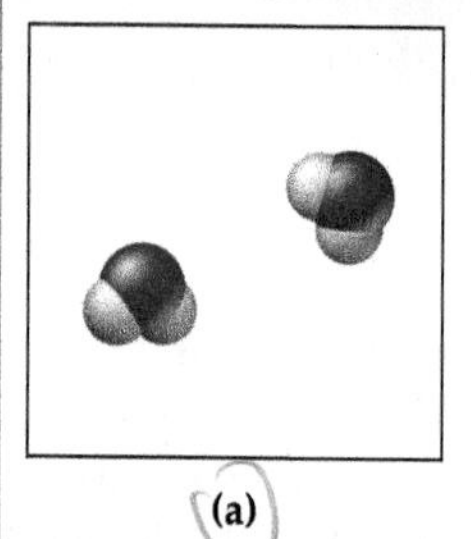

(a)

(b)

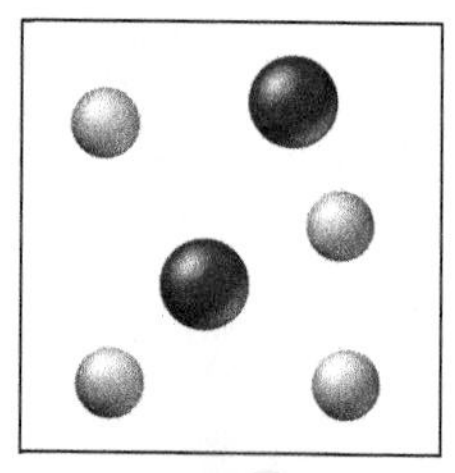

(c)

Note: The answers to all Conceptual Checkpoints appear at the end of the chapter.

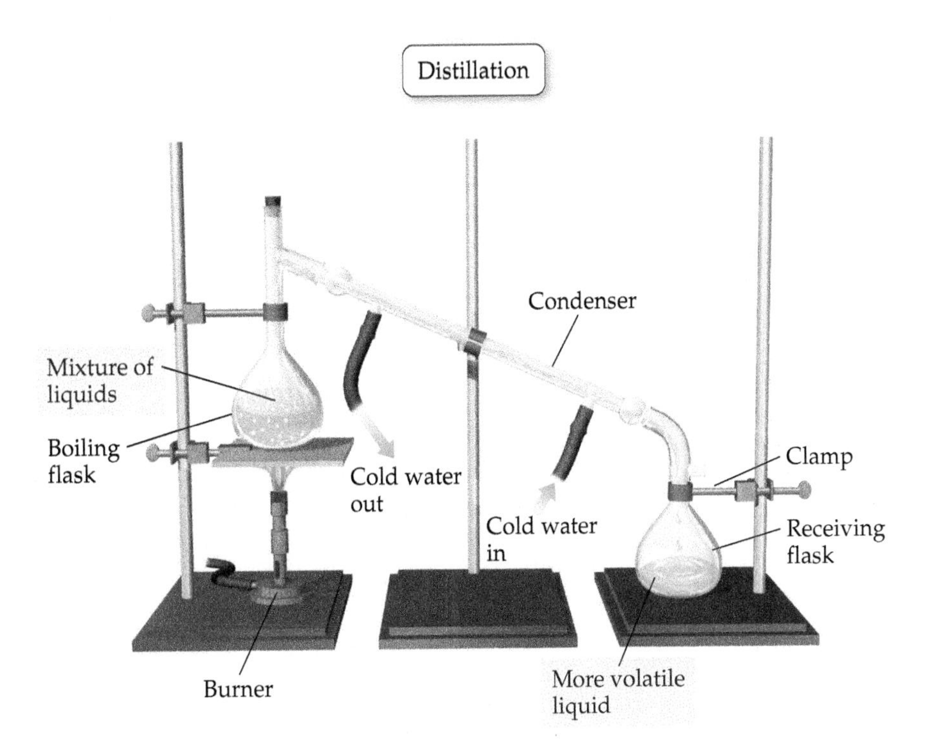

▶ **FIGURE 3.13 Separating a mixture of two liquids by distillation** The liquid with the lower boiling point vaporizes first. The vapors are collected and cooled (with cold water) until they condense back into liquid form.

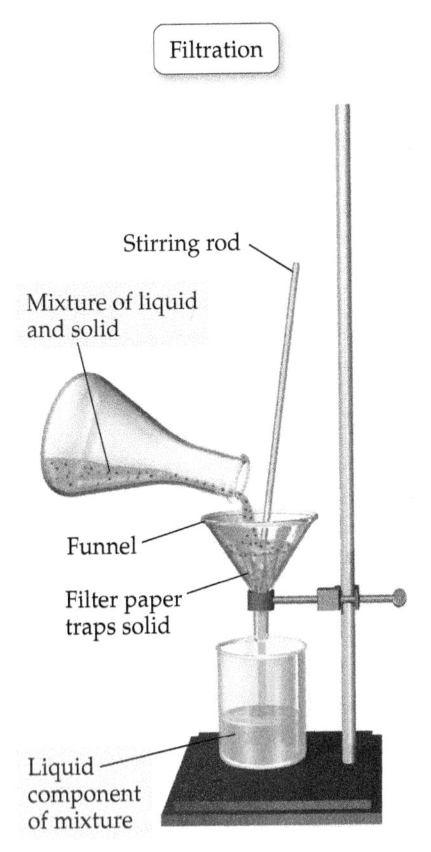

▲ **FIGURE 3.14 Separating a solid from a liquid by filtration**

SEPARATING MIXTURES THROUGH PHYSICAL CHANGES

Chemists often want to separate mixtures into their components. Such separations can be easy or difficult, depending on the components in the mixture. In general, mixtures are separable because the different components have different properties. Various techniques that exploit these differences can be used to achieve separation. For example, oil and water are immiscible (do not mix) and have different densities. For this reason, oil floats on top of water and can be separated from water by **decanting**—carefully pouring off—the oil into another container. Mixtures of miscible liquids can usually be separated by **distillation**, a process in which the mixture is heated to boil off the more **volatile**—the more easily vaporizable—liquid. The volatile liquid is then recondensed in a condenser and collected in a separate flask (▲ Figure 3.13). If a mixture is composed of a solid and a liquid, the two can be separated by **filtration**, in which the mixture is poured through filter paper usually held in a funnel (◀ Figure 3.14).

3.7 Conservation of Mass: There Is No New Matter

As we have seen, our planet, our air, and even our own bodies are composed of matter. Physical and chemical changes do not destroy matter, nor do they create new matter. Recall from Chapter 1 that Antoine Lavoisier, by studying combustion, established the law of conservation of mass, which states:

> Matter is neither created nor destroyed in a chemical reaction.

This law is a slight oversimplification. In nuclear reactions, covered in Chapter 17, significant changes in mass can occur. In chemical reactions, however, the changes are so minute that they can be ignored.

During physical and chemical changes, the total amount of matter remains constant even though it may not initially appear that it has. When we burn butane in a lighter, for example, the butane slowly disappears. Where does it go? It combines with oxygen to form carbon dioxide and water that travel into the surrounding air. The mass of the carbon dioxide and water that form, however, exactly equals the mass of the butane and oxygen that combined.

We examine the quantitative relationships in chemical reactions in Chapter 8.

Suppose that we burn 58 g of butane in a lighter. It will react with 208 g of oxygen to form 176 g of carbon dioxide and 90 g of water.

$$\underbrace{\underset{58\text{ g} + 208\text{ g}}{\text{Butane} + \text{Oxygen}}}_{266\text{ g}} \longrightarrow \underbrace{\underset{176\text{ g} + 90\text{ g}}{\text{Carbon Dioxide} + \text{Water}}}_{266\text{ g}}$$

The sum of the masses of the butane and oxygen, 266 g, is equal to the sum of the masses of the carbon dioxide and water, which is also 266 g. In this chemical reaction, as in all chemical reactions, matter is conserved.

EXAMPLE 3.4 Conservation of Mass

A chemist forms 16.6 g of potassium iodide by combining 3.9 g of potassium with 12.7 g of iodine. Show that these results are consistent with the law of conservation of mass.

SOLUTION

The sum of the masses of the potassium and iodine is:

$$3.9\text{g} + 12.7\text{g} = 16.6\text{g}$$

The sum of the masses of potassium and iodine equals the mass of the product, potassium iodide. The results are consistent with the law of conservation of mass.

▶SKILLBUILDER 3.4 | Conservation of Mass

Suppose 12 g of natural gas combines with 48 g of oxygen in a flame. The chemical change produces 33 g of carbon dioxide. How many grams of water form?

▶FOR MORE PRACTICE Example 3.15; Problems 45, 46, 47, 48, 49, 50.

CONCEPTUAL CHECKPOINT 3.2

Consider a drop of water that is put into a flask, sealed with a cap, and heated until the droplet vaporizes. Is the mass of the container and water different after heating?

3.8 Energy

▲ Water behind a dam contains potential energy.

Matter is one of the two major components of our universe. The other major component is **energy**, *the capacity to do work.* **Work** is defined as the result of a force acting on a distance. For example, if you push this book across your desk, you have done work. You may at first think that chemistry is concerned only with matter, but the behavior of matter is driven in large part by energy, so understanding energy is critical to understanding chemistry. Like matter, energy is conserved. The **law of conservation of energy** states that *energy is neither created nor destroyed.* The total amount of energy is constant; energy can be changed from one form to another or transferred from one object to another, but it cannot be created out of nothing, and it does not vanish into nothing.

Virtually all samples of matter have energy. The total energy of a sample of matter is the sum of its **kinetic energy**, the energy associated with its motion, and its **potential energy**, the energy associated with its position or composition. For example, a moving billiard ball contains *kinetic energy* because it is *moving* at some speed across the billiard table. Water behind a dam contains *potential energy* because it is held at a high *position* in the Earth's gravitational field by the dam.

CHEMISTRY IN THE ENVIRONMENT

Getting Energy out of Nothing?

The law of conservation of energy has significant implications for energy use. The best we can do with energy is break even (and even that is not really possible); we can't continually draw energy from a device without putting energy into it. A device that supposedly produces energy without the need for energy input is sometimes called a *perpetual motion machine* (▼ Figure 3.15) and, according to the law of conservation of energy, cannot exist. Occasionally, the media report or speculate on the discovery of a system that appears to produce more energy than it consumes. For example, I once heard a radio talk show on the subject of energy and gasoline costs. The reporter suggested that we simply design an electric car that recharges itself while being driven. The battery in the electric car would charge during operation in the same way that the battery in a conventional car recharges, except the electric car would run with energy from the battery. Although people have dreamed of machines such as this for decades, such ideas violate the law of conservation of energy because they produce energy without any energy input. In the case of the perpetually moving electric car, the fault lies in the idea that driving the electric car can recharge the battery—it can't.

The battery in a conventional car recharges because energy from gasoline combustion is converted into electrical energy that then charges the battery. The electric car needs energy to move forward, and the battery will eventually discharge as it provides that energy. Hybrid cars (electric and gasoline-powered) such as the Toyota Prius can capture some limited energy from braking and use that energy to recharge the battery. However, they could never run indefinitely without the addition of fuel. Our society has a continual need for energy, and as our current energy resources dwindle, new energy sources will be required. Unfortunately, those sources must also follow the law of conservation of energy—energy must be conserved.

◀ **FIGURE 3.15 A proposed perpetual motion machine** The rolling balls supposedly keep the wheel perpetually spinning. **Question:** Can you explain why this would not work?

CAN YOU ANSWER THIS? *A friend asks you to invest in a new flashlight he invented that never needs batteries. What questions should you ask before writing a check?*

When the water flows through the dam from a higher position to a lower position, it can turn a turbine and produce electrical energy. **Electrical energy** is the energy associated with the flow of electrical charge. **Thermal energy** is the energy associated with the random motions of atoms and molecules in matter. The hotter an object, the more thermal energy it contains.

Chemical systems contain **chemical energy**, a form of potential energy associated with the positions of the particles that compose the chemical system. For example, the molecules that compose gasoline contain a substantial amount of chemical energy. They are a bit like the water behind a dam. Burning the gasoline is analogous to releasing the water from the dam. The chemical energy present in the gasoline is released upon burning. When we drive a car, we use that chemical energy to move the car forward. When we heat a home, we use chemical energy stored in natural gas to produce heat and warm the air in the house.

UNITS OF ENERGY

Several different energy units are in common use. The SI unit of energy is the joule (J), named after the English scientist James Joule (1818–1889), who demonstrated that energy could be converted from one type to another as long as the total energy was conserved. A second unit of energy is the **calorie (cal)**, the amount of energy required to raise the temperature of 1 g of water by 1 °C. A calorie is a larger unit than a joule: 1 cal = 4.184 J. A related energy unit is the nutritional or *capital C* **Calorie (Cal)**, equivalent to 1000 *little c* calories. Electricity bills usually come in yet another energy unit, the **kilowatt-hour (kWh)**. The average cost of residential electricity in the United States is about \$0.12 per kilowatt-hour. Table 3.2 lists various energy units and their conversion factors. Table 3.3 shows the amount of energy required for various processes in each of these units.

TABLE 3.2 Energy Conversion Factors

1 calorie (cal)	=	4.184 joules (J)
1 Calorie (Cal)	=	1000 calories (cal)
1 kilowatt-hour (kWh)	=	3.60×10^6 joules (J)

TABLE 3.3 Energy Use in Various Units

Unit	Energy Required to Raise Temperature of 1 g of Water by 1 °C	Energy Required to Light 100-W Bulb for 1 Hour	Total Energy Used by Average U.S. Citizen in 1 Day
joule (J)	4.18	3.6×10^5	9.0×10^8
calorie (cal)	1.00	8.60×10^4	2.2×10^8
Calorie (Cal)	0.00100	86.0	2.2×10^5
kilowatt-hour (kWh)	1.16×10^{-6}	0.100	2.50×10^2

EXAMPLE 3.5 Conversion of Energy Units

A candy bar contains 225 Cal of nutritional energy. How many joules does it contain?

SORT

Begin by sorting the information in the problem. Here you are *given* energy in Calories and asked to *find* energy in joules.

GIVEN: 225 Cal

FIND: J

STRATEGIZE

Draw a solution map. Begin with Cal, convert to cal, and then convert to J.

SOLUTION MAP

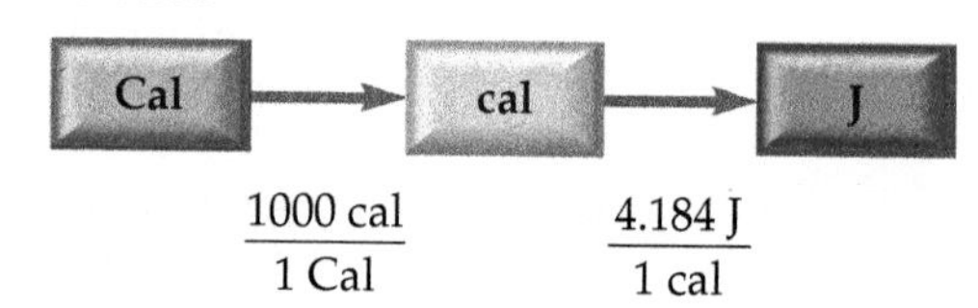

$$\frac{1000\text{ cal}}{1\text{ Cal}} \qquad \frac{4.184\text{ J}}{1\text{ cal}}$$

RELATIONSHIPS USED

1000 calories = 1 Cal (Table 3.2)
4.184 J = 1 cal (Table 3.2)

SOLVE

Follow the solution map to solve the problem. Begin with 225 Cal and multiply by the appropriate conversion factors to arrive at J. Round the answer to the correct number of significant figures (in this case, three because of the three significant figures in 225 Cal).

SOLUTION

$$225\ \cancel{\text{Cal}} \times \frac{1000\ \cancel{\text{cal}}}{1\ \cancel{\text{Cal}}} \times \frac{4.184\text{ J}}{1\ \cancel{\text{cal}}} = 9.41 \times 10^5\text{ J}$$

CHECK

Check your answer. Are the units correct? Does the answer make physical sense?

The units of the answer (J) are the desired units. The magnitude of the answer makes sense because the J is a smaller unit than the Cal; therefore, the quantity of energy in J should be greater than the quantity in Cal.

▶SKILLBUILDER 3.5 | Conversion of Energy Units

The complete combustion of a small wooden match produces approximately 512 cal of heat. How many kilojoules are produced?

▶SKILLBUILDER PLUS

Convert 2.75×10^4 kJ to calories.

▶FOR MORE PRACTICE Example 3.16; Problems 51, 52, 53, 54, 55, 56, 57, 58.

CONCEPTUAL CHECKPOINT 3.3

Suppose a salesperson wants to make an appliance seem as efficient as possible. In which units would the yearly energy consumption of the appliance have the lowest numerical value and therefore seem most efficient?

(a) J

(b) cal

(c) Cal

(d) kWh

3.9 Energy and Chemical and Physical Change

When discussing energy transfer, we often define the object of our study (such as a flask in which a chemical reaction is occurring) as the *system*. The system then exchanges energy with its *surroundings*. In other words, we view energy changes as an exchange of energy between the system and the surroundings.

The physical and chemical changes that we discussed in Section 3.6 are usually accompanied by energy changes. For example, when water evaporates from your skin (a physical change), the water molecules absorb energy, cooling your skin. When you burn natural gas on the stove (a chemical change), energy is released, heating the food you are cooking.

The release of energy during a chemical reaction is analogous to the release of energy that occurs when you drop a weight to the ground. When you lift a weight, you raise its potential energy; when you drop it, the potential energy is released. *Systems with high potential energy—like the raised weight—have a tendency to change in a way that lowers their potential energy.* For this reason, objects or systems with high potential energy tend to be *unstable.* A weight lifted several meters from the ground is unstable because it contains a significant amount of localized potential energy. Unless restrained, the weight will fall, lowering its potential energy.

Some chemical substances are like the raised weight just described. For example, the molecules that compose TNT (trinitrotoluene) have a relatively high potential energy—energy is concentrated in them just as energy is concentrated in the raised weight. TNT molecules therefore tend to undergo rapid chemical changes that lower their potential energy, which is why TNT is explosive. Chemical reactions that *release* energy, like the explosion of TNT, are said to be **exothermic.**

Some chemical reactions behave in just the opposite way—they *absorb* energy from their surroundings as they occur. Such reactions are said to be **endothermic.** The use of a chemical cold pack is a good example of an endothermic reaction. When a barrier separating the reactants in a chemical cold pack is broken, the substances mix, react, and absorb heat from the surroundings. The surroundings—possibly including your bruised ankle—get colder.

We can represent the energy changes that occur during a chemical reaction with an energy diagram, as shown in ◀ Figure 3.16. In an exothermic reaction (Figure 3.16a), the reactants have greater energy than the products, and energy is released as the reaction occurs. In an endothermic reaction (Figure 3.16b), the products have more energy than the reactants, and energy is absorbed as the reaction occurs.

If a particular reaction or process is exothermic, then the reverse process must be endothermic. For example, the evaporation of water from your skin is endothermic (and therefore cools you off), but the condensation of water onto your skin is exothermic (which is why steam burns can be so painful and dangerous).

Exothermic reaction

Energy

Reactants

Energy released

Products

(a)

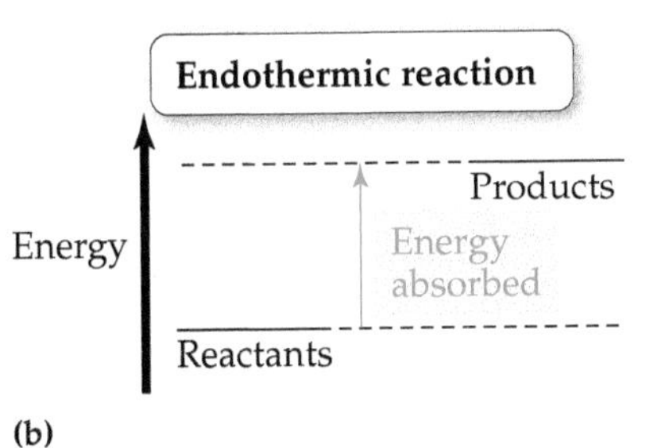

(b)

▲ **FIGURE 3.16 Exothermic and endothermic reactions** **(a)** In an exothermic reaction, energy is released. **(b)** In an endothermic reaction, energy is absorbed.

EXAMPLE 3.6 Exothermic and Endothermic Processes

Identify each change as exothermic or endothermic.

(a) wood burning in a fire
(b) ice melting

SOLUTION

(a) When wood burns, it emits heat into the surroundings. Therefore, the process is exothermic.
(b) When ice melts, it absorbs heat from the surroundings. For example, when ice melts in a glass of water, it cools the water as the melting ice absorbs heat from the water. Therefore, the process is endothermic.

▶**SKILLBUILDER 3.6 | Exothermic and Endothermic Processes**

Identify each change as exothermic or endothermic.

(a) water freezing into ice
(b) natural gas burning

▶**FOR MORE PRACTICE** Problems 61, 62, 63, 64.

3.10 Temperature: Random Motion of Molecules and Atoms

The atoms and molecules that compose matter are in constant random motion—they contain *thermal energy.* The **temperature** of a substance is a measure of its thermal energy. The hotter an object, the greater the random motion of the atoms and molecules that compose it, and the higher its temperature. We must be careful to not confuse *temperature* with *heat.* **Heat,** which has units of energy, is the *transfer* or *exchange* of thermal energy caused by a temperature difference. For example, when a cold ice cube is dropped into a warm cup of water, heat is transferred from the water to the ice, resulting in the cooling of the water. Temperature, by contrast, is a *measure* of the thermal energy of matter (not the exchange of thermal energy).

Three different temperature scales are in common use. The most familiar in the United States is the **Fahrenheit (°F) scale.** On the Fahrenheit scale, water freezes at 32 °F and boils at 212 °F. Room temperature is approximately 72 °F. The Fahrenheit scale was initially set up by assigning 0 °F to the freezing point of a concentrated saltwater solution and 96 °F to normal body temperature (although body temperature is now known to be 98.6 °F).

The scale used by scientists is the **Celsius (°C) scale.** On this scale, water freezes at 0 °C and boils at 100 °C. Room temperature is approximately 22 °C.

The Fahrenheit and Celsius scales differ in both the size of their respective degrees and the temperature each calls "zero" (▶ Figure 3.17). Both the Fahrenheit and Celsius scales contain negative temperatures. A third temperature scale, called the **Kelvin (K) scale,** avoids negative temperatures by assigning 0 K to the coldest temperature possible, absolute zero. Absolute zero (−273.15 °C or −459.7 °F) is the temperature at which molecular motion virtually stops. There is no lower temperature. The kelvin degree, or kelvin (K), is the same size as the Celsius degree—the only difference is the temperature that each scale designates as zero.

We can convert between these temperature scales using the following formulas.

The degree symbol is used with the Celsius and Fahrenheit scales, but not with the Kelvin scale.

$$K = {}^{\circ}C + 273.15$$

$$^{\circ}C = \frac{(^{\circ}F - 32)}{1.8}$$

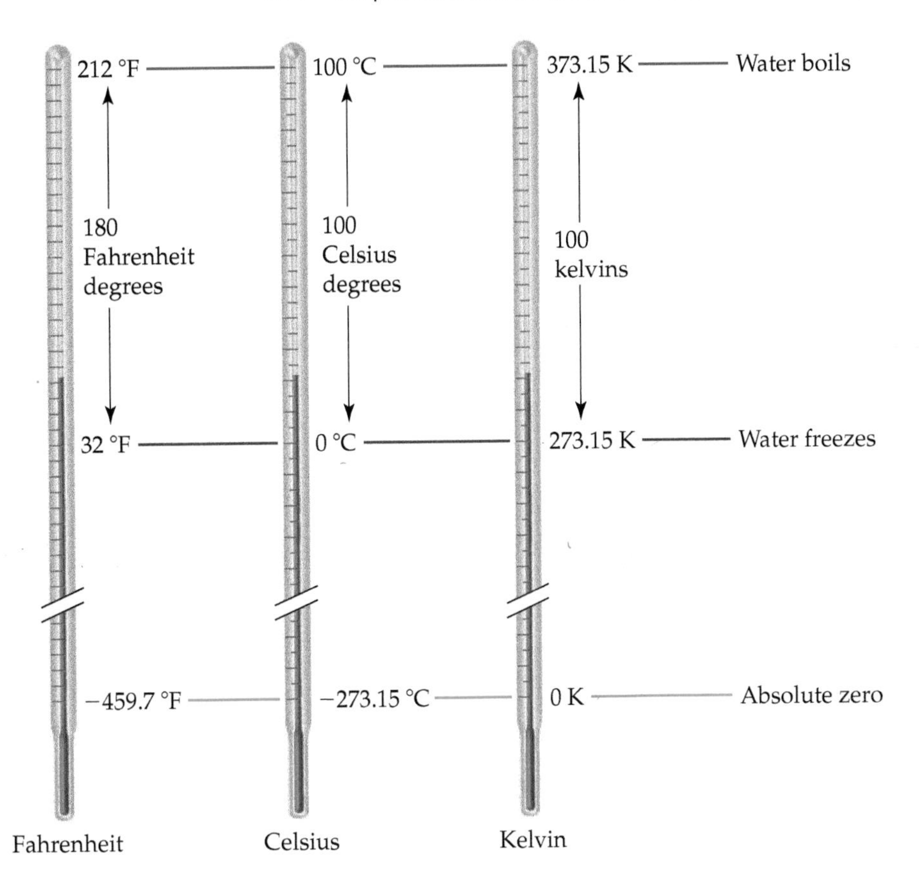

▶ **FIGURE 3.17 Comparison of the Fahrenheit, Celsius, and Kelvin temperature scales** The Fahrenheit degree is five-ninths the size of a Celsius degree. The Celsius degree and the kelvin degree are the same size.

For example, suppose we want to convert 212 K to Celsius. Following the procedure for solving numerical problems (Section 2.6), we first sort the information in the problem statement:

GIVEN: 212 K

FIND: °C

In a solution map involving a formula, the formula establishes the relationship between the variables. However, the formula under the arrow is not necessarily solved for the correct variable until later, as is the case here.

SOLUTION MAP

We then strategize by building a solution map.

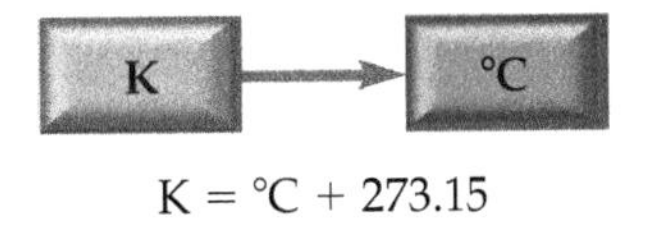

$$K = °C + 273.15$$

RELATIONSHIPS USED

K = °C + 273.15 (This equation relates the *given* quantity (K) to the *find* quantity (°C) and is given in this section.)

SOLUTION

Finally, we follow the solution map to solve the problem. The equation below the arrow shows the relationship between K and °C, but it is not solved for the correct variable. Before using the equation, we must solve it for °C.

$$K = °C + 273.15$$

$$°C = K - 273.15$$

We can now substitute the given value for K and compute the answer to the correct number of significant figures.

$$°C = 212 - 273.15$$

$$= -61\ °C$$

EXAMPLE 3.7 Converting between Celsius and Kelvin Temperature Scales

Convert −25 °C to kelvins.

SORT You are given a temperature in degrees Celsius and asked to find the value of the temperature in kelvins.	**GIVEN:** −25 °C **FIND:** K
STRATEGIZE Draw a solution map. Use the equation that relates the temperature in kelvins to the temperature in Celsius to convert from the given quantity to the quantity you are asked to find.	**SOLUTION MAP**  K = °C + 273.15 **RELATIONSHIPS USED** K = °C + 273.15 (presented in this section)
SOLVE Follow the solution map to solve the problem by substituting the correct value for °C and calculating the answer to the correct number of significant figures.	**SOLUTION** K = °C + 273.15 K = −25 °C + 273.15 = 248 K
CHECK Check your answer. Are the units correct? Does the answer make physical sense?	The units (K) are correct. The answer makes sense because the value in kelvins should be a more positive number than the value in degrees Celsius.

▶**SKILLBUILDER 3.7 | Converting between Celsius and Kelvin Temperature Scales**

Convert 358 K to Celsius.

▶**FOR MORE PRACTICE** Example 3.17; Problems 65c, 66d.

EXAMPLE 3.8 Converting between Fahrenheit and Celsius Temperature Scales

Convert 55 °F to Celsius.

SORT You are given a temperature in degrees Fahrenheit and asked to find the value of the temperature in degrees Celsius.	**GIVEN:** 55 °F **FIND:** °C
STRATEGIZE Draw the solution map. Use the equation that shows the relationship between the given quantity (°F) and the find quantity (°C).	**SOLUTION MAP** 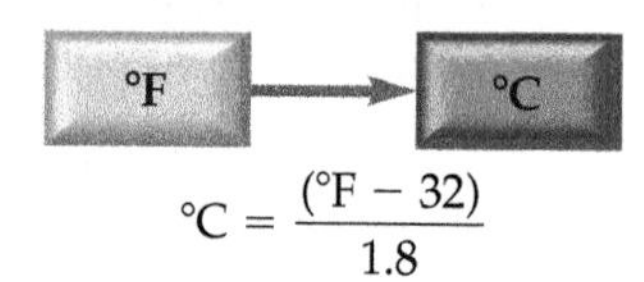 $°C = \frac{(°F - 32)}{1.8}$ **RELATIONSHIPS USED** $°C = \frac{(°F - 32)}{1.8}$ (presented in this section)
SOLVE Substitute the given value into the equation and calculate the answer to the correct number of significant figures.	**SOLUTION** $°C = \frac{(°F - 32)}{1.8}$ $°C = \frac{(55 - 32)}{1.8} = 12.778\ °C = 13\ °C$

CHECK
Check your answer. Are the units correct? Does the answer make physical sense?

The units (°C) are correct. The value of the answer (13 °C) is smaller than the value in degrees Fahrenheit. For positive temperatures, the value of a temperature in degrees Celsius will always be smaller than the value in degrees Fahrenheit because the Fahrenheit degree is smaller than the Celsius degree and the Fahrenheit scale is offset by 32 degrees (see Figure 3.17).

►**SKILLBUILDER 3.8 | Converting between Fahrenheit and Celsius Temperature Scales**
Convert 139 °C to Fahrenheit.

►**FOR MORE PRACTICE** Example 3.18; Problems 65a, 66a, c.

EXAMPLE 3.9 Converting between Fahrenheit and Kelvin Temperature Scales

Convert 310 K to Fahrenheit.

SORT
You are given a temperature in kelvins and asked to find the value of the temperature in degrees Fahrenheit.

GIVEN: 310 K
FIND: °F

STRATEGIZE
Build the solution map, which requires two steps: one to convert kelvins to degrees Celsius and one to convert degrees Celsius to degrees Fahrenheit.

SOLUTION MAP

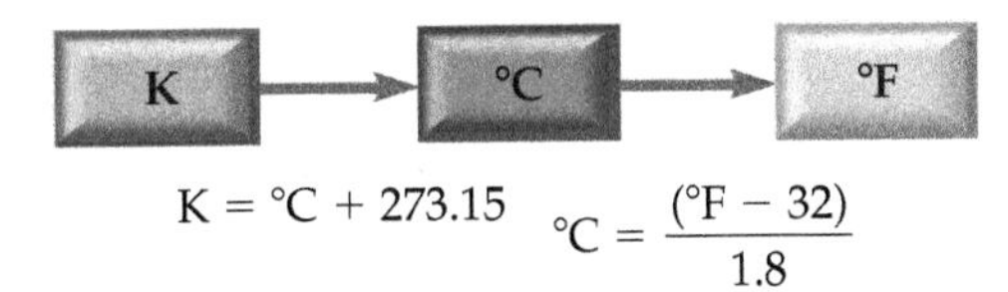

$$K = °C + 273.15 \qquad °C = \frac{(°F - 32)}{1.8}$$

RELATIONSHIPS USED

$K = °C + 273.15$ (presented in this section)

$°C = \frac{(°F - 32)}{1.8}$ (presented in this section)

SOLVE
Solve the first equation for °C and substitute the given quantity in K to convert it to °C.

SOLUTION

$$K = °C + 273.15$$
$$°C = K - 273.15$$
$$°C = 310 - 273.15 = 37\ °C$$

Solve the second equation for °F. Substitute the value of the temperature in °C (from the previous step) to convert it to °F and round the answer to the correct number of significant figures.

$$°C = \frac{(°F - 32)}{1.8}$$
$$1.8\ °C = (°F - 32)$$
$$°F = 1.8\ °C + 32$$
$$°F = 1.8(37) + 32 = 98.6\ °F = 99\ °F$$

CHECK
Check your answer. Are the units correct? Does the answer make physical sense?

The units (°F) are correct. The magnitude of the answer is a bit trickier to judge. In this temperature range, a temperature in Fahrenheit should indeed be smaller than the temperature in kelvins. However, because the Fahrenheit degree is smaller, temperatures in Fahrenheit become larger than temperatures in kelvins above 575 °F.

►**SKILLBUILDER 3.9 | Converting between Fahrenheit and Kelvin Temperature Scales**
Convert −321 °F to kelvins.

►**FOR MORE PRACTICE** Problems 65b, d, 66b.

CONCEPTUAL CHECKPOINT 3.4

Which temperature is identical on both the Celsius and the Fahrenheit scale?

(a) 100°

(b) 32°

(c) 0°

(d) −40°

3.11 Temperature Changes: Heat Capacity

TABLE 3.4 Specific Heat Capacities of Some Common Substances

Substance	Specific Heat Capacity (J/g °C)
Lead	0.128
Gold	0.128
Silver	0.235
Copper	0.385
Iron	0.449
Aluminum	0.903
Ethanol	2.42
Water	4.184

All substances change temperature when they are heated, but how much they change for a given amount of heat varies significantly from one substance to another. For example, if you put a steel skillet on a flame, its temperature rises rapidly. However, if you put some water in the skillet, the temperature increases more slowly. Why? One reason is that when you add water, the same amount of heat energy must warm more matter, so the temperature rise is slower. The second and more interesting reason is that water is more resistant to temperature change than steel because water has a higher *heat capacity*. The **heat capacity** of a substance is the quantity of heat (usually in joules) required to change the temperature of a given amount of the substance by 1 °C. When the amount of the substance is expressed in grams, the heat capacity is called the **specific heat capacity** (or simply the **specific heat**) and has units of joules per gram per degree Celsius (J/g °C). Table 3.4 lists the values of the specific heat capacity for several substances.

Notice that water has the highest specific heat capacity on the list—changing its temperature requires a lot of heat. If you have traveled from an inland geographical region to a coastal one and have felt the drop in temperature, you have experienced the effects of water's high specific heat capacity. On a summer day in California, for example, the temperature difference between Sacramento (an inland city) and San Francisco (a coastal city) can be 30 °F; San Francisco enjoys a cool 68 °F, while Sacramento bakes at near 100 °F. Yet the intensity of sunlight falling on these two cities is the same. Why the large temperature difference? The difference between the two locations is due to the presence of the Pacific Ocean, which practically surrounds San Francisco. Water, with its high heat capacity, absorbs much of the sun's heat without undergoing a large increase in temperature, keeping San Francisco cool. The land surrounding Sacramento, on the other hand, with its low heat capacity, cannot absorb a lot of heat without a large increase in temperature—it has a lower *capacity* to absorb heat without a large temperature increase.

Similarly, only two U.S. states have never recorded a temperature above 100 °F. One of them is obvious: Alaska. It is too far north to get that hot. The other one, however, may come as a surprise. It is Hawaii. The water that surrounds America's only island state moderates the temperature, preventing Hawaii from ever getting too hot.

▲ San Francisco enjoys cool weather even in summer months because of the high heat capacity of the surrounding ocean.

CONCEPTUAL CHECKPOINT 3.5

If you want to heat a metal plate to as high a temperature as possible for a given energy input, you should make the plate out of:

(a) copper

(b) iron

(c) aluminum

(d) it would make no difference

EVERYDAY CHEMISTRY
Coolers, Camping, and the Heat Capacity of Water

Have you ever loaded a cooler with ice and then added room-temperature drinks? If you have, you know that the ice quickly melts. In contrast, if you load your cooler with chilled drinks, the ice lasts for hours. Why the difference? The answer is related to the high heat capacity of the water within the drinks. As we just learned, water must absorb a lot of heat to raise its temperature, and it must also release a lot of heat to lower its temperature. When the warm drinks are placed into the ice, they release heat, which then melts the ice. The chilled drinks, on the other hand, are already cold, so they do not release much heat. It is always better to load your cooler with chilled drinks—that way, the ice will last the rest of the day.

CAN YOU ANSWER THIS? *Suppose you are cold-weather camping and decide to heat some objects to bring into your sleeping bag for added warmth. You place a large water jug and a rock of equal mass close to the fire. Over time, both the rock and the water jug warm to about 38 °C (100 °F). If you could bring only one into your sleeping bag, which one should you bring to keep you the warmest? Why?*

▲ The ice in a cooler loaded with cold drinks lasts much longer than the ice in a cooler loaded with warm drinks.
Question: Can you explain why?

3.12 Energy and Heat Capacity Calculations

When a substance absorbs heat (which we represent with the symbol q), its temperature change (which we represent as ΔT) is in direct proportion to the amount of heat absorbed.

$$\xrightarrow[q]{} \text{System} \quad \Delta T$$

In other words, the more heat absorbed, the greater the temperature change. The specific heat capacity of the substance can be used to *quantify* the relationship between the amount of heat added to a given amount of the substance and the corresponding temperature increase. The equation that relates these quantities is:

$$\text{Heat} = \text{Mass} \times \text{Specific Heat Capacity} \times \text{Temperature Change}$$

$$q = m \times C \times \Delta T$$

ΔT in °C is equal to ΔT in K but is not equal to ΔT in °F.

where q is the amount of heat in joules, m is the mass of the substance in grams, C is the specific heat capacity in joules per gram per degree Celsius, and ΔT is the temperature change in Celsius. The symbol Δ means *the change in*, so ΔT means *the change in temperature.* For example, suppose you are making a cup of tea and want to know how much heat energy will warm 235 g of water (about 8 oz) from 25 °C to 100.0 °C (boiling). We begin by sorting the information in the problem.

GIVEN: 235 g water (m)
25 °C initial temperature (T_i)
100.0 °C final temperature (T_f)

FIND: amount of heat needed (q)

SOLUTION MAP

Then we strategize by building a solution map.

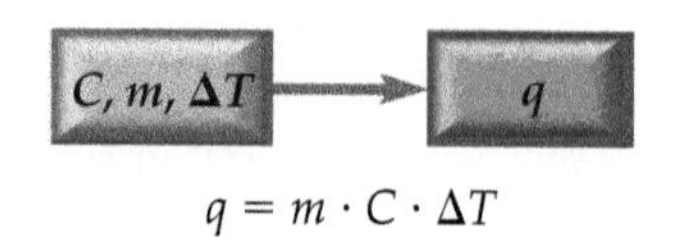

$$q = m \cdot C \cdot \Delta T$$

In addition to m and ΔT, the equation requires C, the specific heat capacity of water. The next step is to gather all of the required quantities for the equation (C, m, and ΔT) in the correct units. These are:

$$C = 4.18\,\text{J/g °C}$$

$$m = 235\,\text{g}$$

The other required quantity is ΔT. The change in temperature is the difference between the final temperature (T_f) and the initial temperature (T_i).

$$\begin{aligned} \Delta T &= T_f - T_i \\ &= 100.0\,°\text{C} - 25\,°\text{C} = 75\,°\text{C} \end{aligned}$$

SOLUTION

Finally, we solve the problem. Substitute the correct values into the equation and calculate the answer to the correct number of significant figures.

$$\begin{aligned} q &= m \cdot C \cdot \Delta T \\ &= 235\,\cancel{\text{g}} \times 4.18 \times \frac{\text{J}}{\cancel{\text{g}}\,\cancel{°\text{C}}} \times 75\,\cancel{°\text{C}} \\ &= 7.367 \times 10^4\,\text{J} = 7.4 \times 10^4\,\text{J} \end{aligned}$$

It is critical that you substitute each of the correct variables into the equation in the correct units and cancel units as you compute the answer. If, during this process, you learn that one of your variables is not in the correct units, convert it to the correct units using the skills you learned in Chapter 2. Notice that the sign of q is positive (+) if the substance is increasing in temperature (heat entering the substance) and negative (−) if the substance is decreasing in temperature (heat leaving the substance).

EXAMPLE 3.10 Relating Heat Energy to Temperature Changes

Gallium is a solid metal at room temperature but melts at 29.9 °C. If you hold gallium in your hand, it melts from your body heat. How much heat must 2.5 g of gallium absorb from your hand to raise its temperature from 25.0 °C to 29.9 °C? The specific heat capacity of gallium is 0.372 J/g °C.

SORT

You are given the mass of gallium, its initial and final temperatures, and its specific heat capacity, and are asked to find the amount of heat absorbed.

GIVEN: 2.5 g gallium (m)

$T_i = 25.0\ °C$

$T_f = 29.9\ °C$

$C = 0.372\,J/g\ °C$

FIND: q

STRATEGIZE

The equation that relates the *given* and *find* quantities is the specific heat capacity equation. The solution map indicates that this equation takes you from the *given* quantities to the quantity you are asked to *find*.

SOLUTION MAP

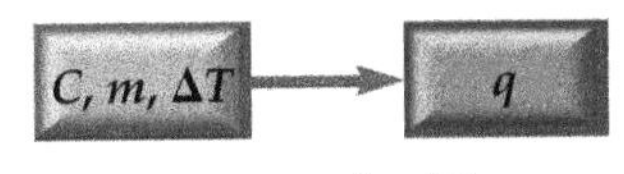

$q = m \cdot C \cdot \Delta T$

RELATIONSHIPS USED

$q = m \cdot C \cdot \Delta T$ (presented in this section)

SOLVE

Before solving the problem, you must gather the necessary quantities—C, m, and ΔT—in the correct units.

SOLUTION

$C = 0.372\,J/g\ °C$

$m = 2.5\ g$

$\Delta T = T_f - T_i$

$= 29.9\ °C - 25.0\ °C$

$= 4.9\ °C$

Substitute C, m, and ΔT into the equation, canceling units, and calculate the answer to the correct number of significant figures.

$q = m \cdot C \cdot \Delta T$

$= 2.5\ \cancel{g} \times 0.372 \frac{J}{\cancel{g}\ \cancel{°C}} \times 4.9\ \cancel{°C} = 4.557\ J = 4.6\ J^*$

CHECK

Check your answer. Are the units correct? Does the answer make physical sense?

The units (J) are correct. The magnitude of the answer makes sense because it takes almost 1 J to heat the 2.5 g sample of the metal by 1 °C; therefore, it should take about 5 J to heat the sample by 5 °C.

▶SKILLBUILDER 3.10 | Relating Heat Energy to Temperature Changes

You find a copper penny (pre-1982) in the snow and pick it up. How much heat is absorbed by the penny as it warms from the temperature of the snow, −5.0 °C, to the temperature of your body, 37.0 °C? Assume the penny is pure copper and has a mass of 3.10 g. You can find the heat capacity of copper in Table 3.4 (p. 74).

▶SKILLBUILDER PLUS |

The temperature of a lead fishing weight rises from 26 °C to 38 °C as it absorbs 11.3 J of heat. What is the mass of the fishing weight in grams?

▶FOR MORE PRACTICE Example 3.19; Problems 75, 76, 77, 78.

* This is the amount of heat required to raise the temperature to the melting point. Actually melting the gallium requires additional heat.

EXAMPLE 3.11 Relating Heat Capacity to Temperature Changes

A chemistry student finds a shiny rock that she suspects is gold. She weighs the rock on a balance and obtains the mass, 14.3 g. She then finds that the temperature of the rock rises from 25 °C to 52 °C upon absorption of 174 J of heat. Find the heat capacity of the rock and determine whether the value is consistent with the heat capacity of gold.

SORT

You are given the mass of the "gold" rock, the amount of heat absorbed, and the initial and final temperature. You are asked to find the heat capacity.

GIVEN: 14.3 g
174 J of heat absorbed
$T_i = 25\ °C$
$T_f = 52\ °C$

FIND: C

STRATEGIZE

The solution map shows how the heat capacity equation relates the given and find quantities.

SOLUTION MAP

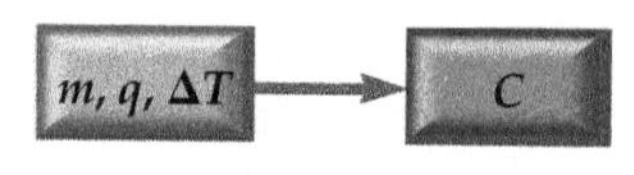

$$q = m \cdot C \cdot \Delta T$$

RELATIONSHIPS USED

$q = m \cdot C \cdot \Delta T$ (presented in this section)

SOLVE

First, gather the necessary quantities—m, q, and ΔT—in the correct units.

SOLUTION

$$m = 14.3\ \text{g}$$
$$q = 174\ \text{J}$$
$$\Delta T = 52\ °C - 25\ °C = 27\ °C$$

Then solve the equation for C and substitute the correct variables into the equation. Finally, calculate the answer to the right number of significant figures.

$$q = m \cdot C \cdot \Delta T$$
$$C = \frac{q}{m \cdot \Delta T}$$
$$C = \frac{174\ \text{J}}{14.3\ \text{g} \times 27\ °C}$$
$$= 0.4507\ \frac{\text{J}}{\text{g}°C} = 0.45\ \frac{\text{J}}{\text{g}°C}$$

By comparing the calculated value of the specific heat capacity (0.45 J/g °C) with the specific heat capacity of gold from Table 3.4 (0.128 J/g °C), we conclude that the rock could not be pure gold.

CHECK

Check your answer. Are the units correct? Does the answer make physical sense?

The units of the answer are those of specific heat capacity, so they are correct. The magnitude of the answer falls in the range of specific heat capacities given in Table 3.4. A value of heat capacity that falls far outside this range would immediately be suspect.

▶SKILLBUILDER 3.11 | Relating Heat Capacity to Temperature Changes

A 328-g sample of water absorbs 5.78×10^3 J of heat. Calculate the change in temperature for the water. If the water is initially at 25.0 °C, what is its final temperature?

▶FOR MORE PRACTICE Problems 85, 86, 87, 88.

CONCEPTUAL CHECKPOINT 3.6

The heat capacity of substance A is twice that of substance B. If samples of equal mass of both substances absorb the same amount of heat, which substance undergoes the largest change in temperature?

CHAPTER IN REVIEW

CHEMICAL PRINCIPLES

Matter: Matter is anything that occupies space and has mass. It is composed of atoms, which are often bonded together as molecules. Matter can exist as a solid, a liquid, or a gas. Solid matter can be either amorphous or crystalline.

Classification of Matter: Matter can be classified according to its composition. Pure matter is composed of only one type of substance; that substance may be an element (a substance that cannot be decomposed into simpler substances), or it may be a compound (a substance composed of two or more elements in fixed definite proportions). Mixtures are composed of two or more different substances the proportions of which may vary from one sample to the next. Mixtures can be either homogeneous, having the same composition throughout, or heterogeneous, having a composition that varies from region to region.

Properties and Changes of Matter: The properties of matter can be divided into two types: physical and chemical. The physical properties of matter do not involve a change in composition. The chemical properties of matter involve a change in composition. The changes in matter can be divided into physical and chemical. In a physical change, the appearance of matter may change, but its composition does not. In a chemical change, the composition of matter changes.

Conservation of Mass: Whether the changes in matter are chemical or physical, matter is always conserved. In a chemical change, the masses of the matter undergoing the chemical change must equal the sum of the masses of matter resulting from the chemical change.

Energy: Besides matter, energy is the other major component of our universe. Like matter, energy is conserved—it can be neither created nor destroyed. Energy exists in various different types, and these can be converted from one to another. Some common units of energy are the joule (J), the calorie (cal), the nutritional Calorie (Cal), and the kilowatt-hour (kWh). Chemical reactions that emit energy are said to be exothermic; those that absorb energy are said to be endothermic.

Temperature: The temperature of matter is related to the random motions of the molecules and atoms that compose it—the greater the motion, the higher the temperature. Temperature is commonly measured on three scales: Fahrenheit (°F), Celsius (°C), and Kelvin (K).

RELEVANCE

Matter: Everything is made of matter—you, me, the chair you sit on, and the air we breathe. The physical universe basically contains only two things: matter and energy. We begin our study of chemistry by defining and classifying these two building blocks of the universe.

Classification of Matter: Since ancient times, humans have tried to understand matter and harness it for their purposes. The earliest humans shaped matter into tools and used the transformation of matter—especially fire—to keep warm and to cook food. To manipulate matter, we must understand it. Fundamental to this understanding is the connection between the properties of matter and the molecules and atoms that compose it.

Properties and Changes of Matter: The physical and chemical properties of matter make the world around us the way it is. For example, a physical property of water is its boiling point at sea level—100 °C. The physical properties of water—and all matter—are determined by the atoms and molecules that compose it. If water molecules were different—even slightly different—water would boil at a different temperature. Imagine a world where water boiled at room temperature.

Conservation of Mass: The conservation of matter is relevant to, for example, pollution. We often think that humans create pollution, but, actually, we are powerless to create anything. Matter cannot be created. So, pollution is simply misplaced matter—matter that has been put into places where it does not belong.

Energy: Our society's energy sources will not last forever because as we burn fossil fuels—our primary energy source—we convert chemical energy, stored in molecules, to kinetic and thermal energy. The kinetic and thermal energy is not readily available to be used again. Consequently, our energy resources are dwindling, and the conservation of energy implies that we will not be able simply to create new energy—it must come from somewhere. All of the chemical reactions that we use for energy are exothermic.

Temperature: The temperature of matter and its measurement are relevant to many everyday phenomena. Humans are understandibly interested in the weather, and air temperature is a fundamental part of weather. We use body temperature as one measure of human health and global temperature as one measure of the planet's health.

Heat Capacity: The temperature change that a sample of matter undergoes upon absorption of a given amount of heat is related to the heat capacity of the substance composing the matter. Water has one of the highest heat capacities, meaning that it is most resistant to rapid temperature changes.

Heat Capacity: The heat capacity of water explains why it is cooler in coastal areas, which are near large bodies of high-heat-capacity water, than in inland areas, which are surrounded by low-heat-capacity land. It also explains why it takes longer to cool a refrigerator filled with liquids than an empty one.

CHEMICAL SKILLS

Classifying Matter (Sections 3.3, 3.4)

Begin by examining the alphabetical listing of elements in the back of this book. If the substance is listed in that table, it is a pure substance and an element.

If the substance is not listed in that table, refer to your everyday experience with the substance to determine whether it is a pure substance. If it is a pure substance not listed in the table, then it is a compound.

If it is not a pure substance, then it is a mixture. Refer to your everyday experience with the mixture to determine whether it has uniform composition throughout (homogeneous) or nonuniform composition (heterogeneous).

EXAMPLES

EXAMPLE 3.12 Classifying Matter

Classify each type of matter as a pure substance or a mixture. If it is a pure substance, classify it as an element or compound. If it is a mixture, classify it as homogeneous or heterogeneous.

(a) pure silver
(b) swimming-pool water
(c) dry ice (solid carbon dioxide)
(d) blueberry muffin

SOLUTION

(a) Pure element; silver appears in the element table.
(b) Homogeneous mixture; pool water contains at least water and chlorine, and it is uniform throughout.
(c) Compound; dry ice is a pure substance (carbon dioxide), but it is not listed in the table.
(d) Heterogeneous mixture; a blueberry muffin is a mixture of several things and has nonuniform composition.

Physical and Chemical Properties (Section 3.5)

To distinguish between physical and chemical properties, consider whether the substance changes composition while displaying the property. If it *does not* change composition, the property is physical; if it *does*, the property is chemical.

EXAMPLE 3.13 Physical and Chemical Properties

Determine whether each property is physical or chemical.

(a) the tendency for platinum jewelry to scratch easily
(b) the ability of sulfuric acid to burn the skin
(c) the ability of hydrogen peroxide to bleach hair
(d) the density of lead relative to other metals

SOLUTION

(a) Physical; scratched platinum is still platinum.
(b) Chemical; the acid chemically reacts with the skin to produce the burn.
(c) Chemical; the hydrogen peroxide chemically reacts with hair to bleach it.
(d) Physical; the heaviness can be felt without changing the lead into anything else.

Physical and Chemical Changes (Section 3.6)

To distinguish between physical and chemical changes, consider whether the substance changes composition during the change. If it *does not* change composition, the change is physical; if it *does*, the change is chemical.

EXAMPLE 3.14 Physical and Chemical Changes

Determine whether each change is physical or chemical.

(a) the explosion of gunpowder in the barrel of a gun
(b) the melting of gold in a furnace
(c) the bubbling that occurs upon mixing baking soda and vinegar
(d) the bubbling that occurs when water boils

SOLUTION

(a) Chemical; the gunpowder reacts with oxygen during the explosion.
(b) Physical; the liquid gold is still gold.
(c) Chemical; the bubbling is a result of a chemical reaction between the two substances to form new substances, one of which is carbon dioxide released as bubbles.
(d) Physical; the bubbling is due to liquid water turning into gaseous water, but it is still water.

Conservation of Mass (Section 3.7)

The sum of the masses of the substances involved in a chemical change must be the same before and after the change.

EXAMPLE 3.15 Conservation of Mass

An automobile runs for 10 minutes and burns 47 g of gasoline. The gasoline combined with oxygen from air and formed 132 g of carbon dioxide and 34 g of water. How much oxygen was consumed in the process?

SOLUTION

The total mass after the chemical change is:

$$132 \text{ g} + 34 \text{ g} = 166 \text{ g}$$

The total mass before the change must also be 166 g.

$$47 \text{ g} + \text{oxygen} = 166 \text{ g}$$

So, the mass of oxygen consumed is the total mass (166 g) minus the mass of gasoline (47 g).

$$\text{grams of oxygen} = 166 \text{ g} - 47 \text{ g} = 119 \text{ g}$$

Conversion of Energy Units (Section 3.8)

Solve unit conversion problems using the problem-solving strategies outlined in Section 2.6.

EXAMPLE 3.16 Conversion of Energy Units

Convert 1.7×10^3 kWh (the amount of energy used by the average U.S. citizen in one week) into calories.

SORT

You are given an amount of energy in kilowatt-hours and asked to find the amount in calories.

GIVEN: 1.7×10^3 kWh

FIND: cal

STRATEGIZE

Draw a solution map. Begin with kilowatt-hours and determine the conversion factors to get to calories.

SOLUTION MAP

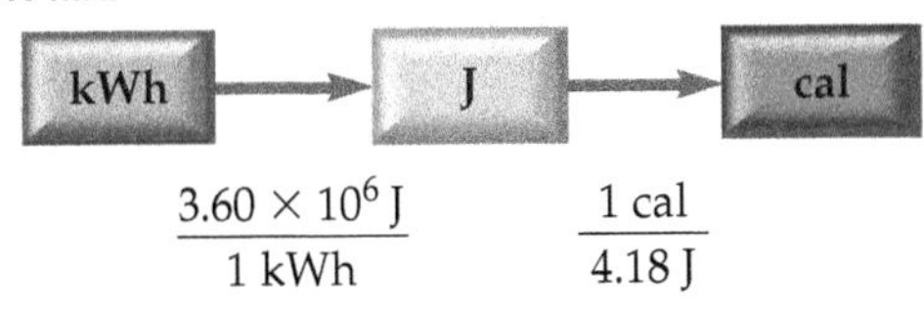

$$\frac{3.60 \times 10^6 \text{ J}}{1 \text{ kWh}} \qquad \frac{1 \text{ cal}}{4.18 \text{ J}}$$

RELATIONSHIPS USED

$$1 \text{ kWh} = 3.60 \times 10^6 \text{ J (Table 3.2)}$$
$$1 \text{ cal} = 4.18 \text{ J (Table 3.2)}$$

SOLVE

Follow the solution map to solve the problem. Begin with the given quantity and multiply by the conversion factors to arrive at calories. Round the answer to the correct number of significant figures.

SOLUTION

$$1.7 \times 10^3 \text{ kWh} \times \frac{3.60 \times 10^6 \text{ J}}{1 \text{ kWh}} \times \frac{1 \text{ cal}}{4.18 \text{ J}} = 1.464 \times 10^9 \text{ cal}$$

$$1.464 \times 10^9 \text{ cal} = 1.5 \times 10^9 \text{ cal}$$

CHECK

Are the units correct? Does the answer make physical sense?

The unit of the answer, cal, is correct. The magnitude of the answer makes sense since cal is a smaller unit than kWh; therefore, the value in cal should be larger than the value in kWh.

Converting between Celsius and Kelvin Temperature Scales (Section 3.10)

Solve temperature conversion problems using the problem-solving procedure in Sections 2.6 and 2.10. Take the steps appropriate for equations.

EXAMPLE 3.17 Converting between Celsius and Kelvin Temperature Scales

Convert 257 K to Celsius.

SORT

You are given the temperature in kelvins and asked to convert it to degrees Celsius.

GIVEN: 257 K

FIND: °C

STRATEGIZE

Draw a solution map. Use the equation that relates the *given* quantity to the *find* quantity.

SOLUTION MAP

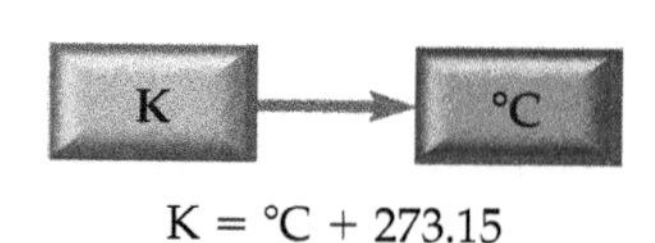

$K = °C + 273.15$

RELATIONSHIPS USED

$$K = °C + 273.15 \text{ (Section 3.10)}$$

SOLVE

Solve the equation for the *find* quantity (°C) and substitute the temperature in K into the equation. Calculate the answer to the correct number of significant figures.

SOLUTION

$$K = °C + 273.15$$
$$°C = K - 273.15$$
$$°C = 257 - 273.15 = -16\ °C$$

CHECK

Are the units correct? Does the answer make physical sense?

The answer has the correct unit, and its magnitude seems correct (see Figure 3.17).

Converting between Fahrenheit and Celsius Temperature Scales (Section 3.10)

Solve temperature conversion problems using the problem-solving procedure in Sections 2.6 and 2.10. Take the steps appropriate for equations.

EXAMPLE 3.18 Converting between Fahrenheit and Celsius Temperature Scales

Convert 62.0 °C to Fahrenheit.

SORT

You are given the temperature in degrees Celsius and asked to convert it to degrees Fahrenheit.

GIVEN: 62.0 °C

FIND: °F

STRATEGIZE

Draw a solution map. Use the equation that relates the *given* quantity to the *find* quantity.

SOLUTION MAP

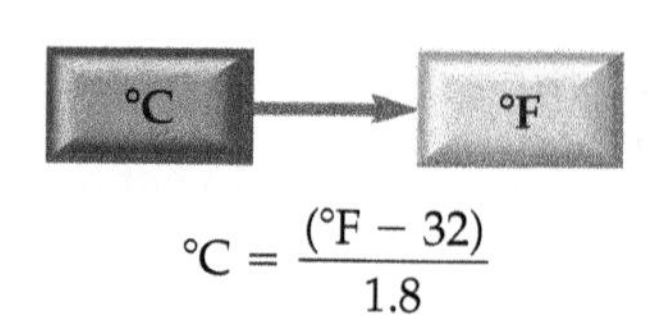

$°C = \frac{(°F - 32)}{1.8}$

RELATIONSHIPS USED

$$°C = \frac{(°F - 32)}{1.8}$$

SOLVE

Solve the equation for the *find* quantity (°F) and substitute the temperature in °C into the equation. Calculate the answer to the correct number of significant figures.

SOLUTION

$$°C = \frac{(°F - 32)}{1.8}$$
$$1.8(°C) = °F - 32$$
$$°F = 1.8(°C) + 32$$
$$°F = 1.8(62.0) + 32 = 143.60\ °F = 144\ °F$$

CHECK

Are the units correct? Does the answer make physical sense?

The answer is in the correct units, and its magnitude seems correct (see Figure 3.17).

Energy, Temperature Change, and Heat Capacity Calculations (Sections 3.11, 3.12)
Solve heat capacity problems using the problem-solving procedure in Sections 2.6 and 2.10. Take the steps appropriate for equations.

EXAMPLE 3.19 Energy, Temperature Change, and Heat Capacity Calculations

What is the temperature change in 355 mL of water upon absorption of 34 kJ of heat?

SORT
You are given the volume of water and the amount of heat absorbed. You are asked to find the change in temperature.

GIVEN: 355 mL water
34 kJ of heat

FIND: ΔT

STRATEGIZE
The solution map shows how the heat capacity equation relates the *given* and *find* quantities.

SOLUTION MAP

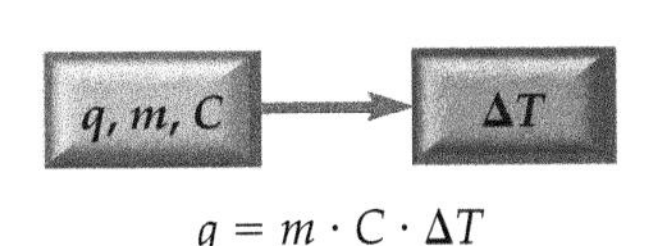

$q = m \cdot C \cdot \Delta T$

RELATIONSHIPS USED

$q = m \cdot C \cdot \Delta T$

SOLVE
First, gather the necessary quantities—m, q, and ΔT—in the correct units. The value for q must be converted from kJ to J.

SOLUTION

$$q = 34\ \text{kJ} \times \frac{1000\ \text{J}}{1\ \text{kJ}} = 3.4 \times 10^4\ \text{J}$$

You must convert the value for m from milliliters to grams; use the density of water, 1.0 g/mL, to convert milliliters to grams.

$$m = 355\ \text{mL} \times \frac{1.0\ \text{g}}{1\ \text{mL}} = 355\ \text{g}$$

Look up the heat capacity for water in Table 3.4.

$$C = 4.18\ \text{J/g}\ ^\circ\text{C}$$

$$q = m \cdot C \cdot \Delta T$$

Then solve the equation for ΔT and substitute the correct variables into the equation. Finally, calculate the answer to the right number of significant figures.

$$\Delta T = \frac{q}{mC}$$

$$\Delta T = \frac{3.4 \times 10^4\ \text{J}}{355\ \text{g} \times 4.18\ \text{J/g}\ ^\circ\text{C}}$$

$$= 22.91\ ^\circ\text{C} = 23\ ^\circ\text{C}$$

CHECK
Check your answer. Are the units correct? Does the answer make physical sense?

The answer has the correct units, and the magnitude seems correct. If the magnitude of the answer were a huge number—3×10^6, for example—we would go back and look for a mistake. Above 100 °C, water boils, so such a large answer would be unlikely.

KEY TERMS

amorphous **[3.3]**
atoms **[3.2]**
calorie (cal) **[3.8]**
Calorie (Cal) **[3.8]**
Celsius (°C) scale **[3.10]**
chemical change **[3.6]**
chemical energy **[3.8]**
chemical property **[3.5]**
chemical reaction **[3.7]**
compound **[3.4]**
compressible **[3.3]**
crystalline **[3.3]**
decanting **[3.6]**
distillation **[3.6]**
electrical energy **[3.8]**
element **[3.4]**
endothermic **[3.9]**
energy **[3.8]**
exothermic **[3.9]**
Fahrenheit (°F) scale **[3.10]**
filtration **[3.6]**
gas **[3.3]**
heat **[3.10]**
heat capacity **[3.11]**
heterogeneous mixture **[3.4]**
homogeneous mixture **[3.4]**
Kelvin (K) scale **[3.10]**
kilowatt-hour (kWh) **[3.8]**
kinetic energy **[3.8]**
law of conservation of energy **[3.8]**
liquid **[3.3]**
matter **[3.2]**
mixture **[3.4]**

molecule [3.2]
physical change [3.6]
physical property [3.5]
potential energy [3.8]
product [3.7]
property [3.5]
pure substance [3.4]
reactant [3.7]
solid [3.3]
specific heat capacity (specific heat) [3.11]
state of matter [3.3]
temperature [3.10]
thermal energy [3.8]
volatile [3.6]
work [3.8]

EXERCISES

QUESTIONS

Answers to all odd-numbered questions (numbered in blue) appear in the Answers section at the back of the book.

1. Define matter and list some examples.
2. What is matter composed of?
3. What are the three states of matter?
4. What are the properties of a solid?
5. What is the difference between a crystalline solid and an amorphous solid?
6. What are the properties of a liquid?
7. What are the properties of a gas?
8. Why are gases compressible?
9. What is a mixture?
10. What is the difference between a homogeneous mixture and a heterogeneous mixture?
11. What is a pure substance?
12. What is an element? A compound?
13. What is the difference between a mixture and a compound?
14. What is the definition of a physical property? What is the definition of a chemical property?
15. What is the difference between a physical change and a chemical change?
16. What is the law of conservation of mass?
17. What is the definition of energy?
18. What is the law of conservation of energy?
19. Expain the difference between kinetic energy and potential energy.
20. What is chemical energy? List some examples of common substances that contain chemical energy.
21. What are three common units for energy?
22. What is an exothermic reaction? Which has greater energy in an exothermic reaction, the reactants or the products?
23. What is an endothermic reaction? Which has greater energy in an endothermic reaction, the reactants or the products?
24. List three common units for measuring temperature.
25. Explain the difference between heat and temperature.
26. How do the three temperature scales differ?
27. What is heat capacity?
28. Why are coastal geographic regions normally cooler in the summer than inland geographic regions?
29. The following equation can be used to convert Fahrenheit temperature to Celsius temperature.

$$°C = \frac{(°F - 32)}{1.8}$$

Use algebra to change the equation to convert Celsius temperature to Fahrenheit temperature.

30. The following equation can be used to convert Celsius temperature to Kelvin temperature.

$$K = °C + 273$$

Use algebra to change the equation to convert Kelvin temperature to Celsius temperature.

PROBLEMS

Note: The exercises in the Problems section are paired, and the answers to the odd-numbered exercises (numbered in blue) appear in the Answers section at the back of the book.

CLASSIFYING MATTER

31. Classify each pure substance as an element or a compound.
    (a) aluminum
    (b) sulfur
    (c) methane
    (d) acetone

32. Classify each pure substance as an element or a compound.
    (a) carbon
    (b) baking soda (sodium bicarbonate)
    (c) nickel
    (d) gold

33. Classify each mixture as homogeneous or heterogeneous.

(a) coffee

(b) chocolate sundae

(c) apple juice

(d) gasoline

34. Classify each mixture as homogeneous or heterogeneous.

(a) baby oil

(b) chocolate chip cookie

(c) water and gasoline

(d) wine

35. Classify each substance as a pure substance or a mixture. If it is a pure substance, classify it as an element or a compound. If it is a mixture, classify it as homogeneous or heterogeneous.

(a) helium gas

(b) clean air

(c) rocky road ice cream

(d) concrete

36. Classify each substance as a pure substance or a mixture. If it is a pure substance, classify it as an element or a compound. If it is a mixture, classify it as homogeneous or heterogeneous.

(a) urine

(b) pure water

(c) Snickers™ bar

(d) soil

PHYSICAL AND CHEMICAL PROPERTIES AND PHYSICAL AND CHEMICAL CHANGES

37. Classify each property as physical or chemical.

(a) the tendency of silver to tarnish

(b) the shine of chrome

(c) the color of gold

(d) the flammability of propane gas

38. Classify each property as physical or chemical.

(a) the boiling point of ethyl alcohol

(b) the temperature at which dry ice sublimes

(c) the flammability of ethyl alcohol

(d) the smell of perfume

39. The following list contains several properties of ethylene (a ripening agent for bananas). Which are physical properties, and which are chemical?

- colorless
- odorless
- flammable
- gas at room temperature
- 1 L has a mass of 1.260 g under standard conditions
- mixes with acetone
- polymerizes to form polyethylene

40. The following list contains several properties of ozone (a pollutant in the lower atmosphere but part of a protective shield against UV light in the upper atmosphere). Which are physical, and which are chemical?

- bluish color
- pungent odor
- very reactive
- decomposes on exposure to ultraviolet light
- gas at room temperature

41. Determine whether each change is physical or chemical.

(a) A balloon filled with hydrogen gas explodes upon contact with a spark.

(b) The liquid propane in a barbecue evaporates away because the user left the valve open.

(c) The liquid propane in a barbecue ignites upon contact with a spark.

(d) Copper metal turns green on exposure to air and water.

42. Determine whether each change is physical or chemical.

(a) Sugar dissolves in hot water.

(b) Sugar burns in a pot.

(c) A metal surface becomes dull because of continued abrasion.

(d) A metal surface becomes dull on exposure to air.

43. A block of aluminum is **(a)** ground into aluminum powder and then **(b)** ignited. It then emits flames and smoke. Classify **(a)** and **(b)** as chemical or physical changes.

44. Several pieces of graphite from a mechanical pencil are **(a)** broken into tiny pieces. Then the pile of graphite is **(b)** ignited with a hot flame. Classify **(a)** and **(b)** as chemical or physical changes.

THE CONSERVATION OF MASS

45. An automobile gasoline tank holds 42 kg of gasoline. When the gasoline burns, 168 kg of oxygen are consumed and carbon dioxide and water are produced. What is the total combined mass of carbon dioxide and water that is produced?

46. In the explosion of a hydrogen-filled balloon, 0.50 g of hydrogen reacted with 4.0 g of oxygen. How many grams of water vapor are formed? (Water vapor is the only product.)

47. Are these data sets on chemical changes consistent with the law of conservation of mass?

(a) A 7.5-g sample of hydrogen gas completely reacts with 60.0 g of oxygen gas to form 67.5 g of water.

(b) A 60.5-g sample of gasoline completely reacts with 243 g of oxygen to form 206 g of carbon dioxide and 88 g of water.

48. Are these data sets on chemical changes consistent with the law of conservation of mass?

(a) A 12.8-g sample of sodium completely reacts with 19.6 g of chlorine to form 32.4 g of sodium chloride.

(b) An 8-g sample of natural gas completely reacts with 32 g of oxygen gas to form 17 g of carbon dioxide and 16 g of water.

49. In a butane lighter, 9.7 g of butane combine with 34.7 g of oxygen to form 29.3 g carbon dioxide and how many grams of water?

50. A 56-g sample of iron reacts with 24 g of oxygen to form how many grams of iron oxide?

CONVERSION OF ENERGY UNITS

51. Perform each conversion.

(a) 588 cal to joules

(b) 17.4 J to Calories

(c) 134 kJ to Calories

(d) 56.2 Cal to joules

52. Perform each conversion.

(a) 45.6 J to calories

(b) 355 cal to joules

(c) 43.8 kJ to calories

(d) 215 cal to kilojoules

53. Perform each conversion.

(a) 25 kWh to joules

(b) 249 cal to Calories

(c) 113 cal to kilowatt-hours

(d) 44 kJ to calories

54. Perform each conversion.

(a) 345 Cal to kilowatt-hours

(b) 23 J to calories

(c) 5.7×10^3 J to kilojoules

(d) 326 kJ to joules

55. Complete the table:

J	cal	Cal	kWh
225 J	______	5.38×10^{-2} Cal	______
______	8.21×10^5 cal	______	______
______	______	______	295 kWh
______	______	155 Cal	______

56. Complete the table:

J	cal	Cal	kWh
7.88×10^6 J	1.88×10^6 cal	______	______
______	______	1154 Cal	______
______	88.4 cal	______	______
______	______	______	125 kWh

57. An energy bill indicates that a customer used 1027 kWh in July. How many joules did the customer use?

58. A television uses 32 kWh of energy per year. How many joules does it use?

59. An adult eats food whose nutritional energy totals approximately 2.2×10^3 Cal per day. The adult burns 2.0×10^3 Cal per day. How much excess nutritional energy, in kilojoules, does the adult consume per day? If 1 lb of fat is stored by the body for each 14.6×10^3 kJ of excess nutritional energy consumed, how long will it take this person to gain 1 lb?

60. How many joules of nutritional energy are in a bag of chips whose label reads 245 Cal? If 1 lb of fat is stored by the body for each 14.6×10^3 kJ of excess nutritional energy consumed, how many bags of chips contain enough nutritional energy to result in 1 lb of body fat?

ENERGY AND CHEMICAL AND PHYSICAL CHANGE

61. A common type of handwarmer contains iron powder that reacts with oxygen to form an oxide of iron. As soon as the handwarmer is exposed to air, the reaction begins and heat is emitted. Is the reaction between the iron and oxygen exothermic or endothermic? Draw an energy diagram showing the relative energies of the reactants and products in the reaction.

62. In a chemical cold pack, two substances are kept separate by a divider. When the divider is broken, the substances mix and absorb heat from the surroundings. The chemical cold pack feels cold. Is the reaction exothermic or endothermic? Draw an energy diagram showing the relative energies of the reactants and products in the reaction.

63. Determine whether each process is exothermic or endothermic.
   (a) gasoline burning in a car
   (b) isopropyl alcohol evaporating from skin
   (c) water condensing as dew during the night

64. Determine whether each process is exothermic or endothermic.
   (a) dry ice subliming (changing from a solid directly to a gas)
   (b) the wax in a candle burning
   (c) a match burning

CONVERTING BETWEEN TEMPERATURE SCALES

65. Perform each temperature conversion.
   (a) 212 °F to Celsius (temperature of boiling water)
   (b) 77 K to Fahrenheit (temperature of liquid nitrogen)
   (c) 25 °C to Kelvin (room temperature)
   (d) 98.6 °F to Kelvin (body temperature)

66. Perform each temperature conversion.
   (a) 102 °F to Celsius
   (b) 0 K to Fahrenheit
   (c) −48 °C to Fahrenheit
   (d) 273 K to Celsius

67. The coldest temperature ever measured in the United States was −80 °F on January 23, 1971, in Prospect Creek, Alaska. Convert that temperature to degrees Celsius and Kelvin. (Assume that −80 °F is accurate to two significant figures.)

68. The warmest temperature ever measured in the United States was 134 °F on July 10, 1913, in Death Valley, California. Convert that temperature to degrees Celsius and Kelvin.

69. Vodka will not freeze in the freezer because it contains a high percentage of ethanol. The freezing point of pure ethanol is −114 °C. Convert that temperature to degrees Fahrenheit and Kelvin.

70. Liquid helium boils at 4.2 K. Convert this temperature to degrees Fahrenheit and Celsius.

71. The temperature in the South Pole during the Antarctic winter is so cold that planes cannot land or take off, effectively leaving the inhabitants of the South Pole isolated for the winter. The average daily temperature at the South Pole in July is −59.7 °C. Convert this temperature to degrees Fahrenheit.

72. The coldest temperature ever recorded in Iowa was −47 °F on February 3, 1998. Convert this temperature to Kelvin and degrees Celsius.

73. Complete the table.

Kelvin	Fahrenheit	Celsius
0.0 K	______	−273.0 °C
______	82.5 °F	______
______	______	8.5 °C

74. Complete the table.

Kelvin	Fahrenheit	Celsius
273.0 K	______	0.0 °C
______	−40.0 °F	______
385 K	______	______

ENERGY, HEAT CAPACITY, AND TEMPERATURE CHANGES

75. Calculate the amount of heat required to raise the temperature of a 65-g sample of water from 32 °C to 65 °C.

76. Calculate the amount of heat required to raise the temperature of a 22-g sample of water from 7 °C to 18 °C.

77. Calculate the amount of heat required to heat a 45-kg sample of ethanol from 11.0 °C to 19.0 °C.

78. Calculate the amount of heat required to heat a 3.5-kg gold bar from 21 °C to 67 °C.

79. If 89 J of heat are added to a pure gold coin with a mass of 12 g, what is its temperature change?

80. If 57 J of heat are added to an aluminum can with a mass of 17.1 g, what is its temperature change?

81. An iron nail with a mass of 12 g absorbs 15 J of heat. If the nail was initially at 28 °C, what is its final temperature?

82. A 45-kg sample of water absorbs 345 kJ of heat. If the water was initially at 22.1 °C, what is its final temperature?

83. Calculate the temperature change that occurs when 248 cal of heat are added to 24 g of water.

84. A lead fishing weight with a mass of 57 g absorbs 146 cal of heat. If its initial temperature is 47 °C, what is its final temperature?

85. An unknown metal with a mass of 28 g absorbs 58 J of heat. Its temperature rises from 31.1 °C to 39.9 °C. Calculate the heat capacity of the metal and identify it referring to Table 3.4.

86. An unknown metal is suspected to be gold. When 2.8 J of heat are added to 5.6 g of the metal, its temperature rises by 3.9 °C. Are these data consistent with the metal being gold?

87. When 56 J of heat are added to 11 g of a liquid, its temperature rises from 10.4 °C to 12.7 °C. What is the heat capacity of the liquid?

88. When 47.5 J of heat are added to 13.2 g of a liquid, its temperature rises by 1.72 °C. What is the heat capacity of the liquid?

89. Two identical coolers are packed for a picnic. Each cooler is packed with eighteen 12-oz soft drinks and 3 lb of ice. However, the drinks that went into cooler A were refrigerated for several hours before they were packed in the cooler, while the drinks that went into cooler B were at room temperature. When the two coolers are opened three hours later, most of the ice in cooler A is still ice, while nearly all of the ice in cooler B has melted. Explain.

90. A 100-g block of iron metal and 100 g of water are each warmed to 75 °C and placed into two identical insulated containers. Two hours later, the two containers are opened and the temperature of each substance is measured. The iron metal has cooled to 38 °C while the water has cooled only to 69 °C. Explain.

CUMULATIVE PROBLEMS

91. Calculate the final temperature of 245 mL of water initially at 32 °C upon absorption of 17 kJ of heat.

92. Calculate the final temperature of 32 mL of ethanol initially at 11 °C upon absorption of 562 J of heat. (density of ethanol = 0.789 g/mL)

93. A pure gold ring with a volume of 1.57 cm^3 is initially at 11.4 °C. When it is put on, it warms to 29.5 °C. How much heat did the ring absorb? (density of gold = 19.3 g/cm^3)

94. A block of aluminum with a volume of 98.5 cm^3 absorbs 67.4 J of heat. If its initial temperature was 32.5 °C, what is its final temperature? (density of aluminum = 2.70 g/cm^3)

95. How much heat in kilojoules is required to heat 56 L of water from 85 °F to 212 °F?

96. How much heat in joules is required to heat a 43-g sample of aluminum from 72 °F to 145 °F?

97. What is the temperature change in Celsius when 29.5 L of water absorbs 2.3 kWh of heat?

98. If 1.45 L of water is initially at 25.0 °C, what will its temperature be after absorption of 9.4×10^{-2} kWh of heat?

99. A water heater contains 55 gal of water. How many kilowatt-hours of energy are necessary to heat the water in the water heater by 25 °C?

100. A room contains 48 kg of air. How many kilowatt-hours of energy are necessary to heat the air in the house from 7 °C to 28 °C? The heat capacity of air is 1.03 J/g °C.

101. A backpacker wants to carry enough fuel to heat 2.5 kg of water from 25 °C to 100.0 °C. If the fuel he carries produces 36 kJ of heat per gram when it burns, how much fuel should he carry? (For the sake of simplicity, assume that the transfer of heat is 100% efficient.)

102. A cook wants to heat 1.35 kg of water from 32.0 °C to 100.0 °C. If he uses the combustion of natural gas (which is exothermic) to heat the water, how much natural gas will he need to burn? Natural gas produces 49.3 kJ of heat per gram. (For the sake of simplicity, assume that the transfer of heat is 100% efficient.)

103. Evaporating sweat cools the body because evaporation is endothermic and absorbs 2.44 kJ per gram of water evaporated. Estimate the mass of water that must evaporate from the skin to cool a body by 0.50 °C, if the mass of the body is 95 kg and its heat capacity is 4.0 J/g °C. (Assume that the heat transfer is 100% efficient.)

104. When ice melts, it absorbs 0.33 kJ per gram. How much ice is required to cool a 12.0-oz drink from 75 °F to 35 °F, if the heat capacity of the drink is 4.18 J/g °C (Assume that the heat transfer is 100% efficient.)

105. A 15.7-g aluminum block is warmed to 53.2 °C and plunged into an insulated beaker containing 32.5 g of water initially at 24.5 °C. The aluminum and the water are allowed to come to thermal equilibrium. Assuming that no heat is lost, what is the final temperature of the water and aluminum?

106. 25.0 mL of ethanol (density = 0.789 g/mL) initially at 7.0 °C is mixed with 35.0 mL of water (density = 1.0 g/mL) initially at 25.3 °C in an insulated beaker. Assuming that no heat is lost, what is the final temperature of the mixture?

107. The wattage of an appliance indicates the average power consumption in watts (W), where 1 W = 1 J/s. What is the difference in the number of kJ of energy consumed per month between a refrigeration unit that consumes 625 W and one that consumes 855 W? If electricity costs $0.15 per kWh, what is the monthly cost difference to operate the two refrigerators? (Assume 30.0 days in one month and 24.0 hours per day.)

108. A portable electric water heater transfers 255 watts (W) of power to 5.5 L of water, where 1 W = 1 J/s. How much time (in minutes) will it take for the water heater to heat the 5.5 L of water from 25 °C to 42 °C? (Assume that the water has a density of 1.0 g/mL.)

109. What temperature is the same whether it is expressed in the Celsius or Fahrenheit scale?

110. What temperature on the Celsius scale is equal to twice its value when expressed on the Fahrenheit scale?

HIGHLIGHT PROBLEMS

111. Classify each molecular picture as a pure substance or a mixture.

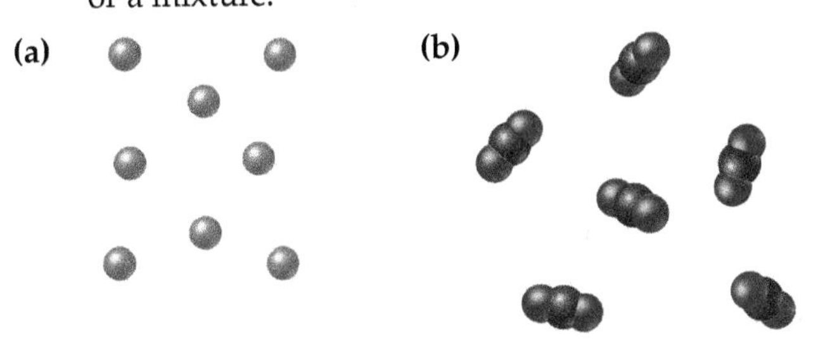

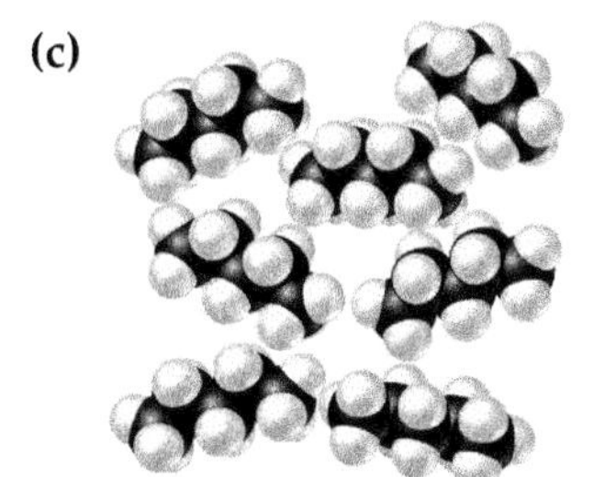

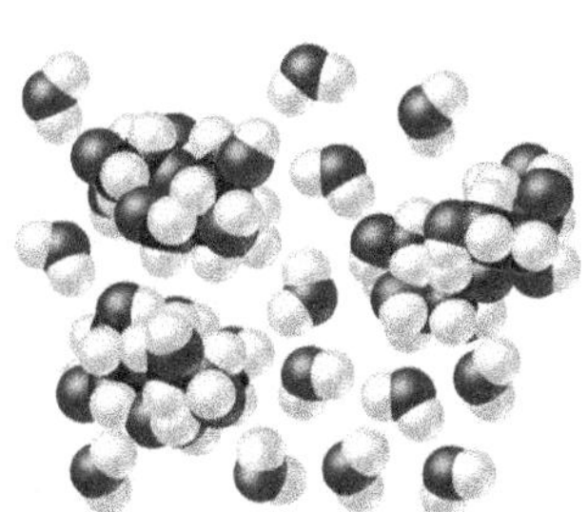

112. Classify each molecular picture as a pure substance or a mixture. If it is a pure substance, classify it as an element or a compound. If it is a mixture, classify it as homogeneous or heterogeneous.

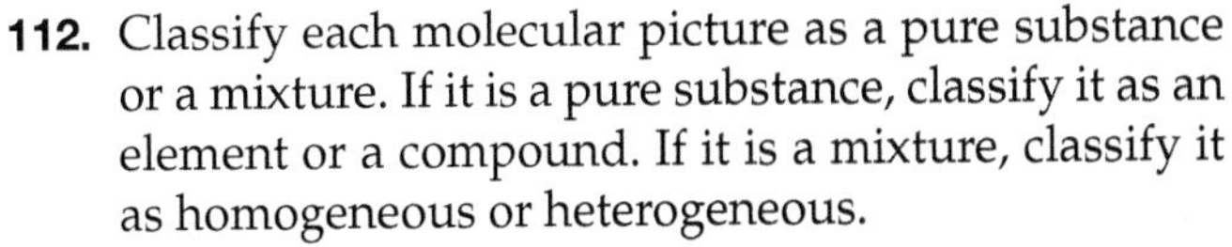

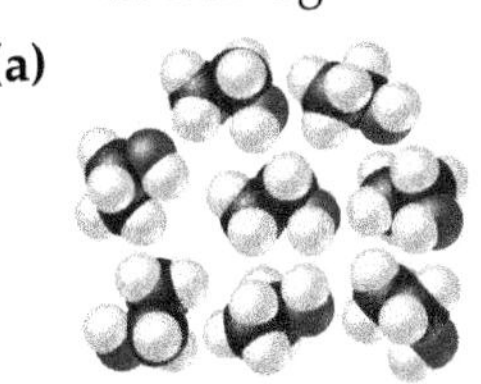

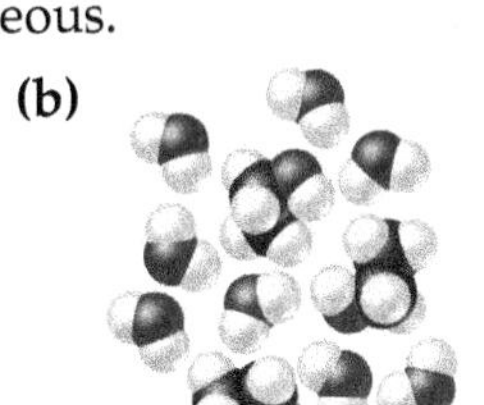

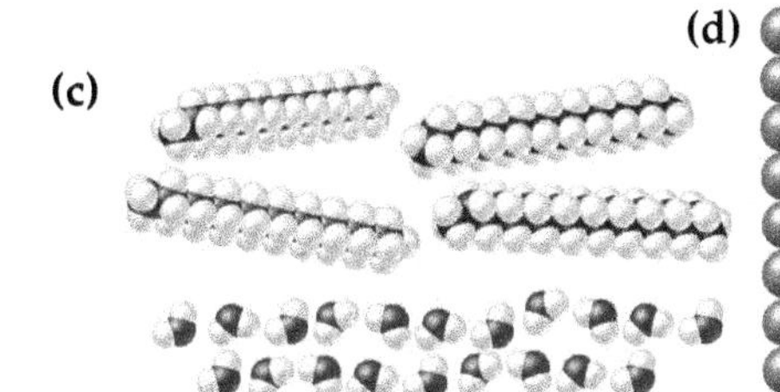

113. This molecular drawing shows images of acetone molecules before and after a change. Was the change chemical or physical?

114. This molecular drawing shows images of methane molecules and oxygen molecules before and after a change. Was the change chemical or physical?

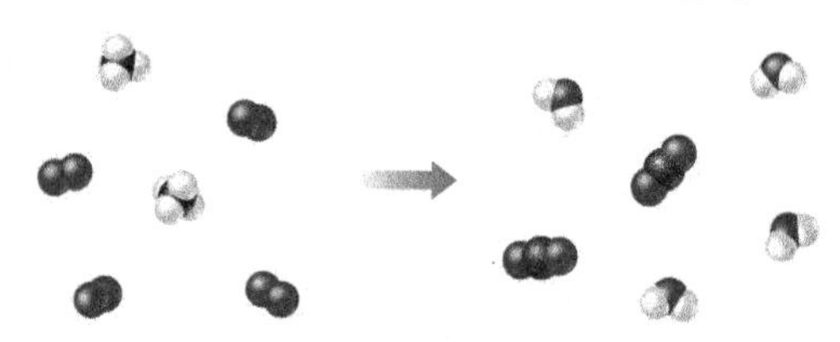

115. A major event affecting global climate is the El Niño/La Niña cycle. In this cycle, equatorial Pacific Ocean waters warm by several degrees Celsius above normal (El Niño) and then cool by several degrees Celsius below normal (La Niña). This cycle affects weather not only in North and South America, but also in places as far away as Africa. Why does a seemingly small change in ocean temperature have such a large impact on weather?

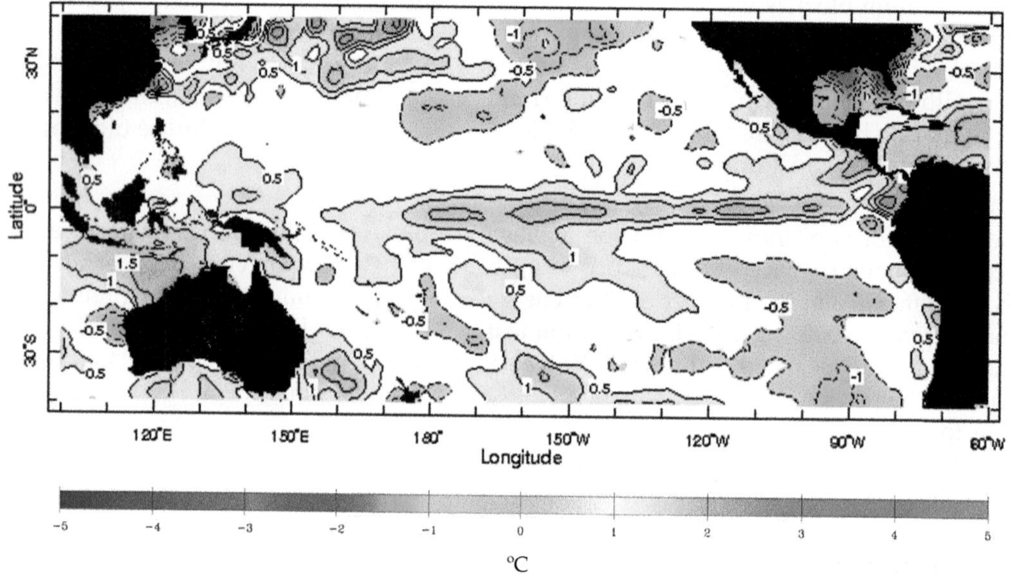

▲ Temperature anomaly plot of the world's oceans for January 17–23, 2010. The large red-orange section in the middle of the map indicates the El Niño effect, a warming of the Pacific Ocean along the equator.

116. Global warming refers to the rise in average global temperature due to the increased concentration of certain gases, called greenhouse gases, in our atmosphere. Earth's oceans, because of their high heat capacity, absorb heat and therefore act to slow down global warming. How much heat would be required to warm Earth's oceans by 1.0 °C? Assume that the volume of water in Earth's oceans is $137 \times 10^7\ km^3$ and that the density of seawater is $1.03\ g/cm^3$. Also assume that the heat capacity of seawater is the same as that of water.

◀ Earth's oceans moderate temperatures by absorbing heat during warm periods.

117. Examine the data for the maximum and minimum average temperatures of San Francisco and Sacramento in the summer and in the winter.

San Francisco (Coastal City)

January		August	
High	Low	High	Low
57.4 °F	43.8 °F	64.4 °F	54.5 °F

Sacramento (Inland City)

January		August	
High	Low	High	Low
53.2 °F	37.7 °F	91.5 °F	57.7 °F

(a) Notice the difference between the August high in San Francisco and Sacramento. Why is it much hotter in the summer in Sacramento?

(b) Notice the difference between the January low in San Francisco and Sacramento. How might the heat capacity of the ocean contribute to this difference?

▶ANSWERS TO SKILLBUILDER EXERCISES

Skillbuilder 3.1
(a) pure substance, element
(b) mixture, homogeneous
(c) mixture, heterogeneous
(d) pure substance, compound

Skillbuilder 3.2
(a) chemical
(b) physical
(c) physical
(d) physical

Skillbuilder 3.3
(a) chemical
(b) physical
(c) physical
(d) chemical

Skillbuilder 3.4 27 g

Skillbuilder 3.5 2.14 kJ

Skillbuilder Plus, p. 68 6.57×10^6 cal

Skillbuilder 3.6
(a) exothermic
(b) exothermic

Skillbuilder 3.7 85 °C

Skillbuilder 3.8 282 °F

Skillbuilder 3.9 77 K

Skillbuilder 3.10 50.1 J

Skillbuilder Plus, p. 77 7.4 g

Skillbuilder 3.11 $\Delta T = 4.21$ °C; $T_f = 29.2$ °C

▶ANSWERS TO CONCEPTUAL CHECKPOINTS

3.1 (a) Vaporization is a physical change, so the water molecules are the same before and after the boiling.

3.2 No In the vaporization, the liquid water becomes gaseous, but its mass does not change. Like chemical changes, physical changes also follow the law of conservation of mass.

3.3 (d) kWh is the largest of the four units listed, so the numerical value of the yearly energy consumption is lowest if expressed in kWh.

3.4 (d) You can confirm this by substituting each of the Fahrenheit temperatures into the equation in Section 3.10 and solving for the Celsius temperature.

3.5 (a) Because copper has the lowest specific heat capacity of the three metals, it experiences the greatest temperature change for a given energy input.

3.6 Substance B will undergo a greater change in temperature because it has the lower heat capacity. A substance with a lower heat capacity is less resistant to temperature changes.

CHAPTER 4

Atoms and Elements

"Nothing exists except atoms and empty space; everything else is opinion."

DEMOCRITUS (460–370 B.C.)

4.1 Experiencing Atoms at Tiburon

As we learned in Chapter 3, many atoms exist not as free particles but as groups of atoms bound together to form molecules. Nevertheless, all matter is ultimately made of atoms.

My wife and I recently enjoyed a visit to the northern California seaside town of Tiburon. Tiburon sits next to San Francisco Bay with views of the water, the city of San Francisco, and the surrounding mountains. As we walked along a waterside path, I could feel the wind as it blew over the bay. I could hear the water splashing on the shore, and I could smell the sea air. What was the cause of these sensations? The answer is simple—atoms.

Since all matter is made of atoms, atoms are at the foundation of our sensations. The atom is the fundamental building block of everything you hear, feel, see, and experience. When you feel wind on your skin, you are feeling atoms. When you hear sounds, you are in a sense hearing atoms. When you touch a shoreside rock, you are touching atoms, and when you smell sea air, you are smelling atoms. You eat atoms, you breathe atoms, and you excrete atoms. Atoms are the building blocks of matter; they are the basic units from which nature builds. They are all around us and compose everything, including our own bodies.

◀ Seaside rocks are typically composed of silicates, compounds of silicon and oxygen atoms. Seaside air, like all air, contains nitrogen and oxygen molecules, and it may also contain substances called amines. The amine shown here is triethylamine, which is emitted by decaying fish. Triethylamine is one of the compounds responsible for the fishy smell of the seaside.

Atoms are incredibly small. A single pebble from the shoreline contains more atoms than you could ever count. The number of atoms in a single pebble far exceeds the number of pebbles on the bottom of San Francisco Bay. To get an idea of how small atoms are, imagine this: If every atom within a small pebble were the size of the pebble itself, the pebble would be larger than Mount Everest (▶ Figure 4.1). Atoms are small—yet they compose everything.

The key to connecting the microscopic world with the macroscopic world is the atom. Atoms compose matter; their properties determine matter's properties. An **atom** is the smallest identifiable unit of an element. Recall from Section 3.4 that an *element* is a substance that cannot be broken down into simpler substances.

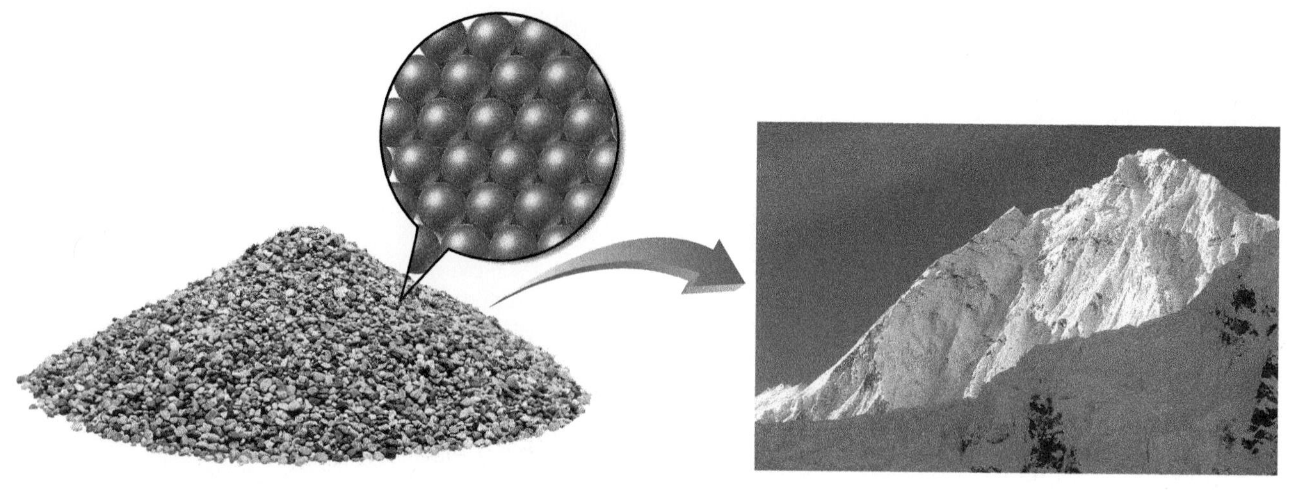

▲ **FIGURE 4.1 The size of the atom** If every atom within a pebble were the size of the pebble itself, then the pebble would be larger than Mount Everest.

The exact number of naturally occurring elements is controversial because some elements previously considered only synthetic may actually occur in nature in very small quantities.

There are about 91 different elements in nature, and consequently about 91 different kinds of atoms. In addition, scientists have succeeded in making about 20 synthetic elements (not found in nature). In this chapter, we examine atoms: what they are made of, how they differ from one another, and how they are structured. We also examine the elements that atoms compose and some of the properties of those elements.

4.2 Indivisible: The Atomic Theory

▲ Diogenes and Democritus, as imagined by a medieval artist. Democritus is the first person on record to have postulated that matter was composed of atoms.

If we simply look at matter, even under a microscope, it is not obvious that matter is composed of tiny particles. In fact, it appears to be just the opposite. If we divide a sample of matter into smaller and smaller pieces, it seems that we could divide it forever. From our perspective, matter seems continuous. The first people recorded as thinking otherwise were Leucippus (fifth century B.C., exact dates unknown) and Democritus (460–370 B.C.). These Greek philosophers theorized that matter was ultimately composed of small, indivisible particles. Democritus suggested that if you divided matter into smaller and smaller pieces, you would eventually end up with tiny, indestructible particles called *atomos,* or "atoms," meaning "indivisible."

The ideas of Leucippus and Democritus were not widely accepted, and it was not until 1808—over 2000 years later—that John Dalton formalized a theory of atoms that gained broad acceptance. Dalton's atomic theory has three parts:

1. Each element is composed of tiny indestructible particles called atoms.
2. All atoms of a given element have the same mass and other properties that distinguish them from the atoms of other elements.
3. Atoms combine in simple, whole-number ratios to form compounds.

Today, the evidence for the atomic theory is overwhelming. Recent advances in microscopy have allowed scientists not only to image individual atoms but also to pick them up and move them (▶ Figure 4.2). Matter is indeed composed of atoms.

EVERYDAY CHEMISTRY

Atoms and Humans

All matter is composed of atoms. What does that mean? What does it imply? It means that everything before you is composed of tiny particles too small to see. It means that even you and I are composed of these same particles. We acquired those particles from the food we have eaten over the years. The average carbon atom in our own bodies has been used by 20 other living organisms before we get to it and will be used by other organisms when we are done with it. In fact, it is likely that at this moment, your body contains over 1 trillion carbon atoms that were at one time part of your chemistry professor.*

The idea that all matter is composed of atoms has far-reaching implications. It implies that our bodies, our hearts, and even our brains are composed of atoms acting according to the laws of chemistry and physics. Some people view this as a devaluation of human life. We have always wanted to distinguish ourselves from everything else, and the idea that we are made of the same basic particles as all other matter takes something away from that distinction . . . or does it?

CAN YOU ANSWER THIS? *Do you find the idea that you are made of atoms disturbing? Why or why not?*

**This calculation assumes that all of the carbon atoms metabolized by your professor over the last 40 years have been uniformly distributed into atmospheric carbon dioxide and subsequently incorporated into plants that you eat.*

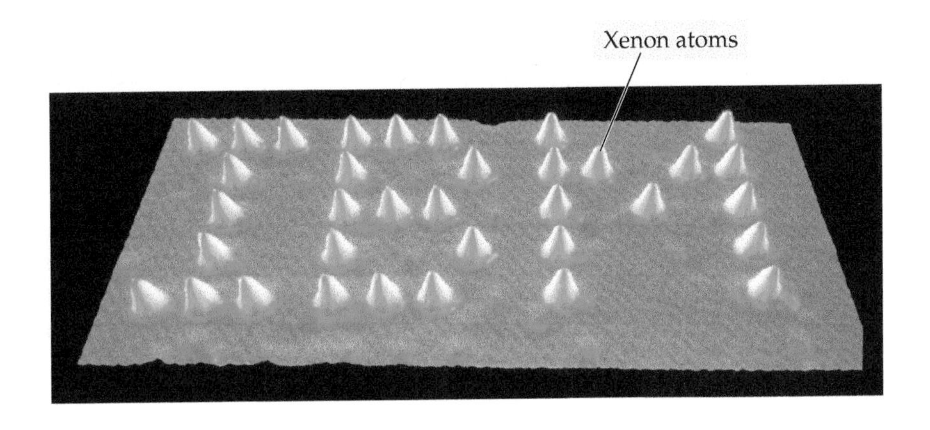

▶ FIGURE 4.2 **Writing with atoms** Scientists at IBM used a special microscope, called a scanning tunneling microscope (STM), to move xenon atoms to form the letters I, B, and M. The cone shape of these atoms is due to the peculiarities of the instrumentation. Atoms are, in general, spherical in shape.

4.3 The Nuclear Atom

By the end of the nineteenth century, scientists were convinced that matter was composed of atoms, the permanent, indestructible building blocks from which all substances are constructed. However, an English physicist named J. J. Thomson (1856–1940) complicated the picture by discovering an even smaller and more fundamental particle called the **electron**. Thomson discovered that electrons are negatively charged, that they are much smaller and lighter than atoms, and that they are uniformly present in many different kinds of substances. The indestructible building block called the atom could apparently be "chipped."

Electric charge is more fully defined in Section 4.4. For now, think of it as an inherent property of electrons that causes them to interact with other charged particles.

The discovery of negatively charged particles within atoms raised the question of a balancing positive charge. Atoms were known to be charge-neutral, so it was believed that they must contain positive charge that balanced the negative charge of electrons. But how did the positive and negative charges within the atom fit together? Were atoms just a jumble of even more fundamental particles? Were they solid spheres, or did they have some internal structure? Thomson proposed that the negatively charged electrons were small particles held within a positively charged sphere. This model, the most popular of the time, became

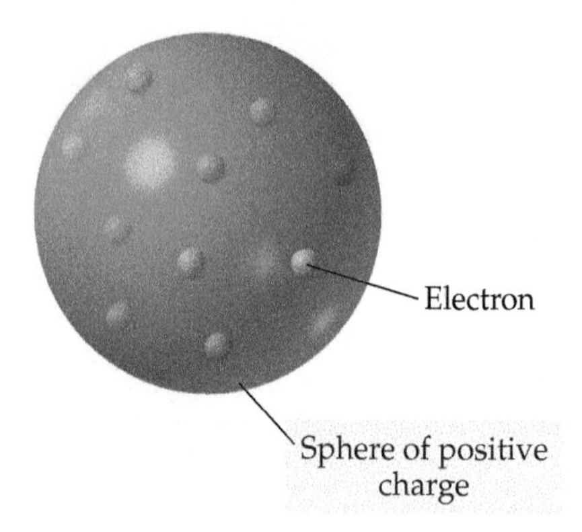

▲ **FIGURE 4.3 Plum pudding model of the atom** In the model suggested by J. J. Thomson, negatively charged electrons (yellow) were held in a sphere of positive charge (red).

known as the plum pudding model (plum pudding is an English dessert) (◀ Figure 4.3). The picture suggested by Thomson was—to those of us not familiar with plum pudding—like a blueberry muffin, where the blueberries are the electrons and the muffin is the positively charged sphere.

In 1909, Ernest Rutherford (1871–1937), who had worked under Thomson and adhered to his plum pudding model, performed an experiment in an attempt to confirm it. His experiment instead proved it wrong. In his experiment, Rutherford directed tiny, positively charged particles—called alpha-particles—at an ultrathin sheet of gold foil (▼ Figure 4.4). Alpha-particles are about 7000 times more massive than electrons and carry a positive charge. These particles were to act as probes of the gold atoms' structure. If the gold atoms were indeed like blueberry muffins or plum pudding—with their mass and charge spread throughout the entire volume of the atom—these speeding probes should pass right through the gold foil with minimum deflection. Rutherford's results were not as he expected. A majority of the particles did pass directly through the foil, but some particles were deflected, and some (1 in 20,000) even bounced back. The results puzzled Rutherford, who found them "about as credible as if you had fired a 15-inch shell at a piece of tissue paper and it came back and hit you." What must the structure of the atom be in order to explain this odd behavior?

Rutherford created a new model to explain his results (▶ Figure 4.5). He concluded that matter must not be as uniform as it appears. It must contain large regions of empty space dotted with small regions of very dense matter. In order to explain the deflections he observed, the mass and positive charge of an atom must all be concentrated in a space much smaller than the size of the atom itself. Based on this idea, he developed the **nuclear theory of the atom**, which has three basic parts:

1. Most of the atom's mass and all of its positive charge are contained in a small core called the *nucleus*.
2. Most of the volume of the atom is empty space through which the tiny, negatively charged electrons are dispersed.
3. There are as many negatively charged electrons outside the nucleus as there are positively charged particles (*protons*) inside the nucleus, so that the atom is electrically neutral.

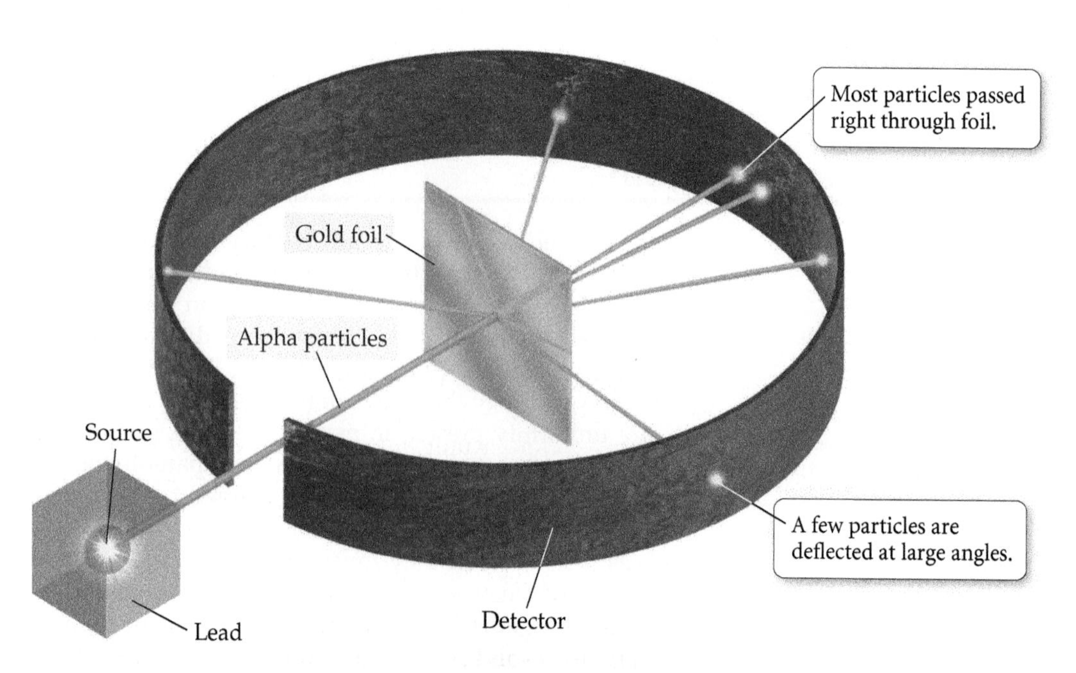

▲ **FIGURE 4.4 Rutherford's gold foil experiment** Tiny particles called alpha-particles were directed at a thin sheet of gold foil. Most of the particles passed directly through the foil. A few, however, were deflected—some of them at sharp angles.

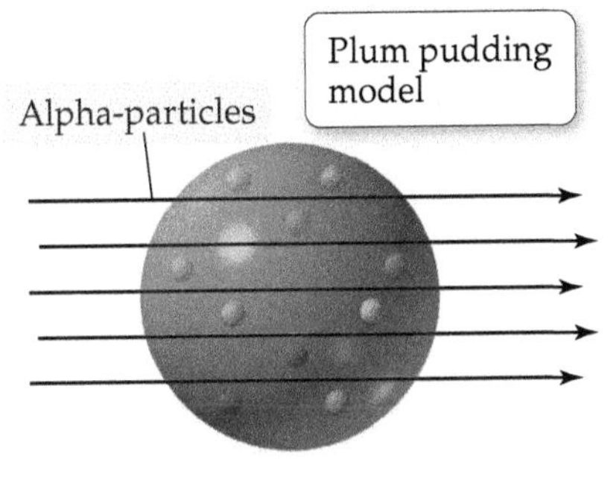

(a) Rutherford's expected result

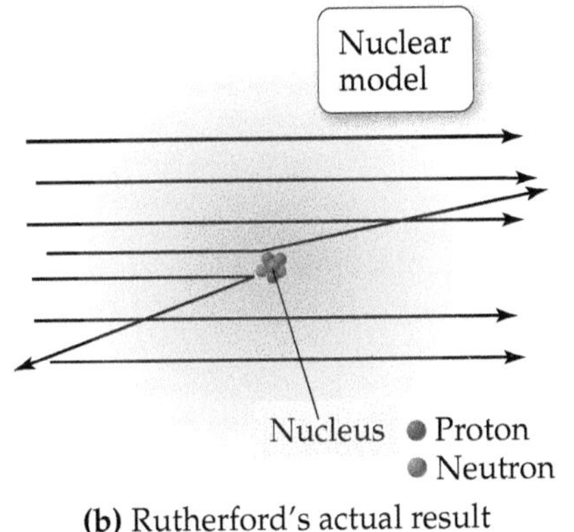

(b) Rutherford's actual result

◀ **FIGURE 4.5 Discovery of the atomic nucleus** **(a)** Expected result of Rutherford's gold foil experiment. If the plum pudding model were correct, the alpha-particles would pass right through the gold foil with minimal deflection. **(b)** Actual result of Rutherford's gold foil experiment. A small number of alpha-particles were deflected or bounced back. The only way to explain the deflections was to suggest that most of the mass and all of the positive charge of an atom must be concentrated in a space much smaller than the size of the atom itself—the nucleus. The nucleus itself is composed of positively charged particles (protons) and neutral particles (neutrons).

Later work by Rutherford and others demonstrated that the atom's **nucleus** contains both positively charged **protons** and neutral particles called **neutrons.** The dense nucleus makes up more than 99.9% of the mass of the atom, but occupies only a small fraction of its volume. The electrons are distributed through a much larger region, but don't have much mass (▼ Figure 4.6). For now, you can think of these electrons like the water droplets that make up a cloud—they are dispersed throughout a large volume but weigh almost nothing.

Rutherford's nuclear theory was a success and is still valid today. The revolutionary part of this theory is the idea that matter—at its core—is much less uniform than it appears. If the nucleus of the atom were the size of this dot ·, the average electron would be about 10 m away. Yet the dot would contain almost the entire mass of the atom. Imagine what matter would be like if atomic structure broke down. What if matter were composed of atomic nuclei piled on top of each other like marbles? Such matter would be incredibly dense; a single grain of sand composed of solid atomic nuclei would have a mass of 5 million kg (or a weight of about 10 million lb). Astronomers believe that black holes and neutron stars are composed of this kind of incredibly dense matter.

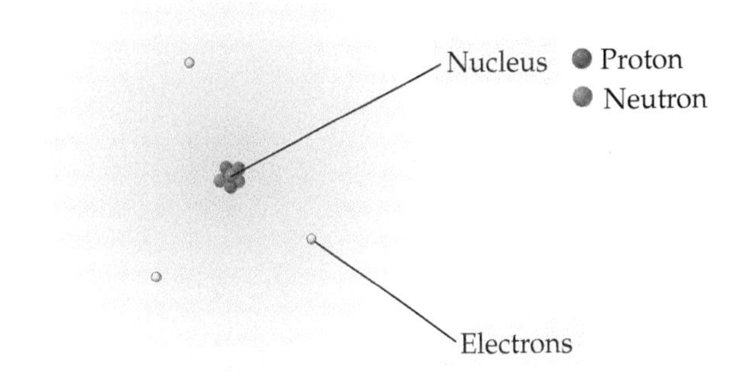

▶ **FIGURE 4.6 The nuclear atom** In this model, 99.9% of the atom's mass is concentrated in a small, dense nucleus that contains protons and neutrons. The rest of the volume of the atom is mostly empty space occupied by negatively charged electrons. The number of electrons outside the nucleus is equal to the number of protons inside the nucleus. In this image, the nucleus is greatly enlarged and the electrons are portrayed as particles.

4.4 The Properties of Protons, Neutrons, and Electrons

Protons and neutrons have very similar masses. In SI units, the mass of the proton is 1.67262×10^{-27} kg, and the mass of the neutron is a close 1.67493×10^{-27} kg. A more common unit to express these masses, however, is the **atomic mass unit (amu),** defined as one-twelfth of the mass of a carbon atom containing six protons and six neutrons. In this unit, a proton has a mass of 1.0073 amu and a neutron has a mass of 1.0087 amu. Electrons, by contrast, have an almost negligible mass of 0.00091×10^{-27} kg, or approximately 0.00055 amu.

◀ If a proton had the mass of a baseball, an electron would have the mass of a rice grain. The proton is nearly 2000 times as massive as an electron.

EVERYDAY CHEMISTRY

Solid Matter?

If matter really is mostly empty space as Rutherford suggested, then why does it appear so solid? Why can I tap my knuckles on the table and feel a solid thump? Matter appears solid because the variation in the density is on such a small scale that our eyes can't see it. Imagine a jungle gym 100 stories high and the size of a football field. It is mostly empty space. Yet if you viewed it from an airplane, it would appear as a solid mass. Matter is similar. When you tap your knuckles on the table, it is much like one giant jungle gym (your finger) crashing into another (the table). Even though they are both primarily empty space, one does not fall into the other.

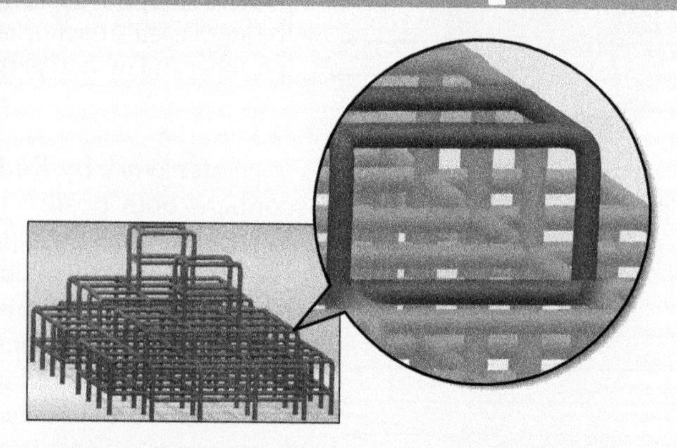

▲ Matter appears solid and uniform because the variation in density is on a scale too small for our eyes to see. Just as this scaffolding appears solid at a distance, so matter appears solid to us.

CAN YOU ANSWER THIS? *Use the jungle gym analogy to explain why most of Rutherford's alpha-particles went right through the gold foil and why a few bounced back. Remember that his gold foil was extremely thin.*

The proton and the electron both have electrical **charge**. The proton's charge is 1+ and the electron's charge is 1−. The charges of the proton and the electron are equal in magnitude but opposite in sign, so that when the two particles are paired, the charges exactly cancel. The neutron has no charge.

What is electrical charge? Electrical charge is a fundamental property of protons and electrons, just as mass is a fundamental property of matter. Most matter is charge-neutral because protons and electrons occur together and their charges cancel. However, you may have experienced excess electrical charge when brushing your hair on a dry day. The brushing action results in the accumulation of electrical charge on the hair strands, which then repel each other, causing your hair to stand on end.

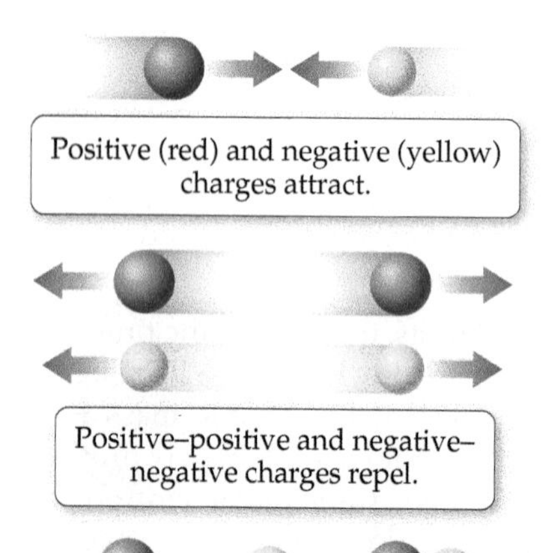
Positive (red) and negative (yellow) charges attract.
Positive–positive and negative–negative charges repel.
1+ + 1− = 0
Positive and negative charges cancel.

▲ **FIGURE 4.7 The properties of electrical charge**

We can summarize the nature of electrical charge as follows (◄ Figure 4.7)

- Electrical charge is a fundamental property of protons and electrons.
- Positive and negative electrical charges attract each other.
- Positive–positive and negative–negative charges repel each other.
- Positive and negative charges cancel each other so that a proton and an electron, when paired, are charge-neutral.

Note that matter is usually charge-neutral due to the canceling effect of protons and electrons. When matter does acquire charge imbalances, these imbalances usually equalize quickly, often in dramatic ways. For example, the shock you receive when touching a doorknob during dry weather is the equalization of a charge imbalance that developed as you walked across the carpet. Lightning is an equalization of charge imbalances that develop during electrical storms.

If you had a sample of matter—even a tiny sample, such as a sand grain—that was composed of only protons or only electrons, the forces around that matter would be extraordinary, and the matter would be unstable. Fortunately, matter is not that way—protons and electrons exist together, canceling each other's charge and making matter charge-neutral. Table 4.1 summarizes the properties of protons, neutrons, and electrons.

▶ Matter is normally charge-neutral, having equal numbers of positive and negative charges that exactly cancel. When the charge balance of matter is disturbed, as in an electrical storm, it quickly rebalances, often in dramatic ways such as lightning.

TABLE 4.1 Subatomic Particles

	Mass (kg)	Mass (amu)	Charge
proton	1.67262×10^{-27}	1.0073	1+
neutron	1.67493×10^{-27}	1.0087	0
electron	0.00091×10^{-27}	0.00055	1−

CONCEPTUAL CHECKPOINT 4.1

An atom composed of which of these particles would have a mass of approximately 12 amu and be charge-neutral?

(a) 6 protons and 6 electrons

(b) 3 protons, 3 neutrons, and 6 electrons

(c) 6 protons, 6 neutrons, and 6 electrons

(d) 12 neutrons and 12 electrons

4.5 Elements: Defined by Their Numbers of Protons

We have seen that atoms are composed of protons, neutrons, and electrons. However, it is the number of protons in the nucleus of an atom that identifies it as a particular element. For example, atoms with 2 protons in their nucleus are helium atoms, atoms with 13 protons in their nucleus are aluminum atoms, and atoms with 92 protons in their nucleus are uranium atoms. The number of protons in an atom's nucleus defines the element (▼ Figure 4.8). Every aluminum atom has

▼ **FIGURE 4.8 The number of protons in the nucleus defines the element**

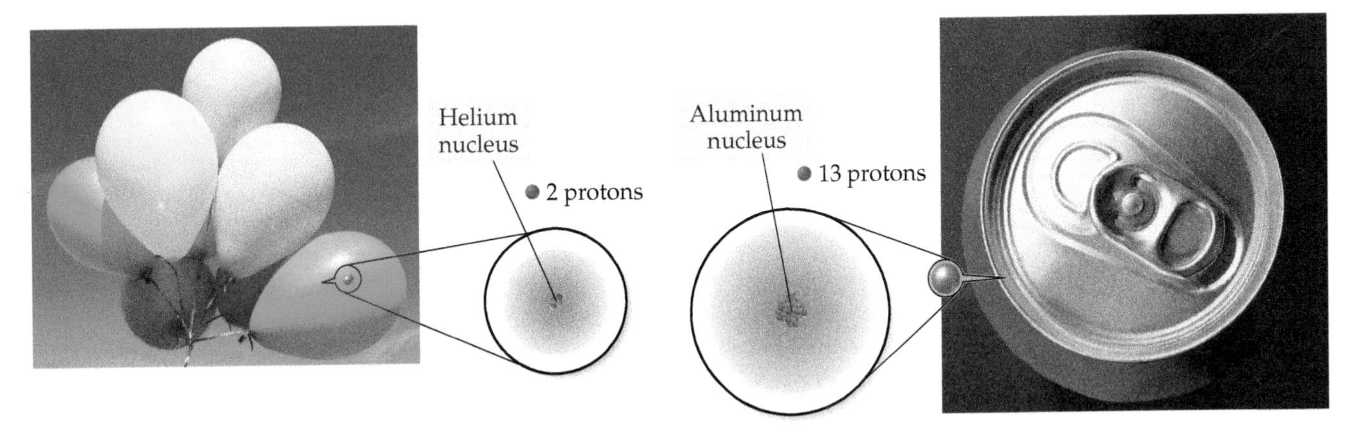

Key: 4 (Atomic number (Z)), Be (Chemical symbol), 9.01 (Atomic mass (defined in section 4.9)), beryllium (Name)

Periods	1A 1	2A 2	3B 3	4B 4	5B 5	6B 6	7B 7	8B 8	8B 9	8B 10	1B 11	2B 12	3A 13	4A 14	5A 15	6A 16	7A 17	8A 18
1	1 H 1.01 hydrogen																	2 He 4.00 helium
2	3 Li 6.94 lithium	4 Be 9.01 beryllium											5 B 10.81 boron	6 C 12.01 carbon	7 N 14.01 nitrogen	8 O 16.00 oxygen	9 F 19.00 fluorine	10 Ne 20.18 neon
3	11 Na 22.99 sodium	12 Mg 24.31 magnesium											13 Al 26.98 aluminum	14 Si 28.09 silicon	15 P 30.97 phosphorus	16 S 32.07 sulfur	17 Cl 35.45 chlorine	18 Ar 39.95 argon
4	19 K 39.10 potassium	20 Ca 40.08 calcium	21 Sc 44.96 scandium	22 Ti 47.88 titanium	23 V 50.94 vanadium	24 Cr 52.00 chromium	25 Mn 54.94 manganese	26 Fe 55.85 iron	27 Co 58.93 cobalt	28 Ni 58.69 nickel	29 Cu 63.55 copper	30 Zn 65.39 zinc	31 Ga 69.72 gallium	32 Ge 72.61 germanium	33 As 74.92 arsenic	34 Se 78.96 selenium	35 Br 79.90 bromine	36 Kr 83.80 krypton
5	37 Rb 85.47 rubidium	38 Sr 87.62 strontium	39 Y 88.91 yttrium	40 Zr 91.22 zirconium	41 Nb 92.91 niobium	42 Mo 95.94 molybdenum	43 Tc (99) technetium	44 Ru 101.07 ruthenium	45 Rh 102.91 rhodium	46 Pd 106.42 palladium	47 Ag 107.87 silver	48 Cd 112.41 cadmium	49 In 114.82 indium	50 Sn 118.71 tin	51 Sb 121.75 antimony	52 Te 127.60 tellurium	53 I 126.90 iodine	54 Xe 131.29 xenon
6	55 Cs 132.91 cesium	56 Ba 137.33 barium	57 La 138.91 lanthanum	72 Hf 178.49 hafnium	73 Ta 180.95 tantalum	74 W 183.85 tungsten	75 Re 186.21 rhenium	76 Os 190.2 osmium	77 Ir 192.22 iridium	78 Pt 195.08 platinum	79 Au 196.97 gold	80 Hg 200.59 mercury	81 Tl 204.38 thallium	82 Pb 207.2 lead	83 Bi 208.98 bismuth	84 Po (209) polonium	85 At (210) astatine	86 Rn (222) radon
7	87 Fr (223) francium	88 Ra (226) radium	89 Ac (227) actinium	104 Rf (261) rutherfordium	105 Db (262) dubnium	106 Sg (263) seaborgium	107 Bh (262) bohrium	108 Hs (265) hassium	109 Mt (266) meitnerium	110 Ds (281) darmstadtium	111 Rg (280) roentgenium	112 Cn (285)	113 — (284)	114 — (289)	115 — (288)	116 — (292)	117 ** (292)	118 — (294)

Lanthanides	58 Ce 140.12 cerium	59 Pr 140.91 praseodymium	60 Nd 144.24 neodymium	61 Pm (147) promethium	62 Sm 150.36 samarium	63 Eu 151.97 europium	64 Gd 157.25 gadolinium	65 Tb 158.93 terbium	66 Dy 162.50 dysprosium	67 Ho 164.93 holmium	68 Er 167.26 erbium	69 Tm 168.93 thulium	70 Yb 173.04 ytterbium	71 Lu 174.97 lutetium
Actinides	90 Th (232) thorium	91 Pa (231) protactinium	92 U (238) uranium	93 Np (237) neptunium	94 Pu (244) plutonium	95 Am (243) americium	96 Cm (247) curium	97 Bk (247) berkelium	98 Cf (251) californium	99 Es (252) einsteinium	100 Fm (257) fermium	101 Md (258) mendelevium	102 No (259) nobelium	103 Lr (260) lawrencium

▲ FIGURE 4.9 The periodic table of the elements

**Element 117 is currently under review by IUPAC.

13 protons in its nucleus; if it had a different number of protons, it would be a different element. The number of protons in the nucleus of an atom is its **atomic number** and is given the symbol **Z**.

The periodic table of the elements (▲ Figure 4.9) lists all known elements according to their atomic numbers. Each element is represented by a unique **chemical symbol**, a one- or two-letter abbreviation for the element that appears directly below its atomic number on the periodic table. The chemical symbol for helium is He; for aluminum, Al; and for uranium, U. The chemical symbol and the atomic number always go together. If the atomic number is 13, the chemical symbol must be Al. If the atomic number is 92, the chemical symbol must be U. This is just another way of saying that the number of protons defines the element.

Most chemical symbols are based on the English name of the element. For example, the symbol for carbon is C; for silicon, Si; and for bromine, Br. Some elements, however, have symbols based on their Latin names. For example, the symbol for potassium is K, from the Latin *kalium*, and the symbol for sodium is Na, from the Latin *natrium*. Additional elements with symbols based on their Greek or Latin names include the following:

lead	Pb	*plumbum*
mercury	Hg	*hydrargyrum*
iron	Fe	*ferrum*
silver	Ag	*argentum*
tin	Sn	*stannum*
copper	Cu	*cuprum*

Early scientists often gave newly discovered elements names that reflected their properties. For example, *argon* originates from the Greek word *argos*, meaning "inactive," referring to argon's chemical inertness (it does not react with other elements). *Bromine* originates from the Greek word *bromos*, meaning "stench," referring to bromine's strong odor. Other elements were named after countries.

For example, polonium was named after Poland, francium after France, and americium after the United States of America. Still other elements were named after scientists. Curium was named after Marie Curie, and mendelevium after Dmitri Mendeleev. Every element's name, symbol, and atomic number are included in the periodic table (inside front cover) and in an alphabetical listing (inside back cover) in this book.

▲ The name *bromine* originates from the Greek word *bromos*, meaning "stench." Bromine vapor, seen as the red-brown gas in this photograph, has a strong odor.

Curium
96
Cm
(247)

▲ Curium is named after Marie Curie, a chemist who helped discover radioactivity and also discovered two new elements. Curie won two Nobel Prizes for her work.

EXAMPLE 4.1 Atomic Number, Atomic Symbol, and Element Name

Find the atomic symbol and atomic number for each element.

(a) silicon
(b) potassium
(c) gold
(d) antimony

SOLUTION

As you become familiar with the periodic table, you will be able to quickly locate elements on it. For now, it might be easier to find them in the alphabetical listing on the inside back cover of this book, but you should also find their position in the periodic table.

Element	Symbol	Atomic Number
silicon	Si	14
potassium	K	19
gold	Au	79
antimony	Sb	51

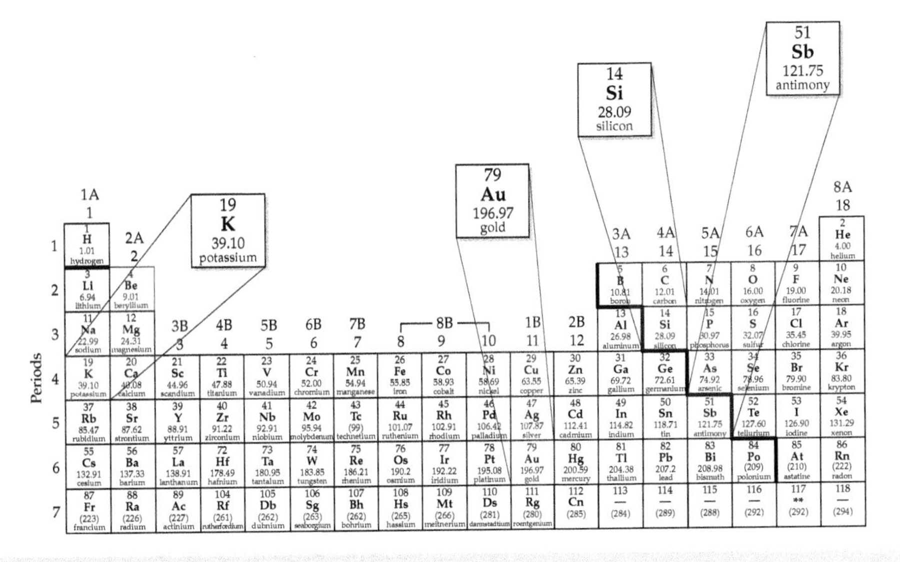

▶SKILLBUILDER 4.1 | Atomic Number, Atomic Symbol, and Element Name

Find the name and atomic number for each element.

(a) Na Sodium 11
(b) Ni Nickel 28
(c) P Phosphorous 15
(d) Ta Tantalum 73

▶FOR MORE PRACTICE Problems 41, 42, 45, 46, 47, 48, 49, 50.

4.6 Looking for Patterns: The Periodic Law and the Periodic Table

▲ Dmitri Mendeleev, a Russian chemistry professor who proposed the periodic law and arranged early versions of the periodic table, shown on a Russian postage stamp.

The organization of the periodic table has its origins in the work of Dmitri Mendeleev (1834–1907), a nineteenth-century Russian chemistry professor. In his time, about 65 different elements had been discovered. Through the work of a number of chemists, much was known about each of these elements, including their relative masses, chemical activity, and some of their physical properties. However, there was no systematic way of organizing them.

1	2	3	4	5	6	7	8	9	10	11	12	13	14	15	16	17	18	19	20
H	He	Li	Be	B	C	N	O	F	Ne	Na	Mg	Al	Si	P	S	Cl	Ar	K	Ca

▲ FIGURE 4.10 **Recurring properties** The elements shown are listed in order of increasing atomic number (Mendeleev used relative mass, which is similar). The color of each element represents its properties. Notice that the properties (colors) of these elements form a repeating pattern.

In 1869, Mendeleev noticed that certain groups of elements had similar properties. He found that if he listed the elements in order of increasing relative mass, those similar properties recurred in a regular pattern (▲ Figure 4.10). Mendeleev summarized these observations in the **periodic law**:

Periodic means "recurring regularly." The properties of the elements, when listed in order of increasing relative mass, formed a *repeating pattern*.

When the elements are arranged in order of increasing relative mass, certain sets of properties recur periodically.

Mendeleev organized all the known elements in a table in which relative mass increased from left to right and elements with similar properties were aligned in the same vertical columns (◀ Figure 4.11). Since many elements had not yet been discovered, Mendeleev's table contained some gaps, which allowed him to predict the existence of yet-undiscovered elements. For example, Mendeleev predicted the existence of an element he called *eka-silicon*, which fell below silicon on the table and between gallium and arsenic. In 1886, eka-silicon was discovered by German chemist Clemens Winkler (1838–1904) and was found to have almost exactly the properties that Mendeleev had anticipated. Winkler named the element germanium, after his home country.

1 H							2 He
3 Li	4 Be	5 B	6 C	7 N	8 O	9 F	10 Ne
11 Na	12 Mg	13 Al	14 Si	15 P	16 S	17 Cl	18 Ar
19 K	20 Ca						

▲ FIGURE 4.11 **Making a periodic table** If we place the elements from Figure 4.10 in a table, we can arrange them in rows so that similar properties align in the same vertical columns. This is similar to Mendeleev's first periodic table.

Mendeleev's original listing has evolved into the modern **periodic table.** In the modern table, elements are listed in order of increasing atomic number rather than increasing relative mass. The modern periodic table also contains more elements than Mendeleev's original table because many more have been discovered since his time.

Mendeleev's periodic law was based on observation. Like all scientific laws, the periodic law summarized many observations but did not give the underlying reason for the observation—only theories do that. For now, we accept the periodic law as it is, but in Chapter 9 we will examine a powerful theory that explains the law and gives the underlying reasons for it.

The elements in the periodic table can be broadly classified as metals, nonmetals, and metalloids (▶ Figure 4.12). **Metals** occupy the left side of the periodic table and have similar properties: They are good conductors of heat and electricity; they can be pounded into flat sheets (malleability); they can be drawn into wires (ductility); they are often shiny; and they tend to lose electrons when they undergo chemical changes. Good examples of metals are iron, magnesium, chromium, and sodium.

Nonmetals occupy the upper right side of the periodic table. The dividing line between metals and nonmetals is the zigzag diagonal line running from boron to astatine (see Figure 4.12). Nonmetals have more varied properties—some are solids at room temperature, others are gases—but as a whole they tend to be poor conductors of heat and electricity, and they all tend to gain electrons when they undergo chemical changes. Good examples of nonmetals are oxygen, nitrogen, chlorine, and iodine.

- Metals
- Nonmetals
- Metalloids

	1A 1	2A 2	3B 3	4B 4	5B 5	6B 6	7B 7	8B 8	8B 9	8B 10	1B 11	2B 12	3A 13	4A 14	5A 15	6A 16	7A 17	8A 18
1	1 H																	2 He
2	3 Li	4 Be											5 B	6 C	7 N	8 O	9 F	10 Ne
3	11 Na	12 Mg											13 Al	14 Si	15 P	16 S	17 Cl	18 Ar
4	19 K	20 Ca	21 Sc	22 Ti	23 V	24 Cr	25 Mn	26 Fe	27 Co	28 Ni	29 Cu	30 Zn	31 Ga	32 Ge	33 As	34 Se	35 Br	36 Kr
5	37 Rb	38 Sr	39 Y	40 Zr	41 Nb	42 Mo	43 Tc	44 Ru	45 Rh	46 Pd	47 Ag	48 Cd	49 In	50 Sn	51 Sb	52 Te	53 I	54 Xe
6	55 Cs	56 Ba	57 La	72 Hf	73 Ta	74 W	75 Re	76 Os	77 Ir	78 Pt	79 Au	80 Hg	81 Tl	82 Pb	83 Bi	84 Po	85 At	86 Rn
7	87 Fr	88 Ra	89 Ac	104 Rf	105 Db	106 Sg	107 Bh	108 Hs	109 Mt	110 Ds	111 Rg	112 Cn	113	114	115	116	117 **	118

Lanthanides	58 Ce	59 Pr	60 Nd	61 Pm	62 Sm	63 Eu	64 Gd	65 Tb	66 Dy	67 Ho	68 Er	69 Tm	70 Yb	71 Lu
Actinides	90 Th	91 Pa	92 U	93 Np	94 Pu	95 Am	96 Cm	97 Bk	98 Cf	99 Es	100 Fm	101 Md	102 No	103 Lr

▲ **FIGURE 4.12 Metals, nonmetals, and metalloids** The elements in the periodic table can be broadly classified as metals, nonmetals, and metalloids.

Most of the elements that lie along the zigzag diagonal line dividing metals and nonmetals are called **metalloids**, or semimetals, and display mixed properties. Metalloids are also called **semiconductors** because of their intermediate electrical conductivity, which can be changed and controlled. This property makes semiconductors useful in the manufacture of the electronic devices that are central to computers, cell phones, and many other modern gadgets. Silicon, arsenic, and germanium are good examples of metalloids.

▲ Silicon is a metalloid used extensively in the computer and electronics industries.

EXAMPLE 4.2 Classifying Elements as Metals, Nonmetals, or Metalloids

Classify each element as a metal, nonmetal, or metalloid.

(a) Ba
(b) I
(c) O
(d) Te

SOLUTION

(a) Barium is on the left side of the periodic table; it is a metal.
(b) Iodine is on the right side of the periodic table; it is a nonmetal.
(c) Oxygen is on the right side of the periodic table; it is a nonmetal.
(d) Tellurium is in the middle-right section of the periodic table, along the line that divides the metals from the nonmetals; it is a metalloid.

▶SKILLBUILDER 4.2 | Classifying Elements as Metals, Nonmetals, or Metalloids

Classify each element as a metal, nonmetal, or metalloid.

(a) S
(b) Cl
(c) Ti
(d) Sb

▶FOR MORE PRACTICE Problems: 51, 52, 53, 54.

▶ FIGURE 4.13 Main-group and transition elements The periodic table can be broadly divided into main-group elements, whose properties can generally be predicted based on their position, and transition elements, whose properties tend to be less predictable based on their position.

Main-group elements | Transition elements | Main-group elements

Group number — Periods

Period	1A	2A	3B	4B	5B	6B	7B	8B	8B	8B	1B	2B	3A	4A	5A	6A	7A	8A
1	1 H																	2 He
2	3 Li	4 Be											5 B	6 C	7 N	8 O	9 F	10 Ne
3	11 Na	12 Mg											13 Al	14 Si	15 P	16 S	17 Cl	18 Ar
4	19 K	20 Ca	21 Sc	22 Ti	23 V	24 Cr	25 Mn	26 Fe	27 Co	28 Ni	29 Cu	30 Zn	31 Ga	32 Ge	33 As	34 Se	35 Br	36 Kr
5	37 Rb	38 Sr	39 Y	40 Zr	41 Nb	42 Mo	43 Tc	44 Ru	45 Rh	46 Pd	47 Ag	48 Cd	49 In	50 Sn	51 Sb	52 Te	53 I	54 Xe
6	55 Cs	56 Ba	57 La	72 Hf	73 Ta	74 W	75 Re	76 Os	77 Ir	78 Pt	79 Au	80 Hg	81 Tl	82 Pb	83 Bi	84 Po	85 At	86 Rn
7	87 Fr	88 Ra	89 Ac	104 Rf	105 Db	106 Sg	107 Bh	108 Hs	109 Mt	110 Ds	111 Rg	112 Cn	113	114	115	116	117 **	118

The periodic table can also be broadly divided into **main-group elements**, whose properties tend to be more predictable based on their position in the periodic table, and **transition elements** or **transition metals**, whose properties are less easily predictable based simply on their position in the periodic table (▲ Figure 4.13). Main-group elements are in columns labeled with a number and the letter A. Transition elements are in columns labeled with a number and the letter B. A competing numbering system does not use letters, but only the numbers 1–18. Both numbering systems are shown in the periodic table in the inside front cover of this book.

The noble gases are inert (or unreactive) compared to other elements. However, some noble gases, especially the heavier ones, will form a limited number of compounds with other elements under special conditions.

Each column within the periodic table is called a **family** or **group** of elements. The elements within a family of main-group elements usually have similar properties, and some have a group name. For example, the Group 8A elements, called the **noble gases**, are chemically inert gases. The most familiar noble gas is probably helium, used to fill balloons. Helium, like the other noble gases, is chemically stable—it won't combine with other elements to form compounds—and is therefore safe to put into balloons. Other noble gases include neon, often used in neon signs; argon, which makes up a small percentage of our atmosphere; krypton; and xenon. The Group 1A elements, called the **alkali metals**, are all very reactive metals. A marble-sized piece of sodium can explode when dropped into water. Other alkali metals include lithium, potassium, and rubidium. The Group 2A elements, called the **alkaline earth metals**, are also fairly reactive, although not quite as reactive as the alkali metals. Calcium, for example, reacts fairly vigorously when

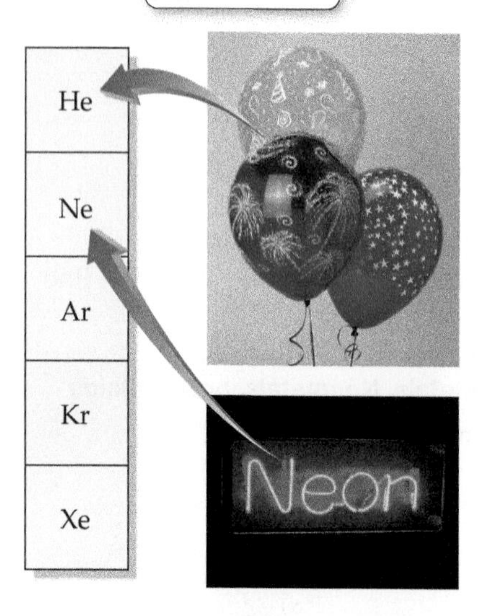

▲ The noble gases include helium (used in balloons), neon (used in neon signs), argon, krypton, and xenon.

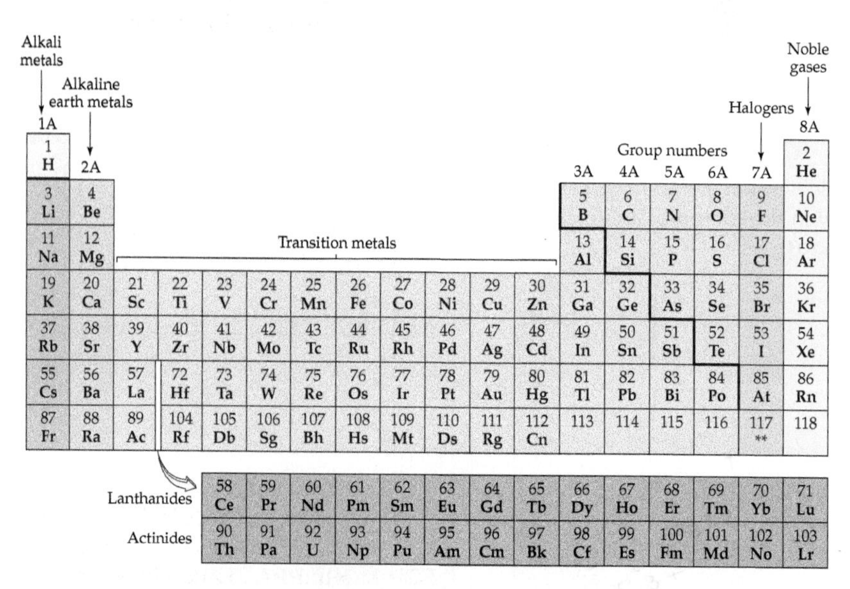

▲ The periodic table with Groups 1A, 2A, 7A, and 8A highlighted.

Alkali metals

Li
Na
K
Rb
Cs

▲ The alkali metals include lithium (shown in the first photo), sodium (shown in the second photo reacting with water), potassium, rubidium, and cesium.

dropped into water but will not explode as readily as sodium. Other alkaline earth metals are magnesium, a common low-density structural metal; strontium; and barium. The Group 7A elements, called the **halogens**, are very reactive nonmetals. Chlorine, a greenish-yellow gas with a pungent odor is probably the most familiar halogen. Because of its reactivity, chlorine is often used as a sterilizing and disinfecting agent (because it reacts with and kills bacteria and other microscopic organisms). Other halogens include bromine, a red-brown liquid that easily evaporates into a gas; iodine, a purple solid; and fluorine, a pale yellow gas.

EXAMPLE 4.3 Groups and Families of Elements

To which group or family of elements does each element belong?

(a) Mg
(b) N
(c) K
(d) Br

SOLUTION

(a) Mg is in Group 2A; it is an alkaline earth metal.
(b) N is in Group 5A.
(c) K is in Group 1A; it is an alkali metal.
(d) Br is in Group 7A; it is a halogen.

▶SKILLBUILDER 4.3 | Groups and Families of Elements

To which group or family of elements does each element belong?

(a) Li
(b) B
(c) I
(d) Ar

▶FOR MORE PRACTICE Problems 57, 58, 59, 60, 61, 62, 63, 64.

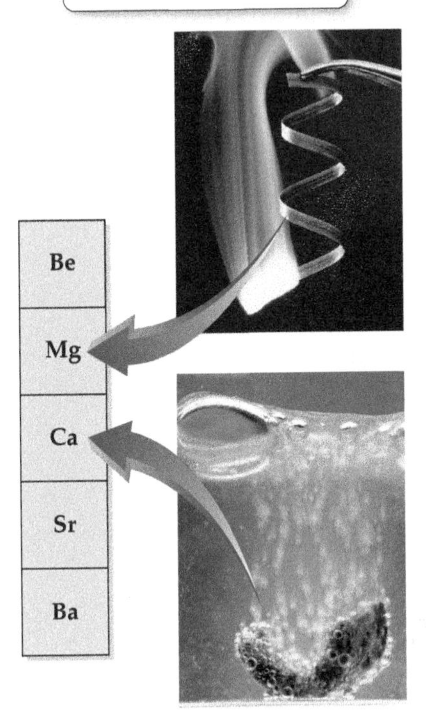

◀ The alkaline earth metals include beryllium, magnesium (shown burning in the first photo), calcium (shown reacting with water in the second photo), strontium, and barium.

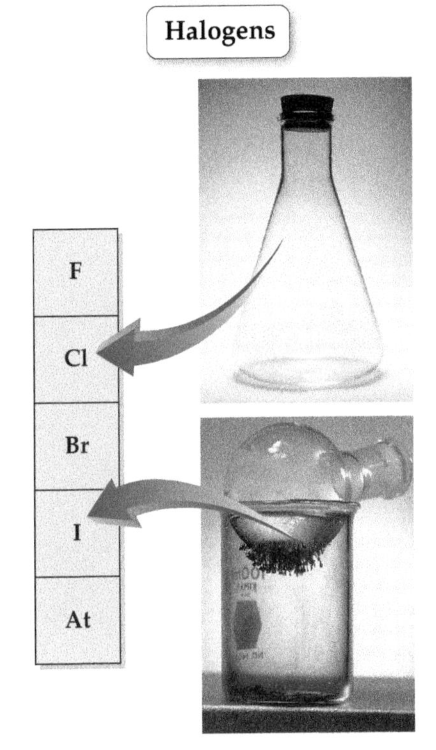

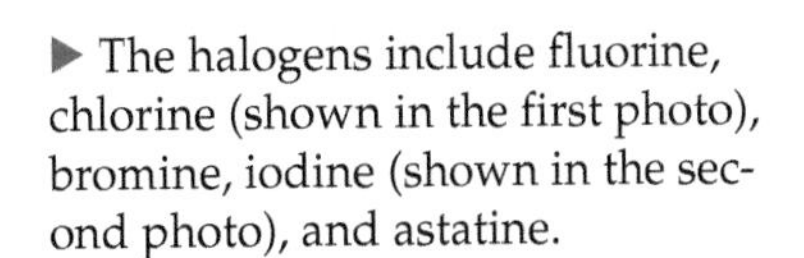

▶ The halogens include fluorine, chlorine (shown in the first photo), bromine, iodine (shown in the second photo), and astatine.

CONCEPTUAL CHECKPOINT 4.2

Which statement can NEVER be true?

(a) An element can be both a transition element and a metal.
(b) An element can be both a transition element and a metalloid.
(c) An element can be both a metalloid and a halogen.
(d) An element can be both a main-group element and a halogen.

4.7 Ions: Losing and Gaining Electrons

The charge of an ion is shown in the upper right corner of the symbol.

In chemical reactions, atoms often lose or gain electrons to form charged particles called **ions.** For example, neutral lithium (Li) atoms contain 3 protons and 3 electrons; however, in reactions, lithium atoms lose one electron (e^-) to form Li^+ ions.

$$Li \longrightarrow Li^+ + e^-$$

The Li^+ *ion* contains 3 protons but only 2 electrons, resulting in a net charge of 1+. Ion charges are usually written with the magnitude of the charge first followed by the sign of the charge. For example, a positive two charge is written as 2+, and a negative two charge is written as 2−. The charge of an ion depends on how many electrons were gained or lost and is given by the formula:

$$\text{Ion charge} = \text{number of protons} - \text{number of electrons}$$
$$= \#p^+ - \#e^-$$

where p^+ stands for *proton* and e^- stands for *electron.*

For the Li^+ ion with 3 protons and 2 electrons the charge is:

$$\text{Ion Charge} = 3 - 2 = 1+$$

Neutral fluorine (F) atoms contain 9 protons and 9 electrons; however, in chemical reactions fluorine atoms gain 1 electron to form F^- ions:

$$F + e^- \longrightarrow F^-$$

The F^- *ion* contains 9 protons and 10 electrons, resulting in a 1− charge.

$$\text{Ion charge} = 9 - 10$$
$$= 1-$$

Positively charged ions, such as Li^+, are **cations**, and negatively charged ions, such as F^-, are **anions.** Ions behave very differently than the atoms from which they are formed. Neutral sodium atoms, for example, are extremely reactive, interacting violently with most things they contact. Sodium cations (Na^+), on the other hand, are relatively inert—we eat them all the time in sodium chloride (table salt). In nature, cations and anions always occur together so that, again, matter is charge-neutral. For example, in table salt, the sodium cation occurs together with the chloride anion (Cl^-).

EXAMPLE 4.4 Determining Ion Charge from Numbers of Protons and Electrons

Determine the charge of each ion.

(a) a magnesium ion with 10 electrons
(b) a sulfur ion with 18 electrons
(c) an iron ion with 23 electrons

SOLUTION

To determine the charge of each ion, use the ion charge equation.

$$\text{Ion charge} = \#\text{p} - \#\text{e}^-$$

The number of electrons is given in the problem. The number of protons is obtained from the element's atomic number in the periodic table.

(a) magnesium with atomic number 12

$$\text{Ion charge} = 12 - 10 = 2+ \ (Mg^{2+})$$

(b) sulfur with atomic number 16

$$\text{Ion charge} = 16 - 18 = 2- \ (S^{2-})$$

(c) iron with atomic number 26

$$\text{Ion charge} = 26 - 23 = 3+ \ (Fe^{3+})$$

▶SKILLBUILDER 4.4 | Determining Ion Charge from Numbers of Protons and Electrons

Determine the charge of each ion.

(a) a nickel ion with 26 electrons
(b) a bromine ion with 36 electrons
(c) a phosphorus ion with 18 electrons

▶FOR MORE PRACTICE Example 4.10; Problems 73, 74.

EXAMPLE 4.5 Determining the Number of Protons and Electrons in an Ion

Find the number of protons and electrons in the Ca^{2+} ion.

From the periodic table, find that the atomic number for calcium is 20, so calcium has 20 protons. The number of electrons can be found using the ion charge equation.

SOLUTION

$$\text{Ion charge} = \#\text{p} - \#\text{e}^-$$

$$2+ = 20 - \#\text{e}^-$$

$$\#\text{e}^- = 20 - 2 = 18$$

Therefore the number of electrons is 18. The Ca^{2+} ion has 20 protons and 18 electrons.

▶SKILLBUILDER 4.5 | Determining the Number of Protons and Electrons in an Ion

Find the number of protons and electrons in the S^{2-} ion.

▶FOR MORE PRACTICE Example 4.11; Problems 75, 76.

IONS AND THE PERIODIC TABLE

For many main-group elements, we can use the periodic table to predict how many electrons tend to be lost or gained when an atom of that particular element ionizes. The number associated with the letter A above each *main-group* column in the periodic table—1 through 8—gives the number of *valence electrons* for the elements in that column. We will discuss the concept of valence electrons more fully in Chapter 9, but for now, think of valence electrons as the outermost electrons in an atom. Since oxygen is in column 6A, we can deduce that it has 6 valence

1A	2A		3A	4A	5A	6A	7A	8A
Li^+	Be^{2+}					O^{2-}	F^-	
Na^+	Mg^{2+}		Al^{3+}			S^{2-}	Cl^-	
K^+	Ca^{2+}		Ga^{3+}			Se^{2-}	Br^-	
Rb^+	Sr^{2+}	Transition metals form cations with various charges	In^{3+}			Te^{2-}	I^-	
Cs^+	Ba^{2+}							

▲ **FIGURE 4.14 Elements that form predictable ions**

electrons; since magnesium is in column 2A, it has 2 valence electrons, and so on. An important exception to this rule is helium—it is in column 8A, but has only 2 valence electrons. Valence electrons are particularly important because, as we shall see in Chapter 10, it is these electrons that take part in chemical bonding.

The key to predicting the charge acquired by a particular element when it ionizes is its position in the periodic table relative to the noble gases:

> Main-group elements tend to form ions that have the same number of valence electrons as the nearest noble gas.

For example, the closest noble gas to oxygen is neon. When oxygen ionizes, it *acquires* two additional electrons for a total of 8 valence electrons—the same number as neon. When determining the closest noble gas, we can move either forward or backward on the periodic table. For example, the closest noble gas to magnesium is also neon, even though neon (atomic number 10) falls before magnesium (atomic number 12) in the periodic table. Therefore magnesium *loses* its 2 valence electrons to attain the same number of valence electrons as neon.

In accordance with this principle, the alkali metals (Group 1A) tend to lose 1 electron and therefore form 1+ ions, while the alkaline earth metals (Group 2A) tend to lose 2 electrons and therefore form 2+ ions. The halogens (Group 7A) tend to gain 1 electron and therefore form 1− ions. The groups in the periodic table that form predictable ions are shown in ▲ Figure 4.14. Be familiar with these groups and the ions they form. In Chapter 9, we will examine a theory that more fully explains why these groups form ions as they do.

EXAMPLE 4.6 Charge of Ions from Position in Periodic Table

Based on their position in the periodic table, what ions do barium and iodine tend to form?

SOLUTION

Since barium is in Group 2A, it tends to form a cation with a 2+ charge (Ba^{2+}). Since iodine is in Group 7A, it tends to form an anion with a 1− charge (I^-).

▶SKILLBUILDER 4.6 | Charge of Ions from Position in Periodic Table

Based on their position in the periodic table, what ions do potassium and selenium tend to form?

▶FOR MORE PRACTICE Problems 79, 80.

CONCEPTUAL CHECKPOINT 4.3

Which of these pairs of ions have the same total number of electrons?

(a) Na^+ and Mg^{2+}
(b) F^- and Cl^-
(c) O^- and O^{2-}
(d) Ga^{3+} and Fe^{3+}

4.8 Isotopes: When the Number of Neutrons Varies

All atoms of a given element have the same number of protons; however, they do not necessarily have the same number of neutrons. Since neutrons and protons have nearly the same mass (approximately 1 amu), and since the number of neutrons in the atoms of a given element can vary, all atoms of a given element *do not* have the same mass (contrary to what John Dalton originally proposed in his atomic theory). For example, all neon atoms in nature contain 10 protons, but they may have 10, 11, or 12 neutrons (▼ Figure 4.15). All three types of neon atoms exist, and each has a slightly different mass. Atoms with the same number of protons but different numbers of neutrons are called **isotopes**. Some elements, such as beryllium (Be) and aluminum (Al), have only one naturally occurring isotope, while other elements, such as neon (Ne) and chlorine (Cl), have two or more.

There are a few exceptions to this rule, such as boron, but they are beyond our scope in this text.

For a given element, the relative amounts of each different isotope in a naturally occurring sample of that element is always the same. For example, in any natural sample of neon atoms, 90.48% of them are the isotope with 10 neutrons, 0.27% are the isotope with 11 neutrons, and 9.25% are the isotope with 12 neutrons as summarized in Table 4.2. This means that out of 10,000 neon atoms, 9048 have

TABLE 4.2 Neon Isotopes

Symbol	Number of Protons	Number of Neutrons	A (Mass Number)	Percent Natural Abundance
Ne-20 or $^{20}_{10}Ne$	10	10	20	90.48%
Ne-21 or $^{21}_{10}Ne$	10	11	21	0.27%
Ne-22 or $^{22}_{10}Ne$	10	12	22	9.25%

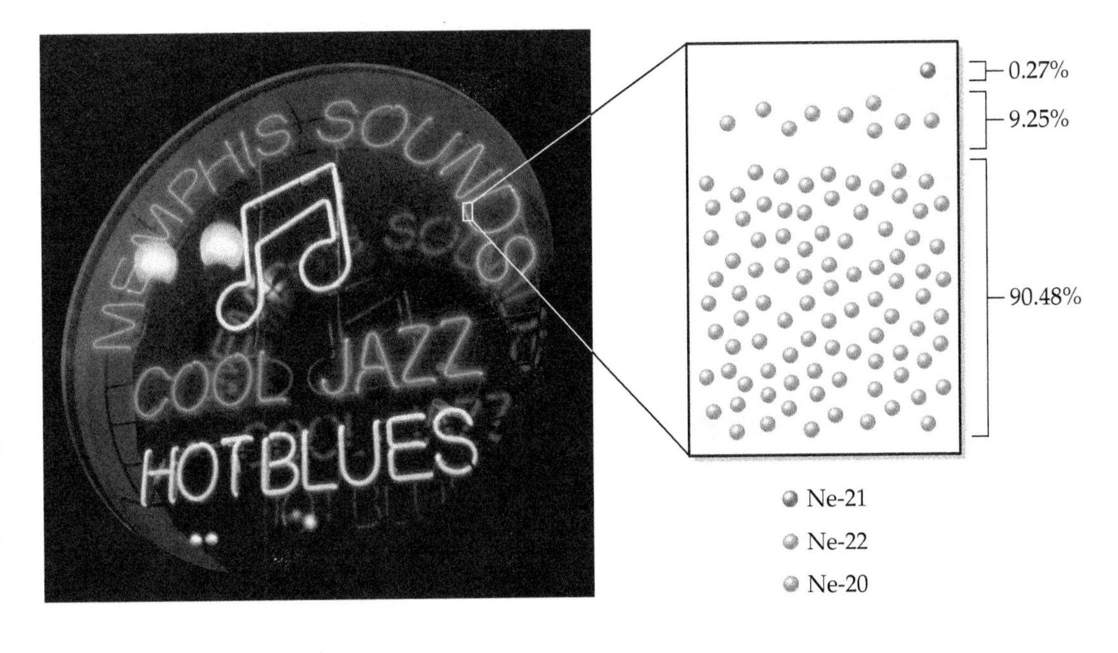

▶ **FIGURE 4.15**
Isotopes of neon
Naturally occurring neon contains three different isotopes, Ne-20 (with 10 neutrons), Ne-21 (with 11 neutrons), and Ne-22 (with 12 neutrons).

Percent means "per hundred." 90.48% means that 90.48 atoms out of 100 are the isotope with 10 neutrons.

10 neutrons, 27 have 11 neutrons, and 925 have 12 neutrons. These percentages are referred to as the **percent natural abundance** of the isotopes. The preceding numbers are for neon only; all elements have their own unique percent natural abundance of isotopes.

The sum of the number of neutrons and protons in an atom is its **mass number** and is given the symbol **A**.

$$A = \text{Number of protons} + \text{Number of neutrons}$$

For neon, which has 10 protons, the mass numbers of the three different naturally occurring isotopes are 20, 21, and 22, corresponding to 10, 11, and 12 neutrons, respectively.

Isotopes are often symbolized in the following way:

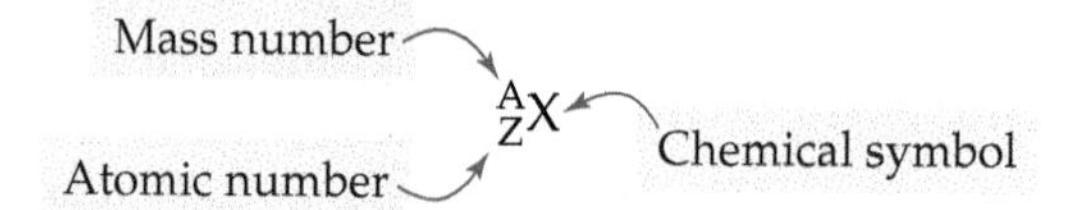

where X is the chemical symbol, A is the mass number, and Z is the atomic number.

For example, the symbols for the neon isotopes are:

$$^{20}_{10}\text{Ne} \quad ^{21}_{10}\text{Ne} \quad ^{22}_{10}\text{Ne}$$

Notice that the chemical symbol, Ne, and the atomic number, 10, are redundant: If the atomic number is 10, the symbol must be Ne, and vice versa. The mass numbers, however, are different, reflecting the different number of neutrons in each isotope.

A second common notation for isotopes is the chemical symbol (or chemical name) followed by a hyphen and the mass number of the isotope.

X—A

Chemical symbol or name → X; Mass number → A

In this notation, the neon isotopes are:

Ne-20	neon-20
Ne-21	neon-21
Ne-22	neon-22

In general, mass number increases with increasing atomic number.

Notice that all isotopes of a given element have the same number of protons (otherwise they would be a different element). Notice also that the mass number is the *sum* of the number of protons and the number of neutrons. The number of neutrons in an isotope is the difference between the mass number and the atomic number.

EXAMPLE 4.7 Atomic Numbers, Mass Numbers, and Isotope Symbols

What are the atomic number (Z), mass number (A), and symbols of the carbon isotope with 7 neutrons?

SOLUTION

Find that the atomic number (Z) of carbon is 6 (from the periodic table). This tells you that carbon atoms have 6 protons. The mass number (A) for the isotope with 7 neutrons is the sum of the number of protons and the number of neutrons.

$$A = 6 + 7 = 13$$

So, Z = 6, A = 13, and the symbols for the isotope are C-13 and $^{13}_{6}\text{C}$.

▶SKILLBUILDER 4.7 | Atomic Numbers, Mass Numbers, and Isotope Symbols

What are the atomic number, mass number, and symbols for the chlorine isotope with 18 neutrons?

▶FOR MORE PRACTICE Example 4.12; Problems: 85, 87, 89, 90.

EXAMPLE 4.8 Numbers of Protons and Neutrons from Isotope Symbols

How many protons and neutrons are in the chromium isotope $^{52}_{24}Cr$?

	SOLUTION
The number of protons is equal to Z (lower left number).	$\#p^+ = Z = 24$
The number of neutrons is equal to A (upper left number) −Z (lower left number).	$\#n = A - Z$ $= 52 - 24$ $= 28$

▶SKILLBUILDER 4.8 | Numbers of Protons and Neutrons from Isotope Symbols

How many protons and neutrons are in the potassium isotope $^{39}_{19}K$?

▶FOR MORE PRACTICE Example 4.13; Problems 91, 92.

CONCEPTUAL CHECKPOINT 4.4

If an atom with a mass number of 27 has 14 neutrons, it is an isotope of which element?

(a) silicon
(b) aluminum
(c) cobalt
(d) niobium

CONCEPTUAL CHECKPOINT 4.5

Throughout this book, we represent atoms as spheres. For example, a carbon atom is represented by a black sphere as shown here. In light of the nuclear theory of the atom, would C-12 and C-13 look different in this representation of atoms? Why or why not?

4.9 Atomic Mass: The Average Mass of an Element's Atoms

An important part of Dalton's atomic theory was that all atoms of a given element have the same mass. But as we just learned, the atoms of a given element may have different masses (because of isotopes). So Dalton was not completely correct. We can, however, calculate an average mass—called the **atomic mass**—for each

CHEMISTRY IN THE ENVIRONMENT

Radioactive Isotopes at Hanford, Washington

Nuclei of the isotopes of a given element are not all equally stable. For example, naturally occurring lead is composed primarily of Pb-206, Pb-207, and Pb-208. Other isotopes of lead also exist, but their nuclei are unstable. Scientists can make some of these other isotopes, such as Pb-185, in the laboratory. However, within seconds Pb-185 atoms emit a few energetic subatomic particles from their nuclei and change into different isotopes of different elements (which are themselves unstable). These emitted subatomic particles are called **nuclear radiation**, and the isotopes that emit them are termed **radioactive**. Nuclear radiation, always associated with unstable nuclei, can be harmful to humans and other living organisms because the energetic particles interact with and damage biological molecules. Some isotopes, such as Pb-185, emit significant amounts of radiation only for a very short time. Others, however, remain radioactive for a long time—in some cases millions or even billions of years.

The nuclear power and nuclear weapons industries produce by-products containing unstable isotopes of several different elements. Many of these isotopes emit nuclear radiation for a long time, and their disposal is an environmental problem. For example, in Hanford, Washington, which for 50 years produced fuel for nuclear weapons, 177 underground storage tanks contain 55 million gallons of highly radioactive nuclear waste. Certain radioactive isotopes within that waste will produce nuclear radiation for the foreseeable future. Unfortunately, some of the underground storage tanks are aging, and leaks have allowed some of the waste to seep into the environment. While the danger from short-term external exposure to this waste is minimal, ingestion of the waste through contamination of drinking water or food supplies would pose significant health risks. Consequently, Hanford is now the site of the largest environmental cleanup project in U.S. history. The U.S. government expects the project to take more than 20 years and cost about $10 billion.

Radioactive isotopes are not always harmful, however, and many have beneficial uses. For example, technetium-99 (Tc-99) is often given to patients to diagnose disease. The radiation emitted by Tc-99 helps doctors image internal organs or detect infection.

CAN YOU ANSWER THIS? *Give the number of neutrons in each of the following isotopes: Pb-206, Pb-207, Pb-208, Pb-185, Tc-99.*

◀ Storage tanks at Hanford, Washington, contain 55 million gallons of high-level nuclear waste. Each tank pictured here holds 1 million gallons.

element. The atomic mass of each element is listed in the periodic table directly beneath the element's symbol; it represents the average mass of the atoms that compose that element. For example, the periodic table lists the atomic mass of chlorine as 35.45 amu. Naturally occurring chlorine consists of 75.77% chlorine-35 (mass 34.97 amu) and 24.23% chlorine-37 (mass 36.97 amu). Its atomic mass is:

Some books call this *average atomic mass* or atomic weight instead of simply *atomic mass.*

$$\text{Atomic mass} = (0.7577 \times 34.97\ \text{amu}) + (0.2423 \times 36.97\ \text{amu})$$
$$= 35.45\ \text{amu}$$

Notice that the atomic mass of chlorine is closer to 35 than 37 because naturally occurring chlorine contains more chlorine-35 atoms than chlorine-37 atoms. Notice also that when percentages are used in these calculations, they must always be converted to their decimal value. To convert a percentage to its decimal value, divide by 100. For example:

$$75.77\% = 75.77/100 = 0.7577$$
$$24.33\% = 24.23/100 = 0.2423$$

In general, atomic mass is calculated according to the following equation:

$$\begin{aligned}\text{Atomic mass} = &(\text{Fraction of isotope 1} \times \text{Mass of isotope 1}) + \\ &(\text{Fraction of isotope 2} \times \text{Mass of isotope 2}) + \\ &(\text{Fraction of isotope 3} \times \text{Mass of isotope 3}) + \ldots\end{aligned}$$

where the fractions of each isotope are the percent natural abundances converted to their decimal values. Atomic mass is useful because it allows us to assign a characteristic mass to each element and, as we will see in Chapter 6, it allows us to quantify the number of atoms in a sample of that element.

EXAMPLE 4.9 Calculating Atomic Mass

Gallium has two naturally occurring isotopes: Ga-69 with mass 68.9256 amu and a natural abundance of 60.11%, and Ga-71 with mass 70.9247 amu and a natural abundance of 39.89%. Calculate the atomic mass of gallium.

	SOLUTION
Convert the percent natural abundances into decimal form by dividing by 100.	$\text{Fraction Ga-69} = \dfrac{60.11}{100} = 0.6011$ $\text{Fraction Ga-71} = \dfrac{39.89}{100} = 0.3989$
Use the fractional abundances and the atomic masses of the isotopes to compute the atomic mass according to the atomic mass definition given earlier.	$\text{Atomic mass} = (0.6011 \times 68.9256\text{ amu}) + (0.3989 \times 70.9247\text{ amu})$ $= 41.4321\text{ amu} + 28.2919\text{ amu}$ $= 69.7231 = 69.72\text{ amu}$

▶SKILLBUILDER 4.9 | Calculating Atomic Mass

Magnesium has three naturally occurring isotopes with masses of 23.99, 24.99, and 25.98 amu and natural abundances of 78.99%, 10.00%, and 11.01%. Calculate the atomic mass of magnesium.

▶FOR MORE PRACTICE Example 4.14; Problems 95, 96.

CONCEPTUAL CHECKPOINT 4.6

A fictitious element is composed of isotopes A and B with masses of 61.9887 and 64.9846 amu, respectively. The atomic mass of the element is 64.52. What can you conclude about the natural abundances of the two isotopes?

(a) The natural abundance of isotope A must be greater than the natural abundance of isotope B.

(b) The natural abundance of isotope B must be greater than the natural abundance of isotope A.

(c) The natural abundances of both isotopes must be about equal.

(d) Nothing can be concluded about the natural abundances of the two isotopes from the given information.

CHAPTER IN REVIEW

CHEMICAL PRINCIPLES	RELEVANCE
The Atomic Theory: Democritus and Leucippus, ancient Greek philosophers, were the first to assert that matter is ultimately composed of small, indestructible particles. It was not until 2000 years later, however, that John Dalton introduced a formal atomic theory stating that matter is composed of atoms; atoms of a given element have unique properties that distinguish them from atoms of other elements; and atoms combine in simple, whole-number ratios to form compounds.	**The Atomic Theory:** The concept of atoms is important because it explains the physical world. You and everything you see are made of atoms. To understand the physical world, we must begin by understanding atoms. Atoms are the key concept—they determine the properties of matter.
Discovery of the Atom's Nucleus: Rutherford's gold foil experiment probed atomic structure, and his results led to the nuclear model of the atom, which, with minor modifications to accommodate neutrons, is still valid today. In this model, the atom is composed of protons and neutrons—which compose most of the atom's mass and are grouped together in a dense nucleus—and electrons, which compose most of the atom's volume. Protons and neutrons have similar masses (1 amu), while electrons have a much smaller mass (0.00055 amu).	**Discovery of the Atom's Nucleus:** We can understand why this is relevant by asking, what if it were otherwise? What if matter were *not* mostly empty space? While we cannot know for certain, it seems probable that such matter would not form the diversity of substances required for life—and then, of course, we would not be around to ask the question.
Charge: Protons and electrons both have electrical charge; the charge of the proton is +1 and the charge of the electron is −1. The neutron has no charge. When protons and electrons combine in atoms, their charges cancel.	**Charge:** Electrical charge is relevant to much of our modern world. Many of the machines and computers we depend on are powered by electricity, which is the movement of electrical charge.
The Periodic Table: The periodic table tabulates all known elements in order of increasing atomic number. The periodic table is arranged so that similar elements are grouped in columns. Columns of elements in the periodic table have similar properties and are called groups or families. Elements on the left side of the periodic table are metals and tend to lose electrons in their chemical changes. Elements on the upper right side of the periodic table are nonmetals and tend to gain electrons in their chemical changes. Elements between the two are called metalloids.	**The Periodic Table:** The periodic table helps us organize the elements in ways that allow us to predict their properties. Helium, for example, is not toxic in small amounts because it is an inert gas—it does not react with anything. The gases in the column below it on the periodic table are also inert gases and form a family or group of elements called the noble gases. By tabulating the elements and grouping similar ones together, we begin to understand their properties.
Atomic Number: The characteristic that defines an element is the number of protons in the nuclei of its atoms; this number is called the atomic number (Z).	**Atomic Number:** Elements are the fundamental building blocks from which all compounds are made.
Ions: When an atom gains or loses electrons, it becomes an ion. Positively charged ions are called cations, and negatively charged ions are called anions. Cations and anions occur together so that matter is ordinarily charge-neutral.	**Ions:** Ions occur in many compounds, such as sodium chloride.

Isotopes: While all atoms of a given element have the same number of protons, they do not necessarily have the same number of neutrons. Atoms of the same element with different numbers of neutrons are called isotopes. Isotopes are characterized by their mass number (A), the sum of the number of protons and the number of neutrons in their nucleus.

Each naturally occurring sample of an element has the same percent natural abundance of each isotope. These percentages, together with the mass of each isotope, are used to compute the atomic mass of the element, a weighted average of the masses of the individual isotopes.

Isotopes: Isotopes are relevant because they influence tabulated atomic masses. To understand these masses, we must understand the presence and abundance of isotopes. In nuclear processes—processes in which the nuclei of atoms actually change—the presence of different isotopes becomes even more important.

Some isotopes are not stable—they lose subatomic particles and are transformed into other elements. The emission of subatomic particles by unstable nuclei is called radioactive decay. In many situations, such as in diagnosing and treating certain diseases, nuclear radiation is extremely useful. In other situations, such as in the disposal of radioactive waste, it can pose environmental problems.

CHEMICAL SKILLS

Determining Ion Charge from Numbers of Protons and Electrons (Section 4.7)

- From the periodic table or from the alphabetical list of elements, find the atomic number of the element; this number is equal to the number of protons.
- Use the ion charge equation to compute charge.

$$\text{Ion charge} = \#p^+ - \#e^-$$

Determining the Number of Protons and Electrons in an Ion (Section 4.7)

- From the periodic table or from the alphabetical list of elements, find the atomic number of the element; this number is equal to the number of protons.
- Use the ion charge equation and substitute in the known values.

$$\text{Ion charge} = \#p^+ - \#e^-$$

- Solve the equation for the number of electrons.

Determining Atomic Numbers, Mass Numbers, and Isotope Symbols for an Isotope (Section 4.8)

- From the periodic table or from the alphabetical list of elements, find the atomic number of the element.
- The mass number (A) is equal to the atomic number plus the number of neutrons.
- Write the symbol for the isotope by writing the symbol for the element with the mass number in the upper left corner and the atomic number in the lower left corner.
- The other symbol for the isotope is simply the chemical symbol followed by a hyphen and the mass number.

EXAMPLES

EXAMPLE 4.10 Determining Ion Charge from Numbers of Protons and Electrons

Determine the charge of a selenium ion with 36 electrons.

SOLUTION

Selenium is atomic number 34; therefore, it has 34 protons.

$$\text{Ion charge} = 34 - 36 = 2-$$

EXAMPLE 4.11 Determining the Number of Protons and Electrons in an Ion

Find the number of protons and electrons in the O^{2-} ion.

SOLUTION

The atomic number of O is 8; therefore, it has 8 protons.

$$\text{Ion charge} = \#p^+ - \#e^-$$

$$2- = 8 - \#e^-$$

$$\#e^- = 8 + 2 = 10$$

The ion has 8 protons and 10 electrons.

EXAMPLE 4.12 Determining Atomic Numbers, Mass Numbers, and Isotope Symbols for an Isotope

What are the atomic number (Z), mass number (A), and symbols for the iron isotope with 30 neutrons?

SOLUTION

The atomic number of iron is 26.

$$A = 26 + 30 = 56$$

The mass number is 56.

$${}^{56}_{26}\text{Fe}$$

Fe-56

Number of Protons and Neutrons from Isotope Symbols (Section 4.8)

- The number of protons is equal to Z (lower left number).
- The number of neutrons is equal to

A (upper left number) − Z (lower left number.)

EXAMPLE 4.13 Number of Protons and Neutrons from Isotope Symbols

How many protons and neutrons are in $^{62}_{28}Ni$?

SOLUTION

28 protons

$\#n = 62 - 28 = 34$ neutrons

Calculating Atomic Mass from Percent Natural Abundances and Isotopic Masses (Section 4.9)

- Convert the natural abundances from percent to decimal values by dividing by 100.
- Find the atomic mass by multiplying the fractions of each isotope by their respective masses and adding.
- Round to the correct number of significant figures.
- Check your work.

EXAMPLE 4.14 Calculating Atomic Mass from Percent Natural Abundances and Isotopic Masses

Copper has two naturally occurring isotopes: Cu-63 with mass 62.9395 amu and a natural abundance of 69.17%, and Cu-65 with mass 64.9278 amu and a natural abundance of 30.83%. Calculate the atomic mass of copper.

SOLUTION

$$\text{Fraction Cu-63} = \frac{69.17}{100} = 0.6917$$

$$\text{Fraction Cu-65} = \frac{30.83}{100} = 0.3083$$

$$\begin{aligned}\text{Atomic mass} &= (0.6917 \times 62.9395 \text{ amu})\\ &= 43.5\underline{3}53 \text{ amu} + 20.0\underline{1}07 \text{ amu}\\ &= 63.5\underline{4}60 \text{ amu}\\ &= 63.55 \text{ amu}\end{aligned}$$

KEY TERMS

alkali metals **[4.6]**
alkaline earth metals **[4.6]**
anions **[4.7]**
atom **[4.1]**
atomic mass **[4.9]**
atomic mass unit (amu) **[4.4]**
atomic number (Z) **[4.5]**
cation **[4.7]**
charge **[4.4]**
chemical symbol **[4.5]**
electron **[4.3]**
family (of elements) **[4.6]**
group (of elements) **[4.6]**
halogens **[4.6]**
ion **[4.7]**
isotope **[4.8]**
main-group elements **[4.6]**
mass number (A) **[4.8]**
metalloids **[4.6]**
metals **[4.6]**
neutron **[4.3]**
noble gases **[4.6]**
nonmetals **[4.6]**
nuclear radiation **[4.9]**
nuclear theory of the atom **[4.3]**
nucleus **[4.3]**
percent natural abundance **[4.8]**
periodic law **[4.6]**
periodic table **[4.6]**
proton **[4.3]**
radioactive **[4.9]**
semiconductor **[4.6]**
transition elements **[4.6]**
transition metals **[4.6]**

EXERCISES

QUESTIONS

1. What did Democritus contribute to our modern understanding of matter?
2. What are three main ideas in Dalton's atomic theory?
3. Describe Rutherford's gold foil experiment and the results of that experiment. How did these results contradict the plum pudding model of the atom?
4. What are the main ideas in the nuclear theory of the atom?
5. List the three subatomic particles and their properties.
6. What is electrical charge?
7. Is matter usually charge-neutral? How would matter be different if it were not charge-neutral?
8. What does the atomic number of an element specify?
9. What is a chemical symbol?
10. List some examples of how elements got their names.

11. What was Dmitri Mendeleev's main contribution to our modern understanding of chemistry?
12. What is the main idea in the periodic law?
13. How is the periodic table organized?
14. What are the properties of metals? Where are metals found on the periodic table?
15. What are the properties of nonmetals? Where are nonmetals found on the periodic table?
16. Where on the periodic table are metalloids found?
17. What is a family or group of elements?
18. Locate each group of elements on the periodic table and list its group number.
  (a) alkali metals
  (b) alkaline earth metals
  (c) halogens
  (d) noble gases

19. What is an ion?
20. What is an anion? What is a cation?
21. Locate each group on the periodic table and list the charge of the ions it tends to form.
  (a) Group 1A
  (b) Group 2A
  (c) Group 3A
  (d) Group 6A
  (e) Group 7A
22. What are isotopes?
23. What is the percent natural abundance of isotopes?
24. What is the mass number of an isotope?
25. What notations are commonly used to specify isotopes? What do each of the numbers in these symbols mean?
26. What is the atomic mass of an element?

PROBLEMS

ATOMIC AND NUCLEAR THEORY

27. Which statements are *inconsistent* with Dalton's atomic theory as it was originally stated? Why?
  (a) All carbon atoms are identical.
  (b) Helium atoms can be split into two hydrogen atoms.
  (c) An oxygen atom combines with 1.5 hydrogen atoms to form water molecules.
  (d) Two oxygen atoms combine with a carbon atom to form carbon dioxide molecules.

28. Which statements are *consistent* with Dalton's atomic theory as it was originally stated? Why?
  (a) Calcium and titanium atoms have the same mass.
  (b) Neon and argon atoms are the same.
  (c) All cobalt atoms are identical.
  (d) Sodium and chlorine atoms combine in a 1:1 ratio to form sodium chloride.

29. Which statements are *inconsistent* with Rutherford's nuclear theory as it was originally stated? Why?
  (a) Helium atoms have two protons in the nucleus and two electrons outside the nucleus.
  (b) Most of the volume of hydrogen atoms is due to the nucleus.
  (c) Aluminum atoms have 13 protons in the nucleus and 22 electrons outside the nucleus.
  (d) The majority of the mass of nitrogen atoms is due to their 7 electrons.

30. Which statements are *consistent* with Rutherford's nuclear theory as it was originally stated? Why?
  (a) Atomic nuclei are small compared to the size of atoms.
  (b) The volume of an atom is mostly empty space.
  (c) Neutral potassium atoms contain more protons than electrons.
  (d) Neutral potassium atoms contain more neutrons than protons.

31. If atoms are mostly empty space, and atoms compose all ordinary matter, then why does solid matter seem to have no space within it?

32. Rutherford's experiment suggested that matter was not as uniform as it appears. What part of his experimental results implied this idea? Explain.

PROTONS, NEUTRONS, AND ELECTRONS

33. Which statements about electrons are true?
  (a) Electrons repel each other.
  (b) Electrons are attracted to protons.
  (c) Some electrons have a charge of 1− and some have no charge.
  (d) Electrons are much lighter than neutrons.

34. Which statements about electrons are false?
  (a) Most atoms have more electrons than protons.
  (b) Electrons have a charge of 1−.
  (c) If an atom has an equal number of protons and electrons, it will be charge-neutral.
  (d) Electrons experience an attraction to protons.

35. Which statements about protons are true?
(a) Protons have twice the mass of neutrons.
(b) Protons have the same magnitude of charge as electrons but are opposite in sign.
(c) Most atoms have more protons than electrons.
(d) Protons have a charge of 1+.

36. Which statements about protons are false?
(a) Protons have about the same mass as neutrons.
(b) Protons have about the same mass as electrons.
(c) Some atoms don't have any protons.
(d) Protons have the same magnitude of charge as neutrons, but are opposite in sign.

37. How many electrons would it take to equal the mass of a proton?

38. A helium nucleus has two protons and two neutrons. How many electrons would it take to equal the mass of a helium nucleus?

39. What mass of electrons would be required to just neutralize the charge of 1.0 g of protons?

40. What mass of protons would be required to just neutralize the charge of 1.0 g of electrons?

ELEMENTS, SYMBOLS, AND NAMES

41. Find the atomic number (Z) for each element.
(a) Fr
(b) Kr
(c) Pa
(d) Ge
(e) Al

42. Find the atomic number (Z) for each element.
(a) Si
(b) W
(c) Ni
(d) Rn
(e) Sr

43. How many protons are in the nucleus of an atom of each element?
(a) Ar
(b) Sn
(c) Xe
(d) O
(e) Tl

44. How many protons are in the nucleus of an atom of each element?
(a) Ti
(b) Li
(c) U
(d) Br
(e) F

45. List the symbol and atomic number corresponding to each element.
(a) carbon
(b) nitrogen
(c) sodium
(d) potassium
(e) copper

46. List the symbol and atomic number corresponding to each element.
(a) boron
(b) neon
(c) silver
(d) mercury
(e) curium

47. List the name and the atomic number corresponding to the symbol for each element.
(a) Mn
(b) Ag
(c) Au
(d) Pb
(e) S

48. List the name and the atomic number corresponding to the symbol for each element.
(a) Y
(b) N
(c) Ne
(d) K
(e) Mo

49. Fill in the blanks to complete the table.

Element Name	Element Symbol	Atomic Number
____	Au	79
Tin	____	____
____	As	____
Copper	____	29
____	Fe	____
____	____	80

50. Fill in the blanks to complete the table.

Element Name	Element Symbol	Atomic Number
____	Al	13
Iodine	____	____
____	Sb	____
Sodium	____	____
____	Rn	86
____	____	82

THE PERIODIC TABLE

51. Classify each element as a metal, nonmetal, or metalloid.
   (a) Sr
   (b) Mg
   (c) F
   (d) N
   (e) As

52. Classify each element as a metal, nonmetal, or metalloid.
   (a) Na
   (b) Ge
   (c) Si
   (d) Br
   (e) Ag

53. Which elements would you expect to lose electrons in chemical changes?
   (a) potassium
   (b) sulfur
   (c) fluorine
   (d) barium
   (e) copper

54. Which elements would you expect to gain electrons in chemical changes?
   (a) nitrogen
   (b) iodine
   (c) tungsten
   (d) strontium
   (e) gold

55. Which elements are main-group elements?
   (a) Te
   (b) K
   (c) V
   (d) Re
   (e) Ag

56. Which elements are *not* main-group elements?
   (a) Al
   (b) Br
   (c) Mo
   (d) Cs
   (e) Pb

57. Which elements are alkaline earth metals?
   (a) sodium
   (b) aluminum
   (c) calcium
   (d) barium
   (e) lithium

58. Which elements are alkaline earth metals?
   (a) rubidium
   (b) tungsten
   (c) magnesium
   (d) cesium
   (e) beryllium

59. Which elements are alkali metals?
   (a) barium
   (b) sodium
   (c) gold
   (d) tin
   (e) rubidium

60. Which elements are alkali metals?
   (a) scandium
   (b) iron
   (c) potassium
   (d) lithium
   (e) cobalt

61. Classify each element as a halogen, a noble gas, or neither.
(a) Cl
(b) Kr
(c) F
(d) Ga
(e) He

62. Classify each element as a halogen, a noble gas, or neither.
(a) Ne
(b) Br
(c) S
(d) Xe
(e) I

63. To what group number does each element belong?
(a) oxygen
(b) aluminum
(c) silicon
(d) tin
(e) phosphorus

64. To what group number does each element belong?
(a) germanium
(b) nitrogen
(c) sulfur
(d) carbon
(e) boron

65. Which element do you expect to be most like sulfur? Why?
(a) nitrogen
(b) oxygen
(c) fluorine
(d) lithium
(e) potassium

66. Which element do you expect to be most like magnesium? Why?
(a) potassium
(b) silver
(c) bromine
(d) calcium
(e) lead

67. Which pair of elements do you expect to be most similar? Why?
(a) Si and P
(b) Cl and F
(c) Na and Mg
(d) Mo and Sn
(e) N and Ni

68. Which pair of elements do you expect to be most similar? Why?
(a) Ti and Ga
(b) N and O
(c) Li and Na
(d) Ar and Br
(e) Ge and Ga

69. Fill in the blanks to complete the table.

Chemical Symbol	Group Number	Group Name	Metal or Nonmetal
K	___	___	metal
Br	___	halogens	___
Sr	___	___	___
He	8A	___	___
Ar	___	___	___

70. Fill in the blanks to complete the table.

Chemical Symbol	Group Number	Group Name	Metal or Nonmetal
Cl	7A	___	___
Ca	___	___	metal
Xe	___	___	nonmetal
Na	___	alkali metal	___
F	___	___	___

IONS

71. Complete each ionization equation.
(a) $Na \longrightarrow Na^+ +$ ___
(b) $O + 2e^- \longrightarrow$ ___
(c) $Ca \longrightarrow Ca^{2+} +$ ___
(d) $Cl + e^- \longrightarrow$ ___

72. Complete each ionization equation.
(a) $Mg \longrightarrow$ ___ $+ 2e^-$
(b) $Ba \longrightarrow Ba^{2+} +$ ___
(c) $I + e^- \longrightarrow$ ___
(d) $Al \longrightarrow$ ___ $+ 3e^-$

73. Determine the charge of each ion.
(a) oxygen ion with 10 electrons
(b) aluminum ion with 10 electrons
(c) titanium ion with 18 electrons
(d) iodine ion with 54 electrons

74. Determine the charge of each ion.
(a) tungsten ion with 68 electrons
(b) tellurium ion with 54 electrons
(c) nitrogen ion with 10 electrons
(d) barium ion with 54 electrons

75. Determine the number of protons and electrons in each ion.
(a) Na^{+}
(b) Ba^{2+}
(c) O^{2+}
(d) Co^{3+}

76. Determine the number of protons and electrons in each ion.
(a) Al^{3+}
(b) S^{2-}
(c) I^{-}
(d) Ag^{+}

77. Determine whether each statement is true or false. If false, correct it.
(a) The Ti^{2+} ion contains 22 protons and 24 electrons.
(b) The I^{-} ion contains 53 protons and 54 electrons.
(c) The Mg^{2+} ion contains 14 protons and 12 electrons.
(d) The O^{2-} ion contains 8 protons and 10 electrons.

78. Determine whether each statement is true or false. If false, correct it.
(a) The Fe^{+} ion contains 29 protons and 26 electrons.
(b) The Cs^{+} ion contains 55 protons and 56 electrons.
(c) The Se^{2-} ion contains 32 protons and 34 electrons.
(d) The Li^{+} ion contains 3 protons and 2 electrons.

79. Predict the ion formed by each element:
(a) Rb
(b) K
(c) Al
(d) O

80. Predict the ion formed by each element:
(a) F
(b) N
(c) Mg
(d) Na

81. Predict how many electrons will most likely be gained or lost by each element:
(a) Ga
(b) Li
(c) Br
(d) S

82. Predict how many electrons will most likely be gained or lost by each element:
(a) I
(b) Ba
(c) Cs
(d) Se

83. Fill in the blanks to complete the table.

Symbol	Ion Commonly Formed	Number of Electrons in Ion	Number of Protons in Ion
Te	___	54	___
In	___	___	49
Sr	Sr^{2+}	___	___
___	Mg^{2+}	___	12
Cl	___	___	___

84. Fill in the blanks to complete the table.

Symbol	Ion Commonly Formed	Number of Electrons in Ion	Number of Protons in Ion
F	___	___	9
___	Be^{2+}	2	___
Br	___	36	___
Al	___	___	13
O	___	___	___

ISOTOPES

85. What are the atomic number and mass number for each isotope?
   (a) the hydrogen isotope with 2 neutrons
   (b) the chromium isotope with 28 neutrons
   (c) the calcium isotope with 22 neutrons
   (d) the tantalum isotope with 109 neutrons

86. How many neutrons are in an atom with each set of atomic numbers and mass numbers?
   (a) Z = 28, A = 59
   (b) Z = 92, A = 235
   (c) Z = 21, A = 46
   (d) Z = 18, A = 42

87. Write isotopic symbols of the form ^A_ZX for each isotope.
   (a) the oxygen isotope with 8 neutrons
   (b) the fluorine isotope with 10 neutrons
   (c) the sodium isotope with 12 neutrons
   (d) the aluminum isotope with 14 neutrons

88. Write isotopic symbols of the form X-A (for example, C-13) for each isotope.
   (a) the iodine isotope with 74 neutrons
   (b) the phosphorus isotope with 16 neutrons
   (c) the uranium isotope with 234 neutrons
   (d) the argon isotope with 22 neutrons

89. Write the symbol for each isotope in the form ^A_ZX.
   (a) cobalt-60
   (b) neon-22
   (c) iodine-131
   (d) plutonium-244

90. Write the symbol for each isotope in the form ^A_ZX.
   (a) U-235
   (b) V-52
   (c) P-32
   (d) Xe-144

91. Determine the number of protons and neutrons in each isotope:
   (a) $^{23}_{11}Na$
   (b) $^{266}_{28}Ra$
   (c) $^{208}_{82}Pb$
   (d) $^{14}_{7}N$

92. Determine the number of protons and neutrons in each isotope:
   (a) $^{33}_{15}P$
   (b) $^{40}_{19}K$
   (c) $^{222}_{86}Rn$
   (d) $^{99}_{43}Tc$

93. Carbon-14, present within living organisms and substances derived from living organisms, is often used to establish the age of fossils and artifacts. Determine the number of protons and neutrons in a carbon-14 isotope and write its symbol in the form ^A_ZX.

94. Plutonium-239 is used in nuclear bombs. Determine the number of protons and neutrons in plutonium-239 and write its symbol in the form ^A_ZX.

ATOMIC MASS

95. Rubidium has two naturally occurring isotopes: Rb-85 with mass 84.9118 amu and a natural abundance of 72.17%, and Rb-87 with mass 86.9092 amu and a natural abundance of 27.83%. Calculate the atomic mass of rubidium.

96. Silicon has three naturally occurring isotopes: Si-28 with mass 27.9769 amu and a natural abundance of 92.21%, Si-29 with mass 28.9765 amu and a natural abundance of 4.69%, and Si-30 with mass 29.9737 amu and a natural abundance of 3.10%. Calculate the atomic mass of silicon.

97. Bromine has two naturally occurring isotopes (Br-79 and Br-81) and an atomic mass of 79.904 amu.
   (a) If the natural abundance of Br-79 is 50.69%, what is the natural abundance of Br-81?
   (b) If the mass of Br-81 is 80.9163 amu, what is the mass of Br-79?

98. Silver has two naturally occurring isotopes (Ag-107 and Ag-109).
   (a) Use the periodic table to find the atomic mass of silver.
   (b) If the natural abundance of Ag-107 is 51.84%, what is the natural abundance of Ag-109?
   (c) If the mass of Ag-107 is 106.905 amu, what is the mass of Ag-109?

99. An element has two naturally occurring isotopes. Isotope 1 has a mass of 120.9038 amu and a relative abundance of 57.4%, and isotope 2 has a mass of 122.9042 amu and a relative abundance of 42.6%. Find the atomic mass of this element and, referring to the periodic table, identify it.

100. Copper has two naturally occurring isotopes. Cu-63 has a mass of 62.939 amu and relative abundance of 69.17%. Use the atomic weight of copper to determine the mass of the other copper isotope.

CUMULATIVE PROBLEMS

101. Electrical charge is sometimes reported in coulombs (C). On this scale, 1 electron has a charge of -1.6×10^{-19} C. Suppose your body acquires −125 mC (millicoulombs) of charge on a dry day. How many excess electrons has it acquired? (*Hint:* Use the charge of an electron in coulombs as a conversion factor between charge and electrons.)

102. How many excess protons are in a positively charged object with a charge of +398 mC (millicoulombs)? The charge of 1 proton is $+1.6 \times 10^{-19}$ C.

103. The hydrogen atom contains 1 proton and 1 electron. The radius of the proton is approximately 1.0 fm (femtometers), and the radius of the hydrogen atom is approximately 53 pm (picometers). Calculate the volume of the nucleus and the volume of the atom for hydrogen. What percentage of the hydrogen atom's volume is occupied by the nucleus?

104. Carbon-12 contains 6 protons and 6 neutrons. The radius of the nucleus is approximately 2.7 fm, and the radius of the atom is approximately 70 pm. Calculate the volume of the nucleus and the volume of the atom. What percentage of the carbon atom's volume is occupied by the nucleus?

105. Prepare a table such as Table 4.2 for the four different isotopes of Sr that have the following natural abundances and masses.

Sr-84	0.56%	83.9134 amu
Sr-86	9.86%	85.9093 amu
Sr-87	7.00%	86.9089 amu
Sr-88	82.58%	87.9056 amu

Use your table and the preceding atomic masses to calculate the atomic mass of strontium.

106. Determine the number of protons and neutrons in each isotope of chromium and use the following natural abundances and masses to calculate its atomic mass.

Cr-50	4.345%	49.9460 amu
Cr-52	83.79%	51.9405 amu
Cr-53	9.50%	52.9407 amu
Cr-54	2.365%	53.9389 amu

107. Fill in the blanks to complete the table.

Symbol	Z	A	Number of Protons	Number of Electrons	Number of Neutrons	Charge
Zn^{+}	___	___	___	___	34	1+
___	25	55	___	22	___	___
___	___	___	15	15	16	___
O^{2-}	___	16	___	___	___	2−
___	___	___	16	18	18	___

108. Fill in the blanks to complete the table.

Symbol	Z	A	Number of Protons	Number of Electrons	Number of Neutrons	Charge
Mg^{2+}	___	25	___	___	13	2+
___	22	48	___	18	___	___
___	16	___	___	___	16	2−
Ga^{3+}	___	71	___	___	___	___
___	___	___	82	80	125	___

109. Europium has two naturally occurring isotopes: Eu-151 with a mass of 150.9198 amu and a natural abundance of 47.8%, and Eu-153. Use the atomic mass of europium to find the mass and natural abundance of Eu-153.

110. Rhenium has two naturally occurring isotopes: Re-185 with a natural abundance of 37.40%, and Re-187 with a natural abundance of 62.60%. The sum of the masses of the two isotopes is 371.9087 amu. Find the masses of the individual isotopes.

111. Chapter 1 describes the difference between observations, laws, and theories. Provide two examples of theories from this chapter and explain why they are theories.

112. Chapter 1 describes the difference between observations, laws, and theories. Provide one example of a law from this chapter and explain why it is a law.

113. The atomic mass of fluorine is 19.00 amu, and all fluorine atoms in a naturally occurring sample of fluorine have this mass. The atomic mass of chlorine is 35.45 amu, but no chlorine atoms in a naturally occurring sample of chlorine have this mass. Explain the difference.

114. The atomic mass of germanium is 72.61 amu. Is it likely that any individual germanium atoms have a mass of 72.61 amu?

115. Copper has only two naturally occurring isotopes, Cu-63 and Cu-65. The mass of Cu-63 is 62.9396 amu, and the mass of Cu-65 is 64.9278 amu. Use the atomic mass of copper to determine the relative abundance of each isotope in a naturally occurring sample.

116. Gallium has only two naturally occurring isotopes, Ga-69 and Ga-71. The mass of Ga-69 is 68.9256 amu, and the mass of Ga-71 is 70.9247 amu. Use the atomic mass of gallium to determine the relative abundance of each isotope in a naturally occurring sample.

HIGHLIGHT PROBLEMS

117. The figure is a representation of 50 atoms of a fictitious element with the symbol Nt and atomic number 120. Nt has three isotopes represented by the following colors: Nt-304 (red), Nt-305 (blue), and Nt-306 (green).

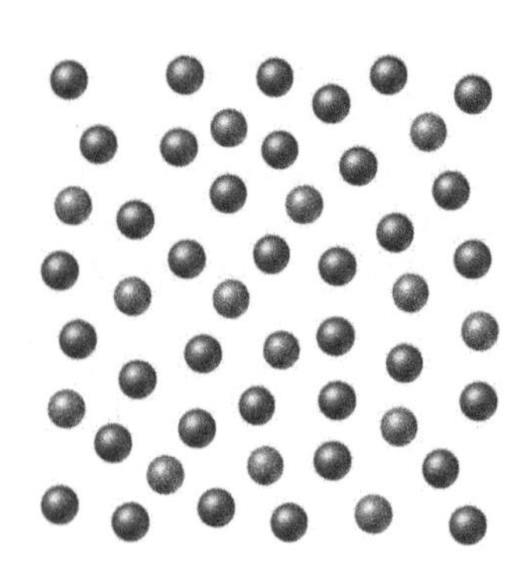

(a) Assuming that the figure is statistically representative of naturally occurring Nt, what is the percent natural abundance of each Nt isotope?

(b) Use the following masses of each isotope to calculate the atomic mass of Nt. Then draw a box for the element similar to the boxes for each element shown in the periodic table in the inside front cover of this book. Make sure your box includes the atomic number, symbol, and atomic mass. (Assume that the percentages from part (a) are correct to four significant figures.)

Nt-304	303.956 amu
Nt-305	304.962 amu
Nt-306	305.978 amu

118. Neutron stars are believed to be composed of solid nuclear matter, primarily neutrons.

(a) If the radius of a neutron is 1.0×10^{-13} cm, calculate its density in g/cm^3.

(volume of a sphere $= \frac{4}{3}\pi r^3$)

(b) Assuming that a neutron star has the same density as a neutron, calculate the mass in kilograms of a small piece of a neutron star the size of a spherical pebble with a radius of 0.10 mm.

▶ANSWERS TO SKILLBUILDER EXERCISES

Skillbuilder 4.1
(a) sodium, 11
(b) nickel, 28
(c) phosphorus, 15
(d) tantalum, 73

Skillbuilder 4.2
(a) nonmetal
(b) nonmetal
(c) metal
(d) metalloid

Skillbuilder 4.3
(a) alkali metal, group 1A
(b) group 3A
(c) halogen, group 7A
(d) noble gas, group 8A

Skillbuilder 4.4
(a) 2+
(b) 1−
(c) 3−

Skillbuilder 4.5 16 protons, 18 electrons

Skillbuilder 4.6 K^+ and Se^{2-}

Skillbuilder 4.7 $Z = 17$, $A = 35$, Cl-35, and ${}^{35}_{17}Cl$

Skillbuilder 4.8 19 protons, 20 neutrons

Skillbuilder 4.9 24.31 amu

▶ANSWERS TO CONCEPTUAL CHECKPOINTS

4.1 (c) The mass in amu is approximately equal to the number of protons plus the number of neutrons. In order to be charge-neutral, the number of protons must equal the number of electrons.

4.2 (b) All of the metalloids are main-group elements (see Figures 4.12 and 4.13).

4.3 (a) Both of these ions have 10 electrons.

4.4 (b) This atom must have $(27 - 14) = 13$ protons; the element with an atomic number of 13 is Al.

4.5 The isotopes C-12 and C-13 would not look different in this representation of atoms because the only difference between the two isotopes is that C-13 has an extra neutron in the nucleus. The illustration represents the whole atom and does not attempt to illustrate its nucleus. Since the nucleus of an atom is miniscule compared to the size of the atom itself, the extra neutron would not affect the size of the atom.

4.6 (b) The natural abundance of isotope B must be greater than the natural abundance of isotope A because the atomic mass is closer to the mass of isotope B than to the mass of isotope A.

Sucrose
AND COMP
$C_{12}H_{22}O_{11}$
H_2O
SUCROSE
O_2
CAFFEINE
23RD
HOMEWOR
MASTERING
CHEMISTRY
CALL
Sucrose
Sucrose

CHAPTER 5

Molecules and Compounds

"Almost all aspects of life are engineered at the molecular level, and without understanding molecules, we can only have a very sketchy understanding of life itself."

FRANCIS HARRY COMPTON CRICK (1916–2004)

5.1 Sugar and Salt

Sodium, a shiny metal (▼ Figure 5.1) that dulls almost instantly upon exposure to air, is extremely reactive and poisonous. If you were to consume any appreciable amount of elemental sodium, you would need immediate medical help. Chlorine, a pale yellow gas (▼ Figure 5.2), is equally reactive and poisonous. Yet the compound formed from these two elements, sodium chloride, is the relatively harmless flavor enhancer that we call table salt (▶ Figure 5.3). When elements combine to form compounds, their properties completely change.

◀ Ordinary table sugar is a compound called sucrose. A sucrose molecule, such as the one shown here, contains carbon, hydrogen, and oxygen atoms. The properties of sucrose are, however, very different from those of carbon (also shown in the form of graphite), hydrogen, and oxygen. The properties of a compound are, in general, different from the properties of the elements that compose it.

▲ FIGURE 5.1 **Elemental sodium** Sodium is an extremely reactive metal that dulls almost instantly upon exposure to air.

▲ FIGURE 5.2 **Elemental chlorine** Chlorine is a yellow gas with a pungent odor. It is highly reactive and poisonous.

▲ **FIGURE 5.3 Sodium chloride** The compound formed by sodium and chlorine is table salt.

Consider ordinary sugar. Sugar is a compound composed of carbon, hydrogen, and oxygen. Each of these elements has its own unique properties. Carbon is most familiar to us as the graphite found in pencils or as the diamonds in jewelry. Hydrogen is an extremely flammable gas used as a fuel for the space shuttle, and oxygen is one of the gases that compose air. When these three elements combine to form sugar, however, a sweet, white, crystalline solid results.

In Chapter 4, we learned how protons, neutrons, and electrons combine to form different elements, each with its own properties and its own chemistry, each different from the other. In this chapter, we learn how these elements combine with each other to form different compounds, each with its own properties and its own chemistry, each different from all the others and different from the elements that compose it. This is the great wonder of nature: how from such simplicity—protons, neutrons, and electrons—we get such great complexity. It is exactly this complexity that makes life possible. Life could not exist with just 91 different elements if they did not combine to form compounds. It takes compounds in all of their diversity to make living organisms.

5.2 Compounds Display Constant Composition

Although some of the substances we encounter in everyday life are elements, most are not—they are compounds. Free atoms are rare in nature. As we learned in Chapter 3, a compound is different from a mixture of elements. In a compound, the elements combine in fixed, definite proportions, whereas in a mixture, they can have any proportions whatsoever. Consider the difference between a mixture of hydrogen and oxygen gas (▼ Figure 5.4) and the compound water (▼ Figure 5.5). A mixture of hydrogen and oxygen gas can contain any propor-

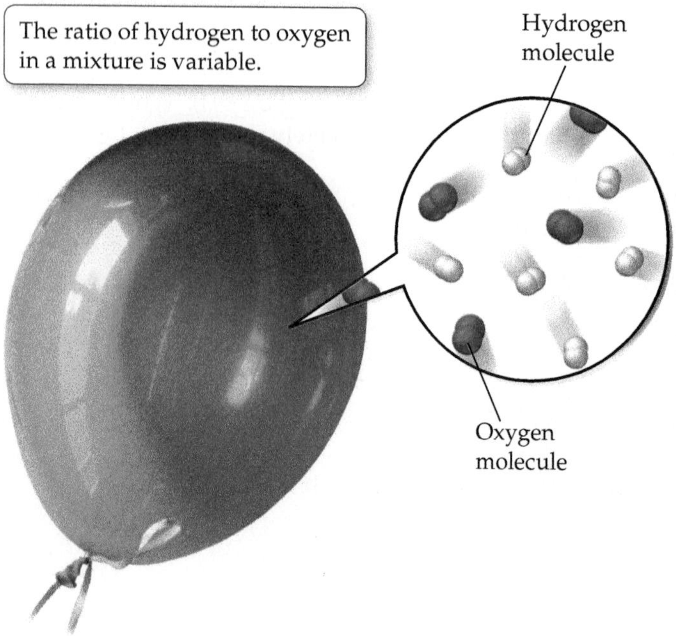

The ratio of hydrogen to oxygen in a mixture is variable.

Hydrogen molecule

Oxygen molecule

▲ **FIGURE 5.4 A mixture** This balloon is filled with a mixture of hydrogen and oxygen gas. The relative amounts of hydrogen and oxygen are variable. We could easily add either more hydrogen or more oxygen to the balloon.

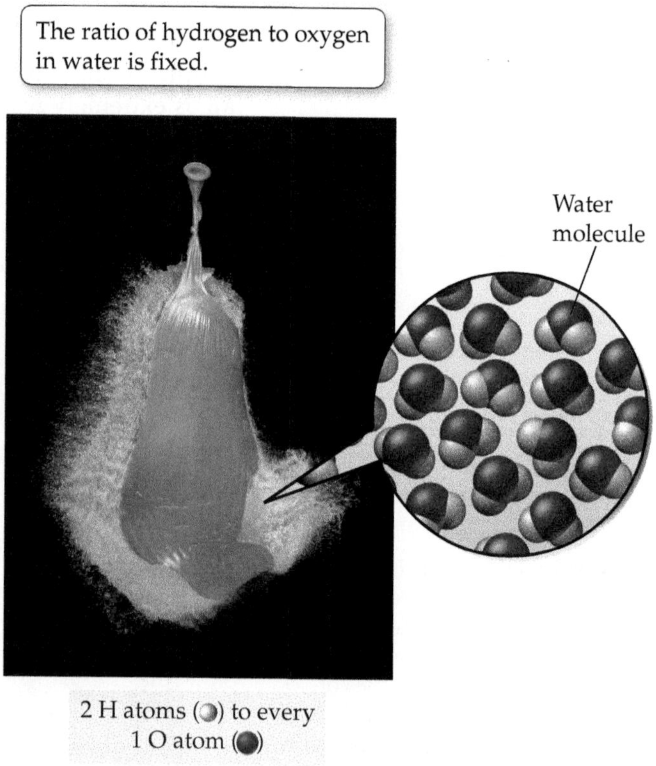

The ratio of hydrogen to oxygen in water is fixed.

Water molecule

2 H atoms to every 1 O atom

▲ **FIGURE 5.5 A chemical compound** This balloon is filled with water, composed of molecules that have a fixed ratio of hydrogen to oxygen. (*Source:* JoLynn E. Funk.)

tions of hydrogen and oxygen. Water, on the other hand, is composed of water molecules that consist of two hydrogen atoms bonded to one oxygen atom. Consequently, water has a definite proportion of hydrogen to oxygen.

The first chemist to formally state the idea that elements combine in fixed proportions to form compounds was Joseph Proust (1754–1826) in the **law of constant composition**, which states:

> All samples of a given compound have the same proportions of their constituent elements.

For example, if we decompose an 18.0 g sample of water, we would get 16.0 g of oxygen and 2.0 g of hydrogen, or an oxygen-to-hydrogen mass ratio of

$$\text{Mass ratio} = \frac{16.0 \text{ g O}}{2.0 \text{ g H}} = 8.0 \quad \text{or} \quad 8.0{:}1$$

This is true of any sample of pure water, no matter what its origin. The law of constant composition applies not only to water, but to every compound. If we decomposed a 17.0 g sample of ammonia, a compound composed of nitrogen and hydrogen, we would get 14.0 g of nitrogen and 3.0 g of hydrogen, or a nitrogen-to-hydrogen mass ratio of

Even though atoms combine in whole-number ratios, their mass ratios are not necessarily whole numbers.

$$\text{Mass ratio} = \frac{14.0 \text{ g N}}{3.0 \text{ g H}} = 4.7 \quad \text{or} \quad 4.7{:}1$$

Again, this ratio is the same for every sample of ammonia—the composition of each compound is constant.

EXAMPLE 5.1 Constant Composition of Compounds

Two samples of carbon dioxide, obtained from different sources, are decomposed into their constituent elements. One sample produces 4.8 g of oxygen and 1.8 g of carbon, and the other sample produces 17.1 g of oxygen and 6.4 g of carbon. Show that these results are consistent with the law of constant composition.

SOLUTION

Compute the mass ratio of one element to the other by dividing the larger mass by the smaller one. For the first sample:

$$\frac{\text{Mass oxygen}}{\text{Mass carbon}} = \frac{4.8 \text{ g}}{1.8 \text{ g}} = 2.7$$

For the second sample:

$$\frac{\text{Mass oxygen}}{\text{Mass carbon}} = \frac{17.1 \text{ g}}{6.4 \text{ g}} = 2.7$$

Since the ratios are the same for the two samples, these results are consistent with the law of constant composition.

▶SKILLBUILDER 5.1 | Constant Composition of Compounds

Two samples of carbon monoxide, obtained from different sources, are decomposed into their constituent elements. One sample produces 4.3 g of oxygen and 3.2 g of carbon, and the other sample produces 7.5 g of oxygen and 5.6 g of carbon. Are these results consistent with the law of constant composition?

▶FOR MORE PRACTICE Example 5.16; Problems 25, 26.

5.3 Chemical Formulas: How to Represent Compounds

Compounds have constant composition with respect to mass (as we learned in the previous section) because they are composed of atoms in fixed ratios.

We represent a compound with a **chemical formula**, which indicates the elements present in the compound and the relative number of atoms of each. For example, H_2O is the chemical formula for water; it indicates that water consists of hydrogen and oxygen atoms in a 2:1 ratio. The formula contains the symbol for each element, accompanied by a subscript indicating the number of atoms of that element. By convention, a subscript of 1 is omitted.

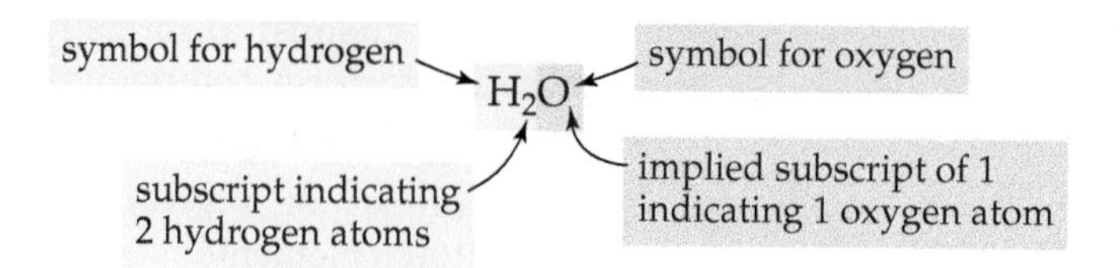

Other common chemical formulas include NaCl for table salt, indicating sodium and chlorine atoms in a 1:1 ratio; CO_2 for carbon dioxide, indicating carbon and oxygen atoms in a 1:2 ratio; and $C_{12}H_{22}O_{11}$ for table sugar (sucrose), indicating carbon, hydrogen, and oxygen atoms in a 12:22:11 ratio. The subscripts in a chemical formula are part of the compound's definition—if they change, the formula no longer specifies the same compound. For example, CO is the chemical formula for carbon monoxide, an air pollutant with adverse health effects on humans. When inhaled, carbon monoxide interferes with the blood's ability to carry oxygen, which can be fatal. CO is the primary substance responsible for the deaths of people who inhale too much automobile exhaust. If you change the subscript of the O in CO from 1 to 2, however, you get the formula for a totally different compound. CO_2 is the chemical formula for carbon dioxide, the relatively harmless product of combustion and human respiration. We breathe small amounts of CO_2 all the time with no harmful effects. So, remember that:

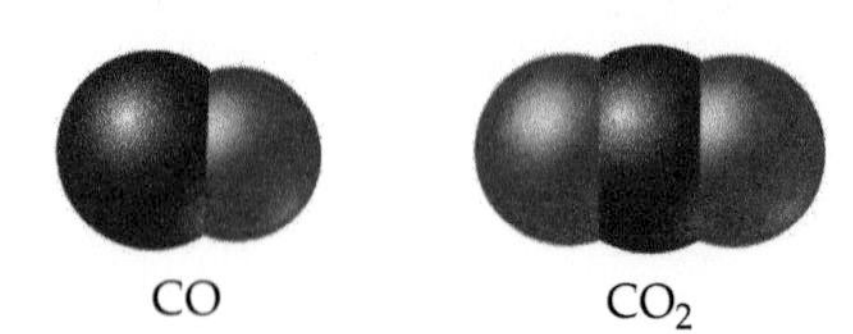

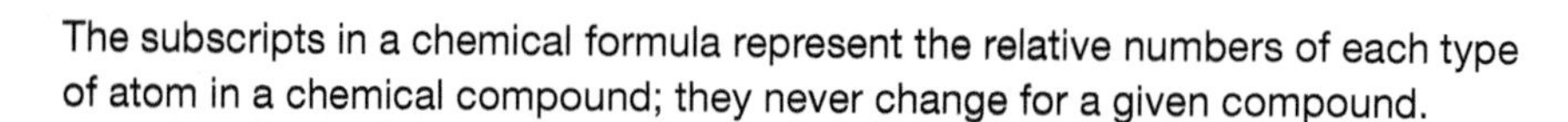
The subscripts in a chemical formula represent the relative numbers of each type of atom in a chemical compound; they never change for a given compound.

Chemical formulas normally list the most metallic elements first. Therefore, the formula for table salt is NaCl, not ClNa. In compounds that do not include a metal, the more metal-like element is listed first. Recall from Chapter 4 that metals are found on the left side of the periodic table and nonmetals on the upper right side. Among nonmetals, those to the left in the periodic table are more metal-like than those to the right and are normally listed first. Therefore, we write CO_2 and NO, not O_2C and ON. Within a single column in the periodic table, elements toward the bottom are more metal-like than elements toward the top. So, we write SO_2, not O_2S. The specific order for listing nonmetal elements in a chemical formula is shown in Table 5.1.

There are a few historical exceptions to the practice in which the most metallic element is listed first, such as the hydroxide ion, which is written as OH^-.

TABLE 5.1 Order of Listing Nonmetal Elements in a Chemical Formula

C	P	N	H	S	I	Br	Cl	O	F

Elements on the left are generally listed before elements on the right.

EXAMPLE 5.2 Writing Chemical Formulas

Write a chemical formula for each compound.

(a) the compound containing two aluminum atoms to every three oxygen atoms
(b) the compound containing three oxygen atoms to every sulfur atom
(c) the compound containing four chlorine atoms to every carbon atom

	SOLUTION
Since aluminum is the metal, it is listed first.	**(a)** Al_2O_3
Since sulfur is below oxygen on the periodic table and since it occurs before oxygen in Table 5.1, it is listed first.	**(b)** SO_3
Since carbon is to the left of chlorine on the periodic table and since it occurs before chlorine in Table 5.1, it is listed first.	**(c)** CCl_4

▶SKILLBUILDER 5.2 | Writing Chemical Formulas

Write a chemical formula for each compound.

(a) the compound containing two silver atoms to every sulfur atom
(b) the compound containing two nitrogen atoms to every oxygen atom
(c) the compound containing two oxygen atoms to every titanium atom

▶FOR MORE PRACTICE Example 5.17; Problems 31, 32, 33, 34.

Some chemical formulas contain groups of atoms that act as a unit. When several groups of the same kind are present, their formula is set off in parentheses with a subscript to indicate the number of that group. Many of these groups of atoms have a charge associated with them and are called **polyatomic ions.** For example, NO_3^- is a polyatomic ion with a 1− charge. Polyatomic ions are described in more detail in Section 5.7.

To determine the total number of each type of atom in a compound containing a group within parentheses, multiply the subscript outside the parentheses by the subscript for each atom inside the parentheses. For example, $Mg(NO_3)_2$ indicates a compound containing one magnesium atom (present as the Mg^{2+} ion) and two NO_3^- groups.

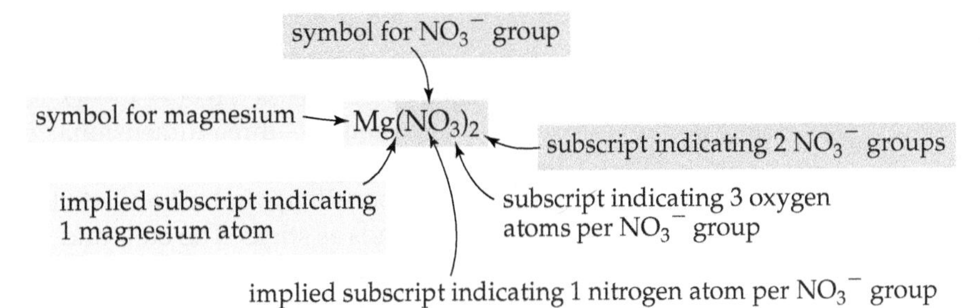

Therefore, the preceding formula has the following numbers of each type of atom.

Mg:	1 Mg	
N:	$1 \times 2 = 2$ N	(implied 1 inside parentheses times 2 outside parentheses)
O:	$3 \times 2 = 6$ O	(3 inside parentheses times 2 outside parentheses)

EXAMPLE 5.3 Total Number of Each Type of Atom in a Chemical Formula

Determine the number of each type of atom in $Mg_3(PO_4)_2$.

SOLUTION

Mg: There are three Mg atoms (present as Mg^{2+} ions), as indicated by the subscript 3.

P: There are two P atoms. We determine this by multiplying the subscript outside the parentheses (2) by the subscript for P inside the parentheses, which is 1 (implied).

O: There are eight O atoms. We determine this by multiplying the subscript outside the parentheses (2) by the subscript for O inside the parentheses (4).

▶SKILLBUILDER 5.3 | Total Number of Each Type of Atom in a Chemical Formula

Determine the number of each type of atom in K_2SO_4.

▶SKILLBUILDER PLUS

Determine the number of each type of atom in $Al_2(SO_4)_3$.

▶FOR MORE PRACTICE Example 5.18; Problems 35, 36, 37, 38.

CONCEPTUAL CHECKPOINT 5.1

Which formula represents the greatest total number of atoms?

(a) $Al(C_2H_3O_2)_3$ (d) $Pb_3(PO_4)_4$

(b) $Al_2(Cr_2O_7)_3$ (e) $(NH_4)_3PO_4$

(c) $Pb(HSO_4)_4$

TYPES OF CHEMICAL FORMULAS

Hydrogen

Carbon

Nitrogen

Oxygen

Fluorine

Phosphorus

Sulfur

Chlorine

We can categorize chemical formulas as three different types: empirical, molecular, and structural. An **empirical formula** gives the simplest whole-number ratio of atoms of each element in a compound. A **molecular formula** gives the *actual* number of atoms of each element in a molecule of the compound. For example, the molecular formula for hydrogen peroxide is H_2O_2, and its empirical formula is HO. The molecular formula is always a whole number multiple of the empirical formula. For many compounds, the molecular and empirical formula are the same. For example, the empirical and molecular formula for water is H_2O because water molecules contain two hydrogen atoms and one oxygen atom; no simpler whole number ratio can express the relative number of hydrogen atoms to oxygen atoms.

A **structural** formula uses lines to represent chemical bonds and shows how the atoms in a molecule are connected to each other. The structural formula for hydrogen peroxide is H—O—O—H. In addition to formulas, we also use **molecular models**—three-dimensional representations of molecules—to represent compounds. In this book, we use two types of molecular models: ball-and-stick and space-filling. In **ball-and-stick models**, we represent atoms as balls and chemical bonds as sticks. The balls and sticks are connected to represent the molecule's shape. The balls are color coded, and each element is assigned a color as shown in the margin.

In **space-filing models**, atoms fill the space between each other to more closely represent our best idea for how a molecule might appear if we could scale it to a visible size. Consider the following ways to represent a molecule of methane, the main component of natural gas:

CH_4

Molecular formula

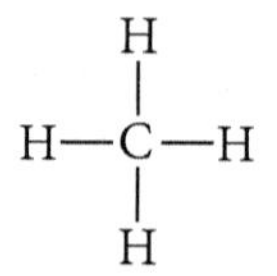

Structural formula

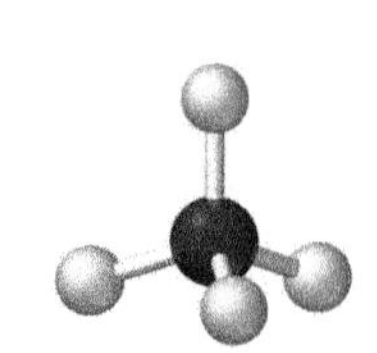

Ball-and-stick model

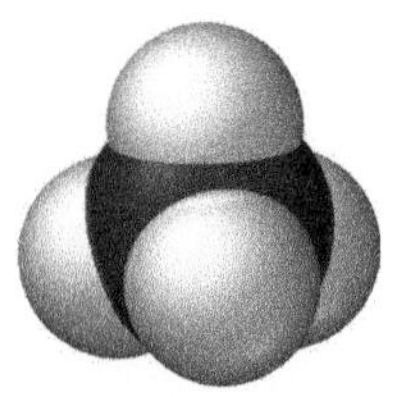

Space-filling model

Macroscopic

Molecular

H_2O

Symbolic

The molecular formula of methane indicates that methane has one carbon atom and four hydrogen atoms. The structural formula shows how the atoms are connected: Each hydrogen atom is bonded to the central carbon atom. The ball-and-stick model and the space-filling model illustrate the *geometry* of the molecule: how the atoms are arranged in three dimensions.

Throughout this book, you have seen and will continue to see images that show the connection between the *macroscopic world* (what we see), the *atomic and molecular world* (the particles that compose matter), and the *symbolic way* that chemists represent the atomic and molecular world. For example, at left is a representation of water using this kind of image.

The main goal of these images is to help you visualize the main theme of this book: *the connection between the world around us and the world of atoms and molecules.*

5.4 A Molecular View of Elements and Compounds

In Chapter 3, we learned that pure substances could be categorized as either elements or compounds. We can further subcategorize elements and compounds according to the basic units that compose them (▼ Figure 5.6). Pure substances may be elements, or they may be compounds. Elements may be either atomic or molecular. Compounds may be either molecular or ionic.

▶ FIGURE 5.6 **A molecular view of elements and compounds**

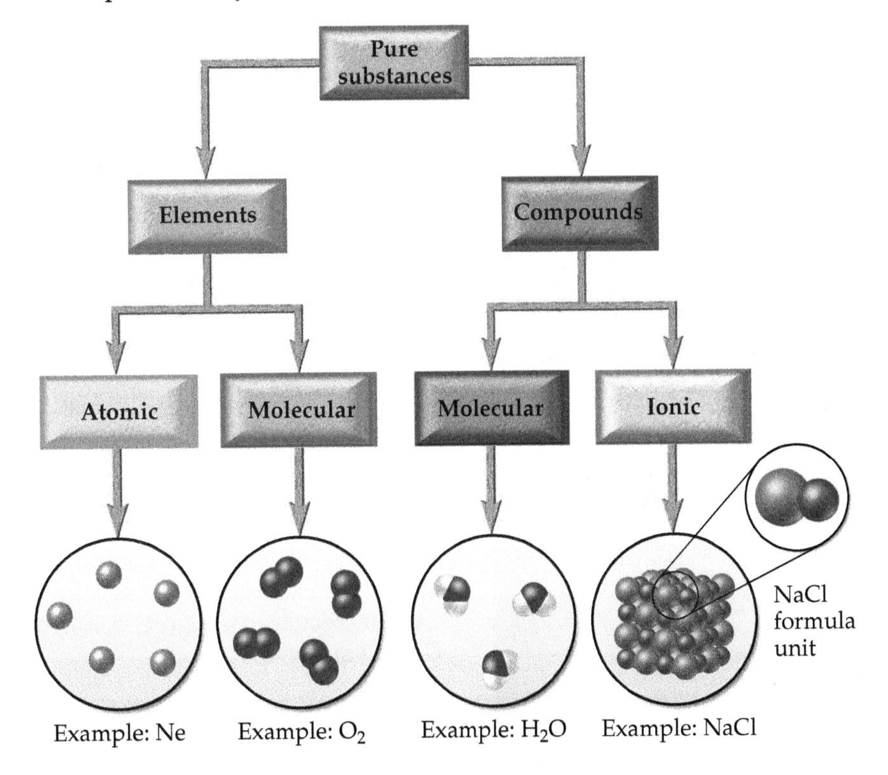

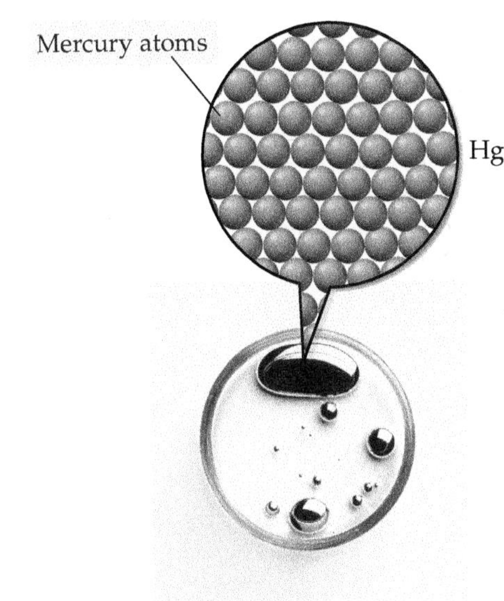

▲ FIGURE 5.7 **An atomic element** The basic units that compose mercury, an atomic element and a metal, are single mercury atoms.

ATOMIC ELEMENTS

Atomic elements are those that exist in nature with single atoms as their basic units. Most elements fall into this category. For example, helium is composed of helium atoms, copper is composed of copper atoms, and mercury of mercury atoms (◀ Figure 5.7).

A few molecular elements, such as S_8 and P_4, are composed of molecules containing several atoms.

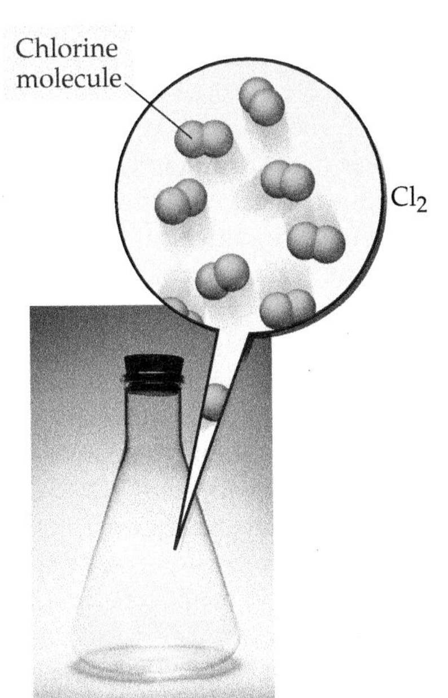

MOLECULAR ELEMENTS

Molecular elements do not normally exist in nature with single atoms as their basic units. Instead, these elements exist as *diatomic molecules*—two atoms of that element bonded together—as their basic units. For example, hydrogen is composed of H_2 molecules, oxygen is composed of O_2 molecules, and chlorine of Cl_2 molecules (◀ Figure 5.8). Elements that exist as diatomic molecules are shown in Table 5.2 and ▶ Figure 5.9.

◀ FIGURE 5.8 **A molecular element** The basic units that compose chlorine, a molecular element, are diatomic chlorine molecules, each composed of two chlorine atoms.

TABLE 5.2 Elements That Occur as Diatomic Molecules

Name of Element	Formula of Basic Unit
hydrogen	H_2
nitrogen	N_2
oxygen	O_2
fluorine	F_2
chlorine	Cl_2
bromine	Br_2
iodine	I_2

Main groups | Transition metals | Main groups

☐ Elements that exist as diatomic molecules

Periods	1A 1	2A 2	3B 3	4B 4	5B 5	6B 6	7B 7	8B 8	8B 9	8B 10	1B 11	2B 12	3A 13	4A 14	5A 15	6A 16	7A 17	8A 18
1	1 H																	2 He
2	3 Li	4 Be											5 B	6 C	7 N	8 O	9 F	10 Ne
3	11 Na	12 Mg											13 Al	14 Si	15 P	16 S	17 Cl	18 Ar
4	19 K	20 Ca	21 Sc	22 Ti	23 V	24 Cr	25 Mn	26 Fe	27 Co	28 Ni	29 Cu	30 Zn	31 Ga	32 Ge	33 As	34 Se	35 Br	36 Kr
5	37 Rb	38 Sr	39 Y	40 Zr	41 Nb	42 Mo	43 Tc	44 Ru	45 Rh	46 Pd	47 Ag	48 Cd	49 In	50 Sn	51 Sb	52 Te	53 I	54 Xe
6	55 Cs	56 Ba	57 La	72 Hf	73 Ta	74 W	75 Re	76 Os	77 Ir	78 Pt	79 Au	80 Hg	81 Tl	82 Pb	83 Bi	84 Po	85 At	86 Rn
7	87 Fr	88 Ra	89 Ac	104 Rf	105 Db	106 Sg	107 Bh	108 Hs	109 Mt	110 Ds	111 Rg	112 Cn	113	114	115	116	117	118

Lanthanides	58 Ce	59 Pr	60 Nd	61 Pm	62 Sm	63 Eu	64 Gd	65 Tb	66 Dy	67 Ho	68 Er	69 Tm	70 Yb	71 Lu
Actinides	90 Th	91 Pa	92 U	93 Np	94 Pu	95 Am	96 Cm	97 Bk	98 Cf	99 Es	100 Fm	101 Md	102 No	103 Lr

▲ **FIGURE 5.9 Elements that form diatomic molecules** Elements that normally exist as diatomic molecules are highlighted in yellow on this periodic table. Note that they are all nonmetals, and include four of the halogens.

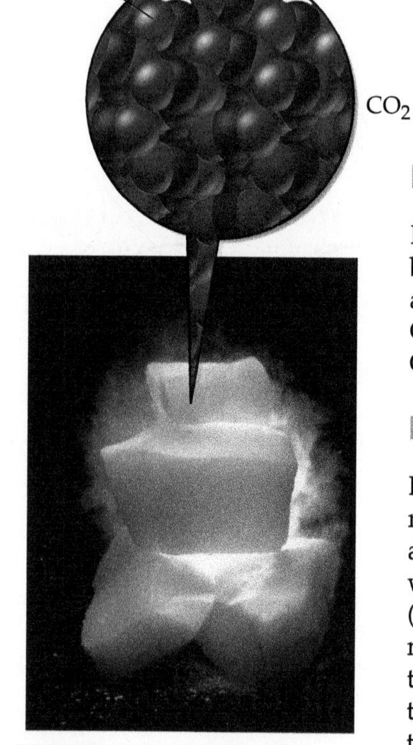

▲ **FIGURE 5.10 A molecular compound** The basic units that compose dry ice, a molecular compound, are CO_2 molecules.

MOLECULAR COMPOUNDS

Molecular compounds are compounds formed from two or more nonmetals. The basic units of molecular compounds are molecules composed of the constituent atoms. For example, water is composed of H_2O molecules, dry ice is composed of CO_2 molecules (◀ Figure 5.10), and acetone (finger nail–polish remover) of C_3H_6O molecules.

IONIC COMPOUNDS

Ionic compounds contain one or more cations paired with one or more anions. In most cases, the cations are metals and the anions are nonmetals. When a metal, which has a tendency to lose electrons (see Section 4.6), combines with a nonmetal, which has a tendency to gain electrons, one or more electrons transfer from the metal to the nonmetal, creating positive and negative ions that are then attracted to each other. You can assume that a compound composed of a metal and a nonmetal is ionic. The basic unit of ionic compounds is the **formula unit**, the smallest electrically neutral collection of ions. Formula units are different from molecules in that they do not exist as discrete entities, but rather as part of a larger lattice. For example, salt (NaCl) is composed of Na^+ and Cl^- ions in a 1:1 ratio. In table salt, Na^+ and Cl^- ions exist in an alternating three-dimensional array (▶ Figure 5.11). However, any one Na^+ ion does not pair with one specific Cl^- ion. Sometimes chemists refer to formula units as molecules, but this is not strictly correct since ionic compounds do not contain distinct molecules.

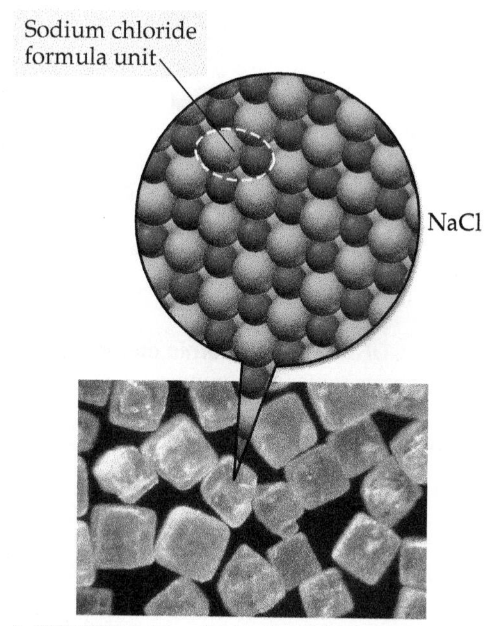

▲ **FIGURE 5.11 An ionic compound** The basic units that compose table salt, an ionic compound, are NaCl formula units. Unlike molecular compounds, ionic compounds do not contain individual molecules but rather sodium and chloride ions in an alternating three-dimensional array.

EXAMPLE 5.4 Classifying Substances as Atomic Elements, Molecular Elements, Molecular Compounds, or Ionic Compounds

Classify each substance as an atomic element, molecular element, molecular compound, or ionic compound.

(a) krypton
(b) $CoCl_2$
(c) nitrogen
(d) SO_2
(e) KNO_3

SOLUTION

(a) Krypton is an element that is not listed as diatomic in Table 5.2; therefore, it is an atomic element.
(b) $CoCl_2$ is a compound composed of a metal (left side of periodic table) and nonmetal (right side of the periodic table); therefore, it is an ionic compound.
(c) Nitrogen is an element that is listed as diatomic in Table 5.2; therefore, it is a molecular element.
(d) SO_2 is a compound composed of two nonmetals; therefore, it is a molecular compound.
(e) KNO_3 is a compound composed of a metal and two nonmetals; therefore, it is an ionic compound.

▶SKILLBUILDER 5.4 | Classifying Substances as Atomic Elements, Molecular Elements, Molecular Compounds, or Ionic Compounds

Classify each substance as an atomic element, molecular element, molecular compound, or ionic compound.

(a) chlorine
(b) NO
(c) Au
(d) Na_2O
(e) $CrCl_3$

▶FOR MORE PRACTICE Example 5.19, Example 5.20; Problems 43, 44, 45, 46.

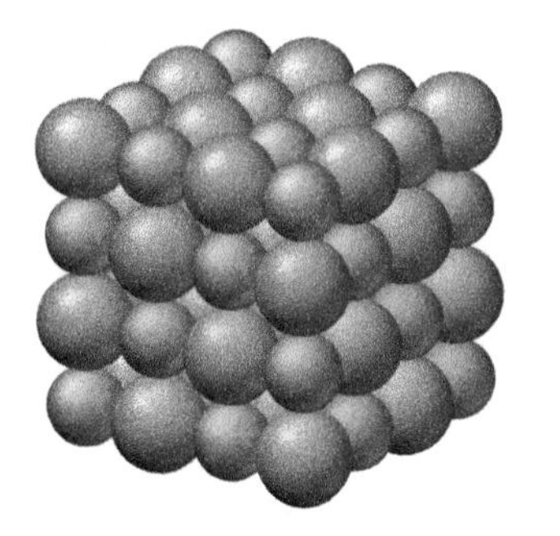

(a)

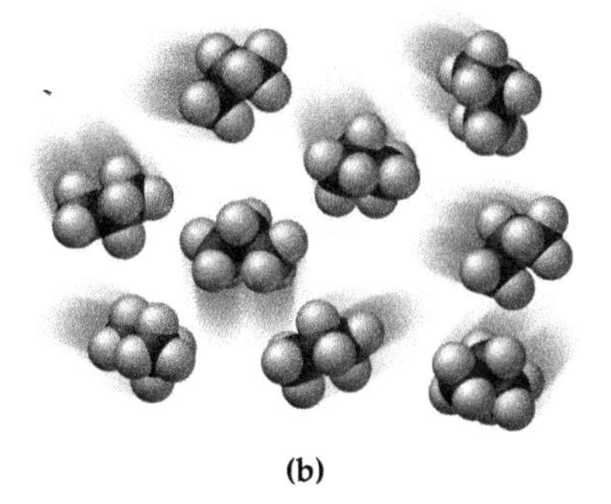

(b)

CONCEPTUAL CHECKPOINT 5.2

Which of the figures at left (in the margin) represents a molecular compound?

5.5 Writing Formulas for Ionic Compounds

Revisit Section 4.7 and Figure 4.14 to review the elements that form ions with a predictable charge.

Since ionic compounds must be charge-neutral, and since many elements form only one type of ion with a predictable charge, we can determine the formulas for many ionic compounds based on their constituent elements. For example, the formula for the ionic compound composed of sodium and chlorine must be NaCl and not anything else because in compounds Na always forms 1+ cations and Cl always forms 1− anions. In order for the compound to be charge-neutral, it must contain one Na^+ cation to every Cl^- anion. The formula for the ionic compound composed of magnesium and chlorine, however, must be $MgCl_2$, because Mg always forms 2+ cations and Cl always forms 1− anions. In order for the compound to be charge-neutral, it must contain one Mg^{2+} cation to every two Cl^- anions. In general:

- Ionic compounds always contain positive and negative ions.
- In the chemical formula, the sum of the charges of the positive ions (cations) must always equal the sum of the charges of the negative ions (anions).

To write the formula for an ionic compound, follow the procedure in the left column of the following table. Two examples of how to apply the procedure are provided in the center and right columns.

Writing Formulas for Ionic Compounds	**EXAMPLE 5.5** Write a formula for the ionic compound that forms from aluminum and oxygen.	**EXAMPLE 5.6** Write a formula for the ionic compound that forms from magnesium and oxygen.
1. Write the symbol for the metal and its charge followed by the symbol of the nonmetal and its charge. For many elements, you can determine these charges from their group number in the periodic table (refer to Figure 4.14).	SOLUTION Al^{3+} O^{2-}	SOLUTION Mg^{2+} O^{2-}
2. Make the magnitude of the charge on each ion (without the sign) become the subscript for the other ion.	Al^{3+} O^{2-} → Al_2O_3	Mg^{2+} O^{2-} → Mg_2O_2
3. If possible, reduce the subscripts to give a ratio with the smallest whole numbers.	In this case, the numbers cannot be reduced any further; the correct formula is Al_2O_3.	To reduce the subscripts, divide both subscripts by 2. $Mg_2O_2 \div 2 = MgO$
4. Check to make sure that the sum of the charges of the cations exactly cancels the sum of the charges of the anions.	Cations: $2(3+) = 6+$ Anions: $3(2-) = 6-$ The charges cancel.	Cations: $2+$ Anions: $2-$ The charges cancel.
	►**SKILLBUILDER 5.5** Write a formula for the compound formed from strontium and chlorine.	►**SKILLBUILDER 5.6** Write a formula for the compound formed from aluminum and nitrogen.
		►**FOR MORE PRACTICE** Example 5.21; Problems 53, 54, 55, 56.

EXAMPLE 5.7 Writing Formulas for Ionic Compounds

Write a formula for the compound composed of potassium and oxygen.

SOLUTION

First write the symbol for each ion along with its appropriate charge from its group number in the periodic table.

$$K^+ \quad O^{2-}$$

Then make the magnitude of each ion's charge become the subscript for the other ion.

$$K^+ \quad O^{2-} \text{ becomes } K_2O$$

No reduction of subscripts is necessary in this case. Finally, check to see that the sum of the charges of the cations [2(1+) = 2+] exactly cancels the sum of the charges of the anion (2−). The correct formula is K_2O.

▶SKILLBUILDER 5.7 | Writing Formulas for Ionic Compounds
Write a formula for the compound that forms from calcium and bromine.

▶FOR MORE PRACTICE Problems 57, 58.

5.6 Nomenclature: Naming Compounds

Since there are so many different compounds, chemists have developed systematic ways to name them. If you learn these naming rules, you can examine a compound's formula and determine its name or vice versa. Many compounds also have a common name. For example, H_2O has the common name *water* and the systematic name *dihydrogen monoxide*. A common name is like a nickname for a compound, used by those who are familiar with it. Since water is such a familiar compound, everyone uses its common name and not its systematic name. In the sections that follow, you will learn how to systematically name simple ionic and molecular compounds. Keep in mind, however, that some compounds also have common names that are often used instead of the systematic name. Common names can be learned only through familiarity.

5.7 Naming Ionic Compounds

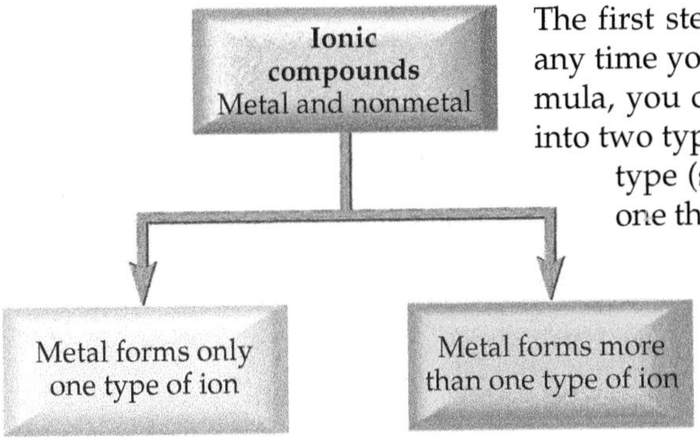

The first step in naming an ionic compound is identifying it as one. Remember, any time you have a metal and one or more nonmetals together in a chemical formula, you can assume the compound is ionic. Ionic compounds are categorized into two types (◀ Figure 5.12) depending on the metal in the compound. The first type (sometimes called Type I) contains a metal with an invariant charge—one that does not vary from one compound to another. Sodium, for instance, has a 1+ charge in all of its compounds. Table 5.3 lists more examples of metals whose charge is invariant from one compound to another. The charge of most of these metals can be inferred from their group number in the periodic table (see Figure 4.14).

Ionic compounds
Metal and nonmetal

Metal forms only one type of ion

Metal forms more than one type of ion

▲ **FIGURE 5.12 Classification of ionic compounds** Ionic compounds can be categorized into two types, depending on the metal in the compound.

TABLE 5.3 Metals Whose Charge Is Invariant from One Compound to Another

Metal	Ion	Name	Group Number
Li	Li^+	lithium	1A
Na	Na^+	sodium	1A
K	K^+	potassium	1A
Rb	Rb^+	rubidium	1A
Cs	Cs^+	cesium	1A
Mg	Mg^{2+}	magnesium	2A
Ca	Ca^{2+}	calcium	2A
Sr	Sr^{2+}	strontium	2A
Ba	Ba^{2+}	barium	2A
Al	Al^{3+}	aluminum	3A
Zn	Zn^{2+}	zinc	*
Ag	Ag^+	silver	*

*The charge of these metals cannot be inferred from their group number.

TABLE 5.4 Some Metals That Form More Than One Type of Ion and Their Common Charges

Metal	Symbol Ion	Name	Older Name*
chromium	Cr^{2+}	chromium(II)	chromous
	Cr^{3+}	chromium(III)	chromic
iron	Fe^{2+}	Iron(II)	ferrous
	Fe^{3+}	iron(III)	ferric
cobalt	Co^{2+}	cobalt(II)	cobaltous
	Co^{3+}	cobalt(III)	cobaltic
copper	Cu^{+}	copper(I)	cuprous
	Cu^{2+}	copper(II)	cupric
tin	Sn^{2+}	tin(II)	stannous
	Sn^{4+}	tin(IV)	stannic
mercury	Hg_2^{2+}	mercury(I)	mercurous
	Hg^{2+}	mercury(II)	mercuric
lead	Pb^{2+}	lead(II)	plumbous
	Pb^{4+}	lead(IV)	plumbic

*An older naming system substitutes the names found in this column for the name of the metal and its charge. Under this system, chromium(II) oxide is named chromous oxide. We do *not* use this older system in this text.

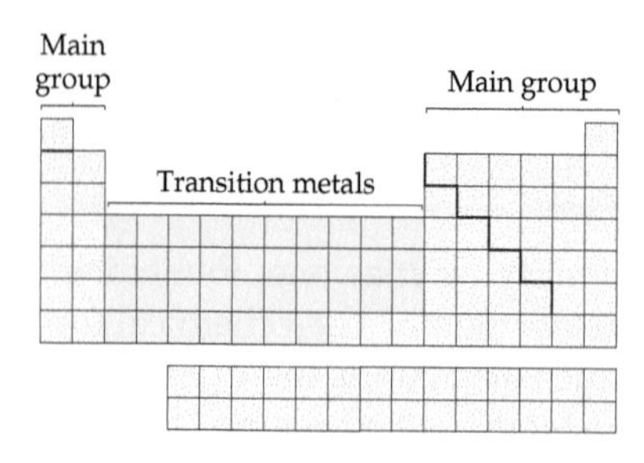

▲ **FIGURE 5.13 The transition metals** The metals that form more than one type of ion are usually (but not always) transition metals.

The second type of ionic compound (sometimes called Type II) contains a metal with a charge that can differ in different compounds. In other words, the metal in this second type of ionic compound can form more than one kind of cation (depending on the compound). Iron, for instance, has a 2+ charge in some of its compounds and a 3+ charge in others. Additional examples of metals that form more than one type of cation are listed in Table 5.4. Such metals are usually (but not always) found in the **transition metals** section of the periodic table (◀ Figure 5.13). However, some transition metals, such as Zn and Ag, form cations with the same charge in all of their compounds, and some main group metals, such as Pb and Sn, form more than one type of cation.

NAMING BINARY IONIC COMPOUNDS CONTAINING A METAL THAT FORMS ONLY ONE TYPE OF CATION

Binary compounds are those that contain only two different elements. The names for binary ionic compounds containing a metal that forms only one type of ion have the form:

name of cation (metal)	base name of anion (nonmetal) + *-ide*

Since the charge of the metal is always the same for these types of compounds, it need not be specified in the compound's name. For example, the name for NaCl consists of the name of the cation, *sodium*, followed by the base name of the anion, *chlor*, with the ending *-ide*. The full name is *sodium chloride*.

The name of the cation in ionic compounds is the same as the name of the metal.

NaCl sodium chloride

The name for MgO consists of the name of the cation, *magnesium*, followed by the base name of the anion, *ox*, with the ending *-ide*. The full name is *magnesium oxide*.

MgO magnesium oxide

Table 5.5 contains the base names for various nonmetals and their most common charges in ionic compounds.

TABLE 5.5 Some Common Anions

Nonmetal	Symbol for Ion	Base Name	Anion Name
fluorine	F^-	fluor-	fluoride
chlorine	Cl^-	chlor-	chloride
bromine	Br^-	brom-	bromide
iodine	I^-	iod-	iodide
oxygen	O^{2-}	ox-	oxide
sulfur	S^{2-}	sulf-	sulfide
nitrogen	N^{3-}	nitr-	nitride

EXAMPLE 5.8 Naming Ionic Compounds Containing a Metal That Forms Only One Type of Cation

Name the compound MgF_2.

SOLUTION

The cation is magnesium. The anion is fluorine, which becomes *fluoride*. Its correct name is *magnesium fluoride*.

▶SKILLBUILDER 5.8 | Naming Ionic Compounds Containing a Metal That Forms Only One Type of Ion

Name the compound KBr.

▶SKILLBUILDER PLUS

Name the compound Zn_3N_2.

▶FOR MORE PRACTICE Example 5.22; Problems 59, 60.

NAMING BINARY IONIC COMPOUNDS CONTAINING A METAL THAT FORMS MORE THAN ONE TYPE OF CATION

Since the charge of the metal cation in these types of compounds is not always the same, the charge must be specified in the metal's name. We specify the charge with a roman numeral (in parentheses) following the name of the metal. For example, we distinguish between Cu^+ and Cu^{2+} by writing a (I) to indicate the 1+ ion or a (II) to indicate the 2+ ion:

Cu^+ Copper(I)

Cu^{2+} Copper(II)

The full name for these types of compounds have the form:

name of cation (metal) (charge of cation (metal) in roman numerals in parentheses) base name of anion (nonmetal) + *-ide*

We can determine the charge of the metal from the chemical formula of the compound—remember that the sum of all the charges must be zero. For example, the charge of iron in $FeCl_3$ must be 3+ in order for the compound to be charge neutral with the three Cl^- anions. The name for $FeCl_3$ is therefore the name of the cation, *iron*, followed by the charge of the cation in parentheses *(III)*, followed by the base name of the anion, *chlor*, with the ending *-ide*. The full name is *iron(III) chloride*.

$FeCl_3$ iron(III) chloride

Likewise, the name for CrO consists of the name of the cation, *chromium*, followed by the charge of the cation in parentheses *(II)*, followed by the base name of the anion, *ox-*, with the ending *-ide*. The full name is *chromium(II) oxide*.

CrO chromium(II) oxide

The charge of chromium must be 2+ in order for the compound to be charge-neutral with one O^{2-} anion.

EXAMPLE 5.9 Naming Ionic Compounds Containing a Metal That Forms More Than One Type of Cation

Name the compound $PbCl_4$.

SOLUTION

The name for $PbCl_4$ consists of the name of the cation, *lead*, followed by the charge of the cation in parentheses *(IV)*, followed by the base name of the anion, *chlor-*, with the ending *-ide*. The full name is *lead(IV) chloride*. We know the charge on Pb is 4+ because the charge on Cl is 1−. Since there are 4 Cl^- anions, the Pb cation must be Pb^{4+}.

$PbCl_4$ lead(IV) chloride

▶SKILLBUILDER 5.9 | Naming Ionic Compounds Containing a Metal That Forms More Than One Type of Cation

Name the compound PbO.

▶FOR MORE PRACTICE Example 5.23; Problems 61, 62.

CONCEPTUAL CHECKPOINT 5.3

Explain why CaO is NOT named calcium(II) oxide.

NAMING IONIC COMPOUNDS CONTAINING A POLYATOMIC ION

As we saw previously, some ionic compounds contain polyatomic ions (ions that are themselves composed of a group of atoms with an overall charge). The most common polyatomic ions are listed in Table 5.6. We name ionic compounds containing polyatomic ions using the same procedure we apply to other ionic compounds, except that we use the name of the polyatomic ion whenever it occurs. For example, KNO_3 is named using its cation, K^+, *potassium*, and its polyatomic anion, NO_3^-, *nitrate*. The full name is *potassium nitrate*.

KNO_3 potassium nitrate

$Fe(OH)_2$ is named according to its cation, *iron*, its charge *(II)*, and its polyatomic ion, *hydroxide*. Its full name is *iron(II) hydroxide*.

$Fe(OH)_2$ iron(II) hydroxide

If the compound contains both a polyatomic cation and a polyatomic anion, use the names of both polyatomic ions. For example, NH_4NO_3 is *ammonium nitrate*.

NH_4NO_3 ammonium nitrate

EVERYDAY CHEMISTRY

Polyatomic Ions

A glance at the labels of household products reveals the importance of polyatomic ions in everyday compounds. For example, the active ingredient in household bleach is sodium hypochlorite, which acts to decompose color-causing molecules in clothes (bleaching action) and to kill bacteria (disinfection). A box of baking soda contains sodium bicarbonate (sodium hydrogen carbonate), which acts as an antacid when consumed in small quantities and as a source of carbon dioxide gas in baking. The pockets of carbon dioxide gas make baked goods fluffy rather than flat.

Calcium carbonate is the active ingredient in many antacids such as Tums™ and Alka-Mints™. It neutralizes stomach acids, relieving the symptoms of indigestion and heartburn. Too much calcium carbonate, however, can cause constipation, so Tums should not be overused. Sodium nitrite is a common food additive used to preserve packaged meats such as ham, hot dogs, and bologna. Sodium nitrite inhibits the growth of bacteria, especially those that cause botulism, an often fatal type of food poisoning.

TUMS
CLOROX
BAKING SODA
Best's
BEEF FRANKFURTERS

◀ Compounds containing polyatomic ions are present in many consumer products.

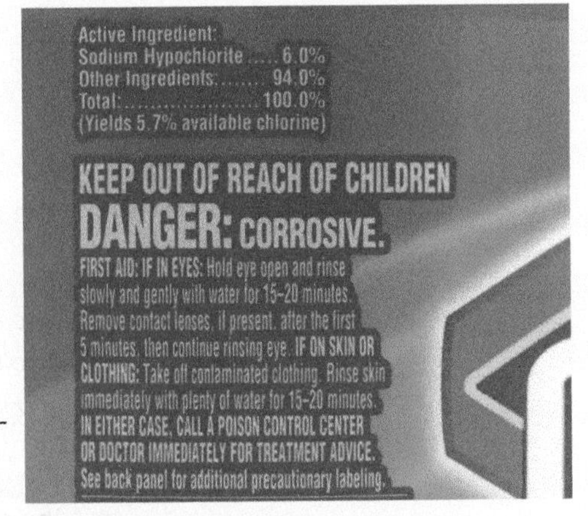
Active Ingredient:
Sodium Hypochlorite 6.0%
Other Ingredients:....... 94.0%
Total:.................. 100.0%
(Yields 5.7% available chlorine)
KEEP OUT OF REACH OF CHILDREN
DANGER: CORROSIVE.
FIRST AID: IF IN EYES: Hold eye open and rinse slowly and gently with water for 15-20 minutes. Remove contact lenses, if present, after the first 5 minutes, then continue rinsing eye. IF ON SKIN OR CLOTHING: Take off contaminated clothing. Rinse skin immediately with plenty of water for 15-20 minutes.
IN EITHER CASE, CALL A POISON CONTROL CENTER OR DOCTOR IMMEDIATELY FOR TREATMENT ADVICE.
See back panel for additional precautionary labeling.

▶ The active ingredient in bleach is sodium hypochlorite.

CAN YOU ANSWER THIS? *Write a formula for each of these compounds that contain polyatomic ions: sodium hypochlorite, sodium bicarbonate, calcium carbonate, sodium nitrite.*

TABLE 5.6 Some Common Polyatomic Ions

Name	Formula	Name	Formula
acetate	$C_2H_3O_2^-$	hypochlorite	ClO^-
carbonate	CO_3^{2-}	chlorite	ClO_2^-
hydrogen carbonate (or bicarbonate)	HCO_3^-	chlorate	ClO_3^-
hydroxide	OH^-	perchlorate	ClO_4^-
nitrate	NO_3^-	permanganate	MnO_4^-
nitrite	NO_2^-	sulfate	SO_4^{2-}
chromate	CrO_4^{2-}	sulfite	SO_3^{2-}
dichromate	$Cr_2O_7^{2-}$	hydrogen sulfite (or bisulfite)	HSO_3^-
phosphate	PO_4^{3-}	hydrogen sulfate (or bisulfate)	HSO_4^-
hydrogen phosphate	HPO_4^{2-}	peroxide	O_2^{2-}
ammonium	NH_4^+	cyanide	CN^-

You will need to be able to recognize polyatomic ions in a chemical formula, so become familiar with Table 5.6. Most polyatomic ions are **oxyanions,** anions containing oxygen. Notice that when a series of oxyanions contain different numbers of oxygen atoms, they are named systematically according to the number of oxygen atoms in the ion. If there are two ions in the series, the one with more oxygen atoms is given the ending *-ate* and the one with fewer is given the ending *-ite*. For example, NO_3^- is called *nitrate* and NO_2^- is called *nitrite.*

NO_3^- nitrate
NO_2^- nitrite

If there are more than two ions in the series, then the prefixes *hypo-*, meaning "less than," and *per-*, meaning "more than," are used. So ClO^- is called *hypochlorite,* meaning "less oxygen than chlorite," and ClO_4^- is called *perchlorate,* meaning "more oxygen than chlorate."

ClO^- hypochlorite
ClO_2^- chlorite
ClO_3^- chlorate
ClO_4^- perchlorate

EXAMPLE 5.10 Naming Ionic Compounds Containing a Polyatomic Ion

Name the compound K_2CrO_4.

SOLUTION

The name for K_2CrO_4 consists of the name of the cation, *potassium,* followed by the name of the polyatomic ion, *chromate.*

K_2CrO_4 potassium chromate

▶SKILLBUILDER 5.10 | Naming Ionic Compounds Containing a Polyatomic Ion

Name the compound $Mn(NO_3)_2$.

▶FOR MORE PRACTICE Example 5.24; Problems 65, 66.

CONCEPTUAL CHECKPOINT 5.4

You have just learned that the anion ClO_3^- is named chlorate. What is the name of the anion IO_3^-?

5.8 Naming Molecular Compounds

The first step in naming a molecular compound is identifying it as one. Remember, nearly all molecular compounds form from two or more nonmetals. In this section, we learn how to name binary (two-element) molecular compounds. Their names have the form:

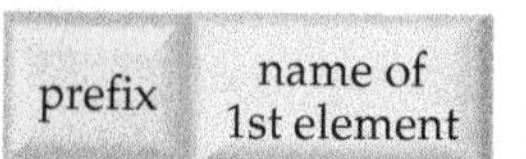

When writing the name of a molecular compound, as when writing the formula, the first element is the more metal-like one (see Table 5.1). The prefixes given to each element indicate the number of atoms present.

mono- 1	*hexa-* 6
di- 2	*hepta-* 7
tri- 3	*octa-* 8
tetra- 4	*nona-* 9
penta- 5	*deca-* 10

If there is only one atom of the *first element* in the formula, the prefix *mono-* is normally omitted. For example, CO_2 is named according to the first element, *carbon*, with no prefix because *mono-* is omitted for the first element, followed by the prefix *di-*, to indicate two oxygen atoms, followed by the base name of the second element, *ox*, with the ending *-ide*.

carbon di- ox -ide

The full name is *carbon dioxide.*

CO_2 carbon dioxide

When the prefix ends with a vowel and the base name starts with a vowel, the first vowel is sometimes dropped, especially in the case of mono oxide, which becomes monoxide.

The compound N_2O, also called laughing gas, is named according to the first element, *nitrogen*, with the prefix *di-*, to indicate that there are two of them, followed by the base name of the second element, *ox*, prefixed by *mono-*, to indicate one, and the suffix *-ide*. Since *mono-* ends with a vowel and *oxide* begins with one, an *o* is dropped and the two are combined as *monoxide*. The entire name is *dinitrogen monoxide.*

N_2O dinitrogen monoxide

EXAMPLE 5.11 Naming Molecular Compounds

Name each compound.

(a) CCl_4
(b) BCl_3
(c) SF_6

SOLUTION

(a) The name of the compound is the name of the first element, *carbon*, followed by the base name of the second element, *chlor*, prefixed by *tetra-* to indicate four, and the suffix *–ide*.

CCl_4 carbon tetrachloride

(b) The name of the compound is the name of the first element, *boron*, followed by the base name of the second element, *chlor*, prefixed by *tri-* to indicate three, and the suffix *-ide*.

BCl_3 boron trichloride

(c) The name of the compound is the name of the first element, *sulfur*, followed by the base name of the second element, *fluor*, prefixed by *hexa-* to indicate six, and the suffix *-ide*. The entire name is *sulfur hexafluoride*.

SF_6 sulfur hexafluoride

▶SKILLBUILDER 5.11 | Naming Molecular Compounds

Name the compound N_2O_4.

▶FOR MORE PRACTICE Example 5.25; Problems 71, 72.

5.9 Naming Acids

Acids are molecular compounds that produce H^+ ions when dissolved in water. They are composed of hydrogen, usually written first in their formula, and one or more nonmetals, written second. Acids are characterized by their sour taste and their ability to dissolve some metals. For example, $HCl(aq)$ is an acid—the (aq) indicates that the compound is "aqueous" or "dissolved in water". $HCl(aq)$ has a characteristically sour taste. Since $HCl(aq)$ is present in stomach fluids, its sour taste becomes painfully obvious during vomiting. $HCl(aq)$ also dissolves some metals. If you drop a strip of zinc into a beaker of $HCl(aq)$, it will slowly disappear as the acid converts the zinc metal into dissolved Zn^{2+} cations.

$HCl(g)$ refers to HCl molecules in the gas phase.

Acids are present in many foods, such as lemons and limes, and they are used in some household products such as toilet bowl cleaner and Lime-A-Way. In this section, we simply learn how to name them, but in Chapter 14 we will learn more about their properties. We can categorize acids into two groups: **binary acids**, those containing only hydrogen and a nonmetal, and **oxyacids**, those containing hydrogen, a nonmetal, and oxygen (◀ Figure 5.14).

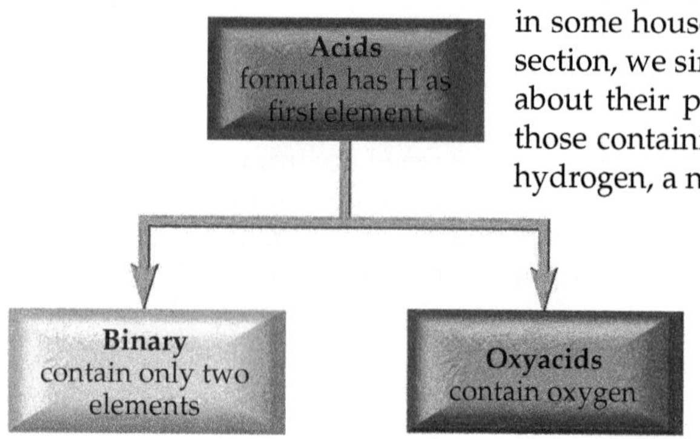

◀ **FIGURE 5.14 Classification of acids** Acids are classified into two types, depending on the number of elements in the acid. If the acid contains only two elements, it is a binary acid. If it contains oxygen, it is an oxyacid.

NAMING BINARY ACIDS

Binary acids are composed of hydrogen and a nonmetal. The names for binary acids have the following form:

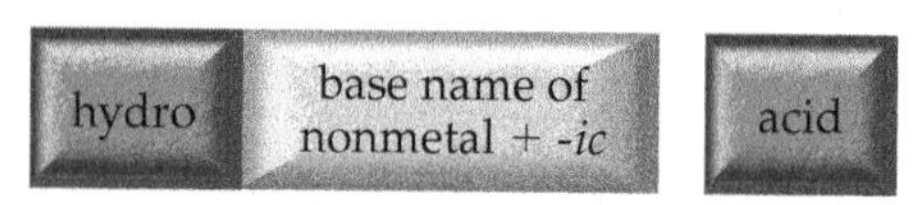

For example, $HCl(aq)$ is hydro*chlor*ic acid and $HBr(aq)$ is hydro*brom*ic acid.

$HCl(aq)$ hydrochloric acid $HBr(aq)$ hydrobromic acid

EXAMPLE 5.12 Naming Binary Acids

Give the name of $H_2S(aq)$.

The base name of S is *sulfur*, so the name is *hydrosulfuric acid*

SOLUTION

$H_2S(aq)$ hydrosulfuric acid

▶**SKILLBUILDER 5.12 | Naming Binary Acids**

Name $HF(aq)$.

▶**FOR MORE PRACTICE** Example 5.26; Problems 77b, 78d.

NAMING OXYACIDS

Oxyacids are acids that contain oxyanions, which can be found in the table of polyatomic ions (Table 5.6). For example, $HNO_3(aq)$ contains the nitrate (NO_3^-) ion, $H_2SO_3(aq)$ contains the sulfite (SO_3^{2-}) ion, and $H_2SO_4(aq)$ contains the sulfate (SO_4^{2-}) ion. All of these acids are a combination of one or more H^+ ions with an oxyanion. The number of H^+ ions depends on the charge of the oxyanion, so that the formula is always charge-neutral. The names of oxyacids depend on the ending of the oxyanion (▶ Figure 5.15).

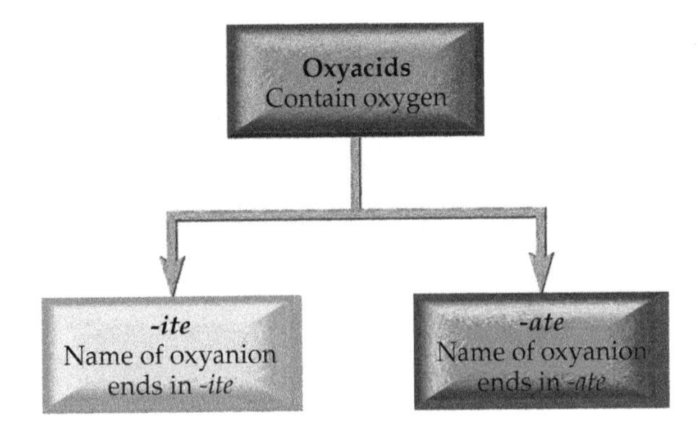

▶ **FIGURE 5.15 Classification of oxyacids** Oxyacids are classified into two types, depending on the endings of the oxyanions that they contain.

The names of acids containing oxyanions ending with *-ite* take this form:

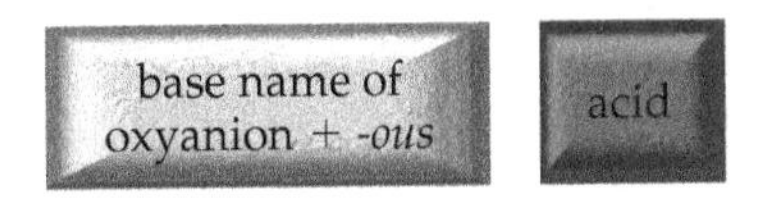

The saying, "*ic* I *ate* an acid" is sometimes used to help remember the association of -ic with *-ate*.

The names of acids containing oxyanions ending with *-ate* take this form:

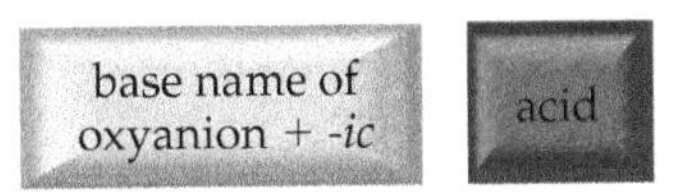

So H_2SO_3 is *sulfurous acid* (oxyanion is sulfite), and HNO_3 is *nitric acid* (oxyanion is nitrate).

$H_2SO_3(aq)$ sulfurous acid $HNO_3(aq)$ nitric acid

Table 5.7 lists the names of some common oxyacids and their oxyanions.

EXAMPLE 5.13 Naming Oxyacids

Name $HC_2H_3O_2(aq)$.

The oxyanion is acetate, which ends in *-ate*; therefore, the name of the acid is *acetic acid*.

SOLUTION

$HC_2H_3O_2(aq)$ acetic acid

▶**SKILLBUILDER 5.13 | Naming Oxyacids**

Name $HNO_2(aq)$.

▶**FOR MORE PRACTICE** Examples 5.27, 5.28; Problems 77acd, 78abc.

TABLE 5.7 Names of Some Common Oxyacids and Their Oxyanions

Acid Formula	Acid Name	Oxyanion Name	Oxyanion Formula
HNO_2	nitrous acid	nitrite	NO_2^-
HNO_3	nitric acid	nitrate	NO_3^-
H_2SO_3	sulfurous acid	sulfite	SO_3^-
H_2SO_4	sulfuric acid	sulfate	SO_4^{2-}
$HClO_2$	chlorous acid	chorite	ClO_2^-
$HClO_3$	chloric acid	chlorate	ClO_3^-
$H_2C_2H_3O_2$	acetic acid	acetate	$C_2H_3O_2^-$
H_2CO_3	carbonic acid	carbonate	CO_3^{2-}

CHEMISTRY IN THE ENVIRONMENT

Acid Rain

Acid rain occurs when rainwater mixes with air pollutants—such as NO, NO_2, and SO_2—that form acids. NO and NO_2, primarily from vehicular emission, combine with water to form HNO_3 *(aq)*. SO_2, primarily from coal-powered electricity generation, combines with water and oxygen in air to form H_2SO_4 *(aq)*. HNO_3 *(aq)* and H_2SO_4 *(aq)* both cause rainwater to become acidic. The problem is greatest in the northeastern United States, where pollutants from midwestern electrical power plants combine with rainwater to produce rain with acid levels that are up to 10 times higher than normal.

When acid rain falls or flows into lakes and streams, it makes them more acidic. Some species of aquatic animals—such as trout, bass, snails, salamanders, and clams—cannot tolerate the increased acidity and die. This then disturbs the ecosystem of the lake, resulting in imbalances that may lead to the death of other aquatic species. Acid rain also weakens trees by dissolving nutrients in the soil and by damaging their leaves. Appalachian red spruce trees have been the hardest hit, with many forests showing significant acid rain damage.

Acid rain also damages building materials. Acids dissolve $CaCO_3$ (limestone), a main component of marble and concrete, and iron, the main component of steel. Consequently, many statues, buildings, and bridges in the northeastern United States show significant deterioration, and some historical gravestones made of limestone are barely legible due to acid rain damage.

Although acid rain has been a problem for many years, innovative legislation has offered hope for change. In 1990, Congress passed several amendments to the Clean Air Act that included provisions requiring electrical utilities to reduce SO_2 emissions. Since then, SO_2 emissions have decreased, and rain in the northeastern United States has become somewhat less acidic. For example, in the early 1990s, scientists categorized 30% of the lakes in the Northeast as being of *acute concern*; today, the percentage of lakes in that category has been reduced to 18%. With time, and continued enforcement of the acid rain program, lakes, streams, and forests damaged by acid rain should recover. However, acid rain continues to worsen in countries such as China, where industrial growth is outpacing environmental controls. International cooperation is essential to solving environmental problems such as acid rain.

CAN YOU ANSWER THIS? *Name each compound, given here as formulas:*

NO, NO_2, SO_2, HNO_3 *(aq)*, $CaCO_3$

▲ A forest damaged by acid rain.

▲ Acid rain harms many materials, including the limestone often used for tombstones, buildings, and statues.

5.10 Nomenclature Summary

Naming compounds requires several steps. The flowchart in ▶ Figure 5.16 summarizes the different categories of compounds that we have covered in the chapter and how to identify and name them. The first step is to decide whether the compound is ionic, molecular, or an acid. You can recognize ionic compounds by the presence of a metal and a nonmetal, molecular compounds by two or more nonmetals, and acids by the presence of hydrogen (written first) and one or more nonmetals.

Acids are technically a subclass of molecular compounds; that is, they are molecular compounds that form H^+ ions when dissolved in water.

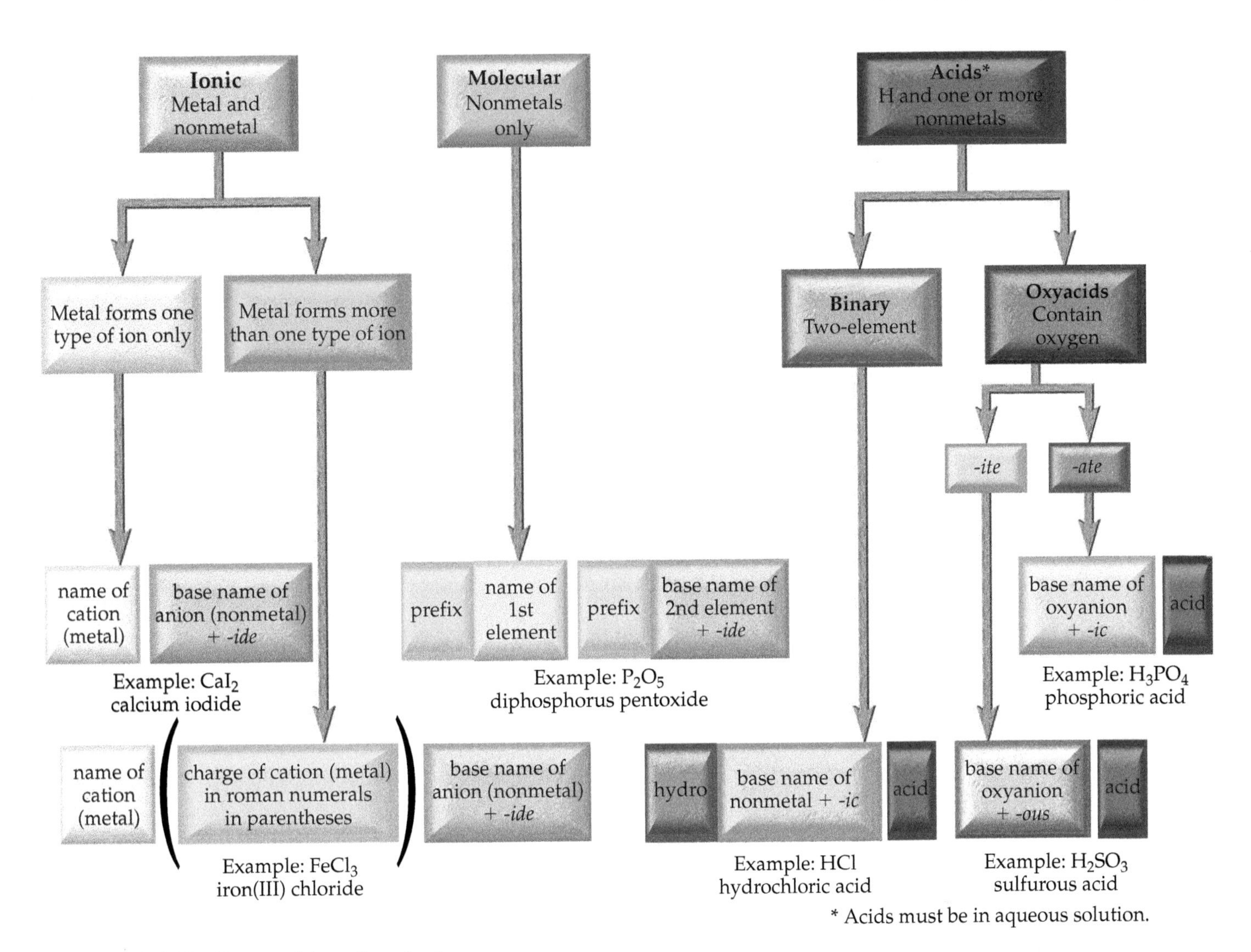

▲ FIGURE 5.16 **Nomenclature flowchart**

IONIC COMPOUNDS

For an ionic compound, you must next decide whether the metal forms only one type of ion or more than one type of ion. Group 1A (alkali) metals, Group 2A (alkaline earth) metals, and aluminum will always form only one type of ion (Figure 4.14). Most of the transition metals will form more than one type of ion. Once you have identified the type of ionic compound, name it according to the scheme in the chart. If the ionic compound contains a polyatomic ion—something you must learn to recognize by familiarity—insert the name of the polyatomic ion in place of the metal (positive polyatomic ion) or the nonmetal (negative polyatomic ion).

Zinc (Zn^{2+}), scandium (Sc^{3+}), and silver (Ag^{+}) also form only one type of ion.

MOLECULAR COMPOUNDS

We have learned how to name only one type of molecular compound, the binary (two-element) compound. If you identify a compound as molecular, name it according to the scheme in Figure 5.16.

ACIDS

To name an acid, you must first decide whether it is a binary (two-element) acid or an oxyacid (an acid containing oxygen). Binary acids are named according to the scheme in Figure 5.16. Oxyacids must be further subdivided based on the name of their corresponding oxyanion. If the oxyanion ends in *-ite*, use one scheme; if it ends with *-ate*, use the other.

EXAMPLE 5.14 Nomenclature Using Figure 5.16

Name each compound: CO, CaF_2, HF(*aq*), $Fe(NO_3)_3$, $HClO_4$ (*aq*), H_2SO_3 (*aq*).

SOLUTION

For each compound, the following table shows how to use Figure 5.16 to arrive at a name for the compound.

Formula	Flowchart Path	Name
CO	molecular	carbon monoxide
CaF_2	ionic ⟶ one type of ion ⟶	calcium fluoride
HF(*aq*)	acid ⟶ binary ⟶	hydrofluoric acid
$Fe(NO_3)_3$	ionic ⟶ more than one type of ion ⟶	iron(III) nitrate
$HClO_4$ (*aq*)	acid ⟶ oxyacid ⟶ *-ate* ⟶	perchloric acid
H_2SO_3 (*aq*)	acid ⟶ oxyacid ⟶ *-ite* ⟶	sulfurous acid

▶**FOR MORE PRACTICE** Problems 93, 94.

5.11 Formula Mass: The Mass of a Molecule or Formula Unit

The terms *molecular mass* and *molecular weight*, which are also commonly used, have the same meaning as formula mass.

In Chapter 4, we discussed atoms and elements and designated the average mass of the atoms that compose an element as the atomic mass for that element. Similarly, in this chapter, which introduces molecules and compounds, we designate the average mass of the molecules (or formula units) that compose a compound as the **formula mass**.

For any compound, the formula mass is the sum of the atomic masses of all the atoms in its chemical formula:

Formula mass = (# atoms of 1st element in chemical formula × Atomic mass of 1st element) + (# atoms of 2nd element in chemical formula × Atomic mass of 2nd element) + . . .

Like atomic mass for atoms, formula mass characterizes the average mass of a molecule or formula unit. For example, the formula mass of water, H_2O, is:

$$\text{Formula mass} = 2(1.01\text{ amu}) + 16.00\text{ amu}$$
$$= 18.02\text{ amu}$$

and that of sodium chloride, NaCl, is:

$$\text{Formula mass} = 22.99\text{ amu} + 35.45\text{ amu}$$
$$= 58.44\text{ amu}$$

In addition to giving a characteristic mass to the molecules or formula units of a compound, formula mass—as we will learn in Chapter 6—allows us to quantify the number of molecules or formula units in a sample of a given mass.

EXAMPLE 5.15 Calculating Formula Mass

Calculate the formula mass of carbon tetrachloride, CCl_4.

SOLUTION

To find the formula mass, sum the atomic masses of each atom in the chemical formula.

$$\begin{aligned}\text{Formula mass} &= 1 \times (\text{Atomic mass C}) + 4 \times (\text{Atomic mass Cl})\\ &= 12.01 \text{ amu} + 4(35.45 \text{ amu})\\ &= 12.01 \text{ amu} + 141.80 \text{ amu}\\ &= 153.8 \text{ amu}\end{aligned}$$

▶SKILLBUILDER 5.15 | Calculating Formula Masses

Calculate the formula mass of dinitrogen monoxide, N_2O, also called laughing gas.

▶FOR MORE PRACTICE Example 5.29; Problems 83, 84.

CONCEPTUAL CHECKPOINT 5.5

Which compound has the greatest formula mass?

(a) O_2 **(b)** O_3 **(c)** H_2O **(d)** H_2O_2

CHAPTER IN REVIEW

CHEMICAL PRINCIPLES	RELEVANCE
Compounds: Matter is ultimately composed of atoms, but those atoms are often combined in compounds. The most important characteristic of a compound is its constant composition. The elements that make up a particular compound are in fixed, definite proportions in all samples of the compound.	**Compounds:** Most of the matter we encounter is in the form of compounds. Water, salt, and carbon dioxide are all examples of common simple compounds. More complex compounds include caffeine, aspirin, acetone, and testosterone.
Chemical Formulas: Compounds are represented by chemical formulas, which indicate the elements present in the compound and the relative number of atoms of each. These formulas represent the basic units that make up a compound. Pure substances can be categorized according to the basic units that compose them. Elements can be composed of atoms or molecules. Compounds can be molecular, in which case their basic units are molecules, or ionic, in which case their basic units are ions. The formulas for many ionic compounds can be written simply by knowing the elements in the compound.	**Chemical Formulas:** To understand compounds, we must understand their composition, which is represented by a chemical formula. The connection between the microscopic world and the macroscopic world hinges on the particles that compose matter. Since most matter is in the form of compounds, the properties of most matter depend on the molecules or ions that compose it. Molecular matter does what its molecules do; ionic matter does what its ions do. The world we see and experience is governed by what these particles are doing.
Chemical Nomenclature: The names of simple ionic compounds, molecular compounds, and acids can all be written by examining their chemical formula. The nomenclature flowchart (Figure 5.16) shows the basic procedure for determining these names.	**Chemical Nomenclature:** Since there are so many compounds, we need a systematic way to name them. By learning these few simple rules, you will be able to name thousands of different compounds. The next time you look at the label on a consumer product, try to identify as many of the compounds as you can by examining their names.

Formula Mass: The formula mass of a compound is the sum of the atomic masses of all the atoms in the chemical formula for the compound. Like atomic mass for elements, formula mass characterizes the average mass of a molecule or formula unit.

Formula Mass: Besides being the characteristic mass of a molecule or formula unit, formula mass is important in many calculations involving the composition of compounds and quantities in chemical reactions.

CHEMICAL SKILLS

Constant Composition of Compounds (Section 5.2)

The law of constant composition states that all samples of a given compound should have the same ratio of their constituent elements.

To determine whether experimental data are consistent with the law of constant composition, compute the ratios of the masses of each element in all samples. When computing these ratios, it is most convenient to put the larger number in the numerator (top) and the smaller one in the denominator (bottom); that way, the ratio is greater than 1. If the ratios are the same, then the data are consistent with the law of constant composition.

EXAMPLES

EXAMPLE 5.16 Constant Composition of Compounds

Two samples said to be carbon disulfide (CS_2) are decomposed into their constituent elements. One sample produced 8.08 g S and 1.51 g C, while the other produced 31.3 g S and 3.85 g C. Are these results consistent with the law of constant composition?

SOLUTION

Sample 1

$$\frac{\text{Mass S}}{\text{Mass C}} = \frac{8.08\text{ g}}{1.51\text{ g}} = 5.35$$

Sample 2

$$\frac{\text{Mass S}}{\text{Mass C}} = \frac{31.3\text{ g}}{3.85\text{ g}} = 8.13$$

These results are not consistent with the law of constant composition, so the information that the two samples are the same substance must therefore be in error.

Writing Chemical Formulas (Section 5.3)

Chemical formulas indicate the elements present in a compound and the relative number of atoms of each. When writing formulas, put the more metallic element first.

EXAMPLE 5.17 Writing Chemical Formulas

Write a chemical formula for the compound containing one nitrogen atom for every two oxygen atoms.

SOLUTION

NO_2

Total Number of Each Type of Atom in a Chemical Formula (Section 5.3)

The numbers of atoms not enclosed in parentheses are given directly by their subscript.

Find the numbers of atoms within parentheses by multiplying their subscript within the parentheses by their subscript outside the parentheses.

EXAMPLE 5.18 Total Number of Each Type of Atom in a Chemical Formula

Determine the number of each type of atom in $Pb(ClO_3)_2$.

SOLUTION

One Pb atom

Two Cl atoms

Six O atoms

Classifying Elements as Atomic or Molecular (Section 5.4)

Most elements exist as atomic elements, their basic units in nature being individual atoms. However, several elements (H_2, N_2, O_2, F_2, Cl_2, Br_2, and I_2) exist as molecular elements, their basic units in nature being diatomic molecules.

EXAMPLE 5.19 Classifying Elements as Atomic or Molecular

Classify each element as atomic or molecular: sodium, iodine, and nitrogen.

SOLUTION

sodium: atomic

iodine: molecular (I_2)

nitrogen: molecular (N_2)

Classifying Compounds as Ionic or Molecular (Section 5.4)

Compounds containing a metal and a nonmetal are ionic. If the metal is a transition metal, it will likely form more than one type of ion (see exceptions in Tables 5.3 and 5.4). If the metal is not a transition metal, it will likely form only one type of ion (see exceptions in Tables 5.3 and 5.4).

Compounds composed of nonmetals are molecular.

EXAMPLE 5.20 Classifying Compounds as Ionic or Molecular

Classify each compound as ionic or molecular. If they are ionic, determine whether the metal forms only one type of ion or more than one type of ion.

$FeCl_3$, K_2SO_4, CCl_4

SOLUTION

$FeCl_3$: ionic, metal forms more than one type of ion

K_2SO_4: ionic, metal forms only one type of ion

CCl_4: molecular

Writing Formulas for Ionic Compounds (Section 5.5)

1. Write the symbol for the metal ion followed by the symbol for the nonmetal ion (or polyatomic ion) and their charges. These charges can be deduced from the group numbers in the periodic table. (In the case of polyatomic ions, the charges come from Table 5.6.)
2. Make the magnitude of the charge on each ion become the subscript for the other ion.
3. Check to see if the subscripts can be reduced to simpler whole numbers. Subscripts of 1 can be dropped, since they are normally implied.
4. Check that the sum of the charges of the cations exactly cancels the sum of the charges of the anions.

EXAMPLE 5.21 Writing Formulas for Ionic Compounds

Write a formula for the compound that forms from lithium and sulfate ions.

SOLUTION

Li^+ SO_4^{2-}

$Li_2(SO_4)$

In this case, the subscripts cannot be further reduced.

Li_2SO_4

Cations	Anions
$2(1+) = 2+$	$2-$

Naming Binary Ionic Compounds Containing a Metal That Forms Only One Type of Ion (Section 5.7)

The name of the metal is unchanged. The name of the nonmetal is its base name with the ending *-ide*.

EXAMPLE 5.22 Naming Binary Ionic Compounds Containing a Metal That Forms Only One Type of Ion

Name the compound Al_2O_3.

SOLUTION

aluminum oxide

Naming Binary Ionic Compounds Containing a Metal That Forms More than One Type of Ion (Section 5.7)

EXAMPLE 5.23 Naming Binary Ionic Compounds Containing a Metal that Forms More than One Type of Ion

Name the compound Fe_2S_3.

SOLUTION

Since the names of these compounds include the charge of the metal ion, you must first determine that charge. To do this, calculate the total charge of the nonmetal ions.

The total charge of the metal ions must equal the total charge of the nonmetal ions, but have the opposite sign.

3 sulfide ions × (2−) = 6−

2 iron ions × (*ion charge*) = 6+

ion charge = 3+

Charge of each iron ion = 3+

The name of the compound is the name of the metal ion, followed by the charge of the metal ion, followed by the base name of the nonmetal + *-ide*.

iron (III) sulfide

Naming Compounds Containing a Polyatomic Ion (Section 5.7)

EXAMPLE 5.24 Naming Compounds Containing a Polyatomic Ion

Name the compound $Co(ClO_4)_2$.

SOLUTION

Name ionic compounds containing a polyatomic ion in the normal way, except substitute the name of the polyatomic ion (from Table 5.6) in place of the nonmetal.

Since the metal in this example forms more than one type of ion, you need to determine the charge on the metal ion. The charge of the metal ion must be equal in magnitude to the sum of the charges of the polyatomic ions but opposite in sign.

2 perchlorate ions × (1−) = 2−

Charge of cobalt ion = 2+

The name of the compound is the name of the metal ion, followed by the charge of the metal ion, followed by the name of the polyatomic ion.

cobalt(II) perchlorate

Naming Molecular Compounds (Section 5.8)

EXAMPLE 5.25 Naming Molecular Compounds

Name the compound NO_2.

SOLUTION

The name consists of a prefix indicating the number of atoms of the first element, followed by the name of the first element, and a prefix for the number of atoms of the second element followed by the base name of the second element plus the suffix *-ide*. When *mono-* occurs on the first element, it is normally dropped.

nitrogen dioxide

Naming Binary Acids (Section 5.9)

EXAMPLE 5.26 Naming Binary Acids

Name the acid HI(*aq*).

SOLUTION

The name begins with *hydro-*, followed by the base name of the nonmetal, plus the suffix *-ic* and then the word *acid*.

hydroiodic acid

Naming Oxyacids with an Oxyanion Ending in *-ate* (Section 5.9)

EXAMPLE 5.27 Naming Oxyacids with an Oxyanion Ending in *-ate*

Name the acid H_2SO_4 (*aq*).

SOLUTION

The name is the base name of the oxyanion + *-ic*, followed by the word *acid* (sulfate violates the rule somewhat, since in strict term, the base name would be *sulf*).

The oxyanion is sulfate. The name of the acid is *sulfuric acid*.

Naming Oxyacids with an Oxyanion Ending in *-ite* (Section 5.9)

The name is the base name of the oxyanion + *-ous*, followed by the word *acid*.

EXAMPLE 5.28 Naming Oxyacids with an Oxyanion Ending in *-ite*

Name the acid $HClO_2(aq)$.

SOLUTION

The oxyanion is chlorite. The name of the acid is *chlorous acid*.

Calculating Formula Mass (Section 5.11)

The formula mass is the sum of the atomic masses of all the atoms in the chemical formula. In determining the number of each type of atom, don't forget to multiply subscripts inside parentheses by subscripts outside parentheses.

EXAMPLE 5.29 Calculating Formula Mass

Calculate the formula mass of $Mg(NO_3)_2$.

SOLUTION

$$\text{Formula mass} = 24.31 + 2(14.01) + 6(16.00) = 148.33 \text{ amu}$$

KEY TERMS

acid [5.9]
atomic element [5.4]
ball-and-stick model [5.3]
binary acid [5.9]
binary compound [5.7]
chemical formula [5.3]
empirical formula [5.3]
formula mass [5.11]
formula unit [5.4]
ionic compound [5.4]
law of constant composition [5.2]
molecular compound [5.4]
molecular element [5.4]
molecular formula [5.3]
molecular model [5.3]
oxyacid [5.9]
oxyanion [5.7]
polyatomic ion [5.7]
space-filling model [5.3]
transition metals [5.7]

EXERCISES

QUESTIONS

1. Do the properties of an element change when it combines with another element to form a compound? Explain.
2. How might the world be different if elements did not combine to form compounds?
3. What is the law of constant composition? Who discovered it?
4. What is a chemical formula? List some examples.
5. In a chemical formula, which element is listed first?
6. In a chemical formula, how do you calculate the number of atoms of an element within parentheses? Give an example.
7. Explain the difference between a molecular formula and an empirical formula.
8. What is structural formula? What is the difference between a structural formula and a molecular model?
9. What is the difference between a molecular element and an atomic element? List the elements that occur as diatomic molecules.
10. What is the difference between an ionic compound and a molecular compound?
11. What is the difference between a common name for a compound and a systematic name?
12. List the metals that form only one type of ion (that is, metals whose charge is invariant from one compound to another). What are the group numbers of these metals?
13. Find the block in the periodic table of metals that tend to form more than one type of ion. What is the name of this block?
14. What is the basic form for the names of ionic compounds containing a metal that forms only one type of ion?
15. What is the basic form for the names of ionic compounds containing a metal that forms more than one type of ion?
16. Why are numbers needed in the names of ionic compounds containing a metal that forms more than one type of ion?
17. How are compounds containing a polyatomic ion named?
18. What polyatomic ions have a 2− charge? What polyatomic ions have a 3− charge?

19. What is the basic form for the names of molecular compounds?

20. How many atoms does each prefix specify? *mono-, di-, tri-, tetra-, penta-, hexa-.*

21. What is the basic form for the names of binary acids?

22. What is the basic form for the name of oxyacids whose oxyanions end with *-ate*?

23. What is the basic form for the name of oxyacids whose oxyanions end with *-ite*?

24. What is the formula mass of a compound?

PROBLEMS

CONSTANT COMPOSITION OF COMPOUNDS

25. Two samples of sodium chloride were decomposed into their constituent elements. One sample produced 4.65 g of sodium and 7.16 g of chlorine, and the other sample produced 7.45 g of sodium and 11.5 g of chlorine. Are these results consistent with the law of constant composition? Explain your answer.

26. Two samples of carbon tetrachloride were decomposed into their constituent elements. One sample produced 32.4 g of carbon and 373 g of chlorine, and the other sample produced 12.3 g of carbon and 112 g of chlorine. Are these results consistent with the law of constant composition? Explain your answer.

27. Upon decomposition, one sample of magnesium fluoride produced 1.65 kg of magnesium and 2.57 kg of fluorine. A second sample produced 1.32 kg of magnesium. How much fluorine (in grams) did the second sample produce?

28. The mass ratio of sodium to fluorine in sodium fluoride is 1.21:1. A sample of sodium fluoride produced 34.5 g of sodium upon decomposition. How much fluorine (in grams) was formed?

29. Use the law of constant composition to complete the table summarizing the amounts of nitrogen and oxygen produced upon the decomposition of several samples of dinitrogen monoxide.

	Mass N_2O	Mass N	Mass O
Sample A	2.85 g	1.82 g	1.03 g
Sample B	4.55 g	______	______
Sample C	______	______	1.35 g
Sample D	______	1.11 g	______

30. Use the law of constant composition to complete the table summarizing the amounts of iron and chlorine produced upon the decomposition of several samples of iron(III) chloride.

	Mass $FeCl_3$	Mass Fe	Mass Cl
Sample A	3.785 g	1.302 g	2.483 g
Sample B	2.175 g	______	______
Sample C	______	2.012 g	______
Sample D	______	______	2.329 g

CHEMICAL FORMULAS

31. Write a chemical formula for the compound containing one nitrogen atom for every three iodine atoms.

32. Write a chemical formula for the compound containing one carbon atom for every four bromine atoms.

33. Write chemical formulas for compounds containing:
  (a) three iron atoms for every four oxygen atoms
  (b) one phosphorus atom for every three chlorine atoms
  (c) one phosphorus atom for every five chlorine atoms
  (d) two silver atoms for every oxygen atom

34. Write chemical formulas for compounds containing:
  (a) one calcium atom for every two iodine atoms
  (b) two nitrogen atoms for every four oxygen atoms
  (c) one silicon atom for every two oxygen atoms
  (d) one zinc atom for every two chlorine atoms

35. How many oxygen atoms are in each chemical formula?
  (a) H_3PO_4
  (b) Na_2HPO_4
  (c) $Ca(HCO_3)_2$
  (d) $Ba(C_2H_3O_2)_2$

36. How many hydrogen atoms are in each of the formulas in Problem 35?

37. Determine the number of each type of atom in each formula.
(a) $MgCl_2$
(b) $NaNO_3$
(c) $Ca(NO_2)_2$
(d) $Sr(OH)_2$

38. Determine the number of each type of atom in each formula.
(a) NH_4Cl
(b) $Mg_3(PO_4)_2$
(c) NaCN
(d) $Ba(HCO_3)_2$

39. Complete the table.

Formula	Number of $C_2H_3O_2^-$ Units	Number of Carbon Atoms	Number of Hydrogen Atoms	Number of Oxygen Atoms	Number of Metal Atoms
$Mg(C_2H_3O_2)_2$					
$NaC_2H_3O_2$					
$Cr_2(C_2H_3O_2)_4$					

40. Complete the table.

Formula	Number of SO_4^{2-} Units	Number of Sulfur Atoms	Number of Oxygen Atoms	Number of Metal Atoms
$CaSO_4$				
$Al_2(SO_4)_3$				
K_2SO_4				

41. Give the empirical formula that corresponds to each molecular formula.
(a) C_2H_6
(b) N_2O_4
(c) $C_4H_6O_2$
(d) NH_3

42. Give the empirical formula that corresponds to each molecular formula.
(a) C_2H_2
(b) CO_2
(c) $C_6H_{12}O_6$
(d) B_2H_6

MOLECULAR VIEW OF ELEMENTS AND COMPOUNDS

43. Classify each element as atomic or molecular.
(a) chlorine
(b) argon
(c) cobalt
(d) hydrogen

44. Which elements have molecules as their basic units?
(a) helium
(b) oxygen
(c) iron
(d) bromine

45. Classify each compound as ionic or molecular.
(a) CS_2
(b) CuO
(c) KI
(d) PCl_3

46. Classify each compound as ionic or molecular.
(a) PtO_2
(b) CF_2Cl_2
(c) CO
(d) SO_3

47. Match the substances on the left with the basic units that compose them on the right.

helium	molecules
CCl_4	formula units
K_2SO_4	diatomic molecules
bromine	single atoms

48. Match the substances on the left with the basic units that compose them on the right.

NI_3	molecules
copper metal	single atoms
$SrCl_2$	diatomic molecules
nitrogen	formula units

49. What are the basic units—single atoms, molecules, or formula units—that compose each substance?
(a) $BaBr_2$
(b) Ne
(c) I_2
(d) CO

50. What are the basic units—single atoms, molecules, or formula units—that compose each substance?
(a) Rb_2O
(b) N_2
(c) $Fe(NO_3)_2$
(d) N_2F_4

51. Classify each compound as ionic or molecular. If it is ionic, determine whether the metal forms only one type of ion or more than one type of ion.
(a) KCl
(b) CBr_4
(c) NO_2
(d) $Sn(SO_4)_2$

52. Classify each compound as ionic or molecular. If it is ionic, determine whether the metal forms only one type of ion or more than one type of ion.
(a) $CoCl_2$
(b) CF_4
(c) $BaSO_4$
(d) NO

WRITING FORMULAS FOR IONIC COMPOUNDS

53. Write a formula for the ionic compound that forms from each pair of elements.
(a) sodium and sulfur
(b) strontium and oxygen
(c) aluminum and sulfur
(d) magnesium and chlorine

54. Write a formula for the ionic compound that forms from each pair of elements.
(a) aluminum and oxygen
(b) beryllium and iodine
(c) calcium and sulfur
(d) calcium and iodine

55. Write a formula for the compound that forms from potassium and
(a) acetate
(b) chromate
(c) phosphate
(d) cyanide

56. Write a formula for the compound that forms from calcium and
(a) hydroxide
(b) carbonate
(c) phosphate
(d) hydrogen phosphate

57. Write formulas for the compounds formed from the element on the left and each element on the right.
(a) Li N, O, F
(b) Ba N, O, F
(c) Al N, O, F

58. Write formulas for the compounds formed from the element on the left and each polyatomic ion on the right.
(a) Rb NO_3^-, SO_4^{2-}, PO_4^{3-}
(b) Sr NO_3^-, SO_4^{2-}, PO_4^{3-}
(c) In NO_3^-, SO_4^{2-}, PO_4^{3-}
(Assume In charge is 3+.)

NAMING IONIC COMPOUNDS

59. Name each ionic compound. In each of these compounds, the metal forms only one type of ion.
(a) CsCl
(b) $SrBr_2$
(c) K_2O
(d) LiF

60. Name each ionic compound. In each of these compounds, the metal forms only one type of ion.
(a) LiI
(b) MgS
(c) BaF_2
(d) NaF

61. Name each ionic compound. In each of these compounds, the metal forms more than one type of ion.
(a) $CrCl_2$
(b) $CrCl_3$
(c) SnO_2
(d) PbI_2

62. Name each ionic compound. In each of these compounds, the metal forms more than one type of ion.
(a) $HgBr_2$
(b) Fe_2O_3
(c) CuI_2
(d) $SnCl_4$

63. Determine whether the metal in each ionic compound forms only one type of ion or more than one type of ion and name the compound accordingly.
   (a) Cr_2O_3
   (b) NaI
   (c) $CaBr_2$
   (d) SnO

64. Determine whether the metal in each ionic compound forms only one type of ion or more than one type of ion and name the compound accordingly.
   (a) FeI_3
   (b) $PbCl_4$
   (c) SrI_2
   (d) BaO

65. Name each ionic compound containing a polyatomic ion.
   (a) $Ba(NO_3)_2$
   (b) $Pb(C_2H_3O_2)_2$
   (c) NH_4I
   (d) $KClO_3$
   (e) $CoSO_4$
   (f) $NaClO_4$

66. Name each ionic compound containing a polyatomic ion.
   (a) $Ba(OH)_2$
   (b) $Fe(OH)_3$
   (c) $Cu(NO_2)_2$
   (d) $PbSO_4$
   (e) KClO
   (f) $Mg(C_2H_3O_2)_2$

67. Name each polyatomic ion.
   (a) BrO^-
   (b) BrO_2^-
   (c) BrO_3^-
   (d) BrO_4^-

68. Name each polyatomic ion.
   (a) IO^-
   (b) IO_2^-
   (c) IO_3^-
   (d) IO_4^-

69. Write a formula for each ionic compound.
   (a) copper(II) bromide
   (b) silver nitrate
   (c) potassium hydroxide
   (d) sodium sulfate
   (e) potassium hydrogen sulfate
   (f) sodium hydrogen carbonate

70. Write a formula for each ionic compound.
   (a) copper(I) chlorate
   (b) potassium permanganate
   (c) lead(II) chromate
   (d) calcium fluoride
   (e) iron(II) phosphate
   (f) lithium hydrogen sulfite

NAMING MOLECULAR COMPOUNDS

71. Name each molecular compound.
   (a) SO_2
   (b) NI_3
   (c) BrF_5
   (d) NO
   (e) N_4Se_4

72. Name each molecular compound.
   (a) XeF_4
   (b) PI_3
   (c) SO_3
   (d) $SiCl_4$
   (e) I_2O_5

73. Write a formula for each molecular compound.
   (a) carbon monoxide
   (b) disulfur tetrafluoride
   (c) dichlorine monoxide
   (d) phosphorus pentafluoride
   (e) boron tribromide
   (f) diphosphorus pentasulfide

74. Write a formula for each molecular compound.
   (a) chlorine monoxide
   (b) xenon tetroxide
   (c) xenon hexafluoride
   (d) carbon tetrabromide
   (e) diboron tetrachloride
   (f) tetraphosphorus triselenide

75. Determine whether the name shown for each molecular compound is correct. If not, provide the compound's correct name.
(a) PBr_5 phosphorus(V) pentabromide
(b) P_2O_3 phosphorus trioxide
(c) SF_4 monosulfur hexafluoride
(d) NF_3 nitrogen trifluoride

76. Determine whether the name shown for each molecular compound is correct. If not, provide the compound's correct name.
(a) NCl_3 nitrogen chloride
(b) CI_4 carbon(IV) iodide
(c) CO carbon oxide
(d) SCl_4 sulfur tetrachloride

NAMING ACIDS

77. Determine whether each acid is a binary acid or an oxyacid and name each acid. If the acid is an oxyacid, also provide the name of the oxyanion.
(a) $HNO_2\,(aq)$
(b) $HI\,(aq)$
(c) $H_2SO_4\,(aq)$
(d) $HNO_3\,(aq)$

78. Determine whether each acid is a binary acid or an oxyacid and name each acid. If the acid is an oxyacid, also provide the name of the oxyanion.
(a) $H_2CO_3\,(aq)$
(b) $HC_2H_3O_2\,(aq)$
(c) $H_3PO_4(aq)$
(d) $HCl\,(aq)$

79. Name each acid.
(a) HClO
(b) $HClO_2$
(c) $HClO_3$
(d) $HClO_4$

80. Name each acid. (*Hint:* The names of the oxyanions are analogous to the names of the oxyanions of chlorine.)
(a) $HBrO_3$
(b) HIO_3

81. Write a formula for each acid.
(a) phosphoric acid
(b) hydrobromic acid
(c) sulfurous acid

82. Write a formula for each acid.
(a) hydrofluoric acid
(b) hydrocyanic acid
(c) chlorous acid

FORMULA MASS

83. Calculate the formula mass for each compound.
(a) HNO_3
(b) $CaBr_2$
(c) CCl_4
(d) $Sr(NO_3)_2$

84. Calculate the formula mass for each compound.
(a) CS_2
(b) $C_6H_{12}O_6$
(c) $Fe(NO_3)_3$
(d) C_7H_{16}

85. Arrange the compounds in order of decreasing formula mass.

Ag_2O, PtO_2, $Al(NO_3)_3$, PBr_3

86. Arrange the compounds in order of decreasing formula mass.

WO_2, Rb_2SO_4, $Pb(C_2H_3O_2)_2$, RbI

CUMULATIVE PROBLEMS

87. Write a molecular formula for each molecular model. (White = hydrogen; red = oxygen; black = carbon; blue = nitrogen; yellow = sulfur)

88. Write a molecular formula for each molecular model. (White = hydrogen; red = oxygen; black = carbon; blue = nitrogen; yellow = sulfur)

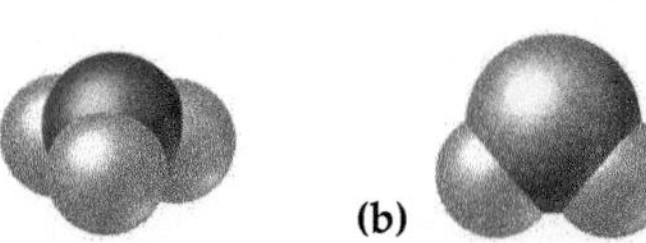

89. How many chlorine atoms are in each set?
  (a) three carbon tetrachloride molecules
  (b) two calcium chloride formula units
  (c) four phosphorus trichloride molecules
  (d) seven sodium chloride formula units

90. How many oxygen atoms are in each set?
  (a) four dinitrogen monoxide molecules
  (b) two calcium carbonate formula units
  (c) three sulfur dioxide molecules
  (d) five perchlorate ions

91. Specify the number of hydrogen atoms (white) represented in each set of molecular models:

(a) (b) (c)

92. Specify the number of oxygen atoms (red) represented in each set of molecular models:

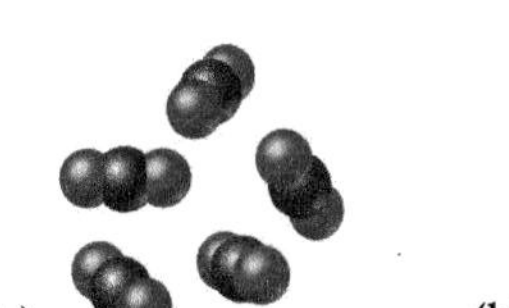
(a)

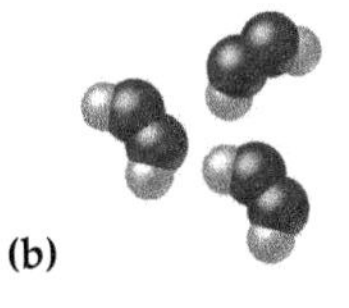
(b)

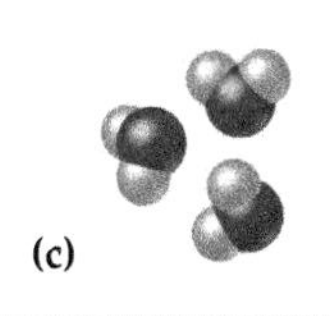
(c)

93. Complete the table:

Formula	Type of Compound (Ionic, Molecular, Acid)	Name
N_2H_4	molecular	______
______	______	potassium chloride
H_2CrO_4 (*aq*)	______	______
______	______	cobalt(III) cyanide

94. Complete the table:

Formula	Type of Compound (Ionic, Molecular, Acid)	Name
$K_2Cr_2O_7$	ionic	______
HBr (*aq*)	______	hydrobromic acid
______	______	dinitrogen pentoxide
PbO_2	______	______

95. Determine whether each name is correct for the given formula. If not, provide the correct name.
  (a) $Ca(NO_2)_2$ calcium nitrate
  (b) K_2O dipotassium monoxide
  (c) PCl_3 phosphorus chloride
  (d) $PbCO_3$ lead(II) carbonate
  (e) KIO_2 potassium hypoiodite

96. Determine whether each name is correct for the given formula. If not, provide the correct name.
  (a) HNO_3 (*aq*) hydrogen nitrate
  (b) $NaClO$ sodium hypochlorite
  (c) CaI_2 calcium diiodide
  (d) $SnCrO_4$ tin chromate
  (e) $NaBrO_3$ sodium bromite

97. For each compound, list the correct formula and calculate the formula mass.
  (a) tin(IV) sulfate
  (b) nitrous acid
  (c) sodium bicarbonate
  (d) phosphorus pentafluoride

98. For each compound, list the correct formula and calculate the formula mass.
  (a) barium bromide
  (b) dinitrogen trioxide
  (c) copper(I) sulfate
  (d) hydrobromic acid

99. Name each compound and calculate its formula mass.
  (a) PtO_2
  (b) N_2O_5
  (c) $Al(ClO_3)_3$
  (d) PBr_5

100. Name each compound and calculate its formula mass.
  (a) $Al_2(SO_4)_3$
  (b) P_2O_3
  (c) $HClO$ (*aq*)
  (d) $Cr(C_2H_3O_2)_3$

101. A compound contains only carbon and hydrogen and has a formula mass of 28.06 amu. What is its molecular formula?

102. A compound contains only nitrogen and oxygen and has a formula mass of 44.02 amu. What is its molecular formula?

103. Carbon has two naturally occurring isotopes: carbon-12 (mass = 12.00 amu) and carbon-13 (mass = 13.00 amu). Chlorine also has two naturally occurring isotopes: chlorine-35 (mass = 34.97 amu) and chlorine-37 (mass = 36.97 amu). How many CCl_4 molecules of different masses can exist? Determine the mass (in amu) of each of them.

104. Nitrogen has two naturally occurring isotopes: nitrogen-14 (mass = 14.00 amu) and nitrogen-15 (mass = 15.00 amu). Bromine also has two naturally occurring isotopes: bromine-79 (mass = 78.92 amu) and bromine-81 (mass = 80.92 amu). How many NBr_3 molecules of different masses can exist? Determine the mass (in amu) of each of them.

HIGHLIGHT PROBLEMS

105. Examine each substance and the corresponding molecular view and classify it as an atomic element, a molecular element, a molecular compound, or an ionic compound.

(a)

(b)

(c)

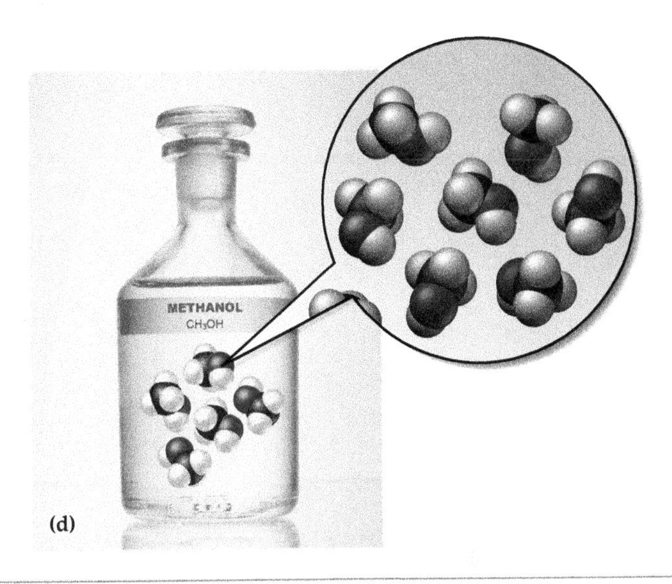

(d)

106. Molecules can be as small as two atoms or as large as thousands of atoms. In 1962, Max F. Perutz and John C. Kendrew were awarded the Nobel Prize for their discovery of the structure of hemoglobin, a very large molecule that transports oxygen from the lungs to cells through the bloodstream. The chemical formula of hemoglobin is $C_{2952}H_{4664}O_{832}N_{812}S_8Fe_4$. Calculate the formula mass of hemoglobin.

▶ Max Perutz and John C. Kendrew won a Nobel Prize in 1962 for determining the structure of hemoglobin by X-ray diffraction.

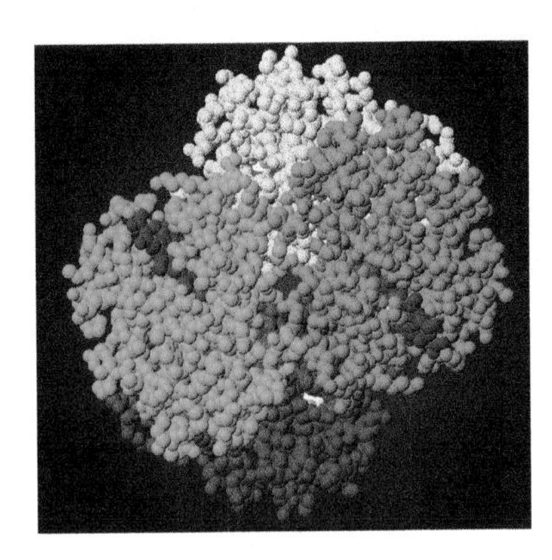

◀ Computer generated model of hemoglobin.

107. Examine each consumer product label. Write chemical formulas for as many of the compounds as possible based on what you have learned in this chapter.

(a)

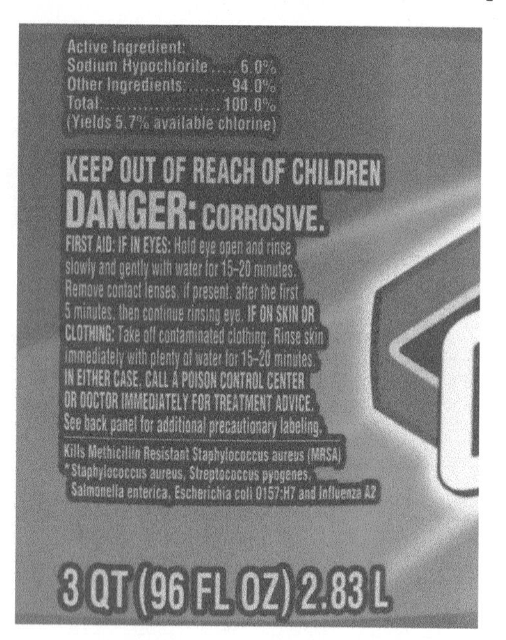

Active Ingredient:
Sodium Hypochlorite 6.0%
Other Ingredients: 94.0%
Total: 100.0%
(Yields 5.7% available chlorine)
KEEP OUT OF REACH OF CHILDREN
DANGER: CORROSIVE.
FIRST AID: IF IN EYES: Hold eye open and rinse slowly and gently with water for 15–20 minutes. Remove contact lenses, if present, after the first 5 minutes, then continue rinsing eye. IF ON SKIN OR CLOTHING: Take off contaminated clothing. Rinse skin immediately with plenty of water for 15–20 minutes. IN EITHER CASE, CALL A POISON CONTROL CENTER OR DOCTOR IMMEDIATELY FOR TREATMENT ADVICE.
See back panel for additional precautionary labeling.
Kills Methicillin Resistant Staphylococcus aureus (MRSA)
*Staphylococcus aureus, Streptococcus pyogenes, Salmonella enterica, Escherichia coli 0157:H7 and Influenza A2
3 QT (96 FL OZ) 2.83 L

(b)

NOTICE! PROTECTIVE INNER SEAL BENEATH CAP. IF MISSING OR DAMAGED, DO NOT USE CONTENTS.
Drug Facts
Active ingredients (in each tablet) Purpose
Calcium carbonate 1000 mg .... Antacid
Simethicone 60 mg .... Antigas
Uses for the relief of
• acid indigestion
• heartburn
• sour stomach
• upset stomach associated with these symptoms
• bloating and pressure commonly referred to as gas
Warning
Do not take more than 8 tablets in a 24-hour period or use the maximum dosage for more than 2 weeks except under the advice and supervision of a physician
Ask a doctor before use if you have
• kidney stones • a calcium-restricted diet
Ask a doctor or pharmacist before use if your are presently taking a prescription drug. Antacids may interact with certain prescription drugs.
When using this product
• at maximum dose, constipation may occur
Stop use and ask a doctor if
• symptoms last more than two weeks
Keep out of reach of children.

(c)

Drug Facts
Active ingredients (in each 5 mL teaspoon) Purposes
Aluminum hydroxide (equivalent to dried gel, USP) 400 mg .... Antacid
Magnesium hydroxide 400 mg .... Antacid
Simethicone 40 mg .... Antigas
Use relieves: ■ heartburn ■ acid indigestion ■ sour stomach ■ upset stomach due to these symptoms ■ pressure and bloating commonly referred to as gas
Warnings
Ask a doctor before use if you have
■ kidney disease ■ a magnesium-restricted diet
Ask a doctor or pharmacist if you are taking a prescription drug. Antacids may interact with certain prescription drugs.
Stop use and ask a doctor if symptoms last more than 2 weeks.
Keep out of reach of children.
Directions ■ shake well ■ adults/children 12 years and older: take 2-4 teaspoonfuls between meals, at bedtime, or as directed by a doctor ■ do not take more than 12 teaspoonfuls in a 24-hour period, or use the maximum dosage for more than 2 weeks ■ children under 12 years: ask a doctor
Other information ■ each teaspoon contains: magnesium 171 mg ■ do not use if breakaway band on plastic cap is broken or missing ■ does not meet USP requirements for preservative effectiveness ■ do not freeze
Inactive ingredients butylparaben, carboxymethylcellulose sodium, flavors, hypromellose, microcrystalline cellulose, propylparaben, purified water, sodium saccharin, sorbitol
Questions or comments?
1-800-469-5268 (English) or
1-888-466-8746 (Spanish)
Johnson & Johnson · MERCK
Consumer Pharmaceuticals Co.
FORT WASHINGTON, PA 19034 USA
7 16837 62412

(d)

Nutrition Facts
Serving Size 1/8 tsp (0.6g)
Servings Per Container about 472
Amount Per Serving
Calories 0
% Daily Value*
Total Fat 0g 0%
Sodium 65mg 3%
Total Carb. 0g 0%
Protein 0g
Calcium 2%
Not a significant source of calories from fat, saturated fat, trans fat, cholesterol, dietary fiber, sugars, vitamin A, vitamin C and iron.
*Percent Daily Values are based on a 2,000 calorie diet.
Ingredients: Cornstarch, Sodium Bicarbonate, Sodium Aluminum Sulfate, Monocalcium Phosphate.
CLABBER GIRL CORPORATION
TERRE HAUTE, IN 47808
davisbakingpowder.com
MADE IN USA

▶ANSWERS TO SKILLBUILDER EXERCISES

Skillbuilder 5.1	Yes, because in both cases $\frac{\text{Mass O}}{\text{Mass C}} = 1.3$
Skillbuilder 5.2	**(a)** Ag_2S **(b)** N_2O **(c)** TiO_2
Skillbuilder 5.3	two K atoms, one S atom, four O atoms
Skillbuilder Plus, p. 131	two Al atoms, three S atoms, twelve O atoms
Skillbuilder 5.4	**(a)** molecular element **(b)** molecular compound **(c)** atomic element **(d)** ionic compound **(e)** ionic compound
Skillbuilder 5.5	$SrCl_2$
Skillbuilder 5.6	AlN
Skillbuilder 5.7	$CaBr_2$
Skillbuilder 5.8	potassium bromide
Skillbuilder Plus, p. 139	zinc nitride
Skillbuilder 5.9	lead(II) oxide
Skillbuilder 5.10	manganese(II) nitrate
Skillbuilder 5.11	dinitrogen tetroxide
Skillbuilder 5.12	hydrofluoric acid
Skillbuilder 5.13	nitrous acid
Skillbuilder 5.15	44.02 amu

▶ANSWERS TO CONCEPTUAL CHECKPOINTS

5.1 (b) This formula represents 2 Al atoms + 3 (2 Cr atoms + 7 O atoms) = 29 atoms.

5.2 (b) The figure represents a molecular compound because the compound exists as individual molecules. Figure (a) represents an ionic compound with formula units in a lattice structure.

5.3 Because calcium forms only one type of ion (Ca^{2+}); therefore, the charge of the ion is not included in the name (because it is always the same, 2+).

5.4 Iodate

5.5 (b)

Moonlight Diner
Specials
Breaksfast Special
Two eggs, Three strips of bacon, Sausage link, Toast ,NaCl
$5.95
Lunch Special
1500 milligrams a day
Omelettes
Served with side of NaCl
Denver Omelette
BP Delight
Atherosclerosis
Sodium Chloride
Hypertension

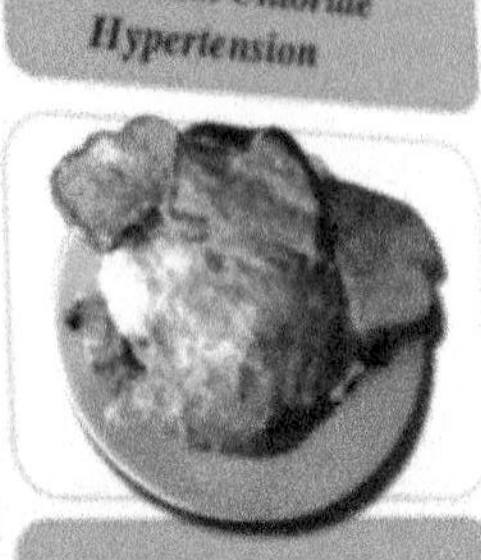

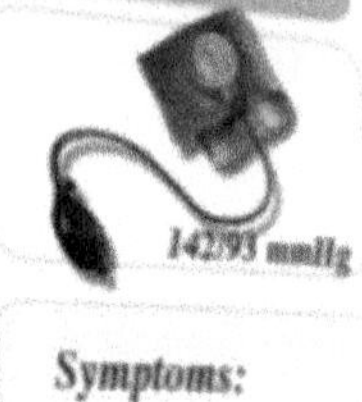
142/93 mmHg
Symptoms:
Chest pain
Confusion
Ear noise or buzzing
Irregular heartbeat
Nosebleed
On the Healthy Side
120/80 mmHg

CHAPTER 6

Chemical Composition

"In science, you don't ask why, you ask how much."

Erwin Chargaff (1905–2002)

6.1 How Much Sodium?

Sodium is an important dietary mineral that we eat in our food, primarily as sodium chloride (table salt). Sodium is involved in the regulation of body fluids, and eating too much of it can lead to high blood pressure. High blood pressure, in turn, increases the risk of stroke and heart attack. Consequently, people with high blood pressure should limit their sodium intake. The FDA recommends that a person consume less than 2.4 g (2400 mg) of sodium per day. However, sodium is usually consumed as sodium chloride, so the mass of sodium that we eat is not the same as the mass of sodium chloride that we eat. How many grams of sodium chloride can we consume and still stay below the FDA recommendation for sodium?

To answer this question, we need to know the *chemical composition* of sodium chloride. From Chapter 5, we are familiar with its formula, NaCl, so we know that there is one sodium ion to every chloride ion. However, since the masses of sodium and chlorine are different, the relationship between the mass of sodium and the mass of sodium chloride is not clear from the chemical formula alone. In this chapter, we learn how to use the information in a chemical formula, together with atomic and formula masses, to calculate the amount of a constituent element in a given amount of a compound (or vice versa).

Chemical composition is important not just for assessing dietary sodium intake, but for addressing many other issues as well. A company that mines iron, for example, wants to know how much iron it can extract from a given amount of iron ore; a company interested in developing hydrogen as a potential fuel would want to know how much hydrogen it can extract from a given amount of water. Many environmental issues also require knowledge of chemical composition. An estimate of the threat of ozone depletion requires knowing how much chlorine is in a given amount of a particular chlorofluorocarbon such as freon-12. To determine

◀ Ordinary table salt is a compound called sodium chloride. The sodium within sodium chloride is linked to high blood pressure. In this chapter, we learn how to determine how much sodium is in a given amount of sodium chloride.

▲ The mining of iron requires knowing how much iron is in a given amount of iron ore.

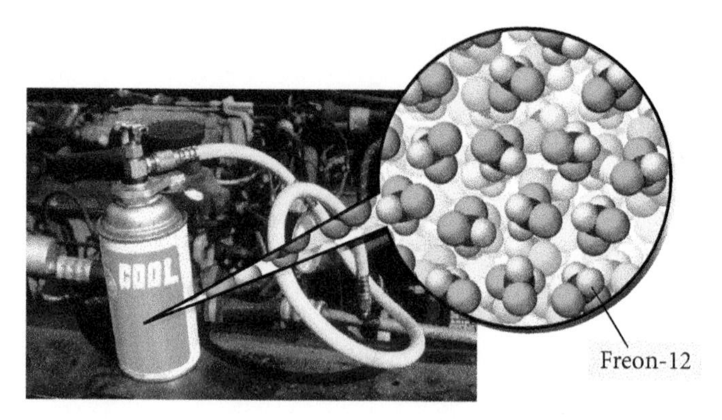

▲ Estimating the threat of ozone depletion requires knowing the amount of chlorine in a given amount of a chlorofluorocarbon.

these kinds of quantities, we must understand the relationships inherent in a chemical formula and the relationship between numbers of atoms or molecules and their masses. In this chapter, we examine these relationships.

6.2 Counting Nails by the Pound

3.4 lbs nails

8.25 grams carbon

▲ Asking how many nails are in a given weight of nails is similar to asking how many atoms are in a given mass of an element. In both cases, we count the objects by weighing them.

Some hardware stores sell nails by the pound, which is easier than selling them by the nail because customers often need hundreds of nails and counting them takes too long. However, a customer may still want to know the number of nails contained in a given weight of nails. This problem is similar to asking how many atoms are in a given mass of an element. With atoms, however, we *must* use their mass as a way to count them because atoms are too small and too numerous to count individually. Even if you could see atoms and counted them 24 hours a day for as long as you lived, you would barely begin to count the number of atoms in something as small as a grain of sand. However, just as the hardware store customer wants to know the number of nails in a given weight, we want to know the number of atoms in a given mass. How do we do that?

Suppose the hardware store customer buys 2.60 lb of medium-sized nails and a dozen nails weigh 0.150 lb. How many nails did the customer buy? This calculation requires two conversions: one between pounds and dozens and another between dozens and number of nails. The conversion factor for the first part is the weight per dozen nails.

$$0.150 \text{ lb nails} = 1 \text{ doz nails}$$

The conversion factor for the second part is the number of nails in one dozen.

$$1 \text{ doz nails} = 12 \text{ nails}$$

The solution map for the problem is:

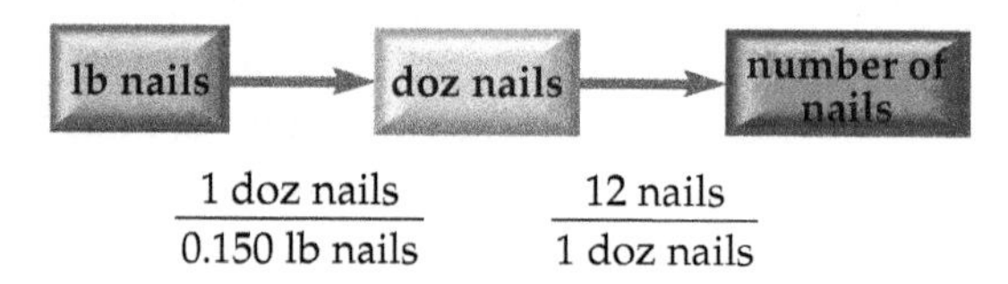

Beginning with 2.60 lb and using the solution map as a guide, we convert from lb to number of nails.

$$2.60 \text{ lb nails} \times \frac{1 \text{ doz nails}}{0.150 \text{ lb nails}} \times \frac{12 \text{ nails}}{1 \text{ doz nails}} = 208 \text{ nails}$$

The customer who bought 2.60 lb of nails has 208 nails. He counted the nails by weighing them. If the customer purchased a different size of nail, the first conversion factor—relating pounds to dozens—would change, but the second conversion factor would not. One dozen corresponds to 12 nails, regardless of their size.

6.3 Counting Atoms by the Gram

1 mole of copper atoms

▲ Twenty-two *copper* pennies contain approximately 1 mol of copper atoms. Pennies were mostly copper until 1982, at which point the U.S. Mint started making them out of zinc with only a copper coating (because copper became too valuable).

The value of the mole is actually an empirically measured quantity.

1 mole of helium atoms

▲ Two large helium balloons contain approximately 1 mol of helium atoms.

Determining the number of atoms in a sample with a certain mass is similar to determining the number of nails in a sample with a certain weight. With nails, we used a dozen as a convenient number in our conversions, but a dozen is too small to use with atoms. We need a larger number because atoms are so small. The chemist's "dozen" is called the **mole (mol)** and has a value of 6.022×10^{23}.

$$1 \text{ mol} = 6.022 \times 10^{23}$$

This number is also called **Avogadro's number**, named after Amadeo Avogadro (1776–1856).

The first thing to understand about the mole is that it can specify Avogadro's number of anything. *One mole of anything is* 6.022×10^{23} *units of that thing*. For example, one mole of marbles corresponds to 6.022×10^{23} marbles, and one mole of sand grains corresponds to 6.022×10^{23} sand grains. One mole of atoms, ions, or molecules generally makes up objects of reasonable size. For example, 22 *copper* pennies (pennies were mostly copper until 1982) contain approximately 1 mol of copper (Cu) atoms, and a couple of large helium balloons contain approximately 1 mol of helium (He) atoms.

The second thing to understand about the mole is how it gets its specific value. *The numerical value of the mole is defined as being equal to the number of atoms in exactly 12 g of pure carbon-12.*

This definition of the mole establishes a relationship between mass (grams of carbon) and number of atoms (Avogadro's number). This relationship, as we will see shortly, allows us to count atoms by weighing them.

CONVERTING BETWEEN MOLES AND NUMBER OF ATOMS

Converting between moles and number of atoms is similar to converting between dozens and number of nails. To convert between moles of atoms and number of atoms, we use the conversion factors:

$$\frac{1 \text{ mol}}{6.022 \times 10^{23} \text{ atoms}} \quad \text{or} \quad \frac{6.022 \times 10^{23} \text{ atoms}}{1 \text{ mol}}$$

For example, suppose we want to convert 3.5 mol of helium to a number of helium atoms. We set up the problem in the standard way.

GIVEN: 3.5 mol He

FIND: He atoms

RELATIONSHIPS USED 1 mol He = 6.022×10^{23} He atoms

SOLUTION MAP We draw a solution map showing the conversion from moles of He to He atoms.

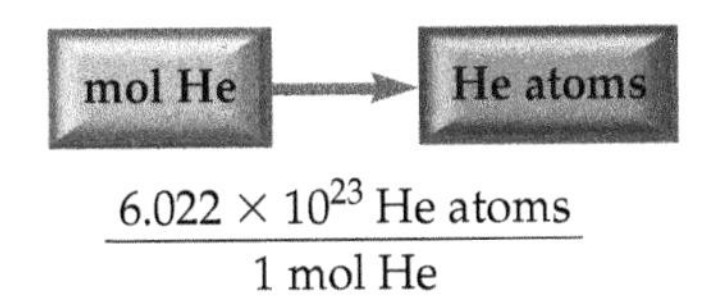

SOLUTION

Beginning with 3.5 mol He, we use the conversion factor to get to He atoms.

$$3.5\ \text{mol He} \times \frac{6.022 \times 10^{23}\ \text{He atoms}}{1\ \text{mol He}} = 2.1 \times 10^{24}\ \text{He atoms}$$

EXAMPLE 6.1 Converting between Moles and Number of Atoms

A silver ring contains 1.1×10^{22} silver atoms. How many moles of silver are in the ring?

SORT You are given the number of silver atoms and asked to find the number of moles.	GIVEN: 1.1×10^{22} Ag atoms FIND: mol Ag
STRATEGIZE Draw a solution map, beginning with silver atoms and ending at moles. The conversion factor is Avogadro's number.	SOLUTION MAP 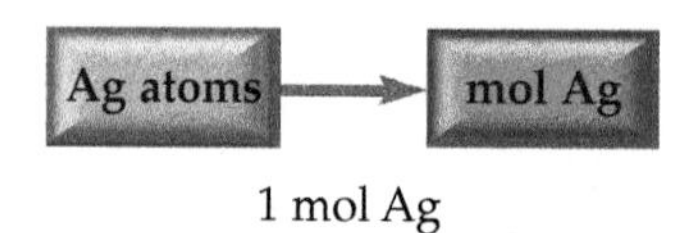 $\frac{1\ \text{mol Ag}}{6.022 \times 10^{23}\ \text{Ag atoms}}$ RELATIONSHIPS USED 1 mol Ag = 6.022×10^{23} Ag atoms (Avogadro's number)
SOLVE Follow the solution map to solve the problem. Beginning with 1.1×10^{22} Ag atoms, use the conversion factor to get to moles of Ag.	SOLUTION $1.1 \times 10^{22}\ \text{Ag atoms} \times \frac{1\ \text{mol Ag}}{6.022 \times 10^{23}\ \text{Ag atoms}} = 1.8 \times 10^{-2}\ \text{mol Ag}$
CHECK Are the units correct? Does the answer make physical sense?	The units, mol Ag, are the desired units. The magnitude of the answer is orders of magnitude smaller than the given quantity because it takes many atoms to make a mole, so we expect the answer to be orders of magnitude smaller than the given quantity.

▶**SKILLBUILDER 6.1 | Converting between Moles and Number of Atoms**

How many gold atoms are in a pure gold ring containing 8.83×10^{-2} mol Au?

▶**FOR MORE PRACTICE** Example 6.13, Problems 17, 18, 19, 20.

CONVERTING BETWEEN GRAMS AND MOLES OF AN ELEMENT

We just learned how to convert between moles and number of atoms, which is like converting between dozens and number of nails. We need one more conversion factor to convert from the mass of a sample to the number of atoms in the sample. For nails, we used the weight of one dozen nails; for atoms, we use the mass of one mole of atoms.

> The mass of 1 mol of atoms of an element is its **molar mass**. The value of an element's molar mass in grams per mole is numerically equal to the element's atomic mass in atomic mass units.

Recall that Avogadro's number, the number of atoms in a mole, is defined as the number of atoms in exactly 12 g of carbon-12. Since the atomic mass unit is defined as one-twelfth of the mass of a carbon-12 atom, it follows that the molar mass of any element—the mass of 1 mol of atoms in grams of that element—is equal to the atomic mass of that element expressed in atomic mass units. For example, copper has an atomic mass of 63.55 amu; therefore, 1 mol of copper atoms has a mass of 63.55 g, and the molar mass of copper is 63.55 g/mol. Just as the weight of 1 doz nails changes for different nails, so the mass of 1 mol of atoms changes for different elements: 1 mol of sulfur atoms (sulfur atoms are lighter than copper atoms) has a mass of 32.07 g; 1 mol of carbon atoms (lighter than sulfur) has a mass of 12.01 g; and 1 mol of lithium atoms (lighter yet) has a mass of 6.94 g.

$$32.07 \text{ g sulfur} = 1 \text{ mol sulfur} = 6.022 \times 10^{23} \text{ S atoms}$$

$$12.01 \text{ g carbon} = 1 \text{ mol carbon} = 6.022 \times 10^{23} \text{ C atoms}$$

$$6.94 \text{ g lithium} = 1 \text{ mol lithium} = 6.022 \times 10^{23} \text{ Li atoms}$$

The lighter the atom, the less mass in one mole of that atom (▼ Figure 6.1).

Therefore, the molar mass of any element becomes a conversion factor between grams of that element and moles of that element. For carbon:

$$12.01 \text{ g C} = 1 \text{ mol C} \quad \text{or} \quad \frac{12.01 \text{ g C}}{1 \text{ mol C}} \quad \text{or} \quad \frac{1 \text{ mol C}}{12.01 \text{ g C}}$$

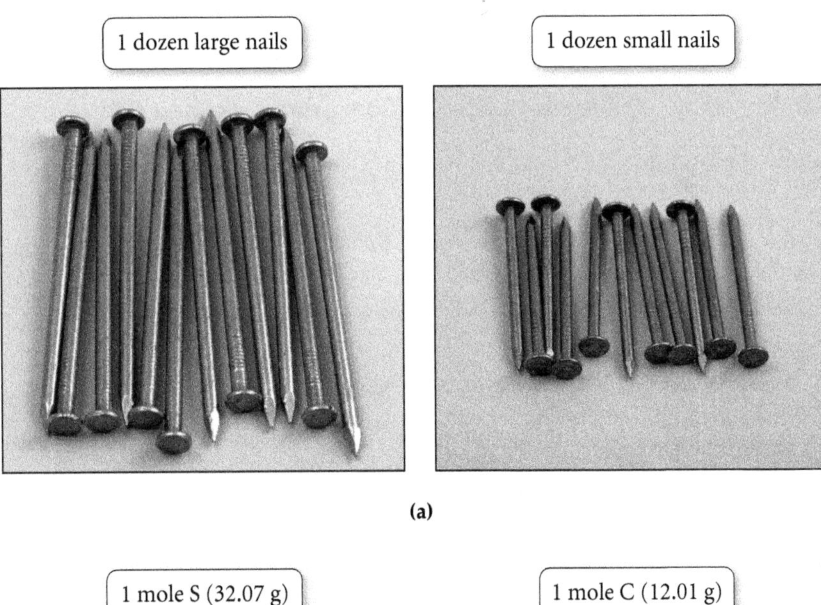

▶ **FIGURE 6.1 The mass of 1 mol** **(a)** Each of these pictures shows the same number of nails: 12. As you can see, 12 large nails have more weight and occupy more space than 12 small nails. The same is true for atoms. **(b)** Each of these samples has the same number of atoms: 6.022×10^{23}. Since sulfur atoms are more massive and larger than carbon atoms, 1 mol of S atoms is heavier and occupies more space than 1 mol of C atoms.

A 0.58-g diamond would be about a three-carat diamond.

Suppose we want to calculate the number of moles of carbon in a 0.58-g diamond (pure carbon).

We first sort the information in the problem.

GIVEN: 0.58 g C

FIND: mol C

SOLUTION MAP We then strategize by drawing a solution map showing the conversion from grams of C to moles of C. The conversion factor is the molar mass of carbon.

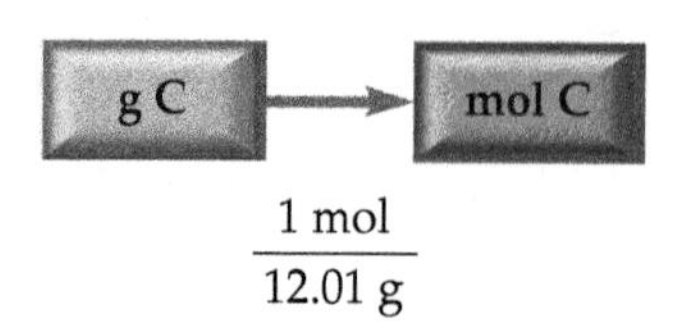

RELATIONSHIPS USED

12.01 g C = 1 mol C (molar mass of carbon, from periodic table)

SOLUTION

Finally, we solve the problem by following the solution map.

$$0.58\ \text{g C} \times \frac{1\ \text{mol C}}{12.01\ \text{g C}} = 4.8 \times 10^{-2}\ \text{mol C}$$

EXAMPLE 6.2 The Mole Concept—Converting between Grams and Moles

Calculate the number of moles of sulfur in 57.8 g of sulfur.

SORT

Begin by sorting the information in the problem. You are given the mass of sulfur and asked to find the number of moles.

GIVEN: 57.8 g S

FIND: mol S

STRATEGIZE

Draw a solution map showing the conversion from g S to mol S. The conversion factor is the molar mass of sulfur.

SOLUTION MAP

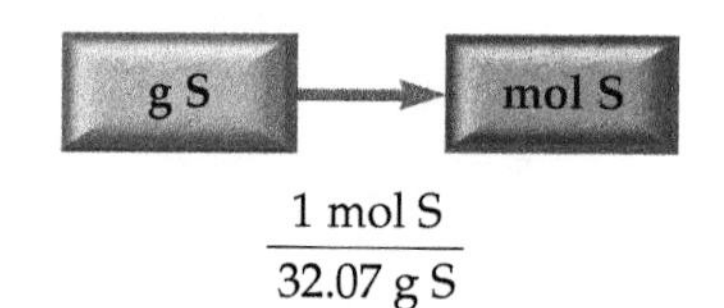

RELATIONSHIPS USED

32.07 g S = 1 mol S (molar mass of sulfur, from periodic table)

SOLVE

Follow the solution map to solve the problem. Begin with 57.8 g S and use the conversion factor to get to mol S.

SOLUTION

$$57.8\ \text{g S} \times \frac{1\ \text{mol S}}{32.07\ \text{g S}} = 1.80\ \text{mol S}$$

CHECK

Check your answer. Are the units correct? Does the answer make physical sense?

The units (mol S) are correct. The magnitude of the answer makes sense because 1 mole of S has a mass of 32.07 g; therefore, 57.8 g of S should be close to 2 moles.

▶SKILLBUILDER 6.2 | The Mole Concept—Converting between Grams and Moles

Calculate the number of grams of sulfur in 2.78 mol of sulfur.

▶FOR MORE PRACTICE Example 6.14; Problems 25, 26, 27, 28, 29, 30.

CONVERTING BETWEEN GRAMS OF AN ELEMENT AND NUMBER OF ATOMS

Now, suppose we want to know the number of carbon *atoms* in the 0.58-g diamond. We first convert from grams to moles and then from moles to number of atoms. The solution map is:

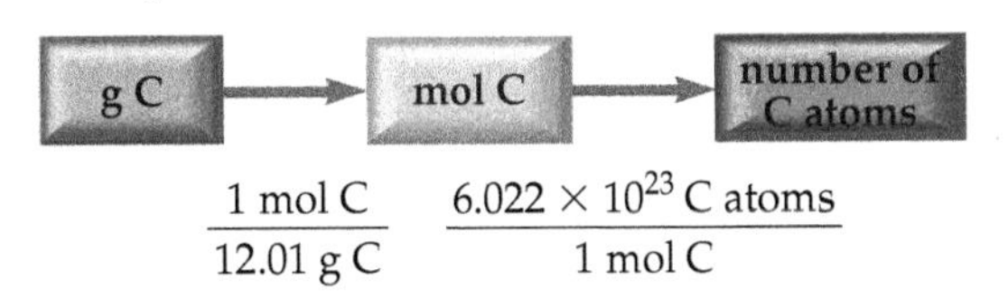

$$\frac{1 \text{ mol C}}{12.01 \text{ g C}} \qquad \frac{6.022 \times 10^{23} \text{ C atoms}}{1 \text{ mol C}}$$

Notice the similarity between this solution map and the one we used for nails:

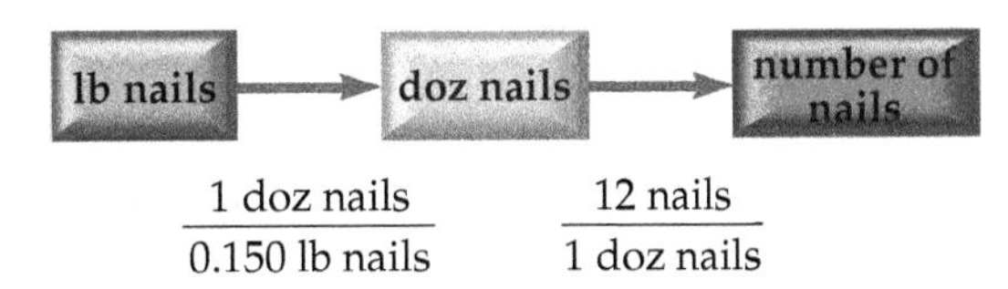

$$\frac{1 \text{ doz nails}}{0.150 \text{ lb nails}} \qquad \frac{12 \text{ nails}}{1 \text{ doz nails}}$$

Beginning with 0.58 g carbon and using the solution map as a guide, we convert to the number of carbon atoms.

$$0.58 \cancel{\text{g C}} \times \frac{1 \cancel{\text{mol C}}}{12.01 \cancel{\text{g C}}} \times \frac{6.022 \times 10^{23} \text{ C atoms}}{1 \cancel{\text{mol C}}} = 2.9 \times 10^{22} \text{ C atoms}$$

EXAMPLE 6.3 The Mole Concept—Converting between Grams and Number of Atoms

How many aluminum atoms are in an aluminum can with a mass of 16.2 g?

SORT
You are given the mass of aluminum and asked to find the number of aluminum atoms.

GIVEN: 16.2 g Al

FIND: Al atoms

STRATEGIZE
The solution map has two steps. In the first step, convert from g Al to mol Al. In the second step, convert from mol Al to the number of Al atoms. The required conversion factors are the molar mass of aluminum and the number of atoms in a mole.

SOLUTION MAP

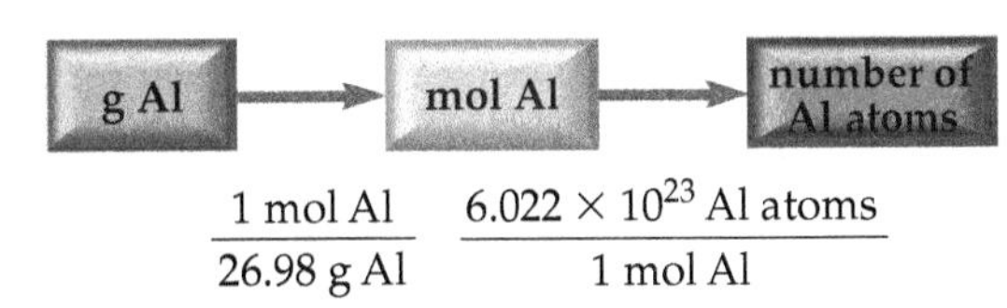

$$\frac{1 \text{ mol Al}}{26.98 \text{ g Al}} \qquad \frac{6.022 \times 10^{23} \text{ Al atoms}}{1 \text{ mol Al}}$$

RELATIONSHIPS USED

26.98 g Al = 1 mol Al (molar mass of aluminum, from periodic table)

6.022×10^{23} = 1 mol (Avogadro's number)

SOLVE
Follow the solution map to solve the problem, beginning with 16.2 g Al and multiplying by the appropriate conversion factors to arrive at Al atoms.

SOLUTION

$$16.2 \cancel{\text{g Al}} \times \frac{1 \cancel{\text{mol Al}}}{26.98 \cancel{\text{g Al}}} \times \frac{6.022 \times 10^{23} \text{ Al atoms}}{1 \cancel{\text{mol Al}}} = 3.62 \times 10^{23} \text{ Al atoms}$$

CHECK
Are the units correct? Does the answer make physical sense?

The units, Al atoms, are correct. The answer makes sense because the number of atoms in any macroscopic-sized sample of matter should be very large.

▶SKILLBUILDER 6.3 | The Mole Concept—Converting between Grams and Number of Atoms
Calculate the mass of 1.23×10^{24} helium atoms.

▶FOR MORE PRACTICE Example 6.15; Problems 35, 36, 37, 38, 39, 40, 41, 42.

Before we move on, notice that numbers with large exponents, such as 6.022×10^{23}, are almost unimaginably large. Twenty-two copper pennies contain 6.022×10^{23} or 1 mol of copper atoms, but 6.022×10^{23} pennies would cover Earth's entire surface to a depth of 300 m. Even objects that are small by everyday standards occupy a huge space when we have a mole of them. For example, one crystal of granulated sugar has a mass of less than 1 mg and a diameter of less than 0.1 mm, yet 1 mol of sugar crystals would cover the state of Texas to a depth of several feet. For every increase of 1 in the exponent of a number, the number increases by 10. So a number with an exponent of 23 is incredibly large. A mole has to be a large number because atoms are so small.

CONCEPTUAL CHECKPOINT 6.1

Which statement is *always* true for samples of atomic elements, regardless of the type of element present in the samples?

(a) If two samples of different elements contain the same number of atoms, they contain the same number of moles.

(b) If two samples of different elements have the same mass, they contain the same number of moles.

(c) If two samples of different elements have the same mass, they contain the same number of atoms.

CONCEPTUAL CHECKPOINT 6.2

Without doing any calculations, determine which sample contains the most atoms.

(a) one gram of cobalt

(b) one gram of carbon

(c) one gram of lead

6.4 Counting Molecules by the Gram

Remember, ionic compounds do not contain individual molecules. In loose language, the smallest electrically neutral collection of ions is sometimes called a molecule but is more correctly called a formula unit.

The calculations we just performed for atoms can also be applied to molecules for covalent compounds or formula units for ionic compounds. We first convert between the mass of a compound and moles of the compound, and then we calculate the number of molecules (or formula units) from moles.

CONVERTING BETWEEN GRAMS AND MOLES OF A COMPOUND

Remember, the formula mass for a compound is the sum of the atomic masses of all of the atoms in a chemical formula.

For elements, the molar mass is the mass of 1 mol of atoms of that element. For compounds, the molar mass is the mass of 1 mol of molecules or formula units of that compound. The molar mass of a compound in grams per mole is numerically equal to the formula mass of the compound in atomic mass units. For example, the formula mass of CO_2 is:

$$\begin{aligned}\text{Formula mass} &= 1(\text{Atomic mass of C}) + 2(\text{Atomic mass of O})\\ &= 1(12.01\text{ amu}) + 2(16.00\text{ amu})\\ &= 44.01\text{ amu}\end{aligned}$$

The molar mass of CO_2 is therefore:

$$\text{Molar mass} = 44.01\text{ g/mol}$$

Just as the molar mass of an element serves as a conversion factor between grams and moles of that element, the molar mass of a compound serves as a conversion factor between grams and moles of that compound. For example, suppose want to find the number of moles in a 22.5-g sample of dry ice (solid CO_2). We set up the problem in the normal way.

We begin by sorting the information.

GIVEN: 22.5 g CO_2

FIND: mol CO_2

SOLUTION MAP

We then strategize by drawing a solution map which shows how the molar mass converts grams of the compound to moles of the compound.

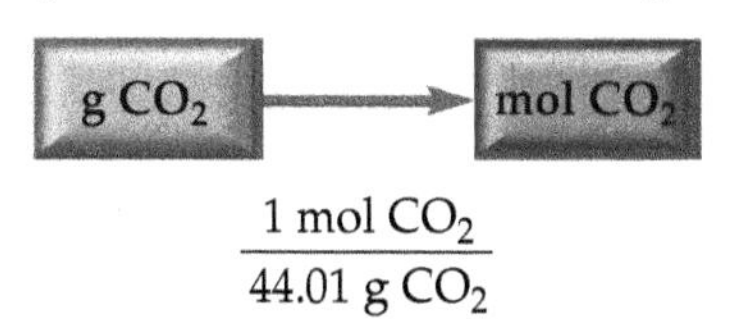

$$\frac{1 \text{ mol } CO_2}{44.01 \text{ g } CO_2}$$

RELATIONSHIPS USED

44.01 g CO_2 = 1 mol CO_2 (molar mass of CO_2)

SOLUTION

Finally, we solve the problem.

$$22.5 \text{ g} \times \frac{1 \text{ mol } CO_2}{44.01 \text{ g}} = 0.511 \text{ mol } CO_2$$

EXAMPLE 6.4 The Mole Concept—Converting between Grams and Moles for Compounds

Calculate the mass (in grams) of 1.75 mol of water.

SORT

You are given moles of water and asked to find the mass.

GIVEN: 1.75 mol H_2O

FIND: g H_2O

STRATEGIZE

Draw a solution map showing the conversion from mol H_2O to g H_2O. The conversion factor is the molar mass of water, which you can determine by summing the atomic masses of all the atoms in the chemical formula.

SOLUTION MAP

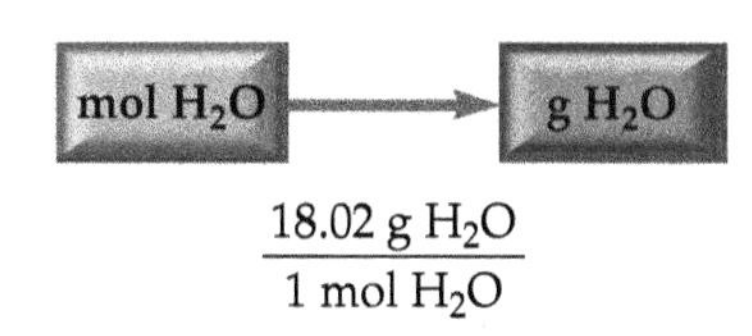

$$\frac{18.02 \text{ g } H_2O}{1 \text{ mol } H_2O}$$

RELATIONSHIPS USED

$$\begin{aligned} H_2O \text{ molar mass} &= 2(\text{Atomic mass H}) + 1(\text{Atomic mass O}) \\ &= 2(1.01) + 1(16.00) \\ &= 18.02 \text{ g/mol} \end{aligned}$$

SOLVE

Follow the solution map to solve the problem. Begin with 1.75 mol of water and use the molar mass to convert to grams of water.

SOLUTION

$$1.75 \text{ mol } H_2O \times \frac{18.02 \text{ g } H_2O}{\text{mol } H_2O} = 31.5 \text{ g } H_2O$$

CHECK

Check your answer. Are the units correct? Does the answer make physical sense?

The units (g H_2O) are the desired units. The magnitude of the answer makes sense because 1 mole of water has a mass of 18.02 g; therefore, 1.75 moles should have a mass that is slightly less than 36 g.

▶**SKILLBUILDER 6.4 | The Mole Concept—Converting between Grams and Moles**

Calculate the number of moles of NO_2 in 1.18 g of NO_2.

▶**FOR MORE PRACTICE** Problems 47, 48, 49, 50.

CONVERTING BETWEEN GRAMS OF A COMPOUND AND NUMBER OF MOLECULES

Suppose that we want to find the *number of CO_2 molecules* in a sample of dry ice (solid CO_2) with a mass of 22.5 g.

The solution map for the problem is:

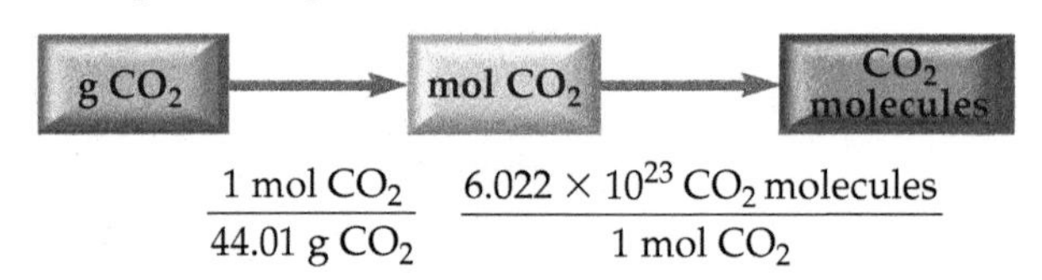

Notice that the first part of the solution map is identical to computing the number of moles of CO_2 in 22.5 g of dry ice. The second part of the solution map shows the conversion from moles to number of molecules. Following the solution map, we calculate:

$$22.5\ \text{g CO}_2 \times \frac{1\ \text{mol CO}_2}{44.01\ \text{g CO}_2} \times \frac{6.022 \times 10^{23}\ \text{CO}_2\ \text{molecules}}{\text{mol CO}_2}$$

$$= 3.08 \times 10^{23}\ \text{CO}_2\ \text{molecules}$$

EXAMPLE 6.5 The Mole Concept—Converting between Mass of a Compound and Number of Molecules

What is the mass of 4.78×10^{24} NO_2 molecules?

SORT

You are given the number of NO_2 molecules and asked to find the mass.

GIVEN: 4.78×10^{24} NO_2 molecules

FIND: g NO_2

STRATEGIZE

The solution map has two steps. In the first step, convert from molecules of NO_2 to moles of NO_2. In the second step, convert from moles of NO_2 to mass of NO_2. The required conversion factors are the molar mass of NO_2 and the number of molecules in a mole.

SOLUTION MAP

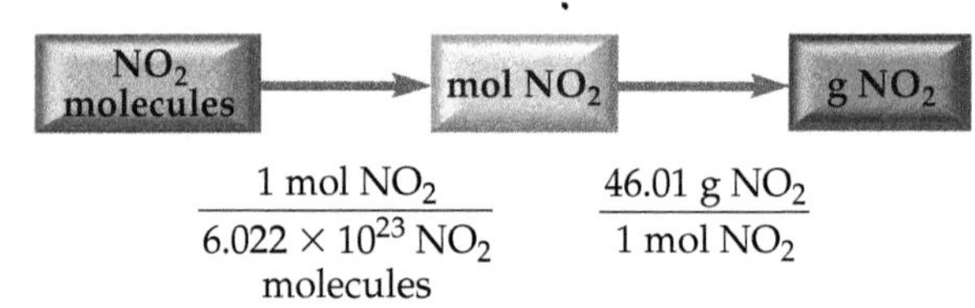

RELATIONSHIPS USED

6.022×10^{23} molecules = 1 mol (Avogadro's number)

$$\begin{aligned} NO_2\ \text{molar mass} &= 1(\text{Atomic mass N}) + 2(\text{Atomic mass O}) \\ &= 14.01 + 2(16.00) \\ &= 46.01\ \text{g/mol} \end{aligned}$$

SOLVE

Using the solution map as a guide, begin with molecules of NO_2 and multiply by the appropriate conversion factors to arrive at g NO_2.

SOLUTION

$$4.78 \times 10^{24}\ \text{NO}_2\ \text{molecules} \times \frac{1\ \text{mol NO}_2}{6.022 \times 10^{23}\ \text{NO}_2\ \text{molecules}} \times \frac{46.1\ \text{g NO}_2}{1\ \text{mol NO}_2} = 365\ \text{g NO}_2$$

CHECK

Check your answer. Are the units correct? Does the answer make physical sense?

The units, g NO_2, are correct. Since the number of NO_2 molecules is more than one mole, the answer should be more than one molar mass (more than 46.01 g), which it is; therefore, the magnitude of the answer is reasonable.

▶**SKILLBUILDER 6.5 | The Mole Concept—Converting between Mass and Number of Molecules**

How many H_2O molecules are in a sample of water with a mass of 3.64 g?

▶**FOR MORE PRACTICE** Problems 51, 52, 53, 54.

CONCEPTUAL CHECKPOINT 6.3

Compound A has a molar mass of 100 g/mol and Compound B has a molar mass of 200 g/mol. If you have samples of equal mass of both compounds, which sample contains the greatest number of molecules?

6.5 Chemical Formulas as Conversion Factors

▲ From our knowledge of clovers, we know that each clover has three leaves. We can express that as a ratio: 3 leaves : 1 clover.

We are almost ready to address the sodium problem in our opening example. To determine how much of a particular element (such as sodium) is in a given amount of a particular compound (such as sodium chloride), we must understand the numerical relationships inherent in a chemical formula. We can understand these relationships with a simple analogy: Asking how much sodium is in a given amount of sodium chloride is similar to asking how many leaves are on a given number of clovers. For example, suppose we want to know the number of leaves on 14 clovers. We need a conversion factor between leaves and clovers. For clovers, the conversion factor comes from our knowledge about them—we know that each clover has 3 leaves. We can express that relationship as a ratio between clovers and leaves.

3 leaves : 1 clover

Like other conversion factors, this ratio gives the relationship between leaves and clovers. With this ratio, we can write a conversion factor to determine the number of leaves in 14 clovers. The solution map is:

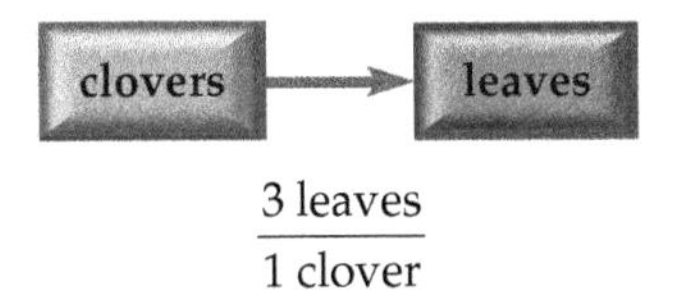

$$\frac{3 \text{ leaves}}{1 \text{ clover}}$$

We solve the problem by beginning with clovers and converting to leaves.

$$14 \text{ clovers} \times \frac{3 \text{ leaves}}{1 \text{ clover}} = 42 \text{ leaves}$$

Similarly, a chemical formula gives us ratios between elements and molecules for a particular compound. For example, the formula for carbon dioxide (CO_2) means there are two O atoms per CO_2 molecule. We write this as:

2 O atoms : 1 CO_2 molecule

Just as 3 leaves : 1 clover can also be written as 3 dozen leaves : 1 dozen clovers, for molecules we can write:

2 doz O atoms : 1 doz CO_2 molecules

However, for atoms and molecules, we normally work in moles.

$$2 \text{ mol O} : 1 \text{ mol } CO_2$$

Chemical formulas are discussed in Chapter 5.

With conversion factors such as these—which come directly from the chemical formula—we can determine the amounts of the constituent elements present in a given amount of a compound.

▶ Each of these shows a ratio.

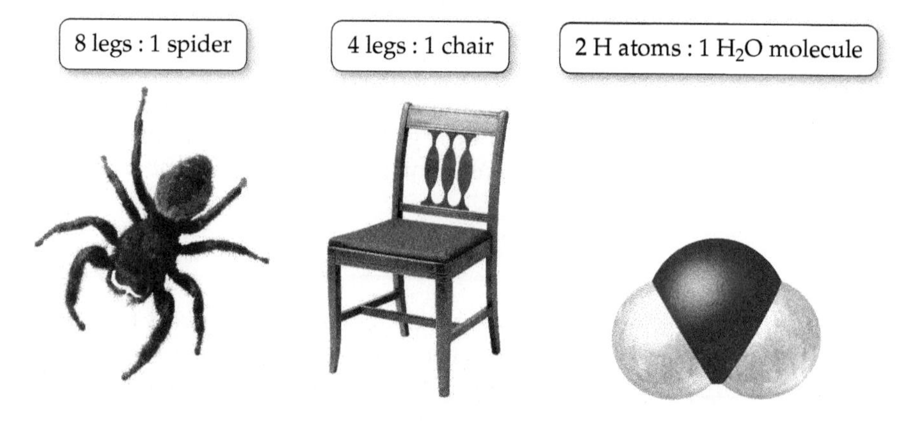

CONVERTING BETWEEN MOLES OF A COMPOUND AND MOLES OF A CONSTITUENT ELEMENT

Suppose we want to know the number of moles of O in 18 mol of CO_2. Our solution map is:

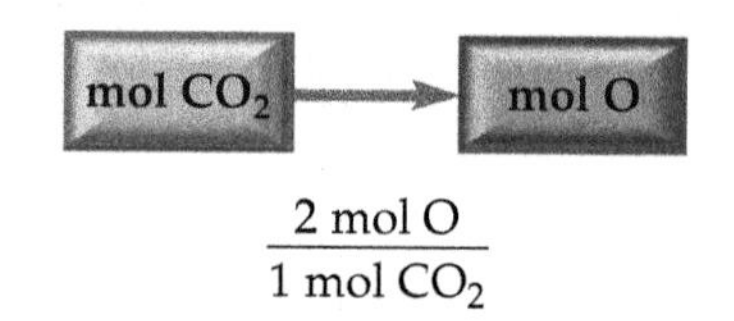

$$\frac{2 \text{ mol O}}{1 \text{ mol } CO_2}$$

We can then calculate the moles of O.

$$18 \cancel{\text{mol } CO_2} \times \frac{2 \text{ mol O}}{1 \cancel{\text{mol } CO_2}} = 36 \text{ mol O}$$

EXAMPLE 6.6 Chemical Formulas as Conversion Factors—Converting between Moles of a Compound and Moles of a Constituent Element

Determine the number of moles of O in 1.7 mol of $CaCO_3$.

SORT You are given the number of moles of $CaCO_3$ and asked to find the number of moles of O.	**GIVEN:** 1.7 mol $CaCO_3$ **FIND:** mol O
STRATEGIZE The solution map begins with moles of calcium carbonate and ends with moles of oxygen. Determine the conversion factor from the chemical formula, which indicates three O atoms for every $CaCO_3$ unit.	**SOLUTION MAP** mol $CaCO_3$ → mol O $\frac{3 \text{ mol O}}{1 \text{ mol } CaCO_3}$ **RELATIONSHIPS USED** 3 mol O : 1 mol $CaCO_3$ (from chemical formula)
SOLVE Follow the solution map to solve the problem. The subscripts in a chemical formula are exact, so they never limit significant figures.	**SOLUTION** $1.7 \cancel{\text{mol } CaCO_3} \times \frac{3 \text{ mol O}}{1 \cancel{\text{mol } CaCO_3}} = 5.1 \text{ mol O}$

CHECK
Check your answer. Are the units correct? Does the answer make physical sense?

The units (mol O) are correct. The magnitude is reasonable as the number of moles of oxygen should be larger than the number of moles of $CaCO_3$ (because each $CaCO_3$ unit contains 3 O atoms).

▶SKILLBUILDER 6.6 | Chemical Formulas as Conversion Factors—Converting between Moles of a Compound and Moles of a Constituent Element

Determine the number of moles of O in 1.4 mol of H_2SO_4.

▶FOR MORE PRACTICE Example 6.16; Problems 63, 64.

CONVERTING BETWEEN GRAMS OF A COMPOUND AND GRAMS OF A CONSTITUENT ELEMENT

Now, we have the tools we need to solve our sodium problem. Suppose we want to know the mass of sodium in 15 g of NaCl. The chemical formula gives us the relationship between moles of Na and moles of NaCl:

$$1 \text{ mol Na} : 1 \text{ mol NaCl}$$

To use this relationship, we need *mol* NaCl, but we have *g* NaCl. We can, however, use the *molar mass* of NaCl to convert from g NaCl to mol NaCl. Then we use the conversion factor from the chemical formula to convert to mol Na. Finally, we use the molar mass of Na to convert to g Na. The solution map is:

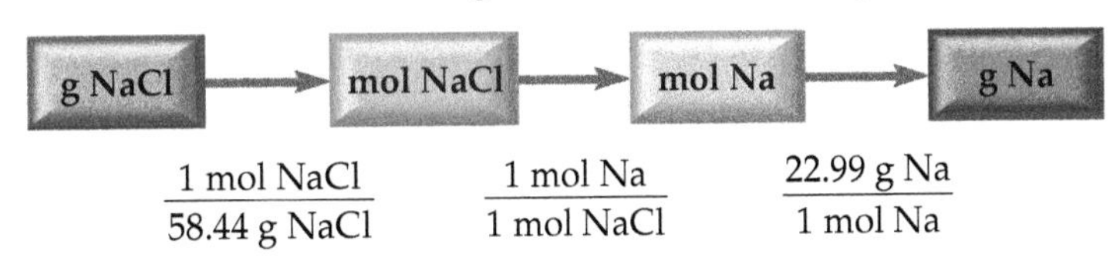

$$\frac{1 \text{ mol NaCl}}{58.44 \text{ g NaCl}} \qquad \frac{1 \text{ mol Na}}{1 \text{ mol NaCl}} \qquad \frac{22.99 \text{ g Na}}{1 \text{ mol Na}}$$

Notice that we must convert from g NaCl to mol NaCl *before* we can use the chemical formula as a conversion factor.

The chemical formula gives us a relationship between moles of substances, not between grams.

We follow the solution map to solve the problem.

$$15 \text{ g NaCl} \times \frac{1 \text{ mol NaCl}}{58.44 \text{ g NaCl}} \times \frac{1 \text{ mol Na}}{1 \text{ mol NaCl}} \times \frac{22.99 \text{ g Na}}{1 \text{ mol Na}} = 5.9 \text{ g Na}$$

The general form for solving problems where you are asked to find the mass of an element present in a given mass of a compound is:

Mass compound ⟶ **Moles** compound ⟶ **Moles** element ⟶ **Mass** element

Use the atomic or molar mass to convert between mass and moles, and use the relationships inherent in the chemical formula to convert between moles and moles (▼ Figure 6.2).

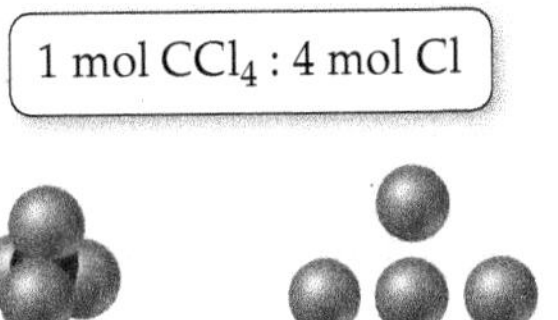

▶ FIGURE 6.2 **Mole relationships from a chemical formula** The relationships inherent in a chemical formula allow us to convert between moles of the compound and moles of a constituent element (or vice versa).

EXAMPLE 6.7 Chemical Formulas as Conversion Factors—Converting between Grams of a Compound and Grams of a Constituent Element

Carvone ($C_{10}H_{14}O$) is the main component of spearmint oil. It has a pleasant aroma and mint flavor. Carvone is often added to chewing gum, liqueurs, soaps, and perfumes. Calculate the mass of carbon in 55.4 g of carvone.

SORT

You are given the mass of carvone and asked to find the mass of one of its constituent elements.

GIVEN: 55.4 g $C_{10}H_{14}O$

FIND: g C

STRATEGIZE

Base the solution map on Grams ⟶ Mole ⟶ Mole ⟶ Grams

SOLUTION MAP

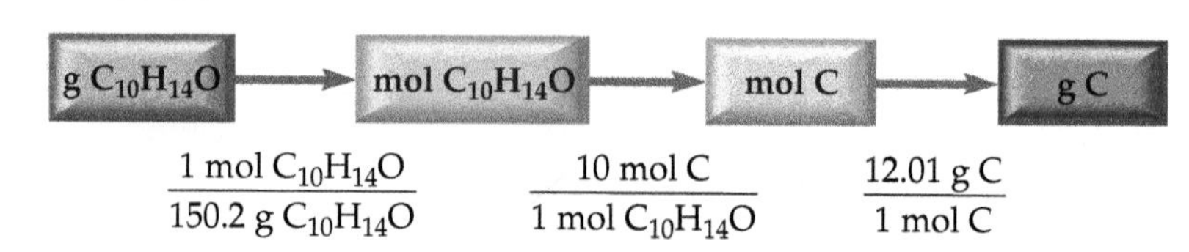

$$\frac{1 \text{ mol } C_{10}H_{14}O}{150.2 \text{ g } C_{10}H_{14}O} \qquad \frac{10 \text{ mol C}}{1 \text{ mol } C_{10}H_{14}O} \qquad \frac{12.01 \text{ g C}}{1 \text{ mol C}}$$

RELATIONSHIPS USED

You need three conversion factors. The first is the molar mass of carvone.

$$\begin{aligned}\text{Molar mass carvone} &= 10(12.01) + 14(1.01) + 1(16.00)\\ &= 120.1 + 14.14 + 16.00\\ &= 150.2 \text{ g/mol}\end{aligned}$$

The second conversion factor is the relationship between moles of carbon and moles of carvone from the molecular formula.

10 mol C : 1 mol $C_{10}H_{14}O$ (from chemical formula)

The third conversion factor is the molar mass of carbon.

1 mol C = 12.01 g C (molar mass C, from periodic table)

SOLVE

Follow the solution map to solve the problem, beginning with g $C_{10}H_{14}O$ and multiplying by the appropriate conversion factors to arrive at g C.

SOLUTION

$$55.4 \text{ g } C_{10}H_{14}O \times \frac{1 \text{ mol } C_{10}H_{14}O}{150.2 \text{ g } C_{10}H_{14}O} \times \frac{10 \text{ mol C}}{1 \text{ mol } C_{10}H_{14}O} \times \frac{12.01 \text{ g C}}{1 \text{ mol C}} = 44.3 \text{ g C}$$

CHECK

Check your answer. Are the units correct? Does the answer make physical sense?

The units, g C, are correct. The magnitude of the answer is reasonable since the mass of carbon with the compound must be less than the mass of the compound itself. If you had arrived at a mass of carbon that was greater than the mass of the compound, you would immediately know that you had made a mistake; the mass of a constituent element can never be greater than the mass of the compound itself.

▶SKILLBUILDER 6.7 | Chemical Formulas as Conversion Factors—Converting between Grams of a Compound and Grams of a Constituent Element

Determine the mass of oxygen in a 5.8-g sample of sodium bicarbonate ($NaHCO_3$).

▶SKILLBUILDER PLUS

Determine the mass of oxygen in a 7.20-g sample of $Al_2(SO_4)_3$.

▶FOR MORE PRACTICE Example 6.17; Problems 67, 68, 69, 70.

CHEMISTRY IN THE ENVIRONMENT

Chlorine in Chlorofluorocarbons

About 30 years ago, scientists began to suspect that synthetic compounds known as chlorofluorocarbons (CFCs) were destroying a vital compound called ozone (O_3) in Earth's upper atmosphere. Upper atmospheric ozone is important because it acts as a shield to protect life on Earth from harmful ultraviolet light (▼ Figure 6.3). CFCs are chemically inert molecules (they do not readily react with other substances) used primarily as refrigerants and industrial solvents. Their inertness has allowed them to leak into the atmosphere and stay there for many years. In the upper atmosphere, however, sunlight eventually breaks bonds within CFCs, resulting in the release of chlorine atoms. The chlorine atoms then react with ozone and destroy it by converting it from O_3 into O_2.

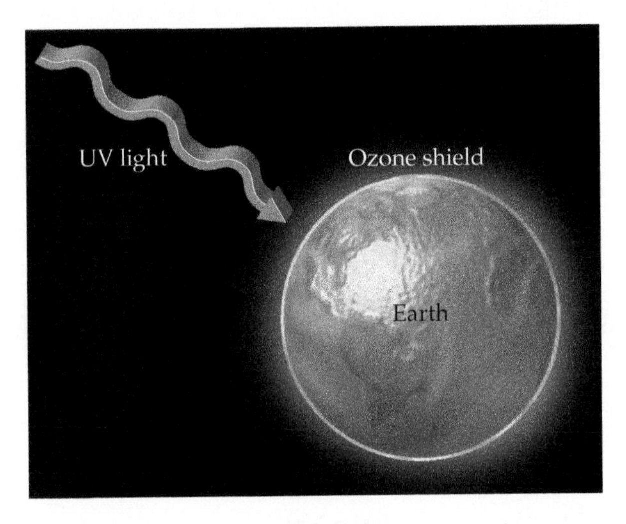

▲ **FIGURE 6.3 The ozone shield** Atmospheric ozone shields life on Earth from harmful ultraviolet light.

In 1985, scientists discovered a large hole in the ozone layer over Antarctica that has since been attributed to CFCs. The amount of ozone over Antarctica had depleted by a startling 50%. The ozone hole is transient, existing only in the Antarctic spring, from late August to November. Examination of data from previous years showed that this gradually expanding ozone hole has formed each spring since 1977 (▼ Figure 6.4), and it continues to form today.

A similar hole has been observed during some years over the North Pole, and a smaller, but still significant, drop in ozone has been observed over more populated areas such as the northern United States and Canada. The thinning of ozone over these areas is dangerous because ultraviolet light can harm living things and induce skin cancer in humans. Based on this evidence, most developed nations banned the production of CFCs on January 1, 1996. However, CFCs still lurk in most older refrigerators and air conditioning units and can leak into the atmosphere and destroy ozone.

CAN YOU ANSWER THIS? *Suppose a car air conditioner contains 2.5 kg of freon-12 (CCl_2F_2), a CFC. How many kilograms of Cl are contained within the freon?*

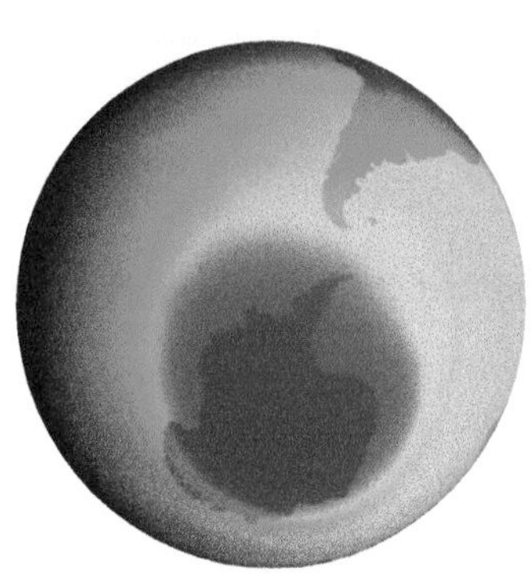

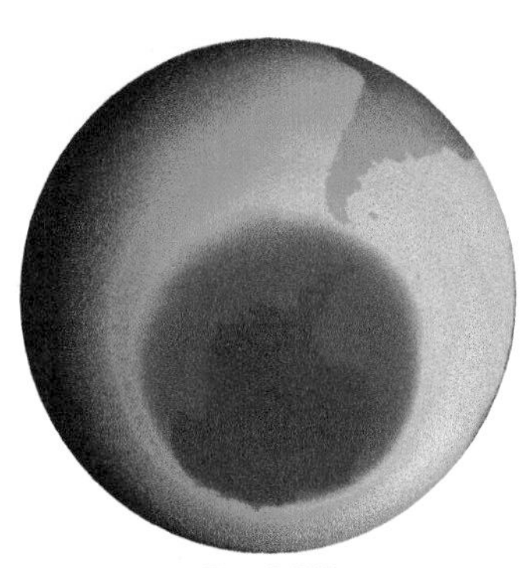

▶ **FIGURE 6.4 Growth of the ozone hole** Antarctic ozone levels in three Septembers from 1979 to 2000. The darkest blue colors indicate the lowest ozone levels.

CONCEPTUAL CHECKPOINT 6.4

Without doing any detailed calculations, determine which sample contains the most fluorine atoms.

(a) 25 g of HF

(b) 1.5 mol of CH_3F

(c) 1.0 mol of F_2

6.6 Mass Percent Composition of Compounds

Another way to express how much of an element is in a given compound is to use the element's mass percent composition for that compound. The **mass percent composition** or simply **mass percent** of an element is the element's percentage of the total mass of the compound. For example, the mass percent composition of sodium in sodium chloride is 39%. This information tells us that a 100-g sample of sodium chloride contains 39 g of sodium. The mass percent composition for a compound can be determined from experimental data using the formula:

$$\text{Mass percent of element } X = \frac{\text{Mass of } X \text{ in a sample of the compound}}{\text{Mass of the sample of the compound}} \times 100\%$$

For example, suppose a 0.358-g sample of chromium reacts with oxygen to form 0.523 g of the metal oxide. Then the mass percent of chromium is:

$$\text{Mass percent Cr} = \frac{\text{Mass Cr}}{\text{Mass metal oxide}} \times 100\%$$

$$= \frac{0.358\text{ g}}{0.523\text{ g}} \times 100\% = 68.5\%$$

We can use mass percent composition as a conversion factor between grams of a constituent element and grams of the compound. For example, we just saw that the mass percent composition of sodium in sodium chloride is 39%. This can be written as:

39 g sodium : 100 g sodium chloride

or in fractional form:

$$\frac{39\text{ g Na}}{100\text{ g NaCl}} \quad \text{or} \quad \frac{100\text{ g NaCl}}{39\text{ g Na}}$$

These fractions are conversion factors between g Na and g NaCl, as shown in Example 6.8.

EXAMPLE 6.8 Using Mass Percent Composition as a Conversion Factor

The FDA recommends that adults consume less than 2.4 g of sodium per day. How many grams of sodium chloride can you consume and still be within the FDA guidelines? Sodium chloride is 39% sodium by mass.

SORT

You are given the mass of sodium and the mass percent of sodium in sodium chloride. When mass percent is given, write it as a fraction. *Percent* means *per hundred*, so 39% sodium indicates that there are 39 g Na per 100 g NaCl. You are asked to find the mass of sodium chloride that contains the given mass of sodium.

GIVEN: 2.4 g Na

$$\frac{39\text{ g Na}}{100\text{ g NaCl}}$$

FIND: g NaCl

STRATEGIZE

Draw a solution map that starts with the mass of sodium and uses the mass percent as a conversion factor to get to the mass of sodium chloride.

SOLUTION MAP

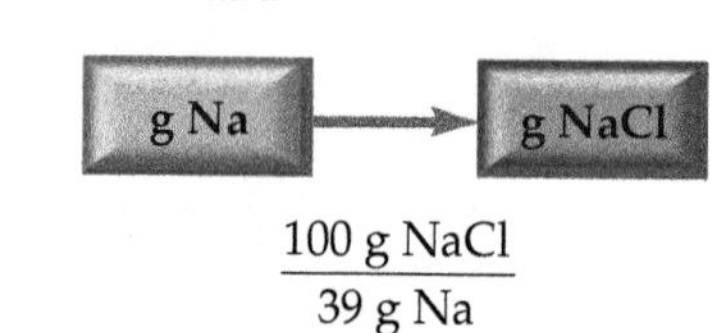

$$\frac{100\text{ g NaCl}}{39\text{ g Na}}$$

RELATIONSHIPS USED

39 g Na : 100 g NaCl (given in the problem)

SOLVE

Follow the solution map to solve the problem, beginning with grams Na and ending with grams of NaCl. The amount of salt you can consume and still be within the FDA guideline is 6.2 g NaCl.

SOLUTION

$$2.4 \text{ g Na} \times \frac{100 \text{ g NaCl}}{39 \text{ g Na}} = 6.2 \text{ g NaCl}$$

CHECK

Check your answer. Are the units correct? Does the answer make physical sense?

The units, g NaCl, are correct. The answer makes physical sense because the mass of NaCl should be *larger* than the mass of Na. The mass of a compound containing a given mass of a particular element is always larger than the mass of the element itself.

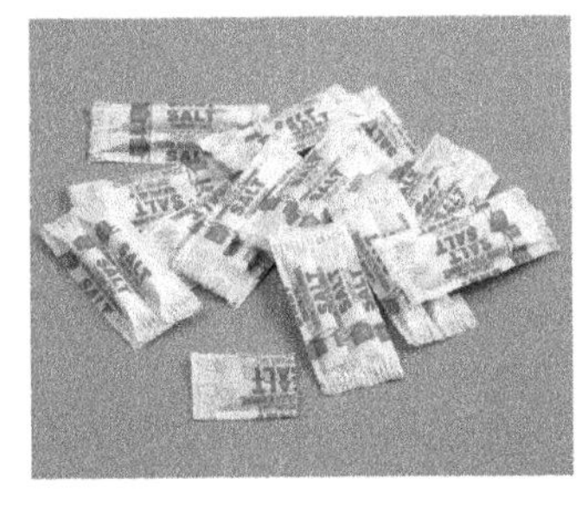

▲ Twelve and a half salt packets contain 6.2 g NaCl.

▶SKILLBUILDER 6.8 | Using Mass Percent Composition as a Conversion Factor

If a woman consumes 22 g of sodium chloride, how much sodium does she consume? Sodium chloride is 39% sodium by mass.

▶FOR MORE PRACTICE Example 6.19; Problems 75, 76, 77, 78.

6.7 Mass Percent Composition from a Chemical Formula

In the previous section, we learned how to calculate mass percent composition from experimental data and how to use mass percent composition as a conversion factor. We can also calculate the mass percent of any element in a compound from the chemical formula for the compound. Based on the chemical formula, the mass percent of element X in a compound is:

$$\text{Mass percent of element } X = \frac{\text{Mass of element } X \text{ in 1 mol of compound}}{\text{Mass of 1 mol of compound}} \times 100\%$$

Suppose, for example, that we want to calculate the mass percent composition of Cl in the chlorofluorocarbon CCl_2F_2. The mass percent of Cl is given by:

CCl_2F_2

$$\text{Mass percent Cl} = \frac{2 \times \text{Molar mass Cl}}{\text{Molar mass } CCl_2F_2} \times 100\%$$

We must multiply the molar mass of Cl by 2 because the chemical formula has a subscript of 2 for Cl, meaning that 1 mol of CCl_2F_2 contains 2 mol of Cl atoms. We calculate the molar mass of CCl_2F_2 as follows:

$$\text{Molar mass} = 1(12.01) + 2(35.45) + 2(19.00) = 120.91 \text{ g/mol}$$

So the mass percent of Cl in CCl_2F_2 is

$$\text{Mass percent Cl} = \frac{2 \times \text{Molar mass Cl}}{\text{Molar mass } CCl_2F_2} \times 100\% = \frac{2 \times 35.45 \text{ g}}{120.91 \text{ g}} \times 100\%$$

$$= 58.64\%$$

EXAMPLE 6.9 Mass Percent Composition

Calculate the mass percent of Cl in freon-114 ($C_2Cl_4F_2$).

SORT

You are given the molecular formula of freon-114 and asked to find the mass percent of Cl.

GIVEN: $C_2Cl_4F_2$

FIND: Mass % Cl

STRATEGIZE

The solution map shows how you can use the information in the chemical formula to substitute into the mass percent equation and obtain the mass percent Cl.

SOLUTION MAP

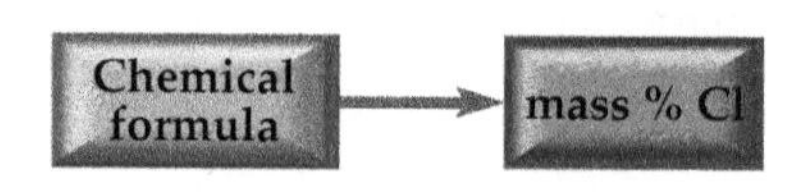

$$\text{Mass \% Cl} = \frac{4 \times \text{Molar mass Cl}}{\text{Molar mass } C_2Cl_4F_2} \times 100\%$$

RELATIONSHIPS USED

$$\text{Mass percent of element } X = \frac{\text{Mass of element } X \text{ in 1 mol of compound}}{\text{Mass of 1 mol of compound}} \times 100\%$$

(mass percent equation, introduced in this section)

SOLVE

Calculate the molar mass of freon-114 and substitute the values into the equation to find mass percent Cl.

SOLUTION

$$4 \times \text{Molar mass Cl} = 4(35.45\text{ g}) = 141.8\text{ g}$$

$$\text{Molar mass } C_2Cl_4F_2 = 2(12.01) + 4(35.45) + 2(19)$$
$$= 24.02 + 141.8 + 38.00$$
$$= \frac{203.8\text{ g}}{\text{mol}}$$

$$\text{Mass \% Cl} = \frac{4 \times \text{Molar mass Cl}}{\text{Molar mass } C_2Cl_4F_2} \times 100\%$$
$$= \frac{141.8\text{ g}}{203.8\text{ g}} \times 100\%$$
$$= 69.58\%$$

CHECK

Check your answer. Are the units correct? Does the answer make physical sense?

The units (%) are correct. The answer makes physical sense. Mass percent composition should never exceed 100%. If your answer is greater than 100%, you have made an error.

▶SKILLBUILDER 6.9 | Mass Percent Composition

Acetic acid ($HC_2H_3O_2$) is the active ingredient in vinegar. Calculate the mass percent composition of O in acetic acid.

▶FOR MORE PRACTICE Example 6.20; Problems 79, 80, 81, 82, 83, 84.

CONCEPTUAL CHECKPOINT 6.5

Which compound has the highest mass percent of O? (You should not have to perform any detailed calculations to answer this question.)

(a) CrO

(b) CrO_2

(c) Cr_2O_3

CHEMISTRY AND HEALTH

Fluoridation of Drinking Water

In the early 1900s, scientists discovered that people whose drinking water naturally contained fluoride (F^-) ions had fewer cavities than people whose water did not. At the proper levels, fluoride strengthens tooth enamel, which prevents tooth decay. In an effort to improve public health, fluoride has been artificially added to drinking water supplies since 1945. In the United States today, about 62% of the population drinks artificially fluoridated drinking water. The American Dental Association and public health agencies estimate that water fluoridation reduces tooth decay by 40 to 65%.

The fluoridation of public drinking water, however, is often controversial. Some opponents argue that fluoride is available from other sources—such as toothpaste, mouthwash, drops, and pills—and therefore should not be added to drinking water. Anyone who wants fluoride can get it from these optional sources, they argue, and the government should not impose fluoride on the general population. Other opponents argue that the risks associated with fluoridation are too great. Indeed, too much fluoride can cause teeth to become brown and spotted, a condition known as dental fluorosis. Extremely high levels can lead to skeletal fluorosis, a condition in which the bones become brittle and arthritic.

The scientific consensus is that, like many minerals, fluoride shows some health benefits at certain levels—about 1–4 mg/day for adults—but can have detrimental effects at higher levels. Consequently, most major cities fluoridate their drinking water at a level of about 1 mg/L. Since adults drink between 1 and 2 L of water per day, they should receive the beneficial amounts of fluoride from the water. Bottled water does not normally contain fluoride, and therefore does not have the benefit of fluoride to teeth. Fluoridated bottled water can sometimes be found in the infant section of supermarkets.

CAN YOU ANSWER THIS? *Fluoride is often added to water as sodium fluoride (NaF). What is the mass percent composition of F^- in NaF? How many grams of NaF should be added to 1500 L of water to fluoridate it at a level of 1.0 mg F^-/L?*

6.8 Calculating Empirical Formulas for Compounds

In Section 6.7, we learned how to calculate mass percent composition from a chemical formula. But can we go the other way? Can we calculate a chemical formula from mass percent composition? This is important because laboratory analyses of compounds do not often give chemical formulas directly; rather, they give the relative masses of each element present in a compound. For example, if we decompose water into hydrogen and oxygen in the laboratory, we could measure the masses of hydrogen and oxygen produced. Can we determine a chemical formula for water from this kind of data?

▶ We just learned how to go from the chemical formula of a compound to its mass percent composition. Can we also go the other way?

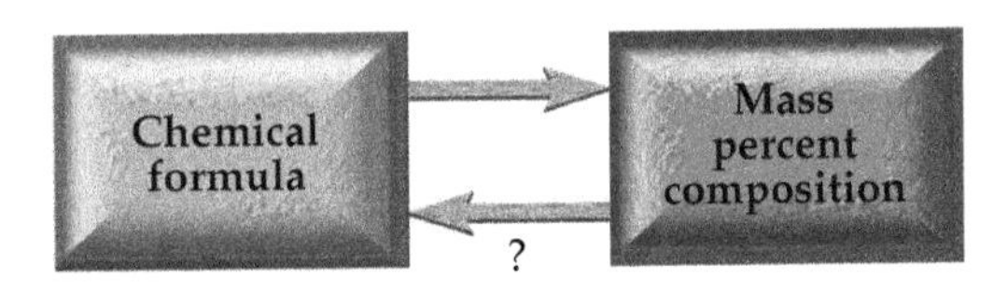

The answer is a qualified yes. We can determine a chemical formula, but it is the **empirical formula**, not the molecular formula. As we saw in Section 5.3, an empirical formula only gives the smallest whole-number ratio of each type of atom in a compound, not the specific number of each type of atom in a molecule. Recall that the **molecular formula** is always a whole-number multiple of the empirical formula: Molecular formula = Empirical formula $\times$ n, where $n = 1, 2, 3 \ldots$

For example, the molecular formula for hydrogen peroxide is H_2O_2, and its empirical formula is HO.

A chemical formula represents a ratio of atoms or moles of atoms, not a ratio of masses.

$$HO \times 2 \longrightarrow H_2O_2$$

CALCULATING AN EMPIRICAL FORMULA FROM EXPERIMENTAL DATA

Suppose we decompose a sample of water in the laboratory and find that it produces 3.0 g of hydrogen and 24 g of oxygen. How do we determine an empirical formula from these data?

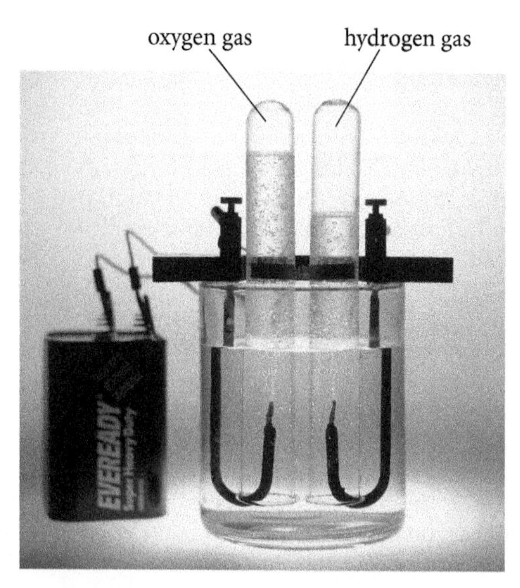

▲ Water can be decomposed by an electric current into hydrogen and oxygen. How can we find the empirical formula for water from the masses of its component elements?

We know that an empirical formula represents a ratio of atoms or a ratio of moles of atoms, but it *does not* represent a ratio of masses. So the first thing we must do is convert our data from grams to moles. How many moles of each element formed during the decomposition? To convert to moles, we divide each mass by the molar mass of that element.

$$\text{Moles H} = 3.0\ \cancel{\text{g H}} \times \frac{1\ \text{mol H}}{1.01\ \cancel{\text{g H}}} = 3.0\ \text{mol H}$$

$$\text{Moles O} = 24\ \cancel{\text{g O}} \times \frac{1\ \text{mol O}}{16.00\ \cancel{\text{g O}}} = 1.5\ \text{mol O}$$

From these data, we know there are 3 mol of H for every 1.5 mol of O. We can now write a pseudoformula for water:

$$H_3O_{1.5}$$

To get whole-number subscripts in our formula, we divide all the subscripts by the smallest one, in this case 1.5.

$$H_{\frac{3}{1.5}}O_{\frac{1.5}{1.5}} = H_2O$$

Our empirical formula for water, which in this case also happens to be the molecular formula, is H_2O. The following procedure can be used to obtain the empirical formula of any compound from experimental data. The left column outlines the procedure, and the center and right columns show two examples of how to apply the procedure.

Obtaining an Empirical Formula from Experimental Data	EXAMPLE 6.10	EXAMPLE 6.11
	A compound containing nitrogen and oxygen is decomposed in the laboratory and produces 24.5 g of nitrogen and 70.0 g of oxygen. Calculate the empirical formula of the compound.	A laboratory analysis of aspirin determines the following mass percent composition: C 60.00% H 4.48% O 35.53% Find the empirical formula.
1. Write down (or calculate) as given the masses of each element present in a sample of the compound. If you are given mass percent composition, assume a 100-g sample and calculate the masses of each element from the given percentages.	GIVEN: 24.5 g N 70.0 g O FIND: empirical formula	GIVEN: In a 100-g sample: 60.00 g C 4.48 g H 35.53 g O FIND: empirical formula
2. Convert each of the masses in Step 1 to moles by using the appropriate molar mass for each element as a conversion factor.	SOLUTION $24.5\ \cancel{g\ N} \times \frac{1\ mol\ N}{14.01\ \cancel{g\ N}} = 1.75\ mol\ N$ $70.0\ \cancel{g\ O} \times \frac{1\ mol\ O}{16.00\ \cancel{g\ O}} = 4.38\ mol\ O$	SOLUTION $60.00\ \cancel{g\ C} \times \frac{1\ mol\ C}{12.01\ \cancel{g\ C}} = 4.996\ mol\ C$ $4.48\ \cancel{g\ H} \times \frac{1\ mol\ H}{1.01\ \cancel{g\ H}} = 4.44\ mol\ H$ $35.53\ \cancel{g\ O} \times \frac{1\ mol\ O}{16.00\ \cancel{g\ O}} = 2.221\ mol\ O$
3. Write down a pseudoformula for the compound, using the moles of each element (from Step 2) as subscripts.	$N_{1.75}O_{4.38}$	$C_{4.996}H_{4.44}O_{2.221}$
4. Divide all the subscripts in the formula by the smallest subscript.	$N_{\frac{1.75}{1.75}}O_{\frac{4.38}{1.75}} \longrightarrow N_1O_{2.5}$	$C_{\frac{4.996}{2.221}}H_{\frac{4.44}{2.221}}O_{\frac{2.221}{2.221}} \longrightarrow C_{2.25}H_2O_1$
5. If the subscripts are not whole numbers, multiply all the subscripts by a small whole number (see the following table) to arrive at whole-number subscripts.	$N_1O_{2.5} \times 2 \longrightarrow N_2O_5$ The correct empirical formula is N_2O_5.	$C_{2.25}H_2O_1 \times 4 \longrightarrow C_9H_8O_4$ The correct empirical formula is $C_9H_8O_4$.
	▶**SKILLBUILDER 6.10** A sample of a compound is decomposed in the laboratory and produces 165 g of carbon, 27.8 g of hydrogen, and 220.2 g O. Calculate the empirical formula of the compound. ▶**FOR MORE PRACTICE** Problems 85, 86, 87, 88.	▶**SKILLBUILDER 6.11** Ibuprofen, an aspirin substitute, has the mass percent composition: C 75.69%; H 8.80%; O 15.51%. Calculate the empirical formula of the ibuprofen. ▶**FOR MORE PRACTICE** Example 6.21; Problems 89, 90, 91, 92.

Fractional Subscript	Multiply by This Number to Get Whole-Number Subscripts
_.10	10
_.20	5
_.25	4
_.33	3
_.50	2
_.66	3
_.75	4

EXAMPLE 6.12 Calculating an Empirical Formula from Reaction Data

A 3.24-g sample of titanium reacts with oxygen to form 5.40 g of the metal oxide. What is the empirical formula of the metal oxide?

You are given the mass of titanium and the mass of the metal oxide that forms. You are asked to find the empirical formula. You must recognize this problem as one requiring a special procedure and apply that procedure, which is outlined below.	GIVEN: 3.24 g Ti 5.40 g metal oxide FIND: empirical formula
1. Write down (or calculate) the masses of each element present in a sample of the compound. In this case, you are given the mass of the initial Ti sample and the mass of its oxide after the sample reacts with oxygen. The mass of oxygen is the difference between the mass of the oxide and the mass of titanium.	SOLUTION 3.24 g Ti Mass O = Mass oxide − Mass titanium = 5.40 g − 3.24 g = 2.16 g O
2. Convert each of the masses in Step 1 to moles by using the appropriate molar mass for each element as a conversion factor.	$3.24\ \text{g Ti} \times \frac{1\ \text{mol Ti}}{47.88\ \text{g Ti}} = 0.0677\ \text{mol Ti}$ $2.16\ \text{g O} \times \frac{1\ \text{mol O}}{16.00\ \text{g O}} = 0.135\ \text{mol O}$
3. Write down a pseudoformula for the compound, using the moles of each element obtained in Step 2 as subscripts.	$Ti_{0.0677}O_{0.135}$
4. Divide all the subscripts in the formula by the smallest subscript.	$Ti_{\frac{0.0677}{0.0677}}O_{\frac{0.135}{0.0677}} \longrightarrow TiO_2$
5. If the subscripts are not whole numbers, multiply all the subscripts by a small whole number to arrive at whole-number subscripts.	Since the subscripts are already whole numbers, this last step is unnecessary. The correct empirical formula is TiO_2.

▶**SKILLBUILDER 6.12 | Calculating an Empirical Formula from Reaction Data**

A 1.56-g sample of copper reacts with oxygen to form 1.95 g of the metal oxide. What is the formula of the metal oxide?

▶**FOR MORE PRACTICE** Problems 93, 94, 95, 96.

6.9 Calculating Molecular Formulas for Compounds

▲ Fructose, a sugar found in fruit.

You can determine the *molecular* formula of a compound from the empirical formula if you also know the molar mass of the compound. Recall from Section 6.8 that the molecular formula is always a whole-number multiple of the empirical formula.

$$\text{Molecular formula} = \text{Empirical formula} \times n, \text{ where } n = 1, 2, 3 \ldots$$

Suppose we want to find the molecular formula for fructose (a sugar found in fruit) from its empirical formula, CH_2O, and its molar mass, 180.2 g/mol. We know that the molecular formula is a whole-number multiple of CH_2O.

$$\text{Molecular formula} = CH_2O \times n$$

We also know that the molar mass is a whole-number multiple of the **empirical formula molar mass**, the sum of the masses of all the atoms in the empirical formula.

$$\text{Molar mass} = \text{Empirical formula molar mass} \times n$$

For a particular compound, the value of n in both cases is the same. Therefore, we can find n by calculating the ratio of the molar mass to the empirical formula molar mass.

$$n = \frac{\text{Molar mass}}{\text{Empirical formula molar mass}}$$

For fructose, the empirical formula molar mass is:

$$\text{Empirical formula molar mass} = 1(12.01) + 2(1.01) + 16.00 = 30.03 \text{ g/mol}$$

Therefore, n is:

$$n = \frac{180.2 \text{ g/mol}}{30.03 \text{ g/mol}} = 6$$

We can then use this value of n to find the molecular formula.

$$\text{Molecular formula} = CH_2O \times 6 = C_6H_{12}O_6$$

EXAMPLE 6.13 Calculating Molecular Formula from Empirical Formula and Molar Mass

Naphthalene is a compound containing carbon and hydrogen that is often used in mothballs. Its empirical formula is C_5H_4 and its molar mass is 128.16 g/mol. What is its molecular formula?

SORT You are given the empirical formula and the molar mass of a compound and asked to find its molecular formula.	**GIVEN:** empirical formula = C_5H_4 molar mass = 128.16 g/mol **FIND:** molecular formula
STRATEGIZE In the first step, use the molar mass (which is given) and the empirical formula molar mass (which you can calculate based on the empirical formula) to determine n (the integer by which you must multiply the empirical formula to get the molecular formula). In the second step, multiply the subscripts in the empirical formula by n to arrive at the molecular formula.	**SOLUTION MAP** 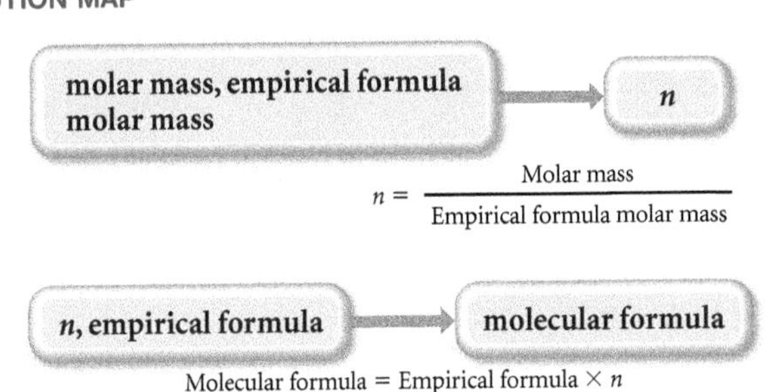
SOLVE First find the empirical formula molar mass.	**SOLUTION** Empirical formula molar mass = 5(12.01) + 4(1.01) = 64.09 g/mol
Now follow the solution map. Find n by dividing the molar mass by the empirical formula molar mass (which you just calculated).	$n = \frac{\text{Molar mass}}{\text{Empirical formula mass}} = \frac{128.16 \text{ g/mol}}{64.09 \text{ g/mol}} = 2$
Multiply the empirical formula by n to get the molecular formula.	Molecular formula = $C_5H_4 \times 2 = C_{10}H_8$
CHECK Check your answer. Does the answer make physical sense?	The answer makes physical sense because it is a whole-number multiple of the empirical formula. Any answer containing fractional subscripts would be an error.

▶SKILLBUILDER 6.13 | Calculating Molecular Formula from Empirical Formula and Molar Mass

Butane is a compound containing carbon and hydrogen that is used as a fuel in butane lighters. Its empirical formula is C_2H_5, and its molar mass is 58.12 g/mol. Find its molecular formula.

▶SKILLBUILDER PLUS

A compound with the following mass percent composition has a molar mass of 60.10 g/mol. Find its molecular formula.

C 39.97% H 13.41% N 46.62%

▶FOR MORE PRACTICE Example 6.22; Problems 97, 98, 99, 100.

CHAPTER IN REVIEW

CHEMICAL PRINCIPLES

The Mole Concept: The mole is a specific number (6.022×10^{23}) that allows us to easily count atoms or molecules by weighing them. One mole of any element has a mass equivalent to its atomic mass in grams, and a mole of any compound has a mass equivalent to its formula mass in grams. The mass of 1 mol of an element or compound is its molar mass.

RELEVANCE

The Mole Concept: The mole concept allows us to determine the number of atoms or molecules in a sample from its mass. Just as a hardware store customer wants to know the number of nails in a certain weight of nails, so we want to know the number of atoms in a certain mass of atoms. Since atoms are too small to count, we use their mass.

Chemical Formulas and Chemical Composition: Chemical formulas indicate the relative number of each kind of element in a compound. These numbers are based on atoms or moles. By using molar masses, we can use the information in a chemical formula to determine the relative masses of each kind of element in a compound. We can then relate the mass of a sample of a compound to the masses of the elements contained in the compound.

Chemical Formulas and Chemical Composition: The chemical composition of compounds is important because it lets us determine how much of a particular element is contained within a particular compound. For example, an assessment of the threat to the Earth's ozone layer from chlorofluorocarbons (CFCs) requires knowing how much chlorine is in a particular CFC.

Empirical and Molecular Formulas from Laboratory Data: We can refer to the relative masses of the elements within a compound to determine the empirical formula of the compound. If the chemist also knows the molar mass of the compound, he or she can also determine its molecular formula.

Empirical and Molecular Formulas from Laboratory Data: The first thing a chemist wants to know about an unknown compound is its chemical formula, because the formula reveals the compound's composition. Chemists often arrive at formulas by analyzing compounds in the laboratory—either by decomposing them or by synthesizing them—to determine the relative masses of the elements they contain.

CHEMICAL SKILLS

Converting between Moles and Number of Atoms (Section 6.3)

SORT

You are given moles of copper and asked to find the number of copper atoms.

STRATEGIZE

To convert between moles and number of atoms, use Avogadro's number, 6.022×10^{23} atoms = 1 mol, as a conversion factor.

EXAMPLES

EXAMPLE 6.13 Converting between Moles and Number of Atoms

Calculate the number of atoms in 4.8 mol of copper.

GIVEN: 4.8 mol Cu

FIND: Cu atoms

SOLUTION MAP

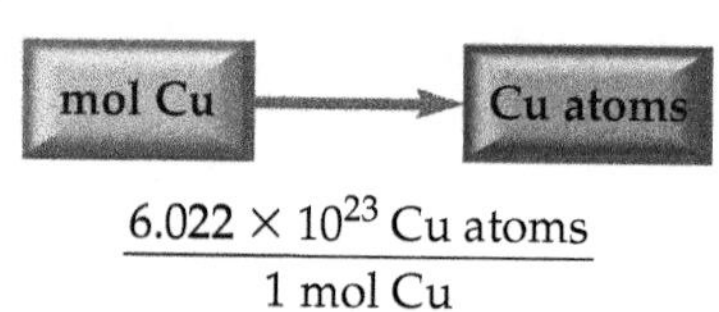

$$\frac{6.022 \times 10^{23} \text{ Cu atoms}}{1 \text{ mol Cu}}$$

RELATIONSHIPS USED

1 mol Cu = 6.022×10^{23} Cu atoms (Avogadro's number, from inside back cover)

SOLVE
Follow the solution map to solve the problem.

SOLUTION

$$4.8 \text{ mol Cu} \times \frac{6.022 \times 10^{23} \text{ Cu atoms}}{1 \text{ mol Cu}} = 2.9 \times 10^{24} \text{ Cu atoms}$$

CHECK
Check your answer. Are the units correct? Does the answer make physical sense?

The units, Cu atoms, are correct. The answer makes physical sense because the number is very large, as you would expect for nearly 5 moles of atoms.

Converting between Grams and Moles (Section 6.3)

EXAMPLE 6.14 Converting between Grams and Moles

Calculate the mass of aluminum (in grams) of 6.73 moles of aluminum.

SORT
You are given the number of moles of aluminum and asked to find the mass of aluminum in grams.

GIVEN: 6.73 mol Al

FIND: g Al

STRATEGIZE
Use the molar mass of aluminum to convert between moles and grams.

SOLUTION MAP

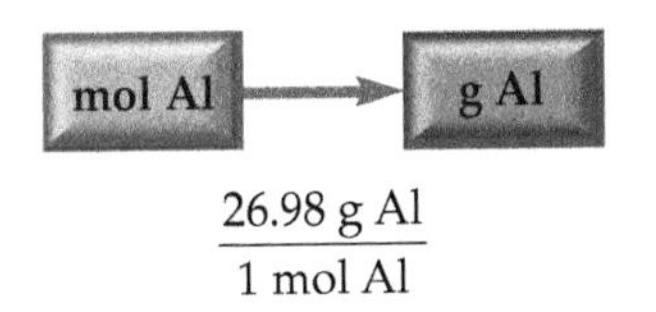

$$\frac{26.98 \text{ g Al}}{1 \text{ mol Al}}$$

RELATIONSHIPS USED

26.98 g Al = 1 mol Al (molar mass of Al from periodic table)

SOLVE
Follow the solution map to solve the problem.

SOLUTION

$$6.73 \text{ mol Al} \times \frac{26.98 \text{ g Al}}{1 \text{ mol Al}} = 182 \text{ g Al}$$

CHECK
Check your answer. Are the units correct? Does the answer make physical sense?

The units, g Al, are correct. The answer makes physical sense because each mole has a mass of about 27 g; therefore, nearly 7 moles should have a mass of nearly 190 g.

Converting between Grams and Number of Atoms or Molecules (Section 6.3)

EXAMPLE 6.15 Converting between Grams and Number of Atoms or Molecules

Determine the number of atoms in a 48.3-g sample of zinc.

SORT

You are given the mass of a zinc sample and asked to find the number of Zn atoms that it contains.

GIVEN: 48.3 g Zn

FIND: Zn atoms

STRATEGIZE

First use the molar mass of the element to convert from grams to moles, and then use Avogadro's number to convert moles to number of atoms.

SOLUTION MAP

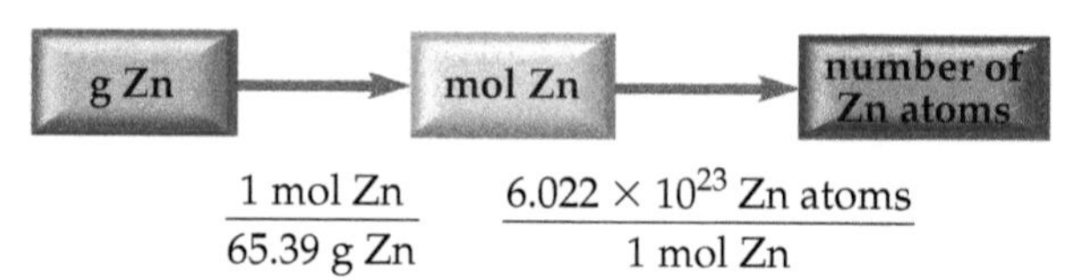

$$\frac{1 \text{ mol Zn}}{65.39 \text{ g Zn}} \qquad \frac{6.022 \times 10^{23} \text{ Zn atoms}}{1 \text{ mol Zn}}$$

RELATIONSHIPS USED

65.39 g Zn = 1 mol Zn (molar mass of Zn from periodic table)

1 mol = 6.022×10^{23} atoms (Avogadro's number, from inside back cover)

SOLVE

Follow the solution map to solve the problem.

SOLUTION

$$48.3 \text{ g Zn} \times \frac{1 \text{ mol Zn}}{65.39 \text{ g Zn}} \times \frac{6.022 \times 10^{23} \text{ Zn atoms}}{1 \text{ mol Zn}} = 4.45 \times 10^{23} \text{ Zn atoms}$$

CHECK

Check your answer. Are the units correct? Does the answer make physical sense?

The units, Zn atoms, are correct. The answer makes physical sense because the number of atoms in any macroscopic-sized sample should be very large.

Converting between Moles of a Compound and Moles of a Constituent Element (Section 6.5)

EXAMPLE 6.16 Converting between Moles of a Compound and Moles of a Constituent Element

Determine the number of moles of oxygen in 7.20 mol of H_2SO_4.

SORT

You are given the number of moles of sulfuric acid and asked to find the number of moles of oxygen.

GIVEN: 7.20 mol H_2SO_4

FIND: mol O

STRATEGIZE

To convert between moles of a compound and moles of a constituent element, use the chemical formula of the compound to determine a ratio between the moles of the element and the moles of the compound.

SOLUTION MAP

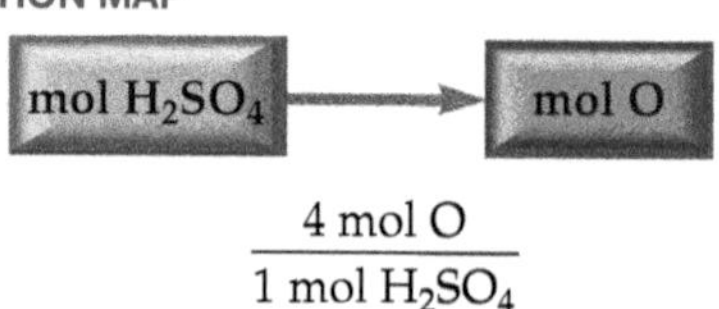

$$\frac{4 \text{ mol O}}{1 \text{ mol } H_2SO_4}$$

RELATIONSHIPS USED

$$4 \text{ mol O} : 1 \text{ mol } H_2SO_4$$

SOLVE

Follow the solution map to solve the problem.

SOLUTION

$$7.20 \text{ mol } H_2SO_4 \times \frac{4 \text{ mol O}}{1 \text{ mol } H_2SO_4} = 28.8 \text{ mol O}$$

CHECK

Check your answer. Are the units correct? Does the answer make physical sense?

The units, mol O, are correct. The answer makes physical sense because the number of moles of an element in a compound is equal to or greater than the number of moles of the compound itself.

Converting between Grams of a Compound and Grams of a Constituent Element (Section 6.5)

EXAMPLE 6.17 Converting between Grams of a Compound and Grams of a Constituent Element

Find the grams of iron in 79.2 g of Fe_2O_3.

SORT

You are given the mass of iron (III) oxide and asked to find the mass of iron contained within it.

GIVEN: 79.2 g Fe_2O_3

FIND: g Fe

STRATEGIZE

Use the molar mass of the compound to convert from grams of the compound to moles of the compound. Then use the chemical formula to obtain a conversion factor to convert from moles of the compound to moles of the constituent element. Finally, use the molar mass of the constituent element to convert from moles of the element to grams of the element.

SOLUTION MAP

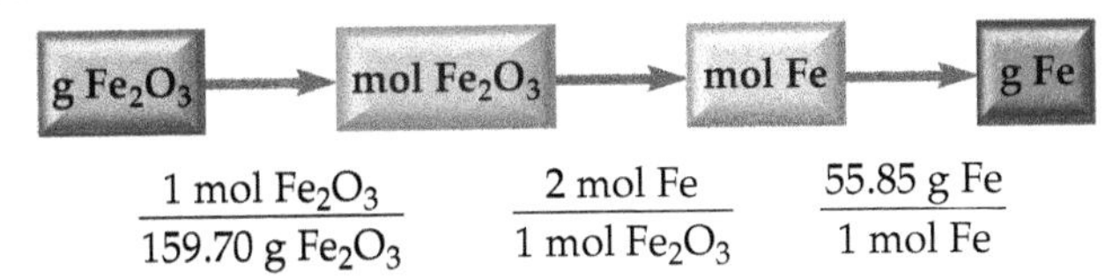

$$\frac{1 \text{ mol } Fe_2O_3}{159.70 \text{ g } Fe_2O_3} \qquad \frac{2 \text{ mol Fe}}{1 \text{ mol } Fe_2O_3} \qquad \frac{55.85 \text{ g Fe}}{1 \text{ mol Fe}}$$

RELATIONSHIPS USED

$$\text{Molar mass } Fe_2O_3 = 2(55.85) + 3(16.00) = 159.70 \text{ g/mol}$$

2 mol Fe : 1 mol Fe_2O_3 (from given chemical formula)

SOLVE

Follow the solution map to solve the problem.

SOLUTION

$$79.2 \text{ g } Fe_2O_3 \times \frac{1 \text{ mol } Fe_2O_3}{159.70 \text{ g } Fe_2O_3} \times \frac{2 \text{ mol Fe}}{1 \text{ mol } Fe_2O_3} \times \frac{55.85 \text{ g Fe}}{1 \text{ mol Fe}} = 55.4 \text{ g Fe}$$

CHECK

Check your answer. Are the units correct? Does the answer make physical sense?

The units, g Fe, are correct. The answer makes physical sense because the mass of a constituent element within a compound should be less than the mass of the compound itself.

Using Mass Percent Composition as a Conversion Factor (Section 6.6)

EXAMPLE 6.18 Using Mass Percent Composition as a Conversion Factor

Determine the mass of titanium in 57.2 g of titanium(IV) oxide. The mass percent of titanium in titanium(IV) oxide is 59.9%.

SORT

You are given the mass of titanium(IV) oxide and the mass percent titanium in the oxide. You are asked to find the mass of titanium in the sample.

GIVEN: 57.2 g TiO_2

$$\frac{59 \text{ g Ti}}{100 \text{ g TiO}_2}$$

FIND: g Ti

STRATEGIZE

Use the percent composition as a conversion factor between grams of titanium(IV) oxide and grams of titanium.

SOLUTION MAP

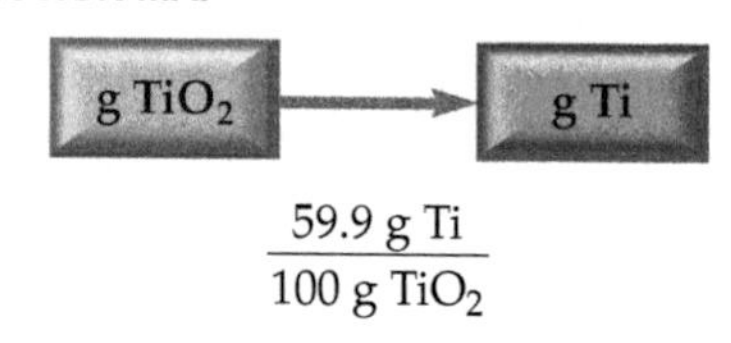

$$\frac{59.9 \text{ g Ti}}{100 \text{ g TiO}_2}$$

RELATIONSHIPS USED

$$59.9 \text{ g Ti} : 100 \text{ g TiO}_2$$

SOLVE

Follow the solution map to solve the problem.

SOLUTION

$$57.2 \text{ g TiO}_2 \times \frac{59.9 \text{ g Ti}}{100 \text{ g TiO}_2} = 34.3 \text{ g Ti}$$

CHECK

Check your answer. Are the units correct? Does the answer make physical sense?

The units, g Ti, are correct. The answer makes physical sense because the mass of an element within a compound should be less than the mass of the compound itself.

Determining Mass Percent Composition from a Chemical Formula (Section 6.7)

EXAMPLE 6.19 Determining Mass Percent Composition from a Chemical Formula

Calculate the mass percent composition of potassium in potassium oxide (K_2O).

SORT

You are given the formula of potassium oxide and asked to determine the mass percent of potassium within it.

GIVEN: K_2O

FIND: Mass % K

STRATEGIZE

The solution map shows how the information derived from the chemical formula can be substituted into the mass percent equation to yield the mass percent of the element.

SOLUTION MAP

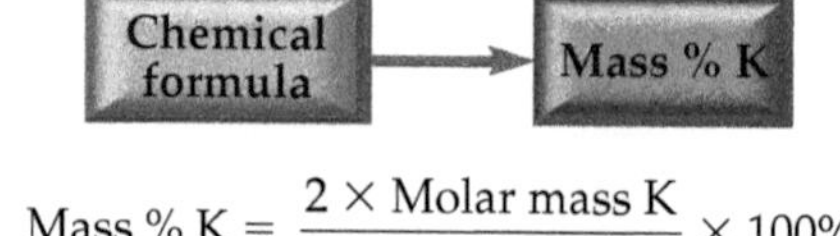

$$\text{Mass \% K} = \frac{2 \times \text{Molar mass K}}{\text{Molar mass K}_2\text{O}} \times 100\%$$

RELATIONSHIPS USED

$$\text{Mass percent of element } X = \frac{\text{Mass of element } X \text{ in 1 mol of compound}}{\text{Mass of 1 mol of compound}} \times 100\%$$

(mass percent equation, from Section 6.6)

SOLVE

Calculate the molar mass of potassium oxide and then follow the solution map to solve the problem.

SOLUTION

$$\text{Molar mass } K_2O = 2(39.10) + 16.00 = 94.20 \text{ g/mol}$$

$$\text{Mass \% K} = \frac{2(39.10 \text{ g K})}{94.20 \text{ g } K_2O} \times 100\% = 83.01\% \text{ K}$$

CHECK

Check your answer. Are the units correct? Does the answer make physical sense?

The units, % K, are correct. The answer makes physical sense because it should be below 100%.

Determining an Empirical Formula from Experimental Data (Section 6.8)

You must recognize this problem as one requiring a special procedure. Follow these steps to solve the problem.

EXAMPLE 6.20 Determining an Empirical Formula from Experimental Data

A laboratory analysis of vanillin, the flavoring agent in vanilla, determined the mass percent composition: C, 63.15%; H, 5.30%; O, 31.55%. Determine the empirical formula of vanillin.

GIVEN: 63.15 % C, 5.30 % H, and 31.55 % O.

FIND: empirical formula

SOLUTION

1. Write down (or calculate) the masses of each element present in a sample of the compound. If you are given mass percent composition, assume a 100-g sample and calculate the masses of each element from the given percentages.

In a 100 g sample:

63.15 g C

5.30 g H

31.55 g O

2. Convert each of the masses in Step 1 to moles by using the appropriate molar mass for each element as a conversion factor.

$$63.15 \text{ g C} \times \frac{1 \text{ mol C}}{12.01 \text{ g C}} = 5.258 \text{ mol C}$$

$$5.30 \text{ g H} \times \frac{1 \text{ mol H}}{1.01 \text{ g H}} = 5.25 \text{ mol H}$$

$$31.55 \text{ g O} \times \frac{1 \text{ mol O}}{16.00 \text{ g O}} = 1.972 \text{ mol O}$$

3. Write down a pseudoformula for the compound using the moles of each element (from Step 2) as subscripts.

$$C_{5.258}H_{5.25}O_{1.972}$$

4. Divide all the subscripts in the formula by the smallest subscript.

$$C_{\frac{5.258}{1.972}}H_{\frac{5.25}{1.972}}O_{\frac{1.972}{1.972}} \longrightarrow C_{2.67}H_{2.66}O_1$$

5. If the subscripts are not whole numbers, multiply all the subscripts by a small whole number to arrive at whole-number subscripts.

$$C_{2.67}H_{2.66}O_1 \times 3 \longrightarrow C_8H_8O_3$$

The correct empirical formula is $C_8H_8O_3$.

Calculating a Molecular Formula from an Empirical Formula and Molar Mass (Section 6.9)

EXAMPLE 6.21 Calculating a Molecular Formula from an Empirical Formula and Molar Mass

Acetylene, a gas often used in welding torches, has the empirical formula CH and a molar mass of 26.04 g/mol. Find its molecular formula.

SORT
You are given the empirical formula and molar mass of acetylene and asked to find the molecular formula.

GIVEN: empirical formula = CH

molar mass = 26.04 g/mol

FIND: molecular formula

STRATEGIZE
In the first step, use the molar mass (which is given) and the empirical formula molar mass (which you can calculate based on the empirical formula) to determine n (the integer by which you must multiply the empirical formula to arrive at the molecular formula).
In the second step, multiply the coefficients in the empirical formula by n to arrive at the molecular formula.

SOLUTION MAP

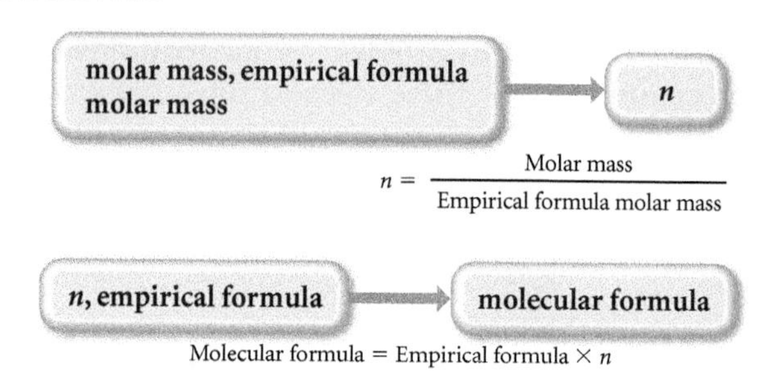

SOLVE
Follow the solution map to solve the problem. Calculate the empirical formula molar mass, which is the sum of the masses of all the atoms in the empirical formula.

SOLUTION
Empirical formula molar mass

$= 12.01 + 1.01$

$= 13.02 \text{ g/mol}$

Next, find n, the ratio of the molar mass to empirical mass.

$$n = \frac{\text{Molar mass}}{\text{Empirical formula molar mass}}$$

$$= \frac{26.04 \text{ g/mol}}{13.02 \text{ g/mol}} = 2$$

Finally, multiply the empirical formula by n to get the molecular formula.

Molecular formula $= CH \times 2 \longrightarrow C_2H_2$

CHECK
Check your answer. Does the answer make physical sense?

The answer makes physical sense because the formula subscripts are all integers. Any answer with fractional integers would be suspect.

KEY TERMS

Avogadro's number **[6.3]**
empirical formula **[6.8]**
empirical formula molar mass **[6.9]**
mass percent (composition) **[6.6]**
molar mass **[6.3]**
mole (mol) **[6.3]**
molecular formula **[6.8]**

EXERCISES

QUESTIONS

1. Why is chemical composition important?
2. How can you determine the number of atoms in a sample of an element? Why is counting them not an option?
3. How many atoms are in 1 mol of atoms?
4. How many molecules are in 1 mol of molecules?
5. What is the mass of 1 mol of atoms for an element?
6. What is the mass of 1 mol of molecules for a compound?
7. What is the mass of 1 mol of atoms of each element?
   (a) P
   (b) Pt
   (c) C
   (d) Cr
8. What is the mass of 1 mol of molecules of each compound?
   (a) CO_2
   (b) CH_2Cl_2
   (c) $C_{12}H_{22}O_{11}$
   (d) SO_2
9. The subscripts in a chemical formula give relationships between moles of the constituent elements and moles of the compound. Explain why these subscripts *do not* give relationships between grams of the constituent elements and grams of the compound.
10. Write the conversion factors between moles of each constituent element and moles of the compound for $C_{12}H_{22}O_{11}$.
11. Mass percent composition can be used as a conversion factor between grams of a constituent element and grams of the compound. Write the conversion factor (including units) inherent in each mass percent composition.
    (a) Water is 11.19% hydrogen by mass.
    (b) Fructose, also known as fruit sugar, is 53.29% oxygen by mass.
    (c) Octane, a component of gasoline, is 84.12% carbon by mass.
    (d) Ethanol, the alcohol in alcoholic beverages, is 52.14% carbon by mass.
12. What is the mathematical formula for calculating mass percent composition from a chemical formula?
13. How are the empirical formula and the molecular formula of a compound related?
14. Why is it important to be able to calculate an empirical formula from experimental data?
15. What is the empirical formula mass of a compound?
16. How are the molar mass and empirical formula mass for a compound related?

PROBLEMS

THE MOLE CONCEPT

17. How many mercury atoms are in 5.8 mol of mercury?
18. How many moles of gold atoms do 3.45×10^{24} gold atoms constitute?
19. How many atoms are in each elemental sample?
    (a) 3.4 mol Cu
    (b) 9.7×10^{-3} mol C
    (c) 22.9 mol Hg
    (d) 0.215 mol Na
20. How many moles of atoms are in each elemental sample?
    (a) 4.6×10^{24} Pb atoms
    (b) 2.87×10^{22} He atoms
    (c) 7.91×10^{23} K atoms
    (d) 4.41×10^{21} Ca atoms

21. Complete the table:

Element	Moles	Number of Atoms
Ne	0.552	———
Ar	———	3.25×10^{24}
Xe	1.78	———
He	———	1.08×10^{20}

22. Complete the table:

Element	Moles	Number of Atoms
Cr	———	9.61×10^{23}
Fe	1.52×10^{-5}	———
Ti	0.0365	———
Hg	———	1.09×10^{23}

23. Consider these definitions.

1 doz = 12

1 gross = 144

1 ream = 500

1 mol = 6.022×10^{23}

Suppose you have 872 sheets of paper. How many ______ of paper do you have?

(a) dozens

(b) gross

(c) reams

(d) moles

24. A pure copper penny contains approximately 3.0×10^{22} copper atoms. Use the definitions in the previous problem to determine how many ______ of copper atoms are in a penny.

(a) dozens

(b) gross

(c) reams

(d) moles

25. How many moles of tin atoms are in a pure tin cup with a mass of 38.1 g?

26. A lead fishing weight contains 0.12 mol of lead atoms. What is its mass?

27. A pure gold coin contains 0.145 mol of gold. What is its mass?

28. A helium balloon contains 0.46 g of helium. How many moles of helium does it contain?

29. How many moles of atoms are in each elemental sample?

(a) 1.34 g Zn

(b) 24.9 g Ar

(c) 72.5 g Ta

(d) 0.0223 g Li

30. What is the mass in grams of each elemental sample?

(a) 6.64 mol W

(b) 0.581 mol Ba

(c) 68.1 mol Xe

(d) 1.57 mol S

31. Complete the table:

Element	Moles	Mass
Ne	______	22.5 g
Ar	0.117	______
Xe	______	1.00 kg
He	1.44×10^{-4}	______

32. Complete the table:

Element	Moles	Mass
Cr	0.00442	______
Fe	______	73.5 mg
Ti	1.009×10^{-3}	______
Hg	______	1.78 kg

33. A pure silver ring contains 0.0134 mmol (millimol) Ag. How many silver atoms does it contain?

34. A pure gold ring contains 0.0102 mmol (millimol) Au. How many gold atoms does it contain?

35. How many aluminum atoms are in 3.78 g of aluminum?

36. What is the mass of 4.91×10^{21} platinum atoms?

37. How many atoms are in each elemental sample?

(a) 16.9 g Sr

(b) 26.1 g Fe

(c) 8.55 g Bi

(d) 38.2 g P

38. Calculate the mass in grams of each elemental sample:

(a) 1.32×10^{20} uranium atoms

(b) 2.55×10^{22} zinc atoms

(c) 4.11×10^{23} lead atoms

(d) 6.59×10^{24} silicon atoms

39. How many carbon atoms are in a diamond (pure carbon) with a mass of 38 mg?

40. How many helium atoms are in a helium blimp containing 495 kg of helium?

41. How many titanium atoms are in a pure titanium bicycle frame with a mass of 1.28 kg?

42. How many copper atoms are in a pure copper statue with a mass of 133 kg?

43. Complete the table:

Element	Mass	Moles	Number of Atoms
Na	38.5 mg	______	______
C	______	1.12	______
V	______	______	214
Hg	1.44 kg	______	______

44. Complete the table:

Element	Mass	Moles	Number of Atoms
Pt	______	0.0449	______
Fe	______	______	1.14×10^{25}
Ti	23.8 mg	______	______
Hg	______	2.05	______

45. Which sample contains the greatest number of atoms?
(a) 27.2 g Cr
(b) 55.1 g Ti
(c) 205 g Pb

46. Which sample contains the greatest number of atoms?
(a) 10.0 g He
(b) 25.0 g Ne
(c) 115 g Xe

47. Determine the number of moles of molecules (or formula units) in each sample.
(a) 38.2 g sodium chloride
(b) 36.5 g nitrogen monoxide
(c) 4.25 kg carbon dioxide
(d) 2.71 mg carbon tetrachloride

48. Determine the mass of each sample.
(a) 1.32 mol carbon tetrafluoride
(b) 0.555 mol magnesium fluoride
(c) 1.29 mmol carbon disulfide
(d) 1.89 kmol sulfur trioxide

49. Complete the table:

Compound	Mass	Moles	Number of molecules
H_2O	112 kg	______	______
N_2O	6.33 g	______	______
SO_2	______	2.44	______
CH_2Cl_2	______	0.0643	______

50. Complete the table:

Compound	Mass	Moles	Number of molecules
CO_2	______	0.0153	______
CO	______	0.0150	______
BrI	23.8 mg	______	______
CF_2Cl_2	1.02 kg	______	______

51. A mothball, composed of naphthalene ($C_{10}H_8$), has a mass of 1.32 g. How many naphthalene molecules does it contain?

52. Calculate the mass in grams of a single water molecule.

53. How many molecules are in each sample?
(a) 3.5 g H_2O
(b) 56.1 g N_2
(c) 89 g CCl_4
(d) 19 g $C_6H_{12}O_6$

54. Calculate the mass in grams of each sample.
(a) 5.94×10^{20} H_2O_2 molecules
(b) 2.8×10^{22} SO_2 molecules
(c) 4.5×10^{25} O_3 molecules
(d) 9.85×10^{19} CH_4 molecules

55. A sugar crystal contains approximately 1.8×10^{17} sucrose ($C_{12}H_{22}O_{11}$) molecules. What is its mass in milligrams?

56. A salt crystal has a mass of 0.12 mg. How many NaCl formula units does it contain?

57. How much money, in dollars, does one mole of pennies represent? If this amount of money were evenly distributed among the entire world's population (about 6.6 billion people), how much would each person get? Would each person be a millionaire? Billionaire? Trillionaire?

58. A typical dust particle has a diameter of about 10.0 μm. If 1.0 mol of dust particles were laid end to end along the equator, how many times would they encircle the planet? The circumference of the Earth at the equator is 40,076 km.

CHEMICAL FORMULAS AS CONVERSION FACTORS

59. Determine the number of moles of Cl in 2.7 mol $CaCl_2$.

60. How many moles of O are in 12.4 mol $Fe(NO_3)_3$?

61. Which sample contains the greatest number of moles of O?
(a) 2.3 mol H_2O
(b) 1.2 mol H_2O_2
(c) 0.9 mol $NaNO_3$
(d) 0.5 mol $Ca(NO_3)_2$

62. Which sample contains the greatest number of moles of Cl?
(a) 3.8 mol HCl
(b) 1.7 mol CH_2Cl_2
(c) 4.2 mol $NaClO_3$
(d) 2.2 mol $Mg(ClO_4)_2$

63. Determine the number of moles of C in each sample.
(a) 2.5 mol CH_4
(b) 0.115 mol C_2H_6
(c) 5.67 mol C_4H_{10}
(d) 25.1 mol C_8H_{18}

64. Determine the number of moles of H in each sample.
(a) 4.67 mol H_2O
(b) 8.39 mol NH_3
(c) 0.117 mol N_2H_4
(d) 35.8 mol $C_{10}H_{22}$

65. For each set of molecular models, write a relationship between moles of hydrogen and moles of molecules. Then determine the total number of hydrogen atoms present. (H—white; O—red; C—black; N—blue)

(a)
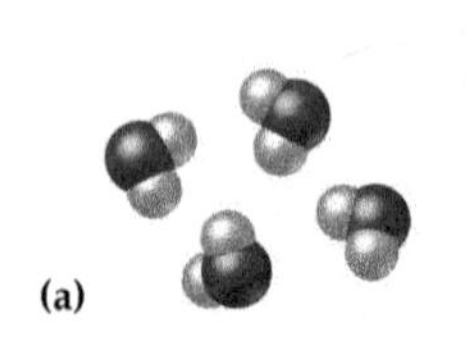
(b)
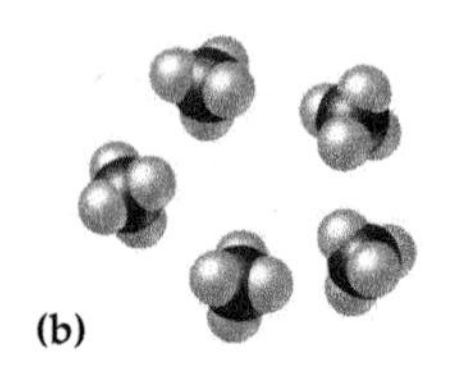
(c)
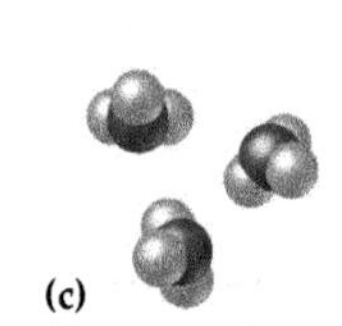

66. For each set of molecular models, write a relationship between moles of oxygen and moles of molecules. Then determine the total number of oxygen atoms present. (H—white; O—red; C—black; S—yellow)

(a)
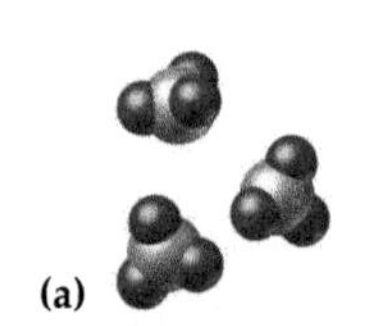
(b)
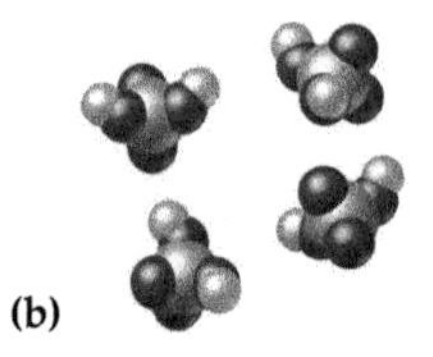
(c)
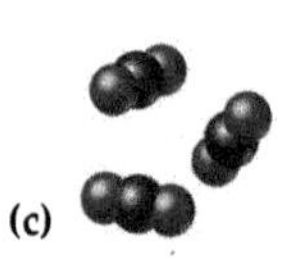

67. How many grams of Cl are in 38.0 g of each sample of chlorofluorocarbons (CFCs)?
(a) CF_2Cl_2
(b) $CFCl_3$
(c) $C_2F_3Cl_3$
(d) CF_3Cl

68. Calculate the number of grams of sodium in 1.00 g of each sodium-containing food additive.
(a) NaCl (table salt)
(b) Na_3PO_4 (sodium phosphate)
(c) $NaC_7H_5O_2$ (sodium benzoate)
(d) $Na_2C_6H_6O_7$ (sodium hydrogen citrate)

69. Iron is found in Earth's crust as several different iron compounds. Calculate the mass (in kg) of each compound that contains 1.0×10^3 kg of iron.
(a) Fe_2O_3 (hematite)
(b) Fe_3O_4 (magnetite)
(c) $FeCO_3$ (siderite)

70. Lead is often found in Earth's crust as several lead compounds. Calculate the mass (in kg) of each compound that contains 1.0×10^3 kg of lead.
(a) PbS (galena)
(b) $PbCO_3$ (cerussite)
(c) $PbSO_4$ (anglesite)

MASS PERCENT COMPOSITION

71. A 2.45-g sample of strontium completely reacts with oxygen to form 2.89 g of strontium oxide. Use this data to calculate the mass percent composition of strontium in strontium oxide.

72. A 4.78-g sample of aluminum completely reacts with oxygen to form 6.67 g of aluminum oxide. Use this data to calculate the mass percent composition of aluminum in aluminum oxide.

73. A 1.912-g sample of calcium chloride is decomposed into its constituent elements and found to contain 0.690 g Ca and 1.222 g Cl. Calculate the mass percent composition of Ca and Cl in calcium chloride.

74. A 0.45-g sample of aspirin is decomposed into its constituent elements and found to contain 0.27 g C, 0.020 g H, and 0.16 g O. Calculate the mass percent composition of C, H, and O in aspirin.

75. Copper(II) fluoride contains 37.42% F by mass. Use this percentage to calculate the mass of fluorine in grams contained in 28.5 g of copper(II) fluoride.

76. Silver chloride, often used in silver plating, contains 75.27% Ag. Calculate the mass of silver chloride in grams required to make 4.8 g of silver plating.

77. In small amounts, the fluoride ion (often consumed as NaF) prevents tooth decay. According to the American Dental Association, an adult female should consume 3.0 mg of fluorine per day. Calculate the amount of sodium fluoride (45.24% F) that a woman should consume to get the recommended amount of fluorine.

78. The iodide ion, usually consumed as potassium iodide, is a dietary mineral essential to good nutrition. In countries where potassium iodide is added to salt, iodine deficiency or goiter has been almost completely eliminated. The recommended daily allowance (RDA) for iodine is 150 μg/day. How much potassium iodide (76.45% I) should you consume to meet the RDA?

MASS PERCENT COMPOSITION FROM CHEMICAL FORMULA

79. Calculate the mass percent composition of nitrogen in each compound.
    (a) N_2O
    (b) NO
    (c) NO_2
    (d) N_2O_5

80. Calculate the mass percent composition of carbon in each compound.
    (a) C_2H_2
    (b) C_3H_6
    (c) C_2H_6
    (d) C_2H_6O

81. Calculate the mass percent composition of each element in each compound.
    (a) $C_2H_4O_2$
    (b) CH_2O_2
    (c) C_3H_9N
    (d) $C_4H_{12}N_2$

82. Calculate the mass percent composition of each element in each compound.
    (a) $FeCl_3$
    (b) TiO_2
    (c) H_3PO_4
    (d) HNO_3

83. Iron ores have different amounts of iron per kilogram of ore. Calculate the mass percent composition of iron for each iron ore: Fe_2O_3 (hematite), Fe_3O_4 (magnetite), $FeCO_3$ (siderite). Which ore has the highest iron content?

84. Plants need nitrogen to grow; so many fertilizers consist of nitrogen-containing compounds. Calculate the mass percent composition of nitrogen in each fertilizer: NH_3, $CO(NH_2)_2$, NH_4NO_3, $(NH_4)_2SO_4$. Which fertilizer has the highest nitrogen content?

CALCULATING EMPIRICAL FORMULAS

85. A compound containing nitrogen and oxygen is decomposed in the laboratory and produces 1.78 g of nitrogen and 4.05 g of oxygen. Calculate the empirical formula of the compound.

86. A compound containing selenium and fluorine is decomposed in the laboratory and produces 2.231 g of selenium and 3.221 g of fluorine. Calculate the empirical formula of the compound.

87. Samples of several compounds were decomposed, and the masses of their constituent elements were measured. Calculate the empirical formula for each compound.

(a) 1.245 g Ni, 5.381 g I

(b) 1.443 g Se, 5.841 g Br

(c) 2.128 g Be, 7.557 g S, 15.107 g O

88. Samples of several compounds were decomposed, and the masses of their constituent elements were measured. Calculate the empirical formula for each compound.

(a) 2.677 g Ba, 3.115 g Br

(b) 1.651 g Ag, 0.1224 g O

(c) 0.672 g Co, 0.569 g As, 0.486 g O

89. The rotten smell of a decaying animal carcass is partially due to a nitrogen-containing compound called putrescine. Elemental analysis of putrescine shows that it consists of 54.50% C, 13.73% H, and 31.77% N. Calculate the empirical formula of putrescine.

90. Citric acid, the compound responsible for the sour taste of lemons, has the elemental composition: C, 37.51%; H, 4.20%; O, 58.29%. Calculate the empirical formula of citric acid.

91. The compounds listed here are often found in many natural flavors and scents. Calculate the empirical formula for each compound.

(a) ethyl butyrate (pineapple oil): C, 62.04%; H, 10.41%; O, 27.55%

(b) methyl butyrate (apple flavor): C, 58.80%; H, 9.87%; O, 31.33%

(c) benzyl acetate (oil of jasmine): C, 71.98%; H, 6.71%; O, 21.31%

92. The compounds listed here are all over-the-counter pain relievers. Calculate the empirical formula for each compound.

(a) acetaminophen (Tylenol): C, 63.56%; H, 6.00%; N, 9.27%; O, 21.17%

(b) naproxen (Aleve): C, 73.03%; H, 6.13%; O, 20.84%

93. A 1.45-g sample of phosphorus burns in air and forms 2.57 g of a phosphorus oxide. Calculate the empirical formula of the oxide.

94. A 2.241-g sample of nickel reacts with oxygen to form 2.852 g of the metal oxide. Calculate the empirical formula of the oxide.

95. A 0.77-mg sample of nitrogen reacts with chlorine to form 6.61 mg of the chloride. What is the empirical formula of the nitrogen chloride?

96. A 45.2-mg sample of phosphorus reacts with selenium to form 131.6 mg of the selenide. What is the empirical formula of the phosphorus selenide?

CALCULATING MOLECULAR FORMULAS

97. A compound containing carbon and hydrogen has a molar mass of 56.11 g/mol and an empirical formula of CH_2. Determine its molecular formula.

98. A compound containing phosphorus and oxygen has a molar mass of 219.9 g/mol and an empirical formula of P_2O_3. Determine its molecular formula.

99. The molar masses and empirical formulas of several compounds containing carbon and chlorine are as follows. Find the molecular formula of each compound.

(a) 284.77 g/mol, CCl

(b) 131.39 g/mol, C_2HCl_3

(c) 181.44 g/mol, C_2HCl

100. The molar masses and empirical formulas of several compounds containing carbon and nitrogen are as follows. Find the molecular formula of each compound.

(a) 163.26 g/mol, $C_{11}C_{17}N$

(b) 186.24 g/mol, C_6C_7N

(c) 312.29 g/mol, C_3C_2N

CUMULATIVE PROBLEMS

101. A pure copper cube has an edge length of 1.42 cm. How many copper atoms does it contain? (volume of a cube = (edge length)^3; density of copper = 8.96 g/cm^3)

102. A pure silver sphere has a radius of 0.886 cm. How many silver atoms does it contain? (volume of a sphere = $\frac{4}{3}\pi r^3$; density of silver = 10.5 g/cm^3)

103. A drop of water has a volume of approximately 0.05 mL. How many water molecules does it contain? (density of water $= 1.0\ g/cm^3$)

104. Fingernail-polish remover is primarily acetone (C_3H_6O). How many acetone molecules are in a bottle of acetone with a volume of 325 mL? (density of acetone $= 0.788\ g/cm^3$)

105. Complete the table:

Substance	Mass	Moles	Number of Particles (atoms or molecules)
Ar	____	4.5×10^{-4}	____
NO_2	____	____	1.09×10^{20}
K	22.4 mg	____	____
C_8H_{18}	3.76 kg	____	____

106. Complete the table:

Substance	Mass	Moles	Number of Particles (atoms or molecules)
$C_6H_{12}O_6$	15.8 g	____	____
Pb	____	____	9.04×10^{21}
CF_4	22.5 kg	____	____
C	____	0.0388	____

107. Determine the chemical formula of each compound and then refer to it to calculate the mass percent composition of each constituent element.

(a) copper(II) iodide

(b) sodium nitrate

(c) lead(II) sulfate

(d) calcium fluoride

108. Determine the chemical formula of each compound and then refer to it to calculate the mass percent composition of each constituent element.

(a) nitrogen triiodide

(b) xenon tetrafluoride

(c) phosphorus trichloride

(d) carbon monoxide

109. The rock in a particular iron ore deposit contains 78% Fe_2O_3 by mass. How many kilograms of the rock must be processed to obtain 1.0×10^3 kg of iron?

110. The rock in a lead ore deposit contains 84% PbS by mass. How many kilograms of the rock must be processed to obtain 1.0 kg of Pb?

111. A leak in the air conditioning system of an office building releases 12 kg of CHF_2Cl per month. If the leak continues, how many kilograms of Cl will be emitted into the atmosphere each year?

112. A leak in the air conditioning system of an older car releases 55 g of CF_2Cl_2 per month. How much Cl is emitted into the atmosphere each year by this car?

113. Hydrogen is a possible future fuel. However, elemental hydrogen is rare, so it must be obtained from a hydrogen-containing compound such as water. If hydrogen were obtained from water, how much hydrogen in grams could be obtained from 1.0 L of water? (density of water $= 1.0\ g/cm^3$)

114. Hydrogen, a possible future fuel mentioned in Problem 113, can also be obtained from other compounds such as ethanol. Ethanol can be made from the fermentation of crops such as corn. How much hydrogen in grams can be obtained from 1.0 kg of ethanol (C_2H_5OH)?

115. Complete the table of compounds that contain only carbon and hydrogen.

Formula	Molar Mass	% C (by mass)	% H (by mass)
C_2H_4	____	____	____
____	58.12	82.66%	____
C_4H_8	____	____	____
____	44.09	____	18.29%

116. Complete the table of compounds that contain only chromium and oxygen.

Formula	Name	Molar Mass	% Cr (by mass)	% O (by mass)
____	Chromium (III) oxide	____	____	____
____	____	84.00	61.90%	____
____	____	100.00	____	48.00%

117. Butanedione, a component of butter and body odor, has a cheesy smell. Elemental analysis of butanedione gave the mass percent composition: C, 55.80%; H, 7.03%; O, 37.17%. The molar mass of butanedione is 86.09 g/mol. Determine the molecular formula of butanedione.

118. Caffeine, a stimulant found in coffee and soda, has the mass percent composition: C, 49.48%; H, 5.19%; N, 28.85%; O, 16.48%. The molar mass of caffeine is 194.19 g/mol. Find the molecular formula of caffeine.

119. Nicotine, a stimulant found in tobacco, has the mass percent composition: C, 74.03%; H, 8.70%; N, 17.27%. The molar mass of nicotine is 162.23 g/mol. Find the molecular formula of nicotine.

120. Estradiol is a female sexual hormone that causes maturation and maintenance of the female reproductive system. Elemental analysis of estradiol gave the mass percent composition: C, 79.37%; H, 8.88%; O, 11.75%. The molar mass of estradiol is 272.37 g/mol. Find the molecular formula of estradiol.

121. A sample contains both KBr and KI in unknown quantities. If the sample has a total mass of 5.00 g and contains 1.51 g K, what are the percentages of KBr and KI in the sample by mass?

122. A sample contains both CO_2 and Ne in unknown quantities. If the sample contains a combined total of 1.75 mol and has a total mass of 65.3 g, what are the percentages of CO_2 and Ne in the sample by mole?

123. Ethanethiol (C_2H_6S) is a compound with a disagreeable odor that can be used to impart an odor to natural gas. When ethanethiol is burned, the sulfur reacts with oxygen to form SO_2. What mass of SO_2 forms upon the complete combustion of 28.7 g of ethanethiol?

124. Methanethiol (CH_4S) has a disagreeable odor and is often a component of bad breath. When methanethiol is burned, the sulfur reacts with oxygen to form SO_2. What mass of SO_2 forms upon the complete combustion of 1.89 g of methanethiol?

125. An iron ore contains 38% Fe_2O_3 by mass. What is the maximum mass of iron that can be recovered from 10.0 kg of this ore?

126. Seawater contains approximately 3.5% NaCl by mass and has a density of 1.02 g/mL. What volume of seawater contains 1.0 g of sodium?

HIGHLIGHT PROBLEMS

127. You can use the concepts in this chapter to obtain an estimate of the number of atoms in the universe. These steps will guide you through this calculation.
    (a) Begin by calculating the number of atoms in the sun. Assume that the sun is pure hydrogen with a density of 1.4 g/cm^3. The radius of the sun is 7×10^8 m, and the volume of a sphere is $V = \frac{4}{3}\pi r^3$.
    (b) Since the sun is an average-sized star, and since stars are believed to compose most of the mass of the visible universe (planets are so small they can be ignored), we can estimate the number of atoms in a galaxy by assuming that every star in the galaxy has the same number of atoms as our sun. The Milky Way galaxy is believed to contain 1×10^{11} stars. Use your answer from part (a) to calculate the number of atoms in the Milky Way galaxy.
    (c) The universe is estimated to contain approximately 1×10^{11} galaxies. If each of these galaxies contains the same number of atoms as the Milky Way galaxy, what is the total number of atoms in the universe?

▲ Our sun is one of the 100 billion stars in the Milky Way galaxy. The universe is estimated to contain about 100 billion galaxies.

128. Because of increasing evidence of damage to the ozone layer, chlorofluorocarbon (CFC) production was banned in 1996. However, there are about 100 million auto air conditioners that still use CFC-12 (CF_2Cl_2). These air conditioners are recharged from stockpiled supplies of CFC-12. If each of the 100 million automobiles contains 1.1 kg of CFC-12 and leaks 25% of its CFC-12 into the atmosphere per year, how much Cl in kilograms is added to the atmosphere each year by auto air conditioners? (Assume two significant figures in your calculations.)

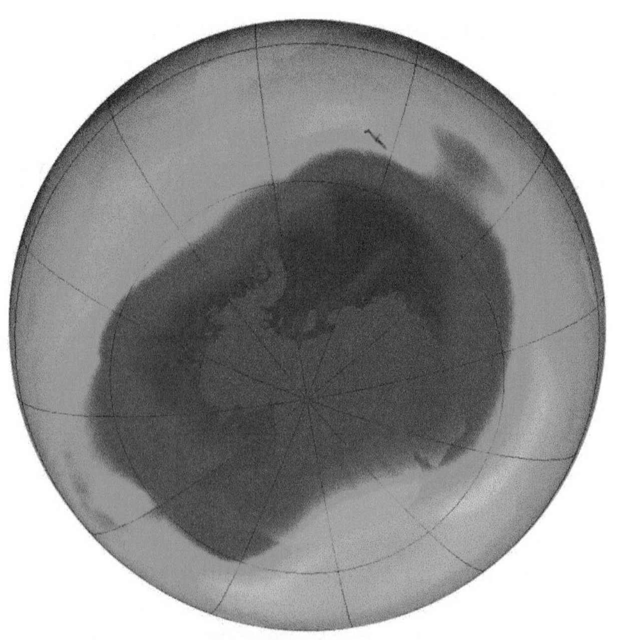

▲ The ozone hole over Antarctica on September 24, 2009. The dark blue and purple areas over the South Pole represent very depressed ozone concentrations.

129. In 1996, the media reported that possible evidence of life on Mars was found on a meteorite called Allan Hills 84001 (AH 84001). The meteorite was discovered in Antarctica in 1984 and is believed to have originated on Mars. Elemental analysis of substances within its crevices revealed carbon-containing compounds that normally derive only from living organisms. Suppose that one of those compounds had a molar mass of 202.23 g/mol and the mass percent composition: C, 95.02%; H, 4.98%. What is the molecular formula for the carbon-containing compound?

▲ The Allan Hills 84001 meteorite. Elemental analysis of the substances within the crevices of this meteorite revealed carbon-containing compounds that normally originate from living organisms.

▸ANSWERS TO SKILLBUILDER EXERCISES

Skillbuilder 6.1	5.32×10^{22} Au atoms
Skillbuilder 6.2	89.2 g S
Skillbuilder 6.3	8.17 g He
Skillbuilder 6.4	2.56×10^{-2} mol NO_2
Skillbuilder 6.5	1.22×10^{23} H_2O molecules
Skillbuilder 6.6	5.6 mol O
Skillbuilder 6.7	3.3 g O
Skillbuilder Plus, p. 178	4.04 g O
Skillbuilder 6.8	8.6 g Na
Skillbuilder 6.9	53.28% O
Skillbuilder 6.10	CH_2O
Skillbuilder 6.11	$C_{13}H_{18}O_2$
Skillbuilder 6.12	CuO
Skillbuilder 6.13	C_4H_{10}
Skillbuilder Plus, p. 187	$C_2H_8N_2$

▸ANSWERS TO CONCEPTUAL CHECKPOINTS

6.1 (a) The mole is a counting unit; it represents a definite number (Avogadro's number, 6.022×10^{23}). Therefore, a given number of atoms always represents a precise number of moles, regardless of what atom is involved. Atoms of different elements have different masses, so if samples of different elements have the same mass, they *cannot* contain the same number of atoms or moles.

6.2 (b) Since carbon has lower molar mass than cobalt or lead, a one-gram sample of carbon contains more atoms than one gram of cobalt or lead.

6.3 (a) Sample A would have the greatest number of molecules. Since sample A has a lower molar mass than sample B, a given mass of sample A has more moles and therefore more molecules than the same mass of sample B.

6.4 (c) 1.0 mole of F_2 contains 2.0 mol of F atoms. The other two options each contain less than two moles of F atoms.

6.5 (b) This compound has the highest ratio of oxygen atoms to chromium atoms and so must have the greatest mass percent of oxygen.

CHAPTER 7

Chemical Reactions

"Chemistry . . . is one of the broadest branches of science if for no other reason than, when we think about it, everything is chemistry."

LUCIANO CAGLIOTI (1933–)

7.1 Kindergarten Volcanoes, Automobiles, and Laundry Detergents

Did you ever make a clay volcano in kindergarten that erupted when filled with vinegar, baking soda, and red food coloring for effect? Have you pushed the gas pedal of a car and felt the acceleration as the car moved forward? Have you wondered why laundry detergents work better than normal soap to clean your clothes? Each of these processes involves a *chemical reaction*—the transformation of one or more substances into different substances.

In the classic kindergarten volcano, the baking soda (which is sodium bicarbonate) reacts with acetic acid in the vinegar to form carbon dioxide gas, water, and sodium acetate. The newly formed carbon dioxide bubbles out of the mixture, causing the eruption. Reactions that occur in liquids and form a gas are *gas evolution reactions*. A similar reaction causes the fizzing of antacids such as Alka-Seltzer™.

Hydrocarbons are covered in detail in Chapter 18.

When you drive a car, hydrocarbons such as octane (in gasoline) react with oxygen from the air to form carbon dioxide gas and water (▶ Figure 7.1). This reaction produces heat, which expands the gases in the car's cylinders, accelerating it forward. Reactions such as this one—in which a substance reacts with oxygen, emitting heat and forming one or more oxygen-containing compounds—are *combustion reactions*. Combustion reactions are a subcategory of *oxidation–reduction reactions*, in which electrons are transferred from one substance to another. The formation of rust and the dulling of automobile paint are other examples of oxidation–reduction reactions.

◀ In the space shuttle's main engines, hydrogen molecules, H_2 (white), and oxygen molecules, O_2 (red), which are stored in the central fuel tank, react violently to form water molecules, H_2O. The reaction emits the energy that helps propel the shuttle into space.

Laundry detergent works better than soap to wash clothes because it contains substances that soften hard water. Hard water contains dissolved calcium (Ca^{2+}) and magnesium (Mg^{2+}) ions. These ions interfere with the action of soap by reacting

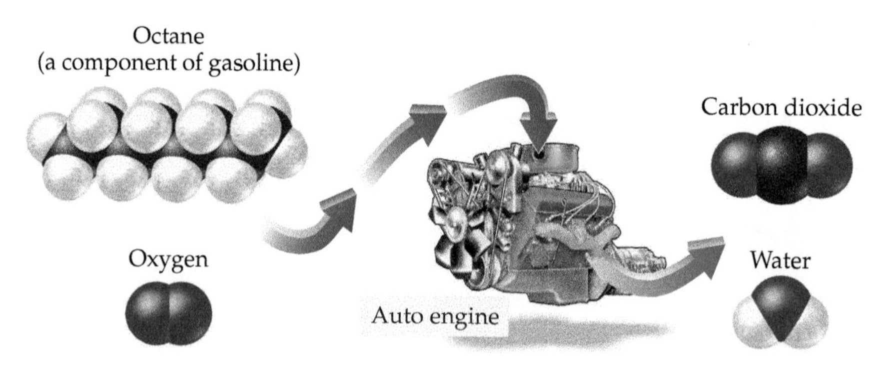

▲ **FIGURE 7.1 A combustion reaction** In an automobile engine, hydrocarbons such as octane (C_8H_{18}) from gasoline combine with oxygen from the air and react to form carbon dioxide and water.

▲ **FIGURE 7.2 Soap and water** Soap forms suds with pure water (left), but reacts with the ions in hard water (right) to form a gray residue that adheres to clothes.

with it to form a gray, slimy substance called *curd* or *soap scum* (◀ Figure 7.2). If you have ever washed your clothes in ordinary soap, you may have noticed gray soap scum residue on your clothes.

Laundry detergents inhibit curd formation because they contain substances such as sodium carbonate (Na_2CO_3) that remove calcium and magnesium ions from the water. When sodium carbonate dissolves in water, it *dissociates*, or separates into sodium ions (Na^+) and carbonate ions (CO_3^{2-}). The dissolved carbonate ions react with calcium and magnesium ions in the hard water to form solid calcium carbonate ($CaCO_3$) and solid magnesium carbonate ($MgCO_3$). These solids simply settle to the bottom of the laundry mixture, resulting in the removal of the ions from the water. In other words, laundry detergents contain substances that react with the ions in hard water to immobilize them. Reactions such as these—that form solid substances in water—are *precipitation reactions*. Precipitation reactions are also used to remove dissolved toxic metals in industrial wastes.

Chemical reactions take place all around us and even inside us. They are involved in many of the products we use daily and in many of our experiences. Chemical reactions can be relatively simple, like the combination of hydrogen and oxygen to form water, or they can be complex, like the synthesis of a protein molecule from thousands of simpler molecules. In some cases, such as the neutralization reaction that occurs in a swimming pool when acid is added to adjust the water's acidity level, chemical reactions are not noticeable to the naked eye. In other cases, such as the combustion reaction that produces a pillar of smoke and fire under the space shuttle during liftoff, chemical reactions are very obvious. In all cases, however, chemical reactions produce changes in the arrangements of the molecules and atoms that compose matter. Often, these molecular changes cause macroscopic changes that we can directly experience.

7.2 Evidence of a Chemical Reaction

If we could see the atoms and molecules that compose matter, we could easily identify a chemical reaction. Do atoms combine with other atoms to form compounds? Do new molecules form? Do the original molecules decompose? Do atoms in one molecule change places with atoms in another? If the answer to one or more of these questions is yes, a chemical reaction has occurred. Of course, we are not normally able to see atoms and molecules, so we need other ways to identify a chemical reaction.

Although we can't see atoms, many chemical reactions do produce easily detectable changes as they occur. For example, when the color-causing molecules in a brightly colored shirt decompose with repeated exposure to sunlight, the color of the shirt fades. Similarly, when the molecules embedded in the plastic of a child's temperature-sensitive spoon transform upon warming, the color of the spoon changes. These *color changes* are evidence that a chemical reaction has occurred.

Solid formation

▲ **FIGURE 7.3 A precipitation reaction** The formation of a solid in a previously clear solution is evidence of a chemical reaction.

Gas formation

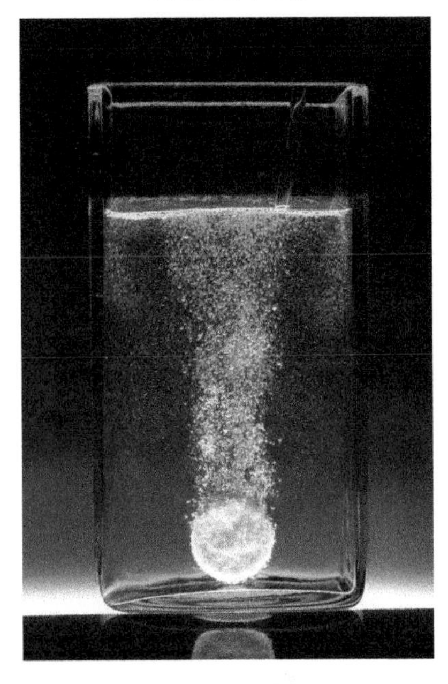

▲ **FIGURE 7.4 A gas evolution reaction** The formation of a gas is evidence of a chemical reaction.

Other changes that identify chemical reactions include the *formation of a solid* (▶ Figure 7.3) or *the formation of a gas* (▶ Figure 7.4). Dropping Alka-Seltzer tablets into water or combining baking soda and vinegar (as in our opening example of the kindergarten volcano) are both good examples of chemical reactions that produce a gas—the gas is visible as bubbles in the liquid.

Recall from Section 3.9 that a reaction that emits heat is an *exothermic* reaction and one that absorbs heat is an *endothermic* reaction.

Heat absorption or *emission*, as well as *light emission*, are also evidence of reactions. For example, a natural gas flame produces heat and light. A chemical cold pack becomes cold when the plastic barrier separating two substances is broken. Both of these changes suggest that a chemical reaction is occurring.

Color change

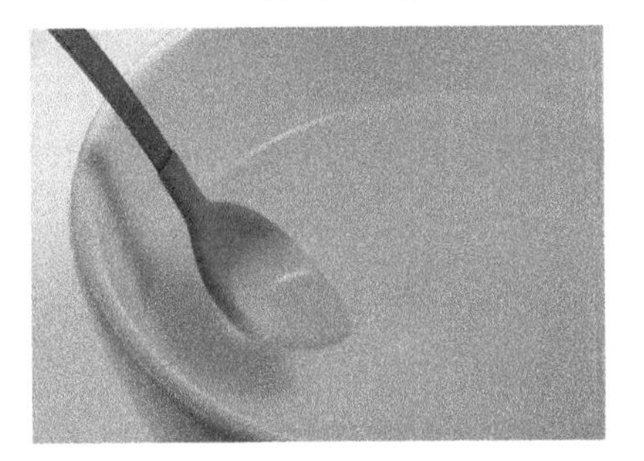

▲ A child's temperature-sensitive spoon changes color upon warming due to a reaction induced by the higher temperature.

Heat absorption

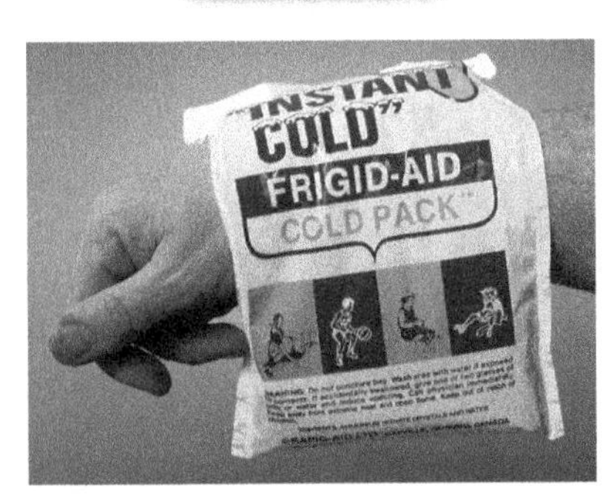

▲ A change in temperature due to absorption or emission of heat is evidence of a chemical reaction. This chemical cold pack becomes cold when the barrier separating two substances is broken.

While these changes provide evidence of a chemical reaction, they are not *definitive* evidence. Only chemical analysis showing that the initial substances have changed into other substances conclusively proves that a chemical reaction has occurred. We can be fooled. For example, when water boils, bubbles form, but no chemical reaction has occurred. Boiling water forms gaseous steam, but both water and steam are composed of water molecules—no chemical change has occurred (◀ Figure 7.5). On the other hand, chemical reactions may occur without any obvious signs, yet chemical analysis may show that a reaction has indeed occurred. The changes occurring at the atomic and molecular level determine whether a chemical reaction has occurred.

▲ **FIGURE 7.5 Boiling: a physical change** When water boils, bubbles are formed and a gas is evolved. However, no chemical change has occurred because the gas, like the liquid water, is also composed of water molecules.

In summary, each of the following provides *evidence of a chemical reaction*.

- a *color change*

- the *formation of a solid* in a previously clear solution

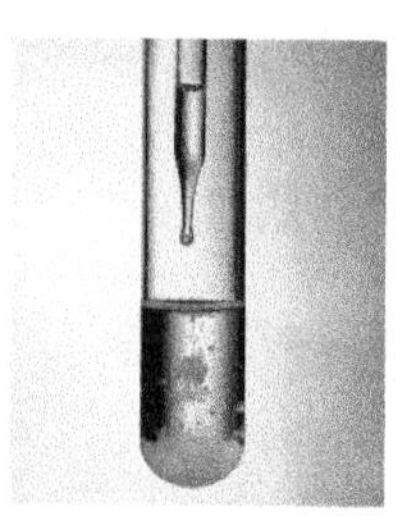

- the *formation of a gas* when you add a substance to a solution

- the *emission of light*

- the *emission* or *absorption of heat*

EXAMPLE 7.1 Evidence of a Chemical Reaction

Which changes involve a chemical reaction? Explain your answers.

(a) ice melting upon warming
(b) an electric current passing through water, resulting in the formation of hydrogen and oxygen gas that appear as bubbles rising in the water
(c) iron rusting
(d) bubbles forming when a soda can is opened

SOLUTION

(a) not a chemical reaction; melting ice forms water, but both the ice and water are composed of water molecules.
(b) chemical reaction; water decomposes into hydrogen and oxygen, as evidenced by the bubbling.
(c) chemical reaction; iron changes into iron oxide, changing color in the process.
(d) not a chemical reaction; even though there is bubbling, it is just carbon dioxide coming out of the liquid.

▶SKILLBUILDER 7.1 | Evidence of a Chemical Reaction

Which changes involve a chemical reaction? Explain your answers.

(a) butane burning in a butane lighter
(b) butane evaporating out of a butane lighter
(c) wood burning
(d) dry ice subliming

▶FOR MORE PRACTICE Example 7.16; Problems 25, 26, 27, 28, 29, 30.

CONCEPTUAL CHECKPOINT 7.1

These images portray molecular views of one substance before and after a change. Determine whether a chemical reaction has occurred in each case.

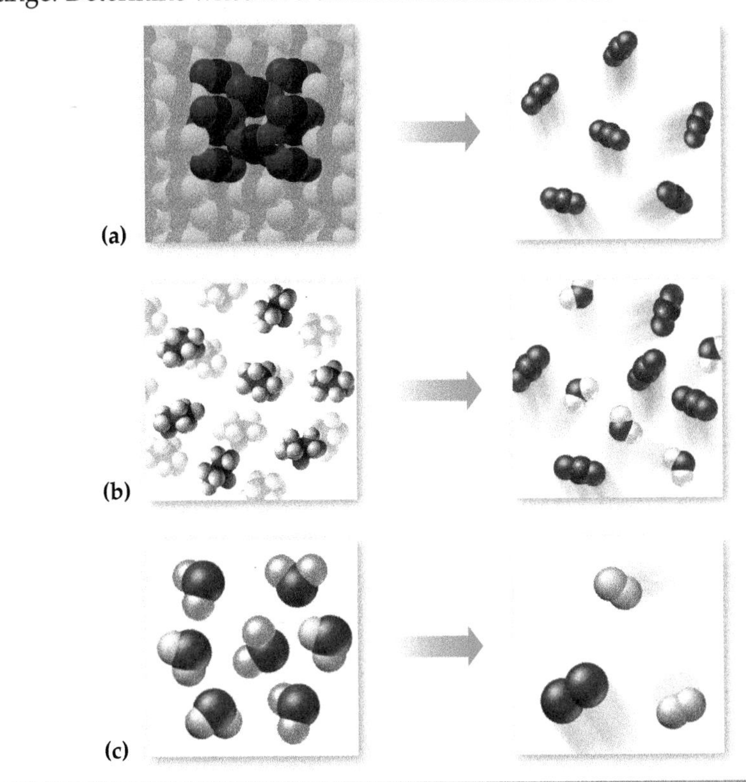

7.3 The Chemical Equation

As we saw in Section 3.6, we represent chemical reactions with *chemical equations*. For example, the reaction occurring in a natural-gas flame, such as the flame on a kitchen stove, is methane (CH_4) reacting with oxygen (O_2) to form carbon dioxide (CO_2) and water (H_2O). We represent this reaction with the equation:

$$\underbrace{CH_4 + O_2}_{\text{reactants}} \longrightarrow \underbrace{CO_2 + H_2O}_{\text{products}}$$

The substances on the left side of the equation are the *reactants*, and the substances on the right side are the *products*. We often specify the state of each reactant or product in parentheses next to the formula. If we add states to our equation, it becomes:

$$CH_4(g) + O_2(g) \longrightarrow CO_2(g) + H_2O(g)$$

TABLE 7.1 Abbreviations Indicating the States of Reactants and Products in Chemical Equations

Abbreviation	State
(g)	gas
(l)	liquid
(s)	solid
(aq)	aqueous (water solution)*

*The (aq) designation stands for *aqueous*, which indicates that a substance is dissolved in water. When a substance dissolves in water, the mixture is called a *solution* (see Section 7.5).

The (g) indicates that these substances are gases in the reaction. Table 7.1 summarizes the common states of reactants and products and their symbols used in chemical reactions.

Let's look more closely at the equation for the burning of natural gas. How many oxygen atoms are on each side of the equation?

2 O atoms 2 O atoms + 1 O atom = 3 O atoms

$$CH_4(g) + O_2(g) \longrightarrow CO_2(g) + H_2O(g)$$

In chemical equations, atoms cannot change from one type to another—hydrogen atoms cannot change into oxygen atoms, for example. Nor can atoms disappear (recall the law of conservation of mass from Section 3.7).

The left side of the equation has two oxygen atoms, and the right side has three. Since chemical equations represent real chemical reactions, atoms cannot simply appear or disappear in chemical equations because, as we know, atoms don't simply appear or disappear in nature. We must account for the atoms on both sides of the equation. Notice also that the left side of the equation has four hydrogen atoms and the right side only two.

4 H atoms 2 H atoms

$$CH_4(g) + O_2(g) \longrightarrow CO_2(g) + H_2O(g)$$

To correct these problems, we must create a **balanced equation**, one in which the numbers of each type of atom on both sides of the equation are equal. To balance an equation, we insert coefficients—not subscripts—in front of the chemical formulas as needed to make the number of each type of atom in the reactants equal to the number of each type of atom in the products. New atoms do not form during a reaction, nor do atoms vanish—matter must be conserved.

When we balance chemical equations by inserting coefficients as needed in front of the formulas of the reactants and products, it changes the number of molecules in the equation, but it does not change the *kinds* of molecules. To balance the preceding equation, for example, we put the coefficient 2 before O_2 in the reactants, and the coefficient 2 before H_2O in the products.

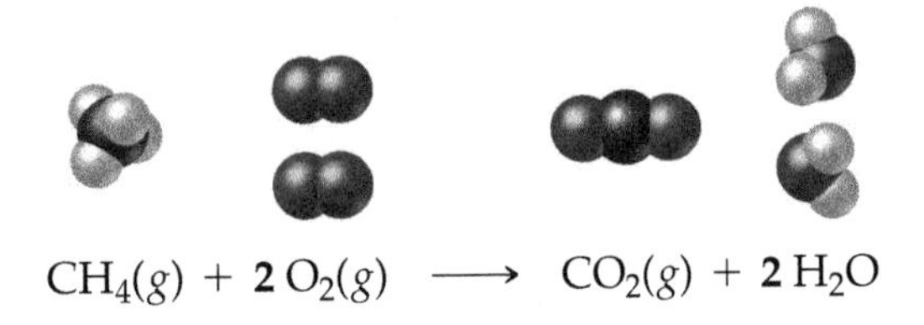

$$CH_4(g) + \mathbf{2}\,O_2(g) \longrightarrow CO_2(g) + \mathbf{2}\,H_2O$$

The equation is now balanced because the numbers of each type of atom on both sides of the equation are equal. We can verify this by summing the number of each type of atom.

> The number of a particular type of atom within a chemical formula embedded in an equation is obtained by multiplying the subscript for the atom by the coefficient for the chemical formula.

If there is no coefficient or subscript, a 1 is implied. So, the balanced equation for the combustion of natural gas is:

$$CH_4(g) + 2\,O_2(g) \longrightarrow CO_2(g) + 2\,H_2O(g)$$

Reactants	Products
1 C atom ($1 \times \underline{C}H_4$)	1 C atom ($1 \times \underline{C}O_2$)
4 H atoms ($1 \times C\underline{H_4}$)	4 H atoms ($2 \times \underline{H_2}O$)
4 O atoms ($2 \times \underline{O_2}$)	4 O atoms ($1 \times C\underline{O_2} + 2 \times H_2\underline{O}$)

The numbers of each type of atom on both sides of the equation are equal—the equation is balanced.

$$CH_4(g) + 2\,O_2(g) \longrightarrow CO_2(g) + 2\,H_2O(g)$$

▶ A balanced chemical equation represents a chemical reaction. In this image, methane molecules combine with oxygen to form carbon dioxide and water.

CONCEPTUAL CHECKPOINT 7.2

In photosynthesis, plants make the sugar glucose, $C_6H_{12}O_6$, from carbon dioxide and water. The equation for the reaction is

$$6\,CO_2 + 6\,H_2O \longrightarrow C_6H_{12}O_6 + x\,O_2$$

In order for this equation to be balanced, the coefficient x must be

(a) 3 **(b)** 6 **(c)** 9 **(d)** 12

7.4 How to Write Balanced Chemical Equations

The following procedure box details the steps for writing balanced chemical equations. As in other procedures, we show the steps in the left column and examples of applying each step in the center and right columns. Remember, change only the *coefficients* to balance a chemical equation; *never change the subscripts.*

Writing Balanced Chemical Equations	**EXAMPLE 7.2** Write a balanced equation for the reaction between solid silicon dioxide and solid carbon to produce solid silicon carbide and carbon monoxide gas.	**EXAMPLE 7.3** Write a balanced equation for the combustion of liquid octane (C_8H_{18}), a component of gasoline, in which it combines with gaseous oxygen to form gaseous carbon dioxide and gaseous water.
1. Write a skeletal equation by writing chemical formulas for each of the reactants and products. Review Chapter 5 for nomenclature rules. (If a skeletal equation is provided, skip this step and go to Step 2.)	SOLUTION $SiO_2(s) + C(s) \longrightarrow SiC(s) + CO(g)$	SOLUTION $C_8H_{18}(l) + O_2(g) \longrightarrow CO_2(g) + H_2O(g)$
2. If an element occurs in only one compound on both sides of the equation, balance it first. If there is more than one such element, balance metals before nonmetals.	Begin with Si $SiO_2(s) + C(s) \longrightarrow SiC(s) + CO(g)$ **1 Si atom ⟶ 1 Si atom** Si is already balanced. Balance O next $SiO_2(s) + C(s) \longrightarrow SiC(s) + CO(g)$ **2 O atoms ⟶ 1 O atom** To balance O, put a 2 before $CO(g)$. $SiO_2(s) + C(s) \longrightarrow SiC(s) + \mathbf{2}\,CO(g)$ **2 O atoms ⟶ 2 O atoms**	Begin with C $C_8H_{18}(l) + O_2(g) \longrightarrow CO_2(g) + H_2O(g)$ **8 C atoms ⟶ 1 C atom** To balance C, put an 8 before $CO_2(g)$. $C_8H_{18}(l) + O_2(g) \longrightarrow 8\,CO_2(g) + H_2O(g)$ **8 C atoms ⟶ 8 C atoms** Balance H next $C_8H_{18}(l) + O_2(g) \longrightarrow 8\,CO_2(g) + H_2O(g)$ **18 H atoms ⟶ 2 H atoms** To balance H, put a 9 before $H_2O(g)$. $C_8H_{18}(l) + O_2(g) \longrightarrow 8\,CO_2(g) + \mathbf{9}\,H_2O(g)$ **18 H atoms ⟶ 18 H atoms**
3. If an element occurs as a free element on either side of the chemical equation, balance it last. Always balance free elements by adjusting the coefficient *on the free element.*	Balance C $SiO_2(s) + C(s) \longrightarrow SiC(s) + 2\,CO(g)$ **1 C atom** ⟶ 1 C + 2 C = **3 C atoms** To balance C, put a 3 before $C(s)$. $SiO_2(s) + \mathbf{3}\,C(s) \longrightarrow SiC(s) + 2\,CO(g)$ **3 C atoms** ⟶ 1 C + 2 C = **3 C atoms**	Balance O $C_8H_{18}(l) + O_2(g) \longrightarrow 8\,CO_2(g) + 9\,H_2O(g)$ **2 O atoms** ⟶ 16 O + 9 O = **25 O atoms** To balance O, put a $\frac{25}{2}$ before $O_2(g)$. $C_8H_{18}(l) + \frac{25}{2}\,O_2(g) \longrightarrow 8\,CO_2(g) + 9\,H_2O(g)$ **25 O atoms** ⟶ 16 O + 9 O = **25 O atoms**
4. If the balanced equation contains coefficient fractions, change these into whole numbers by multiplying the entire equation by the appropriate factor.	This step is not necessary in this example. Proceed to Step 5.	$[C_8H_{18}(l) + \frac{25}{2}\,O_2(g) \longrightarrow 8\,CO_2(g) + 9\,H_2O(g)] \times 2$ $2\,C_8H_{18}(l) + 25\,O_2(g) \longrightarrow 16\,CO_2(g) + 18\,H_2O(g)$

5. Check to make certain the equation is balanced by summing the total number of each type of atom on both sides of the equation.

$SiO_2(s) + 3\,C(s) \longrightarrow SiC(s) + 2\,CO(g)$

Reactants		Products
1 Si atom	⟶	1 Si atom
2 O atoms	⟶	2 O atoms
3 C atoms	⟶	3 C atoms

The equation is balanced.

▶SKILLBUILDER 7.2

Write a balanced equation for the reaction between solid chromium(III) oxide and solid carbon to produce solid chromium and carbon dioxide gas.

$2\,C_8H_{18}(l) + 25\,O_2(g) \longrightarrow 16\,CO_2(g) + 18\,H_2O(g)$

Reactants		Products
16 C atoms	⟶	16 C atoms
36 H atoms	⟶	36 H atoms
50 O atoms	⟶	50 O atoms

The equation is balanced.

▶SKILLBUILDER 7.3

Write a balanced equation for the combustion of gaseous C_4H_{10} in which it combines with gaseous oxygen to form gaseous carbon dioxide and gaseous water.

▶FOR MORE PRACTICE Example 7.17; Problems 33, 34, 35, 36, 37, 38.

EXAMPLE 7.4 Balancing Chemical Equations

Write a balanced equation for the reaction of solid aluminum with aqueous sulfuric acid to form aqueous aluminum sulfate and hydrogen gas.

SOLUTION

Use your knowledge of chemical nomenclature from Chapter 5 to write a skeletal equation containing formulas for each of the reactants and products. The formulas for each compound MUST BE CORRECT before you begin to balance the equation.

$Al(s) + H_2SO_4(aq) \longrightarrow Al_2(SO_4)_3(aq) + H_2(g)$

Since both aluminum and hydrogen occur as pure elements, balance those last. Sulfur and oxygen occur in only one compound on each side of the equation, so balance these first. Sulfur and oxygen are also part of a polyatomic ion that stays intact on both sides of the equation. *Balance polyatomic ions such as these as a unit.* There are 3 SO_4^{2-} ions on the right side of the equation, so put a 3 in front of H_2SO_4.

$Al(s) + \mathbf{3}\,H_2SO_4(aq) \longrightarrow Al_2(SO_4)_3(aq) + H_2(g)$

Balance Al next. Since there are 2 Al atoms on the right side of the equation, place a 2 in front of Al on the left side of the equation.

$\mathbf{2}\,Al(s) + 3\,H_2SO_4(aq) \longrightarrow Al_2(SO_4)_3(aq) + H_2(g)$

Balance H next. Since there are 6 H atoms on the left side, place a 3 in front of $H_2(g)$ on the right side.

$2\,Al(s) + 3\,H_2SO_4(aq) \longrightarrow Al_2(SO_4)_3(aq) + \mathbf{3}\,H_2(g)$

Finally, sum the number of atoms on each side to make sure that the equation is balanced.

$2\,Al(s) + 3\,H_2SO_4(aq) \longrightarrow Al_2(SO_4)_3(aq) + 3\,H_2(g)$

Reactants		Products
2 Al atoms	⟶	2 Al atoms
6 H atoms	⟶	6 H atoms
3 S atoms	⟶	3 S atoms
12 O atoms	⟶	12 O atoms

▶SKILLBUILDER 7.4 | Balancing Chemical Equations

Write a balanced equation for the reaction of aqueous lead(II) acetate with aqueous potassium iodide to form solid lead(II) iodide and aqueous potassium acetate.

▶FOR MORE PRACTICE Problems 39, 40, 41, 42, 43, 44.

EXAMPLE 7.5 Balancing Chemical Equations

Balance this chemical equation.

$$Fe(s) + HCl(aq) \longrightarrow FeCl_3(aq) + H_2(g)$$

	SOLUTION
Since Cl occurs in only one compound on each side of the equation, balance it first. There is 1 Cl atom on the left side of the equation and 3 Cl atoms on the right side. To balance Cl, place a 3 in front of HCl.	$Fe(s) + \mathbf{3}\ HCl(aq) \longrightarrow FeCl_3(aq) + H_2(g)$
Since H and Fe occur as free elements, balance them last. There is 1 Fe atom on the left side of the equation and 1 Fe atom on the right, so Fe is balanced. There are 3 H atoms on the left and 2 H atoms on the right. Balance H by placing a $\frac{3}{2}$ in front of H_2. (That way you don't alter other elements that are already balanced.)	$Fe(s) + 3\ HCl(aq) \longrightarrow FeCl_3(aq) + \mathbf{\frac{3}{2}}\ H_2(g)$
Since the equation now contains a coefficient fraction, clear it by multiplying the entire equation (both sides) by 2.	$[Fe(s) + 3\ HCl(aq) \longrightarrow FeCl_3(aq) + \frac{3}{2}\ H_2(g)] \times 2$ $2\ Fe(s) + 6\ HCl(aq) \longrightarrow 2\ FeCl_3(aq) + 3\ H_2(g)$
Finally, sum the number of atoms on each side to check that the equation is balanced.	$2\ Fe(s) + 6\ HCl(aq) \longrightarrow 2\ FeCl_3(aq) + 3\ H_2(g)$

Reactants		**Products**
2 Fe atoms	$\longrightarrow$	2 Fe atoms
6 Cl atoms	$\longrightarrow$	6 Cl atoms
6 H atoms	$\longrightarrow$	6 H atoms

▶SKILLBUILDER 7.5 | Balancing Chemical Equations

Balance this chemical equation.

$$HCl(g) + O_2(g) \longrightarrow H_2O(l) + Cl_2(g)$$

▶FOR MORE PRACTICE Problems 45, 46, 47, 48, 49, 50.

CONCEPTUAL CHECKPOINT 7.3

Which quantity must always be the same on both sides of a balanced chemical equation?

(a) the number of each type of atom

(b) the number of each type of molecule

(c) the sum of all of the coefficients

7.5 Aqueous Solutions and Solubility: Compounds Dissolved in Water

Reactions occurring in aqueous solution are among the most common and important. An **aqueous solution** is a homogeneous mixture of a substance with water. For example, a sodium chloride (NaCl) solution, also called a saline solution, is composed of sodium chloride dissolved in water. Sodium chloride solutions are common both in the oceans and in living cells. You can form a sodium chloride solution yourself by adding table salt to water. As you stir the salt into the water, it seems to disappear. However, you know the salt is still there because if you taste the water, it has a salty flavor. How does sodium chloride dissolve in water?

When ionic compounds such as NaCl dissolve in water, they usually dissociate into their component ions. A sodium chloride solution, represented as $NaCl(aq)$, does not contain any NaCl units; only dissolved Na^+ ions and Cl^- ions are present.

We know that NaCl is present as independent sodium and chloride ions in solution because sodium chloride solutions conduct electricity, which requires the presence of freely moving charged particles. Substances (such as NaCl) that completely dissociate into ions in solution are called *strong electrolytes* and the resultant solutions are called **strong electrolyte solutions** (▼ Figure 7.6). Similarly, a silver nitrate solution, represented as $AgNO_3(aq)$, does not contain any $AgNO_3$ units, but only dissolved Ag^+ ions and NO_3^- ions. It, too, is a strong electrolyte solution. When compounds containing polyatomic ions such as NO_3^- dissolve, the polyatomic ions dissolve as intact units.

Not all ionic compounds, however, dissolve in water. AgCl, for example, does not. If we add AgCl to water, it remains as solid AgCl and appears as a white solid at the bottom of the beaker.

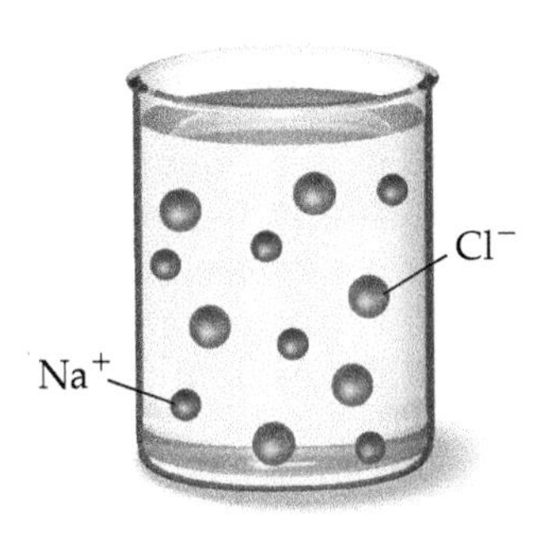

A sodium chloride solution contains independent $\mathbf{Na^+}$ and $\mathbf{Cl^-}$ ions.

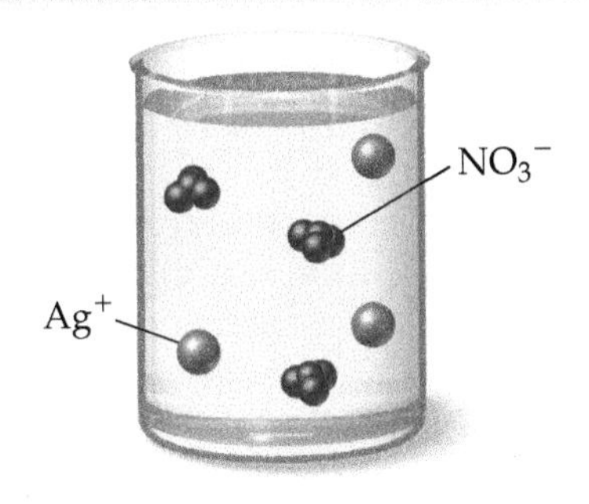

A silver nitrate solution contains independent $\mathbf{Ag^+}$ and $\mathbf{NO_3^-}$ ions.

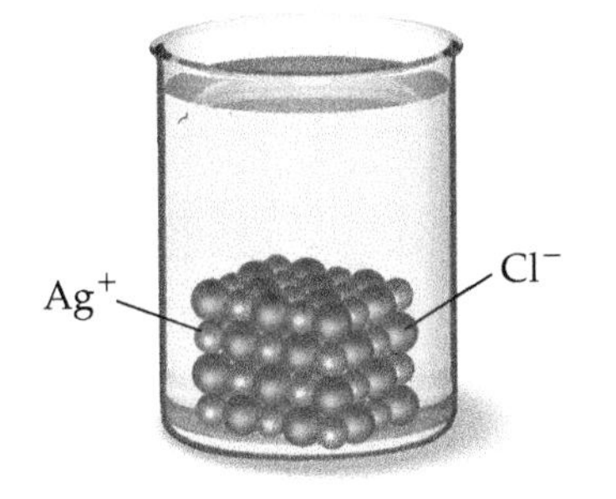

When silver chloride is added to water, it remains as solid AgCl—it does not dissolve into independent ions.

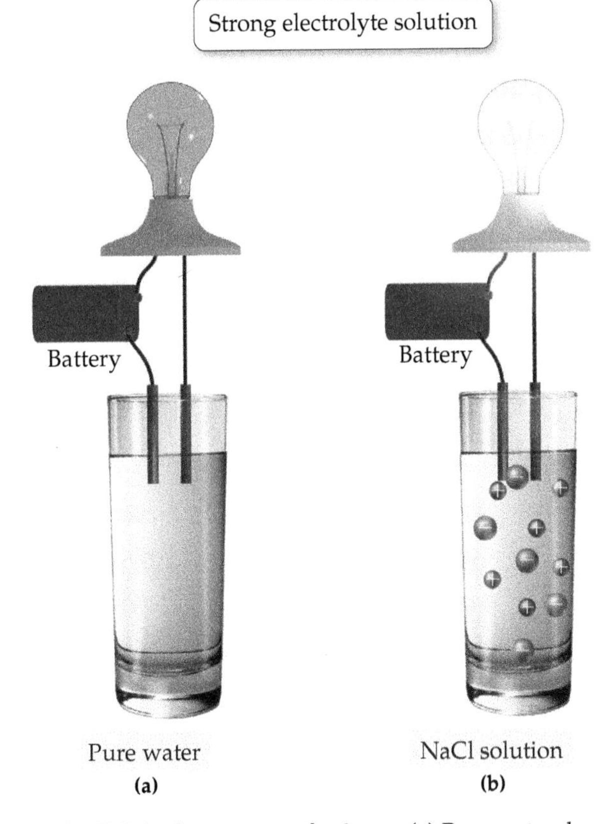

▲ FIGURE 7.6 **Ions as conductors** **(a)** Pure water does not conduct electricity. **(b)** Ions in a sodium chloride solution conduct electricity, causing the bulb to light. Solutions such as NaCl are called strong electrolyte solutions.

SOLUBILITY

A compound is **soluble** in a particular liquid if it dissolves in that liquid; a compound is **insoluble** if it does not dissolve in the liquid. NaCl, for example, is soluble in water. If we mix solid sodium chloride into water, it dissolves and forms a strong electrolyte solution. AgCl, on the other hand, is insoluble in water. If we mix solid silver chloride into water, it remains as a solid within the liquid water.

There is no easy way to tell whether a particular compound will be soluble or insoluble in water. For ionic compounds, however, empirical rules have been deduced from observations of many compounds. These **solubility rules** are summarized in Table 7.2 and ▼ Figure 7.7. For example, the solubility rules indicate that compounds containing the lithium ion are *soluble*. That means that compounds such as LiBr, $LiNO_3$, Li_2SO_4, LiOH, and Li_2CO_3 all dissolve in water to form strong electrolyte solutions. If a compound contains Li^+, it is soluble. Similarly, the solubility rules state that compounds containing the NO_3^- ion are soluble. Therefore, compounds such as $AgNO_3$, $Pb(NO_3)_2$, $NaNO_3$, $Ca(NO_3)_2$ and $Sr(NO_3)_2$ all dissolve in water to form strong electrolyte solutions.

The solubility rules apply only to the solubility of the compounds in water.

The solubility rules also state that, with some exceptions, compounds containing the CO_3^{2-} ion are *insoluble*. Therefore, compounds such as $CuCO_3$, $CaCO_3$, $SrCO_3$, and $FeCO_3$ do not dissolve in water. Note that the solubility rules contain many exceptions. For example, compounds containing CO_3^{2-} are *soluble when paired with* Li^+, Na^+, K^+, or NH_4^+. Thus Li_2CO_3, Na_2CO_3, K_2CO_3, and $(NH_4)_2CO_3$ are all soluble.

▼ **FIGURE 7.7** Solubility rules flowchart.

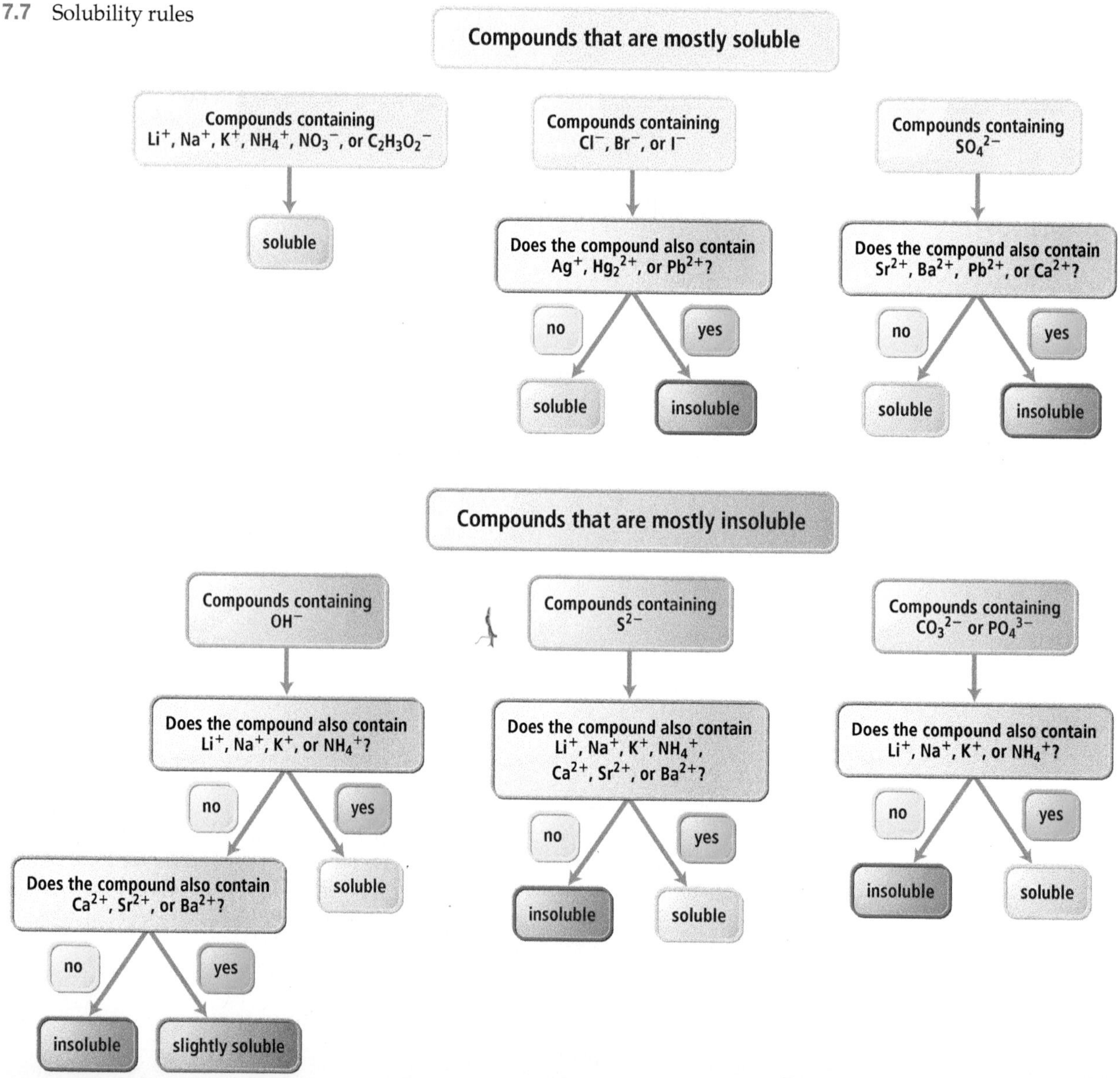

Compounds that are mostly soluble

- Compounds containing Li^+, Na^+, K^+, NH_4^+, NO_3^-, or $C_2H_3O_2^-$ → soluble
- Compounds containing Cl^-, Br^-, or I^- → Does the compound also contain Ag^+, Hg_2^{2+}, or Pb^{2+}? no → soluble; yes → insoluble
- Compounds containing SO_4^{2-} → Does the compound also contain Sr^{2+}, Ba^{2+}, Pb^{2+}, or Ca^{2+}? no → soluble; yes → insoluble

Compounds that are mostly insoluble

- Compounds containing OH^- → Does the compound also contain Li^+, Na^+, K^+, or NH_4^+? yes → soluble; no → Does the compound also contain Ca^{2+}, Sr^{2+}, or Ba^{2+}? no → insoluble; yes → slightly soluble
- Compounds containing S^{2-} → Does the compound also contain Li^+, Na^+, K^+, NH_4^+, Ca^{2+}, Sr^{2+}, or Ba^{2+}? no → insoluble; yes → soluble
- Compounds containing CO_3^{2-} or PO_4^{3-} → Does the compound also contain Li^+, Na^+, K^+, or NH_4^+? no → insoluble; yes → soluble

TABLE 7.2 Solubility Rules

Compounds Containing the Following Ions Are Mostly Soluble	Exceptions
Li^+, Na^+, K^+, NH_4^+	None
NO_3^-, $C_2H_3O_2^-$	None
Cl^-, Br^-, I^-	When any of these ions pairs with Ag^+, Hg_2^{2+}, or Pb^{2+}, the compound is insoluble.
SO_4^{2-}	When SO_4^{2-} pairs with Sr^{2+}, Ba^{2+}, Pb^{2+}, or Ca^{2+}, the compound is insoluble.
Compounds Containing the Following Ions Are Mostly Insoluble	**Exceptions**
OH^-, S^{2-}	When either of these ions pairs with Li^+, Na^+, K^+, or NH_4^+ the compound is soluble. When S^{2-} pairs with Ca^{2+}, Sr^{2+}, or Ba^{2+}, the compound is soluble. When OH^- pairs with Ca^{2+}, Sr^{2+}, or Ba^{2+}, the compound is slightly soluble.*
CO_3^{2-}, PO_4^{3-}	When either of these ions pairs with Li^+, Na^+, K^+, or NH_4^+, the compound is soluble.

*For many purposes these can be considered insoluble.

EXAMPLE 7.6 Determining Whether a Compound Is Soluble

Determine whether each compound is soluble or insoluble.

(a) AgBr **(b)** $CaCl_2$ **(c)** $Pb(NO_3)_2$ **(d)** $PbSO_4$

SOLUTION

(a) Insoluble; compounds containing Br^- are normally soluble, but Ag^+ is an exception.
(b) Soluble; compounds containing Cl^- are normally soluble, and Ca^{2+} is not an exception.
(c) Soluble; compounds containing NO_3^- are always soluble.
(d) Insoluble; compounds containing SO_4^{2-} are normally soluble, but Pb^{2+} is an exception.

▶SKILLBUILDER 7.6 | Determining Whether a Compound Is Soluble

Determine whether each compound is soluble or insoluble.

(a) CuS **(b)** $FeSO_4$ **(c)** $PbCO_3$ **(d)** NH_4Cl

▶FOR MORE PRACTICE Example 7.18; Problems 57, 58, 59, 60, 61, 62.

CONCEPTUAL CHECKPOINT 7.4

Which image best depicts a mixture of $BaCl_2$ and water?

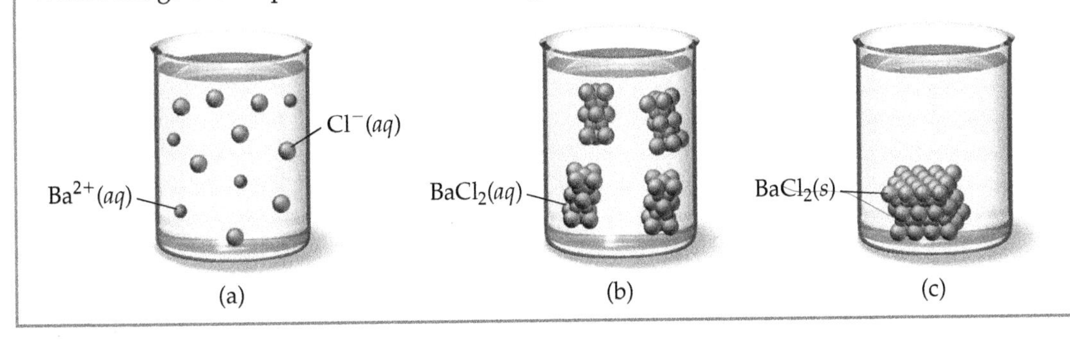

7.6 Precipitation Reactions: Reactions in Aqueous Solution That Form a Solid

Recall from Section 7.1 that sodium carbonate in laundry detergent reacts with dissolved Mg^{2+} and Ca^{2+} ions to form solids that precipitate (or come out of) solution. These reactions are examples of **precipitation reactions**—reactions that form a solid, called a **precipitate**, upon mixing two aqueous solutions.

Precipitation reactions are common in chemistry. Potassium iodide and lead nitrate, for example, both form colorless, strong electrolyte solutions when dissolved in water (see the solubility rules). When the two solutions are combined, however, a brilliant yellow precipitate forms (▼ Figure 7.8). We can describe this precipitation reaction with the chemical equation:

$$2\,KI(aq) + Pb(NO_3)_2(aq) \longrightarrow PbI_2(s) + 2\,KNO_3(aq)$$

Precipitation reactions do not always occur when mixing two aqueous solutions. For example, when solutions of KI(*aq*) and NaCl(*aq*) are combined, nothing happens (▼ Figure 7.9).

$$KI(aq) + NaCl(aq) \longrightarrow \text{NO REACTION}$$

$$2\,KI(aq) + Pb(NO_3)_2(aq) \longrightarrow PbI_2(s) + 2\,KNO_3(aq)$$

▲ **FIGURE 7.8 Precipitation** When a potassium iodide solution is mixed with a lead(II) nitrate solution, a brilliant yellow precipitate of $PbI_2(s)$ forms.

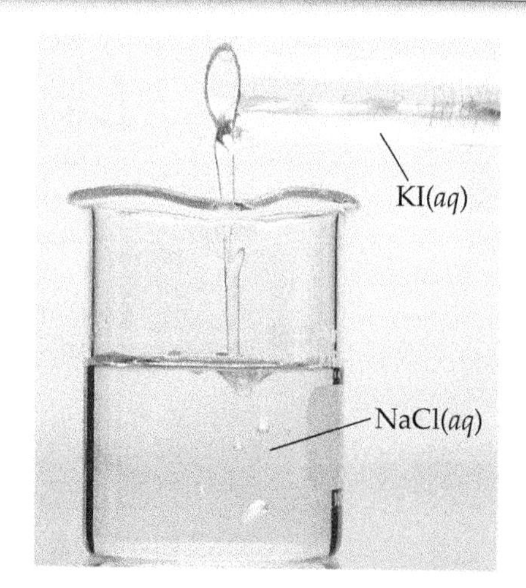

▲ **FIGURE 7.9 No reaction** When a potassium iodide solution is mixed with a sodium chloride solution, no reaction occurs.

PREDICTING PRECIPITATION REACTIONS

The key to predicting precipitation reactions is understanding that *only insoluble compounds form precipitates.* In a precipitation reaction, two solutions containing soluble compounds combine and an insoluble compound precipitates. Consider the precipitation reaction from Figure 7.8.

$$\underset{\text{soluble}}{2\,KI(aq)} + \underset{\text{soluble}}{Pb(NO_3)_2(aq)} \longrightarrow \underset{\text{insoluble}}{PbI_2(s)} + \underset{\text{soluble}}{2\,KNO_3(aq)}$$

KI and $Pb(NO_3)_2$ are both soluble, but the precipitate, PbI_2, is *insoluble.* Before mixing, KI(*aq*) and $Pb(NO_3)_2$(*aq*) are both dissociated in their respective solutions.

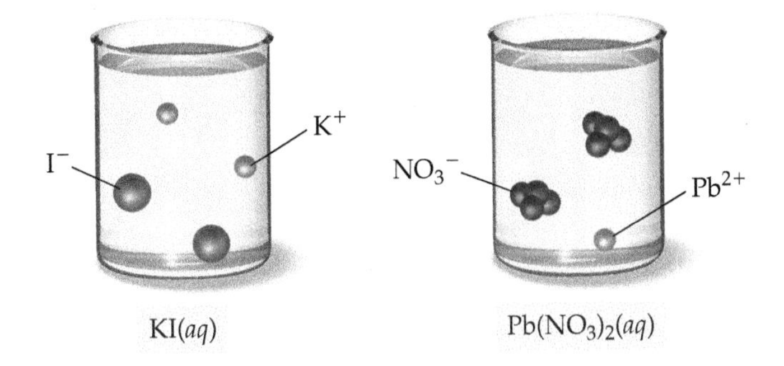

KI(*aq*) $Pb(NO_3)_2$(*aq*)

The instant that the solutions are mixed, all four ions are present.

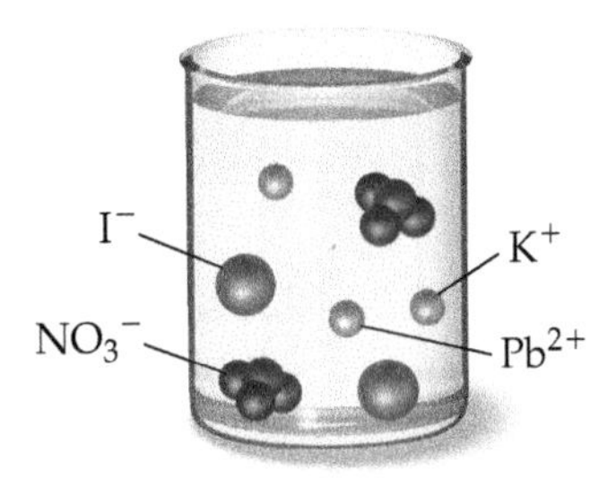

KI(*aq*) and $Pb(NO_3)_2$(*aq*)

However, new compounds—potentially insoluble ones—are now possible. Specifically, the cation from one compound can now pair with the anion from the other compound to form new (and potentially insoluble) products.

Original compounds		*Potentially insoluble products*
K I (*aq*)		KNO_3
	⟶	
Pb $(NO_3)_2$(*aq*)		PbI_2

If the *potentially insoluble* products are both *soluble*, then no reaction occurs. If, on the other hand, one or both of the potentially insoluble products are *indeed insoluble*, a precipitation reaction occurs. In this case, KNO_3 is soluble, but PbI_2 is insoluble. Consequently, PbI_2 precipitates.

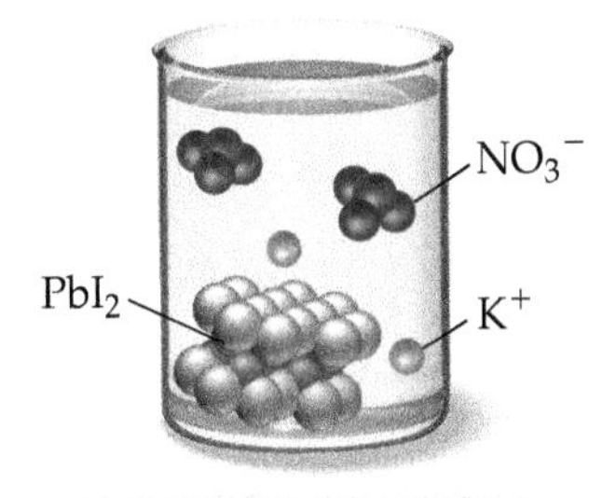

PbI_2(*s*) and KNO_3(*aq*)

To predict whether a precipitation reaction will occur when two solutions are mixed and to write an equation for the reaction, follow the steps in the procedure box. As usual, the steps are shown in the left column, and two examples of applying the procedure are shown in the center and right columns.

Writing Equations for Precipitation Reactions	**EXAMPLE 7.7** Write an equation for the precipitation reaction that occurs (if any) when solutions of sodium carbonate and copper(II) chloride are mixed.	**EXAMPLE 7.8** Write an equation for the precipitation reaction that occurs (if any) when solutions of lithium nitrate and sodium sulfate are mixed.
1. Write the formulas of the two compounds being mixed as reactants in a chemical equation.	SOLUTION $Na_2CO_3(aq) + CuCl_2(aq) \longrightarrow$	SOLUTION $LiNO_3(aq) + Na_2SO_4(aq) \longrightarrow$
2. Below the equation, write the formulas of the potentially insoluble products that could form from the reactants. Obtain these by combining the cation from one reactant with the anion from the other. Make sure to write correct (charge neutral) formulas for these ionic compounds as described in Section 5.5.	$Na_2CO_3(aq) + CuCl_2(aq) \longrightarrow$ **Potentially Insoluble Products** NaCl $CuCO_3$	$LiNO_3(aq) + Na_2SO_4(aq) \longrightarrow$ **Potentially Insoluble Products** $NaNO_3$ Li_2SO_4
3. Use the solubility rules to determine whether any of the potential new products are indeed insoluble.	NaCl is *soluble* (compounds containing Cl^- are usually soluble, and Na^+ is not an exception). $CuCO_3$ is *insoluble* (compounds containing CO_3^{2-} are usually insoluble, and Cu^{2+} is not an exception).	$NaNO_3$ is *soluble* (compounds containing NO_3^- are soluble and Na^+ is not an exception). Li_2SO_4 is *soluble* (compounds containing SO_4^{2-} are soluble and Li^+ is not an exception).
4. If all of the potentially insoluble products are soluble, there will be no precipitate. Write NO REACTION next to the arrow.	Since this example has an insoluble product, proceed to the next step.	$LiNO_3(aq) + Na_2SO_4(aq) \longrightarrow$ NO REACTION
5. If one or both of the potentially insoluble products are insoluble, write their formula(s) as the product(s) of the reaction, using (s) to indicate solid. Write any soluble products with (aq) to indicate aqueous.	$Na_2CO_3(aq) + CuCl_2(aq) \longrightarrow CuCO_3(s) + NaCl(aq)$	
6. Balance the equation. Remember to adjust only coefficients, not subscripts.	$Na_2CO_3(aq) + CuCl_2(aq) \longrightarrow CuCO_3(s) + \mathbf{2}\,NaCl(aq)$	
	▶SKILLBUILDER 7.7 Write an equation for the precipitation reaction that occurs (if any) when solutions of potassium hydroxide and nickel(II) bromide are mixed.	**▶SKILLBUILDER 7.8** Write an equation for the precipitation reaction that occurs (if any) when solutions of ammonium chloride and iron(III) nitrate are mixed. **▶FOR MORE PRACTICE** Example 7.19; Problems 63, 64, 65, 66.

EXAMPLE 7.9 Predicting and Writing Equations for Precipitation Reactions

Write an equation for the precipitation reaction (if any) that occurs when solutions of lead(II) acetate and sodium sulfate are mixed. If no reaction occurs, write *NO REACTION.*

	SOLUTION
1. Write the formulas of the two compounds being mixed as reactants in a chemical equation.	$Pb(C_2H_3O_2)_2(aq) + Na_2SO_4(aq) \longrightarrow$
2. Below the equation, write the formulas of the potentially insoluble products that could form from the reactants. These are obtained by combining the cation from one reactant with the anion from the other. Make sure to adjust the subscripts so that all formulas are charge-neutral.	$Pb(C_2H_3O_2)_2(aq) + Na_2SO_4(aq) \longrightarrow$ **Potentially insoluble products** $NaC_2H_3O_2$ $PbSO_4$
3. Use the solubility rules to determine whether any of the potentially insoluble products are indeed insoluble.	$NaC_2H_3O_2$ is *soluble* (compounds containing Na^+ are always soluble). $PbSO_4$ is *insoluble* (compounds containing SO_4^{2-} are normally soluble, but Pb^{2+} is an exception).
4. If all of the potentially insoluble products are soluble, there will be no precipitate. Write *NO REACTION* next to the arrow.	Since this reaction has an insoluble product, proceed to the next step.
5. If one or both of the potentially insoluble products are indeed insoluble, write their formula(s) as the product(s) of the reaction, using (*s*) to indicate solid. Write any soluble products with (*aq*) to indicate aqueous.	$Pb(C_2H_3O_2)_2(aq) + Na_2SO_4(aq) \longrightarrow PbSO_4(s) + NaC_2H_3O_2(aq)$
6. Balance the equation.	$Pb(C_2H_3O_2)_2(aq) + Na_2SO_4(aq) \longrightarrow PbSO_4(s) + \mathbf{2}\,NaC_2H_3O_2(aq)$

▶SKILLBUILDER 7.9 | Predicting and Writing Equations for Precipitation Reactions

Write an equation for the precipitation reaction (if any) that occurs when solutions of potassium sulfate and strontium nitrate are mixed. If no reaction occurs, write *NO REACTION.*

▶FOR MORE PRACTICE Problems 67, 68.

CONCEPTUAL CHECKPOINT 7.5

Which of these reactions would result in the formation of a precipitate?

(a) $NaNO_3(aq) + CaS(aq)$

(b) $MgSO_4(aq) + CaS(aq)$

(c) $NaNO_3(aq) + MgSO_4(aq)$

7.7 Writing Chemical Equations for Reactions in Solution: Molecular, Complete Ionic, and Net Ionic Equations

Consider the following equation for a precipitation reaction.

$$AgNO_3(aq) + NaCl(aq) \longrightarrow AgCl(s) + NaNO_3(aq)$$

This equation is written as a **molecular equation**, an equation showing the complete neutral formulas for every compound in the reaction. Equations for reactions occurring in aqueous solution may also be written to show that aqueous ionic compounds normally dissociate in solution. For example, the previous equation can be written as:

$$Ag^+(aq) + NO_3^-(aq) + Na^+(aq) + Cl^-(aq) \longrightarrow AgCl(s) + Na^+(aq) + NO_3^-(aq)$$

When writing complete ionic equations, separate only aqueous ionic compounds into their constituent ions. Do NOT separate solid, liquid, or gaseous compounds.

Equations such as this one, showing the reactants and products as they are actually present in solution, are called **complete ionic equations.**

Notice that in the complete ionic equation, some of the ions in solution appear unchanged on both sides of the equation. These ions are called **spectator ions** because they do not participate in the reaction.

$$Ag^+(aq) + NO_3^-(aq) + Na^+(aq) + Cl^-(aq) \longrightarrow AgCl(s) + Na^+(aq) + NO_3^-(aq)$$

Spectator ions

To simplify the equation, and to more clearly show what is happening, spectator ions can be omitted.

$$Ag^+(aq) + Cl^-(aq) \longrightarrow AgCl(s)$$

Species refers to a kind or sort of thing. In this case, the species are all the different molecules and ions that are present during the reaction.

Equations such as this one, which show only the *species* that actually participate in the reaction, are called **net ionic equations.**

As another example, consider the reaction between $HCl(aq)$ and $NaOH(aq)$.

$$HCl(aq) + NaOH(aq) \longrightarrow H_2O(l) + NaCl(aq)$$

HCl, NaOH, and NaCl exist in solution as independent ions. The *complete ionic equation* for this reaction is:

$$H^+(aq) + Cl^-(aq) + Na^+(aq) + OH^-(aq) \longrightarrow H_2O(l) + Na^+(aq) + Cl^-(aq)$$

To write the *net ionic equation,* we remove the spectator ions, those that are unchanged on both sides of the equation.

$$H^+(aq) + \cancel{Cl^-}(aq) + \cancel{Na^+}(aq) + OH^-(aq) \longrightarrow H_2O(l) + \cancel{Na^+}(aq) + \cancel{Cl^-}(aq)$$

Spectator ions

The net ionic equation is $H^+(aq) + OH^-(aq) \longrightarrow H_2O(l)$

To summarize:

- A molecular equation is a chemical equation showing the complete, neutral formulas for every compound in a reaction.
- A complete ionic equation is a chemical equation showing all of the species as they are actually present in solution.
- A net ionic equation is an equation showing only the species that actually participate in the reaction.

EXAMPLE 7.10 Writing Complete Ionic and Net Ionic Equations

Consider this precipitation reaction occurring in aqueous solution.

$$Pb(NO_3)_2(aq) + 2\ LiCl(aq) \longrightarrow PbCl_2(s) + 2\ LiNO_3(aq)$$

Write a complete ionic equation and a net ionic equation for the reaction.

	SOLUTION
Write the complete ionic equation by separating aqueous ionic compounds into their constituent ions. The $PbCl_2(s)$ remains as one unit.	**Complete ionic equation** $Pb^{2+}(aq) + 2\,NO_3^-(aq) + 2\,Li^+(aq) + 2\,Cl^-(aq) \longrightarrow PbCl_2(s) + 2\,Li^+(aq) + 2\,NO_3^-(aq)$
Write the net ionic equation by eliminating the spectator ions, those that do not change during the reaction.	**Net ionic equation** $Pb^{2+}(aq) + 2\,Cl^-(aq) \longrightarrow PbCl_2(s)$

▶SKILLBUILDER 7.10 | Writing Complete Ionic and Net Ionic Equations

Consider this reaction occurring in aqueous solution.

$$2\,HBr(aq) + Ca(OH)_2(aq) \longrightarrow 2\,H_2O(l) + CaBr_2(aq)$$

Write a complete ionic equation and net ionic equation for the reaction.

▶FOR MORE PRACTICE Example 7.20; Problems 69, 70, 71, 72.

7.8 Acid–Base and Gas Evolution Reactions

Basic

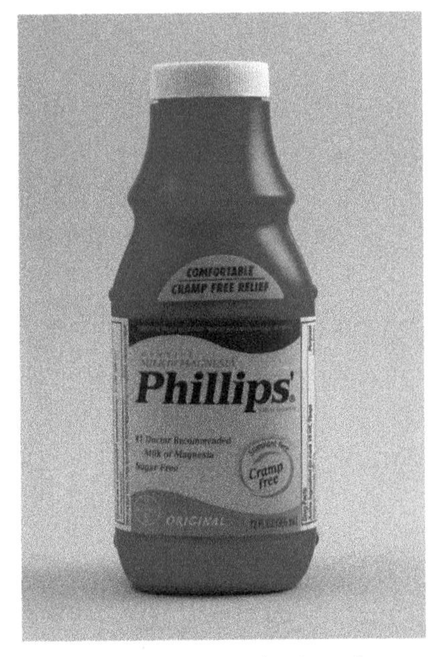

▲ Milk of magnesia is basic and tastes bitter.

Even though coffee itself is acidic overall, it contains some naturally occurring bases (such as caffeine) that give it a bitter taste.

Two other kinds of reactions that occur in solution are **acid–base reactions**—reactions that form water upon mixing of an acid and a base—and **gas evolution reactions**—reactions that evolve a gas. Like precipitation reactions, these reactions occur when the cation of one reactant combines with the anion of another. As we will see in the next section, many gas evolution reactions also happen to be acid–base reactions.

ACID–BASE (NEUTRALIZATION) REACTIONS

As we saw in Chapter 5, an acid is a compound characterized by its sour taste, its ability to dissolve some metals, and its tendency to form H^+ ions in solution. A base is a compound characterized by its bitter taste, its slippery feel, and its tendency to form OH^- ions in solution. Some common acids and bases are listed in Table 7.3. Acids and bases are also found in many everyday substances. Foods such as lemons, limes, and vinegar contain acids. Soap, coffee, and milk of magnesia all contain bases.

When an acid and base are mixed, the $H^+(aq)$ from the acid combines with the $OH^-(aq)$ from the base to form $H_2O(l)$. Consider the reaction between hydrochloric acid and sodium hydroxide mentioned earlier.

$$\underset{\text{Acid}}{HCl(aq)} + \underset{\text{Base}}{NaOH(aq)} \longrightarrow \underset{\text{Water}}{H_2O(l)} + \underset{\text{Salt}}{NaCl(aq)}$$

TABLE 7.3 Some Common Acids and Bases

Acid	Formula	Base	Formula
hydrochloric acid	HCl	sodium hydroxide	$NaOH$
hydrobromic acid	HBr	lithium hydroxide	$LiOH$
nitric acid	HNO_3	potassium hydroxide	KOH
sulfuric acid	H_2SO_4	calcium hydroxide	$Ca(OH)_2$
perchloric acid	$HClO_4$	barium hydroxide	$Ba(OH)_2$
acetic acid	$HC_2H_3O_2$		

Acidic

▲ Common foods and everyday substances such as oranges, lemons, vinegar, and vitamin C contain acids.

Acid–base reactions (also called **neutralization reactions**) generally form water and an ionic compound—called a **salt**—that usually remains dissolved in the solution. The net ionic equation for many acid–base reactions is:

$$H^+(aq) + OH^-(aq) \longrightarrow H_2O(l)$$

Another example of an acid–base reaction is the reaction that occurs between sulfuric acid and potassium hydroxide.

$$\underset{\text{acid}}{H_2SO_4(aq)} + \underset{\text{base}}{2\,KOH} \longrightarrow \underset{\text{water}}{2\,H_2O(l)} + \underset{\text{salt}}{K_2SO_4(aq)}$$

Notice the pattern of acid and base reacting to form water and a salt.

$$\text{Acid} + \text{Base} \longrightarrow \text{Water} + \text{Salt} \qquad \text{(acid–base reactions)}$$

When writing equations for acid–base reactions, write the formula of the salt using the procedure for writing formulas of ionic compounds given in Section 5.5.

EXAMPLE 7.11 Writing Equations for Acid–Base Reactions

Write a molecular and net ionic equation for the reaction between aqueous HNO_3 and aqueous $Ca(OH)_2$.

	SOLUTION
You must recognize these substances as an acid and a base. Write the skeletal reaction following the general pattern of acid plus base goes to water plus salt.	$\underset{\text{acid}}{HNO_3(aq)} + \underset{\text{base}}{Ca(OH)_2(aq)} \longrightarrow \underset{\text{water}}{H_2O(l)} + \underset{\text{salt}}{Ca(NO_3)_2(aq)}$
Next, balance the equation.	$2\,HNO_3(aq) + Ca(OH)_2(aq) \longrightarrow 2\,H_2O(l) + Ca(NO_3)_2(aq)$
Write the net ionic equation by eliminating those ions that remain the same on both sides of the equation.	$2\,H^+(aq) + 2\,OH^-(aq) \longrightarrow 2\,H_2O(l)$ or simply $H^+(aq) + OH^-(aq) \longrightarrow H_2O(l)$

▶**SKILLBUILDER 7.11 | Writing Equations for Acid–Base Reactions**

Write a molecular and net ionic equation for the reaction that occurs between aqueous H_2SO_4 and aqueous KOH.

▶**FOR MORE PRACTICE** Example 7.21; Problems 77, 78, 79, 80.

GAS EVOLUTION REACTIONS

Some aqueous reactions form a gas as a product. These reactions, as we learned in the opening section of this chapter, are called gas evolution reactions. Some gas evolution reactions form a gaseous product directly when the cation of one reactant reacts with the anion of the other. For example, when sulfuric acid reacts with lithium sulfide, dihydrogen sulfide gas is formed.

$$H_2SO_4(aq) + Li_2S(aq) \longrightarrow \underset{\text{Gas}}{H_2S(g)} + Li_2SO_4(aq)$$

Many gas evolution reactions such as this one are also acid–base reactions. In Chapter 14 we learn how ions such as HCO_3^- act as bases in aqueous solution.

Other gas evolution reactions form an intermediate product that then decomposes into a gas. For example, when aqueous hydrochloric acid is mixed with aqueous sodium bicarbonate, the following reaction occurs.

$$HCl(aq) + NaHCO_3(aq) \longrightarrow H_2CO_3(aq) + NaCl(aq) \longrightarrow H_2O(l) + \underset{\text{Gas}}{CO_2(g)} + NaCl(aq)$$

Gas evolution reaction

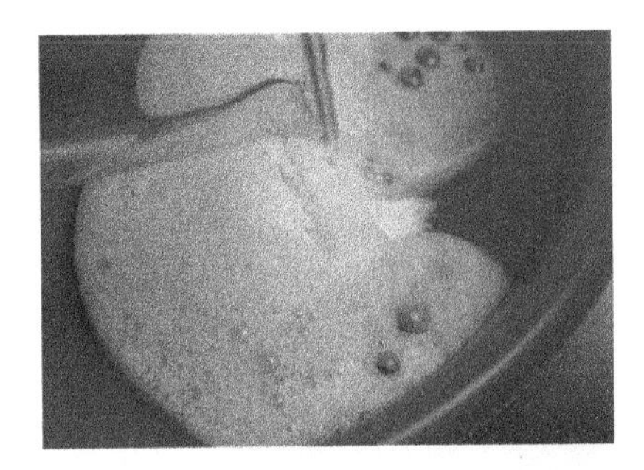

▲ In this gas evolution reaction, vinegar (a dilute solution of acetic acid) and baking soda (sodium bicarbonate) produce carbon dioxide.

The intermediate product, H_2CO_3, is not stable and decomposes to form H_2O and gaseous CO_2. This reaction is almost identical to the reaction in the kindergarten volcano of Section 7.1, which involves the mixing of acetic acid and sodium bicarbonate.

$$HC_2H_3O_2(aq) + NaHCO_3(aq) \longrightarrow H_2CO_3(aq) + NaC_2H_3O_2(aq) \longrightarrow H_2O(l) + CO_2(g) + NaC_2H_3O_2(aq)$$

The bubbling is caused by the newly formed carbon dioxide gas. Other important gas evolution reactions form either H_2SO_3 or NH_4OH as intermediate products.

$$HCl(aq) + NaHSO_3(aq) \longrightarrow H_2SO_3(aq) + NaCl(aq) \longrightarrow H_2O(l) + SO_2(g) + NaCl(aq)$$

$$NH_4Cl(aq) + NaOH(aq) \longrightarrow NH_4OH(aq) + NaCl(aq) \longrightarrow H_2O(l) + NH_3(g) + NaCl(aq)$$

The main types of compounds that form gases in aqueous reactions, as well as the gases that they form, are listed in Table 7.4.

TABLE 7.4 Types of Compounds That Undergo Gas Evolution Reactions

Reactant Type	Intermediate Product	Gas Evolved	Example
sulfides	none	H_2S	$2\,HCl(aq) + K_2S(aq) \longrightarrow H_2S(g) + 2\,KCl(aq)$
carbonates and bicarbonates	H_2CO_3	CO_2	$2\,HCl(aq) + K_2CO_3(aq) \longrightarrow H_2O(l) + CO_2(g) + 2\,KCl(aq)$
sulfites and bisulfites	H_2SO_3	SO_2	$2\,HCl(aq) + K_2SO_3(aq) \longrightarrow H_2O(l) + SO_2(g) + 2\,KCl(aq)$
ammonium	NH_4OH	NH_3	$NH_4Cl(aq) + KOH(aq) \longrightarrow H_2O(l) + NH_3(g) + KCl(aq)$

EXAMPLE 7.12 Writing Equations for Gas Evolution Reactions

Write a molecular equation for the gas evolution reaction that occurs when you mix aqueous nitric acid and aqueous sodium carbonate.

	SOLUTION
Begin by writing a skeletal equation that includes the reactants and products that form when the cation of each reactant combines with the anion of the other.	$HNO_3(aq) + Na_2CO_3(aq) \longrightarrow H_2CO_3(aq) + NaNO_3(aq)$
You must recognize that $H_2CO_3(aq)$ decomposes into $H_2O(l)$ and $CO_2(g)$ and write the corresponding equation.	$HNO_3(aq) + Na_2CO_3(aq) \longrightarrow H_2O(l) + CO_2(g) + NaNO_3(aq)$
Finally, balance the equation.	$2\,HNO_3(aq) + Na_2CO_3(aq) \longrightarrow H_2O(l) + CO_2(g) + 2\,NaNO_3(aq)$

▶SKILLBUILDER 7.12 | Writing Equations for Gas Evolution Reactions

Write a molecular equation for the gas evolution reaction that occurs when you mix aqueous hydrobromic acid and aqueous potassium sulfite.

▶SKILLBUILDER PLUS

Write a net ionic equation for the previous reaction.

▶FOR MORE PRACTICE Example 7.22; Problems 81, 82.

CHEMISTRY AND HEALTH

Neutralizing Excess Stomach Acid

Your stomach normally contains acids that are involved in food digestion. Certain foods and stress, however, can increase the acidity of your stomach to uncomfortable levels, causing acid stomach or heartburn. Antacids are over-the-counter medicines that work by reacting with and neutralizing stomach acid. Antacids employ different bases as neutralizing agents. Tums™, for example, contains $CaCO_3$; milk of magnesia contains $Mg(OH)_2$; and Mylanta™ contains $Al(OH)_3$. They all, however, have the same effect of neutralizing stomach acid and relieving heartburn.

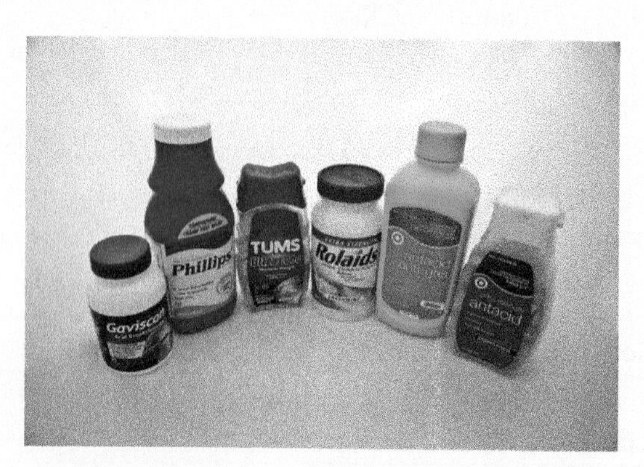

▲ Antacids contain bases such $Mg(OH)_2$, $Al(OH)_3$, and $NaHCO_3$.

CAN YOU ANSWER THIS? *Assume that stomach acid is HCl and write equations showing how each of these antacids neutralizes stomach acid.*

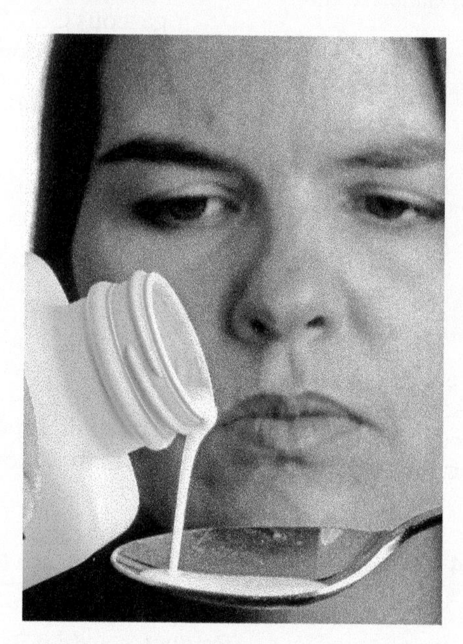

▲ The base in an antacid neutralizes excess stomach acid, relieving heartburn and acid stomach.

7.9 Oxidation–Reduction Reactions

We will cover oxidation–reduction reactions in more detail in Chapter 16.

Reactions involving the transfer of electrons are called **oxidation–reduction reactions** or **redox reactions**. Redox reactions are responsible for the rusting of iron, the bleaching of hair, and the production of electricity in batteries. Many redox reactions involve the reaction of a substance with oxygen.

$$2\,H_2(g) + O_2(g) \longrightarrow 2\,H_2O(g)$$
(reaction that powers the space shuttle)

$$4\,Fe(s) + 3\,O_2(g) \longrightarrow 2\,Fe_2O_3(s)$$
(rusting of iron)

$$CH_4(g) + 2\,O_2(g) \longrightarrow CO_2(g) + 2\,H_2O(g)$$
(combustion of natural gas)

However, redox reactions need not involve oxygen. Consider, for example, the reaction between sodium and chlorine to form table salt (NaCl).

$$2\,Na(s) + Cl_2(g) \longrightarrow 2\,NaCl(s)$$

This reaction is similar to the reaction between sodium and oxygen which can form sodium oxide.

The reaction between sodium and oxygen also forms other oxides besides Na_2O.

$$4\,Na(s) + O_2(g) \longrightarrow 2\,Na_2O(s)$$

Helpful mnemonics: OIL RIG—**O**xidation **I**s **L**oss; **R**eduction **I**s **G**ain. LEO GER—**L**ose **E**lectrons **O**xidation; **G**ain **E**lectrons **R**eduction.

What do these two reactions have in common? In both cases, sodium (a metal with a tendency to lose electrons) reacts with a nonmetal (that has a tendency to gain electrons). In both cases, sodium atoms lose electrons to nonmetal atoms. A fundamental definition of oxidation is *the loss of electrons*, and a fundamental definition of reduction is *the gain of electrons*.

Notice that oxidation and reduction must occur together. If one substance loses electrons (oxidation), then another substance must gain electrons (reduction). For now, you simply need to be able to identify redox reactions. In Chapter 16 we will examine them more thoroughly.

A reaction can be classified as a redox reaction if it meets any one of these requirements.

Redox reactions are those in which:

- A substance reacts with elemental oxygen.
- A metal reacts with a nonmetal.
- More generally, one substance transfers electrons to another substance.

EXAMPLE 7.13 Identifying Redox Reactions

Which of these are redox reactions?

(a) $2\,Mg(s) + O_2(g) \longrightarrow 2\,MgO(s)$
(b) $2\,HBr(aq) + Ca(OH)_2(aq) \longrightarrow 2\,H_2O(l) + CaBr_2(aq)$
(c) $Ca(s) + Cl_2(g) \longrightarrow CaCl_2(s)$
(d) $Zn(s) + Fe^{2+}(aq) \longrightarrow Zn^{2+}(aq) + Fe(s)$

SOLUTION

(a) Redox reaction; Mg reacts with elemental oxygen.
(b) Not a redox reaction; it is an acid–base reaction.
(c) Redox reaction; a metal reacts with a nonmetal.
(d) Redox reaction; Zn transfers two electrons to Fe^{2+}.

▶**SKILLBUILDER 7.13** | Identifying Redox Reactions

Which of these are redox reactions?

(a) $2\,Li(s) + Cl_2(g) \longrightarrow 2\,LiCl(s)$
(b) $2\,Al(s) + 3\,Sn^{2+}(aq) \longrightarrow 2\,Al^{3+}(aq) + 3\,Sn(s)$
(c) $Pb(NO_3)_2(aq) + 2\,LiCl(aq) \longrightarrow PbCl_2(s) + 2\,LiNO_3(aq)$
(d) $C(s) + O_2(g) \longrightarrow CO_2(g)$

▶**FOR MORE PRACTICE** Example 7.23; Problems 83, 84.

COMBUSTION REACTIONS

Combustion reactions are a type of redox reaction. They are important to us because most of our society's energy is derived from combustion reactions. Combustion reactions are characterized by the reaction of a substance with O_2 to form one or more oxygen-containing compounds, often including water. Combustion reactions are exothermic (they emit heat). For example, as we saw in Section 7.3, natural gas (CH_4) reacts with oxygen to form carbon dioxide and water.

The water formed in combustion reactions may be gaseous (*g*) or liquid (*l*) depending on the reaction conditions.

$$CH_4(g) + 2\,O_2(g) \longrightarrow CO_2(g) + 2\,H_2O(g)$$

As mentioned in the opening section of this chapter, combustion reactions power automobiles. For example, octane, a component of gasoline, reacts with oxygen to form carbon dioxide and water.

$$2\,C_8H_{18}(l) + 25\,O_2(g) \longrightarrow 16\,CO_2(g) + 18\,H_2O(g)$$

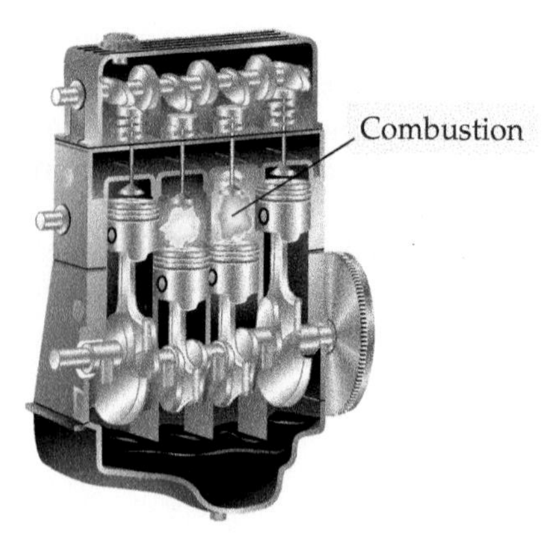

▲ Combustion of octane occurs in the cylinders of an automobile engine.

Ethanol, the alcohol in alcoholic beverages, also reacts with oxygen in a combustion reaction to form carbon dioxide and water.

$$C_2H_5OH(l) + 3\,O_2(g) \longrightarrow 2\,CO_2(g) + 3\,H_2O(g)$$

Compounds containing carbon and hydrogen—or carbon, hydrogen, and oxygen—always form carbon dioxide and water upon combustion. Other combustion reactions include the reaction of carbon with oxygen to form carbon dioxide:

$$C(s) + O_2(g) \longrightarrow CO_2(g)$$

and the reaction of hydrogen with oxygen to form water:

$$2\,H_2(g) + O_2(g) \longrightarrow 2\,H_2O(g)$$

EXAMPLE 7.14 Writing Combustion Reactions

Write a balanced equation for the combustion of liquid methyl alcohol (CH_3OH).

	SOLUTION
Begin by writing a skeletal equation showing the reaction of CH_3OH with O_2 to form CO_2 and H_2O.	$CH_3OH(l) + O_2(g) \longrightarrow CO_2(g) + H_2O(g)$
Balance the skeletal equation using the rules in Section 7.4.	$2\,CH_3OH(l) + 3\,O_2(g) \longrightarrow 2\,CO_2(g) + 4\,H_2O(g)$

▶SKILLBUILDER 7.14 | Writing Combustion Reactions

Write a balanced equation for the combustion of liquid pentane (C_5H_{12}), a component of gasoline.

▶SKILLBUILDER PLUS

Write a balanced equation for the combustion of liquid propanol (C_3H_7OH).

▶FOR MORE PRACTICE Example 7.24; Problems 85, 86.

7.10 Classifying Chemical Reactions

Throughout this chapter, we have examined different types of chemical reactions. We have seen examples of precipitation reactions, acid–base reactions, gas evolution reactions, oxidation–reduction reactions, and combustion reactions. We can organize these different types of reactions with the following flowchart.

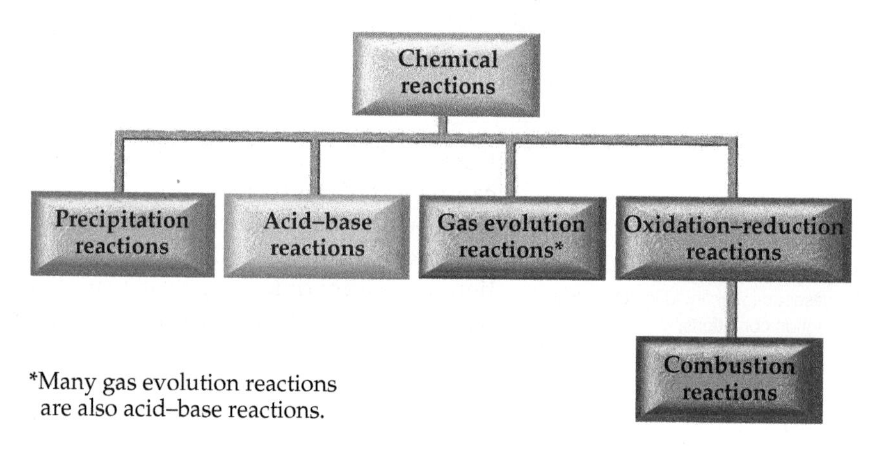

This classification scheme focuses on the type of chemistry or phenomenon that is occurring during the reaction (such as the formation of a precipitate or the transfer of electrons). However, an alternative way to classify chemical reactions is by what atoms or groups of atoms do during the reaction.

CLASSIFYING CHEMICAL REACTIONS BY WHAT ATOMS DO

In this alternative way of classifying reactions, we focus on the pattern of the reaction by classifying it into one of the following four categories. In this classification scheme, the letters (A, B, C, D) represent atoms or groups of atoms.

Type of Reaction	Generic Equation
synthesis or combination	$A + B \longrightarrow AB$
decomposition	$AB \longrightarrow A + B$
displacement	$A + BC \longrightarrow AC + B$
double-displacement	$AB + CD \longrightarrow AD + CB$

SYNTHESIS OR COMBINATION REACTIONS. In a **synthesis** or **combination reaction**, simpler substances combine to form more complex substances. The simpler substances may be elements, such as sodium and chlorine combining to form sodium chloride.

$$2\,Na(s) + Cl_2(g) \longrightarrow 2\,NaCl(s)$$

The simpler substances may also be compounds, such as calcium oxide and carbon dioxide combining to form calcium carbonate.

$$CaO(s) + CO_2(g) \longrightarrow CaCO_3(s)$$

In either case, a synthesis reaction follows the general equation:

$$A + B \longrightarrow AB$$

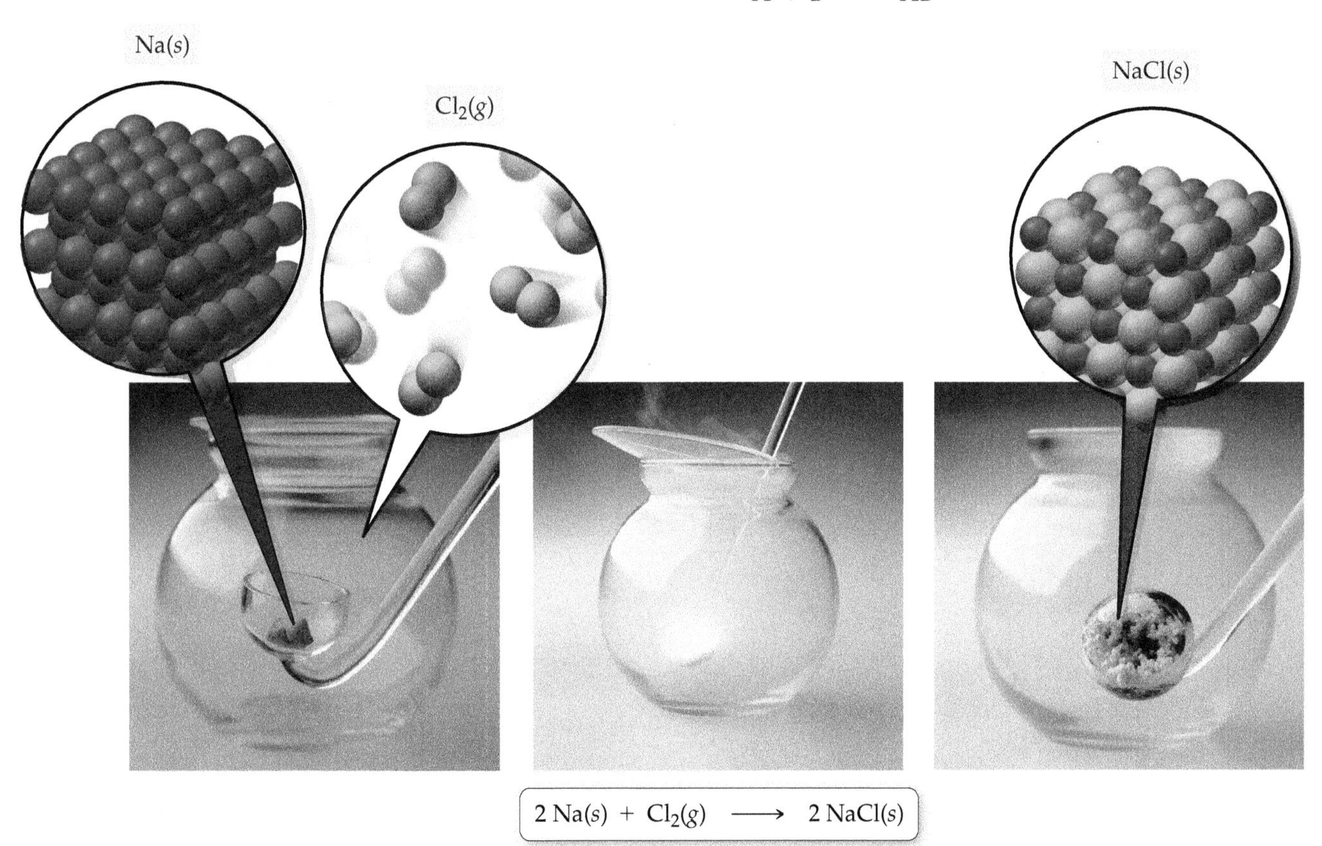

▲ In a synthesis reaction, two simpler substances combine to make a more complex substance. In this series of photographs we see sodium metal and chlorine gas. When they combine, a chemical reaction occurs that forms sodium chloride.

Note that the first two of these reactions are also redox reactions.

Other examples of synthesis reactions include:

$$2\,H_2(g) + O_2(g) \longrightarrow 2\,H_2O(l)$$
$$2\,Mg(s) + O_2(g) \longrightarrow 2\,MgO(s)$$
$$SO_3(g) + H_2O(l) \longrightarrow H_2SO_4(aq)$$

$$2\,H_2O(l) \longrightarrow 2\,H_2(g) + O_2(g)$$

▲ When electrical current is passed through water, the water undergoes a decomposition reaction to form hydrogen gas and oxygen gas.

DECOMPOSITION REACTIONS. In a **decomposition reaction**, a complex substance decomposes to form simpler substances. The simpler substances may be elements, such as the hydrogen and oxygen gases that form upon the decomposition of water when electrical current passes through it.

$$2\,H_2O(l) \xrightarrow[\text{electrical current}]{} 2\,H_2(g) + O_2(g)$$

The simpler substances may also be compounds, such as the calcium oxide and carbon dioxide that form upon heating calcium carbonate.

$$CaCO_3(s) \xrightarrow[\text{heat}]{} CaO(s) + CO_2(g)$$

In either case, a decomposition reaction follows the general equation:

$$AB \longrightarrow A + B$$

Other examples of decomposition reactions include:

$$2\,HgO(s) \xrightarrow[\text{heat}]{} 2\,Hg(l) + O_2(g)$$
$$2\,KClO_3(s) \xrightarrow[\text{heat}]{} 2\,KCl(s) + 3\,O_2(g)$$
$$CH_3I(g) \xrightarrow[\text{light}]{} CH_3(g) + I(g)$$

Notice that these decomposition reactions require energy in the form of heat, electrical current, or light to make them happen. This is because compounds are normally stable and energy is required to decompose them. A number of decomposition reactions require *ultraviolet* or *UV light,* which is light in the ultraviolet region of the spectrum. UV light carries more energy than visible light and can therefore initiate the decomposition of many compounds. (We will discuss light in more detail in Chapter 9.)

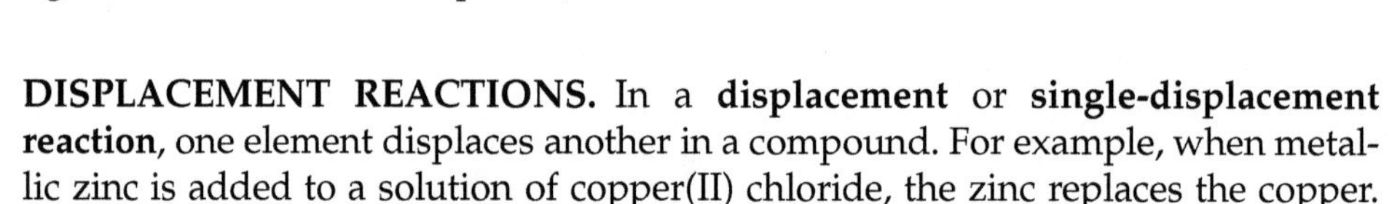

DISPLACEMENT REACTIONS. In a **displacement** or **single-displacement reaction**, one element displaces another in a compound. For example, when metallic zinc is added to a solution of copper(II) chloride, the zinc replaces the copper.

$$Zn(s) + CuCl_2(aq) \longrightarrow ZnCl_2(aq) + Cu(s)$$

A displacement reaction follows the general equation:

$$A + BC \longrightarrow AC + B$$

Other examples of displacement reactions include:

$$Mg(s) + 2\,HCl(aq) \longrightarrow MgCl_2(aq) + H_2(g)$$
$$2\,Na(s) + 2\,H_2O(l) \longrightarrow 2\,NaOH(aq) + H_2(g)$$

The last reaction can be identified more easily as a displacement reaction if we write water as HOH(l).

$$2\,Na(s) + 2\,HOH(l) \longrightarrow 2\,NaOH(aq) + H_2(g)$$

▶ In a single-displacement reaction, one element displaces another in a compound. When zinc metal is immersed in a copper(II) chloride solution, the zinc atoms displace the copper ions in solution.

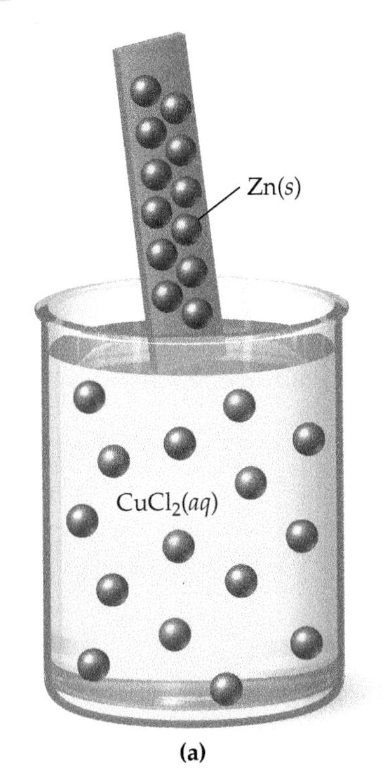

(a)

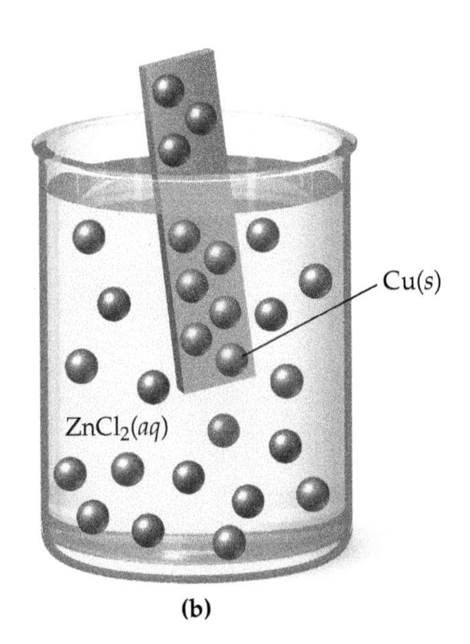

(b)

DOUBLE-DISPLACEMENT REACTIONS. In a **double-displacement reaction**, two elements or groups of elements in two different compounds exchange places to form two new compounds. For example, in aqueous solution, the silver in silver nitrate changes places with the sodium in sodium chloride to form solid silver chloride and aqueous sodium nitrate.

This double-displacement reaction is also a precipitation reaction.

$$AgNO_3(aq) + NaCl(aq) \longrightarrow AgCl(s) + NaNO_3(aq)$$

A double-displacement reaction follows the general form:

$$AB + CD \longrightarrow AD + CB$$

Other examples of double-displacement reactions include:

These double-displacement reactions are also acid–base reactions.

$$HCl(aq) + NaOH(aq) \longrightarrow H_2O(l) + NaCl(aq)$$
$$2\,HCl(aq) + Na_2CO_3(aq) \longrightarrow H_2CO_3(aq) + 2\,NaCl(aq)$$

As we learned in Section 7.8, $H_2CO_3(aq)$ is not stable and decomposes to form $H_2O(l) + CO_2(g)$, so the overall equation is:

This double-displacement reacton is also a gas evolution reaction and an acid–base reaction.

$$2\,HCl(aq) + Na_2CO_3(aq) \longrightarrow H_2O(l) + CO_2(g) + 2\,NaCl(aq)$$

CLASSIFICATION FLOWCHART

A flowchart for this classification scheme of chemical reactions is as follows:

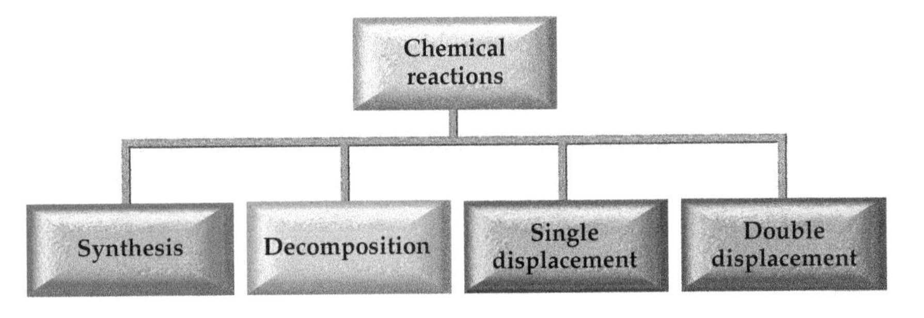

Of course, no single classification scheme is perfect because all chemical reactions are unique in some sense. However, both classification schemes—one that focuses on the type of chemistry occurring and the other that focuses on what atoms or groups of atoms are doing—are helpful because they help us see differences and similarities among chemical reactions.

EXAMPLE 7.15 Classifying Chemical Reactions According to What Atoms Do

Classify each reaction as a synthesis, decomposition, single-displacement, or double-displacement reaction.

(a) $Na_2O(s) + H_2O(l) \longrightarrow 2\,NaOH(aq)$

(b) $Ba(NO_3)_2(aq) + K_2SO_4(aq) \longrightarrow BaSO_4(s) + 2\,KNO_3(aq)$

(c) $2\,Al(s) + Fe_2O_3(s) \longrightarrow Al_2O_3(s) + 2\,Fe(l)$

(d) $2\,H_2O_2(aq) \longrightarrow 2\,H_2O(l) + O_2(g)$

(e) $Ca(s) + Cl_2(g) \longrightarrow CaCl_2(s)$

SOLUTION

(a) Synthesis; a more complex substance forms from two simpler ones.
(b) Double-displacment; Ba and K switch places to form two new compounds.
(c) Single-displacement; Al displaces Fe in Fe_2O_3.
(d) Decomposition; a complex substance decomposes into simpler ones.
(e) Synthesis; a more complex substance forms from two simpler ones.

▶SKILLBUILDER 7.15 | Classifying Chemical Reactions According to What Atoms Do

Classify each reaction as a synthesis, decomposition, single-displacement, or double-displacement reaction.

(a) $2\,Al(s) + 2\,H_3PO_4(aq) \longrightarrow 2\,AlPO_4(aq) + 3\,H_2(g)$

(b) $CuSO_4(aq) + 2\,KOH(aq) \longrightarrow Cu(OH)_2(s) + K_2SO_4(aq)$

(c) $2\,K(s) + Br_2(l) \longrightarrow 2\,KBr(s)$

(d) $CuCl_2(aq) \xrightarrow[\text{electrical current}]{} Cu(s) + Cl_2(g)$

▶FOR MORE PRACTICE Example 7.25; Problems 89, 90, 91, 92.

CONCEPTUAL CHECKPOINT 7.6

Precipitation reactions and acid–base reactions can both also be classified as:

(a) synthesis reactions

(b) decomposition reactions

(c) single-displacement reactions

(d) double-displacement reactions

CHEMISTRY IN THE ENVIRONMENT

The Reactions Involved in Ozone Depletion

Chemistry in the Environment: Chlorine in Chlorofluorocarbons in Chapter 6 explained that chlorine atoms from chlorofluorocarbons deplete the ozone layer, which normally protects life on Earth from harmful ultraviolet light. Through research, chemists have discovered the reactions by which this depletion occurs.

Ozone normally forms in the upper atmosphere according to this reaction.

(a) $O_2(g) + O(g) \longrightarrow O_3(g)$

When chlorofluorocarbons drift to the upper atmosphere, they are exposed to ultraviolet light and undergo the reaction.

(b) $CF_2Cl_2(g) \xrightarrow[\text{UV light}]{} CF_2Cl(g) + Cl(g)$

UV light

Atomic chlorine then reacts with and depletes ozone according to this cycle of reactions.

(c) $Cl(g) + O_3(g) \longrightarrow ClO(g) + O_2(g)$

(d) $O_3(g) \xrightarrow[\text{UV light}]{} O_2(g) + O(g)$

UV light

(e) $O(g) + ClO(g) \longrightarrow O_2(g) + Cl(g)$

Notice that in the final reaction, atomic chlorine is regenerated and can go through the cycle again to deplete more ozone. Through this cycle of reactions, a single chlorofluorocarbon molecule can deplete thousands of ozone molecules.

CAN YOU ANSWER THIS? *Classify each of these reactions (a–e) as a synthesis, decomposition, single-displacement, or double-displacement reaction.*

CHAPTER IN REVIEW

CHEMICAL PRINCIPLES	RELEVANCE
Chemical Reactions: In a chemical reaction, one or more substances—either elements or compounds—changes into a different substance.	**Chemical Reactions:** Chemical reactions are central to many processes, including transportation, energy generation, manufacture of household products, vision, and life itself.
Evidence of a Chemical Reaction: The only absolute evidence for a chemical reaction is chemical analysis showing that one or more substances has changed into another substance. However, one or more of the following often accompanies a chemical reaction: a color change; the formation of a solid or precipitate; the formation of a gas; the emission of light; and the emission or absorption of heat.	**Evidence of a Chemical Reaction:** We can often perceive the changes that accompany chemical reactions. In fact, we often employ chemical reactions for the changes they produce. For example, we use the heat emitted by the combustion of fossil fuels to heat our homes, drive our cars, and generate electricity.
Chemical Equations: Chemical equations represent chemical reactions. They include formulas for the reactants (the substances present before the reaction) and for the products (the new substances formed by the reaction). Chemical equations must be balanced to reflect the conservation of matter in nature; atoms do not spontaneously appear or disappear.	**Chemical Equations:** Chemical equations allow us to represent and understand chemical reactions. For example, the equations for the combustion reactions of fossil fuels let us see that carbon dioxide, a gas that contributes to global warming, is one of the products of these reactions.

Aqueous Solutions and Solubility: Aqueous solutions are mixtures of a substance dissolved in water. If a substance dissolves in water it is soluble. Otherwise, it is insoluble.

Aqueous Solutions and Solubility: Aqueous solutions are common. Oceans, lakes, and most of the fluids in our bodies are aqueous solutions.

Some Specific Types of Reactions:

Precipitation reaction: A solid or precipitate forms upon mixing two aqueous solutions.

Acid–base reaction: Water forms upon mixing an acid and a base.

Gas evolution reaction: A gas forms upon mixing two aqueous solutions.

Redox reaction: Electrons are transferred from one substance to another.

Combustion reaction: A substance reacts with oxygen, emitting heat, and forming an oxygen-containing compound and, in many cases, water.

Some Specific Types of Reactions: Many of the specific types of reactions discussed in this chapter occur in aqueous solutions and are therefore important to living organisms. Acid–base reactions, for example, constantly occur in the blood of living organisms to maintain constant blood acidity levels. In humans, a small change in blood acidity levels would result in death, so the body carries out chemical reactions to prevent this. Combustion reactions are important because they are the main energy source for our society.

Classifying Chemical Reactions: Many chemical reactions can be classified into one of the following four categories according to what atoms or groups of atoms do:

- synthesis: $(A + B \longrightarrow AB)$
- decomposition: $(AB \longrightarrow A + B)$
- single-displacement: $(A + BC \longrightarrow AC + B)$
- double-displacement: $(AB + CD \longrightarrow AD + CB)$

Classifying Chemical Reactions: We classify chemical reactions to better understand them and to recognize similarities and differences among reactions.

CHEMICAL SKILLS

Identifying a Chemical Reaction (Section 7.2)

To identify a chemical reaction, determine whether one or more of the initial substances changed into a different substance. If so, a chemical reaction occurred. One or more of the following often accompanies a chemical reaction: a color change; the formation of a solid or precipitate; the formation of a gas; the emission of light; and the emission or absorption of heat.

EXAMPLES

EXAMPLE 7.16 Identifying a Chemical Reaction

Which of these are chemical reactions?

(a) Copper turns green on exposure to air.
(b) When sodium bicarbonate is combined with hydrochloric acid, bubbling is observed.
(c) Liquid water freezes to form solid ice.
(d) A pure copper penny forms bubbles of a dark brown gas when dropped into nitric acid. The nitric acid solution turns blue.

SOLUTION

(a) Chemical reaction, as evidenced by the color change.
(b) Chemical reaction, as evidenced by the evolution of a gas.
(c) Not a chemical reaction; solid ice is still water.
(d) Chemical reaction, as evidenced by the evolution of a gas and by a color change.

Writing Balanced Chemical Equations (Sections 7.3, 7.4)

To write balanced chemical equations, follow these steps.

1. Write a skeletal equation by writing chemical formulas for each of the reactants and products. (If a skeletal equation is provided, proceed to Step 2.)
2. If an element occurs in only one compound on both sides of the equation, balance that element first. If there is more than one such element, and the equation contains both metals and nonmetals, balance metals before nonmetals.
3. If an element occurs as a free element on either side of the chemical equation, balance that element last.
4. If the balanced equation contains coefficient fractions, clear these by multiplying the entire equation by the appropriate factor.
5. Check to make certain the equation is balanced by summing the total number of each type of atom on both sides of the equation.

Reminders

- Change only the *coefficients* to balance a chemical equation, *never the subscripts*. Changing the subscripts would change the compound itself.
- If the equation contains polyatomic ions that stay intact on both sides of the equation, balance the polyatomic ions as a group.

EXAMPLE 7.17 Writing Balanced Chemical Equations

Write a balanced chemical equation for the reaction of solid vanadium(V) oxide with hydrogen gas to form solid vanadium(III) oxide and liquid water.

$$V_2O_5(s) + H_2(g) \longrightarrow V_2O_3(s) + H_2O(l)$$

SOLUTION

Skeletal equation is given. Proceed to Step 2.

Vanadium occurs in only one compound on both sides of the equation. However, it is balanced, so you can proceed and balance oxygen by placing a 2 in front of H_2O on the right side.

$$V_2O_5(s) + H_2(g) \longrightarrow V_2O_3(s) + \mathbf{2}\,H_2O(l)$$

Hydrogen occurs as a free element, so balance it last by placing a 2 in front of H_2 on the left side.

$$V_2O_5(s) + \mathbf{2}\,H_2(g) \longrightarrow V_2O_3(s) + 2\,H_2O(l)$$

Equation does not contain coefficient fractions. Proceed to Step 5.

Check the equation.

$$V_2O_5(s) + 2\,H_2(g) \longrightarrow V_2O_3(s) + 2\,H_2O(l)$$

Reactants		Products
2 V atoms	⟶	2 V atoms
5 O atoms	⟶	5 O atoms
4 H atoms	⟶	4 H atoms

Determining Whether a Compound Is Soluble (Section 7.5)

To determine whether a compound is soluble, refer to the solubility rules in Table 7.2. It is easiest to begin by looking for those ions that always form soluble compounds (Li^+, Na^+, K^+, NH_4^+, NO_3^-, and $C_2H_3O_2^-$). If a compound contains one of those, it is soluble. If it does not, look at the anion and determine whether it is mostly soluble (Cl^-, Br^-, I^-, or SO_4^{2-}) or mostly insoluble (OH^-, S^{2-}, CO_3^{2-}, or PO_4^{3-}). Look also at the cation to determine whether it is one of the exceptions.

EXAMPLE 7.18 Determining Whether a Compound Is Soluble

Determine whether each compound is soluble.

(a) $CuCO_3$
(b) $BaSO_4$
(c) $Fe(NO_3)_3$

SOLUTION

(a) Insoluble; compounds containing CO_3^{2-} are insoluble, and Cu^{2+} is not an exception.
(b) Insoluble; compounds containing SO_4^{2-} are usually soluble, but Ba^{2+} is an exception.
(c) Soluble; all compounds containing NO_3^- are soluble.

Predicting Precipitation Reactions (Section 7.6)

To predict whether a precipitation reaction occurs when two solutions are mixed and to write an equation for the reaction, follow these steps.

1. Write the formulas of the two compounds being mixed as reactants in a chemical equation.
2. Below the equation, write the formulas of the potentially insoluble products that could form from the reactants. These are obtained by combining the cation from one reactant with the anion from the other. Make sure to adjust the subscripts so that all formulas are charge-neutral.
3. Use the solubility rules to determine whether any of the potentially insoluble products are indeed insoluble.
4. If all of the potentially insoluble products are soluble, there will be no precipitate. Write *NO REACTION* next to the arrow.
5. If one or both of the potentially insoluble products are insoluble, write their formula(s) as the product(s) of the reaction using (*s*) to indicate *solid*. Write any soluble products with (*aq*) to indicate *aqueous*.
6. Balance the equation.

EXAMPLE 7.19 Predicting Precipitation Reactions

Write an equation for the precipitation reaction that occurs, if any, when solutions of sodium phosphate and cobalt(II) chloride are mixed.

SOLUTION

$$Na_3PO_4(aq) + CoCl_2(aq) \longrightarrow$$

Potentially Insoluble Products:

$NaCl$ $\quad$ $Co_3(PO_4)_2$

$NaCl$ is soluble.
$Co_3(PO_4)_2$ is insoluble.

Reaction contains an insoluble product; proceed to Step 5.

$$Na_3PO_4(aq) + CoCl_2(aq) \longrightarrow Co_3(PO_4)_2(s) + NaCl(aq)$$

$$\mathbf{2}\,Na_3PO_4(aq) + \mathbf{3}\,CoCl_2(aq) \longrightarrow CO_3(PO_4)_2(s) + \mathbf{6}\,NaCl(aq)$$

Writing Complete Ionic and Net Ionic Equations (Section 7.7)

To write a complete ionic equation from a molecular equation, separate all aqueous ionic compounds into independent ions. Do not separate solid, liquid, or gaseous compounds.

To write a net ionic equation from a complete ionic equation, eliminate all species that do not change (spectator ions) in the course of the reaction.

EXAMPLE 7.20 Writing Complete Ionic and Net Ionic Equations

Write a complete ionic and net ionic equation for the reaction.

$$2\,NH_4Cl(aq) + Hg_2(NO_3)_2(aq) \longrightarrow Hg_2Cl_2(s) + 2\,NH_4NO_3(aq)$$

SOLUTION

Complete ionic equation:

$$2\,NH_4^+(aq) + 2\,Cl^-(aq) + Hg_2^{2+}(aq) + 2\,NO_3^-(aq) \longrightarrow Hg_2Cl_2(s) + 2\,NH_4^+(aq) + 2\,NO_3^-(aq)$$

Net ionic equation:

$$2\,Cl^-(aq) + Hg_2^{2+}(aq) \longrightarrow Hg_2Cl_2(s)$$

Writing Equations for Acid–Base Reactions (Section 7.8)

When you see an acid and a base (see Table 7.3) as reactants in an equation, write a reaction in which the acid and the base react to form water and a salt.

EXAMPLE 7.21 Writing Equations for Acid–Base Reactions

Write an equation for the reaction that occurs when aqueous hydroiodic acid is mixed with aqueous barium hydroxide.

SOLUTION

$$\underset{\text{acid}}{2\,HI(aq)} + \underset{\text{base}}{Ba(OH)_2(aq)} \longrightarrow \underset{\text{water}}{2\,H_2O(l)} + \underset{\text{salt}}{BaI_2(aq)}$$

Writing Equations for Gas Evolution Reactions (Section 7.8)

See Table 7.4 to identify gas evolution reactions.

EXAMPLE 7.22 Writing Equations for Gas Evolution Reactions

Write an equation for the reaction that occurs when aqueous hydrobromic acid is mixed with aqueous potassium bisulfite.

SOLUTION

$$HBr(aq) + KHSO_3(aq) \longrightarrow H_2SO_3(aq) + KBr(aq) \longrightarrow H_2O(l) + SO_2(g) + KBr(aq)$$

Identifying Redox Reactions (Section 7.9)

Redox reactions are those in which any of the following occurs:

- a substance reacts with elemental oxygen
- a metal reacts with a nonmetal
- one substance transfers electrons to another substance

EXAMPLE 7.23 Identifying Redox Reactions

Which of these reactions is a redox reaction?

(a) $4\,Fe(s) + 3\,O_2(g) \longrightarrow 2\,Fe_2O_3(s)$
(b) $CaO(s) + CO_2(g) \longrightarrow CaCO_3(s)$
(c) $AgNO_3(aq) + NaCl(aq) \longrightarrow AgCl(s) + NaNO_3(aq)$

SOLUTION

Only **(a)** is a redox reaction.

Writing Equations for Combustion Reactions (Section 7.9)

In a combustion reaction, a substance reacts with O_2 to form one or more oxygen-containing compounds and, in many cases, water.

EXAMPLE 7.24 Writing Equations for Combustion Reactions

Write a balanced equation for the combustion of gaseous ethane (C_2H_6), a minority component of natural gas.

SOLUTION

The skeletal equation is:

$$C_2H_6(g) + O_2(g) \longrightarrow CO_2(g) + H_2O(g)$$

The balanced equation is:

$$2\,C_2H_6(g) + 7\,O_2(g) \longrightarrow 4\,CO_2(g) + 6\,H_2O(g)$$

Classifying Chemical Reactions (Section 7.10)

Chemical reactions can be classified by inspection. The four major categories are:

Synthesis or combination

$$A + B \longrightarrow AB$$

Decomposition

$$AB \longrightarrow A + B$$

Single-displacement

$$A + BC \longrightarrow AC + B$$

Double-displacement

$$AB + CD \longrightarrow AD + CB$$

EXAMPLE 7.25 Classifying Chemical Reactions

Classify each chemical reaction as a synthesis, decomposition, single-displacement, or double-displacement reaction.

(a) $2\,K(s) + Br_2(g) \longrightarrow 2\,KBr(s)$
(b) $Fe(s) + 2\,AgNO_3(aq) \longrightarrow Fe(NO_3)_2(aq) + 2\,Ag(s)$
(c) $CaSO_3(s) \longrightarrow CaO(s) + SO_2(g)$
(d) $CaCl_2(aq) + Li_2SO_4(aq) \longrightarrow CaSO_4(s) + 2\,LiCl(aq)$

SOLUTION

(a) Synthesis; KBr, a more complex substance, is formed from simpler substances.
(b) Single-displacement; Fe displaces Ag in $AgNO_3$.
(c) Decomposition; $CaSO_3$ decomposes into simpler substances.
(d) Double-displacement; Ca and Li switch places to form new compounds.

KEY TERMS

acid–base reaction [7.8]
aqueous solution [7.5]
balanced equation [7.3]
combination reaction [7.10]
combustion reaction [7.9]
complete ionic equation [7.7]
decomposition reaction [7.10]
displacement reaction [7.10]
double-displacement reaction [7.10]
gas evolution reaction [7.8]
insoluble [7.5]
molecular equation [7.7]
net ionic equation [7.7]
neutralization reaction [7.8]
oxidation–reduction (redox) reaction [7.9]
precipitate [7.6]
precipitation reaction [7.6]
salt [7.8]
single-displacement reaction [7.10]
solubility rules [7.5]
soluble [7.5]
spectator ion [7.7]
strong electrolyte solution [7.5]
synthesis reaction [7.10]

EXERCISES

QUESTIONS

1. What is a chemical reaction? List some examples.
2. If you could observe atoms and molecules, what would you look for as conclusive evidence of a chemical reaction?
3. What are the main indications that a chemical reaction has occurred?
4. What is a chemical equation? Provide an example and identify the reactants and products.
5. What does each abbreviation, often used in chemical equations, represent?
   (a) (g) **(b)** (l) **(c)** (s) **(d)** (aq)
6. To balance a chemical equation, adjust the ______ as necessary to make the numbers of each type of atom on both sides of the equation equal. Never adjust the ______ to balance a chemical equation.
7. List the number of each type of atom on both sides of each equation. Are the equations balanced?
   (a) $2\,Ag_2O(s) + C(s) \longrightarrow CO_2(g) + 4\,Ag(s)$
   (b) $Pb(NO_3)_2(aq) + 2\,NaCl(aq) \longrightarrow PbCl_2(s) + 2\,NaNO_3(aq)$
   (c) $C_3H_8(g) + O_2(g) \longrightarrow 3\,CO_2(g) + 4\,H_2O(g)$
8. What is an aqueous solution? List two examples.
9. What does it mean for a compound to be soluble? Insoluble?
10. Explain what happens to an ionic substance when it dissolves in water.
11. Do polyatomic ions dissociate when they dissolve in water, or do they remain intact?
12. What is a strong electrolyte solution?
13. What are the solubility rules, and how are they useful?
14. What is a precipitation reaction? Provide an example and identify the precipitate.
15. Will the precipitate in a precipitation reaction always be a compound that is soluble or insoluble? Explain.
16. Describe the differences between a molecular equation, a complete ionic equation, and net ionic equation. Give an example of each to illustrate the differences.
17. What is an acid–base reaction? List an example and identify the acid and the base.
18. What are the properties of acids and bases?
19. What is a gas evolution reaction? Give an example.
20. What is a redox reaction? Give an example.
21. What is a combustion reaction? Give an example.
22. What are two different ways to classify chemical reactions presented in Section 7.10? Explain the differences between them.
23. Explain the difference between a synthesis reaction and a decomposition reaction and give an example of each.
24. Explain the difference between a single-displacement reaction and a double-displacement reaction and give an example of each.

PROBLEMS

EVIDENCE OF CHEMICAL REACTIONS

25. Which observation is consistent with a chemical reaction occurring? Why?
   (a) Solid copper deposits on a piece of aluminum foil when the foil is placed in a blue copper nitrate solution. The blue color of the solution fades.
   (b) Liquid ethyl alcohol turns into a solid when placed in a low-temperature freezer.
   (c) A white precipitate forms when solutions of barium nitrate and sodium sulfate are mixed.
   (d) A mixture of sugar and water bubbles when yeasts are added. After several days, the sugar is gone and ethyl alcohol is found in the water.
26. Which observation is consistent with a chemical reaction occurring? Why?
   (a) Propane forms a flame and emits heat as it burns.
   (b) Acetone feels cold as it evaporates from the skin.
   (c) Bubbling is observed when potassium carbonate and hydrochloric acid solutions are mixed.
   (d) Heat is felt when a warm object is placed in your hand.

27. Vinegar forms bubbles when it is poured onto the calcium deposits on a faucet, and some of the calcium dissolves. Has a chemical reaction occurred? Explain your answer.

28. When a chemical drain opener is added to a clogged sink, bubbles form and the water in the sink gets warmer. Has a chemical reaction occurred? Explain your answer.

29. When a commercial hair bleaching mixture is applied to brown hair, the hair turns blond. Has a chemical reaction occurred? Explain your answer.

30. When water is boiled in a pot, it bubbles. Has a chemical reaction occurred? Explain your answer.

WRITING AND BALANCING CHEMICAL EQUATIONS

31. Consider the unbalanced chemical equation:

$$H_2O(l) \xrightarrow[\text{electrical current}]{} H_2(g) + O_2(g)$$

A chemistry student tries to balance the equation by placing the subscript 2 after the oxygen atom in H_2O. Explain why this is not correct. What is the correct balanced equation?

32. Consider the unbalanced chemical equation:

$$Al(s) + Cl_2(g) \longrightarrow AlCl_3(s)$$

A student tries to balance the equation by changing the subscript 2 on Cl to a 3. Explain why this is not correct. What is the correct balanced equation?

33. Write a balanced chemical equation for each chemical reaction:

(a) Solid lead(II) sulfide reacts with aqueous hydrochloric acid to form solid lead(II) chloride and dihydrogen sulfide gas.

(b) Gaseous carbon monoxide reacts with hydrogen gas to form gaseous methane (CH_4) and liquid water.

(c) Solid iron(III) oxide reacts with hydrogen gas to form solid iron and liquid water.

(d) Gaseous ammonia (NH_3) reacts with gaseous oxygen to form gaseous nitrogen monoxide and gaseous water.

34. Write a balanced chemical equation for each chemical reaction:

(a) Solid copper reacts with solid sulfur to form solid copper(I) sulfide.

(b) Sulfur dioxide gas reacts with oxygen gas to form sulfur trioxide gas.

(c) Aqueous hydrochloric acid reacts with solid manganese(IV) oxide to form aqueous manganese(II) chloride, liquid water, and chlorine gas.

(d) Liquid benzene (C_6H_6) reacts with gaseous oxygen to form carbon dioxide and liquid water.

35. Write a balanced chemical equation for each chemical reaction:

(a) Solid magnesium reacts with aqueous copper(I) nitrate to form aqueous magnesium nitrate and solid copper.

(b) Gaseous dinitrogen pentoxide decomposes to form nitrogen dioxide and oxygen gas.

(c) Solid calcium reacts with aqueous nitric acid to form aqueous calcium nitrate and hydrogen gas.

(d) Liquid methanol (CH_3OH) reacts with oxygen gas to form gaseous carbon dioxide and gaseous water.

36. Write a balanced chemical equation for each chemical reaction:

(a) Gaseous acetylene (C_2H_2) reacts with oxygen gas to form gaseous carbon dioxide and gaseous water.

(b) Chlorine gas reacts with aqueous potassium iodide to form solid iodine and aqueous potassium chloride.

(c) Solid lithium oxide reacts with liquid water to form aqueous lithium hydroxide.

(d) Gaseous carbon monoxide reacts with oxygen gas to form carbon dioxide gas.

37. Hydrogen has been widely proposed as a potential fuel to replace fossil fuels. Some scientists are trying to anticipate any potential problems that might be associated with a hydrogen-based economy. One group of scientists has calculated that the amount of atmospheric hydrogen could increase by a factor of four due to leaks in hydrogen transport and storage. Upper atmospheric hydrogen gas reacts with oxygen gas to form liquid water. An increase in upper atmospheric water would enhance processes that release atmospheric chlorine atoms. The gaseous chlorine atoms would then react with gaseous ozone (O_3) to form gaseous chlorine monoxide and gaseous oxygen, resulting in the depletion of ozone. Write balanced chemical equations for the two reactions described in this problem.

38. Waste water from certain industrial chemical processes contains aqueous Hg_2^{2+} ions. Since the mercury ion is toxic, it is removed from the waste water by reaction with aqueous sodium sulfide. The products of the reaction are solid mercury(I) sulfide and aqueous sodium ions. Write a balanced equation for this reaction.

39. When solid sodium is added to liquid water, it reacts with the water to produce hydrogen gas and aqueous sodium hydroxide. Write a balanced chemical equation for this reaction.

40. When iron rusts, solid iron reacts with gaseous oxygen to form solid iron(III) oxide. Write a balanced chemical equation for this reaction.

41. Sulfuric acid in acid rain forms when gaseous sulfur dioxide pollutant reacts with gaseous oxygen and liquid water to form aqueous sulfuric acid. Write a balanced chemical equation for this reaction.

42. Nitric acid in acid rain forms when gaseous nitrogen dioxide pollutant reacts with gaseous oxygen and liquid water to form aqueous nitric acid. Write a balanced chemical equation for this reaction.

43. Write a balanced chemical equation for the reaction of solid vanadium(V) oxide with hydrogen gas to form solid vanadium(III) oxide and liquid water.

44. Write a balanced chemical equation for the reaction of gaseous nitrogen dioxide with hydrogen gas to form gaseous ammonia and liquid water.

45. Write a balanced chemical equation for the fermentation of sugar ($C_{12}H_{22}O_{11}$) by yeasts in which the aqueous sugar reacts with water to form aqueous ethyl alcohol (C_2H_5OH) and carbon dioxide gas.

46. Write a balanced chemical equation for the photosynthesis reaction in which gaseous carbon dioxide and liquid water react in the presence of chlorophyll to produce aqueous glucose ($C_6H_{12}O_6$) and oxygen gas.

47. Balance each chemical equation.

(a) $Na_2S(aq) + Cu(NO_3)_2(aq) \longrightarrow NaNO_3(aq) + CuS(s)$

(b) $HCl(aq) + O_2(g) \longrightarrow H_2O(l) + Cl_2(g)$

(c) $H_2(g) + O_2(g) \longrightarrow H_2O(l)$

(d) $FeS(s) + HCl(aq) \longrightarrow FeCl_2(aq) + H_2S(g)$

48. Balance each chemical equation.

(a) $N_2H_4(l) \longrightarrow NH_3(g) + N_2(g)$

(b) $H_2(g) + N_2(g) \longrightarrow NH_3(g)$

(c) $Cu_2O(s) + C(s) \longrightarrow Cu(s) + CO(g)$

(d) $H_2(g) + Cl_2(g) \longrightarrow HCl(g)$

49. Balance each chemical equation.

(a) $BaO_2(s) + H_2SO_4(aq) \longrightarrow BaSO_4(s) + H_2O_2(aq)$

(b) $Co(NO_3)_3(aq) + (NH_4)_2S(aq) \longrightarrow Co_2S_3(s) + NH_4NO_3(aq)$

(c) $Li_2O(s) + H_2O(l) \longrightarrow LiOH(aq)$

(d) $Hg_2(C_2H_3O_2)_2(aq) + KCl(aq) \longrightarrow Hg_2Cl_2(s) + KC_2H_3O_2(aq)$

50. Balance each chemical equation.

(a) $MnO_2(s) + HCl(aq) \longrightarrow Cl_2(g) + MnCl_2(aq) + H_2O(l)$

(b) $CO_2(g) + CaSiO_3(s) + H_2O(l) \longrightarrow SiO_2(s) + Ca(HCO_3)_2(aq)$

(c) $Fe(s) + S(l) \longrightarrow Fe_2S_3(s)$

(d) $NO_2(g) + H_2O(l) \longrightarrow HNO_3(aq) + NO(g)$

51. Determine whether each chemical equation is correctly balanced. If not, correct it.
(a) $Rb(s) + H_2O(l) \longrightarrow RbOH(aq) + H_2(g)$
(b) $2\,N_2H_4(g) + N_2O_4(g) \longrightarrow 3\,N_2(g) + 4\,H_2O(g)$
(c) $NiS(s) + O_2(g) \longrightarrow NiO(s) + SO_2(g)$
(d) $PbO(s) + 2\,NH_3(g) \longrightarrow Pb(s) + N_2(g) + H_2O(l)$

52. Determine whether each chemical equation is correctly balanced. If not, correct it.
(a) $SiO_2(s) + 4\,HF(aq) \longrightarrow SiF_4(g) + 2\,H_2O(l)$
(b) $2\,Cr(s) + 3\,O_2(g) \longrightarrow Cr_2O_3(s)$
(c) $Al_2S_3(s) + H_2O(l) \longrightarrow 2\,Al(OH)_3(s) + 3\,H_2S(g)$
(d) $Fe_2O_3(s) + CO(g) \longrightarrow 2\,Fe(s) + CO_2(g)$

53. Human cells obtain energy from a reaction called cellular respiration. Balance the skeletal equation for cellular respiration.

$$C_6H_{12}O_6(aq) + O_2(g) \longrightarrow CO_2(g) + H_2O(l)$$

54. Propane camping stoves produce heat by the combustion of gaseous propane (C_3H_8). Balance the skeletal equation for the combustion of propane.

$$C_3H_8(g) + O_2(g) \longrightarrow CO_2(g) + H_2O(g)$$

55. Catalytic converters work to remove nitrogen oxides and carbon monoxide from exhaust. Balance the skeletal equation for one of the reactions that occurs in a catalytic converter.

$$NO(g) + CO(g) \longrightarrow N_2(g) + CO_2(g)$$

56. Billions of pounds of urea are produced annually for use as a fertilizer. Balance the skeletal equation for the synthesis of urea.

$$NH_3(g) + CO_2(g) \longrightarrow CO(NH_2)_2(s) + H_2O(l)$$

SOLUBILITY

57. Determine whether each compound is soluble or insoluble. For the soluble compounds, identify the ions present in solution.
(a) $NaC_2H_3O_2$
(b) $Sn(NO_3)_2$
(c) AgI
(d) $Na_3(PO_4)$

58. Determine whether each compound is soluble or insoluble. For the soluble compounds, identify the ions present in solution.
(a) $(NH_4)_2S$
(b) $CuCO_3$
(c) ZnS
(d) $Pb(C_2H_3O_2)_2$

59. Pair each cation on the left with an anion on the right that will form an *insoluble* compound with it and write a formula for the insoluble compound. Use each anion only once.

Ag^+	SO_4^{2-}
Ba^{2+}	Cl^-
Cu^{2+}	CO_3^{2-}
Fe^{3+}	S^{2-}

60. Pair each cation on the left with an anion on the right that will form a *soluble* compound with it and write a formula for the soluble compound. Use each anion only once.

Na^+	NO_3^-
Sr^{2+}	SO_4^{2-}
Co^{2+}	S^{2-}
Pb^{2+}	CO_3^{2-}

61. Determine whether each compound is in the correct column. Move any misplaced compounds to the correct column.

Soluble	Insoluble
K_2S	K_2SO_4
$PbSO_4$	Hg_2I_2
BaS	$Cu_3(PO_4)_2$
$PbCl_2$	MgS
Hg_2Cl_2	$CaSO_4$
NH_4Cl	SrS
Na_2CO_3	Li_2S

62. Determine whether each compound is in the correct column. Move any misplaced compounds to the correct column.

Soluble	Insoluble
$LiOH$	$CaCl_2$
Na_2CO_3	$Cu(OH)_2$
$AgCl$	$Ca(C_2H_3O_2)_2$
K_3PO_4	$SrSO_4$
CuI_2	Hg_2Br_2
$Pb(NO_3)_2$	$PbBr_2$
$CoCO_3$	PbI_2

PRECIPITATION REACTIONS

63. Complete and balance each equation. If no reaction occurs, write *NO REACTION.*
   (a) $KI(aq) + BaS(aq) \longrightarrow$
   (b) $K_2SO_4(aq) + BaBr_2(aq) \longrightarrow$
   (c) $NaCl(aq) + Hg_2(C_2H_3O_2)_2(aq) \longrightarrow$
   (d) $NaC_2H_3O_2(aq) + Pb(NO_3)_2(aq) \longrightarrow$

64. Complete and balance each equation. If no reaction occurs, write *NO REACTION.*
   (a) $NaOH(aq) + FeBr_3(aq) \longrightarrow$
   (b) $BaCl_2(aq) + AgNO_3(aq) \longrightarrow$
   (c) $Na_2CO_3(aq) + CoCl_2(aq) \longrightarrow$
   (d) $K_2S(aq) + BaCl_2(aq) \longrightarrow$

65. Write a molecular equation for the precipitation reaction that occurs (if any) when each pair of solutions is mixed. If no reaction occurs, write *NO REACTION.*
   (a) sodium carbonate and lead(II) nitrate
   (b) potassium sulfate and lead(II) acetate
   (c) copper(II) nitrate and barium sulfide
   (d) calcium nitrate and sodium iodide

66. Write a molecular equation for the precipitation reaction that occurs (if any) when each pair of solutions is mixed. If no reaction occurs, write *NO REACTION.*
   (a) potassium chloride and lead(II) acetate
   (b) lithium sulfate and strontium chloride
   (c) potassium bromide and calcium sulfide
   (d) chromium(III) nitrate and potassium phosphate

67. Determine whether each equation for a precipitation reaction is correct. Correct any incorrect equations. If no reaction occurs, write *NO REACTION.*
   (a) $Ba(NO_3)_2(aq) + (NH_4)_2SO_4(aq) \longrightarrow BaSO_4(s) + 2\,NH_4NO_3(aq)$
   (b) $BaS(aq) + 2\,KCl(aq) \longrightarrow BaCl_2(s) + K_2S(aq)$
   (c) $2\,KI(aq) + Pb(NO_3)_2(aq) \longrightarrow PbI_2(s) + 2\,KNO_3(aq)$
   (d) $Pb(NO_3)_2(aq) + 2\,LiCl(aq) \longrightarrow 2\,LiNO_3(s) + PbCl_2(aq)$

68. Determine whether each equation for a precipitation reaction is correct. Correct any incorrect equations. If no reaction occurs, write *NO REACTION.*
   (a) $AgNO_3(aq) + NaCl(aq) \longrightarrow NaCl(s) + AgNO_3(aq)$
   (b) $K_2SO_4(aq) + Co(NO_3)_2(aq) \longrightarrow CoSO_4(s) + 2\,KNO_3(aq)$
   (c) $Cu(NO_3)_2(aq) + (NH_4)_2S(aq) \longrightarrow CuS(s) + 2\,NH_4NO_3(aq)$
   (d) $Hg_2(NO_3)_2(aq) + 2\,LiCl(aq) \longrightarrow Hg_2Cl_2(s) + 2\,LiNO_3(aq)$

IONIC AND NET IONIC EQUATIONS

69. Identify the spectator ions in the complete ionic equation.

$$2\,K^+(aq) + S^{2-}(aq) + Pb^{2+}(aq) + 2\,NO_3^-(aq) \longrightarrow PbS(s) + 2\,K^+(aq) + 2\,NO_3^-(aq)$$

70. Identify the spectator ions in the complete ionic equation.

$$Ba^{2+}(aq) + 2\,I^-(aq) + 2\,Na^+(aq) + SO_4^{2-}(aq) \longrightarrow BaSO_4(s) + 2\,I^-(aq) + 2\,Na^+(aq)$$

71. Write balanced complete ionic and net ionic equations for each reaction.
   (a) $AgNO_3(aq) + KCl(aq) \longrightarrow AgCl(s) + KNO_3(aq)$
   (b) $CaS(aq) + CuCl_2(aq) \longrightarrow CuS(s) + CaCl_2(aq)$
   (c) $NaOH(aq) + HNO_3(aq) \longrightarrow H_2O(l) + NaNO_3(aq)$
   (d) $2\,K_3PO_4(aq) + 3\,NiCl_2(aq) \longrightarrow Ni_3(PO_4)_2(s) + 6\,KCl(aq)$

72. Write balanced complete ionic and net ionic equations for each reaction.
   (a) $HI(aq) + KOH(aq) \longrightarrow H_2O(l) + KI(aq)$
   (b) $Na_2SO_4(aq) + CaI_2(aq) \longrightarrow CaSO_4(s) + 2\,NaI(aq)$
   (c) $2\,HC_2H_3O_2(aq) + Na_2CO_3(aq) \longrightarrow H_2O(l) + CO_2(g) + 2\,NaC_2H_3O_2(aq)$
   (d) $NH_4Cl(aq) + NaOH(aq) \longrightarrow H_2O(l) + NH_3(g) + NaCl(aq)$

73. Mercury(I) ions (Hg_2^{2+}) can be removed from solution by precipitation with Cl^-. Suppose a solution contains aqueous $Hg_2(NO_3)_2$. Write complete ionic and net ionic equations to show the reaction of aqueous $Hg_2(NO_3)_2$ with aqueous sodium chloride to form solid Hg_2Cl_2 and aqueous sodium nitrate.

74. Lead ions can be removed from solution by precipitation with sulfate ions. Suppose a solution contains lead(II) nitrate. Write a complete ionic and net ionic equation to show the reaction of aqueous lead(II) nitrate with aqueous potassium sulfate to form solid lead(II) sulfate and aqueous potassium nitrate.

75. Write complete ionic and net ionic equations for each of the reactions in Problem 65.

76. Write complete ionic and net ionic equations for each of the reactions in Problem 66.

ACID–BASE AND GAS EVOLUTION REACTIONS

77. When a hydrochloric acid solution is combined with a potassium hydroxide solution, an acid–base reaction occurs. Write a balanced molecular equation and a net ionic equation for this reaction.

78. A beaker of nitric acid is neutralized with calcium hydroxide. Write a balanced molecular equation and a net ionic equation for this reaction.

79. Complete and balance each acid–base reaction.
   - **(a)** $HCl(aq) + Ba(OH)_2(aq) \longrightarrow$
   - **(b)** $H_2SO_4(aq) + KOH(aq) \longrightarrow$
   - **(c)** $HClO_4(aq) + NaOH(aq) \longrightarrow$

80. Complete and balance each acid–base reaction.
   - **(a)** $HC_2H_3O_2(aq) + Ca(OH)_2(aq) \longrightarrow$
   - **(b)** $HBr(aq) + LiOH(aq) \longrightarrow$
   - **(c)** $H_2SO_4(aq) + Ba(OH)_2(aq) \longrightarrow$

81. Complete and balance each gas evolution reaction.
   - **(a)** $HBr(aq) + NaHCO_3(aq) \longrightarrow$
   - **(b)** $NH_4I(aq) + KOH(aq) \longrightarrow$
   - **(c)** $HNO_3(aq) + K_2SO_3(aq) \longrightarrow$
   - **(d)** $HI(aq) + Li_2S(aq) \longrightarrow$

82. Complete and balance each gas evolution reaction.
   - **(a)** $HClO_4(aq) + K_2CO_3(aq) \longrightarrow$
   - **(b)** $HC_2H_3O_2(aq) + LiHSO_3(aq) \longrightarrow$
   - **(c)** $(NH_4)_2SO_4(aq) + Ca(OH)_2(aq) \longrightarrow$
   - **(d)** $HCl(aq) + ZnS(s) \longrightarrow$

OXIDATION–REDUCTION AND COMBUSTION

83. Which reactions are redox reactions?
   - **(a)** $Ba(NO_3)_2(aq) + K_2SO_4(aq) \longrightarrow BaSO_4(s) + 2\,KNO_3(aq)$
   - **(b)** $Ca(s) + Cl_2(g) \longrightarrow CaCl_2(s)$
   - **(c)** $HCl(aq) + NaOH(aq) \longrightarrow H_2O(l) + NaCl(aq)$
   - **(d)** $Zn(s) + Fe^{2+}(aq) \longrightarrow Zn^{2+}(aq) + Fe(s)$

84. Which reactions are redox reactions?
   - **(a)** $Al(s) + 3\,Ag^{+}(aq) \longrightarrow Al^{3+}(aq) + 3\,Ag(s)$
   - **(b)** $4\,K(s) + O_2(g) \longrightarrow 2\,K_2O(s)$
   - **(c)** $SO_3(g) + H_2O(l) \longrightarrow H_2SO_4(aq)$
   - **(d)** $Mg(s) + Br_2(l) \longrightarrow MgBr_2(s)$

85. Complete and balance each combustion reaction.
   - **(a)** $C_2H_6(g) + O_2(g) \longrightarrow$
   - **(b)** $Ca(s) + O_2(g) \longrightarrow$
   - **(c)** $C_3H_8O(l) + O_2(g) \longrightarrow$
   - **(d)** $C_4H_{10}S(l) + O_2(g) \longrightarrow$

86. Complete and balance each combustion reaction.
   - **(a)** $S(s) + O_2(g) \longrightarrow$
   - **(b)** $C_7H_{16}(l) + O_2(g) \longrightarrow$
   - **(c)** $C_4H_{10}O(l) + O_2(g) \longrightarrow$
   - **(d)** $CS_2(l) + O_2(g) \longrightarrow$

87. Write a balanced chemical equation for the synthesis reaction of $Br_2(g)$ with each metal:
   - **(a)** $Ag(s)$
   - **(b)** $K(s)$
   - **(c)** $Al(s)$
   - **(d)** $Ca(s)$

88. Write a balanced chemical equation for the synthesis reaction of $Cl_2(g)$ with each metal:
   - **(a)** $Zn(s)$
   - **(b)** $Ga(s)$
   - **(c)** $Rb(s)$
   - **(d)** $Mg(s)$

CLASSIFYING CHEMICAL REACTIONS BY WHAT ATOMS DO

89. Classify each chemical reaction as a synthesis, decomposition, single-displacement, or double-displacement reaction.
   - **(a)** $K_2S(aq) + Co(NO_3)_2(aq) \longrightarrow 2\,KNO_3(aq) + CoS(s)$
   - **(b)** $3\,H_2(g) + N_2(g) \longrightarrow 2\,NH_3(g)$
   - **(c)** $Zn(s) + CoCl_2(aq) \longrightarrow ZnCl_2(aq) + Co(s)$
   - **(d)** $CH_3Br(g) \xrightarrow{\text{UV light}} CH_3(g) + Br(g)$

90. Classify each chemical reaction as a synthesis, decomposition, single-displacement, or double-displacement reaction.
   - **(a)** $CaSO_4(s) \xrightarrow{\text{heat}} CaO(s) + SO_3(g)$
   - **(b)** $2\,Na(s) + O_2(g) \longrightarrow Na_2O_2(s)$
   - **(c)** $Pb(s) + 2\,AgNO_3(aq) \longrightarrow Pb(NO_3)_2(aq) + 2\,Ag(s)$
   - **(d)** $HI(aq) + NaOH(aq) \longrightarrow H_2O(l) + NaI(aq)$

91. NO is a pollutant emitted by motor vehicles. It is formed by the reaction:

(a) $N_2(g) + O_2(g) \longrightarrow 2\,NO(g)$
Once in the atmosphere, NO (through a series of reactions) adds one oxygen atom to form NO_2. NO_2 then interacts with UV light according to the reaction:

(b) $NO_2(g) \xrightarrow[\text{UV light}]{} NO(g) + O(g)$

These freshly formed oxygen atoms then react with O_2 in the air to form ozone (O_3), a main component of smog:

(c) $O(g) + O_2(g) \longrightarrow O_3(g)$
Classify each of the preceding reactions as a synthesis, decomposition, single-displacement, or double-displacement reaction.

92. A main source of sulfur oxide pollutants are smelters where sulfide ores are converted into metals. The first step in this process is the reaction of the sulfide ore with oxygen in reactions such as:

(a) $2\,PbS(s) + 3\,O_2(g) \longrightarrow 2\,PbO(s) + 2\,SO_2(g)$
Sulfur dioxide can then react with oxygen in air to form sulfur trioxide:

(b) $2\,SO_2(g) + O_2(g) \longrightarrow 2\,SO_3(g)$
Sulfur trioxide can then react with water from rain to form sulfuric acid that falls as acid rain:

(c) $SO_3(g) + H_2O(l) \longrightarrow H_2SO_4(aq)$
Classify each of the preceding reactions as a synthesis, decomposition, single-displacement, or double-displacement reaction.

CUMULATIVE PROBLEMS

93. Predict the products of each reaction and write balanced complete ionic and net ionic equations for each. If no reaction occurs, write *NO REACTION*.

(a) $NaI(aq) + Hg_2(NO_3)_2(aq) \longrightarrow$

(b) $HClO_4(aq) + Ba(OH)_2(aq) \longrightarrow$

(c) $Li_2CO_3(aq) + NaCl(aq) \longrightarrow$

(d) $HCl(aq) + Li_2CO_3(aq) \longrightarrow$

94. Predict the products of each reaction and write balanced complete ionic and net ionic equations for each. If no reaction occurs, write *NO REACTION*.

(a) $LiCl(aq) + AgNO_3(aq) \longrightarrow$

(b) $H_2SO_4(aq) + Li_2SO_3(aq) \longrightarrow$

(c) $HC_2H_3O_2(aq) + Ca(OH)_2(aq) \longrightarrow$

(d) $HCl(aq) + KBr(aq) \longrightarrow$

95. Predict the products of each reaction and write balanced complete ionic and net ionic equations for each. If no reaction occurs, write *NO REACTION*.

(a) $BaS(aq) + NH_4Cl(aq) \longrightarrow$

(b) $NaC_2H_3O_2(aq) + KCl(aq) \longrightarrow$

(c) $KHSO_3(aq) + HNO_3(aq) \longrightarrow$

(d) $MnCl_3(aq) + K_3PO_4(aq) \longrightarrow$

96. Predict the products of each reaction and write balanced complete ionic and net ionic equations for each. If no reaction occurs, write *NO REACTION*.

(a) $H_2SO_4(aq) + HNO_3(aq) \longrightarrow$

(b) $NaOH(aq) + LiOH(aq) \longrightarrow$

(c) $Cr(NO_3)_3(aq) + LiOH(aq) \longrightarrow$

(d) $HCl(aq) + Hg_2(NO_3)_2(aq) \longrightarrow$

97. Predict the type of reaction (if any) that occurs between each pair of substances. Write balanced molecular equations for each. If no reaction occurs, write *NO REACTION*.

(a) aqueous potassium hydroxide and aqueous acetic acid

(b) aqueous hydrobromic acid and aqueous potassium carbonate

(c) gaseous hydrogen and gaseous oxygen

(d) aqueous ammonium chloride and aqueous lead(II) nitrate

98. Predict the type of reaction (if any) that occurs between each pair of substances. Write balanced molecular equations for each. If no reaction occurs, write *NO REACTION*.

(a) aqueous hydrochloric acid and aqueous copper(II) nitrate

(b) liquid pentanol ($C_5H_{12}O$) and gaseous oxygen

(c) aqueous ammonium chloride and aqueous calcium hydroxide

(d) aqueous strontium sulfide and aqueous copper(II) sulfate

99. Classify each reaction in as many ways as possible.
   (a) $2\ Al(s) + 3\ Cu(NO_3)_2(aq) \longrightarrow 2\ Al(NO_3)_3(aq) + 3\ Cu(s)$
   (b) $HBr(aq) + KHSO_3(aq) \longrightarrow H_2O(l) + SO_2(g) + NaBr(aq)$
   (c) $2\ HI(aq) + Na_2S(aq) \longrightarrow H_2S(g) + 2\ NaI(aq)$
   (d) $K_2CO_3(aq) + FeBr_2(aq) \longrightarrow FeCO_3(s) + 2\ KBr(aq)$

100. Classify each reaction in as many ways as possible.
   (a) $NaCl(aq) + AgNO_3(aq) \longrightarrow AgCl(s) + NaNO_3(aq)$
   (b) $2\ Rb(s) + Br_2(g) \longrightarrow 2\ RbBr(s)$
   (c) $Zn(s) + NiBr_2(aq) \longrightarrow Ni(s) + ZnBr_2(aq)$
   (d) $Ca(s) + 2\ H_2O(l) \longrightarrow Ca(OH)_2(aq) + H_2(g)$

101. Hard water often contains dissolved Ca^{2+} and Mg^{2+} ions. One way to soften water is to add phosphates. The phosphate ion forms insoluble precipitates with calcium and magnesium ions, removing them from solution. Suppose that a solution contains aqueous calcium chloride and aqueous magnesium nitrate. Write molecular, complete ionic, and net ionic equations showing how the addition of sodium phosphate precipitates the calcium and magnesium ions.

102. Lakes that have been acidified by acid rain (HNO_3 and H_2SO_4) can be neutralized by a process called *liming*, in which limestone ($CaCO_3$) is added to the acidified water. Write ionic and net ionic equations to show how limestone reacts with HNO_3 and H_2SO_4 to neutralize them. How would you be able to tell if the neutralization process was working?

103. What solution can you add to each cation mixture to precipitate one cation while keeping the other cation in solution? Write a net ionic equation for the precipitation reaction that occurs.
   (a) $Fe^{2+}(aq)$ and $Pb^{2+}(aq)$
   (b) $K^+(aq)$ and $Ca^{2+}(aq)$
   (c) $Ag^+(aq)$ and $Ba^{2+}(aq)$
   (d) $Cu^{2+}(aq)$ and $Hg_2^{2+}(aq)$

104. What solution can you add to each cation mixture to precipitate one cation while keeping the other cation in solution? Write a net ionic equation for the precipitation reaction that occurs.
   (a) $Sr^{2+}(aq)$ and $Hg_2^{2+}(aq)$
   (b) $NH_4^+(aq)$ and $Ca^{2+}(aq)$
   (c) $Ba^{2+}(aq)$ and $Mg^{2+}(aq)$
   (d) $Ag^+(aq)$ and $Zn^{2+}(aq)$

105. A solution contains one or more of the following ions: Ag^+, Ca^{2+}, and Cu^{2+}. When sodium chloride is added to the solution, no precipitate occurs. When sodium sulfate is added to the solution, a white precipitate occurs. The precipitate is filtered off and sodium carbonate is added to the remaining solution, producing a precipitate. Which ions were present in the original solution? Write net ionic equations for the formation of each of the precipitates observed.

106. A solution contains one or more of the following ions: Hg_2^{2+}, Ba^{2+}, and Fe^{2+}. When potassium chloride is added to the solution, a precipitate forms. The precipitate is filtered off and potassium sulfate is added to the remaining solution, producing no precipitate. When potassium carbonate is added to the remaining solution, a precipitate occurs. Which ions were present in the original solution? Write net ionic equations for the formation of each of the precipitates observed.

107. A solution contains an unknown amount of dissolved calcium. Addition of 0.112 mol of K_3PO_4 causes complete precipitation of all of the calcium. How many moles of calcium were dissolved in the solution? What mass of calcium was dissolved in the solution?

108. A solution contains an unknown amount of dissolved magnesium. Addition of 0.0877 mol of Na_2CO_3 causes complete precipitation of all of the magnesium. What mass of magnesium was dissolved in the solution?

109. A solution contains 0.133 g of dissolved lead. How many moles of sodium chloride must be added to the solution to completely precipitate all of the dissolved lead? What mass of sodium chloride must be added?

110. A solution contains 1.77 g of dissolved silver. How many moles of potassium chloride must be added to the solution to completely precipitate all of the silver? What mass of potassium chloride must be added?

HIGHLIGHT PROBLEMS

111. The following are molecular views of two different possible mechanisms by which an automobile air bag might function. One of these mechanisms involves a chemical reaction and the other does not. By looking at the molecular views, can you tell which mechanism operates via a chemical reaction?

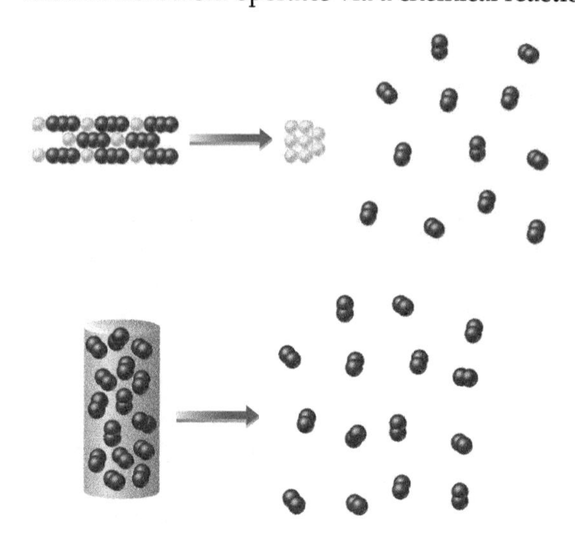

▲ When an airbag is detonated, the bag inflates. These figures show two possible ways in which the inflation may happen.

112. Precipitation reactions often produce brilliant colors. Look at the photographs of each precipitation reaction and write molecular, complete ionic, and net ionic equations for each one.

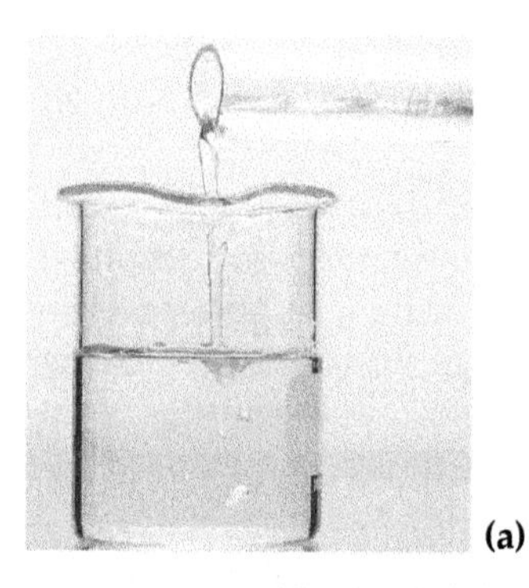

(a)

(b)

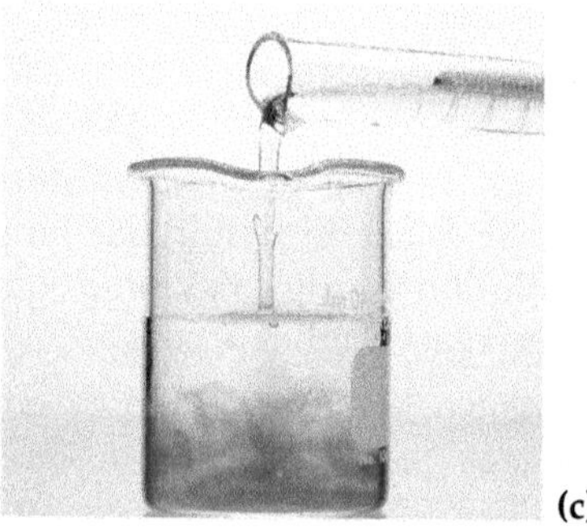

(c)

▲ (a) The precipitation reaction that occurs when aqueous iron(III) nitrate is added to aqueous sodium hydroxide. (b) The precipitation reaction that occurs when aqueous cobalt(II) chloride is added to aqueous potassium hydroxide. (c) The precipitation reaction that occurs when aqueous $AgNO_3$ is added to aqueous sodium iodide.

▸ANSWERS TO SKILLBUILDER EXERCISES

Skillbuilder 7.1 **(a)** Chemical reaction; heat and light are emitted. **(b)** Not a chemical reaction; gaseous and liquid butane are both butane. **(c)** Chemical reaction; heat and light are emitted. **(d)** Not a chemical reaction; solid dry ice is made of carbon dioxide, which sublimes (evaporates) as carbon dioxide gas.

Skillbuilder 7.2

$$2\,Cr_2O_3(s) + 3\,C(s) \longrightarrow 4\,Cr(s) + 3\,CO_2(g)$$

Skillbuilder 7.3

$$2\,C_4H_{10}(g) + 13\,O_2(g) \longrightarrow 8\,CO_2(g) + 10\,H_2O(g)$$

Skillbuilder 7.4

$$Pb(C_2H_3O_2)_2(aq) + 2\,KI(aq) \longrightarrow PbI_2(s) + 2\,KC_2H_3O_2(aq)$$

Skillbuilder 7.5 $4\,HCl(g) + O_2(g) \longrightarrow 2\,H_2O(l) + 2\,Cl_2(g)$

Skillbuilder 7.6 **(a)** insoluble **(b)** soluble **(c)** insoluble **(d)** soluble

Skillbuilder 7.7

$$2\,KOH(aq) + NiBr_2(aq) \longrightarrow Ni(OH)_2(s) + 2\,KBr(aq)$$

Skillbuilder 7.8

$$NH_4Cl(aq) + Fe(NO_3)_3(aq) \longrightarrow \text{NO REACTION}$$

Skillbuilder 7.9

$$K_2SO_4(aq) + Sr(NO_3)_2(aq) \longrightarrow SrSO_4(s) + 2\,KNO_3(aq)$$

Skillbuilder 7.10 Complete ionic equation:

$$2\,H^+(aq) + 2\,Br^-(aq) + Ca^{2+}(aq) + 2\,OH^-(aq) \longrightarrow 2\,H_2O(l) + Ca^{2+}(aq) + 2\,Br^-(aq)$$

Net ionic equation:

$2\,H^+(aq) + 2\,OH^-(aq) \longrightarrow 2\,H_2O(l)$, or simply

$H^+(aq) + OH^-(aq) \longrightarrow H_2O(l)$

Skillbuilder 7.11 Molecular equation:

$H_2SO_4(aq) + 2\,KOH(aq) \longrightarrow 2\,H_2O(l) + K_2SO_4(aq)$

Net ionic equation:

$2\,H^+(aq) + 2\,OH^-(aq) \longrightarrow 2\,H_2O(l)$

Skillbuilder 7.12

$2\,HBr(aq) + K_2SO_3(aq) \longrightarrow H_2O(l) + SO_2(g) + 2\,KBr(aq)$

Skillbuilder Plus, p. 225

$2\,H^+(aq) + SO_3^{2-}(aq) \longrightarrow H_2O(l) + SO_2(g)$

Skillbuilder 7.13 **(a)**, **(b)**, and **(d)** are all redox reactions; **(c)** is a precipitation reaction.

Skillbuilder 7.14

$C_5H_{12}(l) + 8\,O_2(g) \longrightarrow 5\,CO_2(g) + 6\,H_2O(g)$

Skillbuilder Plus, p. 228

$2\,C_3H_7OH(l) + 9\,O_2(g) \longrightarrow 6\,CO_2(g) + 8\,H_2O(g)$

Skillbuilder 7.15 **(a)** single-displacement **(b)** double-displacement **(c)** synthesis **(d)** decomposition

▶ANSWERS TO CONCEPTUAL CHECKPOINTS

7.1 **(a)** No reaction occurred. The molecules are the same before and after the change.
(b) A reaction occurred; the molecules have changed.
(c) A reaction occurred; the molecules have changed.

7.2 **(b)** There are 18 oxygen atoms on the left side of the equation, so the same number is needed on the right: $6 + 6(2) = 18$.

7.3 **(a)** (a) The number of each type of atom must be the same on both sides of a balanced chemical equation. Since molecules change during a chemical reaction, their number is not the same on both sides (b), nor is the sum of all of the coefficients the same (c).

7.4 **(a)** Since chlorides are soluble, and since Ba^{2+} is not an exception, $BaCl_2$ is soluble and will dissolve in water. When it dissolves, it dissociates into its component ions, as shown in (a).

7.5 **(b)** Both of the possible products, MgS and $CaSO_4$, are insoluble. The possible products of the other reactions—Na_2S, $Ca(NO_3)_2$, Na_2SO_4, and $Mg(NO_3)_2$—are all soluble.

7.6 **(d)** In a precipitation reaction, cations and anions "exchange partners" to produce at least one insoluble product. In an acid–base reaction, H^+ and OH^- combine to form water, and their partners pair off to form a salt.

Octane
2.2.4 ISO

CHAPTER 8

Quantities in Chemical Reactions

"Man masters nature not by force but by understanding. That is why science has succeeded where magic failed: because it has looked for no spell to cast."

JACOB BRONOWSKI (1908–1974)

8.1 Global Warming: Too Much Carbon Dioxide

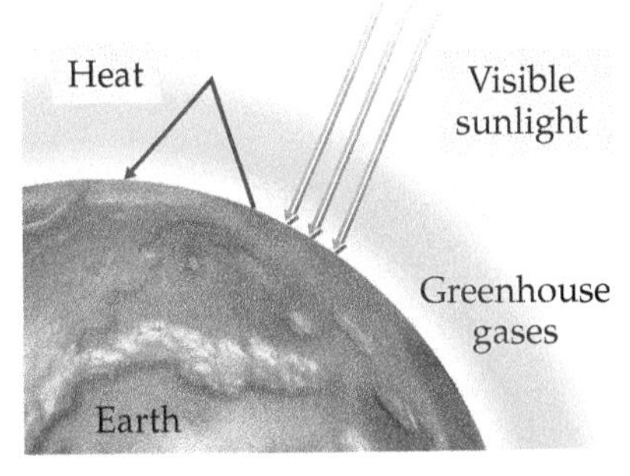

Outgoing heat is trapped by atmospheric greenhouse gases.
Heat
Visible sunlight
Greenhouse gases
Earth

▲ **FIGURE 8.1 The greenhouse effect** Greenhouse gases act like glass in a greenhouse, allowing visible-light energy to enter the atmosphere but preventing heat energy from escaping.

◀ The combustion of fossil fuels such as octane (shown here) produces water and carbon dioxide as products. Carbon dioxide is a greenhouse gas that is believed to be responsible for global warming.

Average global temperatures depend on the balance between incoming sunlight, which warms Earth, and outgoing heat lost to space, which cools it. Certain gases in Earth's atmosphere, called **greenhouse gases**, affect that balance by acting like glass in a greenhouse. They allow sunlight into the atmosphere to warm Earth but prevent heat from escaping (◀ Figure 8.1). Without greenhouse gases, more heat would escape, and Earth's average temperature would be about 60 °F (15 °C) colder. Caribbean tourists would freeze at an icy 21 °F, instead of baking at a tropical 81 °F. On the other hand, if the concentration of greenhouse gases in the atmosphere were to increase, Earth's average temperature would rise.

In recent years scientists have become concerned because the atmospheric concentration of carbon dioxide (CO_2)—Earth's most significant greenhouse gas in terms of its contribution to climate—is rising. This rise in CO_2 concentration enhances the atmosphere's ability to hold heat and may therefore lead to **global warming**, an increase in Earth's average temperature. Since 1860, atmospheric CO_2 levels have risen by 25%, and Earth's average temperature has increased by 0.6 °C (about 1.1 °F) (▶ Figure 8.2 on the next page).

The primary cause of rising atmospheric CO_2 concentration is the burning of fossil fuels. Fossil fuels—natural gas, petroleum, and coal—provide approximately 90% of our society's energy. Combustion of fossil fuels, however, produces CO_2. As an example, consider the combustion of octane (C_8H_{18}), a component of gasoline.

$$2\,C_8H_{18}(l) + 25\,O_2(g) \longrightarrow 16\,CO_2(g) + 18\,H_2O(g)$$

The balanced chemical equation shows that 16 mol of CO_2 are produced for every 2 mol of octane burned. Since we know the world's annual fossil fuel consumption, we can estimate the world's annual CO_2 production. A simple calculation shows that the world's annual CO_2 production—from fossil fuel

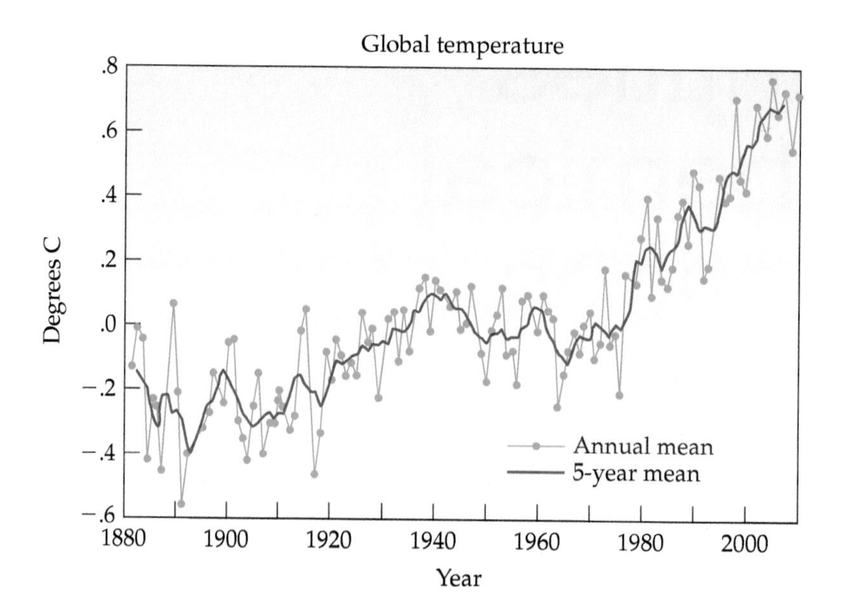

▶ **FIGURE 8.2 Global warming** Yearly temperature differences from the 120-year average temperature. Earth's average temperature has increased by about 0.6 °C since 1880. (*Source:* NASA GISS Surface Temperature Analysis)

combustion—matches the measured annual atmospheric CO_2 increase, implying that fossil fuel combustion is indeed responsible for increased atmospheric CO_2 levels.

The numerical relationship between chemical quantities in a balanced chemical equation is called reaction **stoichiometry**. Stoichiometry allows us to predict the amounts of products that form in a chemical reaction based on the amounts of reactants. Stoichiometry also allows us to predict how much of the reactants are necessary to form a given amount of product, or how much of one reactant is required to completely react with another reactant. These calculations are central to chemistry, allowing chemists to plan and carry out chemical reactions to obtain products in the desired quantities.

8.2 Making Pancakes: Relationships between Ingredients

The concepts of stoichiometry are similar to the concepts we use in following a cooking recipe. Calculating the amount of carbon dioxide produced by the combustion of a given amount of a fossil fuel is similar to calculating the number of pancakes that can be made from a given number of eggs. For example, suppose you use the following pancake recipe.

For the sake of simplicity, this recipe omits liquid ingredients.

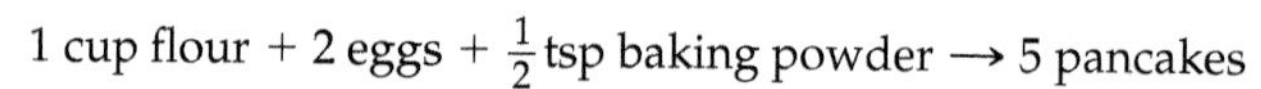

$$1 \text{ cup flour} + 2 \text{ eggs} + \tfrac{1}{2} \text{ tsp baking powder} \longrightarrow 5 \text{ pancakes}$$

▲ A recipe gives numerical relationships between the ingredients and the number of pancakes.

The recipe shows the numerical relationships between the pancake ingredients. It says that if we have 2 eggs—and enough of everything else—we can make 5 pancakes. We can write this relationship as a ratio.

2 eggs : 5 pancakes

What if we have 8 eggs? Assuming that we have enough of everything else, how many pancakes can we make? Using the preceding ratio as a conversion factor, we can determine that 8 eggs are sufficient to make 20 pancakes.

$$8\ \text{eggs} \times \frac{5\ \text{pancakes}}{2\ \text{eggs}} = 20\ \text{pancakes}$$

The pancake recipe contains numerical conversion factors between the pancake ingredients and the number of pancakes. Other conversion factors from this recipe include:

1 cup flour : 5 pancakes

$\frac{1}{2}$ tsp baking powder : 5 pancakes

The recipe also gives us relationships among the ingredients themselves. For example, how much baking powder is required to go with 3 cups of flour? From the recipe:

1 cup flour : $\frac{1}{2}$ tsp baking powder

With this ratio, we can form the conversion factor to calculate the appropriate amount of baking powder.

$$3\ \text{cups flour} \times \frac{\frac{1}{2}\ \text{tsp baking powder}}{1\ \text{cup flour}} = \frac{3}{2}\ \text{tsp baking powder}$$

8.3 Making Molecules: Mole-to-Mole Conversions

In a balanced chemical equation, we have a "recipe" for how reactants combine to form products. For example, the following equation shows how hydrogen and nitrogen combine to form ammonia (NH_3).

$$3\ H_2(g) + N_2(g) \longrightarrow 2\ NH_3(g)$$

The balanced equation shows that 3 H_2 molecules react with 1 N_2 molecule to form 2 NH_3 molecules. We can express these relationships as the following ratios.

3 H_2 molecules : 1 N_2 molecule : 2 NH_3 molecules

Since we do not ordinarily deal with individual molecules, we can express the same ratios in moles.

$$3 \text{ mol } H_2 : 1 \text{ mol } N_2 : 2 \text{ mol } NH_3$$

If we have 3 mol of N_2, and more than enough H_2, how much NH_3 can we make? We first sort the information in the problem.

GIVEN: 3 mol N_2

FIND: mol NH_3

SOLUTION MAP

We then strategize by drawing a solution map that begins with mol N_2 and ends with mol NH_3. The conversion factor comes from the balanced chemical equation.

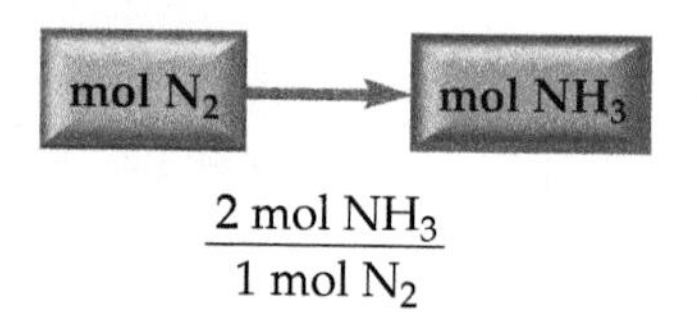

$$\frac{2 \text{ mol } NH_3}{1 \text{ mol } N_2}$$

RELATIONSHIPS USED

1 mol N_2:2 mol NH_3 (from balanced equation)

SOLUTION

We can then do the conversion.

$$3 \text{ mol } N_2 \times \frac{2 \text{ mol } NH_3}{1 \text{ mol } N_2} = 6 \text{ mol } NH_3$$

We have enough N_2 to make 6 mol of NH_3.

EXAMPLE 8.1 Mole-to-Mole Conversions

Sodium chloride, NaCl, forms by this reaction between sodium and chlorine.

$$2 \text{ Na}(s) + \text{Cl}_2(g) \longrightarrow 2 \text{ NaCl}(s)$$

How many moles of NaCl result from the complete reaction of 3.4 mol of Cl_2? Assume that there is more than enough Na.

SORT

You are given the number of moles of a reactant (Cl_2) and asked to find the number of moles of product (NaCl) that will form if the reactant completely reacts.

GIVEN: 3.4 mol Cl_2

FIND: mol NaCl

STRATEGIZE

Draw the solution map beginning with moles of chlorine and using the stoichiometric conversion factor to calculate moles of sodium chloride. The conversion factor comes from the balanced chemical equation.

SOLUTION MAP

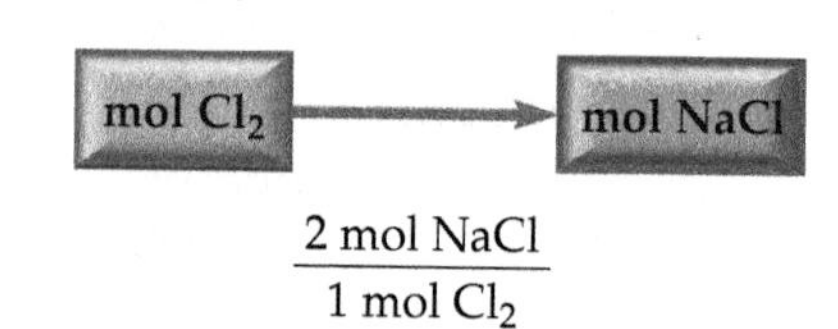

$$\frac{2 \text{ mol NaCl}}{1 \text{ mol } Cl_2}$$

RELATIONSHIPS USED

1 mol Cl_2:2 mol NaCl (from balanced chemical equation)

SOLVE

Follow the solution map to solve the problem. There is enough Cl_2 to produce 6.8 mol of NaCl.

SOLUTION

$$3.4 \text{ mol } Cl_2 \times \frac{2 \text{ mol NaCl}}{1 \text{ mol } Cl_2} = 6.8 \text{ mol NaCl}$$

CHECK

Check your answer. Are the units correct? Does the answer make physical sense?

The answer has the correct units, moles. The answer is reasonable because each mole of Cl_2 makes two moles of NaCl.

▶**SKILLBUILDER 8.1 | Mole-to-Mole Conversions**

Water is formed when hydrogen gas reacts explosively with oxygen gas according to the balanced equation:

$$O_2(g) + 2\,H_2(g) \longrightarrow 2\,H_2O(g)$$

How many moles of H_2O result from the complete reaction of 24.6 mol of O_2? Assume that there is more than enough H_2.

▶**FOR MORE PRACTICE** Example 8.8; Problems 15, 16, 17, 18.

CONCEPTUAL CHECKPOINT 8.1

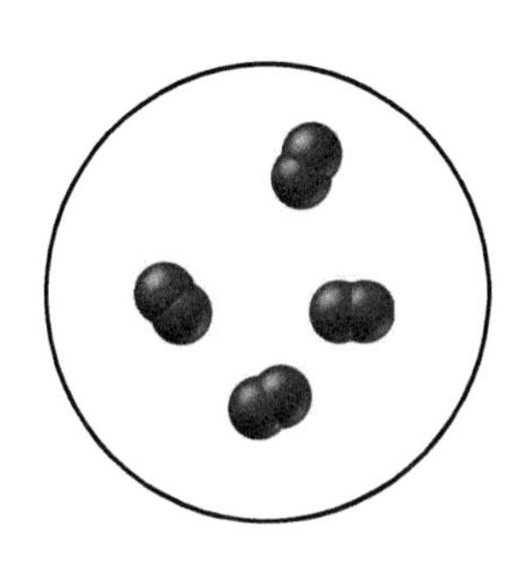

Methane (CH_4) undergoes combustion according to the reaction:

$$CH_4(g) + 2\,O_2(g) \longrightarrow CO_2(g) + 2\,H_2O(g)$$

If the figure at left represents the amount of oxygen available to react, which of the following best represents the amount of CH_4 required to completely react with all of the oxygen?

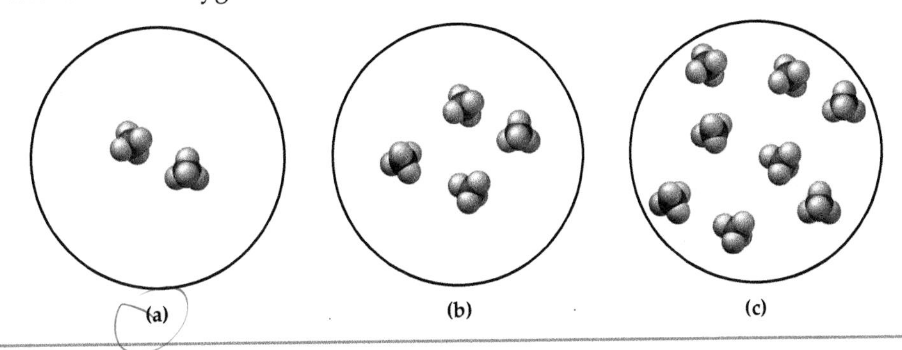

8.4 Making Molecules: Mass-to-Mass Conversions

In Chapter 6, we learned how a chemical *formula* contains conversion factors for converting between moles of a compound and moles of its constituent elements. In this chapter, we have seen how a chemical *equation* contains conversion factors between moles of reactants and moles of products. However, we are often interested in relationships between *mass* of reactants and *mass* of products. For example, we might want to know the mass of carbon dioxide emitted by an automobile per kilogram of gasoline used. Or we might want to know the mass of each reactant required to obtain a certain mass of a product in a synthesis reaction. These calculations are similar to calculations covered in Section 6.5, where we converted between mass of a compound and mass of a constituent element. The general outline for these types of calculations is:

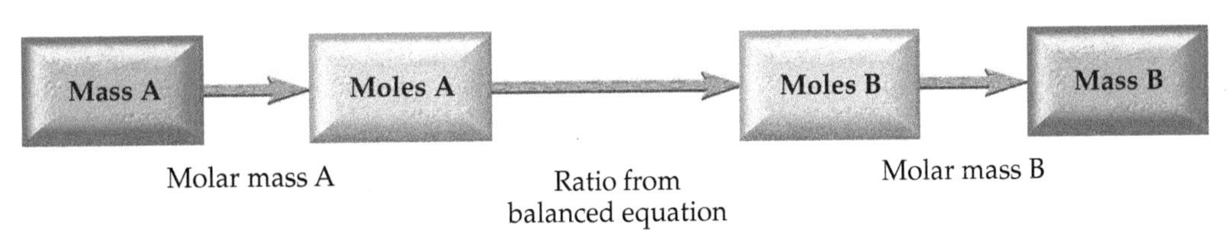

where A and B are two different substances involved in the reaction. We use the molar mass of A to convert from mass of A to moles of A. We use the ratio from the balanced equation to convert from moles of A to moles of B, and we use the molar mass of B to convert moles of B to mass of B. For example, suppose we want to calculate the mass of CO_2 emitted upon the combustion of 5.0×10^2 g of pure octane. The balanced chemical equation for octane combustion is:

$$2\,C_8H_{18}(l) + 25\,O_2(g) \longrightarrow 16\,CO_2(g) + 18\,H_2O(g)$$

CHEMISTRY IN THE MEDIA

The Controversy over Oxygenated Fuels

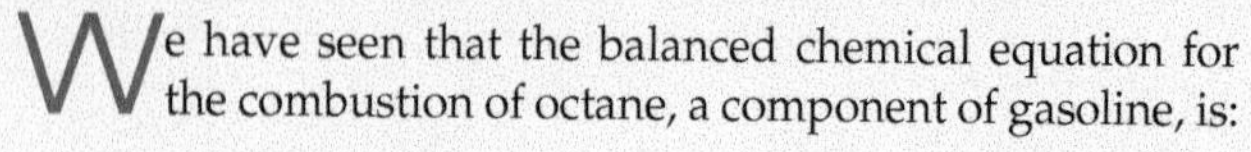

We have seen that the balanced chemical equation for the combustion of octane, a component of gasoline, is:

$$2\,C_8H_{18}(l) + 25\,O_2(g) \longrightarrow 16\,CO_2(g) + 18\,H_2O(g)$$

We have also learned how balanced chemical equations give numerical relationships between reactants. The preceding equation shows that 25 mol of O_2 are required to completely react with 2 mol of C_8H_{18}. What if there were not enough O_2 in the cylinders of an automobile engine to fully react with the amount of octane flowing into them? For many reactions, a shortage of one reactant simply means that less product forms, something we will learn more about later in this chapter. However, for some reactions, a shortage of one reactant causes other reactions—called *side reactions*—to occur along with the desired reaction. In the case of octane and the other major components of gasoline, those side reactions result in pollutants such as carbon monoxide (CO) and ozone (O_3).

In 1990, the U.S. Congress, in efforts to lower air pollution, passed amendments to the Clean Air Act requiring oil companies to add substances to gasoline that prevent these side reactions. Since these additives have the effect of increasing the amount of oxygen during combustion, the resulting gasoline is called oxygenated fuel. The additive of choice among oil companies used to be a compound called MTBE (methyl tertiary butyl ether). The immediate results were positive. Carbon monoxide and ozone levels in many major cities decreased significantly.

Over time, however, MTBE—a compound that does not readily biodegrade—began to appear in drinking-water supplies across the nation. MTBE made its way into drinking water through gasoline spills at gas stations, from boat motors, and from leaking underground storage tanks. The consequences have been significant. MTBE, even at low levels, imparts a turpentine-like odor and foul taste to drinking water. It is also a suspected carcinogen.

Public response was swift and dramatic. Several multimillion dollar class-action lawsuits were filed and settled against the manufacturers of MTBE, against gas stations suspected of leaking it, and against the oil companies that put MTBE into gasoline. Most states have completely banned MTBE from gasoline. Ethanol, made from the fermentation of grains, has been used as a substitute for MTBE because it has many of the same pollution-reducing effects without the associated health hazards. Oil companies did not use ethanol originally because it was more expensive than MTBE, but now ethanol has become the additive of choice.

▲ The 1990 amendments to the Clean Air Act required oil companies to put additives in gasoline that increased its oxygen content.

CAN YOU ANSWER THIS? *How many moles of oxygen (O_2) are required to completely react with 425 mol of octane (approximate capacity of a 15-gal automobile gasoline tank)?*

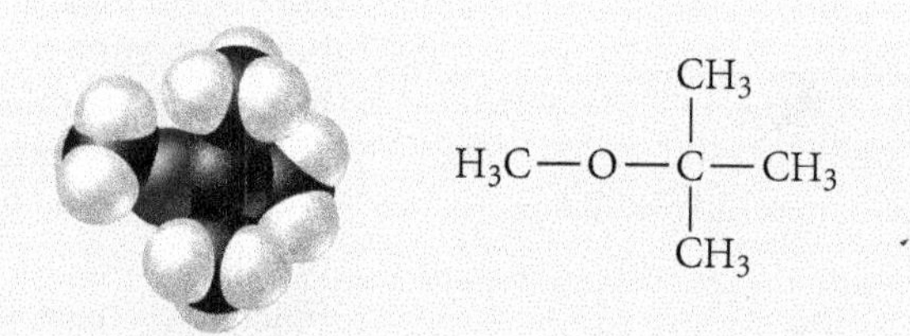

▲ MTBE was the additive of choice.

We begin by sorting the information in the problem.

GIVEN: 5.0×10^2 g C_8H_{18}

FIND: g CO_2

Notice that we are given g C_8H_{18} and asked to find g CO_2. The balanced chemical equation, however, gives us a relationship between moles of C_8H_{18} and moles of CO_2. Consequently, before using that relationship, we must convert from grams to moles.

The solution map uses the general outline

$$\text{Mass A} \longrightarrow \text{Moles A} \longrightarrow \text{Moles B} \longrightarrow \text{Mass B}$$

where A is octane and B is carbon dioxide.

SOLUTION MAP

We strategize by drawing the solution map, which begins with mass of octane and ends with mass of carbon dioxide.

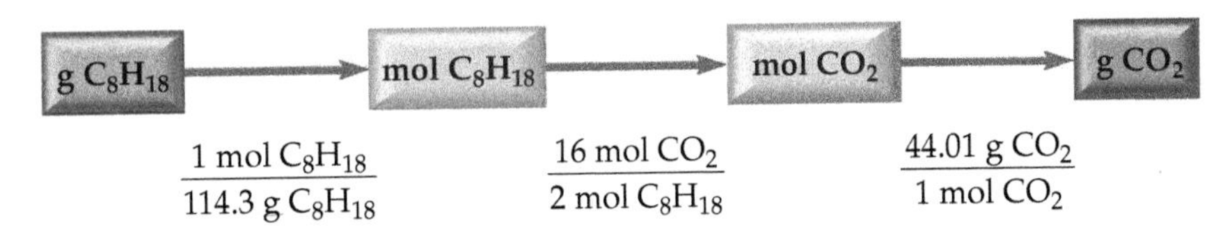

RELATIONSHIPS USED

$2 \text{ mol } C_8H_{18} \equiv 16 \text{ mol } CO_2$ (from chemical equation)

Molar mass $C_8H_{18} = 114.3$ g/mol

Molar mass $CO_2 = 44.01$ g/mol

SOLUTION

We then follow the solution map to solve the problem, beginning with g C_8H_{18} and canceling units to arrive at g CO_2.

$$5.0 \times 10^2 \text{ g } C_8H_{18} \times \frac{1 \text{ mol } C_8H_{18}}{114.3 \text{ g } C_8H_{18}} \times \frac{16 \text{ mol } CO_2}{2 \text{ mol } C_8H_{18}} \times \frac{44.01 \text{ g } CO_2}{1 \text{ mol } CO_2} = 1.5 \times 10^3 \text{ g } CO_2$$

Upon combustion, 5.0×10^2 g of octane produces 1.5×10^3 g of carbon dioxide.

EXAMPLE 8.2 Mass-to-Mass Conversions

In photosynthesis, plants convert carbon dioxide and water into glucose ($C_6H_{12}O_6$) according to the reaction:

$$6\,CO_2(g) + 6\,H_2O(l) \xrightarrow[\text{sunlight}]{} 6\,O_2(g) + C_6H_{12}O_6(aq)$$

How many grams of glucose can be synthesized from 58.5 g of CO_2? Assume that there is more than enough water present to react with all of the CO_2.

SORT

You are given the mass of carbon dioxide and asked to find the mass of glucose that can form if the carbon dioxide completely reacts.

GIVEN: 58.5 g CO_2

FIND: g $C_6H_{12}O_6$

STRATEGIZE

The solution map uses the general outline

Mass A $\longrightarrow$ Moles A $\longrightarrow$ Moles B $\longrightarrow$ Mass B

where A is carbon dioxide and B is glucose.

The main conversion factor is the stoichiometric relationship between moles of carbon dioxide and moles of glucose. This conversion factor comes from the balanced equation. The other conversion factors are simply the molar masses of carbon dioxide and glucose.

SOLUTION MAP

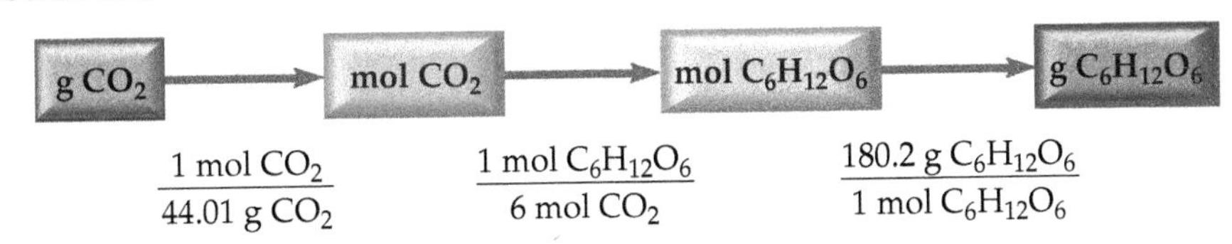

RELATIONSHIPS USED

$6 \text{ mol } CO_2 : 1 \text{ mol } C_6H_{12}O_6$ (from balanced chemical equation)

Molar mass $CO_2 = 44.01$ g/mol

Molar mass $C_6H_{12}O_6 = 180.2$ g/mol

SOLVE Follow the solution map to solve the problem. Begin with grams of carbon dioxide and multiply by the appropriate factors to arrive at grams of glucose.	**SOLUTION** $58.5\ \text{g}\ CO_2 \times \frac{1\ \text{mol}\ CO_2}{44.01\ \text{g}\ CO_2} \times \frac{1\ \text{mol}\ C_6H_{12}O_6}{6\ \text{mol}\ CO_2} \times \frac{180.2\ \text{g}\ C_6H_{12}O_6}{1\ \text{mol}\ C_6H_{12}O_6} = 39.9\ \text{g}\ C_6H_{12}O_6$
CHECK Are the units correct? Does the answer make physical sense?	The units, g $C_6H_{12}O_6$, are correct. The magnitude of the answer seems reasonable because it is of the same order of magnitude as the given mass of carbon dioxide. An answer that is orders of magnitude different would immediately be suspect.

▶SKILLBUILDER 8.2 | Mass-to-Mass Conversions

Magnesium hydroxide, the active ingredient in milk of magnesia, neutralizes stomach acid, primarily HCl, according to the reaction:

$$Mg(OH)_2(aq) + 2\ HCl(aq) \longrightarrow 2\ H_2O(l) + MgCl_2(aq)$$

How much HCl in grams can be neutralized by 5.50 g of $Mg(OH)_2$?

▶FOR MORE PRACTICE Example 8.9; Problems 31, 32, 33, 34.

EXAMPLE 8.3 Mass-to-Mass Conversions

One of the components of acid rain is nitric acid, which forms when NO_2, a pollutant, reacts with oxygen and rainwater according to the following simplified reaction.

$$4\ NO_2(g) + O_2(g) + 2\ H_2O(l) \longrightarrow 4\ HNO_3(aq)$$

Assuming that there is more than enough O_2 and H_2O, how much HNO_3 in kilograms forms from 1.5×10^3 kg of NO_2 pollutant?

SORT You are given the mass of nitrogen dioxide (a reactant) and asked to find the mass of nitric acid that can form if the nitrogen dioxide completely reacts.	**GIVEN:** 1.5×10^3 kg NO_2 **FIND:** kg HNO_3
STRATEGIZE The solution map follows the general format of: Mass ⟶ Moles ⟶ Moles ⟶ Mass However, since the original quantity of NO_2 is given in kilograms, you must first convert to grams. Since the final quantity is requested in kilograms, you must convert back to kilograms at the end. The main conversion factor is the stoichiometric relationship between moles of nitrogen dioxide and moles of nitric acid. This conversion factor comes from the balanced equation. The other conversion factors are simply the molar masses of nitrogen dioxide and nitric acid and the relationship between kilograms and grams.	**SOLUTION MAP** 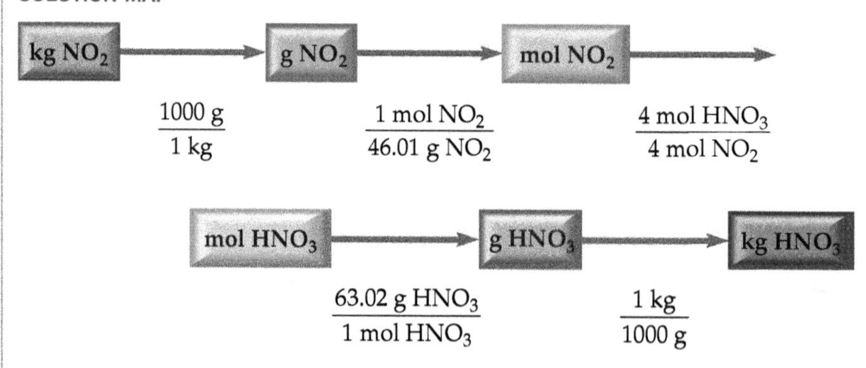 **RELATIONSHIPS USED** 4 mol NO_2 : 4 mol HNO_3 (from balanced chemical equation) Molar mass NO_2 = 46.01 g/mol Molar mass HNO_3 = 63.02 g/mol 1 kg = 1000 g

SOLVE Follow the solution map to solve the problem. Begin with kilograms of nitrogen dioxide and multiply by the appropriate conversion factors to arrive at kilograms of nitric acid.	**SOLUTION** $1.5 \times 10^3 \text{ kg } \cancel{NO_2} \times \frac{1000 \text{ g}}{1 \text{ kg}} \times \frac{1 \text{ mol } NO_2}{46.01 \text{ g } NO_2} \times \frac{4 \text{ mol } HNO_3}{4 \text{ mol } NO_2} \times \frac{63.02 \text{ g } HNO_3}{1 \text{ mol } HNO_3} \times \frac{1 \text{ kg}}{1000 \text{ g}} = 2.1 \times 10^3 \text{ kg } HNO_3$
CHECK Are the units correct? Does the answer make physical sense?	The units, kg HNO_3 are correct. The magnitude of the answer seems reasonable because it is of the same order of magnitude as the given mass of nitrogen dioxide. An answer that is orders of magnitude different would immediately be suspect.

▶SKILLBUILDER 8.3 | Mass-to-Mass Conversions

Another component of acid rain is sulfuric acid, which forms when SO_2, also a pollutant, reacts with oxygen and rainwater according to the following reaction.

$$2\,SO_2(g) + O_2(g) + 2\,H_2O(l) \longrightarrow 2\,H_2SO_4(aq)$$

Assuming that there is more than enough O_2 and H_2O, how much H_2SO_4 in kilograms forms from 2.6×10^3 kg of SO_2?

▶FOR MORE PRACTICE Problems 35, 36, 37, 38.

8.5 More Pancakes: Limiting Reactant, Theoretical Yield, and Percent Yield

Let's return to our pancake analogy to understand two more concepts important in reaction stoichiometry: limiting reactant and percent yield. Recall our pancake recipe:

$$1 \text{ cup flour} + 2 \text{ eggs} + \tfrac{1}{2} \text{ tsp baking powder} \longrightarrow 5 \text{ pancakes}$$

Suppose we have 3 cups flour, 10 eggs, and 4 tsp baking powder. How many pancakes can we make? We have enough flour to make:

$$3 \text{ cups flour} \times \frac{5 \text{ pancakes}}{1 \text{ cup flour}} = 15 \text{ pancakes}$$

We have enough eggs to make:

$$10 \text{ eggs} \times \frac{5 \text{ pancakes}}{2 \text{ eggs}} = 25 \text{ pancakes}$$

We have enough baking powder to make:

$$4 \text{ tsp baking powder} \times \frac{5 \text{ pancakes}}{\tfrac{1}{2} \text{ tsp baking powder}} = 40 \text{ pancakes}$$

We have enough flour for 15 pancakes, enough eggs for 25 pancakes, and enough baking powder for 40 pancakes. Consequently, unless we get more ingredients, *we can make only 15 pancakes*. The amount of flour we have *limits* the number of pancakes we can make. If this were a chemical reaction, the flour would be the *limiting reactant*, the reactant that limits the amount of product in a chemical reaction. Notice that the **limiting reactant** is simply the reactant that makes *the least amount of product*. If this were a chemical reaction, 15 pancakes would be the **theoretical yield**, the amount of product that can be made in a chemical reaction based on the amount of limiting reactant.

The term *limiting reagent* is sometimes used in place of limiting reactant.

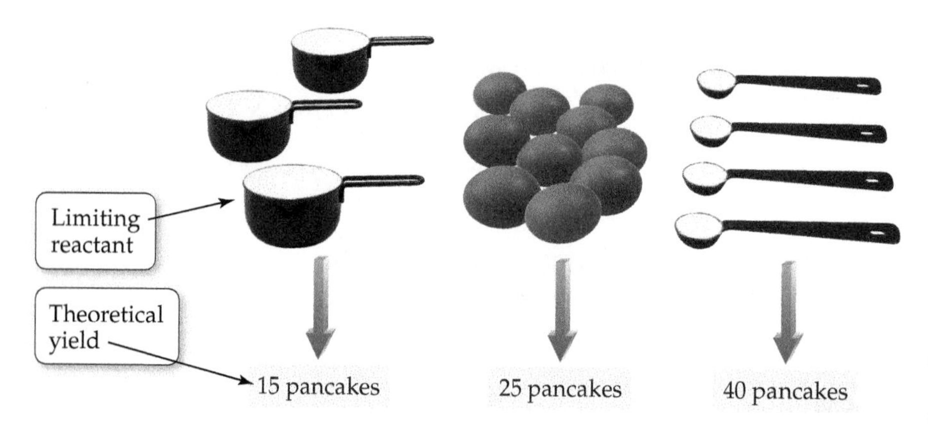

▲ If this were a chemical reaction, the flour would be the limiting reactant and 15 pancakes would be the theoretical yield.

Let us carry this analogy one step further. Suppose we go on to cook our pancakes. We accidentally burn three of them and one falls on the floor. So even though we had enough flour for 15 pancakes, we finished with only 11 pancakes. If this were a chemical reaction, the 11 pancakes would be our **actual yield**, the amount of product actually produced by a chemical reaction. Finally, our **percent yield**, the percentage of the theoretical yield that was actually attained, is:

$$\text{Percent yield} = \frac{11 \text{ pancakes}}{15 \text{ pancakes}} \times 100\% = 73\%$$

Since four of the pancakes were ruined, we got only 73% of our theoretical yield. In a chemical reaction, the actual yield is almost always less than 100% because at least some of the product does not form or is lost in the process of recovering it (in analogy to some of the pancakes being burned).

The actual yield of a chemical reaction, which must be determined experimentally, often depends in various ways on the reaction conditions. We will explore some of the factors involved in Chapter 15.

To summarize:

- **Limiting reactant (or limiting reagent)**—the reactant that is completely consumed in a chemical reaction.
- **Theoretical yield**—the amount of product that can be made in a chemical reaction based on the amount of limiting reactant.
- **Actual yield**—the amount of product actually produced by a chemical reaction.
- $\textbf{Percent yield} = \dfrac{\textbf{Actual yield}}{\textbf{Theoretical yield}} \times 100\%$

Consider the reaction.

$$Ti(s) + 2\,Cl_2(g) \longrightarrow TiCl_4(s)$$

If we begin with 1.8 mol of titanium and 3.2 mol of chlorine, what is the limiting reactant and theoretical yield of $TiCl_4$ in moles? We begin by sorting the information in the problem according to our standard problem-solving procedure.

GIVEN: 1.8 mol Ti

3.2 mol Cl_2

FIND: limiting reactant

theoretical yield

SOLUTION MAP

As in our pancake analogy, we determine the limiting reactant by calculating how much product can be made from each reactant. The reactant that makes the *least amount of product* is the limiting reactant.

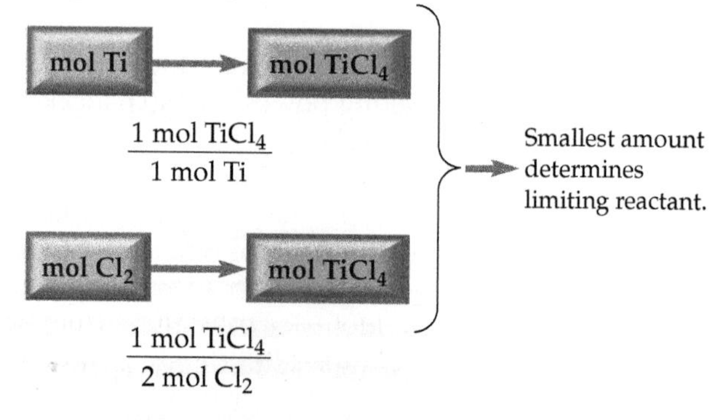

RELATIONSHIPS USED

The conversion factors come from the balanced chemical equation and give the relationships between moles of each of the reactants and moles of product.

$$1 \text{ mol Ti} : 1 \text{ mol TiCl}_4$$

$$2 \text{ mol Cl}_2 : 1 \text{ mol TiCl}_4$$

SOLUTION

$$1.8 \text{ mol Ti} \times \frac{1 \text{ mol TiCl}_4}{1 \text{ mol Ti}} = 1.8 \text{ mol TiCl}_4$$

$$3.2 \text{ mol Cl}_2 \times \frac{1 \text{ mol TiCl}_4}{2 \text{ mol Cl}_2} = 1.6 \text{ mol TiCl}_4$$

Limiting reactant (3.2 mol Cl_2) — Least amount of product (1.6 mol $TiCl_4$)

In many industrial applications, the more costly reactant or the reactant that is most difficult to remove from the product mixture is chosen to be the limiting reactant.

Since the 3.2 mol of Cl_2 make the least amount of $TiCl_4$, Cl_2 is the limiting reactant. Notice that we began with more moles of Cl_2 than Ti, but since the reaction requires 2 Cl_2 for each Ti, Cl_2 is still the limiting reactant. The theoretical yield is 1.6 mol of $TiCl_4$.

EXAMPLE 8.4 Limiting Reactant and Theoretical Yield from Initial Moles of Reactants

Consider the reaction:

$$2\,\text{Al}(s) + 3\,\text{Cl}_2(g) \longrightarrow 2\,\text{AlCl}_3(s)$$

If you begin with 0.552 mol of aluminum and 0.887 mol of chlorine, what is the limiting reactant and theoretical yield of $AlCl_3$ in moles?

SORT

You are given the number of moles of aluminum and chlorine and asked to find the limiting reactant and theoretical yield of aluminum chloride.

GIVEN

0.552 mol Al
0.887 mol Cl_2

FIND

limiting reactant
theoretical yield of $AlCl_3$

STRATEGIZE

Draw a solution map that shows how to get from moles of each reactant to moles of $AlCl_3$. The reactant that makes the *least amount of $AlCl_3$* is the limiting reactant. The conversion factors are the stoichiometric relationships (from the balanced equation).

SOLUTION MAP

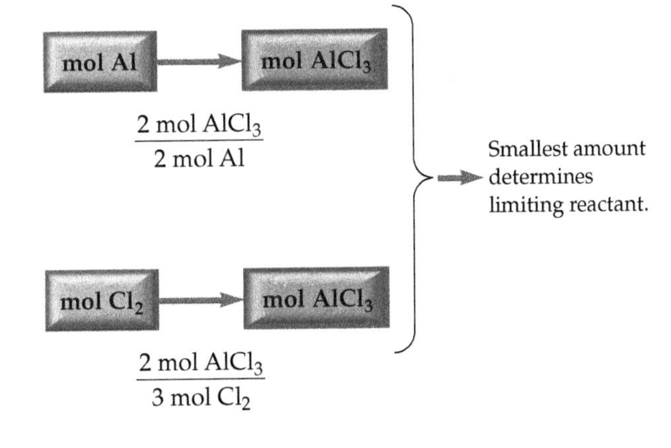

RELATIONSHIPS USED

$2 \text{ mol Al} : 2 \text{ mol AlCl}_3$ (from balanced equation)
$3 \text{ mol Cl}_2 : 2 \text{ mol AlCl}_3$ (from balanced equation)

SOLVE
Follow the solution map to solve the problem.

SOLUTION

$$0.552 \text{ mol Al} \times \frac{2 \text{ mol AlCl}_3}{2 \text{ mol Al}} = 0.552 \text{ mol AlCl}_3$$

Limiting reactant — Least amount of product

$$0.887 \text{ mol Cl}_2 \times \frac{2 \text{ mol AlCl}_3}{3 \text{ mol Cl}_2} = 0.591 \text{ mol AlCl}_3$$

Since the 0.552 mol of Al makes the least amount of $AlCl_3$, Al is the limiting reactant. The theoretical yield is 0.552 mol of $AlCl_3$.

CHECK
Are the units correct? Does the answer make physical sense?

The units, mol $AlCl_3$, are correct. The magnitude of the answer seems reasonable because it is of the same order of magnitude as the given number of moles of Al and Cl_2. An answer that is orders of magnitude different would immediately be suspect.

▶SKILLBUILDER 8.4 | Limiting Reactant and Theoretical Yield from Initial Moles of Reactants

Consider the reaction:

$$2 \text{ Na}(s) + \text{F}_2(g) \longrightarrow 2 \text{ NaF}(s)$$

If you begin with 4.8 mol of sodium and 2.6 mol of fluorine, what is the limiting reactant and theoretical yield of NaF in moles?

▶FOR MORE PRACTICE Problems 43, 44, 45, 46, 47, 48, 49, 50.

CONCEPTUAL CHECKPOINT 8.2

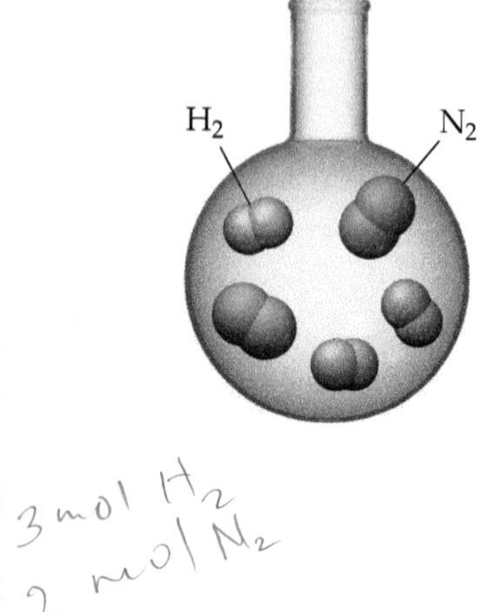

Consider the reaction:

$$\text{N}_2(g) + 3 \text{ H}_2(g) \longrightarrow 2 \text{ NH}_3(g)$$

If the flask at left represents the mixture before the reaction, which flask represents the products after the limiting reactant has completely reacted?

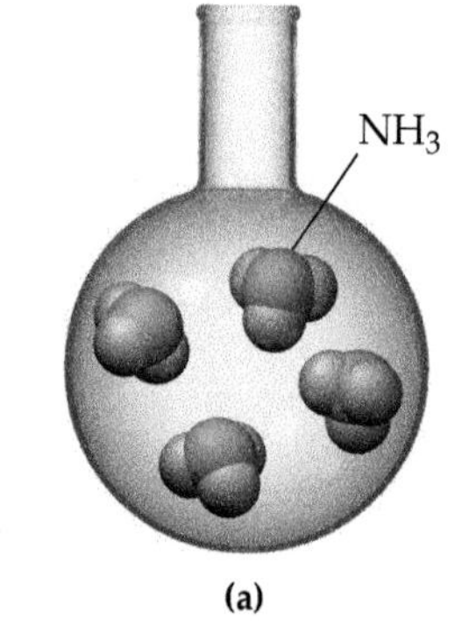

(a)

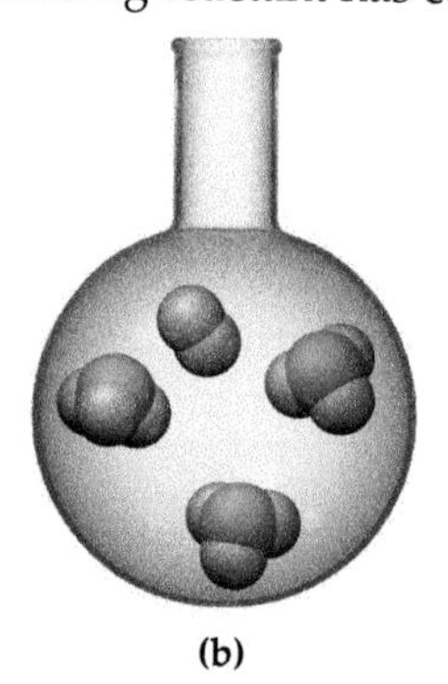

(b)

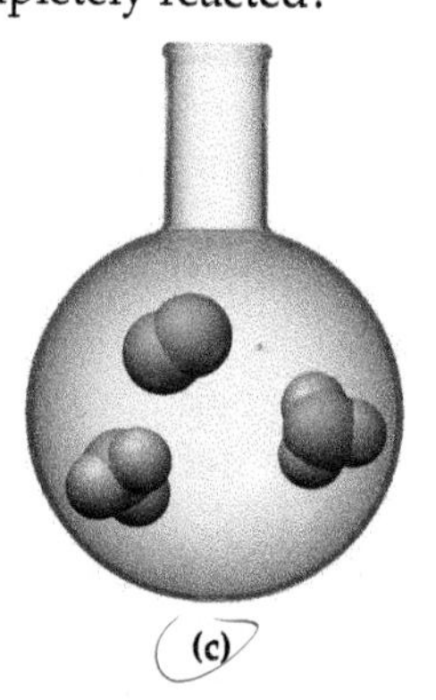

(c)

8.6 Limiting Reactant, Theoretical Yield, and Percent Yield from Initial Masses of Reactants

When working in the laboratory, we normally measure the initial amounts of reactants in grams. To find limiting reactants and theoretical yields from initial masses, we must add two steps to our calculations. Consider, for example, the synthesis reaction:

$$2 \text{ Na}(s) + \text{Cl}_2(g) \longrightarrow 2 \text{ NaCl}(s)$$

If we have 53.2 g of Na and 65.8 g of Cl_2, what is the limiting reactant and theoretical yield? We begin by sorting the information in the problem.

GIVEN: 53.2 g Na

65.8 g Cl_2

FIND: limiting reactant

theoretical yield

SOLUTION MAP

Again, we find the limiting reactant by calculating how much product can be made from each reactant. Since we are given the initial amounts in grams, we must first convert to moles. After we convert to moles of product, we convert back to grams of product. The reactant that makes the *least amount of product* is the limiting reactant.

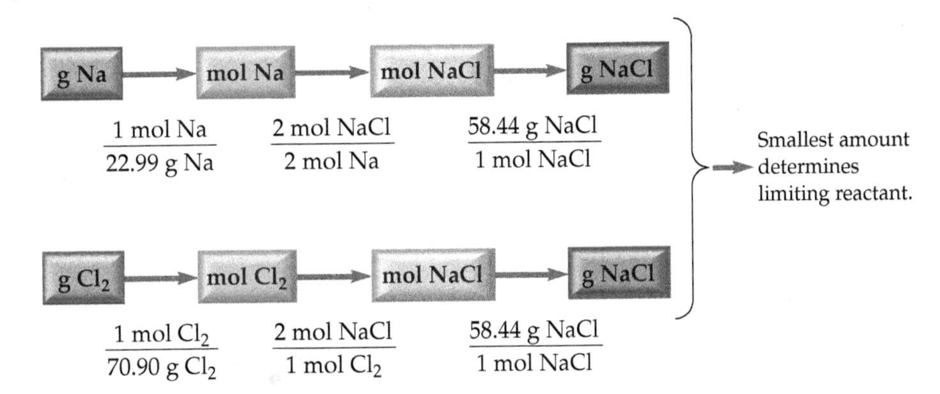

RELATIONSHIPS USED

From the balanced chemical equation, we know:

$$2 \text{ mol Na} : 2 \text{ mol NaCl}$$
$$1 \text{ mol } Cl_2 : 2 \text{ mol NaCl}$$

We also use these molar masses:

$$\text{Molar mass Na} = \frac{22.99 \text{ g Na}}{1 \text{ mol Na}}$$

$$\text{Molar mass } Cl_2 = \frac{70.90 \text{ g } Cl_2}{1 \text{ mol } Cl_2}$$

$$\text{Molar mass NaCl} = \frac{58.44 \text{ g NaCl}}{1 \text{ mol NaCl}}$$

SOLUTION

Beginning with the actual amounts of each reactant, we follow the solution map to calculate how much product can be made from each.

The limiting reactant can also be found by calculating the number of moles of NaCl (rather than grams) that can be made from each reactant. However, since theoretical yields are normally calculated in grams, we take the calculation all the way to grams to determine limiting reactant.

$$53.2 \text{ g Na} \times \frac{1 \text{ mol Na}}{22.99 \text{ g Na}} \times \frac{2 \text{ mol NaCl}}{2 \text{ mol Na}} \times \frac{58.44 \text{ g NaCl}}{1 \text{ mol NaCl}} = 135 \text{ g NaCl}$$

$$65.8 \text{ g } Cl_2 \times \frac{1 \text{ mol } Cl_2}{70.90 \text{ g } Cl_2} \times \frac{2 \text{ mol NaCl}}{1 \text{ mol } Cl_2} \times \frac{58.44 \text{ g NaCl}}{1 \text{ mol NaCl}} = 108 \text{ g NaCl}$$

Limiting reactant (65.8 g Cl_2) — **Least amount of product** (108 g NaCl)

The limiting reactant is not necessarily the reactant with the least mass.

Since Cl_2 makes the least amount of product, it is the limiting reactant. Notice that the limiting reactant is not necessarily the reactant with the least mass. In this case, we had fewer grams of Na than Cl_2, yet Cl_2 was the limiting reactant because it made less NaCl. The theoretical yield is therefore 108 g of NaCl, the amount of product possible based on the limiting reactant.

Now suppose that when the synthesis was carried out, the actual yield of NaCl was 86.4 g. What is the percent yield? The percent yield is:

The actual yield is always less than the theoretical yield because at least a small amount of product is usually lost or does not form during a reaction.

$$\text{Percent yield} = \frac{\text{Actual yield}}{\text{Theoretical yield}} \times 100\% = \frac{86.4 \text{ g}}{108 \text{ g}} \times 100\% = 80.0\%$$

EXAMPLE 8.5 Finding Limiting Reactant and Theoretical Yield

Ammonia, NH_3, can be synthesized by the reaction:

$$2\,NO(g) + 5\,H_2(g) \longrightarrow 2\,NH_3(g) + 2\,H_2O(g)$$

What maximum amount of ammonia in grams can be synthesized from 45.8 g of NO and 12.4 g of H_2?

SORT

You are given the masses of two reactants and asked to find the maximum mass of ammonia that can be formed. Although this problem does not specifically ask for the limiting reactant, it must be found to determine the theoretical yield, which is the maximum amount of ammonia that can be synthesized.

GIVEN: 45.8 g NO, 12.4 g H_2

FIND: maximum amount of NH_3 in g (this is the theoretical yield)

STRATEGIZE

Find the limiting reactant by calculating how much product can be made from each reactant. The reactant that makes the *least amount of product* is the limiting reactant. The mass of ammonia formed by the limiting reactant is the maximum amount of ammonia that can be synthesized.

SOLUTION MAP

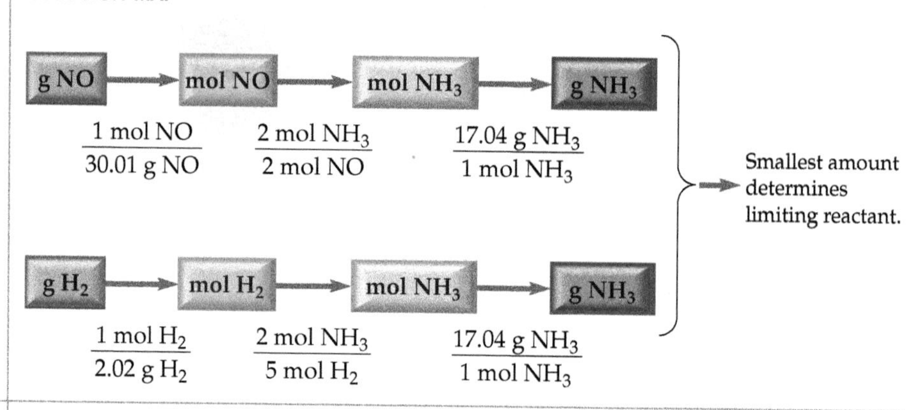

The main conversion factors come from the stoichiometric relationship between moles of each reactant and moles of ammonia. The other conversion factors are the molar masses of nitrogen monoxide, hydrogen gas, and ammonia.

RELATIONSHIPS USED

2 mol NO : 2 mol NH_3 5 mol H_2 : 2 mol NH_3

$$\text{Molar mass NO} = \frac{30.01 \text{ g NO}}{1 \text{ mol NO}} \qquad \text{Molar mass } H_2 = \frac{2.02 \text{ g } H_2}{1 \text{ mol } H_2}$$

$$\text{Molar mass } NH_3 = \frac{17.04 \text{ g } NH_3}{1 \text{ mol } NH_3}$$

SOLVE

Follow the solution map, beginning with the actual amount of each reactant given, to calculate the amount of product that can be made from each reactant.

SOLUTION

$$45.8 \text{ g NO} \times \frac{1 \text{ mol NO}}{30.01 \text{ g NO}} \times \frac{2 \text{ mol } NH_3}{2 \text{ mol NO}} \times \frac{17.04 \text{ g } NH_3}{1 \text{ mol } NH_3} = 26.0 \text{ g } NH_3$$

Limiting reactant — Least amount of product

$$12.4 \text{ g } H_2 \times \frac{1 \text{ mol } H_2}{2.02 \text{ g } H_2} \times \frac{2 \text{ mol } NH_3}{5 \text{ mol } H_2} \times \frac{17.04 \text{ g } NH_3}{1 \text{ mol } NH_3} = 41.8 \text{ g } NH_3$$

There is enough NO to make 26.0 g of NH_3 and enough H_2 to make 41.8 g of NH_3. Therefore, NO is the limiting reactant, and the maximum amount of ammonia that can possibly be made is 26.0 g, which is the theoretical yield.

CHECK Are the units correct? Does the answer make physical sense?	The units of the answer, g NH_3, are correct. The magnitude of the answer seems reasonable because it is of the same order of magnitude as the given masses of NO and H_2. An answer that is orders of magnitude different would immediately be suspect.

▶SKILLBUILDER 8.5 | Finding Limiting Reactant and Theoretical Yield

Ammonia can also be synthesized by the reaction:

$$3\,H_2(g) + N_2(g) \longrightarrow 2\,NH_3(g)$$

What maximum amount of ammonia in grams can be synthesized from 25.2 g of N_2 and 8.42 g of H_2?

▶SKILLBUILDER PLUS

What maximum amount of ammonia in kilograms can be synthesized from 5.22 kg of H_2 and 31.5 kg of N_2?

▶FOR MORE PRACTICE Problems 55, 56, 57, 58.

EXAMPLE 8.6 Finding Limiting Reactant, Theoretical Yield, and Percent Yield

Consider the reaction:

$$Cu_2O(s) + C(s) \longrightarrow 2\,Cu(s) + CO(g)$$

When 11.5 g of C are allowed to react with 114.5 g of Cu_2O, 87.4 g of Cu are obtained. Find the limiting reactant, theoretical yield, and percent yield.

SORT You are given the mass of the reactants, carbon and copper(I) oxide, as well as the mass of copper formed by the reaction. You are asked to find the limiting reactant, theoretical yield, and percent yield.	**GIVEN:** 11.5 g C 114.5 g Cu_2O 87.4 g Cu produced **FIND:** limiting reactant theoretical yield percent yield
STRATEGIZE The solution map shows how to find the mass of Cu formed by the initial masses of Cu_2O and C. The reactant that makes the *least amount of product* is the limiting reactant and determines the theoretical yield.	**SOLUTION MAP** 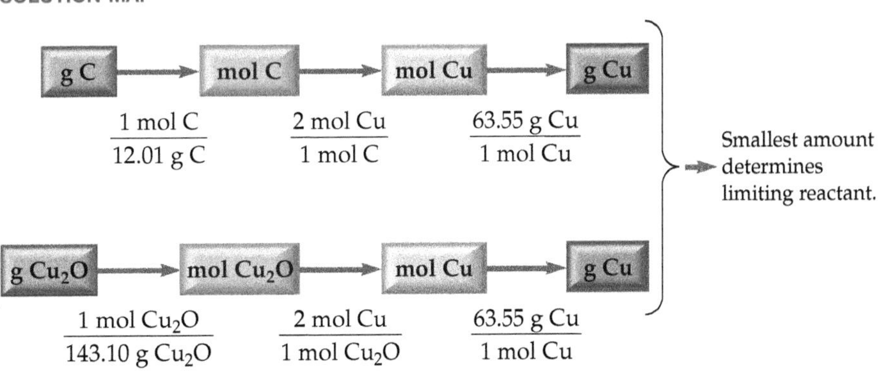
The main conversion factors are the stoichiometric relationships between moles of each reactant and moles of copper. The other conversion factors are the molar masses of copper(I) oxide, carbon, and copper.	**RELATIONSHIPS USED** 1 mol Cu_2O : 2 mol Cu 1 mol C : 2 mol Cu Molar mass Cu_2O = 143.10 g/mol Molar mass C = 12.01 g/mol Molar mass Cu = 63.55 g/mol

SOLVE

Follow the solution map, beginning with the actual amount of each reactant given, to calculate the amount of product that can be made from each reactant.

Since Cu_2O makes the least amount of product, Cu_2O is the limiting reactant. The theoretical yield is then the amount of product made by the limiting reactant. The percent yield is the actual yield (87.4 g Cu) divided by the theoretical yield (101.7 g Cu) multiplied by 100%.

SOLUTION

$$11.5\ \text{g C} \times \frac{1\ \text{mol C}}{12.01\ \text{g C}} \times \frac{2\ \text{mol Cu}}{1\ \text{mol C}} \times \frac{63.55\ \text{g Cu}}{1\ \text{mol Cu}} = 122\ \text{g Cu}$$

$$114.5\ \text{g Cu}_2\text{O} \times \frac{1\ \text{mol Cu}_2\text{O}}{143.10\ \text{g Cu}_2\text{O}} \times \frac{2\ \text{mol Cu}}{1\ \text{mol Cu}_2\text{O}} \times \frac{63.55\ \text{g Cu}}{1\ \text{mol Cu}} = 101.7\ \text{g Cu}$$

Limiting reactant

Least amount of product

Theoretical yield = 101.7 g Cu

$$\text{Percent yield} = \frac{\text{Actual yield}}{\text{Theoretical yield}} \times 100\%$$

$$= \frac{87.4\ \text{g}}{101.7\ \text{g}} \times 100\% = 85.9\%$$

CHECK

Are the units correct? Does the answer make physical sense?

The theoretical yield has the right units (g Cu). The magnitude of the theoretical yield seems reasonable because it is of the same order of magnitude as the given masses of C and Cu_2O. The theoretical yield is reasonable because it is less than 100%. Any calculated theoretical yield above 100% would be suspect.

▶SKILLBUILDER 8.6 | Finding Limiting Reactant, Theoretical Yield, and Percent Yield

This reaction is used to obtain iron from iron ore:

$$Fe_2O_3(s) + 3\,CO(g) \longrightarrow 2\,Fe(s) + 3\,CO_2(g)$$

The reaction of 185 g of Fe_2O_3 with 95.3 g of CO produces 87.4 g of Fe. Find the limiting reactant, theoretical yield, and percent yield.

▶FOR MORE PRACTICE Example 8.10; Problems 61, 62, 63, 64, 65, 66.

CONCEPTUAL CHECKPOINT 8.3

Limiting Reactant and Theoretical Yield

Ammonia can by synthesized by the reaction of nitrogen monoxide and hydrogen gas.

$$2\,NO(g) + 5\,H_2(g) \longrightarrow 2\,NH_3(g) + 2\,H_2O(g)$$

A reaction vessel initially contains 4.0 mol of NO and 15.0 mol of H_2. What is in the reaction vessel once the reaction has occurred to the fullest extent possible?

(a) 2 mol NO; 5 mol H_2; 2 mol NH_3; and 2 mol H_2O

(b) 0 mol NO; 0 mol H_2; 6 mol NH_3; and 6 mol H_2O

(c) 2 mol NO; 0 mol H_2; 4 mol NH_3; and 2 mol H_2O

(d) 0 mol NO; 5 mol H_2; 4 mol NH_3; and 4 mol H_2O

8.7 Enthalpy: A Measure of the Heat Evolved or Absorbed in a Reaction

Chapter 3 (see Section 3.9) describes how chemical reactions can be *exothermic* (in which case they *emit* thermal energy when they occur) or *endothermic* (in which case they *absorb* thermal energy when they occur). The *amount* of thermal energy

EVERYDAY CHEMISTRY

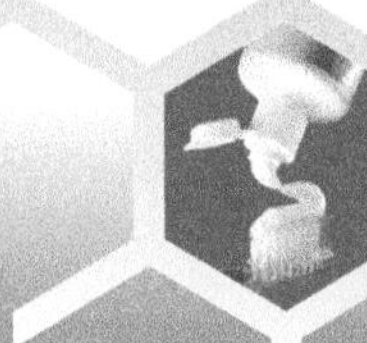

Bunsen Burners

In the laboratory, we often use Bunsen burners as heat sources. These burners are normally fueled by methane. The balanced equation for methane (CH_4) combustion is:

$$CH_4(g) + 2\,O_2(g) \longrightarrow CO_2(g) + 2\,H_2O(g)$$

Most Bunsen burners have a mechanism to adjust the amount of air (and therefore of oxygen) that is mixed with the methane. If you light the burner with the air completely closed off, you get a yellow, smoky flame that is not very hot. As you increase the amount of air going into the burner, the flame becomes bluer, less smoky, and hotter. When you reach the optimum adjustment, the flame has a sharp, inner blue triangle, no smoke, and is hot enough to melt glass easily. Continuing to increase the air beyond this point causes the flame to become cooler again and may actually extinguish it.

CAN YOU ANSWER THIS? *Can you use the concepts from this chapter to explain the changes in the Bunsen burner as the air intake is adjusted?*

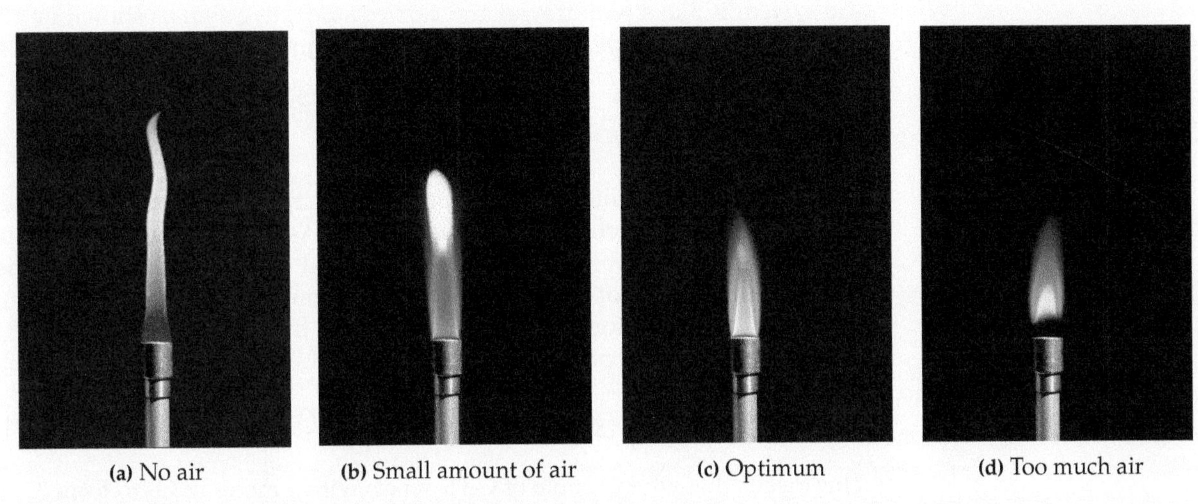

(a) No air (b) Small amount of air (c) Optimum (d) Too much air

▲ Bunsen burner at various stages of air intake adjustment.

emitted or absorbed by a chemical reaction, under conditions of constant pressure (which are common for most everyday reactions), can be quantified with a function called **enthalpy**. Specifically, we define a quantity called the **enthalpy of reaction** (ΔH_{rxn}) as the amount of thermal energy (or heat) that flows when a reaction occurs at constant pressure.

SIGN OF ΔH_{rxn}

The *sign* of ΔH_{rxn} (positive or negative) depends on the *direction* in which thermal energy flows when the reaction occurs. If thermal energy flows out of the reaction and into the surroundings (as in an exothermic reaction), then ΔH_{rxn} is negative. For example, we can specify the enthalpy of reaction for the combustion of CH_4, the main component in natural gas, as:

$$CH_4(g) + 2\,O_2(g) \longrightarrow CO_2(g) + 2\,H_2O(g) \qquad \Delta H_{rxn} = -802.3\text{ kJ}$$

This reaction is exothermic and therefore has a negative enthalpy of reaction. The magnitude of ΔH_{rxn} tells us that 802.3 kJ of heat are emitted when 1 mol of CH_4 reacts with 2 mol of O_2.

If, by contrast, thermal energy flows into the reaction and out of the surroundings (as in an endothermic reaction), then ΔH_{rxn} is positive. For example, we specify the enthalpy of reaction for the reaction between nitrogen and oxygen gas to form nitrogen monoxide as:

$$N_2(g) + O_2(g) \longrightarrow 2\,NO(g) \qquad \Delta H_{rxn} = +182.6\text{ kJ}$$

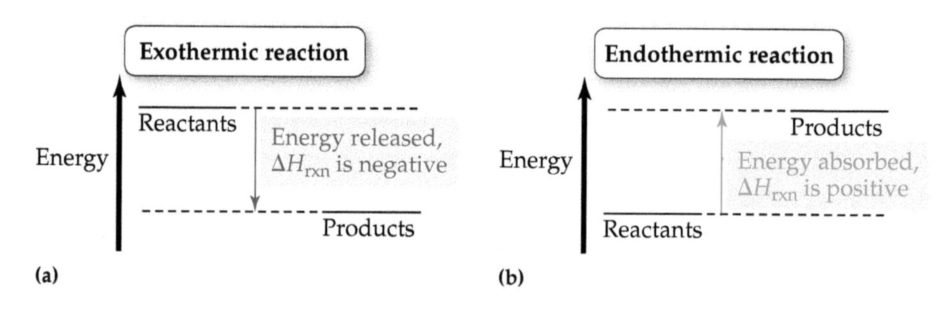

▶ **FIGURE 8.3 Exothermic and endothermic reactions** **(a)** In an exothermic reaction, energy is released into the surroundings. **(b)** In an endothermic reaction, energy is absorbed from the surroundings.

This reaction is endothermic and therefore has a positive enthalpy of reaction. When 1 mol of N_2 reacts with 1 mol of O_2, 182.6 kJ of heat are absorbed from the surroundings.

You can think of the energy of a chemical system in the same way that you think about the balance in your checking account. Energy flowing *out* of the chemical system is like a withdrawal and carries a negative sign as shown in ▲ Figure 8.3a. Energy flowing *into* the system is like a deposit and carries a positive sign as shown in Figure 8.3b.

STOICHIOMETRY OF ΔH_{rxn}

The amount of heat emitted or absorbed when a chemical reaction occurs depends on the *amounts* of reactants that actually react. As we have just seen, we usually specify ΔH_{rxn} in combination with the balanced chemical equation for the reaction. The magnitude of ΔH_{rxn} is for the stoichiometric amounts of reactants and products for the reaction *as written*. For example, the balanced equation and ΔH_{rxn} for the combustion of propane (the fuel used in LP gas) is:

$$C_3H_8(g) + 5\,O_2(g) \longrightarrow 3\,CO_2(g) + 4\,H_2O(g) \qquad \Delta H_{rxn} = -2044 \text{ kJ}$$

This means that when 1 mole of C_3H_8 reacts with 5 moles of O_2 to form 3 moles of CO_2 and 4 moles of H_2O, 2044 kJ of heat are emitted. We can write these relationships in the same way that we express stoichiometric relationships: as ratios between two quantities. For example, for the reactants, we write:

$$1 \text{ mol } C_3H_8 : -2044 \text{ kJ} \quad \text{or} \quad 5 \text{ mol } O_2 : -2044 \text{ kJ}$$

The ratios mean that 2044 kJ of thermal energy are evolved when 1 mole of C_3H_8 and 5 moles of O_2 completely react. These ratios can then be used to construct conversion factors between amounts of reactants or products and the quantity of heat emitted (for exothermic reactions) or absorbed (for endothermic reactions). To find out how much heat is emitted upon the combustion of a certain mass in grams of C_3H_8, we can use the following solution map:

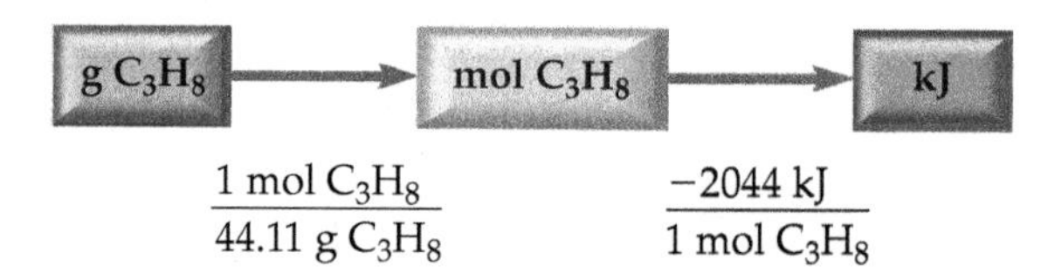

$$\frac{1 \text{ mol } C_3H_8}{44.11 \text{ g } C_3H_8} \qquad \frac{-2044 \text{ kJ}}{1 \text{ mol } C_3H_8}$$

We use the molar mass to convert between grams and moles, and the stoichiometric relationship between moles of C_3H_8 and kJ to convert between moles and kJ, as shown in the following example.

EXAMPLE 8.7 Stoichiometry Involving ΔH

An LP gas tank in a home barbecue contains 11.8×10^3 g of propane (C_3H_8). Calculate the heat (in kJ) associated with the complete combustion of all of the propane in the tank.

$$C_3H_8(g) + 5\,O_2(g) \longrightarrow 3\,CO_2(g) + 4\,H_2O(g) \qquad \Delta H_{rxn} = -2044 \text{ kJ}$$

SORT You are given the mass of propane and asked to find the heat evolved (in kJ) in its combustion.	**GIVEN:** 11.8×10^3 g C_3H_8 **FIND:** kJ
STRATEGIZE Start with the given mass of propane and then use its molar mass to find the number of moles. Next, use the stoichiometric relationship between moles of propane and kilojoules of heat to find the heat evolved.	**SOLUTION MAP** 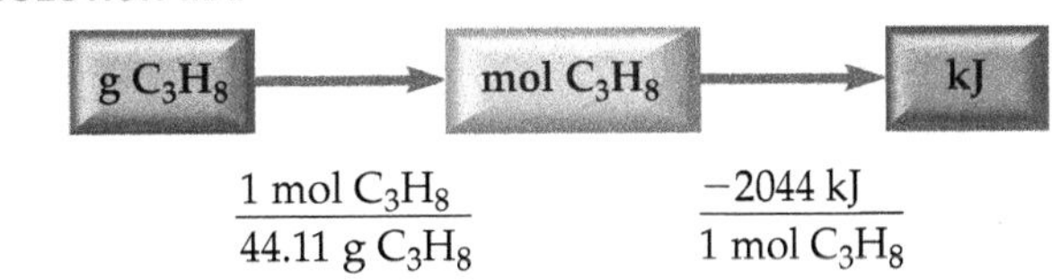 $\frac{1 \text{ mol } C_3H_8}{44.11 \text{ g } C_3H_8}$ $\frac{-2044 \text{ kJ}}{1 \text{ mol } C_3H_8}$ **RELATIONSHIPS USED** 1 mol C_3H_8: −2044 kJ (from balanced equation) Molar mass C_3H_8 = 44.11 g/mol
SOLVE Follow the solution map to solve the problem. Begin with 11.8×10^3 g C_3H_8 and multiply by the appropriate conversion factors to arrive at kJ.	**SOLUTION** $11.8 \times 10^3 \text{ g } C_3H_8 \times \frac{1 \text{ mol } C_3H_8}{44.11 \text{ g } C_3H_8} \times \frac{-2044 \text{ kJ}}{1 \text{ mol } C_3H_8} = -5.47 \times 10^5 \text{ kJ}$
CHECK Check your answer. Are the units correct? Does the answer make physical sense?	The units, kJ, are correct. The answer is negative, as it should be when heat is evolved by a reaction.

▶SKILLBUILDER 8.7 | Stoichiometry Involving ΔH

Ammonia reacts with oxygen according to the equation:

$$4\,NH_3(g) + 5\,O_2(g) \longrightarrow 4\,NO(g) + 6\,H_2O \qquad \Delta H_{rxn} = -906 \text{ kJ}$$

Calculate the heat (in kJ) associated with the complete reaction of 155 g of NH_3.

▶SKILLBUILDER PLUS

What mass of butane in grams is necessary to produce 1.5×10^3 kJ of heat? What mass of CO_2 is produced?

$$C_4H_{10}(g) + \tfrac{13}{2}\,O_2(g) \longrightarrow 4\,CO_2(g) + 5\,H_2O(g) \qquad \Delta H_{rxn} = -2658 \text{ kJ}$$

▶FOR MORE PRACTICE Example 8.11; Problems 71, 72, 73, 74, 75, 76.

CONCEPTUAL CONNECTION 8.4

Stoichiometry Involving ΔH

Consider the generic reaction:

$$2A + 3B \longrightarrow 2C \qquad \Delta H_{rxn} = -100 \text{ kJ}$$

If a reaction mixture initially contains 5 mol of A and 6 mol of B, how much heat (in kJ) will be evolved once the reaction has occurred to the greatest extent possible?

(a) 100 kJ

(b) 150 kJ

(c) 200 kJ

(d) 300 kJ

CHAPTER IN REVIEW

CHEMICAL PRINCIPLES

Stoichiometry: A balanced chemical equation gives quantitative relationships between the amounts of reactants and products. For example, the reaction $2\,H_2 + O_2 \longrightarrow 2\,H_2O$ says that 2 mol of H_2 reacts with 1 mol of O_2 to form 2 mol of H_2O. These relationships can be used to calculate quantities such as the amount of product possible with a certain amount of reactant, or the amount of one reactant required to completely react with a certain amount of another reactant. The quantitative relationship between reactants and products in a chemical reaction is called reaction stoichiometry.

Limiting Reactant, Theoretical Yield, and Percent Yield: The limiting reactant in a chemical reaction is the reactant that limits the amount of product that can be made. The theoretical yield in a chemical reaction is the amount of product that can be made based on the amount of the limiting reactant. The actual yield in a chemical reaction is the amount of product actually produced. The percent yield in a chemical reaction is the actual yield divided by theoretical yield times 100%.

Enthalpy of Reaction: The amount of heat released or absorbed by a chemical reaction under conditions of constant pressure, is the enthalpy of reaction (ΔH_{rxn}).

RELEVANCE

Stoichiometry: Reaction stoichiometry is important because we often want to know the numerical relationship between the reactants and products in a chemical reaction. For example, we might want to know how much carbon dioxide, a greenhouse gas, is formed when a certain amount of a particular fossil fuel burns.

Limiting Reactant, Theoretical Yield, and Percent Yield: Calculations of limiting reactant, theoretical yield, and percent yield are central to chemistry because they allow for quantitative understanding of chemical reactions. Just as you need to know relationships between ingredients to follow a recipe, so you must know relationships between reactants and products to carry out a chemical reaction. The percent yield in a chemical reaction is often used as a measure of the success of the reaction. Imagine following a recipe and making only 1% of the final product—your cooking would be a failure. Similarly, low percent yields in chemical reactions are usually considered poor, and high percent yields are considered good.

Enthalpy of Reaction: The enthalpy of reaction describes the relationship between the amount of reactant that undergoes reaction and the amount of thermal energy produced. This is important, for example, in determining quantities such as the amount of fuel needed to produce a given amount of energy.

CHEMICAL SKILLS

Mole-to-Mole Conversions (Section 8.3)

EXAMPLES

EXAMPLE 8.8 Mole-to-Mole Conversions

How many moles of sodium oxide can be synthesized from 4.8 mol of sodium? Assume that more than enough oxygen is present. The balanced equation is:

$$4\,Na(s) + O_2(g) \longrightarrow 2\,Na_2O(s)$$

SORT

You are given the number of moles of sodium and asked to find the number of moles of sodium oxide formed by the reaction.

GIVEN: 4.8 mol Na

FIND: mol Na_2O

STRATEGIZE

Draw a solution map beginning with the number of moles of the given substance and then use the conversion factor from the balanced chemical equation to determine the number of moles of the substance you are trying to find.

SOLUTION MAP

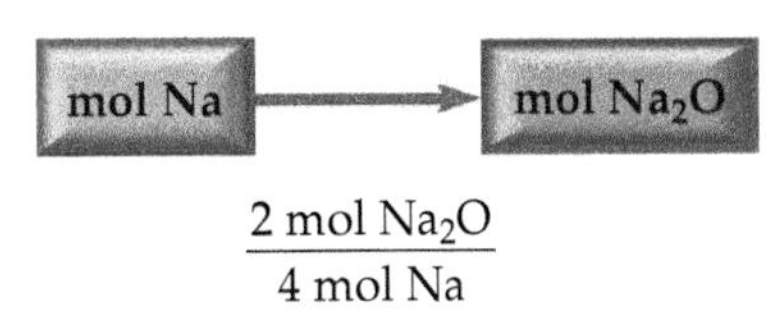

$$\frac{2 \text{ mol Na}_2\text{O}}{4 \text{ mol Na}}$$

RELATIONSHIPS USED

4 mol Na : 2 mol Na_2O

SOLVE

Follow the solution map to get to the number of moles of the substance you are trying to find.

SOLUTION

$$4.8 \text{ mol Na} \times \frac{2 \text{ mol Na}_2\text{O}}{4 \text{ mol Na}} = 2.4 \text{ mol Na}_2\text{O}$$

CHECK

Are the units correct? Does the answer make physical sense?

The units of the answer, mol Na_2O, are correct. The magnitude of the answer seems reasonable because it is of the same order of magnitude as the given number of moles of Na.

Mass-to-Mass Conversions (Section 8.4)

EXAMPLE 8.9 Mass-to-Mass Conversions

How many grams of sodium oxide can be synthesized from 17.4 g of sodium? Assume that more than enough oxygen is present. The balanced equation is:

$$4\,\text{Na}(s) + \text{O}_2(g) \longrightarrow 2\,\text{Na}_2\text{O}(s)$$

SORT

You are given the mass of sodium and asked to find the mass of sodium oxide that forms upon reaction.

GIVEN: 17.4 g Na

FIND: g Na_2O

STRATEGIZE

Draw the solution map by beginning with the mass of the given substance. Convert to moles using the molar mass and then convert to moles of the substance you are trying to find, using the conversion factor obtained from the balanced chemical equation. Finally, convert to mass of the substance you are trying to find, using its molar mass.

SOLUTION MAP

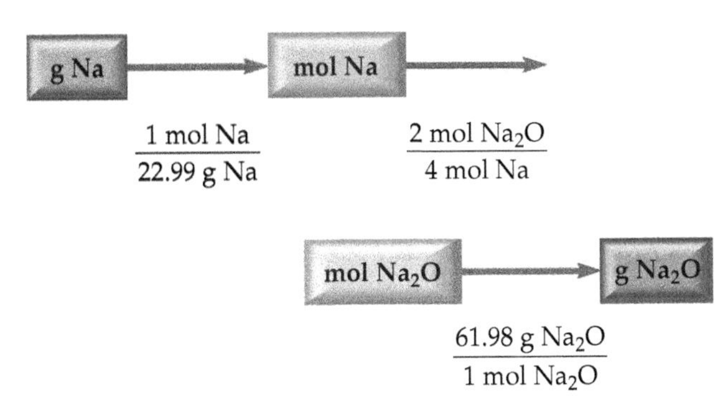

$$\frac{1 \text{ mol Na}}{22.99 \text{ g Na}} \qquad \frac{2 \text{ mol Na}_2\text{O}}{4 \text{ mol Na}} \qquad \frac{61.98 \text{ g Na}_2\text{O}}{1 \text{ mol Na}_2\text{O}}$$

RELATIONSHIPS USED

4 mol Na : 2 mol Na_2O (from balanced equation)

Molar mass Na = 22.99 g/mol

Molar mass Na_2O = 61.98 g/mol

SOLVE

Follow the solution map and calculate the answer by beginning with the mass of the given substance and multiplying by the appropriate conversion factors to determine the mass of the substance you are trying to find.

SOLUTION

$$17.4 \text{ g Na} \times \frac{1 \text{ mol Na}}{22.99 \text{ g Na}} \times \frac{2 \text{ mol Na}_2\text{O}}{4 \text{ mol Na}} \times \frac{61.98 \text{ g Na}_2\text{O}}{1 \text{ mol Na}_2\text{O}} = 23.5 \text{ g Na}_2\text{O}$$

CHECK

Are the units correct? Does the answer make physical sense?

The units of the answer, g Na_2O, are correct. The magnitude of the answer seems reasonable because it is of the same order of magnitude as the given mass of Na.

Limiting Reactant, Theoretical Yield, and Percent Yield (Sections 8.5, 8.6)

EXAMPLE 8.10 Limiting Reactant, Theoretical Yield, and Percent Yield

10.4 g of As reacts with 11.8 g of S to produce 14.2 g of As_2S_3. Find the limiting reactant, theoretical yield, and percent yield for this reaction. The balanced chemical equation is:

$$2\,As(s) + 3\,S(l) \longrightarrow As_2S_3(s)$$

SORT

You are given the masses of iron and sulfur as well as the mass of iron(III) sulfide formed by the reaction. You are asked to find the limiting reactant, theoretical yield, and percent yield.

GIVEN: 10.4 g As
11.8 g S
14.2 g As_2S_3

FIND: limiting reactant
theoretical yield
percent yield

STRATEGIZE

The solution map for limiting-reactant problems shows how to convert from the mass of each of the reactants to mass of the product for each reactant. These are mass-to-mass conversions with the basic outline of

$$\text{Mass} \longrightarrow \text{Moles} \longrightarrow \text{Moles} \longrightarrow \text{Mass}$$

The reactant that forms the least amount of product is the limiting reactant.

The conversion factors you need are the stoichiometric relationships between each of the reactants and the product. You also need the molar masses of each reactant and product.

SOLUTION MAP

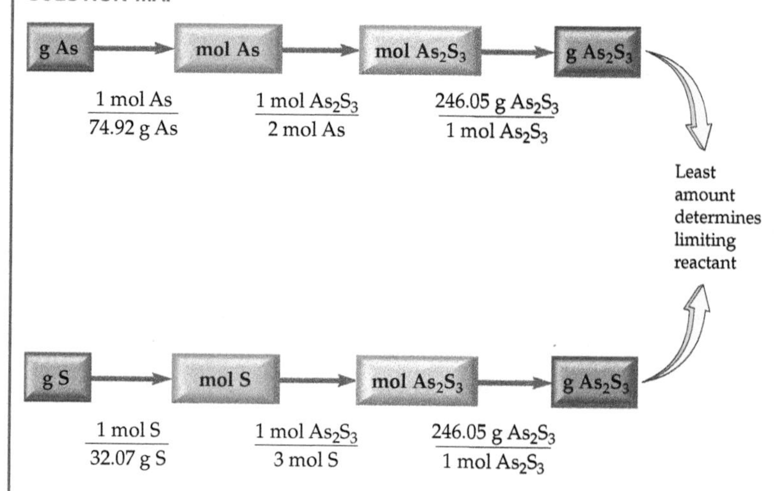

RELATIONSHIPS USED

$2\text{ mol As} : 1\text{ mol } As_2S_3$

$3\text{ mol S} : 1\text{ mol } As_2S_3$

Molar mass As = 74.92 g/mol

Molar mass S = 32.07 g/mol

Molar mass As_2S_3 = 246.05 g/mol

SOLVE

To calculate the amount of product formed by each reactant, begin with the given amount of each reactant and multiply by the appropriate conversion factors, as shown in the solution map, to arrive at the mass of product for each reactant. The reactant that forms the least amount of product is the limiting reactant.

SOLUTION

$$10.4\text{ g As} \times \frac{1\text{ mol As}}{74.92\text{ g As}} \times \frac{1\text{ mol }As_2S_3}{2\text{ mol As}} \times \frac{246.05\text{ g }As_2S_3}{1\text{ mol }As_2S_3} = 17.1\text{ g }As_2S_3$$

Limiting reactant (As); Least amount of product (17.1 g As_2S_3)

$$11.8\text{ g S} \times \frac{1\text{ mol S}}{32.07\text{ g S}} \times \frac{1\text{ mol }As_2S_3}{3\text{ mol S}} \times \frac{246.05\text{ g }As_2S_3}{1\text{ mol }As_2S_3} = 30.2\text{ g }As_2S_3$$

The limiting reactant is As.

The theoretical yield is the amount of product formed by the limiting reactant.
The percent yield is the actual yield divided by the theoretical yield times 100%.

The theoretical yield is 17.1 g of As_2S_3.

$$\text{Percent yield} = \frac{\text{Actual yield}}{\text{Theoretical yield}} \times 100\%$$

$$= \frac{14.2 \text{ g}}{17.1 \text{ g}} \times 100\% = 83.0\%$$

The percent yield is 83.0%.

CHECK
Check your answer. Are the units correct? Does the answer make physical sense?

The theoretical yield has the right units (g As_2S_3). The magnitude of the theoretical yield seems reasonable because it is of the same order of magnitude as the given masses of As and S. The theoretical yield is reasonable because it is less than 100%. Any calculated theoretical yield above 100% would be suspect.

Stoichiometry Involving ΔH (Section 8.7)

EXAMPLE 8.11 Stoichiometry Involving ΔH
Calculate the heat evolved (in kJ) upon complete combustion of 25.0 g of methane (CH_4).

$$CH_4(g) + 2\,O_2(g) \longrightarrow CO_2(g) + 2\,H_2O(g) \qquad \Delta H_{rxn} = -802 \text{ kJ}$$

SORT
You are given the mass of methane and asked to find the quantity of heat in kJ emitted upon combustion.

GIVEN: 25 g CH_4
FIND: kJ

Draw the solution map by beginning with the mass of the given substance. Convert to moles using molar mass and then to kJ using ΔH.

SOLUTION MAP

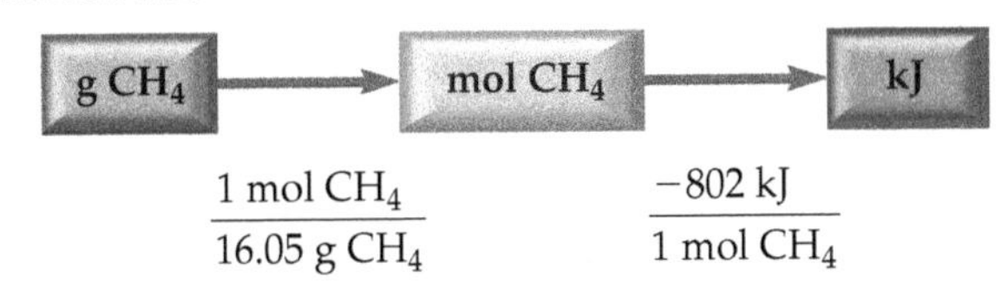

$$\frac{1 \text{ mol } CH_4}{16.05 \text{ g } CH_4} \qquad \frac{-802 \text{ kJ}}{1 \text{ mol } CH_4}$$

RELATIONSHIPS USED
1 mol CH_4: −802 kJ (from balanced equation)
Molar mass CH_4 = 16.05 g/mol

SOLVE
Follow the solution map to solve the problem. Begin with the mass of the given substance and multiply by the appropriate conversion factors to arrive at kJ. A negative answer means that heat is evolved into the surroundings. A positive answer means that heat is absorbed from the surroundings.

SOLUTION

$$25.0 \text{ g } CH_4 \times \frac{1 \text{ mol } CH_4}{16.05 \text{ g } CH_4} \times \frac{-802 \text{ kJ}}{1 \text{ mol } CH_4} = -1.25 \times 10^3 \text{ kJ}$$

CHECK
Are the units correct? Does the answer make physical sense?

The units, kJ, are correct. The answer is negative, as it should be since heat is evolved by the reaction.

KEY TERMS

actual yield **[8.5]**
enthalpy **[8.7]**
enthalpy of reaction (ΔH_{rxn}) **[8.7]**
global warming **[8.1]**
greenhouse gases **[8.1]**
limiting reactant **[8.5]**
percent yield **[8.5]**
stoichiometry **[8.1]**
theoretical yield **[8.5]**

EXERCISES

QUESTIONS

1. Why is reaction stoichiometry important? Give some examples.
2. Nitrogen and hydrogen can react to form ammonia.

   $N_2(g) + 3\,H_2(g) \longrightarrow 2\,NH_3(g)$

   (a) Write ratios showing the relationships between moles of each of the reactants and products in the reaction.
   (b) How many molecules of H_2 are required to completely react with two molecules of N_2?
   (c) How many moles of H_2 are required to completely react with 2 mol of N_2?
3. Write the conversion factor that you would use to convert from moles of Cl_2 to moles of NaCl in the reaction:

   $$2\,Na(s) + Cl_2(g) \longrightarrow 2\,NaCl$$

4. What is wrong with this statement in reference to the reaction in the previous problem? "Two grams of Na react with 1 g of Cl_2 to form 2 g of NaCl." Correct the statement to make it true.
5. What is the general form of the solution map for problems in which you are given the mass of a reactant in a chemical reaction and asked to find the mass of the product that can be made from the given amount of reactant?
6. Consider the recipe for making tomato and garlic pasta.

   $$2 \text{ cups noodles} + 12 \text{ tomatoes} + 3 \text{ cloves garlic} \longrightarrow 4 \text{ servings pasta}$$

   If you have 7 cups of noodles, 27 tomatoes, and 9 cloves of garlic, how many servings of pasta can you make? Which ingredient limits the amount of pasta that it is possible to make?
7. In a chemical reaction, what is the limiting reactant?
8. In a chemical reaction, what is the theoretical yield?
9. In a chemical reaction, what are the actual yield and percent yield?
10. If you are given a chemical equation and specific amounts for each reactant in grams, how would you determine how much product can possibly be made?
11. Consider the generic chemical reaction:

    $A + 2\,B \longrightarrow C + D$

    Suppose you have 12 g of A and 24 g of B. Which statement is true?
    (a) A will definitely be the limiting reactant.
    (b) B will definitely be the limiting reactant.
    (c) A will be the limiting reactant if its molar mass is less than B.
    (d) A will be the limiting reactant if its molar mass is greater than B.
12. Consider the generic chemical equation:

    $$A + B \longrightarrow C$$

    Suppose 25 g of A were allowed to react with 8 g of B. Analysis of the final mixture showed that A was completely used up and 4 g of B remained. What was the limiting reactant?
13. What is the enthalpy of reaction (ΔH_{rxn}). Why is this quantity important?
14. Explain the relationship between the sign of ΔH_{rxn} and whether a reaction is exothermic or endothermic.

PROBLEMS

MOLE-TO-MOLE CONVERSIONS

15. Consider the generic chemical reaction:

    $$A + 2\,B \longrightarrow C$$

    How many moles of C are formed upon complete reaction of:
    (a) 2 mol of A
    (b) 2 mol of B
    (c) 3 mol of A
    (d) 3 mol of B
16. Consider the generic chemical reaction:

    $$2\,A + 3\,B \longrightarrow 3\,C$$

    How many moles of B are required to completely react with:
    (a) 6 mol of A
    (b) 2 mol of A
    (c) 7 mol of A
    (d) 11 mol of A

17. For the reaction shown, calculate how many moles of NO_2 form when each amount of reactant completely reacts.

$$2\,N_2O_5(g) \longrightarrow 4\,NO_2(g) + O_2(g)$$

(a) 1.3 mol N_2O_5
(b) 5.8 mol N_2O_5
(c) 4.45×10^3 mol N_2O_5
(d) 1.006×10^{-3} mol N_2O_5

18. For the reaction shown, calculate how many moles of NH_3 form when each amount of reactant completely reacts.

$$3\,N_2H_4(l) \longrightarrow 4\,NH_3(g) + N_2(g)$$

(a) 5.3 mol N_2H_4
(b) 2.28 mol N_2H_4
(c) 5.8×10^{-2} mol N_2H_4
(d) 9.76×10^7 mol N_2H_4

19. Dihydrogen monosulfide reacts with sulfur dioxide according to the balanced equation:

$$2\,H_2S(g) + SO_2(g) \longrightarrow 3\,S(s) + 2\,H_2O(g)$$

= SO_2

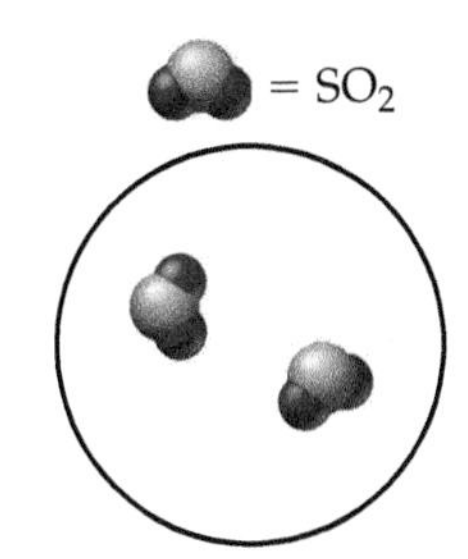

If the above figure represents the amount of SO_2 available to react, which figure best represents the amount of H_2S required to completely react with all of the SO_2?

= H_2S

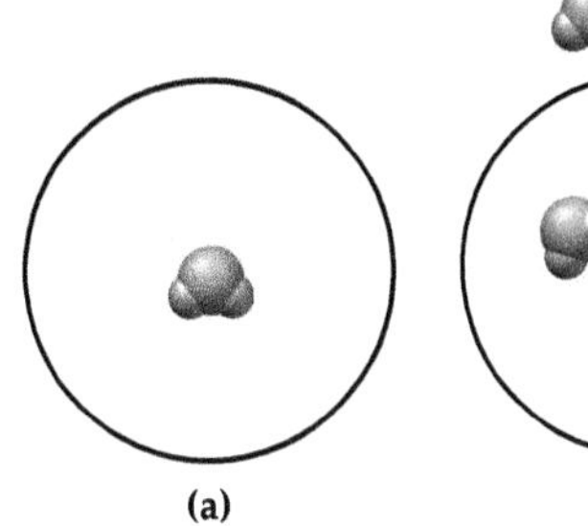

(a)

(b)

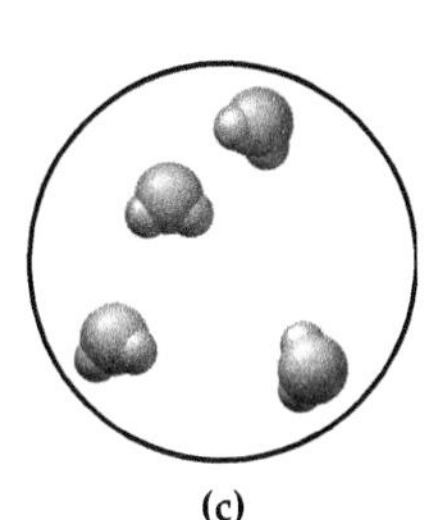

(c)

20. Chlorine gas reacts with fluorine gas according to the balanced equation:

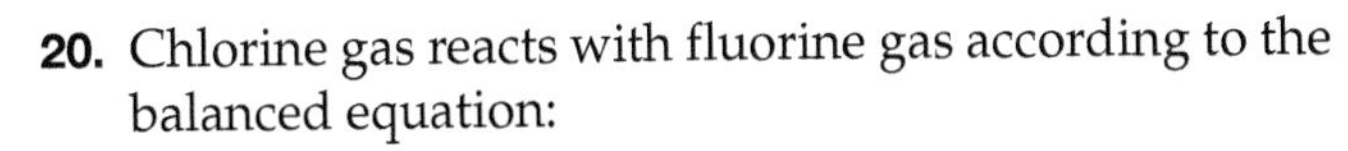

$$Cl_2(g) + 3\,F_2(g) \longrightarrow 2\,ClF_3(g)$$

= F_2

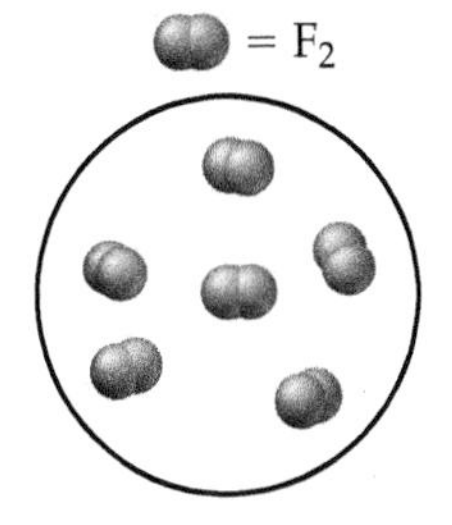

If the above figure represents the amount of fluorine available to react, and assuming that there is more than enough chlorine, which figure best represents the amount of chlorine trifluoride that would form upon complete reaction of all of the fluorine?

= ClF_3

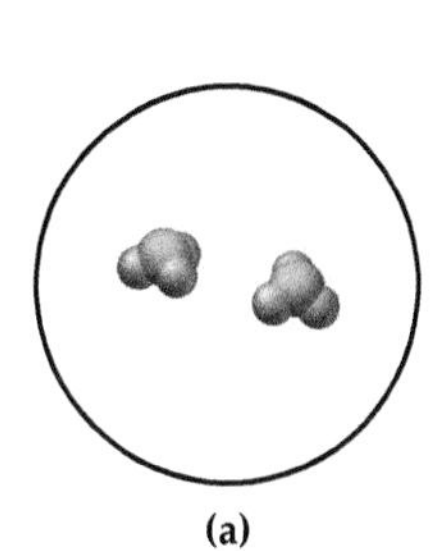

(a)

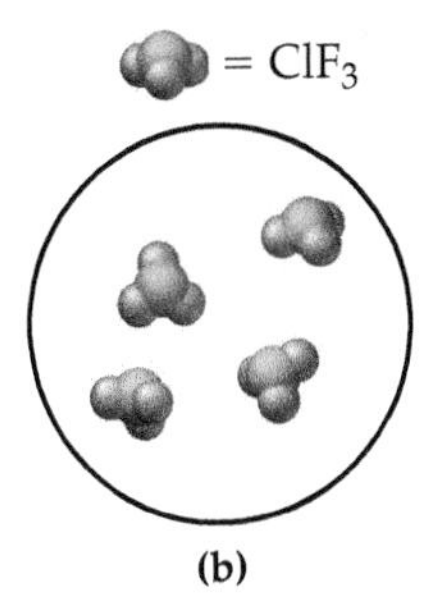

(b)

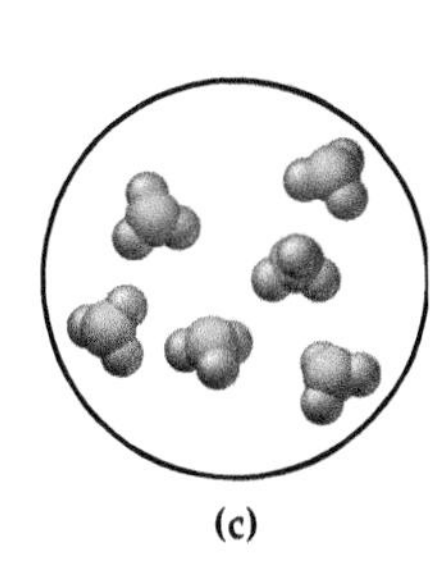

(c)

21. For each reaction, calculate how many moles of product form when 1.75 mol of the reactant in color completely reacts. Assume there is more than enough of the other reactant.

(a) $H_2(g) + Cl_2(g) \longrightarrow 2\,HCl(g)$
(b) $2\,H_2(g) + O_2(g) \longrightarrow 2\,H_2O(l)$
(c) $2\,Na(s) + O_2(g) \longrightarrow Na_2O_2(s)$
(d) $2\,S(s) + 3\,O_2(g) \longrightarrow 2\,SO_3(g)$

22. For each reaction, calculate how many moles of the product form when 0.112 mol of the reactant in color completely reacts. Assume there is more than enough of the other reactant.

(a) $2\,Ca(s) + O_2(g) \longrightarrow 2\,CaO(s)$
(b) $4\,Fe(s) + 3\,O_2(g) \longrightarrow 2\,Fe_2O_3(s)$
(c) $4\,K(s) + O_2(g) \longrightarrow 2\,K_2O(s)$
(d) $4\,Al(s) + 3\,O_2(g) \longrightarrow 2\,Al_2O_3(s)$

23. For the reaction shown, calculate how many moles of each product form when the given amount of each reactant completely reacts. Assume there is more than enough of the other reactant.

$$2\ PbS(s) + 3\ O_2(g) \longrightarrow 2\ PbO(s) + 2\ SO_2(g)$$

(a) 2.4 mol PbS

(b) 2.4 mol O_2

(c) 5.3 mol PbS

(d) 5.3 mol O_2

24. For the reaction shown, calculate how many moles of each product form when the given amount of each reactant completely reacts. Assume there is more than enough of the other reactant.

$$C_3H_8(g) + 5\ O_2(g) \longrightarrow 3\ CO_2(g) + 4\ H_2O(g)$$

(a) 4.6 mol C_3H_8

(b) 4.6 mol O_2

(c) 0.0558 mol C_3H_8

(d) 0.0558 mol O_2

25. Consider the balanced equation:

$$2\ N_2H_4(g) + N_2O_4(g) \longrightarrow 3\ N_2(g) + 4\ H_2O(g)$$

Complete the table showing the appropriate number of moles of reactants and products. If the number of moles of a reactant is provided, fill in the required amount of the other reactant, as well as the moles of each product formed. If the number of moles of a product is provided, fill in the required amount of each reactant to make that amount of product, as well as the amount of the other product that is made.

mol N_2H_4	mol N_2O_4	mol N_2	mol H_2O
____	2	____	____
6	____	____	____
____	____	____	8
____	5.5	____	____
3	____	____	____
____	____	12.4	____

26. Consider the balanced equation:

$$SiO_2(s) + 3\ C(s) \longrightarrow SiC(s) + 2\ CO(g)$$

Complete the table showing the appropriate number of moles of reactants and products. If the number of moles of a reactant is provided, fill in the required amount of the other reactant, as well as the moles of each product formed. If the number of moles of a product is provided, fill in the required amount of each reactant to make that amount of product, as well as the amount of the other product that is made.

mol SiO_2	mol C	mol SiC	mol CO
____	6	____	____
3	____	____	____
____	____	____	10
____	9.5	____	____
3.2	____	____	____

27. Consider the unbalanced equation for the combustion of butane:

$$C_4H_{10}(g) + O_2(g) \longrightarrow CO_2(g) + H_2O(g)$$

Balance the equation and determine how many moles of O_2 are required to react completely with 4.9 mol of C_4H_{10}.

28. Consider the unbalanced equation for the neutralization of acetic acid:

$$HC_2H_3O_2(aq) + Ca(OH)_2(aq) \longrightarrow H_2O(l) + Ca(C_2H_3O_2)_2(aq)$$

Balance the equation and determine how many moles of $Ca(OH)_2$ are required to completely neutralize 1.07 mol of $HC_2H_3O_2$.

29. Consider the unbalanced equation for the reaction of solid lead with silver nitrate:

$$Pb(s) + AgNO_3(aq) \longrightarrow Pb(NO_3)_2(aq) + Ag(s)$$

(a) Balance the equation.

(b) How many moles of silver nitrate are required to completely react with 9.3 mol of lead?

(c) How many moles of Ag are formed by the complete reaction of 28.4 mol of Pb?

30. Consider the unbalanced equation for the reaction of aluminum with sulfuric acid:

$$Al(s) + H_2SO_4(aq) \longrightarrow Al_2(SO_4)_3(aq) + H_2(g)$$

(a) Balance the equation.

(b) How many moles of H_2SO_4 are required to completely react with 8.3 mol of Al?

(c) How many moles of H_2 are formed by the complete reaction of 0.341 mol of Al?

MASS-TO-MASS CONVERSIONS

31. For the reaction shown, calculate how many grams of oxygen form when each quantity of reactant completely reacts.

$$2\ HgO(s) \longrightarrow 2\ Hg(l) + O_2(g)$$

(a) 2.13 g HgO
(b) 6.77 g HgO
(c) 1.55 kg HgO
(d) 3.87 mg HgO

32. For the reaction shown, calculate how many grams of oxygen form when each quantity of reactant completely reacts.

$$2\ KClO_3(s) \longrightarrow 2\ KCl(s) + 3\ O_2(g)$$

(a) 2.72 g $KClO_3$
(b) 0.361g $KClO_3$
(c) 83.6 kg $KClO_3$
(d) 22.4 mg $KClO_3$

33. For each of the reactions shown, calculate how many grams of the product form when 2.4 g of the reactant in color completely reacts. Assume there is more than enough of the other reactant.

(a) $2\ Na(s) + Cl_2(g) \longrightarrow 2\ NaCl(s)$
(b) $CaO(s) + CO_2(g) \longrightarrow CaCO_3(s)$
(c) $2\ Mg(s) + O_2(g) \longrightarrow 2\ MgO(s)$
(d) $Na_2O(s) + H_2O(l) \longrightarrow 2\ NaOH(aq)$

34. For each of the reactions shown, calculate how many grams of the product form when 17.8 g of the reactant in color completely reacts. Assume there is more than enough of the other reactant.

(a) $Ca(s) + Cl_2(g) \longrightarrow CaCl_2(s)$
(b) $2\ K(s) + Br_2(l) \longrightarrow 2\ KBr(s)$
(c) $4Cr(s) + 3O_2(g) \longrightarrow 2Cr_2O_3(s)$
(d) $2\ Sr(s) + O_2(g) \longrightarrow 2\ SrO(s)$

35. For the reaction shown, calculate how many grams of each product form when the given amount of each reactant completely reacts to form products. Assume there is more than enough of the other reactant.

$$2\ Al(s) + Fe_2O_3(s) \longrightarrow Al_2O_3(s) + 2\ Fe(l)$$

(a) 4.7 g Al
(b) 4.7 g Fe_2O_3

36. For the reaction shown, calculate how many grams of each product form when the given amount of each reactant completely reacts to form products. Assume there is more than enough of the other reactant.

$$2\ HCl(aq) + Na_2CO_3(aq) \longrightarrow 2\ NaCl(aq) + H_2O(l) + CO_2(g)$$

(a) 10.8 g HCl
(b) 10.8 g Na_2CO_3

37. Consider the balanced equation for the combustion of methane, a component of natural gas:

$$CH_4(g) + 2\ O_2(g) \longrightarrow CO_2(g) + 2\ H_2O(g)$$

Complete the table with the appropriate masses of reactants and products. If the mass of a reactant is provided, fill in the mass of other reactants required to completely react with the given mass, as well as the mass of each product formed. If the mass of a product is provided, fill in the required masses of each reactant to make that amount of product, as well as the mass of the other product that is formed.

Mass CH_4	Mass O_2	Mass CO_2	Mass H_2O
____	2.57 g	____	____
22.32 g	____	____	____
____	____	____	11.32 g
____	____	2.94 g	____
3.18 kg	____	____	____
____	____	2.35×10^3 kg	____

38. Consider the balanced equation for the combustion of butane, a fuel often used in lighters:

$$2\ C_4H_{10}(g) + 13\ O_2(g) \longrightarrow 8\ CO_2(g) + 10\ H_2O(g)$$

Complete the table showing the appropriate masses of reactants and products. If the mass of a reactant is provided, fill in the mass of other reactants required to completely react with the given mass, as well as the mass of each product formed. If the mass of a product is provided, fill in the required masses of each reactant to make that amount of product, as well as the mass of the other product that is formed.

Mass C_4H_{10}	Mass O_2	Mass CO_2	Mass H_2O
____	1.11 g	____	____
5.22 g	____	____	____
____	____	10.12 g	____
____	____	____	9.04 g
232 mg	____	____	____
____	____	118 mg	____

39. For each acid–base reaction, calculate how many grams of acid are necessary to completely react with and neutralize 2.5 g of the base.

(a) $HCl(aq) + NaOH(aq) \longrightarrow H_2O(l) + NaCl(aq)$

(b) $2\ HNO_3(aq) + Ca(OH)_2(aq) \longrightarrow 2\ H_2O(l) + Ca(NO_3)_2(aq)$

(c) $H_2SO_4(aq) + 2\ KOH(aq) \longrightarrow 2\ H_2O(l) + K_2SO_4(aq)$

40. For each precipitation reaction, calculate how many grams of the first reactant are necessary to completely react with 17.3 g of the second reactant.

(a) $2\ KI(aq) + Pb(NO_3)_2(aq) \longrightarrow PbI_2(s) + 2\ KNO_3(aq)$

(b) $Na_2CO_3(aq) + CuCl_2(aq) \longrightarrow CuCO_3(s) + 2\ NaCl(aq)$

(c) $K_2SO_4(aq) + Sr(NO_3)_2(aq) \longrightarrow SrSO_4(s) + 2\ KNO_3(aq)$

41. Sulfuric acid can dissolve aluminum metal according to the reaction:

$$2\ Al(s) + 3\ H_2SO_4(aq) \longrightarrow Al_2(SO_4)_3(aq) + 3\ H_2(g)$$

Suppose you wanted to dissolve an aluminum block with a mass of 22.5 g. What minimum amount of H_2SO_4 in grams would you need? How many grams of H_2 gas would be produced by the complete reaction of the aluminum block?

42. Hydrochloric acid can dissolve solid iron according to the reaction:

$$Fe(s) + 2\ HCl(aq) \longrightarrow FeCl_2(aq) + H_2(g)$$

What minimum mass of HCl in grams would dissolve a 2.8-g iron bar on a padlock? How much H_2 would be produced by the complete reaction of the iron bar?

LIMITING REACTANT, THEORETICAL YIELD, AND PERCENT YIELD

43. Consider the generic chemical equation:

$$2\ A + 4\ B \longrightarrow 3\ C$$

What is the limiting reactant when each of the initial quantities of A and B is allowed to react?

(a) 2 mol A; 5 mol B

(b) 1.8 mol A; 4 mol B

(c) 3 mol A; 4 mol B

(d) 22 mol A; 40 mol B

44. Consider the generic chemical equation:

$$A + 3\ B \longrightarrow C$$

What is the limiting reactant when each of the initial quantities of A and B is allowed to react?

(a) 1 mol A; 4 mol B

(b) 2 mol A; 3 mol B

(c) 0.5 mol A; 1.6 mol B

(d) 24 mol A; 75 mol B

45. Determine the theoretical yield of C when each of the initial quantities of A and B is allowed to react in the generic reaction:

$$A + 2\ B \longrightarrow 3\ C$$

(a) 1 mol A; 1 mol B

(b) 2 mol A; 2 mol B

(c) 1 mol A; 3 mol B

(d) 32 mol A; 68 mol B

46. Determine the theoretical yield of C when each of the initial quantities of A and B is allowed to react in the generic reaction:

$$2\ A + 3\ B \longrightarrow 2\ C$$

(a) 2 mol A; 4 mol B

(b) 3 mol A; 3 mol B

(c) 5 mol A; 6 mol B

(d) 4 mol A; 5 mol B

47. For the reaction shown, find the limiting reactant for each of the initial quantities of reactants.

$$2\ K(s) + Cl_2(g) \longrightarrow 2\ KCl(s)$$

(a) 1 mol K; 1 mol Cl_2

(b) 1.8 mol K; 1 mol Cl_2

(c) 2.2 mol K; 1 mol Cl_2

(d) 14.6 mol K; 7.8 mol Cl_2

48. For the reaction shown, find the limiting reactant for each of the initial quantities of reactants.

$$4\ Cr(s) + 3\ O_2(g) \longrightarrow 2\ Cr_2O_3(s)$$

(a) 1 mol Cr; 1 mol O_2

(b) 4 mol Cr; 2.5 mol O_2

(c) 12 mol Cr; 10 mol O_2

(d) 14.8 mol Cr; 10.3 mol O_2

49. For the reaction shown, calculate the theoretical yield of product in moles for each of the initial quantities of reactants.

$$2\,Mn(s) + 3\,O_2(g) \longrightarrow 2\,MnO_3(s)$$

(a) 2 mol Mn; 2 mol O_2
(b) 4.8 mol Mn; 8.5 mol O_2
(c) 0.114 mol Mn; 0.161 mol O_2
(d) 27.5 mol Mn; 43.8 mol O_2

50. For the reaction shown, calculate the theoretical yield of the product in moles for each of the initial quantities of reactants.

$$Ti(s) + 2\,Cl_2(g) \longrightarrow TiCl_4(s)$$

(a) 2 mol Ti; 2 mol Cl_2
(b) 5 mol Ti; 9 mol Cl_2
(c) 0.483 mol Ti; 0.911 mol Cl_2
(d) 12.4 mol Ti; 15.8 mol Cl_2

51. Consider the generic reaction between reactants A and B:

$$3\,A + 4\,B \longrightarrow 2\,C$$

If a reaction vessel initially contains 9 mol A and 8 mol B, how many moles of A, B, and C will be in the reaction vessel once the reactants have reacted as much as possible? (Assume 100% actual yield.)

52. Consider the reaction between reactants S and O_2:

$$2\,S(s) + 3\,O_2(g) \longrightarrow 2\,SO_3(g)$$

If a reaction vessel initially contains 5 mol S and 9 mol O_2, how many moles of S, O_2, and SO_3 will be in the reaction vessel once the reactants have reacted as much as possible? (Assume 100% actual yield.)

53. Consider the reaction:

$$4\,HCl(g) + O_2(g) \longrightarrow 2\,H_2O(g) + 2\,Cl_2(g)$$

Each molecular diagram represents an initial mixture of the reactants. How many molecules of Cl_2 would be formed by complete reaction in each case? (Assume 100% actual yield.)

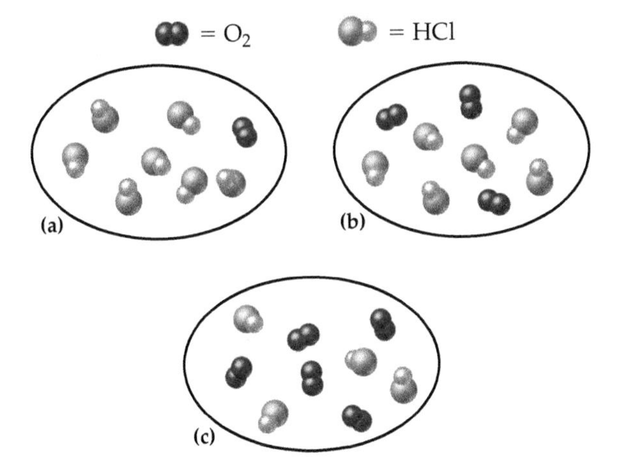

54. Consider the reaction:

$$2\,CH_3OH(g) + 3\,O_2(g) \longrightarrow 2\,CO_2(g) + 4\,H_2O(g)$$

Each molecular diagram represents an initial mixture of the reactants. How many CO_2 molecules would be formed by complete reaction in each case? (Assume 100% actual yield.)

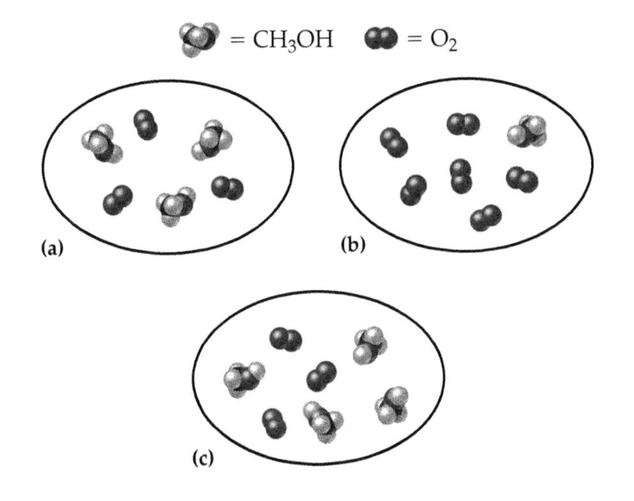

55. For the reaction shown, find the limiting reactant for each of the initial quantities of reactants.

$$2\,Li(s) + F_2(g) \longrightarrow 2\,LiF(s)$$

(a) 1.0 g Li; 1.0 g F_2
(b) 10.5 g Li; 37.2 g F_2
(c) 2.85×10^3 g Li; 6.79×10^3 g F_2

56. For the reaction shown, find the limiting reactant for each of the initial quantities of reactants.

$$4\,Al(s) + 3\,O_2(g) \longrightarrow 2\,Al_2O_3(s)$$

(a) 1.0 g Al; 1.0 g O_2
(b) 2.2 g Al; 1.8 g O_2
(c) 0.353 g Al; 0.482 g O_2

57. For the reaction shown, calculate the theoretical yield of the product in grams for each of initial quantities of reactants.

$$2\,Al(s) + 3\,Cl_2(g) \longrightarrow 2\,AlCl_3(s)$$

(a) 1.0 g Al; 1.0 g Cl_2

(b) 5.5 g Al; 19.8 g Cl_2

(c) 0.439 g Al; 2.29 g Cl_2

58. For the reaction shown, calculate the theoretical yield of the product in grams for each of the initial quantities of reactants.

$$Ti(s) + 2\,F_2(g) \longrightarrow TiF_4(s)$$

(a) 1.0 g Ti; 1.0 g F_2

(b) 4.8 g Ti; 3.2 g F_2

(c) 0.388 g Ti; 0.341 g F_2

59. If the theoretical yield of a reaction is 24.8 g and the actual yield is 18.5 g, what is the percent yield?

60. If the theoretical yield of a reaction is 0.118 g and the actual yield is 0.104 g, what is the percent yield?

61. Consider the reaction between calcium oxide and carbon dioxide:

$$CaO(s) + CO_2(g) \longrightarrow CaCO_3(s)$$

A chemist allows 14.4 g of CaO and 13.8 g of CO_2 to react. When the reaction is finished, the chemist collects 19.4 g of $CaCO_3$. Determine the limiting reactant, theoretical yield, and percent yield for the reaction.

62. Consider the reaction between sulfur trioxide and water:

$$SO_3(g) + H_2O(l) \longrightarrow H_2SO_4(aq)$$

A chemist allows 61.5 g of SO_3 and 11.2 g of H_2O to react. When the reaction is finished, the chemist collects 54.9 g of H_2SO_4. Determine the limiting reactant, theoretical yield, and percent yield for the reaction.

63. Consider the reaction between NiS_2 and O_2:

$$2\,NiS_2(s) + 5\,O_2(g) \longrightarrow 2\,NiO(s) + 4\,SO_2(g)$$

When 11.2 g of NiS_2 react with 5.43 g of O_2, 4.86 g of NiO are obtained. Determine the limiting reactant, theoretical yield of NiO, and percent yield for the reaction.

64. Consider the reaction between HCl and O_2:

$$4\,HCl(g) + O_2(g) \longrightarrow 2\,H_2O(l) + 2\,Cl_2(g)$$

When 63.1 g of HCl react with 17.2 g of O_2, 49.3 g of Cl_2 are collected. Determine the limiting reactant, theoretical yield of Cl_2, and percent yield for the reaction.

65. Lead ions can be precipitated from solution with NaCl according to the reaction:

$$Pb^{2+}(aq) + 2\,NaCl(aq) \longrightarrow PbCl_2(s) + 2\,Na^{+}(aq)$$

When 135.8 g of NaCl are added to a solution containing 195.7 g of Pb^{2+}, a $PbCl_2$ precipitate forms. The precipitate is filtered and dried and found to have a mass of 252.4 g. Determine the limiting reactant, theoretical yield of $PbCl_2$, and percent yield for the reaction.

66. Magnesium oxide can be produced by heating magnesium metal in the presence of oxygen. The balanced equation for the reaction is:

$$2\,Mg(s) + O_2(g) \longrightarrow 2\,MgO(s)$$

When 10.1 g of Mg react with 10.5 g of O_2, 11.9 g of MgO are collected. Determine the limiting reactant, theoretical yield, and percent yield for the reaction.

67. Consider the reaction between TiO_2 and C:

$$TiO_2(s) + 2\,C(s) \longrightarrow Ti(s) + 2\,CO(g)$$

A reaction vessel initially contains 10.0 g of each of the reactants. Calculate the masses of TiO_2, C, Ti, and CO that will be in the reaction vessel once the reactants have reacted as much as possible. (Assume 100% yield.)

68. Consider the reaction between N_2H_4 and N_2O_4:

$$2\,N_2H_4(g) + N_2O_4(g) \longrightarrow 3\,N_2(g) + 4\,H_2O(g)$$

A reaction vessel initially contains 27.5 g N_2H_4 and 74.9 g of N_2O_4, Calculate the masses of N_2H_4, N_2O_4, N_2, and H_2O that will be in the reaction vessel once the reactants have reacted as much as possible. (Assume 100% yield.)

ENTHALPY AND STOICHIOMETRY OF ΔH_{rxn}

69. Classify each process as exothermic or endothermic and indicate the sign of ΔH.
   (a) butane gas burning in a lighter
   (b) the reaction that occurs in the chemical cold packs used to ice athletic injuries
   (c) the burning of wax in a candle

70. Classify each process as exothermic or endothermic and indicate the sign of ΔH.
   (a) ice melting
   (b) a sparkler burning
   (c) acetone evaporating from skin

71. Consider the generic reaction:

$$A + 2\,B \longrightarrow C \qquad \Delta H_{rxn} = -55\text{ kJ}$$

Determine the amount of heat emitted when each amount of reactant completely reacts (assume that there is more than enough of the other reactant):
   (a) 1 mol A
   (b) 2 mol A
   (c) 1 mol B
   (d) 2 mol B

72. Consider the generic reaction:

$$2\,A + 3\,B \longrightarrow C \qquad \Delta H_{rxn} = -125\text{ kJ}$$

Determine the amount of heat emitted when each amount of reactant completely reacts (assume that there is more than enough of the other reactant):
   (a) 2 mol A
   (b) 3 mol A
   (c) 3 mol B
   (d) 5 mol B

73. Consider the equation for the combustion of acetone (C_3H_6O), the main ingredient in nail polish remover.

$$C_3H_6O(l) + 4\,O_2(g) \longrightarrow 3\,CO_2(g) + 3\,H_2O(g) \qquad \Delta H_{rxn} = -1790\text{ kJ}$$

If a bottle of nail polish remover contains 155 g of acetone, how much heat is released by its complete combustion?

74. The equation for the combustion of CH_4 (the main component of natural gas) is shown below. How much heat is produced by the complete combustion of 237 g of CH_4?

$$CH_4(g) + 2\,O_2(g) \longrightarrow CO_2(g) + 2\,H_2O(g) \qquad \Delta H^\circ_{rxn} = -802.3\text{ kJ}$$

75. Octane (C_8H_{18}) is a component of gasoline that burns according to the equation:

$$C_8H_{18}(l) + \tfrac{25}{2}\,O_2(g) \longrightarrow 8\,CO_2(g) + 9\,H_2O(g) \qquad \Delta H^\circ_{rxn} = -5074.1\text{ kJ}$$

What mass of octane (in g) is required to produce 1.55×10^3 kJ of heat?

76. The evaporation of water is endothermic:

$$H_2O(l) \longrightarrow H_2O(g) \qquad \Delta H^\circ_{rxn} = +44.01\text{ kJ}$$

What minimum mass of water (in g) has to evaporate to absorb 175 kJ of heat?

CUMULATIVE PROBLEMS

77. Consider the reaction:

$$2\,N_2(g) + 5\,O_2(g) + 2\,H_2O(g) \longrightarrow 4\,HNO_3(g)$$

If a reaction mixture contains 28 g of N_2, 150 g of O_2, and 36 g of H_2O, what is the limiting reactant? (Try to do this problem in your head without any written calculations.)

78. Consider the reaction:

$$2\,CO(g) + O_2(g) \longrightarrow 2\,CO_2(g)$$

If a reaction mixture contains 28 g of CO and 32 g of O_2, what is the limiting reactant? (Try to do this problem in your head without any written calculations.)

79. A solution contains an unknown mass of dissolved barium ions. When sodium sulfate is added to the solution, a white precipitate forms. The precipitate is filtered and dried and found to have a mass of 258 mg. What mass of barium was in the original solution? (Assume that all of the barium was precipitated out of solution by the reaction.)

80. A solution contains an unknown mass of dissolved silver ions. When potassium chloride is added to the solution, a white precipitate forms. The precipitate is filtered and dried and found to have a mass of 212 mg. What mass of silver was in the original solution? (Assume that all of the silver was precipitated out of solution by the reaction.)

81. Sodium bicarbonate is often used as an antacid to neutralize excess hydrochloric acid in an upset stomach. How much hydrochloric acid in grams can be neutralized by 3.5 g of sodium bicarbonate? (*Hint:* Begin by writing a balanced equation for the reaction between aqueous sodium bicarbonate and aqueous hydrochloric acid.)

82. Toilet bowl cleaners often contain hydrochloric acid to dissolve the calcium carbonate deposits that accumulate within a toilet bowl. How much calcium carbonate in grams can be dissolved by 5.8 g of HCl? (*Hint:* Begin by writing a balanced equation for the reaction between hydrochloric acid and calcium carbonate.)

83. The combustion of gasoline produces carbon dioxide and water. Assume gasoline to be pure octane (C_8H_{18}) and calculate how many kilograms of carbon dioxide are added to the atmosphere per 1.0 kg of octane burned. (*Hint:* Begin by writing a balanced equation for the combustion reaction.)

84. Many home barbecues are fueled with propane gas (C_3H_8.) How much carbon dioxide in kilograms is produced upon the complete combustion of 18.9 L of propane (approximate contents of one 5-gal tank)? Assume that the density of the liquid propane in the tank is 0.621 g/mL. (*Hint:* Begin by writing a balanced equation for the combustion reaction.)

85. A hard water solution contains 4.8 g of calcium chloride. How much sodium phosphate in grams should be added to the solution to completely precipitate all of the calcium?

86. Magnesium ions can be precipitated from seawater by the addition of sodium hydroxide. How much sodium hydroxide in grams must be added to a sample of seawater to completely precipitate the 88.4 mg of magnesium present?

87. Hydrogen gas can be prepared in the laboratory by a single-displacement reaction in which solid zinc reacts with hydrochloric acid. How much zinc in grams is required to make 14.5 g of hydrogen gas through this reaction?

88. Sodium peroxide (Na_2O_2) reacts with water to form sodium hydroxide and oxygen gas. Write a balanced equation for the reaction and determine how much oxygen in grams is formed by the complete reaction of 35.23 g of Na_2O_2.

89. Ammonium nitrate reacts explosively upon heating to form nitrogen gas, oxygen gas, and gaseous water. Write a balanced equation for this reaction and determine how much oxygen in grams is produced by the complete reaction of 1.00 kg of ammonium nitrate.

90. Pure oxygen gas can be prepared in the laboratory by the decomposition of solid potassium chlorate to form solid potassium chloride and oxygen gas. How much oxygen gas in grams can be prepared from 45.8 g of potassium chlorate?

91. Aspirin can be made in the laboratory by reacting acetic anhydride ($C_4H_6O_3$) with salicylic acid ($C_7H_6O_3$) to form aspirin ($C_9H_8O_4$) and acetic acid ($C_2H_4O_2$). The balanced equation is:

$$C_4H_6O_3 + C_7H_6O_3 \longrightarrow C_9H_8O_4 + C_2H_4O_2$$

In a laboratory synthesis, a student begins with 5.00 mL of acetic anhydride (density = 1.08 g/mL) and 2.08 g of salicylic acid. Once the reaction is complete, the student collects 2.01 g of aspirin. Determine the limiting reactant, theoretical yield of aspirin, and percent yield for the reaction.

92. The combustion of liquid ethanol (C_2H_5OH) produces carbon dioxide and water. After 3.8 mL of ethanol (density = 0.789 g/mL) is allowed to burn in the presence of 12.5 g of oxygen gas, 3.10 mL of water (density = 1.00 g/mL) is collected. Determine the limiting reactant, theoretical yield of H_2O, and percent yield for the reaction. (*Hint:* Write a balanced equation for the combustion of ethanol.)

93. Urea (CH_4N_2O), a common fertilizer, can be synthesized by the reaction of ammonia (NH_3) with carbon dioxide:

$$2\,NH_3(aq) + CO_2(aq) \longrightarrow CH_4N_2O(aq) + H_2O(l)$$

An industrial synthesis of urea obtains 87.5 kg of urea upon reaction of 68.2 kg of ammonia with 105 kg of carbon dioxide. Determine the limiting reactant, theoretical yield of urea, and percent yield for the reaction.

94. Silicon, which occurs in nature as SiO_2, is the material from which most computer chips are made. If SiO_2 is heated until it melts into a liquid, it reacts with solid carbon to form liquid silicon and carbon monoxide gas. In an industrial preparation of silicon, 52.8 kg of SiO_2 reacts with 25.8 kg of carbon to produce 22.4 kg of silicon. Determine the limiting reactant, theoretical yield, and percent yield for the reaction.

95. The ingestion of lead from food, water, or other environmental sources can cause lead poisoning, a serious condition that affects the central nervous system, causing symptoms such as distractibility, lethargy, and loss of motor function. Lead poisoning is treated with chelating agents, substances that bind to lead and allow it to be eliminated in the urine. A modern chelating agent used for this purpose is succimer ($C_4H_6O_4S_2$). Suppose you are trying to determine the appropriate dose for succimer treatment of lead poisoning. Assume that a patient's blood lead levels are 0.550 mg/L, that total blood volume is 5.0 L, and that 1 mol of succimer binds 1 mol of lead. What minimum mass of succimer in milligrams is needed to bind all of the lead in this patient's bloodstream?

96. An emergency breathing apparatus placed in mines or caves works via the chemical reaction:

$$4\,KO_2(s) + 2\,CO_2(g) \longrightarrow 2\,K_2CO_3(s) + 3\,O_2(g)$$

If the oxygen supply becomes limited or if the air becomes poisoned, a worker can use the apparatus to breathe while exiting the mine. Notice that the reaction produces O_2, which can be breathed, and absorbs CO_2, a product of respiration. What minimum amount of KO_2 is required for the apparatus to produce enough oxygen to allow the user 15 minutes to exit the mine in an emergency? Assume that an adult consumes approximately 4.4 g of oxygen in 15 minutes of normal breathing.

97. The propane fuel (C_3H_8) used in gas barbecues burns according to the equation:

$$C_3H_8(g) + 5\,O_2(g) \longrightarrow 3\,CO_2(g) + 4\,H_2O(g) \qquad \Delta H^\circ_{rxn} = -2044\text{ kJ}$$

If a pork roast must absorb 1.6×10^3 kJ to fully cook, and if only 10% of the heat produced by the barbecue is actually absorbed by the roast, what mass of CO_2 is emitted into the atmosphere during the grilling of the pork roast?

98. Charcoal is primarily carbon. Determine the mass of CO_2 produced by burning enough carbon to produce 5.00×10^2 kJ of heat.

$$C(s) + O_2(g) \longrightarrow CO_2(g) \qquad \Delta H^\circ_{rxn} = -393.5\text{ kJ}$$

HIGHLIGHT PROBLEMS

99. A loud classroom demonstration involves igniting a hydrogen-filled balloon. The hydrogen within the balloon reacts explosively with oxygen in the air to form water.

$$2\,H_2(g) + O_2(g) \longrightarrow 2\,H_2O(g)$$

If the balloon is filled with a mixture of hydrogen and oxygen, the explosion is even louder than if the balloon is filled with only hydrogen; the intensity of the explosion depends on the relative amounts of oxygen and hydrogen within the balloon. Consider the molecular views representing different amounts of hydrogen and oxygen in four different balloons. Based on the balanced chemical equation, which balloon will make the loudest explosion?

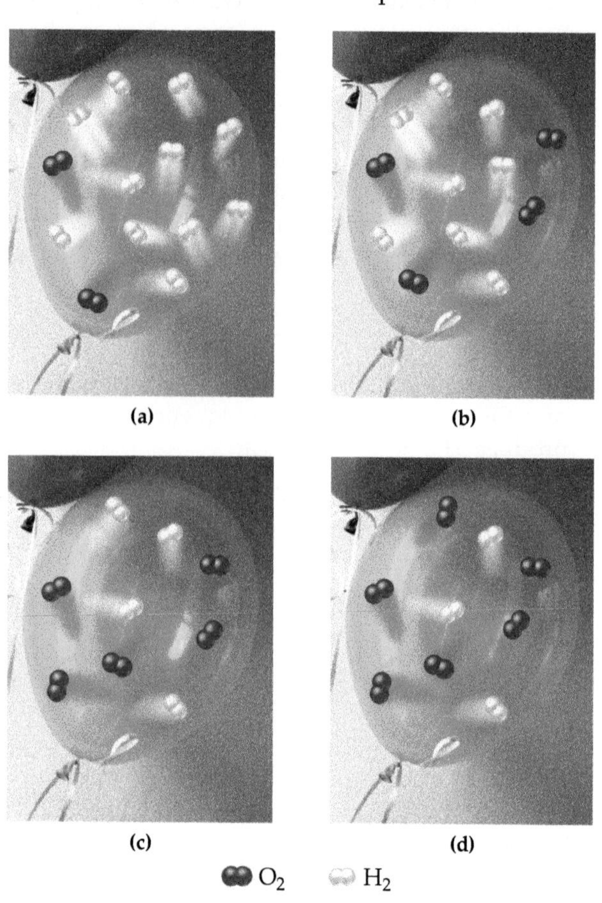

100. A hydrochloric acid solution will neutralize a sodium hydroxide solution. Consider the molecular views showing one beaker of HCl and four beakers of NaOH. Which NaOH beaker will just neutralize the HCl beaker? Begin by writing a balanced chemical equation for the neutralization reaction.

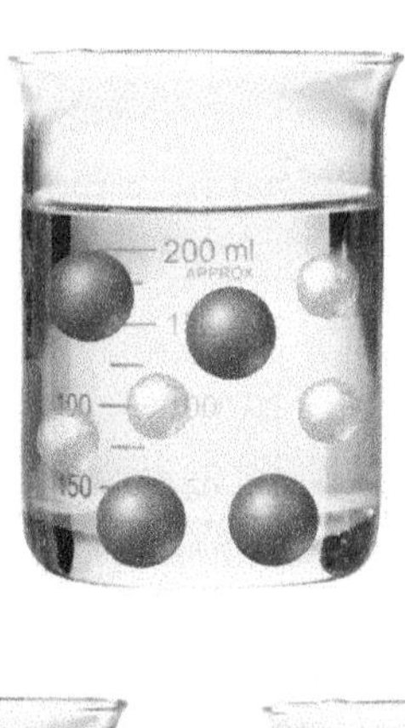

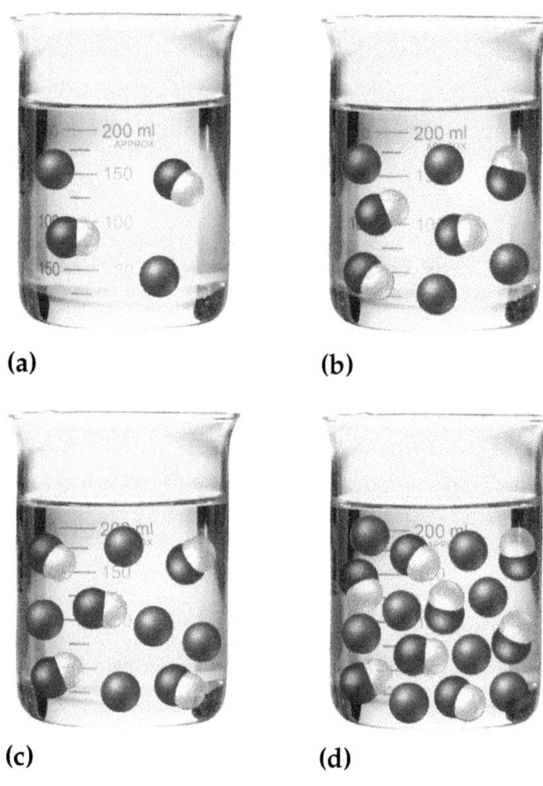

101. As we have seen, scientists have grown progressively more worried about the potential for global warming caused by increasing atmospheric carbon dioxide levels. The world burns the fossil fuel equivalent of approximately 9.0×10^{12} kg of petroleum per year. Assume that all of this petroleum is in the form of octane (C_8H_{18}) and calculate how much CO_2 in kilograms is produced by world fossil fuel combustion per year. (*Hint:* Begin by writing a balanced equation for the combustion of octane.) If the atmosphere currently contains approximately 3.0×10^{15} kg of CO_2, how long will it take for the world's fossil fuel combustion to double the amount of atmospheric carbon dioxide?

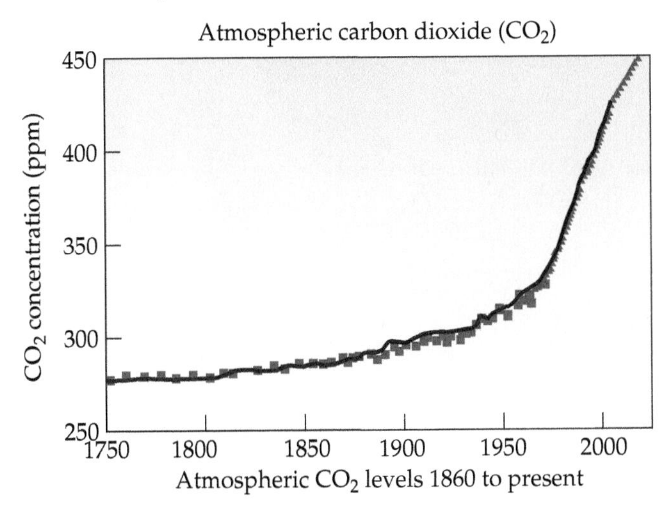

Atmospheric CO_2 levels 1860 to present

102. Lakes that have been acidified by acid rain can be neutralized by the addition of limestone ($CaCO_3$). How much limestone in kilograms would be required to completely neutralize a 5.2×10^9-L lake containing 5.0×10^{-3} g of H_2SO_4 per liter?

▸ANSWERS TO SKILLBUILDER EXERCISES

Skillbuilder 8.1	49.2 mol H_2O
Skillbuilder 8.2	6.88 g HCl
Skillbuilder 8.3	4.0×10^3 kg H_2SO_4
Skillbuilder 8.4	Limiting reactant is Na; theoretical yield is 4.8 mol of NaF
Skillbuilder 8.5	30.7 g NH_3
Skillbuilder Plus, p. 263	29.4 kg NH_3
Skillbuilder 8.6	Limiting reactant is CO; theoretical yield = 127 g Fe; percent yield = 68.8%
Skillbuilder 8.7	-2.06×10^3 kJ
Skillbuilder Plus, p. 267	33 g C_4H_{10} necessary; 99 g CO_2 produced

▸ANSWERS TO CONCEPTUAL CHECKPOINTS

8.1(a) Since the reaction requires 2 O_2 molecules to react with 1 CH_4 molecule, and since there are 4 O_2 molecules available to react, then 2 CH_4 molecules are required for complete reaction.

8.2(c) Hydrogen is the limiting reactant. The reaction mixture contains 3 H_2 molecules; therefore 2 NH_3 molecules will form when the reactants have reacted as completely as possible. Nitrogen is in excess, and there is one leftover nitrogen molecule.

8.3(d) NO is the limiting reagent. The reaction mixture initially contains 4 mol NO; therefore 10 moles of H_2 will be consumed, leaving 5 mol H_2 unreacted. The products will be 4 mol NH_3 and 4 mol H_2O.

8.4(c) B is the limiting reactant. If 4 mol B react, then 200 kJ of heat is produced.

Gases

"The generality of men are so accustomed to judge of things by their senses that, because the air is invisible, they ascribe but little to it, and think it but one removed from nothing."

ROBERT BOYLE (1627–1691)

11.1 Extra-Long Straws

◀ When you drink from a straw, you remove some of the molecules from inside the straw. This creates a pressure difference between the inside of the straw and the outside of thestraw that results in the liquid being pushed up the straw. The pushing is done by molecules in the atmosphere—primarily nitrogen and oxygen—as shown here.

Like too many kids, I grew up preferring fast-food restaurants to home cooking. My favorite stunt at the burger restaurant was drinking my orange soda from an extra-long straw that I pieced together from several smaller straws. I would pinch the end of one straw and squeeze it into the end of another. By attaching several straws together in this way, I could put my orange soda on the floor and drink it while standing on my chair (for some reason, my parents did not appreciate my scientific curiosity). I sometimes planned ahead and brought duct tape to the restaurant to form extra-tight seals between adjacent straws. My brother and I would compete to see who could make the longest working straw. Since I was older, I usually won.

I often wondered how long the straw could be if I made perfect seals between the straws. Could I drink my orange soda from a cup on the ground while I sat in my tree house? Could I drink it from the top of a 10-story building? It seemed to me that I could; but I was wrong. Even if the extended straw had perfect seals and rigid walls, and even if I could create a perfect vacuum (the absence of all air), I could never suck my orange soda from a straw longer than about 10.3 m (34 ft). Why?

Straws work because sucking creates a *pressure* difference between the inside of the straw and the outside. We define pressure and its units more thoroughly later; for now think of pressure as the force exerted per unit area by gas molecules as they collide with the surfaces around them (▶ Figure 11.1). Just as a ball exerts a force when it bounces against a wall, so a molecule exerts a force when it collides with a surface. The result of many of these collisions is pressure. The total amount of pressure exerted by a gas sample depends on several factors, including the concentration of gas molecules in the sample. On Earth at sea level, the gas molecules in our atmosphere exert an average pressure of 101,325 N/m^2 or, in English units, 14.7 lb/in^2.

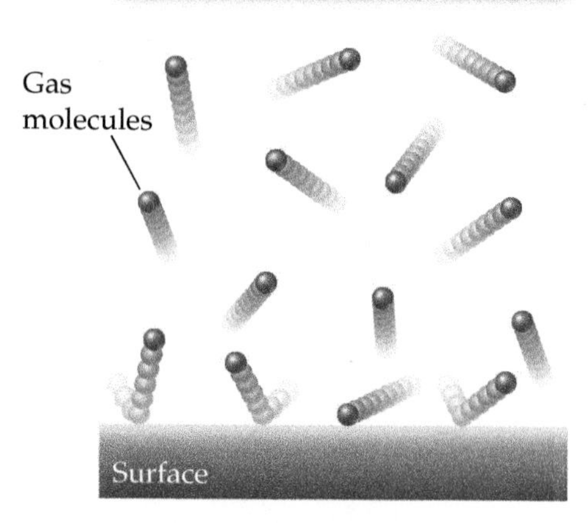
Pressure is the result of collisions between gas molecules and the surfaces around them.
Gas molecules
Surface

▲ **FIGURE 11.1 Gas pressure** Pressure is the force exerted by gas molecules as they collide with the surfaces around them.

When you put a straw in a glass of soda, the pressure inside and outside the straw are the same, so the soda does not rise within the straw (▼ Figure 11.2a). When you suck on the straw, you remove some of the air molecules from inside the straw, lowering the number of collisions that occur and therefore lowering the pressure inside the straw (▼ Figure 11.2b). However, the pressure outside the straw remains the same. The result is a pressure differential—the pressure outside the straw becomes greater than the pressure inside of the straw. This greater external pressure pushes the liquid up the straw and into your mouth.

How high can this greater external pressure push the liquid up the straw? If you formed a perfect vacuum within the straw, the pressure outside of the straw at sea level would be enough to push the orange soda (which is mostly water) to a total height of about 10.3 m (▼ Figure 11.3). This is because a 10.3-m column of water exerts the same pressure—101,325 N/m^2 or 14.7 lb/in.^{2}—as do the gas molecules in our atmosphere. In other words, the orange soda would rise up the straw until the pressure exerted by its weight equaled the pressure exerted by the molecules in our atmosphere.

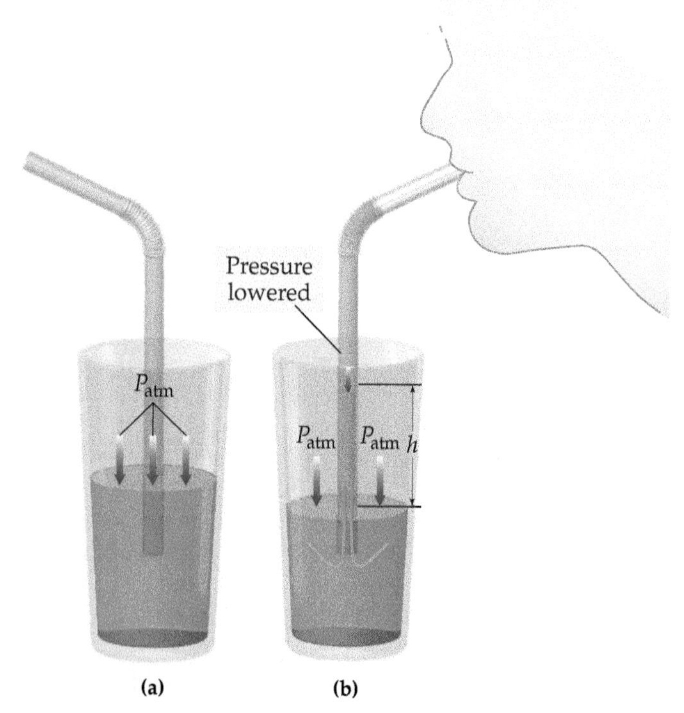
Pressure lowered
P_{atm}
P_{atm}
P_{atm}
h
(a)
(b)

▲ **FIGURE 11.2 Sipping soda** **(a)** When a straw is put into a glass of orange soda, the pressure inside and outside the straw is the same, so the liquid levels inside and outside the straw are the same. **(b)** When a person sucks on the straw, the pressure inside the straw is lowered. The greater pressure on the surface of the liquid outside the straw pushes the liquid up the straw.

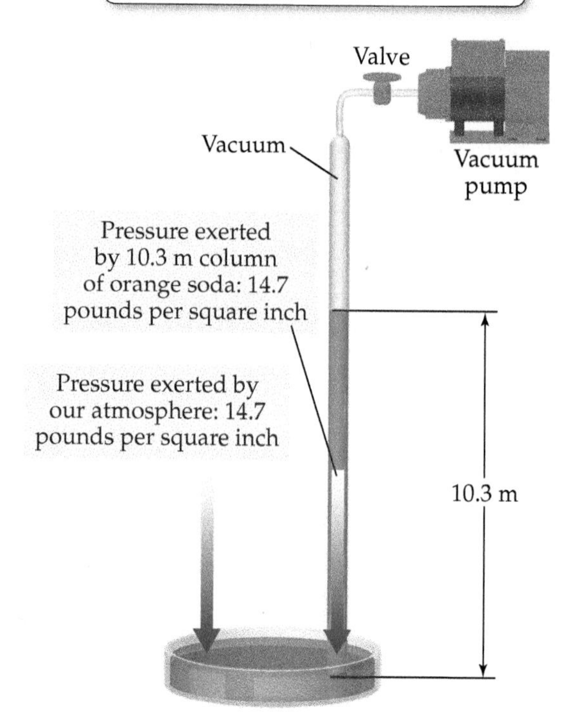
The pressure exerted by the atmosphere is equal to the pressure exerted by a 10.3 m column of water
Valve
Vacuum
Vacuum pump
Pressure exerted by 10.3 m column of orange soda: 14.7 pounds per square inch
Pressure exerted by our atmosphere: 14.7 pounds per square inch
10.3 m

▲ **FIGURE 11.3 Atmospheric pressure** Even if you formed a perfect vacuum, atmospheric pressure could only push orange soda to a total height of about 10 m. This is because a column of water (or soda) 10.3 m high exerts the same pressure (14.7 lb/in.^{2}) as the gas molecules in our atmosphere.

11.2 Kinetic Molecular Theory: A Model for Gases

In prior chapters we have seen the importance of models or theories in understanding nature. A simple model for understanding the behavior of gases is the **kinetic molecular theory**. This model predicts the correct behavior for most gases under many conditions. Like other models, the kinetic molecular theory is not

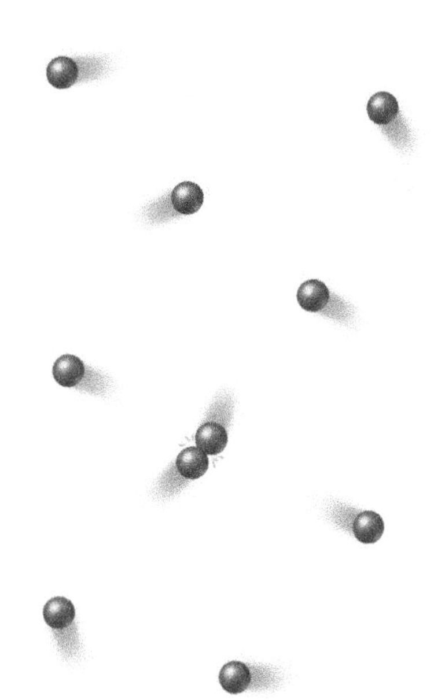

Kinetic molecular theory
1. Collection of particles in constant motion
2. No attractions or repulsions between particles; collisions like billiard ball collisions
3. A lot of space between the particles compared to the size of the particles themselves
4. The speed of the particles increases with increasing temperature

▲ **FIGURE 11.4 Simplified representation of an ideal gas** In reality, the spaces between the gas molecules would be larger in relation to the size of the molecules than shown here.

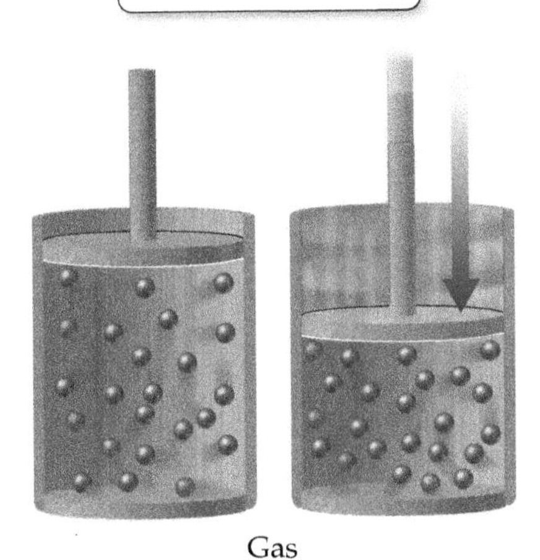

▲ **FIGURE 11.5 Compressibility of gases** Gases are compressible because there is so much empty space between gas particles.

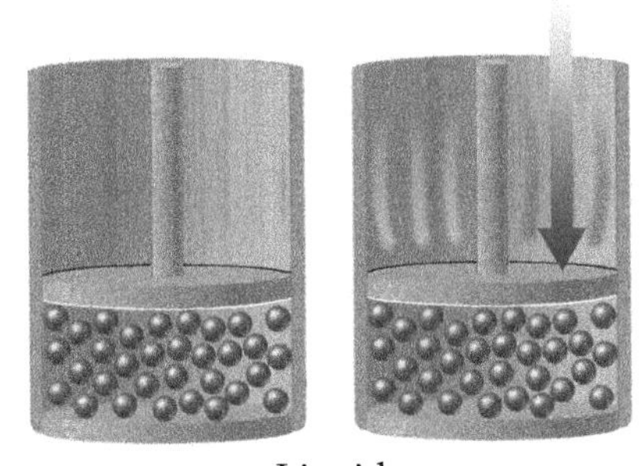

▲ **FIGURE 11.6 Incompressibility of liquids** Liquids are not compressible because there is so little space between the liquid particles.

perfect and breaks down under certain conditions. In this book, however, we focus on conditions where it works well.

Kinetic molecular theory makes the following assumptions (▲ Figure 11.4):

1. A gas is a collection of particles (molecules or atoms) in constant, straight-line motion.
2. Gas particles do not attract or repel each other—they do not interact. The particles collide with each other and with the surfaces around them, but they bounce back from these collisions like idealized billiard balls.
3. There is a lot of space between gas particles compared with the size of the particles themselves.
4. The average kinetic energy—energy due to motion—of gas particles is proportional to the temperature of the gas in kelvins. This means that as the temperature increases, the particles move faster and therefore have more energy.

Kinetic molecular theory is consistent with, and indeed predicts, the properties of gases. As described in Section 3.3, gases:

- are compressible
- assume the shape and volume of their container
- have low densities in comparison with liquids and solids

Gases are compressible because the atoms or molecules that compose them have a lot of space between them. By applying external pressure to a gas sample, the atoms or molecules are forced closer together, compressing the gas. Liquids and solids, in contrast, are not compressible because the atoms or molecules composing them are already in close contact—they cannot be forced any closer together. The compressibility of a gas can be seen, for example, by pushing a piston into a cylinder containing a gas. The piston goes down (◀ Figure 11.5) in response to the external pressure. If the cylinder were filled with a liquid or a solid, however, the piston would not move when pushed (◀ Figure 11.6).

Gases assume the shape and volume of their container because gaseous atoms or molecules are in constant, straight-line motion. In contrast to a solid or liquid, whose atoms or molecules interact with one another, the atoms or molecules in a

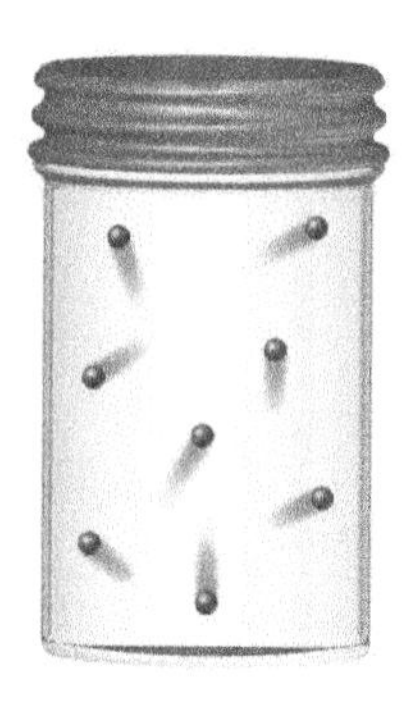

▲ **FIGURE 11.7 A gas assumes the shape of its container** Since the attractions between molecules in a gas are negligible, and since the particles are in constant motion, a gas expands to fill the volume of its container.

gas do not interact with one another (or more precisely, their interactions are negligible). They simply move in straight lines, colliding with each other and with the walls of their container. As a result, they fill the entire container, collectively assuming its shape (◀ Figure 11.7).

Gases have a low density in comparison with solids and liquids because there is so much empty space between the atoms or molecules in a gas. For example, if the water in a 350-mL (12-oz) can of soda were converted to steam (gaseous water), the steam would occupy a volume of 595 L (the equivalent of 1700 soda cans).

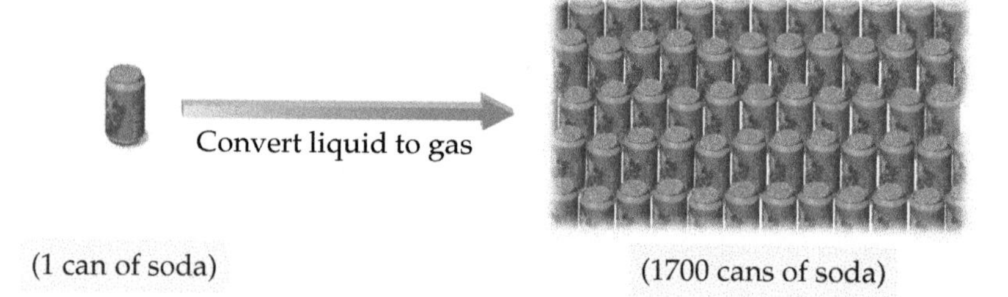

▲ If all of the water in a 12-oz (350-mL) can of orange soda were converted to gaseous steam (at 1 atm pressure and 100 °C), the steam would occupy a volume equal to 1700 soda cans.

11.3 Pressure: The Result of Constant Molecular Collisions

A prediction of kinetic molecular theory—which we already encountered in explaining how straws work—is the very existence of pressure. **Pressure** is the result of the constant collisions between the atoms or molecules in a gas and the surfaces around them. Because of pressure, we can drink from straws, inflate basketballs, and move air into and out of our lungs. Variation in pressure in Earth's atmosphere creates wind, and changes in pressure help predict weather. Pressure is all around us and even inside us. The pressure exerted by a gas sample is defined as the force per unit area that results from the collisions of gas particles with surrounding surfaces.

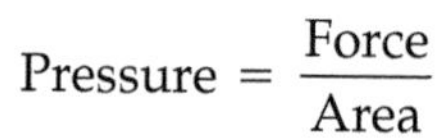

$$\text{Pressure} = \frac{\text{Force}}{\text{Area}}$$

The pressure exerted by a gas depends on several factors, including the number of gas particles in a given volume (◀ Figure 11.8). The fewer the gas particles, the lower the pressure. Pressure decreases, for example, with increasing altitude. As we climb a mountain or ascend in an airplane, there are fewer molecules per unit volume in air and the pressure consequently drops. For this reason, most airplane cabins are artificially pressurized (see the *Everyday Chemistry* box on page 365.)

You may feel the effect of a drop in pressure as a pain in your ears. This pain is caused by air-containing cavities within your ear (▶ Figure 11.9). When you climb a mountain, for example, the external pressure (that pressure that surrounds you) drops while the pressure within your ear cavities (the internal pressure) remains the same. This creates an imbalance—the lower external pressure causes your eardrum to bulge outward, causing pain. With time and a yawn or two, the excess air within your ears' cavities escapes, equalizing the internal and external pressure and relieving the pain.

Lower pressure

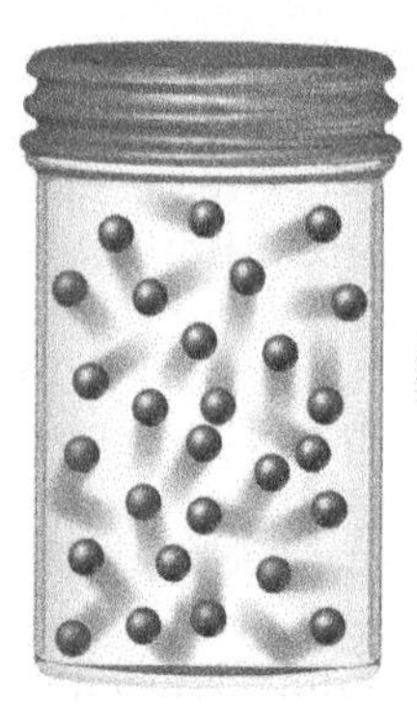

◀ **FIGURE 11.8 Pressure** Since pressure is a result of collisions between gas particles and the surfaces around them, the amount of pressure increases when the number of particles in a given volume increases.

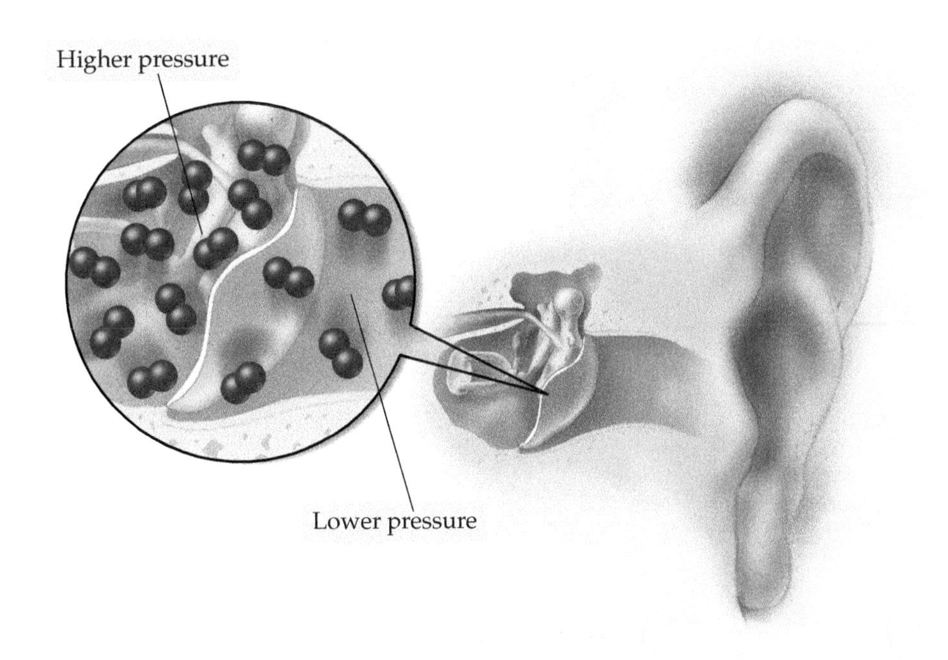

▶ FIGURE 11.9 **Pressure imbalance** The pain you feel in your ears upon climbing a mountain or ascending in an airplane is caused by an imbalance of pressure between the cavities inside your ear and the outside air.

CONCEPTUAL CHECKPOINT 11.1

Which sample of an ideal gas will have the *lowest* pressure? Assume that all of the particles are identical and that the three samples are the same temperature.

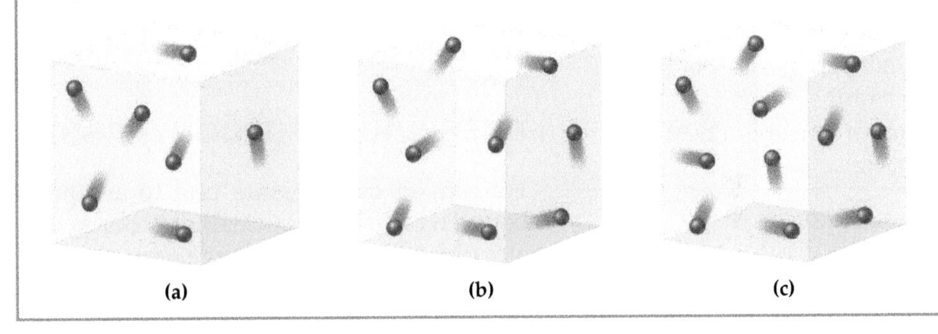

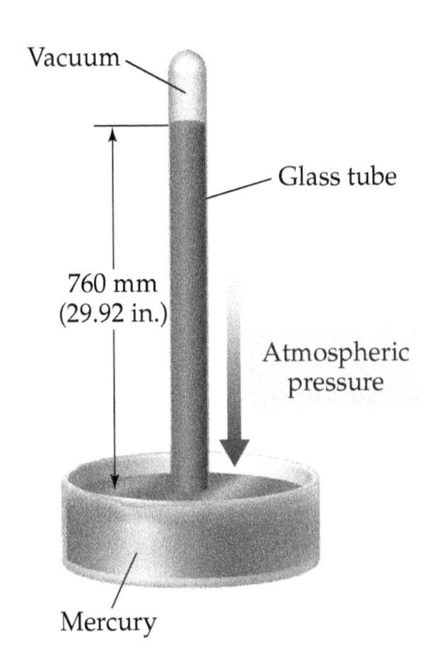

▲ FIGURE 11.10 **The mercury barometer** Average atmospheric pressure at sea level pushes a column of mercury to a height of 760 mm (29.92 in.). Question: What happens to the height of the mercury column if the external pressure decreases? increases?

PRESSURE UNITS

The simplest unit of pressure is the **atmosphere (atm)**, the average pressure at sea level. The SI unit of pressure is the **pascal (Pa)**, defined as 1 newton (N) per square meter.

$$1\ \text{Pa} = 1\ \text{N/m}^2$$

The pascal is a much smaller unit of pressure; 1 atm is equal to 101,325 Pa.

$$1\ \text{atm} = 101{,}325\ \text{Pa}$$

The pressure in a fully inflated mountain bike tire is about 6 atm, and the pressure on top of Mount Everest is about 0.31 atm.

A third unit of pressure, the **millimeter of mercury (mm Hg)**, originates from how pressure is measured with a barometer (◀ Figure 11.10). A barometer is an evacuated glass tube whose tip is submerged in a pool of mercury. As described in Section 11.1, liquid is pushed up an evacuated tube by the atmospheric pressure on the liquid's surface. We learned that water is pushed up to a height of 10.3 m by the average pressure at sea level. Mercury, however, with its higher density, is

Since mercury is 13.5 times as dense as water, it is pushed up 1/13.5 times as high as water by atmospheric pressure.

pushed up to a height of only 0.760 m, or 760 mm, by the average pressure at sea level. This shorter length—0.760 m instead of 10.3 m—makes a column of mercury a convenient way to measure pressure.

In a barometer, the mercury column rises or falls with changes in atmospheric pressure. If the pressure increases, the level of mercury within the column rises. If the pressure decreases, the level of mercury within the column falls. Since 1 atm of pressure pushes a column of mercury to a height of 760 mm, 1 atm and 760 mm Hg are equal.

$$1 \text{ atm} = 760 \text{ mm Hg}$$

A millimeter of mercury is also called a **torr** after Italian physicist Evangelista Torricelli (1608–1647), who invented the barometer.

$$1 \text{ mm Hg} = 1 \text{ torr}$$

Inches of mercury is still a widely used unit in weather reports. You have probably heard a weather forecaster say, "The barometer is 30.07 and rising," meaning that the atmospheric pressure is currently 30.07 in. Hg.

Other common units of pressure include inches of mercury (in. Hg) and **pounds per square inch (psi).**

$$1 \text{ atm} = 14.7 \text{ psi} \qquad 1 \text{ atm} = 29.92 \text{ in. Hg}$$

All these units are summarized in Table 11.1.

TABLE 11.1 Common Units of Pressure

Unit	Average Air Pressure at Sea Level
pascal (Pa)	101,325 Pa
atmosphere (atm)	1 atm
millimeter of mercury (mm Hg)	760 mm Hg (exact)
torr (torr)	760 torr (exact)
pounds per square inch (psi)	14.7 psi
inches of mercury (in. Hg)	29.92 atm

CONCEPTUAL CHECKPOINT 11.2

A liquid that is about twice as dense as water is used in a barometer. With this barometer, normal atmospheric pressure would be about:

(a) 0.38 m **(b)** 1.52 m **(c)** 5.15 m **(d)** 20.6 m

PRESSURE UNIT CONVERSION

See Section 2.6.

We convert one pressure unit to another in the same way that we converted between other units in Chapter 2. For example, suppose we want to convert 0.311 atm (the approximate average pressure at the top of Mount Everest) to millimeters of mercury. We begin by sorting the information in the problem statement.

GIVEN: 0.311 atm
FIND: mm Hg

SOLUTION MAP

We then strategize by building a solution map that shows how to convert from atm to mm Hg.

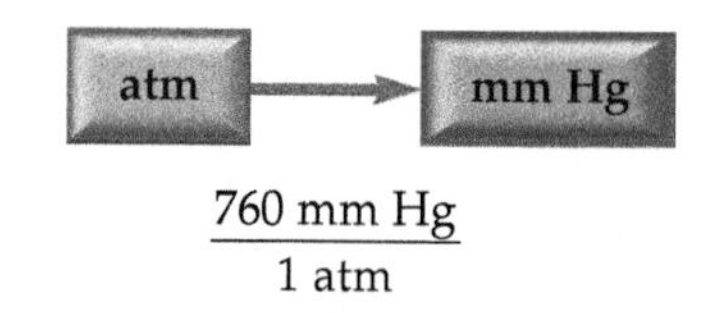

$$\frac{760 \text{ mm Hg}}{1 \text{ atm}}$$

RELATIONSHIPS USED

$$1 \text{ atm} = 760 \text{ mm Hg (from Table 11.1)}$$

SOLUTION

The solution begins with the given value (0.311 atm) and converts it to mm Hg.

$$0.311 \text{ atm} \times \frac{760 \text{ mm Hg}}{1 \text{ atm}} = 236 \text{ mm Hg}$$

EVERYDAY CHEMISTRY

Airplane Cabin Pressurization

Most commercial airplanes fly at elevations between 25,000 and 40,000 ft. At these elevations, atmospheric pressure is below 0.50 atm, much less than the normal atmospheric pressure to which our bodies are accustomed. The physiological effects of these lowered pressures—and the correspondingly lowered oxygen levels (see Section 11.9)—include dizziness, headache, shortness of breath, and even unconsciousness. Consequently, commercial airplanes pressurize the air in their cabins. If, for some reason, an airplane cabin should lose its pressurization, passengers are directed to breathe oxygen through an oxygen mask.

Cabin air pressurization is accomplished as part of the cabin's overall air circulation system. As air flows into the plane's jet engines, the large turbines at the front of the engines compress it. Most of this compressed (or pressurized) air exits out the back of the engines, creating the thrust that drives the plane forward. However, some of the pressurized air is directed into the cabin, where it is cooled and mixed with existing cabin air. This air is then circulated through the cabin through the overhead vents. The air leaves the cabin through ducts that direct it into the lower portion of the airplane. About half of this exiting air is mixed with incoming, pressurized air to circulate again. The other half is vented out of the plane through an outflow valve. This valve is adjusted to maintain the desired cabin pressure. Federal regulations require that cabin pressure in commercial airliners be greater than the equivalent of outside air pressure at 8000 ft.

CAN YOU ANSWER THIS? *Atmospheric pressure at elevations of 8000 ft average about 0.72 atm. Convert this pressure to millimeters of mercury, inches of mercury, and pounds per square inch. Would a cabin pressurized at 500 mm Hg meet federal standards?*

◀ Commercial airplane cabins must be pressurized to a pressure greater than the equivalent atmospheric pressure at an elevation of 8000 ft.

EXAMPLE 11.1 Converting between Pressure Units

A high-performance road bicycle tire is inflated to a total pressure of 125 psi. What is this pressure in millimeters of mercury?

SORT
You are given a pressure in psi and asked to convert it to mm Hg.

GIVEN: 125 psi
FIND: mm Hg

STRATEGIZE
Begin the solution map with the given units of psi. Use the conversion factors to convert first to atm and then to mm Hg.

SOLUTION MAP

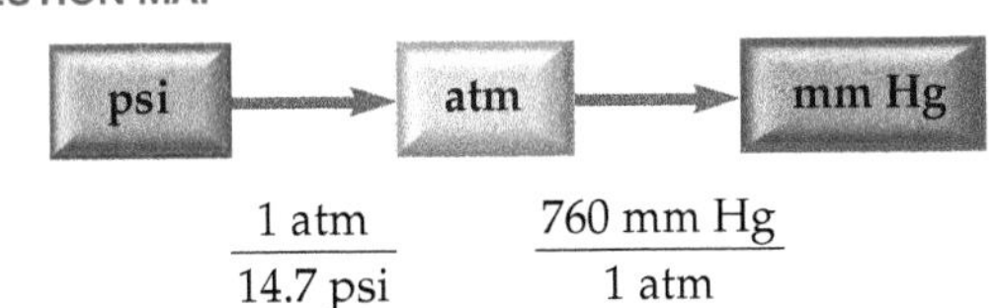

$$\frac{1 \text{ atm}}{14.7 \text{ psi}} \qquad \frac{760 \text{ mm Hg}}{1 \text{ atm}}$$

RELATIONSHIPS USED

1 atm = 14.7 psi (Table 11.1)
760 mm Hg = 1 atm (Table 11.1)

SOLVE
Follow the solution map to solve the problem.

SOLUTION

$$125 \text{ psi} \times \frac{1 \text{ atm}}{14.7 \text{ psi}} \times \frac{760 \text{ mm Hg}}{1 \text{ atm}} = 6.46 \times 10^3 \text{ mm Hg}$$

CHECK
Check your answer. Are the units correct? Does the answer make physical sense?

The answer has the correct units, mm Hg. The answer is reasonable because the mm Hg is a smaller unit than psi; therefore the value of the pressure in mm Hg should be greater than the value of the same pressure in psi.

▶SKILLBUILDER 11.1 | Converting between Pressure Units
Convert a pressure of 173 in. Hg into pounds per square inch.

▶SKILLBUILDER PLUS
Convert a pressure of 23.8 in. Hg into kilopascals.

▶FOR MORE PRACTICE Example 11.13; Problems 23, 24, 25, 26, 29, 30, 31, 32.

11.4 Boyle's Law: Pressure and Volume

The pressure of a gas sample depends, in part, on its volume. If the temperature and the amount of gas are constant, the pressure of a gas sample *increases* for a *decrease* in volume and *decreases* for an *increase* in volume. A simple hand pump, for example, works on this principle. A hand pump is basically a cylinder equipped with a moveable piston (▼ Figure 11.11). The volume in the cylinder increases when you pull the handle up (the upstroke) and decreases when you push the handle down (the downstroke). On the upstroke, the *increasing* volume causes a *decrease* in the internal pressure (the pressure within the pump's cylinder). This, in turn, draws air into the pump's cylinder through a one-way valve. On the downstroke, the *decreasing* volume causes an *increase* in the internal pressure. This increase forces the air out of the pump, through a different one-way valve, and into the tire or whatever else is being inflated.

The relationships between gas properties—such as the relationship between pressure and volume—are described by gas laws. These laws show how a change in one of these properties affects one or more of the others. The relationship between volume and pressure was discovered by Robert Boyle (1627–1691) and is called **Boyle's law**.

Boyle's law assumes constant temperature and a constant number of gas particles.

Boyle's law: The volume of a gas and its pressure are inversely proportional.

$$V \propto \frac{1}{P} \quad \alpha \text{ means "proportional to"}$$

If two quantities are inversely proportional, then increasing one decreases the other (▶ Figure 11.12). As we saw for the hand pump, when the volume of a gas sample is decreased, its pressure increases and vice versa. Kinetic molecular theory explains the observed change in pressure. If the volume of a gas sample is decreased, the same number of gas particles is crowded into a smaller volume, causing more collisions with the walls of the container and therefore increasing the pressure (▶ Figure 11.13).

Scuba divers learn about Boyle's law during certification courses because it explains why ascending too quickly toward the surface is dangerous. For every 10 m of depth that a diver descends in water, he experiences an additional 1 atm of pressure due to the weight of the water above him (▶ Figure 11.14). The pressure regulator used in scuba diving delivers air at a pressure that matches the external pressure; otherwise the diver

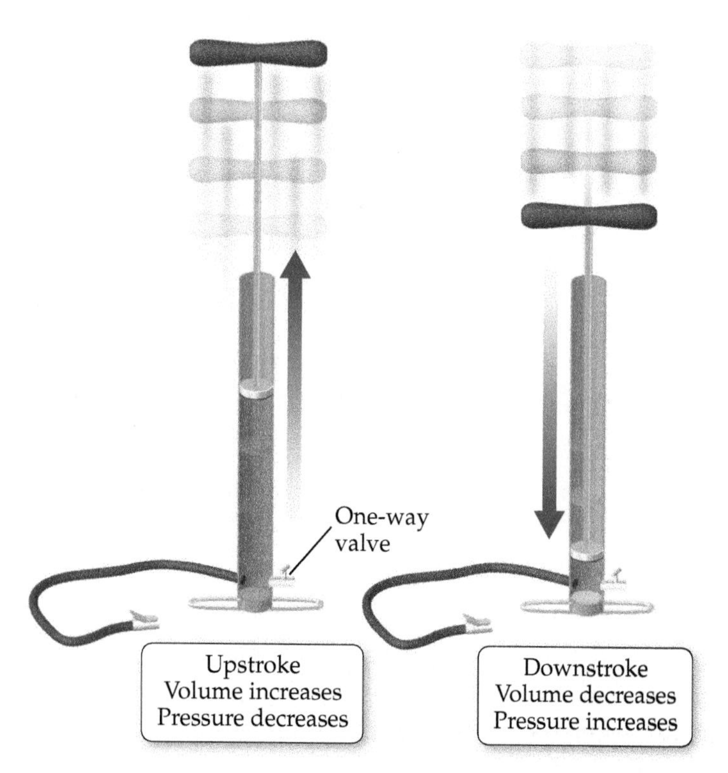

◀ FIGURE 11.11 **Operation of a hand pump**

▶ **FIGURE 11.12 Volume versus pressure** **(a)** A J-tube, such as the one shown here, can be used to measure the volume of a gas at different pressures. Adding mercury to the J-tube causes the pressure on the gas sample to increase and its volume to decrease. **(b)** A plot of the volume of a gas as a function of pressure.

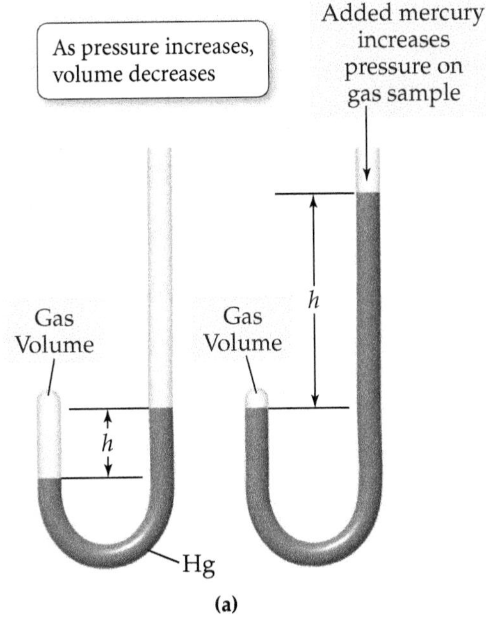

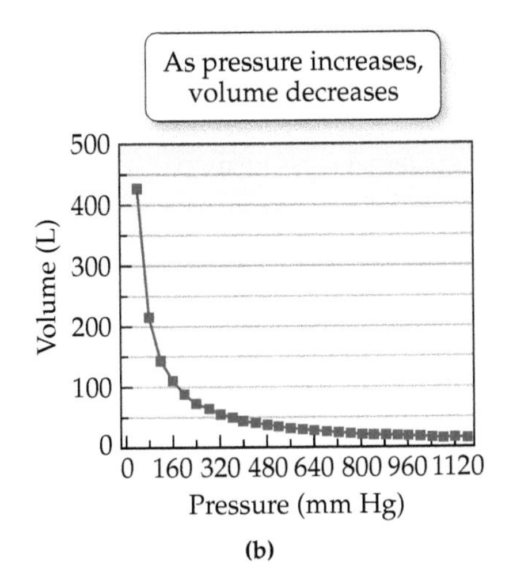

▶ **FIGURE 11.13 Volume versus pressure: a molecular view** As the volume of a sample of gas is decreased, the number of collisions between the gas molecules and each square meter of the container increases. This raises the pressure exerted by the gas.

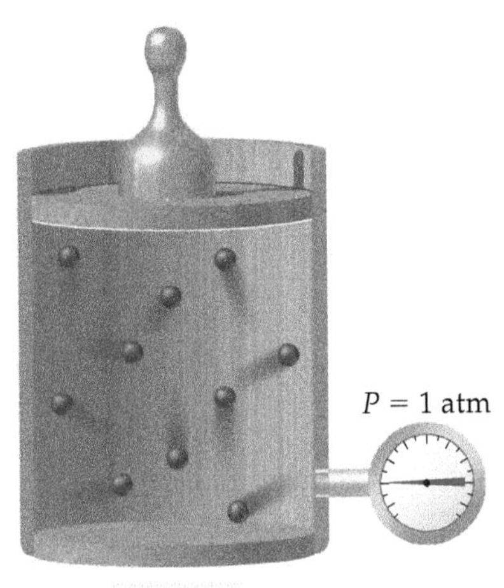

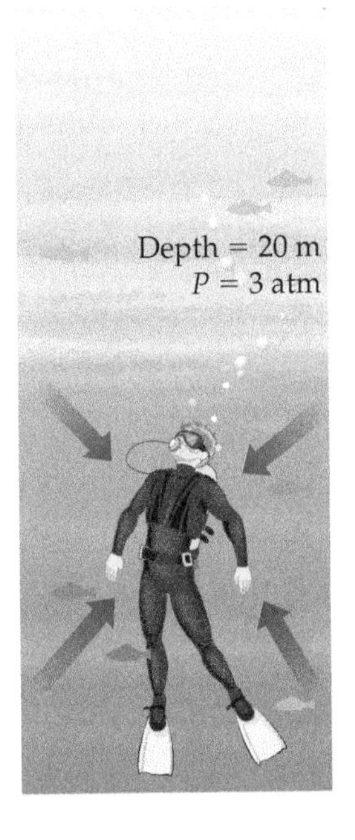

could not inhale the air (see the *Everyday Chemistry* box on page 371). For example, when a diver is at 20 m of depth, the regulator delivers air at a pressure of 3 atm to match the 3 atm of pressure around the diver—1 atm due to normal atmospheric pressure and 2 additional atmospheres due to the weight of the water at 20 m (▶ Figure 11.15).

Suppose that a diver inhaled a lungful of 3-atm air and swam quickly to the surface (where the pressure drops to 1 atm) while holding his breath. What would happen to the volume of air in his lungs? Since the pressure decreases by a factor of 3, the volume of the air in his lungs would increase by a factor of 3, severely damaging his lungs and possibly killing him. Of course, the volume increase in the diver's lungs would be so great that the diver would not be able to hold his breath all the way to the surface—the air would force itself out of his mouth. So the most important rule in diving is *never hold your breath.*

◀ **FIGURE 11.14 Pressure at depth** For every 10 m of depth, a diver experiences an additional 1 atm of pressure due to the weight of the water surrounding him. At 20 m, the diver experiences a total pressure of 3 atm (1 atm from atmospheric pressure plus an additional 2 atm from the weight of the water).

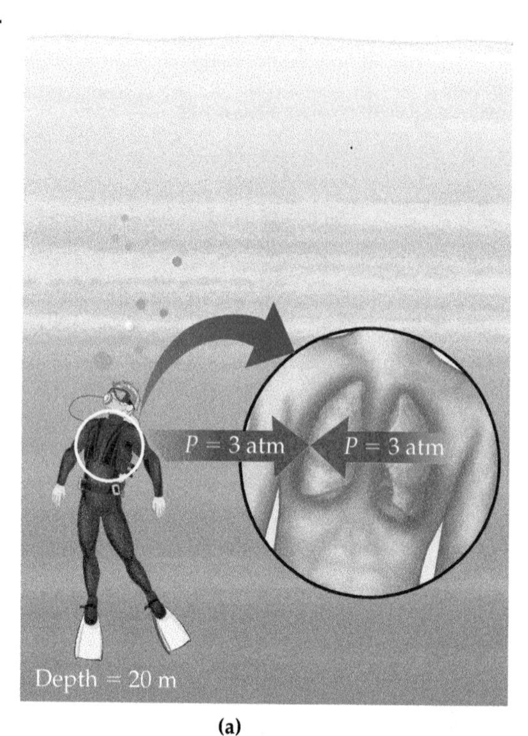

(a)

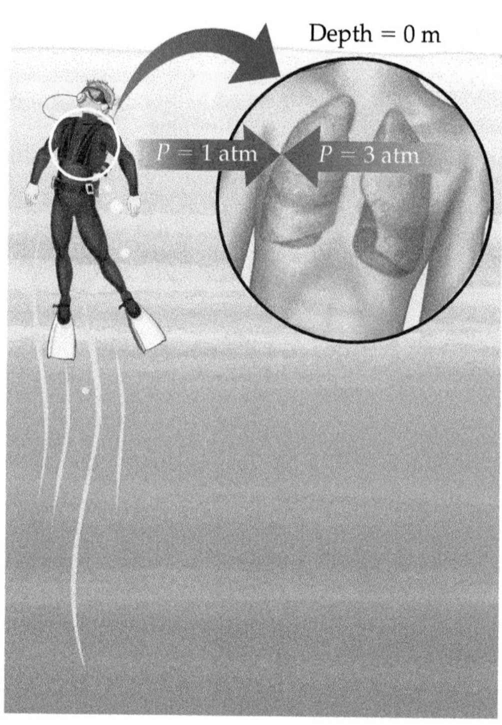

(b)

▶ **FIGURE 11.15 The dangers of decompression** **(a)** A diver at 20 m experiences an external pressure of 3 atm and breathes air pressurized at 3 atm. **(b)** If the diver shoots toward the surface with lungs full of 3 atm air, his lungs will expand as the external pressure drops to 1 atm.

Divers must ascend slowly and breathe continuously, allowing the regulator to bring the air pressure in their lungs back to 1 atm by the time they reach the surface.

Boyle's law can be used to calculate the volume of a gas following a pressure change or the pressure of a gas following a volume change *as long as the temperature and the amount of gas remain constant*. For these calculations, we write Boyle's law in a slightly different way.

$$\text{Since } V \propto \frac{1}{P}, \text{ then } V = \frac{\text{Constant}}{P}$$

If we multiply both sides by P, we get:

$$PV = \text{Constant}$$

This relationship is true because if the pressure increases, the volume decreases, but the product $P \times V$ is always equal to the same constant. For two different sets of conditions, we can say that

$$P_1V_1 = \text{Constant} = P_2V_2, \text{ or}$$

$$P_1V_1 = P_2V_2$$

where P_1 and V_1 are the initial pressure and volume of the gas, and P_2 and V_2 are the final volume and pressure. For example, suppose we want to calculate the pressure of a gas that was initially at 765 mm Hg and 1.78 L and later compressed to 1.25 L. We first sort the information in the problem.

Based on Boyle's law, and before doing any calculations, do you expect P_2 to be greater than or less than P_1?

GIVEN: $P_1 = 765$ mm Hg

$V_1 = 1.78$ L

$V_2 = 1.25$ L

FIND: P_2

SOLUTION MAP

We then draw a solution map showing how the equation takes us from the given quantities (what we have) to the find quantity (what we want).

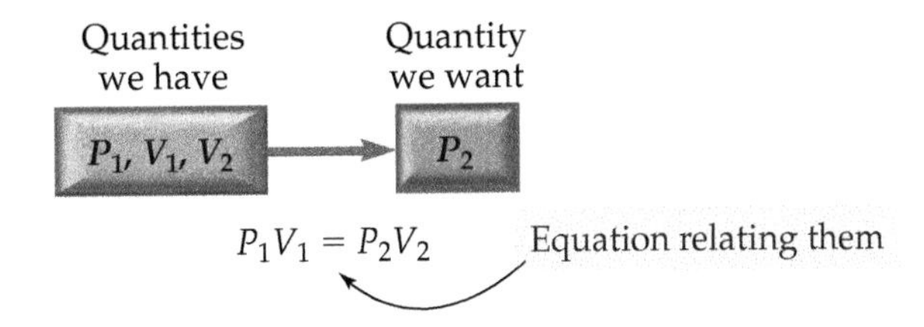

$P_1V_1 = P_2V_2$ Equation relating them

RELATIONSHIPS USED

$P_1V_1 = P_2V_2$ (Boyle's law, presented in this section)

SOLUTION

We then solve the equation for the quantity we are trying to find (P_2).

$$P_1V_1 = P_2V_2$$

$$P_2 = \frac{P_1V_1}{V_2}$$

Lastly, we substitute the numerical values into the equation and calculate the answer.

$$P_2 = \frac{P_1V_1}{V_2} = \frac{(765 \text{ mm Hg})(1.78 \text{ L})}{1.25 \text{ L}}$$

$$= 1.09 \times 10^3 \text{ mm Hg}$$

EXAMPLE 11.2 Boyle's Law

A cylinder equipped with a moveable piston has an applied pressure of 4.0 atm and a volume of 6.0 L. What is the volume of the cylinder if the applied pressure is decreased to 1.0 atm?

SORT You are given an initial pressure, an initial volume, and a final pressure. You are asked to find the final volume.	GIVEN: $P_1 = 4.0$ atm $V_1 = 6.0$ L $P_2 = 1.0$ atm FIND: V_2
STRATEGIZE Draw a solution map beginning with the given quantities. Boyle's law shows the relationship necessary to get to the find quantity.	SOLUTION MAP 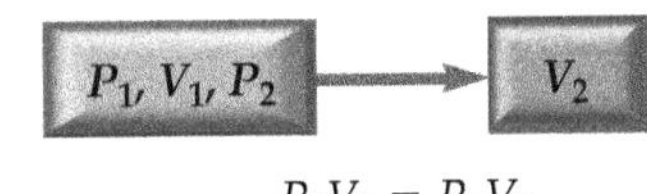 $P_1V_1 = P_2V_2$ RELATIONSHIPS USED $P_1V_1 = P_2V_2$ (Boyle's law, presented in this section)
SOLVE Solve the equation for the quantity you are trying to find (V_2), and then substitute the numerical quantities into the equation to compute the answer.	SOLUTION $P_1V_1 = P_2V_2$ $V_2 = \frac{V_1P_1}{P_2}$ $= \frac{(6.0\text{L})(4.0 \text{ atm})}{1.0 \text{ atm}}$ $= 24$ L
CHECK Check your answer. Are the units correct? Does the answer make physical sense?	The answer has units of volume (L) as expected. The answer is reasonable because we expect the volume to increase as the pressure decreases.

▶SKILLBUILDER 11.2 | Boyle's Law

A snorkeler takes a syringe filled with 16 mL of air from the surface, where the pressure is 1.0 atm, to an unknown depth. The volume of the air in the syringe at this depth is 7.5 mL. What is the pressure at this depth? If the pressure increases by an additional 1 atm for every 10 m of depth, how deep is the snorkeler?

▶FOR MORE PRACTICE Example 11.14; Problems 33, 34, 35, 36.

CONCEPTUAL CHECKPOINT 11.3

A flask contains a gas sample at pressure x. If the volume of the container triples at constant temperature and constant amount of gas, the pressure becomes:

(a) $3x$

(b) $\frac{1}{3}x$

(c) $9x$

11.5 Charles's Law: Volume and Temperature

Recall from Section 2.9 that Density = Mass/Volume. If the volume increases and the mass remains constant, the density must decrease.

Have you ever noticed that hot air rises? You may have walked upstairs in your house and noticed it getting warmer. Or you may have witnessed a hot-air balloon take flight. The air that fills a hot-air balloon is warmed with a burner, which then causes the balloon to rise in the cooler air around it. Why does hot air rise? Hot air rises because the volume of a gas sample at constant pressure increases with increasing temperature. As long as the amount of gas (and therefore its mass) remains constant, warming it decreases its density because density is mass divided by volume. A lower-density gas floats in a higher-density gas just as wood floats in water.

▲ Heating the air in a balloon makes it expand (Charles's law). As the volume occupied by the hot air increases, its density decreases, allowing the balloon to float in the cooler, denser air that surrounds it.

Suppose you keep the pressure of a gas sample constant and measure its volume at a number of different temperatures. The results of a number of such measurements are shown in ▼Figure 11.16. The plot reveals the relationship

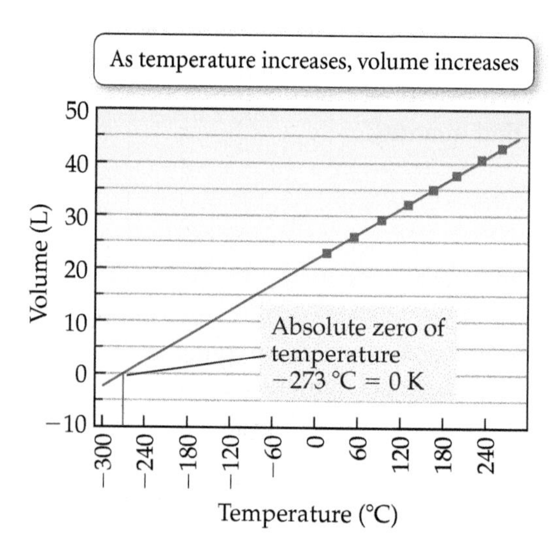

▲ **FIGURE 11.16 Volume versus temperature** The volume of a gas increases linearly with increasing temperature. **Question:** How does this graph demonstrate that −273 °C is the coldest possible temperature?

The extrapolated line could not be measured experimentally because all gases would condense into liquids before −273 °C is reached.

EVERYDAY CHEMISTRY

Extra-long Snorkels

Several episodes of *The Flintstones* featured Fred Flintstone and Barney Rubble snorkeling. Their snorkels, however, were not the modern kind, but long reeds that stretched from the surface of the water down to many meters of depth. Fred and Barney swam around in deep water while breathing air provided to them by these extra-long snorkels. Would this work? Why do people bother with scuba diving equipment if they could simply use 10-m snorkels the way that Fred and Barney did?

When we breathe, we expand the volume of our lungs, lowering the pressure within them (Boyle's law). Air from outside our lungs then flows into them. Extra-long snorkels, such as those used by Fred and Barney, do not work because of the pressure caused by water at depth. A diver at 10 m experiences a pressure of 2 atm that compresses the air in his lungs to a pressure of 2 atm. If the diver had a snorkel that went to the surface—where the air pressure is 1 atm—air would flow out of his lungs, not into them. It would be impossible to breathe.

CAN YOU ANSWER THIS? *Suppose a diver takes a balloon with a volume of 2.5 L from the surface, where the pressure is 1.0 atm, to a depth of 20 m, where the pressure is 3.0 atm. What would happen to the volume of the balloon? What if the end of the balloon was on a long tube that went to the surface and was attached to another balloon, as shown in the drawing below? Which way would air flow as the diver descends?*

◀ Fred and Barney used reeds to breathe air from the surface, even when they were at depth. This would not work because the pressure at depth would push air out of their lungs, preventing them from breathing.

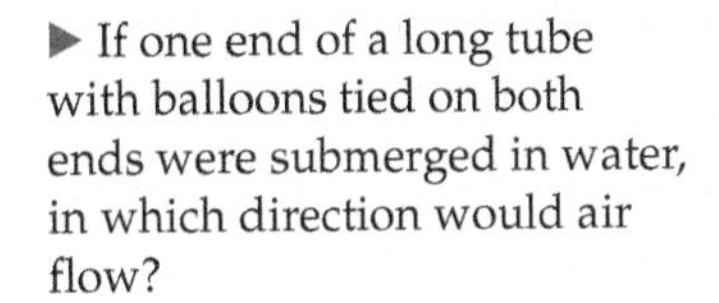

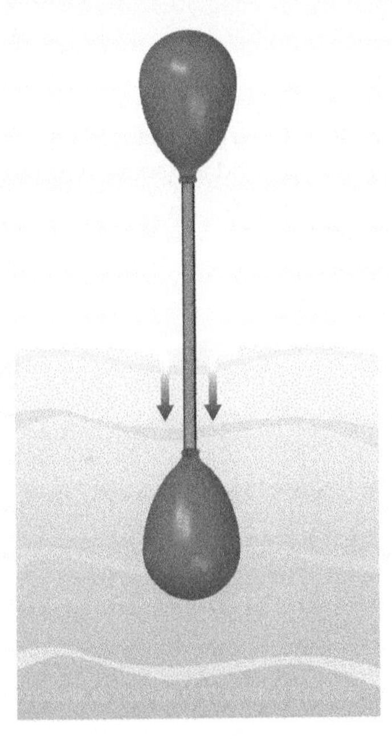

▶ If one end of a long tube with balloons tied on both ends were submerged in water, in which direction would air flow?

Section 3.10 summarizes the three different temperature scales.

between volume and temperature: The volume of a gas increases with increasing temperature. Note also that temperature and volume are *linearly related.* If two variables are linearly related, then plotting one against the other produces a straight line.

We can predict an important property of matter by extending the line on our plot backward from the lowest measured point—a process called *extrapolation.* Our extrapolated line shows that the gas should have a zero volume at −273 °C. Recall from Chapter 3 that −273 °C corresponds to 0 K, the coldest possible temperature. Our extrapolated line shows that below −273 °C, our gas would have a negative volume, which is physically impossible. For this reason, we refer to 0 K as **absolute zero**—colder temperatures do not exist.

The first person to carefully quantify the relationship between the volume of a gas and its temperature was J. A. C. Charles (1746–1823), a French mathematician and physicist. Charles was interested in gases and was among the first people to ascend in a hydrogen-filled balloon. The law he formulated is called **Charles's law**.

Charles's law assumes constant pressure and a constant amount of gas.

Charles's law: The volume (V) of a gas and its Kelvin temperature (T) are directly proportional.

$$V \propto T$$

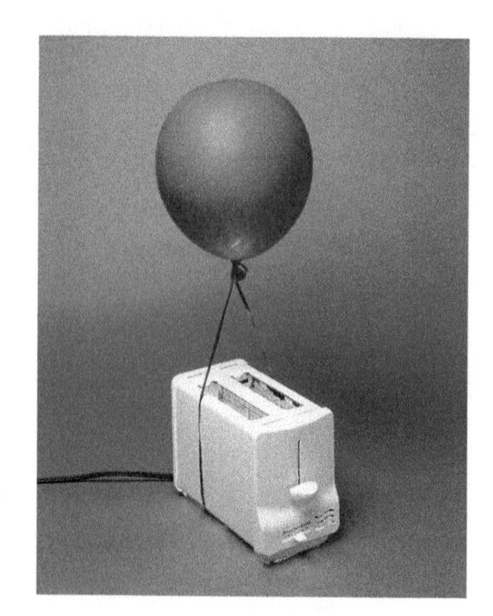

▲ If you hold a partially inflated balloon over a warm toaster, the balloon will expand as the air within the balloon warms.

If two variables are directly proportional, then increasing one by some factor increases the other by the same factor. For example, when the temperature of a gas sample (in kelvins) is doubled, its volume doubles; when the temperature is tripled, its volume triples; and so on. The observed relationship between the temperature and volume of a gas follows from kinetic molecular theory. If the temperature of a gas sample is increased, the gas particles move faster, and if the pressure is to remain constant, the volume must increase (▼ Figure 11.17).

You can experience Charles's law directly by holding a partially inflated balloon over a warm toaster. As the air in the balloon warms, you can feel the balloon expanding. Alternatively, you can put an inflated balloon in the freezer or take it outside on a very cold day (below freezing) and see that it becomes smaller as it cools.

Charles's law can be used to calculate the volume of a gas following a temperature change or the temperature of a gas following a volume change *as long as the pressure and the amount of gas are constant.* For these calculations, we express Charles's law in a different way as follows:

$$\text{Since } V \propto T, \text{ then } V = \text{Constant} \times T$$

If we divide both sides by T, we get:

$$V/T = \text{Constant}$$

If the temperature increases, the volume increases in direct proportion so that the quotient, V/T, is always equal to the same constant. So, for two different measurements, we can say that

$$V_1/T_1 = \text{Constant} = V_2/T_2, \text{ or}$$

$$\frac{V_1}{T_1} = \frac{V_2}{T_2}$$

As temperature increases, the volume of the balloon increases

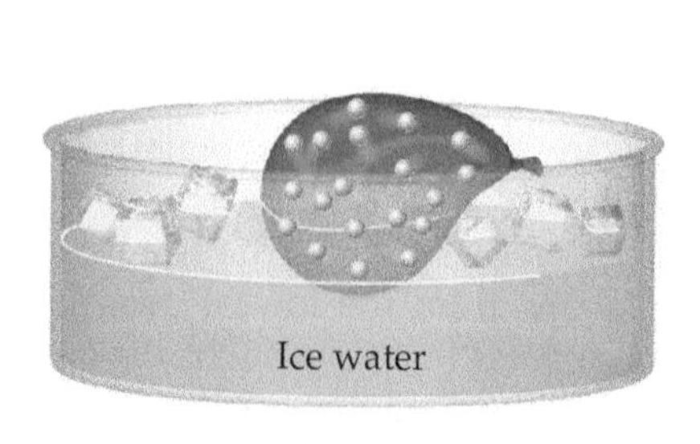

▲ **FIGURE 11.17 Volume versus temperature: a molecular view** If a balloon is moved from an ice-water bath into a boiling-water bath, the gas molecules inside it move faster due to the increased temperature. If the external pressure remains constant, the molecules will expand the balloon and collectively occupy a larger volume.

where V_1 and T_1 are the initial volume and temperature of the gas and V_2 and T_2 are the final volume and temperature. *All temperatures must be expressed in kelvins.*

For example, suppose we have a 2.37-L sample of a gas at 298 K that is then heated to 354 K with no change in pressure. To determine the final volume of the gas, we begin by sorting the information in the problem statement.

GIVEN: $T_1 = 298\text{ K}$

$V_1 = 2.37\text{ L}$

$T_2 = 354\text{ K}$

FIND: V_2

SOLUTION MAP

We then strategize by building a solution map that shows how the equation takes us from the given quantities to the unknown quantity.

Based on Charles's law, and before doing any calculations, do you expect V_2 to be greater than or less than V_1?

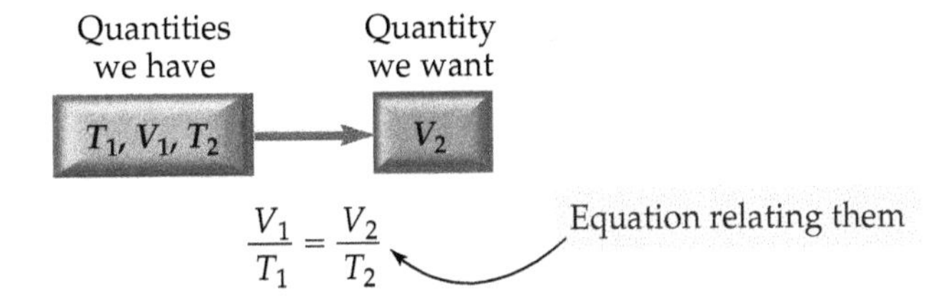

RELATIONSHIPS USED

$$\frac{V_1}{T_1} = \frac{V_2}{T_2} \text{ (Charles's law, presented in this section)}$$

SOLUTION

We then solve the equation for the quantity we are trying to find (V_2).

$$\frac{V_1}{T_1} = \frac{V_2}{T_2}$$

$$V_2 = \frac{V_1}{T_1} T_2$$

Lastly, we substitute the numerical values into the equation and calculate the answer.

$$V_2 = \frac{V_1}{T_1} T_2$$

$$= \frac{2.37\text{ L}}{298\text{ K}} 354\text{ K}$$

$$= 2.82\text{ L}$$

EXAMPLE 11.3 Charles's Law

A sample of gas has a volume of 2.80 L at an unknown temperature. When the sample is submerged in ice water at $t = 0\ °C$, its volume decreases to 2.57 L. What was its initial temperature (in kelvins and in Celsius)? Assume a constant pressure. (To distinguish between the two temperature scales, use t for temperature in °C and T for temperature in K.)

SORT

You are given an initial volume, a final volume, and a final temperature. You are asked to find the intitial temperature in both kelvins (T_1) and degrees Celsius (t_1).

GIVEN:

$$V_1 = 2.80\ \text{L}$$

$$V_2 = 2.57$$

$$t_2 = 0\ °\text{C}$$

FIND: T_1 and t_1

STRATEGIZE

Draw a solution map beginning with the given quantities. Charles's law shows the relationship necessary to get to the find quantity.

SOLUTION MAP

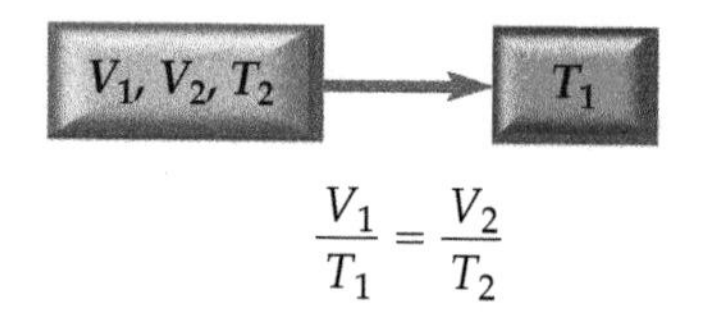

$$\frac{V_1}{T_1} = \frac{V_2}{T_2}$$

RELATIONSHIPS USED

$$\frac{V_1}{T_1} = \frac{V_2}{T_2}$$ (Charles's law, presented in this section)

SOLVE

Solve the equation for the quantity you are trying to find (T_1).

Before you substitute in the numerical values, you must convert the temperature to kelvins. *Remember, gas law problems must always be worked using Kelvin temperatures.* Once you have converted the temperature to kelvins, substitute into the equation to find T_1. Convert the temperature to degrees Celsius to find t_1.

SOLUTION

$$\frac{V_1}{T_1} = \frac{V_2}{T_2}$$

$$T_1 = \frac{V_1}{V_2} T_2$$

$$T_2 = 0 + 273 = 273\ \text{K}$$

$$T_1 = \frac{V_1}{V_2} T_2$$

$$= \frac{2.80\ \cancel{\text{L}}}{2.57\ \cancel{\text{L}}} 273\ \text{K}$$

$$= 297\ \text{K}$$

$$t_1 = 297 - 273 = 24\ °\text{C}$$

CHECK

Check your answer. Are the units correct? Does the answer make physical sense?

The answers have the correct units, K and °C. The answer is reasonable because the initial volume was larger than the final volume; therefore the initial temperature must be higher than the final temperature.

▶SKILLBUILDER 11.3 | Charles's Law

A gas in a cylinder with a moveable piston has an initial volume of 88.2 mL and is heated from 35 °C to 155 °C. What is the final volume of the gas in milliliters?

▶FOR MORE PRACTICE Problems 39, 40, 41, 42.

11.6 The Combined Gas Law: Pressure, Volume, and Temperature

Boyle's law shows how P and V are related at constant temperature, and Charles's law shows how V and T are related at constant pressure. But what if two of these variables change at once? For example, what happens to the volume of a gas if both its pressure and its temperature are changed?

Since volume is inversely proportional to pressure ($V \propto 1/P$) and directly proportional to temperature ($V \propto T$), we can write:

$$V \propto \frac{T}{P} \quad \text{or} \quad \frac{PV}{T} = \text{Constant}$$

For a sample of gases under two different sets of conditions we use the **combined gas law**:

The combined gas law encompasses both Boyle's law and Charles's law and can be used in place of them. If one physical property (P, V, or T) is constant, it will cancel out of your calculations when you use the combined gas law.

The combined gas law: $$\frac{P_1V_1}{T_1} = \frac{P_2V_2}{T_2}$$

The combined gas law applies only when the *amount* of gas is constant. The temperature (as with Charles's law) must be expressed in kelvins.

Suppose you carry a cylinder with a moveable piston that has an initial volume of 3.65 L up a mountain. The pressure at the bottom of the mountain is 755 mm Hg, and the temperature is 302 K. The pressure at the top of the mountain is 687 mm Hg, and the temperature is 291 K. What is the volume of the cylinder at the top of the mountain? We begin by sorting the information in the problem statement.

GIVEN:

$P_1 = 755$ mm Hg $\quad T_2 = 291$ K

$V_1 = 3.65$ L $\quad P_2 = 687$ mm Hg

$T_1 = 302$ K

FIND: V_2

SOLUTION MAP

We strategize by building a solution map that shows how the combined gas law equation takes us from the given quantities to the find quantity.

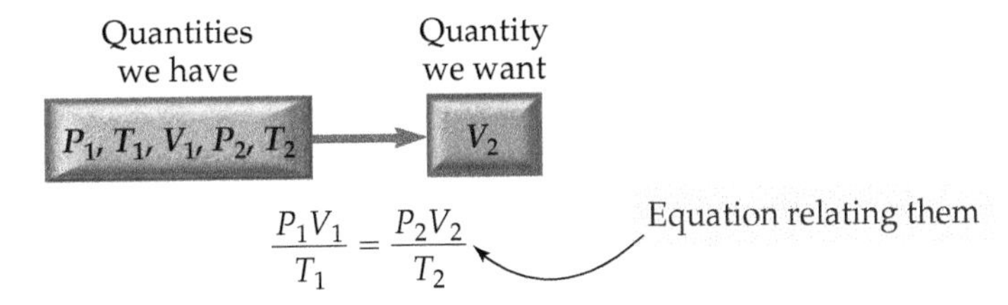

RELATIONSHIPS USED

$$\frac{P_1V_1}{T_1} = \frac{P_2V_2}{T_2} \quad \text{(Combined gas law, presented in this section)}$$

SOLUTION

We then solve the equation for the quantity we are trying to find (V_2).

$$\frac{P_1V_1}{T_1} = \frac{P_2V_2}{T_2}$$

$$V_2 = \frac{P_1V_1T_2}{T_1P_2}$$

Lastly, we substitute in the appropriate values and calculate the answer.

$$V_2 = \frac{P_1V_1T_2}{T_1P_2}$$

$$= \frac{755 \cancel{\text{mm Hg}} \times 3.65 \text{ L} \times 291 \cancel{\text{K}}}{302 \cancel{\text{K}} \times 687 \cancel{\text{mm Hg}}}$$

$$= 3.87 \text{ L}$$

EXAMPLE 11.4 The Combined Gas Law

A sample of gas has an initial volume of 158 mL at a pressure of 735 mm Hg and a temperature of 34 °C. If the gas is compressed to a volume of 108 mL and heated to a temperature of 85 °C, what is its final pressure in millimeters of mercury?

SORT

You are given an initial pressure, temperature, and volume as well as a final temperature and volume. You are asked to find the final pressure.

GIVEN:

$P_1 = 735$ mm Hg

$t_1 = 34$ °C $t_2 = 85$ °C

$V_1 = 158$ mL $V_2 = 108$ mL

FIND: P_2

STRATEGIZE

Draw a solution map beginning with the given quantities. The combined gas law shows the relationship necessary to get to the find quantity.

SOLUTION MAP

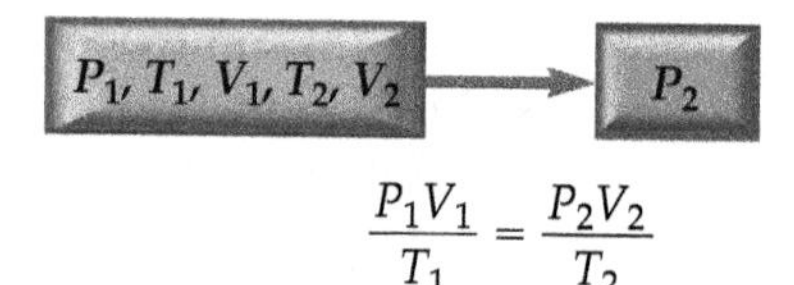

$$\frac{P_1V_1}{T_1} = \frac{P_2V_2}{T_2}$$

RELATIONSHIPS USED

$$\frac{P_1V_1}{T_1} = \frac{P_2V_2}{T_2}$$ (Combined gas law, presented in this section)

SOLVE

Solve the equation for the quantity you are trying to find (P_2).

SOLUTION

$$\frac{P_1V_1}{T_1} = \frac{P_2V_2}{T_2}$$

$$P_2 = \frac{P_1V_1T_2}{T_1V_2}$$

Before you substitute in the numerical values, you must convert the temperatures to kelvins.

$$T_1 = 34 + 273 = 307 \text{ K}$$

$$T_2 = 85 + 273 = 358 \text{ K}$$

Once you have converted the temperature to kelvins, substitute into the equation to find P_2.

$$P_2 = \frac{735 \text{ mm Hg} \times 158 \cancel{\text{mL}} \times 358 \cancel{\text{K}}}{307 \cancel{\text{K}} \times 108 \cancel{\text{mL}}}$$

$$= 1.25 \times 10^3 \text{ mm Hg}$$

CHECK

Check your answer. Are the units correct? Does the answer make physical sense?

The answer has the correct units, mm Hg. The answer is reasonable because the decrease in volume and the increase in temperature should result in a pressure that is higher than the initial pressure.

▶SKILLBUILDER 11.4 | The Combined Gas Law

A balloon has a volume of 3.7 L at a pressure of 1.1 atm and a temperature of 30 °C. If the balloon is submerged in water to a depth where the pressure is 4.7 atm and the temperature is 15 °C, what will its volume be (assume that any changes in pressure caused by the skin of the balloon are negligible)?

▶FOR MORE PRACTICE Example 11.15; Problems 51, 52, 53, 54, 55, 56.

CONCEPTUAL CHECKPOINT 11.4

A volume of gas is confined to a cylinder with a freely moveable piston at one end. If you apply enough heat to double the Kelvin temperature of the gas,

(a) the pressure and volume will both double.

(b) the pressure will double but the volume will remain the same.

(c) the volume will double but the pressure will remain the same.

(d) the volume will double but the pressure will be halved.

11.7 Avogadro's Law: Volume and Moles

So far, we have learned how V, P, and T are interrelated, but we have considered only a constant amount of a gas. What happens when the amount of gas changes? If we make several measurements of the volume of a gas sample (at constant temperature and pressure) while varying the number of moles in the sample, we get results similar to those shown in ▼ Figure 11.18. We can see that the relationship between volume and number of moles is linear. An extrapolation to zero moles shows a zero volume, as we might expect. This relationship was first stated formally by Amedeo Avogadro (1776–1856) and is called **Avogadro's law**.

Avogadro's law assumes constant temperature and pressure.

Avogadro's law: The volume of a gas and the amount of the gas in moles (n) are directly proportional.

$$V \propto n$$

When the amount of gas in a sample is increased, its volume increases in direct proportion, which is yet another prediction of kinetic molecular theory. If the number of gas particles increases at constant pressure and temperature, the particles must occupy more volume.

Since $V \propto n$, then V/n = Constant. If the number of moles increases, then the volume increases in direct proportion so that the quotient, V/n, is always equal to the same constant. Thus, for two different measurements, we can say that $\frac{V_1}{n_1} = \text{Constant} = \frac{V_2}{n_2}$ or $\frac{V_1}{n_1} = \frac{V_2}{n_2}$.

You experience Avogadro's law when you inflate a balloon, for example. With each exhaled breath, you add more gas particles to the inside of the balloon, increasing its volume (▼ Figure 11.19). Avogadro's law can be used to calculate the volume of a gas following a change in the amount of the gas *as long as the pressure and temperature of the gas are constant*. For these calculations, Avogadro's law is expressed as

$$\frac{V_1}{n_1} = \frac{V_2}{n_2}$$

where V_1 and n_1 are the initial volume and number of moles of the gas and V_2 and n_2 are the final volume and number of moles. In calculations, Avogadro's law is used in a manner similar to the other gas laws, as shown in Example 11.5.

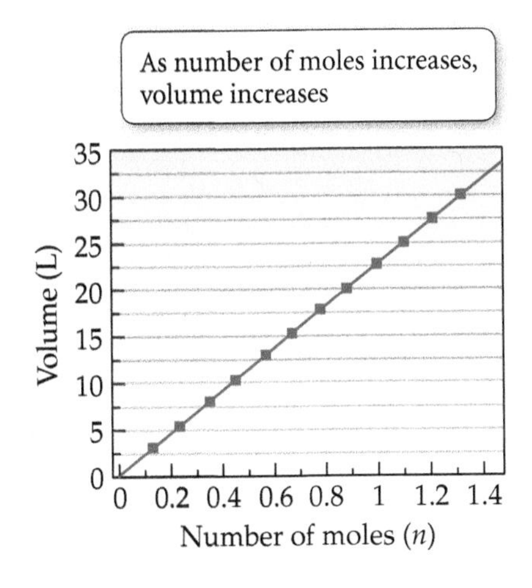

◀ FIGURE 11.18 **Volume versus number of moles** The volume of a gas sample increases linearly with the number of moles in the sample.

▶ FIGURE 11.19 **Blow-up** As you exhale into a balloon, you add gas molecules to the inside of the balloon, increasing its volume.

EXAMPLE 11.5 Avogadro's Law

A 4.8-L sample of helium gas contains 0.22 mol of helium. How many additional moles of helium gas must be added to the sample to obtain a volume of 6.4 L? Assume constant temperature and pressure.

SORT

You are given an initial volume, an initial number of moles, and a final volume. You are (essentially) asked to find the final number of moles.

GIVEN:

$V_1 = 4.8\ \text{L}$

$n_1 = 0.22\ \text{mol}$

$V_2 = 6.4\ \text{L}$

FIND: n_2

STRATEGIZE

Draw a solution map beginning with the given quantities. Avogadro's law shows the relationship necessary to get to the find quantity.

SOLUTION MAP

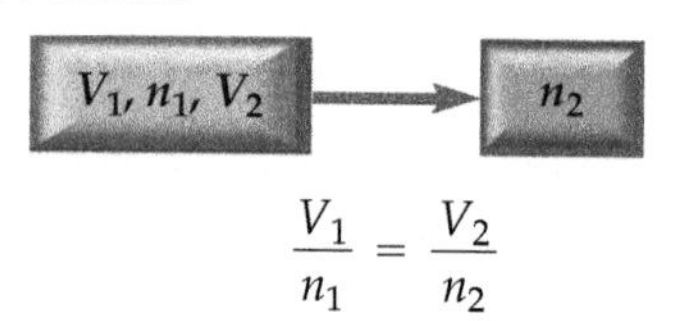

$$\frac{V_1}{n_1} = \frac{V_2}{n_2}$$

RELATIONSHIPS USED

$$\frac{V_1}{n_1} = \frac{V_2}{n_2}$$ (Avogadro's law, presented in this section)

SOLVE

Solve the equation for the quantity you are trying to find (n_2) and substitute the appropriate quantities to calculate n_2.

SOLUTION

$$\frac{V_1}{n_1} = \frac{V_2}{n_2}$$

$$n_2 = \frac{V_2}{V_1} n_1$$

$$= \frac{6.4\ \cancel{\text{L}}}{4.8\ \cancel{\text{L}}} 0.22\ \text{mol}$$

$$= 0.29\ \text{mol}$$

Since the balloon already contains 0.22 mol, subtract this quantity from the final number of moles to determine how much must be added.

mol to add = 0.29 − 0.22 = 0.07 mol

CHECK

Check your answer. Are the units correct? Does the answer make physical sense?

The answer has the correct units, moles. The answer is reasonable because the increase in the number of moles is proportional to the given increase in the volume.

▶SKILLBUILDER 11.5 | Avogadro's Law

A chemical reaction occurring in a cylinder equipped with a moveable piston produces 0.58 mol of a gaseous product. If the cylinder contained 0.11 mol of gas before the reaction and had an initial volume of 2.1 L, what was its volume after the reaction?

▶FOR MORE PRACTICE Problems 45, 46, 47, 48.

CONCEPTUAL CHECKPOINT 11.5

If each gas sample has the same temperature and pressure, which will have the greatest volume?

(a) 1 g O_2

(b) 1 g Ar

(c) 1 g H_2

11.8 The Ideal Gas Law: Pressure, Volume, Temperature, and Moles

The relationships covered so far can be combined into a single law that encompasses all of them. So far, we know that:

$V \propto \frac{1}{P}$ (Boyle's law)
$V \propto T$ (Charles's law)
$V \propto n$ (Avogadro's law)

Combining these three expressions, we get:

$$V \propto \frac{nT}{P}$$

The volume of a gas is directly proportional to the number of moles of gas and the temperature of the gas and is inversely proportional to the pressure of the gas. We can replace the proportional sign with an equal sign by adding R, a proportionality constant called the **ideal gas constant.**

$$V = \frac{RnT}{P}$$

Rearranging, we get the **ideal gas law**:

The ideal gas law: $PV = nRT$

The value of R, the ideal gas constant, is:

R can also be expressed in other units, but its numerical value will be different.

$$R = 0.0821 \frac{\text{L} \cdot \text{atm}}{\text{mol} \cdot \text{K}}$$

The ideal gas law contains within it the simple gas laws that we have learned. For example, recall that Boyle's law states that $V \propto 1/P$ when the amount of gas (n) and the temperature of the gas (T) are kept constant. To derive Boyle's law, we can rearrange the ideal gas law as follows:

$$PV = nRT$$

First, divide both sides by P.

$$V = \frac{nRT}{P}$$

Then put the variables that are constant in parentheses.

$$V = (nRT)\frac{1}{P}$$

Since n and T are constant in this case and since R is always a constant,

$$V = (\text{Constant}) \times \frac{1}{P}$$

which gives us Boyle's law $\left(V \propto \frac{1}{P}\right)$.

The ideal gas law also shows how other pairs of variables are related. For example, from Charles's law we know that volume is proportional to temperature at constant pressure and a constant number of moles. But what if we heat a sample of gas at constant *volume* and a constant number of moles? This question applies to the warning labels on aerosol cans such as hair spray or deodorants. These labels warn the user against excessive heating or incineration of the can, even after the contents are used up. Why? An aerosol can that appears empty actually contains a fixed amount of gas trapped in a fixed volume. What would happen if you heated the can? Let's rearrange the ideal gas law to clearly see the relationship between pressure and temperature at constant volume and a constant number of moles.

$$PV = nRT$$

If we divide both sides by V, we get:

$$P = \frac{nRT}{V}$$

$$P = \left(\frac{nR}{V}\right)T$$

The relationship between pressure and temperature is also known as Gay-Lussac's law.

Since n and V are constant and since R is always a constant:

$$P = \text{Constant} \times T$$

As the temperature of a fixed amount of gas in a fixed volume increases, the pressure increases. In an aerosol can, this pressure increase can cause the can to explode, which is why aerosol cans should not be heated or incinerated. Table 11.2 summarizes the relationships between all of the simple gas laws and the ideal gas law.

TABLE 11.2 Relationships between Simple Gas Laws and Ideal Gas Law

Variable Quantities	Constant Quantities	Ideal Gas Law in Form of Variables-constant	Simple Gas Law	Name of Simple Law
V and P	n and T	$PV = nRT$	$P_1V_1 = P_2V_2$	Boyle's law
V and T	n and P	$\frac{V}{T} = \frac{nR}{P}$	$\frac{V_1}{T_1} = \frac{V_2}{T_2}$	Charles's law
P and T	n and V	$\frac{P}{T} = \frac{nR}{V}$	$\frac{P_1}{T_1} = \frac{P_2}{T_2}$	Gay-Lussac's law
P and n	V and T	$\frac{P}{n} = \frac{RT}{V}$	$\frac{P_1}{n_1} = \frac{P_2}{n_2}$	
V and n	T and P	$\frac{V}{n} = \frac{RT}{P}$	$\frac{V_1}{n_1} = \frac{V_2}{n_2}$	Avogadro's law

The ideal gas law can be used to determine the value of any one of the four variables (P, V, n, or T) given the other three. However, each of the quantities in the ideal gas law *must be expressed* in the units within R.

- Pressure **(P)** must be expressed in atmospheres.
- Volume **(V)** must be expressed in liters.
- Amount of gas **(n)** must be expressed in moles.
- Temperature **(T)** must be expressed in kelvins.

For example, suppose we want to know the pressure of 0.18 mol of a gas in a 1.2-L flask at 298 K. We begin by sorting the information in the problem statement.

GIVEN: $n = 0.18$ mol
$V = 1.2$ L
$T = 298$ K

FIND: P

SOLUTION MAP

We then strategize by drawing a solution map that shows how the ideal gas law takes us from the given quantities to the find quantity.

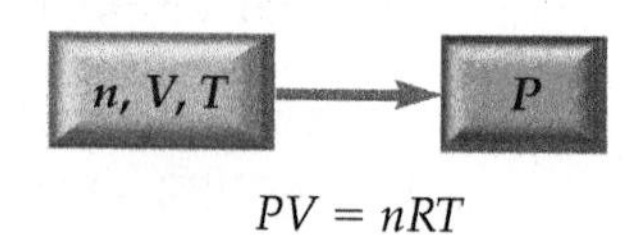

$PV = nRT$

RELATIONSHIPS USED

$$PV = nRT \text{ (Ideal gas law, presented in this section)}$$

SOLUTION

We then solve the equation for the quantity we are trying to find (in this case, P).

$$PV = nRT$$

$$P = \frac{nRT}{V}$$

Next we substitute in the numerical values and calculate the answer.

$$P = \frac{0.18 \text{ mol} \times 0.0821 \frac{\text{L} \cdot \text{atm}}{\text{mol} \cdot \text{K}} \times 298 \text{ K}}{1.2 \text{ L}}$$

$$= 3.7 \text{ atm}$$

Notice that all units cancel except the units of the quantity we need (atm).

EXAMPLE 11.6 The Ideal Gas Law

Calculate the volume occupied by 0.845 mol of nitrogen gas at a pressure of 1.37 atm and a temperature of 315 K.

SORT

You are given the number of moles, the pressure, and the temperature of a gas sample. You are asked to find the volume.

GIVEN:

$n = 0.845$ mol

$P = 1.37$ atm

$T = 315$ K

FIND: V

STRATEGIZE

Draw a solution map beginning with the given quantities. The ideal gas law shows the relationship necessary to get to the find quantity.

SOLUTION MAP

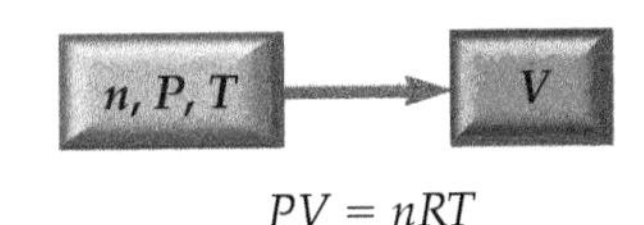

$PV = nRT$

RELATIONSHIPS USED

$PV = nRT$ (Ideal gas law, presented in this section)

SOLVE

Solve the equation for the quantity you are trying to find (V) and substitute the appropriate quantities to compute V.

SOLUTION

$$PV = nRT$$

$$V = \frac{nRT}{P}$$

$$V = \frac{0.845 \text{ mol} \times 0.0821 \frac{\text{L} \cdot \text{atm}}{\text{mol} \cdot \text{K}} \times 315 \text{ K}}{1.37 \text{ atm}} = 16.0 \text{ L}$$

CHECK

Check your answer. Are the units correct? Does the answer make physical sense?

The answer has the correct units for volume, liters. The *value* of the answer is a bit more difficult to judge. However, at standard temperature and pressure ($T = 0$ °C or 273.15 K and $P = 1$ atm), 1 mol gas occupies 22.4 L (see Section 11.10). Therefore our answer of 16.0 L seems reasonable for the volume of 0.85 mol of gas under conditions that are not too far from standard temperature and pressure.

▶SKILLBUILDER 11.6 | The Ideal Gas Law

An 8.5-L tire is filled with 0.55 mol of gas at a temperature of 305 K. What is the pressure of the gas in the tire?

▶FOR MORE PRACTICE Example 11.16; Problems 59, 60, 61, 62.

If the units given in an ideal gas law problem are different from those of the ideal gas constant (atm, L, mol, and K), you must convert to the correct units before you substitute into the ideal gas equation, as demonstrated in Example 11.7.

EXAMPLE 11.7 The Ideal Gas Law Requiring Unit Conversion

Calculate the number of moles of gas in a basketball inflated to a total pressure of 24.2 psi with a volume of 3.2 L at 25 °C.

SORT

You are given the pressure, the volume, and the temperature of a gas sample. You are asked to find the number of moles.

GIVEN:

$P = 24.2\text{ psi}$

$V = 3.2\text{ L}$

$t = 25\ ^\circ\text{C}$

FIND: n

STRATEGIZE

Draw a solution map beginning with the given quantities. The ideal gas law shows the relationship necessary to get to the find quantity.

SOLUTION MAP

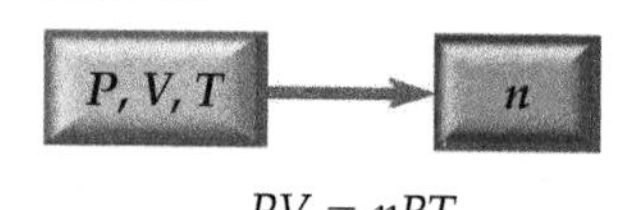

$PV = nRT$

RELATIONSHIPS USED

$PV = nRT$ (Ideal gas law, presented in this section)

SOLVE

Solve the equation for the quantity you are trying to find (n).

SOLUTION

$$PV = nRT$$

$$n = \frac{PV}{RT}$$

Before substituting into the equation, you must convert P and t into the correct units. (Since 1.6462 atm is an intermediate answer, mark the least significant digit, but don't round until the end.)

$$P = 24.2\ \cancel{\text{psi}} \times \frac{1\text{ atm}}{14.7\ \cancel{\text{psi}}} = 1.6\underline{4}62\text{ atm}$$

$$T = t + 273$$

$$= 25 + 273 = 298\text{ K}$$

Finally, substitute into the equation to calculate n.

$$n = \frac{1.6\underline{4}62\ \cancel{\text{atm}} \times 3.2\ \cancel{\text{L}}}{0.0821\ \dfrac{\cancel{\text{L}}\cdot\cancel{\text{atm}}}{\text{mol}\cdot\cancel{\text{K}}} \times 298\ \cancel{\text{K}}}$$

$$= 0.22\text{ mol}$$

CHECK

Check your answer. Are the units correct? Does the answer make physical sense?

The answer has the correct units, moles. The *value* of the answer is a bit more difficult to judge. Again, knowing that at standard temperature and pressure ($T = 0\ ^\circ\text{C}$ or 273.15 K and $P = 1$ atm), 1 mol of gas occupies 22.4 L can help (see Check step in Example 11.6). A 3.2 L sample of gas at STP would contain about 0.15 mol; therefore at a greater pressure, the sample should contain a bit more than 0.15 mol, which is consistent with the answer.

▶SKILLBUILDER 11.7 | The Ideal Gas Law Requiring Unit Conversion

How much volume does 0.556 mol of gas occupy when its pressure is 715 mm Hg and its temperature is 58 °C?

▶SKILLBUILDER PLUS

Find the pressure in millimeters of mercury of a 0.133-g sample of helium gas at 32 °C and contained in a 648-mL container.

▶FOR MORE PRACTICE Problems 63, 64, 67, 68.

MOLAR MASS OF A GAS FROM THE IDEAL GAS LAW

The ideal gas law can be used in combination with mass measurements to calculate the molar mass of a gas. For example, a sample of gas has a mass of 0.136 g. Its volume is 0.112 L at a temperature of 298 K and a pressure of 1.06 atm. Find its molar mass.

We begin by sorting the information given in the problem.

GIVEN:

$m = 0.136\text{ g}$ $\quad\quad V = 0.112\text{ L}$

$T = 298\text{ K}$ $\quad\quad P = 1.06\text{ atm}$

FIND: molar mass (g/mol)

SOLUTION MAP

We then strategize by drawing a solution map, which in this case has two parts. In the first part, we use P, V, and T to find the number of moles of gas. In the second part, we use the number of moles of gas and the given mass to find the molar mass.

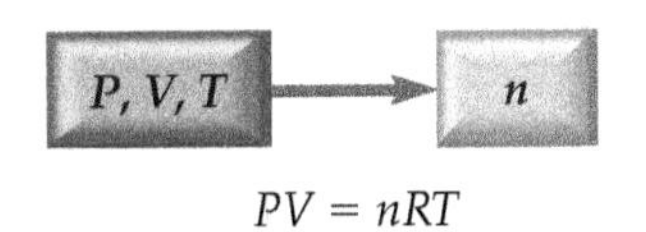

$$PV = nRT$$

n, m → Molar mass

$$\text{Molar mass} = \frac{\text{Mass } (m)}{\text{Moles } (n)}$$

RELATIONSHIPS USED

$$PV = nRT \text{ (Ideal gas law, presented in this section)}$$

$$\text{Molar mass} = \frac{\text{Mass}}{\text{Moles}} \text{ (Definition of molar mass from Section 6.3)}$$

SOLUTION

$$PV = nRT$$

$$n = \frac{PV}{RT}$$

$$= \frac{1.06\ \text{atm} \times 0.112\ \text{L}}{0.0821\ \frac{\text{L} \cdot \text{atm}}{\text{mol} \cdot \text{K}} \times 298\ \text{K}}$$

$$= 4.8\underline{5}25 \times 10^{-3}\ \text{mol}$$

$$\text{Molar mass} = \frac{\text{Mass } (m)}{\text{Moles } (n)}$$

$$= \frac{0.136\ \text{g}}{4.8\underline{5}25 \times 10^{-3}\ \text{mol}}$$

$$= 28.0\ \text{g/mol}$$

EXAMPLE 11.8 Molar Mass Using the Ideal Gas Law and Mass Measurement

A sample of gas has a mass of 0.311 g. Its volume is 0.225 L at a temperature of 55 °C and a pressure of 886 mm Hg. Find its molar mass.

SORT

You are given the mass, the volume, the temperature, and the pressure of a gas sample. You are asked to find the molar mass of the gas.

GIVEN:

$$m = 0.311 \text{ g}$$
$$V = 0.225 \text{ L}$$
$$t = 55\ °\text{C}$$
$$P = 886 \text{ mm Hg}$$

FIND: Molar mass (g/mol)

STRATEGIZE

In the first part of the solution map, use the ideal gas law to find the number of moles of gas from the other given quantities.

SOLUTION MAP

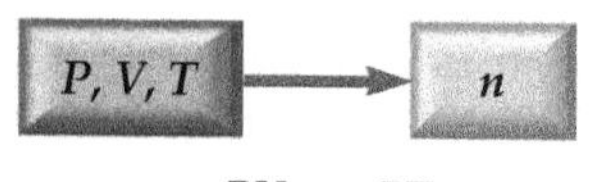

$$PV = nRT$$

In the second part, use the number of moles from the first part, as well as the given mass, to find the molar mass.

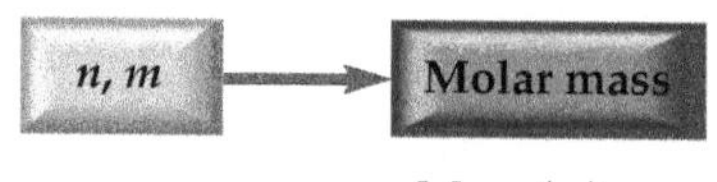

$$\text{Molar mass} = \frac{\text{Mass } (m)}{\text{Moles } (n)}$$

RELATIONSHIPS USED

$PV = nRT$ (Ideal gas law, presented in this section)

$\text{Molar mass} = \dfrac{\text{Mass } (m)}{\text{Moles } (n)}$ (Definition of molar mass from Section 6.3)

SOLVE

First, solve the ideal gas law for n.

SOLUTION

$$PV = nRT$$
$$n = \frac{PV}{RT}$$

Before substituting into the equation, you must convert the pressure to atm and temperature to K.

$$P = 886 \text{ mm Hg} \times \frac{1 \text{ atm}}{760 \text{ mm Hg}} = 1.1\underline{6}58 \text{ atm}$$

$$T = 55\ °\text{C} + 273 = 328 \text{ K}$$

Now, substitute into the equation to calculate n, the number of moles.

$$n = \frac{1.1\underline{6}58 \text{ atm} \times 0.225 \text{ L}}{0.0821 \dfrac{\text{L} \cdot \text{atm}}{\text{mol} \cdot \text{K}} \times 328 \text{ K}}$$
$$= 9.7\underline{4}06 \times 10^{-3} \text{ mol}$$

Finally, use the number of moles just found and the given mass (m) to find the molar mass.

$$\text{Molar mass} = \frac{\text{Mass } (m)}{\text{Moles } (n)}$$
$$= \frac{0.311 \text{ g}}{9.7\underline{4}06 \times 10^{-3} \text{ mol}}$$
$$= 31.9 \text{ g/mol}$$

CHECK

Check your answer. Are the units correct? Does the answer make physical sense?

The answer has the correct units, g/mol. The answer is reasonable because its value is within the range of molar masses for common compounds.

▶SKILLBUILDER 11.8 | Molar Mass Using the Ideal Gas Law and Mass Measurement

A sample of gas has a mass of 827 mg. Its volume is 0.270 L at a temperature of 88 °C and a pressure of 975 mm Hg. Find its molar mass.

▶FOR MORE PRACTICE Problems 69, 70, 71, 72.

Although a complete derivation is beyond the scope of this book, the ideal gas law follows directly from the kinetic molecular theory of gases. Consequently, the ideal gas law holds only under conditions where the kinetic molecular theory holds. The ideal gas law works exactly only for gases that are acting ideally (◀ Figure 11.20), which means that (a) the volume of the gas particles is small compared to the space between them and (b) the forces between the gas particles are not significant. These assumptions break down (▼ Figure 11.21) under conditions of high pressure (because the space between particles is no longer much larger than the size of the particles themselves) or low temperatures (because the gas particles move so slowly that their interactions become significant). For all of the problems encountered in this book, you may assume ideal gas behavior.

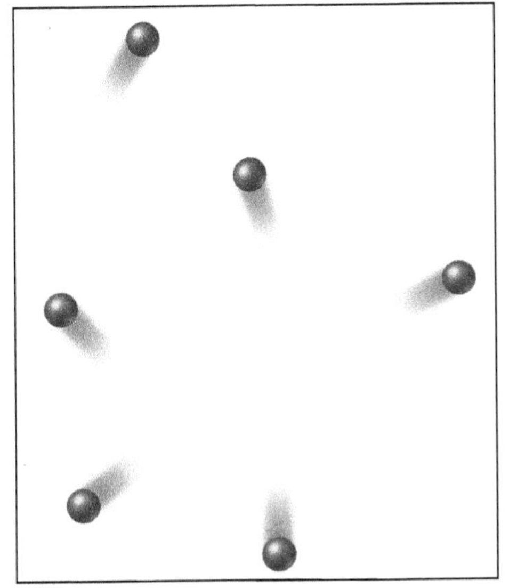

Ideal gas conditions
•High temperature
•Low pressure
•Particle size small compared to space between particles.
•Interactions between particles are insignificant.

▲ FIGURE 11.20 Conditions for ideal gas behavior At high temperatures and low pressures, the assumptions of the kinetic molecular theory apply.

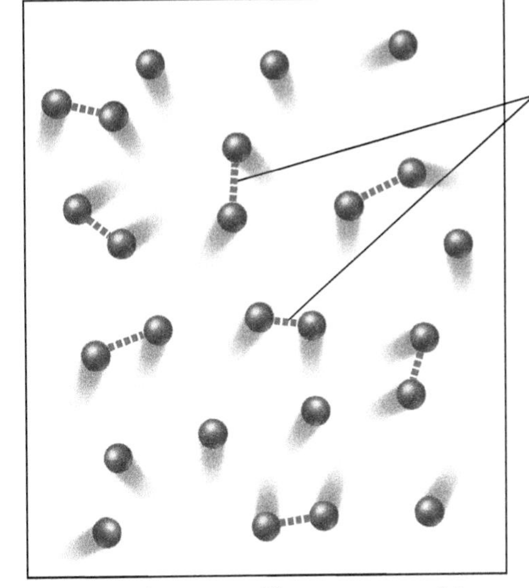

▶ FIGURE 11.21 Conditions for nonideal gas behavior At low temperatures and high pressures, the assumptions of the kinetic molecular theory are not valid.

11.9 Mixtures of Gases: Why Deep-Sea Divers Breathe a Mixture of Helium and Oxygen

Many gas samples are not pure but consist of mixtures of gases. The air in our atmosphere, for example, is a mixture containing 78% nitrogen, 21% oxygen, 0.9% argon, 0.04% carbon dioxide (Table 11.3), and a few other gases in smaller amounts.

According to the kinetic molecular theory, each of the components in a gas mixture acts independently of the others. For example, the nitrogen molecules in air exert a certain pressure—78% of the total pressure—that is independent of the

TABLE 11.3 Composition of Dry Air

Gas	Percent by Volume (%)
nitrogen (N_2)	78
oxygen (O_2)	21
argon (Ar)	0.9
carbon dioxide (CO_2)	0.04

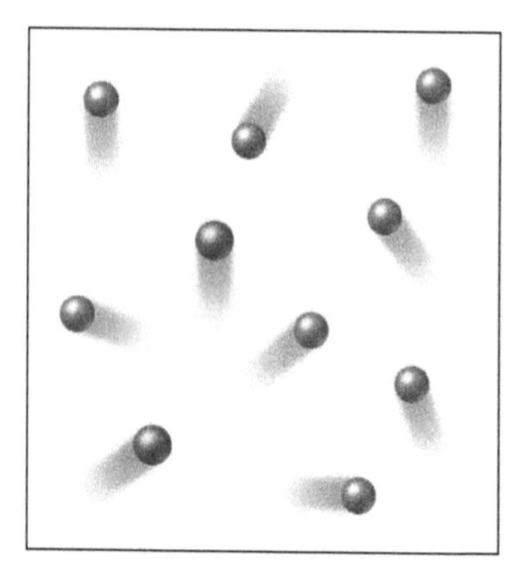

Gas mixture (80% He, 20% Ne)
$P_{tot} = 1.0$ atm
$P_{He} = 0.80$ atm
$P_{Ne} = 0.20$ atm

▲ **FIGURE 11.22 Partial pressures** A gas mixture at a total pressure of 1.0 atm consisting of 80% helium and 20% neon will have a helium partial pressure of 0.80 atm and a neon partial pressure of 0.20 atm.

The fractional composition is the percent composition divided by 100.

We can ignore the contribution of CO_2 and other trace gases because they are present in very small amounts.

presence of the other gases in the mixture. Likewise, the oxygen molecules in air exert a certain pressure—21% of the total pressure—that is also independent of the presence of the other gases in the mixture. The pressure due to any individual component in a gas mixture is called the **partial pressure** of that component. The partial pressure of any component is that component's fractional composition times the total pressure of the mixture (◀ Figure 11.22).

Partial pressure of component:

$$= \text{Fractional composition of component} \times \text{Total pressure}$$

For example, the partial pressure of nitrogen (P_{N_2}) in air at 1.0 atm is:

$$P_{N_2} = 0.78 \times 1.0 \text{ atm}$$
$$= 0.78 \text{ atm}$$

Similarly, the partial pressure of oxygen in air at 1.0 atm is:

$$P_{O_2} = 0.21 \times 1.0 \text{ atm}$$
$$= 0.21 \text{ atm}$$

The sum of the partial pressures of each of the components in a gas mixture must equal the total pressure, as expressed by **Dalton's law of partial pressures**:

Dalton's law of partial pressures:

$$P_{tot} = P_a + P_b + P_c + \ldots$$

where P_{tot} is the total pressure and P_a, P_b, P_c, . . . are the partial pressures of the components.

For 1 atm air:

$$P_{tot} = P_{N_2} + P_{O_2} + P_{Ar}$$
$$P_{tot} = 0.78 \text{ atm} + 0.21 \text{ atm} + 0.01 \text{ atm}$$
$$= 1.00 \text{ atm}$$

EXAMPLE 11.9 Total Pressure and Partial Pressure

A mixture of helium, neon, and argon has a total pressure of 558 mm Hg. If the partial pressure of helium is 341 mm Hg and the partial pressure of neon is 112 mm Hg, what is the partial pressure of argon?

You are given the total pressure of a gas mixture and the partial pressures of two (of its three) components. You are asked to find the partial pressure of the third component.	**GIVEN:** $P_{tot} = 558$ mm Hg $P_{He} = 341$ mm Hg $P_{Ne} = 112$ mm Hg **FIND:** P_{Ar}
To solve this problem, solve Dalton's law for the partial pressure of argon and substitute the correct values to calculate it.	**SOLUTION** $P_{tot} = P_{He} + P_{Ne} + P_{Ar}$ $P_{Ar} = P_{tot} - P_{He} - P_{Ne}$ $= 558 \text{ mm Hg} - 341 \text{ mm Hg} - 112 \text{ mm Hg}$ $= 105 \text{ mm Hg}$

▶**SKILLBUILDER 11.9 | Total Pressure and Partial Pressure**

A sample of hydrogen gas is mixed with water vapor. The mixture has a total pressure of 745 torr, and the water vapor has a partial pressure of 24 torr. What is the partial pressure of the hydrogen gas?

▶**FOR MORE PRACTICE** Example 11.17; Problems 73, 74, 75, 76.

DEEP-SEA DIVING AND PARTIAL PRESSURE

Our lungs have evolved to breathe oxygen at a partial pressure of $P_{O_2} = 0.21$ atm. If the total pressure decreases—as happens when we climb a mountain, for example—the partial pressure of oxygen also decreases. For example, on top of Mount Everest, where the total pressure is 0.311 atm, the partial pressure of oxygen is only 0.065 atm. As we learned earlier, low oxygen levels can have negative physiological effects, a condition called **hypoxia**, or oxygen starvation. Mild hypoxia causes dizziness, headache, and shortness of breath. Severe hypoxia, which occurs when P_{O_2} drops below 0.1 atm, may cause unconsciousness or even death. For this reason, climbers hoping to make the summit of Mount Everest usually carry oxygen to breathe.

▲ Mountain climbers on Mount Everest require oxygen because the pressure is so low that the lack of oxygen causes hypoxia, a condition that in severe cases can be fatal.

High oxygen levels can also have negative physiological effects. Scuba divers, as we have learned, breathe pressurized air. At 30 m, a scuba diver breathes air at a total pressure of 4.0 atm, making P_{O_2} about 0.84 atm. This increased partial pressure of oxygen causes a higher density of oxygen molecules in the lungs (▼ Figure 11.23), which results in a higher concentration of oxygen in body tissues. When P_{O_2} increases beyond 1.4 atm, the increased oxygen concentration in body tissues causes a condition called **oxygen toxicity**, which is characterized by muscle twitching, tunnel vision, and convulsions (▶ Figure 11.24). Divers who venture too deep without proper precautions have drowned because of oxygen toxicity.

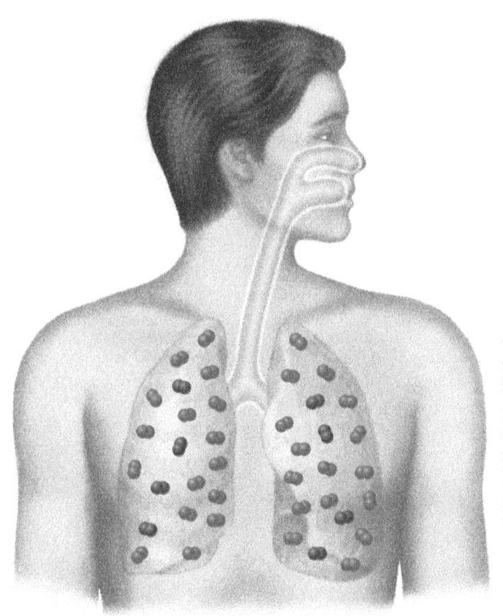

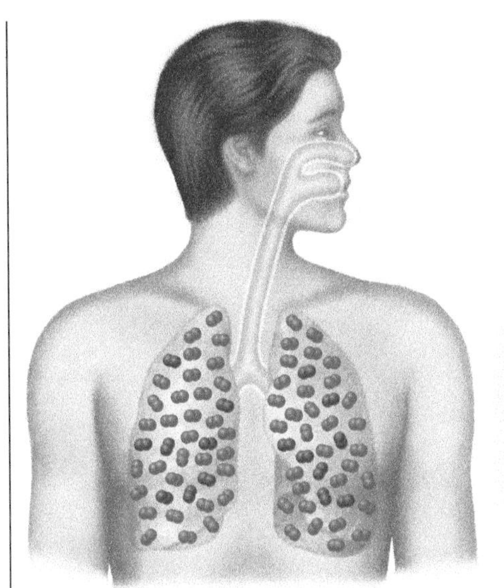

▲ **FIGURE 11.23 Too much of a good thing** When a person is breathing compressed air, there is a larger partial pressure of oxygen in the lungs. A large oxygen partial pressure in the lungs results in a larger amount of oxygen in bodily tissues. When the oxygen partial pressure increases beyond 1.4 atm, oxygen toxicity results. (In this figure, the red molecules are oxygen and the blue ones are nitrogen.)

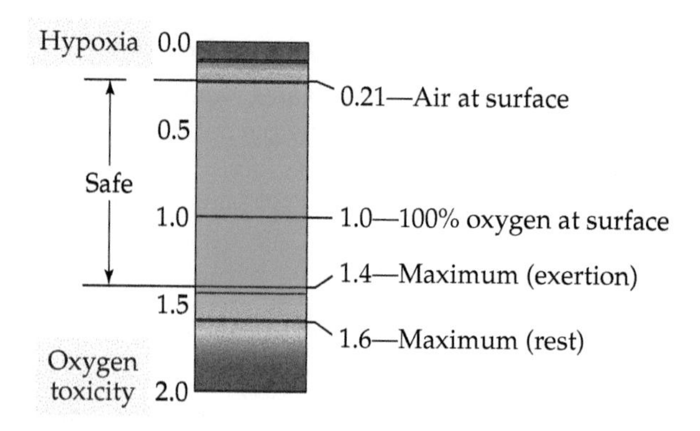

▶ **FIGURE 11.24 Oxygen partial pressure limits** The partial pressure of oxygen in air at sea level is 0.21 atm. If this pressure drops by 50%, fatal hypoxia can result. High oxygen levels can also be harmful, but only if the partial pressure of oxygen increases by a factor of 7 or more.

A second problem associated with breathing pressurized air is the increase in nitrogen in the lungs. At 30 m a scuba diver breathes nitrogen at $P_{N_2} = 3.1$ atm, which causes an increase in nitrogen concentration in bodily tissues and fluids. When P_{N_2} increases beyond about 4 atm, a condition called **nitrogen narcosis**, which is also referred to as *rapture of the deep*, results. Divers describe this condition as a feeling of being tipsy. A diver breathing compressed air at 60 m feels as if he has had too much wine.

To avoid oxygen toxicity and nitrogen narcosis, deep-sea divers—those venturing beyond 50 m—breathe specialized mixtures of gases. One common mixture is called heliox, a mixture of helium and oxygen. These mixtures usually contain a smaller percentage of oxygen than would be found in air, thereby lowering the risk of oxygen toxicity. Heliox also contains helium instead of nitrogen, eliminating the risk of nitrogen narcosis.

EXAMPLE 11.10 Partial Pressure, Total Pressure, and Percent Composition

Calculate the partial pressure of oxygen that a diver breathes with a heliox mixture containing 2.0% oxygen at a depth of 100 m where the total pressure is 10.0 atm.

You are given the percent oxygen in the mixture and the total pressure. You are asked to find the partial pressure of oxygen.	**GIVEN:** O_2 percent = 2.0% P_{tot} = 10.0 atm **FIND:** P_{O_2}
The partial pressure of a component in a gas mixture is equal to the fractional composition of the component multiplied by the total pressure. Calculate the fractional composition of O_2 by dividing the percent composition by 100. Calculate the partial pressure of O_2 by multiplying the fractional composition by the total pressure.	**SOLUTION** Partial pressure of component = Fractional composition of component × Total pressure Fractional composition of $O_2 = \frac{2.0}{100} = 0.020$ $P_{O_2} = 0.020 \times 10.0 \text{ atm} = 0.20 \text{ atm}$

▶**SKILLBUILDER 11.10 | Partial Pressure, Total Pressure, and Percent Composition**

A diver breathing heliox with an oxygen composition of 5.0% wants to adjust the total pressure so that $P_{O_2} = 0.21$ atm. What must the total pressure be?

▶**FOR MORE PRACTICE** Problems 79, 80, 81, 82.

COLLECTING GASES OVER WATER

When the product of a chemical reaction is gaseous, it is often collected by the displacement of water. For example, suppose the following reaction is used as a source of hydrogen gas.

$$Zn(s) + 2\,HCl(aq) \longrightarrow ZnCl_2(aq) + H_2(g)$$

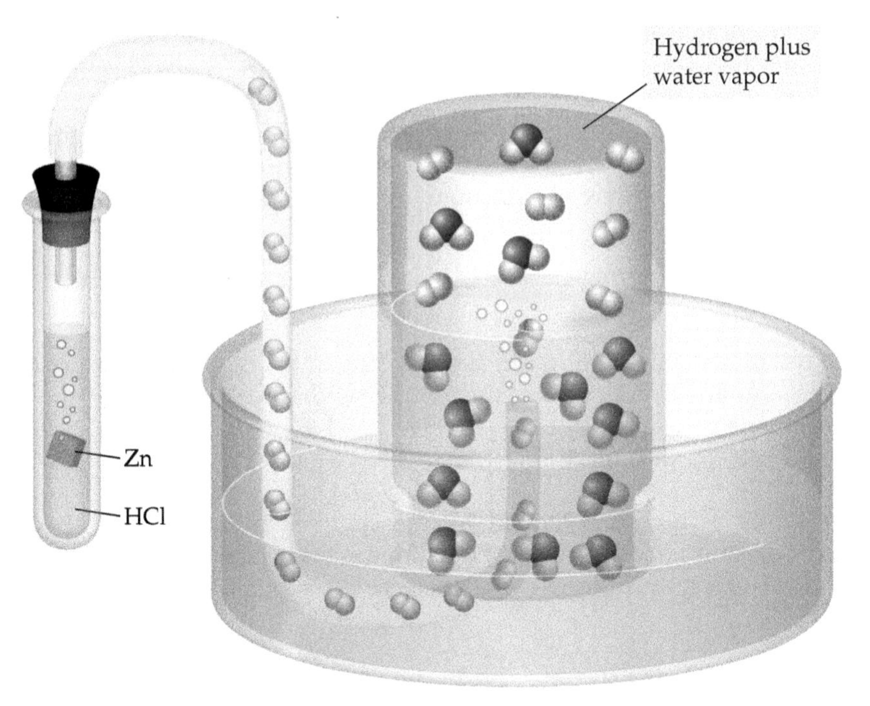

▲ **FIGURE 11.25 Vapor pressure** When a gas from a chemical reaction is collected through water, water molecules become mixed with the gas molecules. The pressure of water vapor in the final mixture is the vapor pressure of water at the temperature at which the gas is collected.

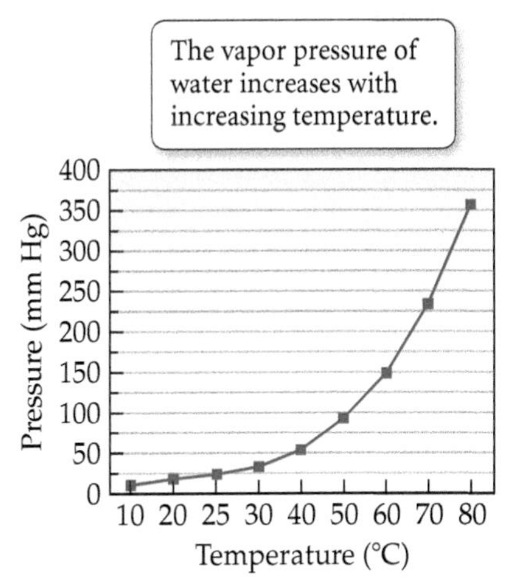

▲ **FIGURE 11.26 Vapor pressure of water as a function of temperature** Vapor pressure increases with increasing temperature.

Vapor pressure is covered in detail in Chapter 12.

TABLE 11.4 Vapor Pressure of Water versus Temperature

Temperature (°C)	Pressure (mm Hg)
10 °C	9.2
20 °C	17.5
25 °C	23.8
30 °C	31.8
40 °C	55.3
50 °C	92.5
60 °C	149.4
70 °C	233.7
80 °C	355.1

As the hydrogen gas forms, it bubbles through the water and gathers in the collection flask (▲ Figure 11.25). However, the hydrogen gas collected in this way is not pure but is mixed with water vapor because some water molecules evaporate and become mixed with the hydrogen molecules. The partial pressure of water in the mixture depends on the temperature and is called its **vapor pressure** (Table 11.4 and ▲ Figure 11.26). Vapor pressure increases with increasing temperature because higher temperatures cause more water molecules to evaporate.

Suppose we collect the hydrogen gas over water at a total pressure of 758 mm Hg and a temperature of 25 °C. What is the partial pressure of the hydrogen gas? We know that the total pressure is 758 mm Hg and that the partial pressure of water is 23.8 mm Hg (its vapor pressure at 25 °C).

$$P_{tot} = P_{H_2} + P_{H_2O}$$

$$758 \text{ mm Hg} = P_{H_2} + 23.8 \text{ mm Hg}$$

Therefore,

$$P_{H_2} = 758 \text{ mm Hg} - 23.8 \text{ mm Hg}$$
$$= 734 \text{ mm Hg}$$

The partial pressure of the hydrogen in the mixture will be 734 mm Hg.

11.10 Gases in Chemical Reactions

See Section 8.3.

Chapter 8 describes how the coefficients in chemical equations can be used as conversion factors between moles of reactants and moles of products in a chemical reaction. These conversion factors could be used to determine, for example, the amount of product obtained in a chemical reaction based on a given amount of reactant or the amount of one reactant needed to completely react with a given amount of another reactant. The general solution map for these kinds of calculations is

$$\text{Moles A} \longrightarrow \text{Moles B}$$

where A and B are two different substances involved in the reaction and the conversion factor between them comes from the stoichiometric coefficients in the balanced chemical equation.

In reactions involving gaseous reactants or products, the amount of gas is often specified in terms of its volume at a given temperature and pressure. In cases like this, we can use the ideal gas law to convert pressure, volume, and temperature to moles.

$$n = \frac{PV}{RT}$$

We can then use the stoichiometric coefficients to convert to other quantities in the reaction. For example, consider the reaction for the synthesis of ammonia.

$$3\,H_2(g) + N_2(g) \longrightarrow 2\,NH_3(g)$$

How many moles of NH_3 are formed by the complete reaction of 2.5 L of hydrogen at 381 K and 1.32 atm? Assume that there is more than enough N_2.

We begin by sorting the information in the problem statement.

GIVEN:

$V = 2.5\text{ L}$

$T = 381\text{ K}$

$P = 1.32\text{ atm (of } H_2)$

FIND: mol NH_3

SOLUTION MAP

We strategize by drawing a solution map. The solution map for this problem is similar to the solution maps for other stoichiometric problems (see Sections 8.3 and 8.4). However, we first use the ideal gas law to find mol H_2 from P, V, and T. Then we use the stoichiometric coefficients from the equation to convert mol H_2 to mol NH_3.

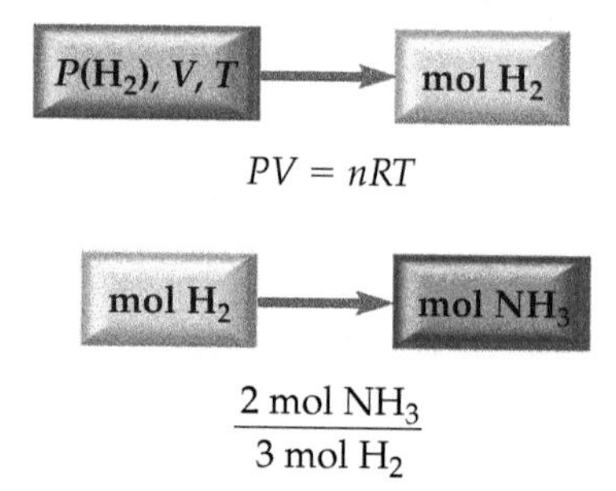

RELATIONSHIPS USED

$PV = nRT$ (ideal gas law, Section 11.8)

3 mol H_2 : 2 mol NH_3 (from balanced equation given in problem)

SOLUTION

We first solve the ideal gas equation for n.

$$PV = nRT$$

$$n = \frac{PV}{RT}$$

Then we substitute in the appropriate values.

$$n = \frac{1.32\,\cancel{\text{atm}} \times 2.5\,\cancel{\text{L}}}{0.0821\,\dfrac{\cancel{\text{L}} \cdot \cancel{\text{atm}}}{\text{mol} \cdot \cancel{\text{K}}} \times 381\,\cancel{\text{K}}}$$

$$= 0.1\underline{0}55\text{ mol } H_2$$

Next, we convert mol H_2 to mol NH_3.

$$0.1\underline{0}55 \text{ mol } H_2 \times \frac{2 \text{ mol } NH_3}{3 \text{ mol } H_2} = 0.070 \text{ mol } NH_3$$

There is enough H_2 to form 0.070 mol NH_3.

EXAMPLE 11.11 Gases in Chemical Reactions

How many liters of oxygen gas form when 294 g of $KClO_3$ completely react in this reaction (which is used in the ignition of fireworks)?

$$2\,KClO_3(s) \longrightarrow 2\,KCl(s) + 3\,O_2(g)$$

Assume that the oxygen gas is collected at $P = 755$ mm Hg and $T = 305$ K.

SORT

You are given the mass of a reactant in a chemical reaction. You are asked to find the volume of a gaseous product at a given pressure and temperature.

GIVEN:

294 g $KClO_3$

$P = 755$ mm Hg (of oxygen gas)

$T = 305$ K

FIND: Volume of O_2 in liters

STRATEGIZE

The solution map has two parts. In the first part, convert from g $KClO_3$ to mol $KClO_3$ and then to mol O_2.

In the second part, use mol O_2 as n in the ideal gas law to find the volume of O_2.

You will need the molar mass of $KClO_3$ and the stoichiometric relationship between $KClO_3$ and O_2 (from the balanced chemical equation). You will also need the ideal gas law.

SOLUTION MAP

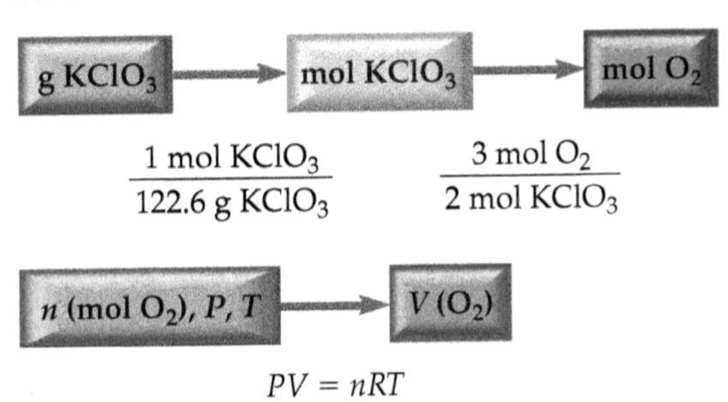

RELATIONSHIPS USED

1 mol $KClO_3$ = 122.6 g (molar mass of $KClO_3$)

2 mol $KClO_3$: 3 mol O_2 (from balanced equation given in problem)

$PV = nRT$ (ideal gas law, Section 11.8)

SOLVE

Begin by converting mass $KClO_3$ to mol $KClO_3$ and then to mol O_2.

SOLUTION

$$294 \text{ g } KClO_3 \times \frac{1 \text{ mol } KClO_3}{122.5 \text{ g } KClO_3} \times \frac{3 \text{ mol } O_2}{2 \text{ mol } KClO_3} = 3.60 \text{ mol } O_2$$

Then solve the ideal gas equation for V.

$$PV = nRT$$

$$V = \frac{nRT}{P}$$

Before substituting the values into this equation, you must convert the pressure to atm.

$$P = 755 \text{ mm Hg} \times \frac{1 \text{ atm}}{760 \text{ mm Hg}} = 0.99\underline{3}42 \text{ atm}$$

Finally, substitute the given quantities along with the number of moles just calculated to calculate the volume.

$$V = \frac{3.60 \text{ mol} \times 0.0821 \dfrac{\text{L} \cdot \text{atm}}{\text{mol} \cdot \text{K}} \times 305 \text{ K}}{0.99\underline{3}42 \text{ atm}}$$

$$= 90.7 \text{ L}$$

CHECK

Check your answer. Are the units correct? Does the answer make physical sense?

The answer has the correct units, liters. The *value* of the answer is a bit more difficult to judge. Again, knowing that at standard temperature and pressure ($T = 0$ °C or 273.15 K and $P = 1$ atm), 1 mol of gas occupies 22.4 L can help (see Check step in Example 11.6). A 90.7 L sample of gas at STP would contain about 4 mol; since we started with a little more than 2 mol $KClO_3$, and since 2 mol $KClO_3$ forms 3 mol O_2, an answer that corresponds to about 4 mol O_2 is reasonable.

▶**SKILLBUILDER 11.11 | Gases in Chemical Reactions**

In this reaction, 4.58 L of O_2 were formed at 745 mm Hg and 308 K. How many grams of Ag_2O decomposed?

$$2\ Ag_2O(s) \longrightarrow 4\ Ag(s) + O_2(g)$$

▶**FOR MORE PRACTICE** Problems 89, 90, 91, 92, 93, 94.

MOLAR VOLUME AT STANDARD TEMPERATURE AND PRESSURE

In Example 11.6 (in the Check step), we saw that the volume occupied by 1 mol of gas at 0 °C (273.15 K) and 1 atm is 22.4 L. These conditions are called **standard temperature and pressure (STP)**, and the volume occupied by 1 mol of gas under these conditions is called the **molar volume** of an ideal gas at STP. Using the ideal gas law, we can confirm that the molar volume at STP is 22.4 L.

$$V = \frac{nRT}{P}$$

$$= \frac{1.00\ \cancel{\text{mol}} \times 0.821\ \frac{\text{L} \cdot \cancel{\text{atm}}}{\cancel{\text{mol}} \cdot \text{K}} \times 273\ \text{K}}{1.00\ \cancel{\text{atm}}}$$

$$= 22.4\ \text{L}$$

Under standard conditions, therefore, we can use this ratio as a conversion factor.

The molar volume of 22.4 L applies only at STP.

$$1\ \text{mol} : 22.4\ \text{L}$$

One mole of any gas at standard temperature and pressure (STP) occupies 22.4 L.

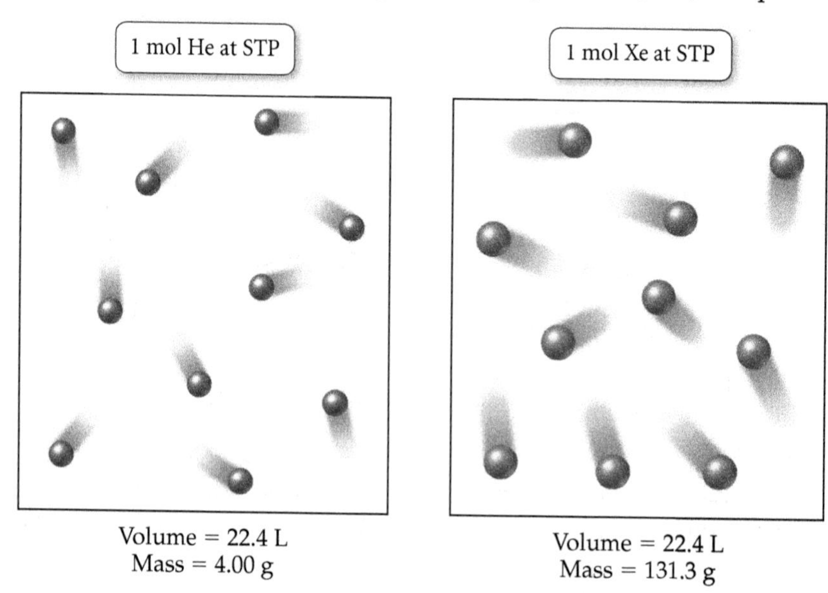

For example, suppose we wanted to calculate the number of liters of $\mathbf{CO_2}$ gas that forms at STP when 0.879 moles of $\mathbf{CaCO_3}$ undergoes this reaction:

$$CaCO_3(s) \longrightarrow CaO(s) + CO_2(g)$$

We begin by sorting the information in the problem statement.

GIVEN: 0.879 mol $CaCO_3$

FIND: $CO_2(g)$ in liters

SOLUTION MAP

We strategize by drawing a solution map that shows how to convert from mol $CaCO_3$ to mol CO_2 to L CO_2 using the molar volume at STP.

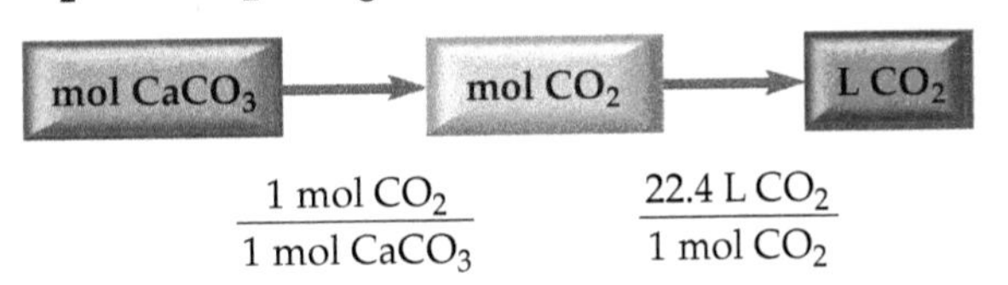

$$\frac{1 \text{ mol } CO_2}{1 \text{ mol } CaCO_3} \qquad \frac{22.4 \text{ L } CO_2}{1 \text{ mol } CO_2}$$

RELATIONSHIPS USED

1 mol $CaCO_3$: 1 mol CO_2 (from balanced equation given in problem)

1 mol = 22.4 L (at STP) (molar volume at STP, presented in this section)

SOLUTION

$$0.879 \text{ mol } CaCO_3 \times \frac{1 \text{ mol } CO_2}{1 \text{ mol } CaCO_3} \times \frac{22.4 \text{ L } CO_2}{1 \text{ mol } CO_2} = 19.7 \text{ L } CO_2$$

EXAMPLE 11.12 Using Molar Volume in Calculations

How many grams of water form when 1.24 L of H_2 gas at STP completely reacts with O_2?

$$2\,H_2(g) + O_2(g) \longrightarrow 2\,H_2O(g)$$

SORT You are given the volume of a reactant at STP and asked to find the mass of the product formed.	GIVEN: 1.24 L H_2 FIND: g H_2O
STRATEGIZE In the solution map, use the molar volume to convert from volume H_2 to mol H_2. Then use the stoichiometric relationship to convert to mol H_2O and finally the molar mass of H_2O to get to mass H_2O.	SOLUTION MAP 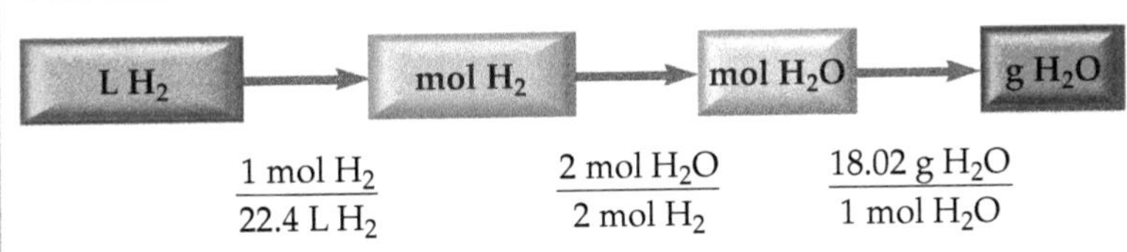 $\frac{1 \text{ mol } H_2}{22.4 \text{ L } H_2}$ $\frac{2 \text{ mol } H_2O}{2 \text{ mol } H_2}$ $\frac{18.02 \text{ g } H_2O}{1 \text{ mol } H_2O}$ RELATIONSHIPS USED 1 mol = 22.4 L (molar volume at STP, presented in this section) 2 mol H_2 : 2 mol H_2O (from balanced equation given in problem) 18.02 g H_2O = 1 mol H_2O (molar mass of H_2O)
SOLVE Begin with the volume of H_2 and follow the solution map to arrive at mass H_2O in grams.	SOLUTION $1.24 \text{ L } H_2 \times \frac{1 \text{ mol } H_2}{22.4 \text{ L } H_2} \times \frac{2 \text{ mol } H_2O}{2 \text{ mol } H_2} \times \frac{18.02 \text{ g } H_2O}{1 \text{ mol } H_2O} = 0.998 \text{ g } H_2O$
CHECK Check your answer. Are the units correct? Does the answer make physical sense?	The answer has the correct units, g H_2O. The answer is reasonable because 1.24 L of a gas is about 0.05 mol of reactant (at STP) and 1 g H_2O is about 0.05 mol product (1 g/18 g/mol ≈ 0.05 mol). Since the reaction produces 1 mol H_2O to 1 mol H_2, we expect the number of moles of H_2O produced to be equal to the number of moles of H_2 that react.

▶**SKILLBUILDER 11.12 | Using Molar Volume in Calculations**

How many liters of oxygen (at STP) are required to form 10.5 g of H_2O?

$$2\,H_2(g) + O_2(g) \longrightarrow 2\,H_2O(g)$$

▶**FOR MORE PRACTICE** Problems 95, 96, 97, 98.

CHEMISTRY IN THE ENVIRONMENT

Air Pollution

All major cities in the world have polluted air. This pollution comes from a number of sources, including electricity generation, motor vehicles, and industrial waste. While there are many different kinds of air pollutants, some of the major gaseous air pollutants are:

Sulfur dioxide (SO_2)—Sulfur dioxide is emitted primarily as a by-product of electricity generation and industrial metal refining. SO_2 is a lung and eye irritant that affects the respiratory system. SO_2 is also one of the main precursors of acid rain.

Carbon monoxide (CO)—Carbon monoxide is formed by the incomplete combustion of fossil fuels (petroleum, natural gas, and coal). It is emitted mainly by motor vehicles. CO displaces oxygen in the blood and causes the heart and lungs to work harder. At high levels, CO can cause sensory impairment, decreased thinking ability, unconsciousness, and even death.

Ozone (O_3)—Ozone in the upper atmosphere is a normal part of our environment. Upper atmospheric ozone filters out part of the harmful UV light contained in sunlight. Lower-atmospheric or *ground-level* ozone, on the other hand, is a pollutant that results from the action of sunlight on motor vehicle emissions. Ground-level ozone is an eye and lung irritant. Prolonged exposure to ozone has been shown to permanently damage the lungs.

Nitrogen dioxide (NO_2)—Nitrogen dioxide is emitted by motor vehicles and by electricity generation plants. It is an orange-brown gas that causes the dark haze often seen over polluted cities. NO_2 is an eye and lung irritant and a precursor of acid rain.

In the United States, the U.S. Environmental Protection Agency (EPA) has set standards for these pollutants. Beginning in the 1970s, the U.S. Congress passed the Clean Air Act and its amendments, requiring U.S. cities to reduce their pollution and maintain levels below the limits set by the EPA. As a result of this legislation, pollutant levels in U.S. cities have decreased significantly over the last 30 years, even as the number of vehicles has increased. For example, according to the EPA, the levels of all four of the previously mentioned pollutants in major U.S cities decreased during 1980–2008. The amounts of these decreases are shown in Table 11.5.

TABLE 11.5 Changes in Pollutant Levels for Major U.S. Cities, 1980–2008

Pollutant	Change, 1980–2008
SO_2	−71%
CO	−79%
O_3	−25%
NO_2	−46%

(*Source:* U.S. EPA)

Although the levels of pollutants (especially ozone) in many cities are still above what the EPA considers safe, much progress has been made. These trends demonstrate that good legislation can clean up our environment.

CAN YOU ANSWER THIS? *Calculate the amount (in grams) of SO_2 emitted when 1.0 kg of coal containing 4.0% S by mass is completely burned. Under standard conditions, what volume in liters would this SO_2 occupy?*

▲ Air pollution plagues most large cities.

CHAPTER IN REVIEW

CHEMICAL PRINCIPLES	RELEVANCE
Kinetic Molecular Theory: The kinetic molecular theory is a model for gases. In this model, gases are composed of widely spaced, noninteracting particles whose average kinetic energy depends on temperature.	**Kinetic Molecular Theory:** The kinetic molecular theory predicts many of the properties of gases, including their low density in comparison to solids, their compressibility, and their tendency to assume the shape and volume of their container. The kinetic molecular theory also predicts the ideal gas law.
Pressure: Pressure is the force per unit area that results from the collision of gas particles with surfaces. The SI unit of pressure is the pascal, but pressure is often expressed in other units such as atmospheres, millimeters of mercury, torr, pounds per square inch, and inches of mercury.	**Pressure:** Pressure is a fundamental property of a gas. It allows tires to be inflated and makes it possible to drink from straws.
Simple Gas Laws: The simple gas laws show how one of the properties of a gas varies with another. They are: **Volume (V) and Pressure (P)** $V \propto \frac{1}{P}$ (Boyle's law) **Volume (V) and Temperature (T)** $V \propto T$ (Charles's law) **Volume (V) and Moles (n)** $V \propto n$ (Avogadro's law)	**Simple Gas Laws:** Each of the simple gas laws allows us to see how two properties of a gas are interrelated. They are also useful in calculating how one of the properties of a gas changes when another does. Boyle's law, for example, can be used to calculate how the volume of a gas will change in response to a change in pressure, or vice versa.
The Combined Gas Law: The combined gas law joins Boyle's law and Charles's law. $\frac{P_1 V_1}{T_1} = \frac{P_2 V_2}{T_2}$	**The Combined Gas Law:** The combined gas law is used to calculate how a property of a gas (pressure, volume, or temperature) changes when two other properties are changed at the same time.
The Ideal Gas Law: The ideal gas law combines the four properties of a gas—pressure, volume, temperature, and number of moles—in a single equation showing their interrelatedness. $PV = nRT$	**The Ideal Gas Law:** The ideal gas law lets you find any one of the four properties of a gas if you know the other three.
Mixtures of Gases: The pressure due to an individual component in a mixture of gases is its partial pressure and is defined as the fractional composition of the component multiplied by the total pressure: Partial pressure of component = Fractional composition of component × Total pressure Dalton's law states that the total pressure of a mixture of gases is equal to the sum of the partial pressures of its components: $P_{tot} = P_a + P_b + P_c + \ldots$	**Mixtures of Gases:** Since many gases are not pure but mixtures of several components, it is useful to know how each component contributes to the properties of the entire mixture. The concepts of partial pressure are relevant to deep-sea diving, for example, and to collecting gases over water, where water vapor mixes with the gas being collected.

Gases in Chemical Reactions: Stoichiometric calculations involving gases are similar to those that do not involve gases in that the coefficients in a balanced chemical equation provide conversion factors among moles of reactants and products in the reaction. For gases, the amount of a reactant or product is often specified by the volume of reactant or product at a given temperature and pressure. The ideal gas law is then used to convert from these quantities to moles of reactant or product. Alternatively, at standard temperature and pressure, volume can be converted directly to moles with the equality:

$$1 \text{ mol} = 22.4 \text{ L (at STP)}$$

Gases in Chemical Reactions: Reactions involving gases are common in chemistry. For example, many atmospheric reactions—some of which are important to the environment—occur as gaseous reactions.

CHEMICAL SKILLS

Pressure Unit Conversion (Section 11.3)

SORT

You are given a pressure in inches of mercury asked to convert the units to torr.

STRATEGIZE

Begin with the quantity you are given and multiply by the appropriate conversion factor(s) to get to the quantity you are trying to find.

SOLVE

Follow the solution map to solve the problem.

CHECK

Are the units correct? Does the answer make physical sense?

EXAMPLES

EXAMPLE 11.13 Pressure Unit Conversion

Convert 18.4 in. Hg to torr.

GIVEN: 18.4 in. Hg
FIND: torr

SOLUTION MAP

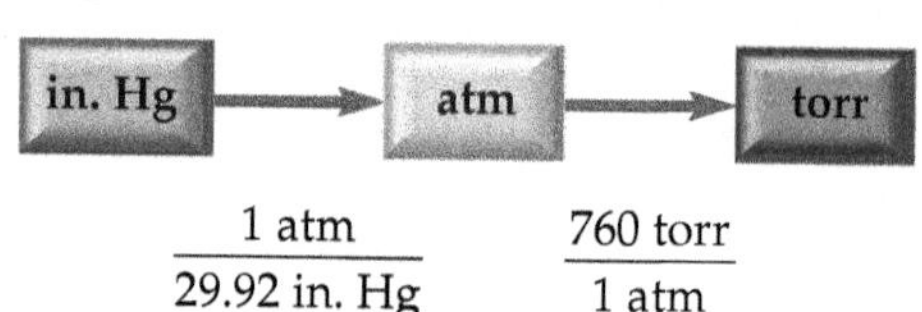

$$\frac{1 \text{ atm}}{29.92 \text{ in. Hg}} \qquad \frac{760 \text{ torr}}{1 \text{ atm}}$$

RELATIONSHIPS USED

$$1 \text{ atm} = 29.92 \text{ in. Hg} \quad \text{(Table 11.1)}$$

$$760 \text{ torr} = 1 \text{ atm} \quad \text{(Table 11.1)}$$

SOLUTION

$$18.4 \text{ in. Hg} \times \frac{1 \text{ atm}}{29.92 \text{ in. Hg}} \times \frac{760 \text{ torr}}{1 \text{ atm}} = 467 \text{ torr}$$

The units (torr) are correct. The value of the answer is reasonable because the torr is a smaller unit than in. Hg; therefore the value of a pressure in torr should be larger than in in. Hg.

Simple Gas Laws (Sections 11.4, 11.5, 11.7)

SORT

You are given the initial and final pressures and the initial volume. You are asked to find the final volume.

EXAMPLE 11.14 Simple Gas Laws

A gas has a volume of 5.7 L at a pressure of 3.2 atm. What is its volume at 4.7 atm? (Assume constant temperature.)

GIVEN:

$P_1 = 3.2$ atm

$V_1 = 5.7$ L

$P_2 = 4.7$ atm

FIND: V_2

STRATEGIZE

Calculations involving the simple gas laws usually consist of finding one of the initial or final conditions given the other initial and final conditions. In this case, use Boyle's law to find V_2 given P_1, V_1, and V_2.

SOLUTION MAP

P_1, V_1, P_2 → V_2

$$P_1V_1 = P_2V_2$$

RELATIONSHIPS USED

$$P_1V_1 = P_2V_2 \text{ (Boyle's law, Section11.4)}$$

SOLVE

Solve Boyle's law for V_2 and substitute the correct variables to calculate its value.

SOLUTION

$$P_1V_1 = P_2V_2 \text{ torr}$$

$$V_2 = \frac{P_1}{P_2}V_1$$

$$= \frac{3.2 \text{ atm}}{4.7 \text{ atm}} 5.7 \text{ L}$$

$$= 3.9 \text{ L}$$

CHECK

Are the units correct? Does the answer make physical sense?

The units (L) are correct. The value is reasonable because as the pressure increases the volume should decrease.

The Combined Gas Law (Section 11.6)

EXAMPLE 11.15 The Combined Gas Law

A sample of gas has an initial volume of 2.4 L at a pressure of 855 mm Hg and a temperature of 298 K. If the gas is heated to a temperature of 387 K and expanded to a volume of 4.1 L, what is its final pressure in millimeters of mercury?

SORT

You are given the initial and final volume and temperature, and you are given the initial pressure. You are asked to find the final pressure.

GIVEN:

$P_1 = 855$ mm Hg

$V_1 = 2.4$ L

$T_1 = 298$ K

$V_2 = 4.1$ L

$T_2 = 387$ K

FIND: P_2

STRATEGIZE

Problems involving the combined gas law usually consist of finding one of the initial or final conditions given the other initial and final conditions. In this case, use the combined gas law to find the unknown quantity, P_2.

SOLUTION MAP

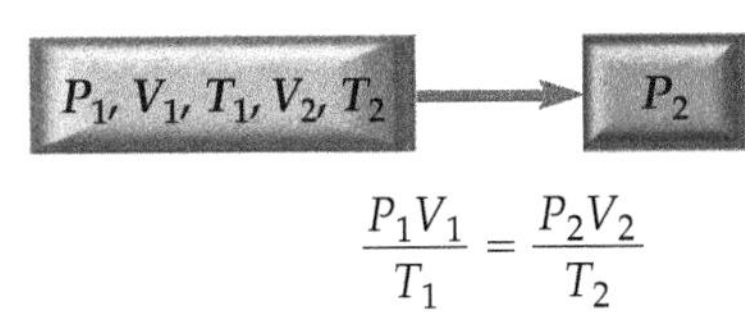

$$\frac{P_1V_1}{T_1} = \frac{P_2V_2}{T_2}$$

RELATIONSHIPS USED

$$\frac{P_1V_1}{T_1} = \frac{P_2V_2}{T_2} \text{ (Combined gas law, Section 11.6)}$$

SOLVE

Solve the combined gas law for the quantity you are trying to find, in this case P_2, and substitute the known quantities to calculate the value of P_2.

SOLUTION

$$\frac{P_1V_1}{T_1} = \frac{P_2V_2}{T_2}$$

$$P_2 = \frac{P_1V_1T_2}{T_1V_2}$$

$$= \frac{855 \text{ mm Hg} \times 2.4 \cancel{\text{L}} \times 387 \cancel{\text{K}}}{298 \cancel{\text{K}} \times 4.1 \cancel{\text{L}}}$$

$$= 6.5 \times 10^2 \text{ mm Hg}$$

CHECK

Are the units correct? Does the answer make physical sense?

The units, mm Hg, are correct. The value of the answer makes sense because the volume increase was proportionally more than the temperature decrease; therefore you would expect the pressure to decrease.

The Ideal Gas Law (Section 11.8)

EXAMPLE 11.16 The Ideal Gas Law

Calculate the pressure exerted by 1.2 mol of gas in a volume of 28.2 L and at a temperature of 334 K.

SORT

You are given the number of moles of a gas, its volume, and its temperature. You are asked to find its pressure.

GIVEN:

$n = 1.2$ mol

$V = 28.2$ L

$T = 334$ K

FIND: P

STRATEGIZE

Calculations involving the ideal gas law often involve finding one of the four variables (P, V, n, or T) given the other three. In this case, you are asked to find P. Use the given variables and the ideal gas law to arrive at P.

SOLUTION MAP

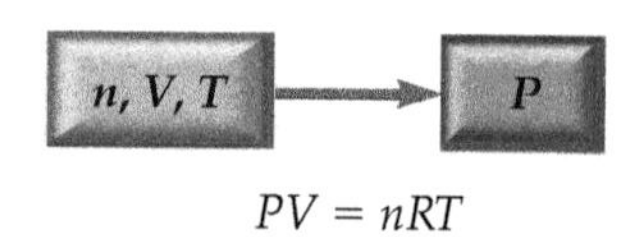

$PV = nRT$

RELATIONSHIPS USED

$PV = nRT$ (Ideal gas law, Section 11.8)

SOLVE

Solve the ideal gas law equation for P and substitute the given variables to calculate P.

SOLUTION

$$PV = nRT$$

$$P = \frac{nRT}{V}$$

$$= \frac{1.2 \cancel{\text{mol}} \times 0.0821 \frac{\cancel{\text{L}} \cdot \text{atm}}{\cancel{\text{mol}} \cdot \cancel{\text{K}}} \times 334 \cancel{\text{K}}}{28.2 \cancel{\text{L}}}$$

$$= 1.2 \text{ atm}$$

CHECK

Are the units correct? Does the answer make physical sense?

The units (atm) are correct units for pressure. The *value* of the answer is a bit more difficult to judge. However, knowing that at standard temperature and pressure ($T = 0$ °C or 273.15 K and $P = 1$ atm), 1 mol of gas occupies 22.4 L, we can see that the answer is reasonable because we have a bit more than one mole of a gas at a temperature not too far from standard temperature. The volume of the gas is a bit higher than 22.4 L; therefore we might expect the pressure to be a bit higher than 1 atm.

Total Pressure and Partial Pressure (Section 11.9)

EXAMPLE 11.17 Total Pressure and Partial Pressure

A mixture of three gases has the partial pressures.

$$P_{CO_2} = 289 \text{ mm Hg}$$
$$P_{O_2} = 342 \text{ mm Hg}$$
$$P_{N_2} = 122 \text{ mm Hg}$$

What is the total pressure of the mixture?

You are given the partial pressures of three gases in a mixture and asked to find the total pressure.

GIVEN:

$$P_{CO_2} = 289 \text{ mm Hg}$$
$$P_{O_2} = 342 \text{ mm Hg}$$
$$P_{N_2} = 122 \text{ mm Hg}$$

FIND: P_{tot}

Use Dalton's law of partial pressures ($P_{tot} = P_a + P_b + P_c + \ldots$) to solve the problem. Sum the partial pressures to obtain the total pressure.

SOLUTION

$$\begin{aligned} P_{tot} &= P_{CO_2} + P_{O_2} + P_{N_2} \\ &= 289 \text{ mm Hg} + 342 \text{ mm Hg} + 122 \text{ mm Hg} \\ &= 753 \text{ mm Hg} \end{aligned}$$

KEY TERMS

absolute zero **[11.5]**
atmosphere (atm) **[11.3]**
Avogadro's law **[11.7]**
Boyle's law **[11.4]**
Charles's law **[11.5]**
combined gas law **[11.6]**
Dalton's law of partial pressures **[11.9]**
hypoxia **[11.9]**
ideal gas constant (*R*) **[11.8]**
ideal gas law **[11.8]**
kinetic molecular theory **[11.2]**
millimeter of mercury (mm Hg) **[11.3]**
molar volume **[11.10]**
nitrogen narcosis **[11.9]**
oxygen toxicity **[11.9]**
partial pressure **[11.9]**
pascal (Pa) **[11.3]**
pounds per square inch (psi) **[11.3]**
pressure **[11.3]**
standard temperature and pressure (STP) **[11.10]**
torr **[11.3]**
vapor pressure **[11.9]**

EXERCISES

QUESTIONS

1. What is pressure?
2. Explain how drinking from a straw works. What causes the drink to go up the straw? Is there an upper limit to how long a straw can theoretically be and still work as a drinking straw?
3. What are the main assumptions of kinetic molecular theory?
4. Describe the main properties of a gas. How are these predicted by kinetic molecular theory?
5. Why do we experience pain in our ears during changes in altitude?
6. What units are used to measure pressure?
7. What is Boyle's law? Explain Boyle's law from the perspective of kinetic molecular theory.
8. Explain why scuba divers should not hold their breath as they ascend to the surface.
9. Why would it be impossible to breathe air through an extra-long snorkel (greater than a couple of meters) while swimming underwater?
10. What is Charles's law? Explain Charles's law from the perspective of kinetic molecular theory.
11. Explain why hot-air balloons float above the ground.
12. What is the combined gas law? When is it useful?
13. What is Avogadro's law? Explain Avogadro's law from the perspective of kinetic molecular theory.
14. What is the ideal gas law? When is it useful?

15. Under what conditions is the ideal gas law most accurate? Under what conditions does the ideal gas law break down? Why?
16. What is partial pressure?
17. What is Dalton's law?
18. Describe hypoxia and oxygen toxicity.
19. Why do deep-sea divers breathe a mixture of helium and oxygen?
20. When a gas is collected over water, is the gas pure? Why or why not?
21. What is vapor pressure?
22. What is standard temperature and pressure (STP)? What is the molar volume of a gas at STP?

PROBLEMS

CONVERTING BETWEEN PRESSURE UNITS

23. Convert each pressure measurement to atm.
    (a) 1277 mm Hg
    (b) 2.38×10^5 Pa
    (c) 127 psi
    (d) 455 torr

24. Convert each pressure measurement to atm.
    (a) 921 torr
    (b) 4.8×10^4 Pa
    (c) 87.5 psi
    (d) 34.22 in. Hg

25. Perform each pressure conversion.
    (a) 2.3 atm to torr
    (b) 4.7×10^{-2} atm to millimeters of mercury
    (c) 24.8 psi to millimeters of mercury
    (d) 32.84 in. Hg to torr

26. Perform each pressure conversion.
    (a) 1.06 atm to millimeters of mercury
    (b) 95,422 Pa to millimeters of mercury
    (c) 22.3 psi to torr
    (d) 35.78 in. Hg to millimeters of mercury

27. Complete the table:

Pascals	Atmospheres	Millimeters of Mercury	Torr	Pounds per Square Inch
882 Pa	_____	6.62 mm Hg	_____	_____
_____	0.558 atm	_____	_____	_____
_____	_____	_____	_____	24.8 psi
_____	_____	_____	764 torr	_____
_____	_____	249 mm Hg	_____	_____

28. Complete the table:

Pascals	Atmospheres	Millimeters of Mercury	Torr	Pounds per Square Inch
_____	1.91 atm	_____	1.45×10^3 torr	_____
1.15×10^4 Pa	_____	_____	_____	_____
_____	_____	_____	721 torr	_____
_____	_____	109 mm Hg	_____	_____
_____	_____	_____	_____	38.9 psi

29. The pressure in Denver, Colorado (5280-ft elevation), averages about 24.9 in. Hg. Convert this pressure to:
    (a) atmospheres
    (b) millimeters of mercury
    (c) pounds per square inch
    (d) pascals

30. The pressure on top of Mount Everest averages about 235 mm Hg. Convert this pressure to:
    (a) torr
    (b) pounds per square inch
    (c) inches of mercury
    (d) atmospheres

31. The North American record for highest recorded barometric pressure is 31.85 in. Hg, set in 1989 in Northway, Alaska. Convert this pressure to:
    (a) millimeters of mercury
    (b) atmospheres
    (c) torr
    (d) kilopascals

32. The world record for lowest pressure (at sea level) was 658 mm Hg, recorded inside Typhoon Ida on September 24, 1958, in the Philippine Sea. Convert this pressure to:
    (a) torr
    (b) atmospheres
    (c) inches of mercury
    (d) pounds per square inch

SIMPLE GAS LAWS

33. A sample of gas has an initial volume of 3.95 L at a pressure of 705 mm Hg. If the volume of the gas is increased to 5.38 L, what will the pressure be? (Assume constant temperature.)

34. A sample of gas has an initial volume of 22.8 L at a pressure of 1.65 atm. If the sample is compressed to a volume of 10.7 L, what will its pressure be? (Assume constant temperature.)

35. A snorkeler with a lung capacity of 6.3 L inhales a lungful of air at the surface, where the pressure is 1.0 atm. The snorkeler then descends to a depth of 25 m, where the pressure increases to 3.5 atm. What is the capacity of the snorkeler's lungs at this depth? (Assume constant temperature.)

36. A scuba diver with a lung capacity of 5.2 L inhales a lungful of air at a depth of 45 m and a pressure of 5.5 atm. If the diver were to ascend to the surface (where the pressure is 1.0 atm) while holding her breath, to what volume would the air in her lungs expand? (Assume constant temperature.)

37. Use Boyle's law to complete the table (assume temperature and number of moles of gas to be constant):

P_1	V_1	P_2	V_2
755 mm Hg	2.85 L	885 mm Hg	______
______	1.33 L	4.32 atm	2.88 L
192 mm Hg	382 mL	______	482 mm Hg
2.11 atm	______	3.82 atm	125 mL

38. Use Boyle's law to complete the table (assume temperature and number of moles of gas to be constant):

P_1	V_1	P_2	V_2
______	1.90 L	4.19 atm	1.09 L
755 mm Hg	118 mL	709 mm Hg	______
2.75 atm	6.75 mL	______	49.8 mL
343 torr	______	683 torr	8.79 L

39. A balloon with an initial volume of 3.2 L at a temperature of 299 K is warmed to 376 K. What is its volume at the final temperature?

40. A dramatic classroom demonstration involves cooling a balloon from room temperature (298 K) to liquid nitrogen temperature (77 K). If the initial volume of the balloon is 2.7 L, what will its volume be after it cools?

41. A 48.3-mL sample of gas in a cylinder equipped with a piston is warmed from 22 °C to 87 °C. What is its volume at the final temperature?

42. A syringe containing 1.55 mL of oxygen gas is cooled from 95.3 °C to 0.0 °C. What is the final volume of oxygen gas?

43. Use Charles's law to complete the table (assume pressure and number of moles of gas to be constant):

V_1	T_1	V_2	T_2
1.08 L	25.4 °C	1.33 L	______
______	77 K	228 mL	298 K
115 cm^3	______	119 cm^3	22.4 °C
232 L	18.5 °C	______	96.2 °C

44. Use Charles's law to complete the table (assume pressure and number of moles of gas to be constant):

V_1	T_1	V_2	T_2
119 L	10.5 °C	______	112.3 °C
______	135 K	176 mL	315 K
2.11 L	15.4 °C	2.33 L	______
15.4 cm^3	______	19.2 cm^3	10.4 °C

45. A 0.12-mole sample of nitrogen gas occupies a volume of 2.55 L. What is the volume of 0.32 mol of nitrogen gas under the same conditions?

46. A 0.48-mole sample of helium gas occupies a volume of 11.7 L. What is the volume of 0.72 mol of helium gas under the same conditions?

47. A balloon contains 0.128 mol of gas and has a volume of 2.76 L. If an additional 0.073 mol of gas is added to the balloon, what will its final volume be?

48. A cylinder with a moveable piston contains 0.87 mol of gas and has a volume of 334 mL. What will its volume be if an additional 0.22 mol of gas is added to the cylinder?

49. Use Avogadro's law to complete the table (assume pressure and temperature to be constant):

V_1	n_1	V_2	n_2
38.5 mL	1.55×10^{-3} mol	49.4 mL	______
______	1.37 mol	26.8 L	4.57 mol
11.2 L	0.628 mol	______	0.881 mol
422 mL	______	671 mL	0.0174 mol

50. Use Avogadro's law to complete the table (assume pressure and temperature to be constant):

V_1	n_1	V_2	n_2
25.2 L	5.05 mol	______	3.03 mol
______	1.10 mol	414 mL	0.913 mol
8.63 L	0.0018 mol	10.9 L	______
53 mL	______	13 mL	2.61×10^{-4} mol

THE COMBINED GAS LAW

51. A sample of gas with an initial volume of 28.4 L at a pressure of 725 mm Hg and a temperature of 305 K is compressed to a volume of 14.8 L and warmed to a temperature of 375 K. What is the final pressure of the gas?

52. A cylinder with a moveable piston contains 218 mL of nitrogen gas at a pressure of 1.32 atm and a temperature of 298 K. What must the final volume be for the pressure of the gas to be 1.55 atm at a temperature of 335 K?

53. A scuba diver takes a 2.8-L balloon from the surface, where the pressure is 1.0 atm and the temperature is 34 °C, to a depth of 25 m, where the pressure is 3.5 atm and the temperature is 18 °C. What is the volume of the balloon at this depth?

54. A bag of potato chips contains 585 mL of air at 25 °C and a pressure of 765 mm Hg. Assuming the bag does not break, what will be its volume at the top of a mountain where the pressure is 442 mm Hg and the temperature is 5.0 °C?

55. A gas sample with a volume of 5.3 L has a pressure of 735 mm Hg at 28 °C. What is the pressure of the sample if the volume remains at 5.3 L but the temperature rises to 86 °C?

56. The total pressure in a 11.7-L automobile tire is 44 psi at 11 °C. How much does the pressure in the tire rise if it warms to a temperature of 37 °C and the volume remains at 11.7 L?

57. Use the combined gas law to complete the table (assume the number of moles of gas to be constant):

P_1	V_1	T_1	P_2	V_2	T_2
1.21 atm	1.58 L	12.2 °C	1.54 atm	______	32.3 °C
721 torr	141 mL	135 K	801 torr	152 mL	______
5.51 atm	0.879 L	22.1 °C	______	1.05 L	38.3 °C

58. Use the combined gas law to complete the table (assume the number of moles of gas to be constant):

P_1	V_1	T_1	P_2	V_2	T_2
1.01 atm	______	2.7 °C	0.54 atm	0.58 L	42.3 °C
123 torr	41.5 mL	______	626 torr	36.5 mL	205 K
______	1.879 L	20.8 °C	0.412 atm	2.05 L	48.1 °C

THE IDEAL GAS LAW

59. What is the volume occupied by 0.255 mol of helium gas at a pressure of 1.25 atm and a temperature of 305 K?

60. What is the pressure in a 20.0-L cylinder filled with 0.683 mol of nitrogen gas at a temperature of 325 K?

61. A cylinder contains 28.5 L of oxygen gas at a pressure of 1.8 atm and a temperature of 298 K. How many moles of gas are in the cylinder?

62. What is the temperature of 0.52 mol of gas at a pressure of 1.3 atm and a volume of 11.8 L?

63. A cylinder contains 11.8 L of air at a total pressure of 43.2 psi and a temperature of 25 °C. How many moles of gas does the cylinder contain?

64. What is the pressure in millimeters of mercury of 0.0115 mol of helium gas with a volume of 214 mL at a temperature of 45 °C?

65. Use the ideal gas law to complete the table:

P	*V*	*n*	*T*
1.05 atm	1.19 L	0.112 mol	______
112 torr	______	0.241 mol	304 K
______	28.5 mL	1.74×10^{-3} mol	25.4 °C
0.559 atm	0.439 L	______	255 K

66. Use the ideal gas law to complete the table:

P	*V*	*n*	*T*
2.39 atm	1.21 L	______	205 K
512 torr	______	0.741 mol	298 K
0.433 atm	0.192 L	0.0131 mol	______
______	20.2 mL	5.71×10^{-3} mol	20.4 °C

67. How many moles of gas must be forced into a 3.5-L ball to give it a gauge pressure of 9.4 psi at 25 °C? The gauge pressure is relative to atmospheric pressure. Assume that atmospheric pressure is 14.7 psi so that the total pressure in the ball is 24.1 psi.

68. How many moles of gas must be forced into a 4.8-L tire to give it a gauge pressure of 32.4 psi at 25 °C? The gauge pressure is relative to atmospheric pressure. Assume that atmospheric pressure is 14.7 psi so that the total pressure in the tire is 47.1 psi.

69. An experiment shows that a 248-mL gas sample has a mass of 0.433 g at a pressure of 745 mm Hg and a temperature of 28 °C. What is the molar mass of the gas?

70. An experiment shows that a 113-mL gas sample has a mass of 0.171 g at a pressure of 721 mm Hg and a temperature of 32 °C. What is the molar mass of the gas?

71. A sample of gas has a mass of 38.8 mg. Its volume is 224 mL at a temperature of 55 °C and a pressure of 886 torr. Find the molar mass of the gas.

72. A sample of gas has a mass of 0.555 g. Its volume is 117 mL at a temperature of 85 °C and a pressure of 753 mm Hg. Find the molar mass of the gas.

PARTIAL PRESSURE

73. A gas mixture contains each gas at the indicated partial pressure.

N_2	217 torr
O_2	106 torr
He	248 torr

What is the total pressure of the mixture?

74. A gas mixture contains each gas at the indicated partial pressure.

CO_2	422 mm Hg
Ar	102 mm Hg
O_2	165 mm Hg
H_2	52 mm Hg

What is the total pressure of the mixture?

75. A heliox deep-sea diving mixture delivers an oxygen partial pressure of 0.30 atm when the total pressure is 11.0 atm. What is the partial pressure of helium in this mixture?

76. A mixture of helium, nitrogen, and oxygen has a total pressure of 752 mm Hg. The partial pressures of helium and nitrogen are 234 mm Hg and 197 mm Hg, respectively. What is the partial pressure of oxygen in the mixture?

77. The hydrogen gas formed in a chemical reaction is collected over water at 30 °C at a total pressure of 732 mm Hg. What is the partial pressure of the hydrogen gas collected in this way?

78. The oxygen gas emitted from an aquatic plant during photosynthesis is collected over water at a temperature of 25 °C and a total pressure of 753 torr. What is the partial pressure of the oxygen gas?

79. A gas mixture contains 78% nitrogen and 22% oxygen. If the total pressure is 1.12 atm, what are the partial pressures of each component?

80. An air sample contains 0.038% CO_2. If the total pressure is 758 mm Hg, what is the partial pressure of CO_2?

81. A heliox deep-sea diving mixture contains 4.0% oxygen and 96.0% helium. What is the partial pressure of oxygen when this mixture is delivered at a total pressure of 8.5 atm?

82. A scuba diver breathing normal air descends to 100 m of depth, where the total pressure is 11 atm. What is the partial pressure of oxygen that the diver experiences at this depth? Is the diver in danger of experiencing oxygen toxicity?

MOLAR VOLUME

83. Calculate the volume of each gas sample at STP.
   (a) 22.5 mol Cl_2
   (b) 3.6 mol nitrogen
   (c) 2.2 mol helium
   (d) 27 mol CH_4

84. Calculate the volume of each gas sample at STP.
   (a) 21.2 mol N_2O
   (b) 0.215 mol CO
   (c) 0.364 mol CO_2
   (d) 8.6 mol C_2H_6

85. Calculate the volume of each gas sample at STP.
   (a) 73.9 g N_2
   (b) 42.9 g O_2
   (c) 148 g NO_2
   (d) 245 mg CO_2

86. Calculate the volume of each gas sample at STP.
   (a) 48.9 g He
   (b) 45.2 g Xe
   (c) 48.2 mg Cl_2
   (d) 3.83 kg SO_2

87. Calculate the mass of each gas sample at STP.
   (a) 178 mL CO_2
   (b) 155 mL O_2
   (c) 1.25 L SF_6

88. Calculate the mass of each gas sample at STP.
   (a) 5.82 L NO
   (b) 0.324 L N_2
   (c) 139 cm^3 Ar

GASES IN CHEMICAL REACTIONS

89. Consider the chemical reaction:

$$C(s) + H_2O(g) \longrightarrow CO(g) + H_2(g)$$

How many liters of hydrogen gas are formed from the complete reaction of 1.07 mol of C? Assume that the hydrogen gas is collected at a pressure of 1.0 atm and temperature of 315 K.

90. Consider the chemical reaction:

$$2\,H_2O(l) \longrightarrow 2\,H_2(g) + O_2(g)$$

How many moles of H_2O are required to form 1.3 L of O_2 at a temperature of 325 K and a pressure of 0.988 atm?

91. CH_3OH can be synthesized by the reaction:

$$CO(g) + 2\,H_2(g) \longrightarrow CH_3OH(g)$$

How many liters of H_2 gas, measured at 748 mm Hg and 86 °C, are required to synthesize 0.55 mol of CH_3OH? How many liters of CO gas, measured under the same conditions, are required?

92. Oxygen gas reacts with powdered aluminum according to the reaction:

$$4\,Al(s) + 3\,O_2(g) \longrightarrow 2\,Al_2O_3(s)$$

How many liters of O_2 gas, measured at 782 mm Hg and 25 °C, are required to completely react with 2.4 mol of Al?

93. Nitrogen reacts with powdered aluminum according to the reaction:

$$2\,Al(s) + N_2(g) \longrightarrow 2\,AlN(s)$$

How many liters of N_2 gas, measured at 892 torr and 95 °C, are required to completely react with 18.5 g of Al?

94. Sodium reacts with chlorine gas according to the reaction:

$$2\,Na(s) + Cl_2(g) \longrightarrow 2\,NaCl(s)$$

What volume of Cl_2 gas, measured at 687 torr and 35 °C, is required to form 28 g of NaCl?

95. How many grams of NH_3 form when 24.8 L of $H_2(g)$ (measured at STP) reacts with N_2 to form NH_3 according to this reaction?

$$N_2(g) + 3\,H_2(g) \longrightarrow 2\,NH_3(g)$$

96. Lithium reacts with nitrogen gas according to the reaction:

$$6\,Li(s) + N_2(g) \longrightarrow 2\,Li_3N(s)$$

How many grams of lithium are required to completely react with 58.5 mL of N_2 gas measured at STP?

97. How many grams of calcium are consumed when 156.8 mL of oxygen gas, measured at STP, reacts with calcium according to this reaction?

$$2\,Ca(s) + O_2(g) \longrightarrow 2\,CaO(s)$$

98. How many grams of magnesium oxide are formed when 14.8 L of oxygen gas, measured at STP, completely reacts with magnesium metal according to this reaction?

$$2\,Mg(s) + O_2(g) \longrightarrow 2\,MgO(s)$$

CUMULATIVE PROBLEMS

99. Use the ideal gas law to show that the molar volume of a gas at STP is 22.4 L.

100. Use the ideal gas law to show that 28.0 g of nitrogen gas and 4.00 g of helium gas occupy the same volume at any temperature and pressure.

101. The mass of an evacuated 255-mL flask is 143.187 g. The mass of the flask filled with 267 torr of an unknown gas at 25 °C is 143.289 g. Calculate the molar mass of the unknown gas.

102. A 118-mL flask is evacuated, and its mass is measured as 97.129 g. When the flask is filled with 768 torr of helium gas at 35 °C, it is found to have a mass of 97.171 g. Is the gas pure helium?

103. A gaseous compound containing hydrogen and carbon is decomposed and found to contain 82.66% carbon and 17.34% hydrogen by mass. The mass of 158 mL of the gas, measured at 556 mm Hg and 25 °C, is 0.275 g. What is the molecular formula of the compound?

104. A gaseous compound containing hydrogen and carbon is decomposed and found to contain 85.63% C and 14.37% H by mass. The mass of 258 mL of the gas, measured at STP, is 0.646 g. What is the molecular formula of the compound?

105. The reaction between zinc and hydrochloric acid is carried out as a source of hydrogen gas in the laboratory:

$$Zn(s) + 2\,HCl(aq) \longrightarrow ZnCl_2(aq) + H_2(g)$$

If 325 mL of hydrogen gas is collected over water at 25 °C at a total pressure of 748 mm Hg, how many grams of Zn reacted?

106. Consider the reaction:

$$2\,NiO(s) \longrightarrow 2\,Ni(s) + O_2(g)$$

If O_2 is collected over water at 40 °C and a total pressure of 745 mm Hg, what volume of gas will be collected for the complete reaction of 24.78 g of NiO?

107. How many grams of hydrogen are collected in a reaction where 1.78 L of hydrogen gas is collected over water at a temperature of 40 °C and a total pressure of 748 torr?

108. How many grams of oxygen are collected in a reaction where 235 mL of oxygen gas is collected over water at a temperature of 25 °C and a total pressure of 697 torr?

109. The decomposition of a silver oxide sample forms 15.8 g of Ag(s):

$$2\,Ag_2O(s) \longrightarrow 4\,Ag(s) + O_2(g)$$

What total volume of gas forms if it is collected over water at a temperature of 25 °C and a total pressure of 752 mm Hg?

110. The following reaction consumes 2.45 kg of CO(g):

$$CO(g) + H_2O(g) \longrightarrow CO_2(g) + H_2(g)$$

How many total liters of gas are formed if the products are collected at STP?

111. When hydrochloric acid is poured over a sample of sodium bicarbonate, 28.2 mL of carbon dioxide gas is produced at a pressure of 0.954 atm and a temperature of 22.7 °C. Write an equation for the gas evolution reaction and determine how much sodium bicarbonate reacted.

112. When hydrochloric acid is poured over potassium sulfide, 42.9 mL of hydrogen sulfide gas is produced at a pressure of 752 torr and a temperature of 25.8 °C. Write an equation for the gas evolution reaction and determine how much potassium sulfide (in grams) reacted.

113. Consider the reaction:

$$2\,SO_2(g) + O_2(g) \longrightarrow 2\,SO_3(g)$$

(a) If 285.5 mL of SO_2 is allowed to react with 158.9 mL of O_2 (both measured at STP), what is the limiting reactant and the theoretical yield of SO_3?

(b) If 187.2 mL of SO_3 is collected (measured at STP), what is the percent yield for the reaction?

114. Consider the reaction:

$$P_4(s) + 6\,H_2(g) \longrightarrow 4\,PH_3(g)$$

(a) If 88.6 L of $H_2(g)$, measured at STP, is allowed to react with 158.3 g of P_4, what is the limiting reactant?

(b) If 48.3 L of PH_3, measured at STP, forms, what is the percent yield?

115. Consider the reaction for the synthesis of nitric acid:

$$3\,NO_2(g) + H_2O(l) \longrightarrow 2\,HNO_3(aq) + NO(g)$$

(a) If 12.8 L of $NO_2(g)$, measured at STP, is allowed to react with 14.9 g of water, find the limiting reagent and the theoretical yield of HNO_3 in grams.

(b) If 14.8 g of HNO_3 forms, what is the percent yield?

116. Consider the reaction for the production of NO_2 from NO:

$$2\,NO(g) + O_2(g) \longrightarrow 2\,NO_2(g)$$

(a) If 84.8 L of $O_2(g)$, measured at 35 °C and 632 mm Hg, is allowed to react with 158.2 g of NO, find the limiting reagent.

(b) If 97.3 L of NO_2 forms, measured at 35 °C and 632 mm Hg, what is the percent yield?

117. Ammonium carbonate decomposes upon heating according to the balanced equation:

$$(NH_4)_2CO_3(s) \longrightarrow 2\,NH_3(g) + CO_2(g) + H_2O(g)$$

Calculate the total volume of gas produced at 22 °C and 1.02 atm by the complete decomposition of 11.83 g of ammonium carbonate.

118. Ammonium nitrate decomposes explosively upon heating according to the balanced equation:

$$2\,NH_4NO_3(s) \longrightarrow 2\,N_2(g) + O_2(g) + 4\,H_2O(g)$$

Calculate the total volume of gas (at 25 °C and 748 mm Hg) produced by the complete decomposition of 1.55 kg of ammonium nitrate.

119. A mixture containing 235 mg of helium and 325 mg of neon has a total pressure of 453 torr. What is the partial pressure of helium in the mixture?

120. A mixture containing 4.33 g of CO_2 and 3.11 g of CH_4 has a total pressure of 1.09 atm. What is the partial pressure of CO_2 in the mixture?

121. Consider the reaction:

$$2\,SO_2(g) + O_2(g) \longrightarrow 2\,SO_3(g)$$

A reaction flask initially contains 0.10 atm of SO_2 and 0.10 atm of O_2. What is the total pressure in the flask once the limiting reactant is completely consumed? Assume a constant temperature and volume and a 100% reaction yield.

122. Consider the reaction:

$$CO(g) + 2\,H_2(g) \longrightarrow CH_3OH(g)$$

A reaction flask initially contains 112 torr of CO and 282 torr of H_2. The reaction is allowed to proceed until the pressure stops changing, at which point the total pressure is 196 torr. Determine the percent yield for the reaction. Assume a constant temperature and that no other reactions occur other than the one indicated.

HIGHLIGHT PROBLEMS

123. Which gas sample depicted, all at the same temperature, will have the greatest pressure? Explain.

(a)

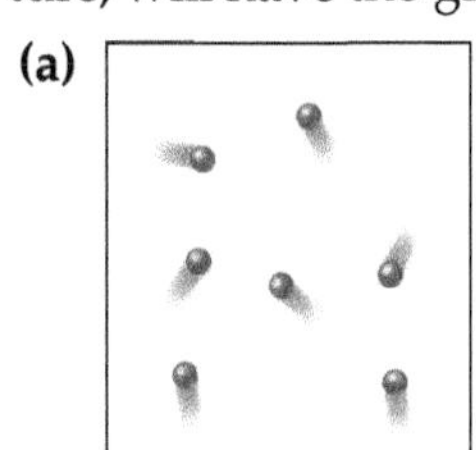

(b)

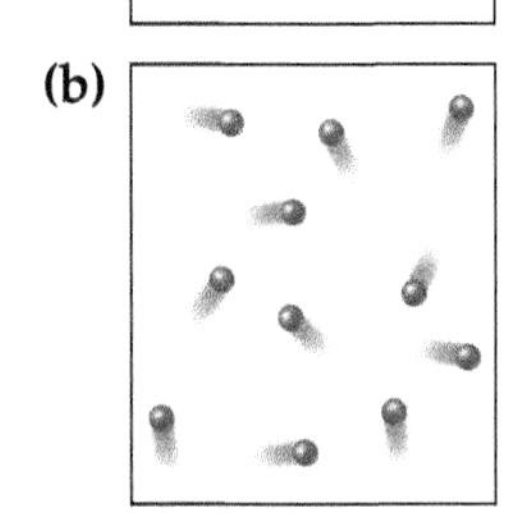

(c)

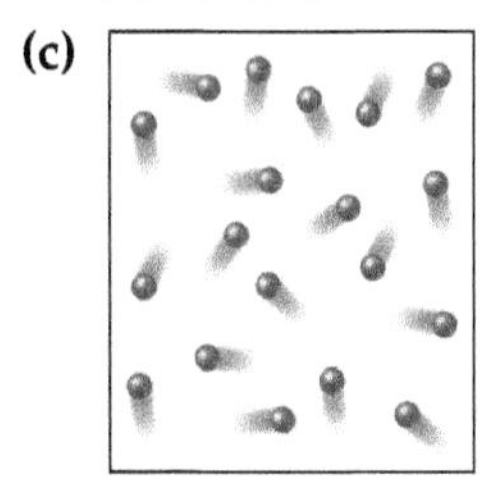

124. This image represents a sample of gas at a pressure of 1 atm, a volume of 1 L, and a temperature of 25 °C. Draw a similar picture showing what happens if the volume were reduced to 0.5 L and the temperature increased to 250 °C. What happens to the pressure?

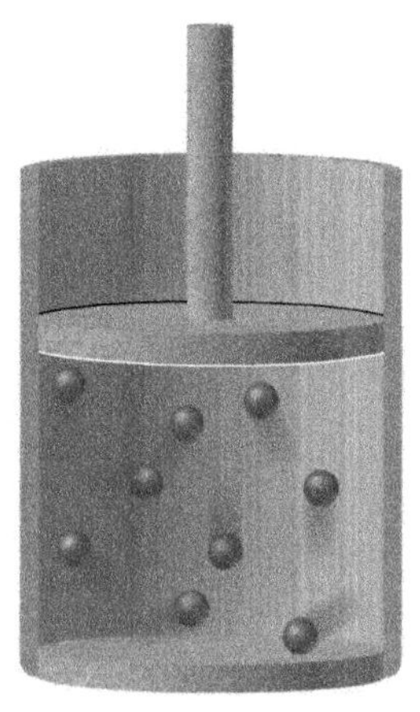

$V = 1.0$ L
$T = 25$ °C
$P = 1.0$ atm

125. Automobile air bags inflate following a serious impact. The impact triggers the chemical reaction:

$$2\ NaN_3(s) \rightarrow 2\ Na(s) + 3\ N_2(g)$$

If an automobile air bag has a volume of 11.8 L, how much NaN_3 in grams is required to fully inflate the air bag upon impact? Assume STP conditions.

126. Olympic cyclists fill their tires with helium to make them lighter. Calculate the mass of air in an air-filled tire and the mass of helium in a helium-filled tire. What is the mass difference between the two? Assume that the volume of the tire is 855 mL, that it is filled with a total pressure of 125 psi, and that the temperature is 25 °C. Also, assume an average molar mass for air of 28.8 g/mol.

127. In a common classroom demonstration, a balloon is filled with air and submerged into liquid nitrogen. The balloon contracts as the gases within the balloon cool. Suppose the balloon initially contains 2.95 L of air at a temperature of 25.0 °C and a pressure of 0.998 atm. Calculate the expected volume of the balloon upon cooling to −196 °C (the boiling point of liquid nitrogen). When the demonstration is carried out, the actual volume of the balloon decreases to 0.61 L. How well does the observed volume of the balloon compare to your calculated value? Can you explain the difference?

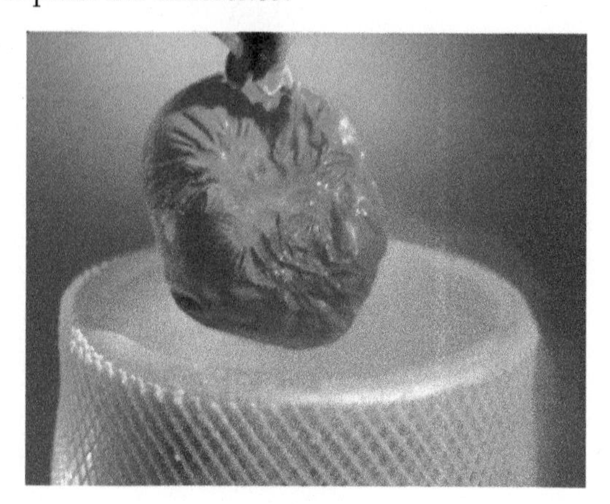

128. Aerosol cans carry clear warnings against incineration because of the high pressures that can develop upon heating. Suppose a can contains a residual amount of gas at a pressure of 755 mm Hg and a temperature of 25 °C. What would the pressure be if the can were heated to 1155 °C?

▶ANSWERS TO SKILLBUILDER EXERCISES

Skillbuilder 11.1	85.0 psi
Skillbuilder Plus, p. 366	80.6 kPa
Skillbuilder 11.2	P_2 = 2.1 atm; depth is approximately 11 m
Skillbuilder 11.3	123 mL
Skillbuilder 11.4	0.82 L
Skillbuilder 11.5	13 L
Skillbuilder 11.6	1.6 atm
Skillbuilder 11.7	16.1 L
Skillbuilder Plus, p. 382	977 mm Hg
Skillbuilder 11.8	70.8 g/mol
Skillbuilder 11.9	721 torr
Skillbuilder 11.10	P_{tot} = 4.2 atm
Skillbuilder 11.11	82.3 g
Skillbuilder 11.12	6.53 L O_2

▶ANSWERS TO CONCEPTUAL CHECKPOINTS

11.1 (a) Since the particles are all identical, and since (a) has the smallest number of particles per unit volume, it will have the lowest pressure.

11.2 (c) Atmospheric pressure will support a column of water 10.3 m in height. If the liquid in a barometer were twice as dense as water, a column of it would be twice as heavy and the pressure it exerted at its base would be twice as great. Therefore, atmospheric pressure would be able to support a column only half as high.

11.3 (b) Since the volume triples, and since according to Boyle's law the volume and pressure are inversely proportional, the pressure will fall by a factor of 3.

11.4 (c) The piston will move in response to any pressure difference, keeping the pressure of the gas in the cylinder equal to that of the surrounding atmosphere. Thus, we know that the final pressure of the gas will be the same as it was initially. At constant pressure, the volume of the gas will be proportional to the temperature—if the Kelvin temperature doubles, the volume will double.

11.5 (c) Since hydrogen gas has the lowest molar mass of the set, 1 g will have the greatest number of moles and therefore the greatest volume.

CHAPTER 12

Liquids, Solids, and Intermolecular Forces

"It will be found that everything depends on the composition of the forces with which the particles of matter act upon one another; and from these forces ... all phenomena of nature take their origin."

ROGER JOSEPH BOSCOVICH (1711–1787)

12.1 Interactions between Molecules

Bite into a candy bar and taste its sweetness. Drink a cup of strong coffee and experience its bitterness. What causes these flavors? Most tastes originate from interactions between molecules. Certain molecules in coffee, for example, interact with molecular receptors on the surface of specialized cells on the tongue. The receptors are highly specific, recognizing only certain types of molecules. The interaction between the molecule and the receptor triggers a signal that goes to the brain, which we interpret as a bitter taste. Bitter tastes are usually unpleasant because many of the molecules that cause them are poisons. The sensation of bitterness is probably an evolutionary adaptation that helps us avoid these poisons.

The interaction between the molecules in coffee that taste bitter and the taste receptors on the tongue is caused by **intermolecular forces**—attractive forces that exist *between* molecules. Living organisms depend on intermolecular forces not only for taste but also for many other physiological processes. For example, in Chapter 19, we will see how intermolecular forces help determine the shapes of protein molecules—the workhorse molecules in living organisms. Later in this chapter—in the *Chemistry and Health* box in Section 12.6—we learn how intermolecular forces are central to DNA, the inheritable molecules that serve as blueprints for life.

The interactions between bitter molecules in coffee and molecular receptors on the tongue are highly specific. However, less specific intermolecular forces exist between all molecules and atoms. These intermolecular forces are responsible for the very existence of liquids and solids. The state of a sample of matter—solid, liquid, or gas—depends on the magnitude of intermolecular forces relative to the amount of thermal energy in the sample. Recall from Section 3.10 that the molecules and atoms that compose matter are in constant random motion that increases with increasing temperature. The energy associated with this motion is

◀ Flavors are caused by the interactions of molecules in foods or drinks with molecular receptors on the surface of the tongue. This image shows a caffeine molecule, one of the substances responsible for the sometimes bitter flavors in coffee.

called **thermal energy**. The weaker the intermolecular forces relative to thermal energy, the more likely the sample will be gaseous. The stronger the intermolecular forces relative to thermal energy, the more likely the sample will be liquid or solid.

12.2 Properties of Liquids and Solids

We are all familiar with solids and liquids. Water, gasoline, rubbing alcohol, and fingernail-polish remover are all common liquids. Ice, dry ice, and diamond are familiar solids. In contrast to gases—in which molecules or atoms are separated by large distances—the molecules or atoms that compose liquids and solids are in close contact with one another (▼ Figure 12.1).

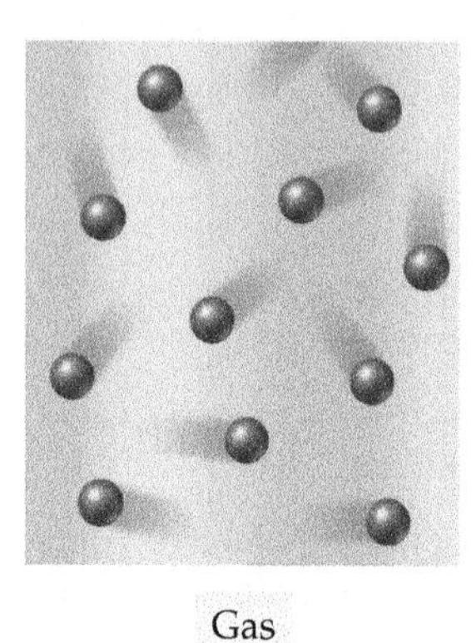

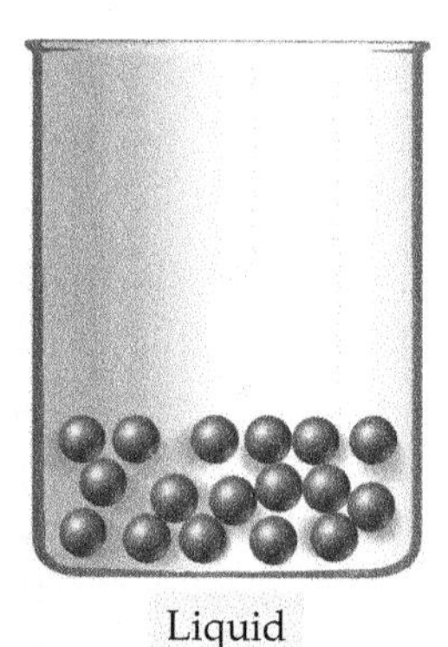

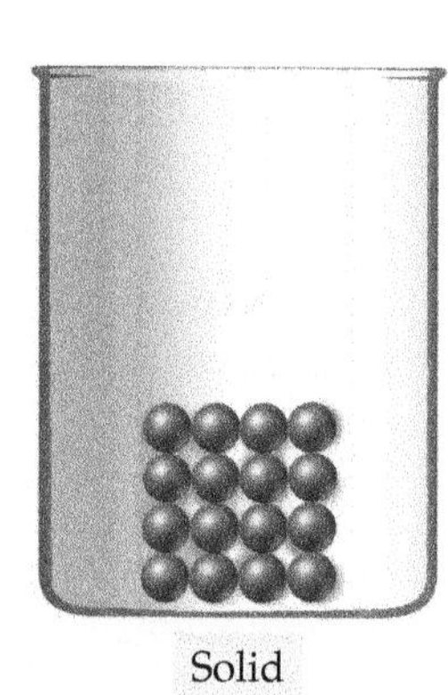

▶ FIGURE 12.1 **Gas, liquid, and solid states**

The difference between solids and liquids is in the freedom of movement of the constituent molecules or atoms. In liquids, even though the atoms or molecules are in close contact, they are still free to move around each other. In solids, the atoms or molecules are fixed in their positions, although thermal energy causes them to vibrate about a fixed point. These molecular properties of solids and liquids result in the following macroscopic properties.

Properties of Liquids

- High densities in comparison to gases.
- Indefinite shape; they assume the shape of their container.
- Definite volume; they are not easily compressed.

Properties of Solids

- High densities in comparison to gases.
- Definite shape; they do not assume the shape of their container.
- Definite volume; they are not easily compressed.
- May be crystalline (ordered) or amorphous (disordered).

Table 12.1 summarizes these properties, as well as the properties of gases for comparison.

TABLE 12.1 Properties of the States of Matter

Phase	Density	Shape	Volume	Strength of Intermolecular Forces[a]	Example
gas	low	indefinite	indefinite	weak	carbon dioxide gas (CO_2)
liquid	high	indefinite	definite	moderate	liquid water (H_2O)
solid	high	definite	definite	strong	sugar ($C_{12}H_{22}O_{11}$)

[a]Relative to thermal energy.

Liquids have high densities in comparison to gases because the atoms or molecules that compose liquids are much closer together. The density of liquid water, for example, is 1.0 g/cm^3 (at 25 °C), while the density of gaseous water at 100 °C and 1 atm is 0.59 g/L, or 5.9×10^{-4} g/cm^3. Liquids assume the shape of their containers because the atoms or molecules that compose them are free to flow. When you pour water into a flask, the water flows and assumes the shape of the flask (▼ Figure 12.2). Liquids are not easily compressed because the molecules or atoms that compose them are in close contact—they cannot be pushed closer together.

Like liquids, solids have high densities in comparison to gases because the atoms or molecules that compose solids are also close together. The densities of solids are usually just slightly greater than those of the corresponding liquids. A major exception is water, whose solid (ice) is slightly less dense than liquid water. Solids have a definite shape because, in contrast to liquids or gases, the molecules or atoms that compose solids are fixed in place (▼ Figure 12.3). Each molecule or atom only vibrates about a fixed point. Like liquids, solids have a definite volume and cannot be compressed because the molecules or atoms composing them are in close contact. As described in Section 3.3, solids may be *crystalline*, in which case the atoms or molecules that compose them arrange themselves in a well-ordered, three-dimensional array, or they may be *amorphous*, in which case the atoms or molecules that compose them have no long-range order.

As we will see in Section 12.8, ice is less dense than liquid water because water expands when it freezes due to its unique crystalline structure.

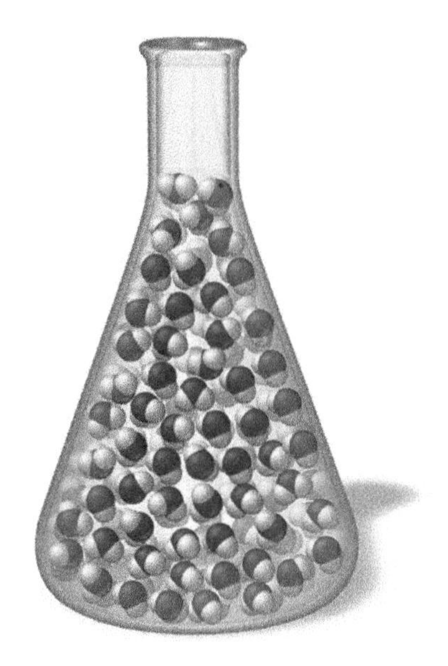

▲ FIGURE 12.2 **A liquid assumes the shape of its container** Because the molecules in liquid water are free to move around each other, they flow and assume the shape of their container.

▲ FIGURE 12.3 **Solids have a definite shape** In a solid such as ice, the molecules are fixed in place. However, they vibrate about fixed points.

12.3 Intermolecular Forces in Action: Surface Tension and Viscosity

The most important manifestation of intermolecular forces is the very existence of liquids and solids. Without intermolecular forces, solids and liquids would not exist and all matter would be gaseous. In liquids, we can observe several other manifestations of intermolecular forces including surface tension and viscosity.

SURFACE TENSION

A fly fisherman delicately casts a small metal hook (with a few feathers and strings attached to make it look like an insect) onto the surface of a moving stream. The hook floats on the surface of the water and attracts trout (▶ Figure 12.4).

▲ **FIGURE 12.4 Floating flies** Even though they are denser than water, fly-fishing lures float on the surface of a stream or lake because of surface tension.

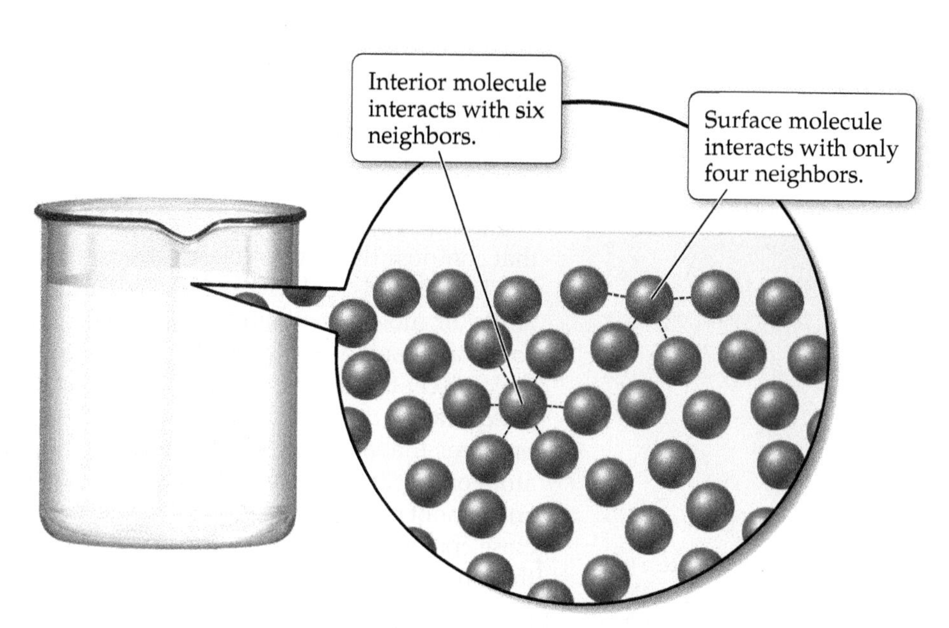
Interior molecule interacts with six neighbors.
Surface molecule interacts with only four neighbors.

▲ **FIGURE 12.5 Origin of surface tension** Molecules at the surface of a liquid interact only with neighbors below them, resulting in a net inward force that creates tension at the surface. This tension tends to minimize the area of the surface and makes it resist penetration.

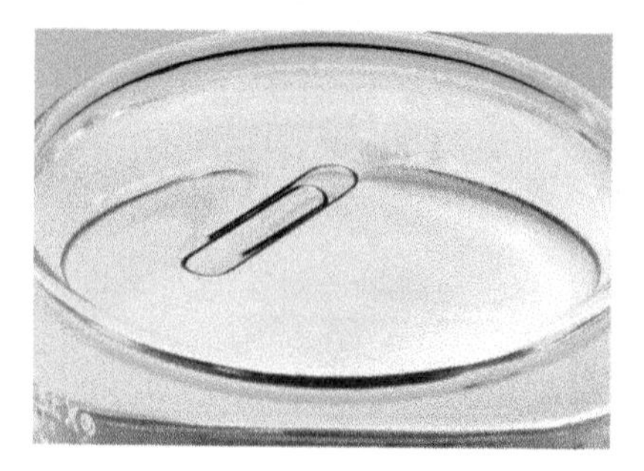

▲ **FIGURE 12.6 Surface tension at work** A paper clip will float on water if it is carefully placed on the surface of the water. It is held up by surface tension.

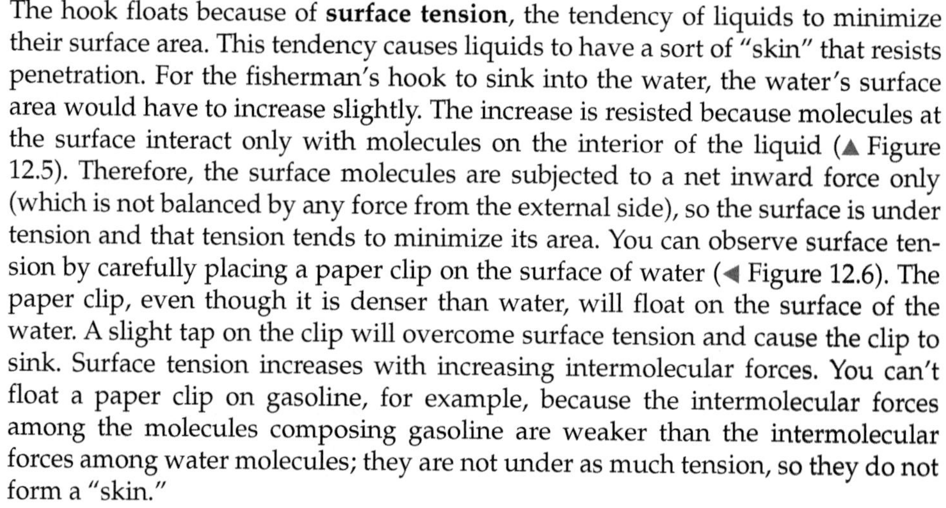

The hook floats because of **surface tension**, the tendency of liquids to minimize their surface area. This tendency causes liquids to have a sort of "skin" that resists penetration. For the fisherman's hook to sink into the water, the water's surface area would have to increase slightly. The increase is resisted because molecules at the surface interact only with molecules on the interior of the liquid (▲ Figure 12.5). Therefore, the surface molecules are subjected to a net inward force only (which is not balanced by any force from the external side), so the surface is under tension and that tension tends to minimize its area. You can observe surface tension by carefully placing a paper clip on the surface of water (◀ Figure 12.6). The paper clip, even though it is denser than water, will float on the surface of the water. A slight tap on the clip will overcome surface tension and cause the clip to sink. Surface tension increases with increasing intermolecular forces. You can't float a paper clip on gasoline, for example, because the intermolecular forces among the molecules composing gasoline are weaker than the intermolecular forces among water molecules; they are not under as much tension, so they do not form a "skin."

VISCOSITY

Another manifestation of intermolecular forces is **viscosity**, the resistance of a liquid to flow. Liquids that are viscous flow more slowly than liquids that are not viscous. For example, motor oil is more viscous than gasoline, and maple syrup is more viscous than water (◀ Figure 12.7). Viscosity is greater in substances with stronger intermolecular forces because molecules cannot move around each other as freely, hindering flow. Long molecules, such as the hydrocarbons in motor oil, also tend to form viscous liquids because of molecular entanglement (the long chainlike molecules get tangled together).

◀ **FIGURE 12.7 Viscosity** Maple syrup is more viscous than water because its molecules interact strongly, and so cannot flow past one another easily.

EVERYDAY CHEMISTRY

Why Are Water Drops Spherical?

Have you ever seen a close-up photograph of tiny water droplets (▼ Figure 12.8) or carefully watched water in free fall? In both cases, the distorting effects of gravity are diminished, and the water forms nearly perfect spheres. On the space shuttle, the complete absence of gravity results in floating spheres of water (▼ Figure 12.9). Why? Water drops are spherical because of the surface tension caused by the attractive forces between water molecules. Just as gravity pulls matter within a planet or star inward to form a sphere, so intermolecular forces pull water molecules inward to form a sphere. The sphere minimizes the surface-area-to-volume ratio, thereby minimizing the number of molecules at the surface.

A collection of magnetic marbles provides a good physical model of a water drop. Each magnetic marble is like a water molecule, attracted to the marbles around it. If you agitate these marbles slightly, so that they can find their preferred configuration, they tend toward a spherical shape (▼ Figure 12.10) because the attractions between the marbles cause them to minimize the number of marbles at the surface.

▲ **FIGURE 12.8 An almost perfect sphere** If a water droplet is small enough, it will largely be free of the distorting effects of gravity and be almost perfectly spherical.

▲ **FIGURE 12.9 A perfect sphere** In the absence of gravity, as in this picture taken on the space shuttle, water assumes the shape of a sphere.

▲ **FIGURE 12.10 An analogy for surface tension** Magnetic marbles tend to arrange themselves in a spherical shape.

CAN YOU ANSWER THIS? *How does the tendency of a liquid to form spherical drops depend on the strength of intermolecular forces? Do liquids with weaker intermolecular forces have a higher or lower tendency to form spherical drops?*

12.4 Evaporation and Condensation

Leave a glass of water in the open for several days and the water level within the glass slowly drops. Why? The first reason is that water molecules at the surface of the liquid—which experience fewer attractions to neighboring molecules and are therefore held less tightly—can break away from the rest of the liquid. The second reason is that all of the molecules in the liquid have a *distribution of kinetic energy* at

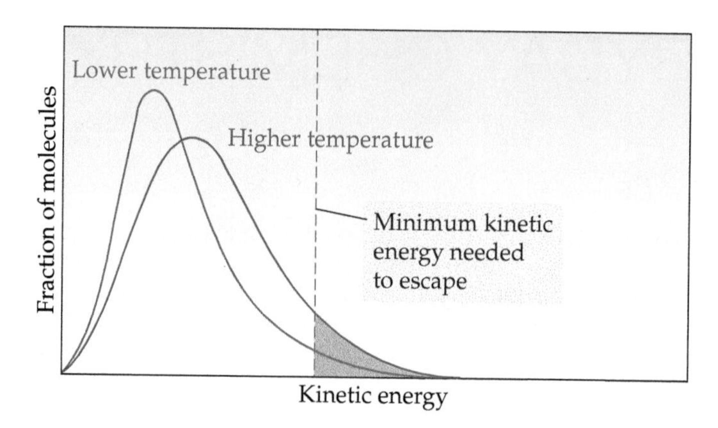

▶ **FIGURE 12.11 Energy distribution** At a given temperature, a sample of molecules or atoms will have a distribution of kinetic energies, as shown here. Only a small fraction of molecules have enough energy to escape. At a higher temperature, the fraction of molecules with enough energy to escape increases.

In evaporation or vaporization, a substance is converted from its liquid state into its gaseous state.

any given temperature (▲ Figure 12.11). At any given moment, some molecules in the liquid are moving faster than the average (higher energy), and others are moving more slowly (lower energy). Some of the molecules that are moving faster have enough energy to break free from the surface, resulting in **evaporation** or **vaporization**, a physical change in which a substance is converted from its liquid state to its gaseous state (◀ Figure 12.12).

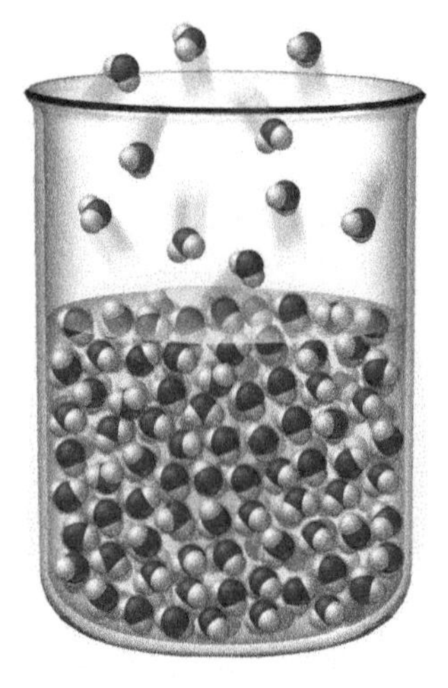

▲ **FIGURE 12.12 Evaporation** Because molecules on the surface of a liquid are held less tightly than those in the interior, the most energetic among them can break away into the gas state in the process called *evaporation*.

If you spill the same amount of water (as was in the glass) on a table, it evaporates more quickly, probably within a few hours. Why? The surface area of the spilled water is greater, leaving more molecules susceptible to evaporation. If you warm the glass of water, it also evaporates more quickly because the greater thermal energy causes a greater fraction of molecules to have enough energy to break away from the surface (see Figure 12.11). If you fill the glass with rubbing alcohol instead of water, the liquid again evaporates more quickly because the intermolecular forces between the alcohol molecules are weaker than the intermolecular forces between water molecules. In general, the rate of vaporization increases with:

- Increasing surface area
- Increasing temperature
- Decreasing strength of intermolecular forces

Liquids that evaporate easily are termed **volatile**, while those that do not vaporize easily are termed **nonvolatile**. Rubbing alcohol, for example, is more volatile than water. Motor oil at room temperature is virtually nonvolatile.

If you leave water in a *closed* container, its level remains constant because the molecules that leave the liquid are trapped in the air space above the water. These gaseous molecules bounce off of the walls of the container and eventually hit the surface of the water again and recondense. **Condensation** is a physical change in which a substance is converted from its gaseous state to its liquid state.

Evaporation and condensation are opposites: Evaporation is a liquid turning into a gas, and condensation is a gas turning into a liquid. When liquid water is initially put into a closed container, more evaporation happens than condensation because there are so few gaseous water molecules in the space above the water (▶ Figure 12.13a). However, as the number of gaseous water molecules increases, the rate of condensation also increases (▶ Figure 12.13b). At the point where the rates of condensation and evaporation become equal (▶ Figure 12.13c), **dynamic equilibrium** is reached and the number of gaseous water molecules above the liquid remains constant. The **vapor pressure** of a liquid is the partial pressure of its vapor in dynamic equilibrium with its liquid. For water at 25 °C, the vapor pressure is 23.8 mm Hg. Vapor pressure increases with:

Dynamic equilibrium is so named because both condensation and evaporation of individual molecules continue, but at the same rate.

- Increasing temperature
- Decreasing strength of intermolecular forces

See Table 11.4 for the vapor pressure of water at different temperatures.

Vapor pressure is independent of surface area because an increase in surface area at equilibrium equally affects the rate of evaporation and the rate of condensation.

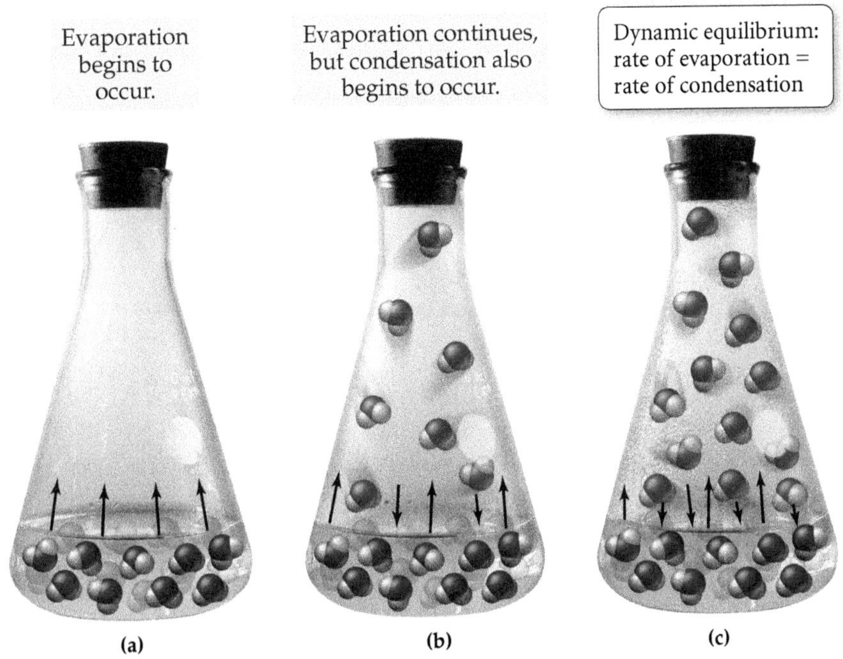

Evaporation begins to occur.

Evaporation continues, but condensation also begins to occur.

Dynamic equilibrium: rate of evaporation = rate of condensation

(a) (b) (c)

▶ **FIGURE 12.13 Evaporation and condensation** **(a)** When water is first put into a closed container, water molecules begin to evaporate. **(b)** As the number of gaseous molecules increases, some of the molecules begin to collide with the liquid and are recaptured—that is, they recondense into liquid. **(c)** When the rate of evaporation equals the rate of condensation, dynamic equilibrium occurs, and the number of gaseous molecules remains constant.

BOILING

Sometimes you see bubbles begin to form in hot water below 100 °C. These bubbles are dissolved air—not gaseous water—leaving the liquid. Dissolved air comes out of water as you heat it because the solubility of a gas in a liquid decreases with increasing temperature (Section 13.4).

As you increase the temperature of water in an open container, the increasing thermal energy causes molecules to leave the surface and vaporize at a faster and faster rate. At the **boiling point**—the temperature at which the vapor pressure of a liquid is equal to the pressure above it—the thermal energy is enough for molecules within the *interior* of the liquid (not just those at the surface) to break free into the gas phase (▼ Figure 12.14). Water's **normal boiling point**—its boiling point at a pressure of 1 atmosphere—is 100 °C. When a sample of water reaches 100 °C, you can see bubbles form within the liquid. These bubbles are pockets of gaseous water. The bubbles quickly rise to the surface of the liquid, and the water molecules that were in the bubble leave as gaseous water, or steam. Once the boiling point of a liquid is reached, additional heating only causes more rapid boiling; it does not raise the temperature of the liquid above its boiling point (▶ Figure 12.15). A mixture of boiling water *and* steam will always have a temperature of 100 °C (at 1 atm pressure). Only after all the water has been converted to steam can the temperature of the steam rise beyond 100 °C.

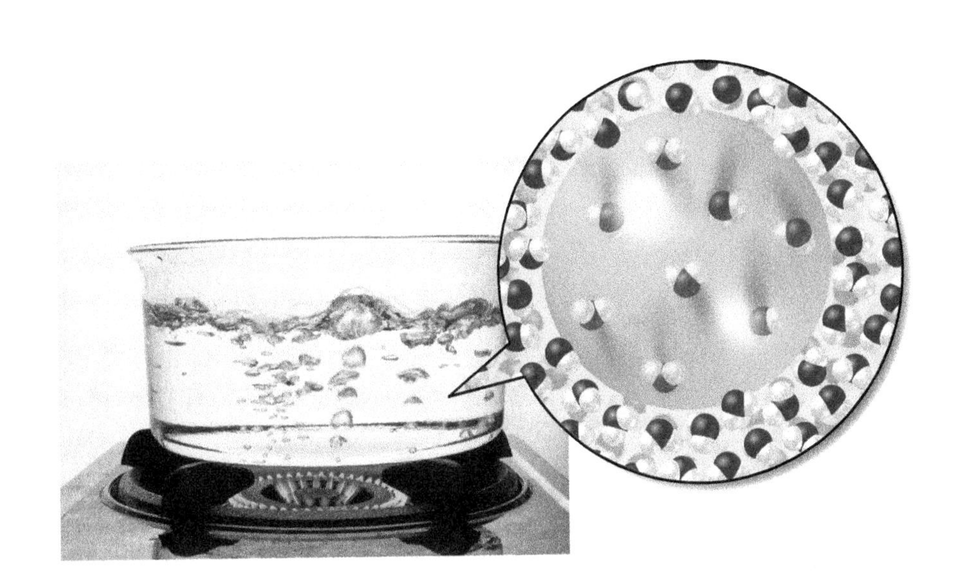

▶ **FIGURE 12.14 Boiling** During boiling, thermal energy is enough to cause water molecules in the interior of the liquid to become gaseous, forming bubbles containing gaseous water molecules.

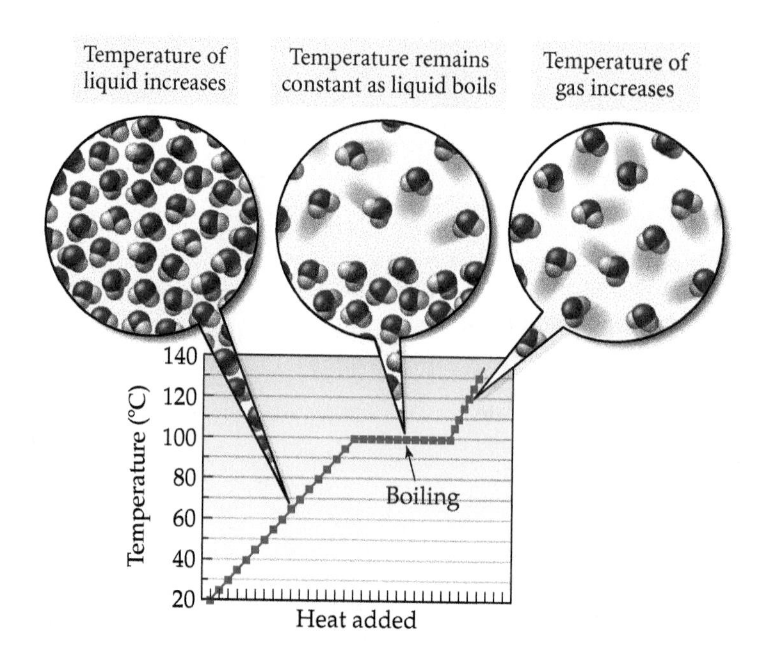

▶ **FIGURE 12.15 Heating curve during boiling** The temperature of water as it is heated from room temperature through boiling. During boiling, the temperature remains at 100 °C until all the liquid is evaporated.

CONCEPTUAL CHECKPOINT 12.1

The gas over a rapidly boiling pot of water is sampled and analyzed. Which substance do you expect to compose a large fraction of the gas sample?

(a) $H_2(g)$ **(b)** $H_2O(g)$ **(c)** $O_2(g)$ **(d)** $H_2O_2(g)$

ENERGETICS OF EVAPORATION AND CONDENSATION

In an endothermic process, heat is absorbed; in an exothermic process, heat is released.

Evaporation is *endothermic*—when a liquid is converted into a gas, it absorbs heat because energy is required to break molecules away from the rest of the liquid. Imagine a collection of water molecules in the liquid state. As the water evaporates, it cools—typical of endothermic processes—because only the fastest-moving molecules break away, which leaves the slower-moving molecules behind. Under ordinary conditions, the slight decrease in temperature of water as it evaporates is counteracted by thermal energy transfer from the surroundings, which warms the water back up. However, if the evaporating water were thermally isolated from the surroundings, it would continue to cool down as it evaporated.

You can observe the endothermic nature of evaporation by turning off the heat beneath a boiling pot of water; it will quickly stop boiling as the heat lost due to vaporization causes the water to cool below its boiling point. Our bodies use the endothermic nature of evaporation for cooling. When we overheat, we sweat, causing our skin to be covered with liquid water. As this water evaporates it absorbs heat from our bodies, cooling us down. A fan intensifies the cooling effect because it blows newly vaporized water away from the skin, allowing more sweat to vaporize and cause even more cooling. High humidity, on the other hand, slows down evaporation, preventing cooling. When the air already contains high amounts of water vapor, sweat does not evaporate as easily, making our cooling system less efficient.

Condensation, the opposite of evaporation, is *exothermic*—heat is released when a gas condenses to a liquid. If you have ever accidentally put your hand above a steaming kettle, you may have experienced a *steam burn*. As the steam condenses to a liquid on your skin, it releases heat, causing a severe burn. The exothermic nature of condensation is also the reason that winter overnight temperatures in coastal cities, which tend to have water vapor in the air, do not get as low as in deserts, which tend to have dry air. As the air temperature in a coastal city drops, water condenses out of the air, releasing heat and preventing the temperature from dropping further. In deserts, there is little moisture in the air to condense, so the temperature drop is greater.

HEAT OF VAPORIZATION

The amount of heat required to vaporize one mole of liquid is the **heat of vaporization** (ΔH_{vap}). The heat of vaporization of water at its normal boiling point (100 °C) is 40.7 kJ/mole.

$$H_2O(l) \longrightarrow H_2O(g) \quad \Delta H = +40.7 \text{ kJ (at 100 °C)}$$

ΔH is positive because vaporization is endothermic; energy must be added to the water to vaporize it.

The same amount of heat is involved when 1 mol of gas condenses, but *the heat is emitted* rather than absorbed.

$$H_2O(g) \longrightarrow H_2O(l) \quad \Delta H = -40.7 \text{ kJ (at 100 °C)}$$

ΔH is negative because condensation is exothermic; energy is given off as the water condenses.

Different liquids have different heats of vaporization (Table 12.2). Heats of vaporization are also *temperature dependent* (they change with temperature). The higher the temperature, the easier it is to vaporize a given liquid and therefore the lower the heat of vaporization.

TABLE 12.2 Heats of Vaporization of Several Liquids at Their Boiling Points and at 25 °C

Liquid	Chemical Formula	Normal Boiling Point (°C)	Heat of Vaporization (kJ/mol) at Boiling Point	Heat of Vaporization (kJ/mol) at 25 °C
water	H_2O	100.0	40.7	44.0
isopropyl alcohol (rubbing alcohol)	C_3H_8O	82.3	39.9	45.4
acetone	C_3H_6O	56.1	29.1	31.0
diethyl ether	$C_4H_{10}O$	34.5	26.5	27.1

We can use the heat of vaporization of a liquid to calculate the amount of heat energy required to vaporize a given amount of that liquid. To do so, we use the heat of vaporization as a conversion factor between moles of the liquid and the amount of heat required to vaporize it. For example, suppose we want to calculate the amount of heat required to vaporize 25.0 g of water at its boiling point. We begin by sorting the information in the problem statement.

GIVEN: 25.0 g H_2O

FIND: heat (kJ)

SOLUTION MAP

We then strategize by building a solution map that begins with the mass of water and ends with the energy required to vaporize it.

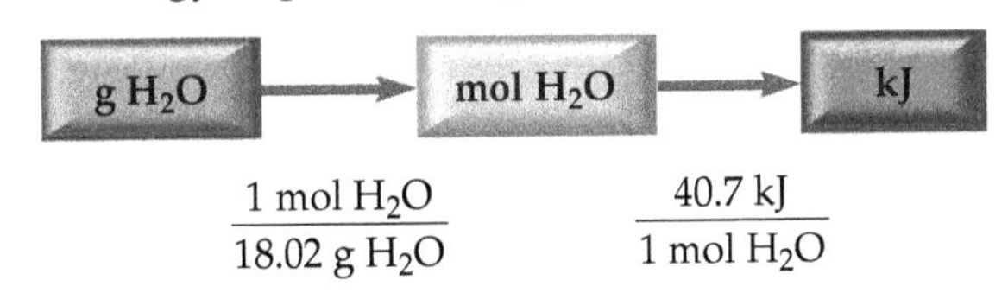

RELATIONSHIPS USED

$$\Delta H_{vap} = 40.7 \text{ kJ/mol at 100 °C (Table 12.2)}$$

$$1 \text{ mol } H_2O = 18.02 \text{ g } H_2O \text{ (molar mass of water)}$$

SOLUTION

$$25.0 \text{ g } H_2O \times \frac{1 \text{ mol } H_2O}{18.02 \text{ g } H_2O} \times \frac{40.7 \text{ kJ}}{1 \text{ mol } H_2O} = 56.5 \text{ kJ}$$

EXAMPLE 12.1 Using the Heat of Vaporization in Calculations

Calculate the amount of water in grams that can be vaporized at its boiling point with 155 kJ of heat.

SORT

You are given the number of kilojoules of heat energy and asked to find the mass of water that can be vaporized with the given amount of energy.

GIVEN: 155 kJ
FIND: g H_2O

STRATEGIZE

Draw the solution map beginning with the energy in kilojoules and converting to moles of water and then to grams of water.

SOLUTION MAP

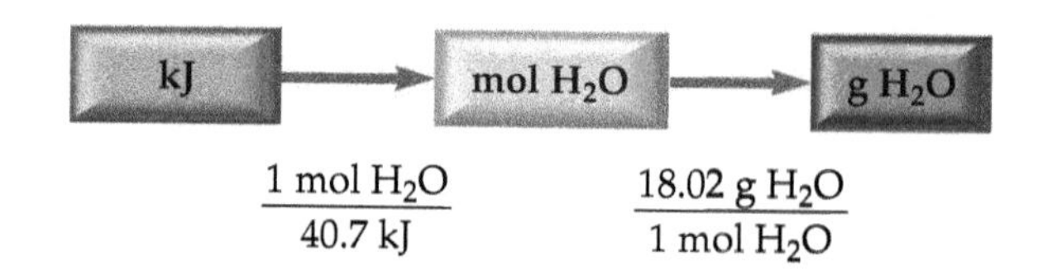

$$\frac{1\ \text{mol}\ H_2O}{40.7\ \text{kJ}} \qquad \frac{18.02\ \text{g}\ H_2O}{1\ \text{mol}\ H_2O}$$

RELATIONSHIPS USED

$\Delta H_{vap} = 40.7\ \text{kJ/mol at } 100\ °\text{C}$ (Table 12.2)

$18.02\ \text{g}\ H_2O = 1\ \text{mol}\ H_2O$ (molar mass of water)

SOLVE

Follow the solution map to solve the problem.

SOLUTION

$$155\ \text{kJ} \times \frac{1\ \text{mol}\ H_2O}{40.7\ \text{kJ}} \times \frac{18.02\ \text{g}}{1\ \text{mol}\ H_2O} = 68.6\ \text{g}$$

CHECK

Check your answer. Are the units correct? Does the answer make physical sense?

The units (g) are correct. The magnitude of the answer makes sense because each mole of water absorbs about 40 kJ of energy upon vaporization. Therefore 155 kJ should vaporize close to 4 mol of water, which is consistent with the answer (4 mol of water has a mass of about 72 g)

▶**SKILLBUILDER 12.1 | Using the Heat of Vaporization in Calculations**

Calculate the amount of heat in kilojoules required to vaporize 2.58 kg of water at its boiling point.

▶**SKILLBUILDER PLUS**

A drop of water weighing 0.48 g condenses on the surface of a 55-g block of aluminum that is initially at 25 °C. If the heat released during condensation goes only toward heating the metal, what is the final temperature in Celsius of the metal block? (The specific heat capacity of aluminum is given in Table 3.4 and is 0.903 J/g °C.)

▶**FOR MORE PRACTICE** Example 12.7; Problems 47, 48, 49, 50, 51, 52.

12.5 Melting, Freezing, and Sublimation

As the temperature of a solid increases, thermal energy causes the molecules and atoms composing the solid to vibrate faster. At the **melting point**, atoms and molecules have enough thermal energy to overcome the intermolecular forces that hold them at their stationary points, and the solid turns into a liquid. The melting point of ice, for example, is 0 °C. Once the melting point of a solid is reached, additional heating only causes more rapid melting; it does not raise the temperature of the solid above its melting point (▶ Figure 12.16). Only after all of the ice has melted will additional heating raise the temperature of the liquid water past 0 °C. A mixture of water *and* ice will always have a temperature of 0 °C (at 1 atm pressure).

ENERGETICS OF MELTING AND FREEZING

The most common way to cool down a drink is to drop several ice cubes into it. As the ice melts, the drink cools because melting is endothermic—heat is absorbed

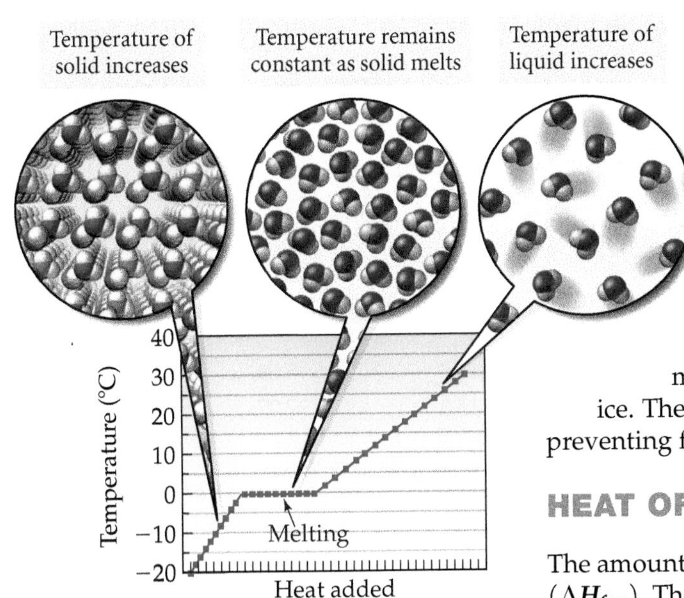

▲ **FIGURE 12.16 Heating curve during melting** A graph of the temperature of ice as it is heated from −20 °C to 35 °C. During melting, the temperature of the solid and the liquid remain at 0 °C until the entire solid is melted.

when a solid is converted into a liquid. The melting ice absorbs heat from the liquid in the drink and cools the liquid. Melting is endothermic because energy is required to partially overcome the attractions between molecules in the solid and free them into the liquid state.

Freezing, the opposite of melting, is exothermic—heat is released when a liquid freezes into a solid. For example, as water in your freezer turns into ice, it releases heat, which must be removed by the refrigeration system of the freezer. If the refrigeration system did not remove the heat, the water would not completely freeze into ice. The heat released as it began to freeze would warm the freezer, preventing further freezing.

HEAT OF FUSION

The amount of heat required to melt 1 mol of a solid is the **heat of fusion** (ΔH_{fus}). The heat of fusion for water is 6.02 kJ/mol.

$$H_2O(s) \longrightarrow H_2O(l) \quad \Delta H = +6.02 \text{ kJ}$$

ΔH is positive because melting is endothermic; energy must be added to the ice to melt it.

The same amount of heat is involved when 1 mol of liquid water freezes, but the heat is emitted rather than absorbed.

$$H_2O(l) \longrightarrow H_2O(s) \quad \Delta H = -6.02 \text{ kJ}$$

ΔH is negative because freezing is exothermic; energy is given off as the water freezes.

Different substances have different heats of fusion (Table 12.3 on p. 422). Notice that, in general, the heat of fusion is significantly less than the heat of vaporization. It takes less energy to melt 1 mol of ice than it does to vaporize 1 mol of liquid water. Why? Vaporization requires complete separation of one molecule

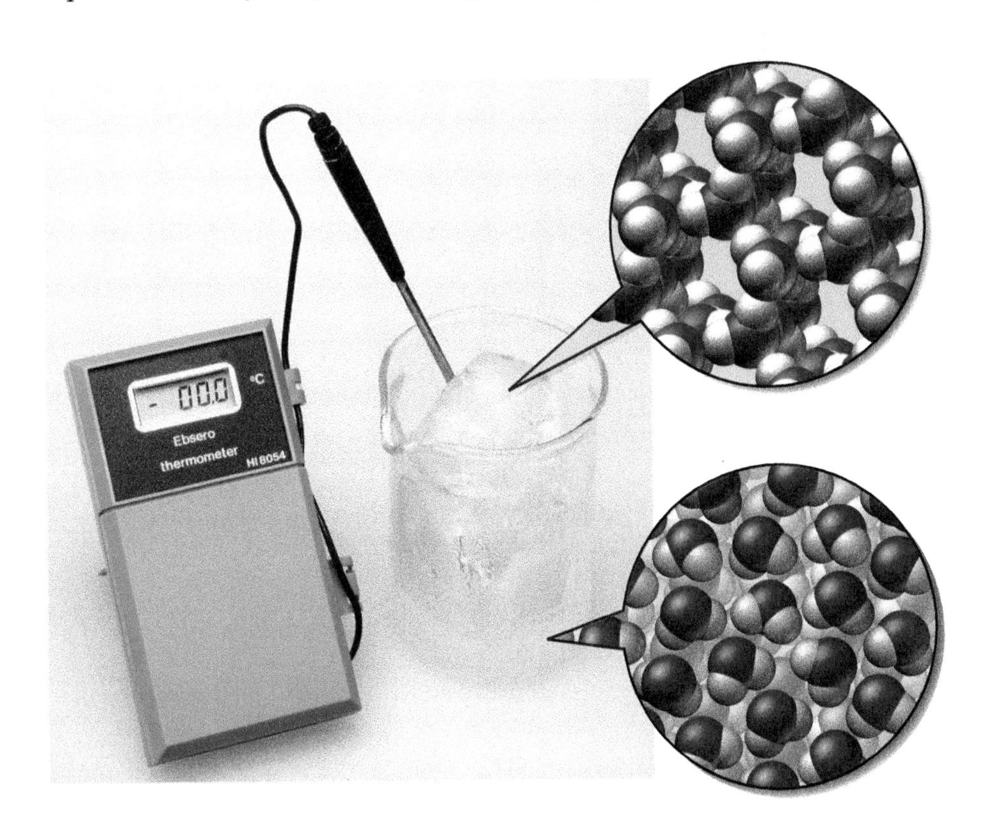

▶ When ice melts, water molecules break free from the solid structure and become liquid. As long as ice and water are both present, the temperature will be 0.0 °C.

from another, so the intermolecular forces must be completely overcome. Melting, on the other hand, requires that intermolecular forces be only partially overcome, allowing molecules to move around one another while still remaining in contact.

TABLE 12.3 Heats of Fusion of Several Substances

Liquid	Chemical Formula	Melting Point (°C)	Heat of Fusion (kJ/mol)
water	H_2O	0.00	6.02
isopropyl alcohol (rubbing alcohol)	C_3H_8O	−89.5	5.37
acetone	C_3H_6O	−94.8	5.69
diethyl ether	$C_4H_{10}O$	−116.3	7.27

We can use the heat of fusion to calculate the amount of heat energy required to melt a given amount of a solid. The heat of fusion is a conversion factor between moles of a solid and the amount of heat required to melt it. For example, suppose we want to calculate the amount of heat required to melt 25.0 g of ice (at 0 °C). We first sort the information in the problem statement.

GIVEN: 25.0 g H_2O

FIND: heat (kJ)

SOLUTION MAP

We then draw the solution map, beginning with the mass of water and ending with the energy required to melt it.

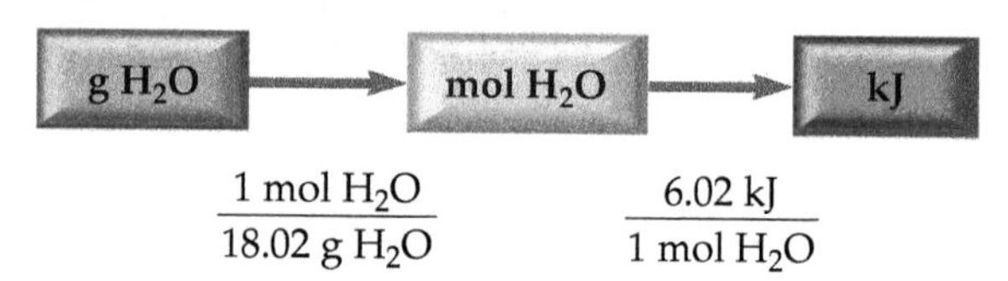

RELATIONSHIPS USED

$$\Delta H_{fus} = 6.02 \text{ kJ/mol (Table 12.3)}$$
$$1 \text{ mol } H_2O = 18.02 \text{ g } H_2O \text{ (molar mass of water)}$$

SOLUTION

$$25.0 \text{ g } H_2O \times \frac{1 \text{ mol } H_2O}{18.02 \text{ g } H_2O} \times \frac{6.02 \text{ kJ}}{1 \text{ mol } H_2O} = 8.35 \text{ kJ}$$

EXAMPLE 12.2 Using the Heat of Fusion in Calculations

Calculate the amount of ice in grams that, upon melting (at 0 °C), absorbs 237 kJ of heat.

SORT You are given the number of kJ of heat energy and asked to find the mass of ice that absorbs the given amount of energy upon melting.	GIVEN: 237 kJ FIND: g H_2O (ice)
STRATEGIZE Draw the solution map beginning with the energy in kilojoules and converting to moles of water and then to grams of water.	SOLUTION MAP 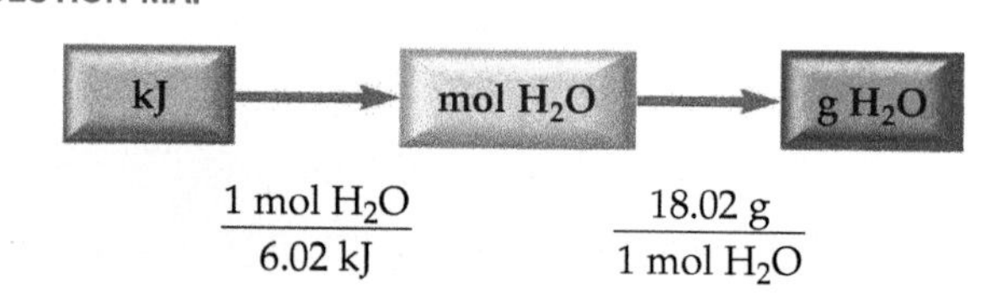

	RELATIONSHIPS USED $\Delta H_{fus} = 6.02\,kJ/mol$ (Table 12.3) $1\,mol\ H_2O = 18.02\ g\ H_2O$ (molar mass of water)
SOLVE Follow the solution map to solve the problem.	**SOLUTION** $237\ kJ \times \frac{1\ \cancel{mol\ H_2O}}{6.02\ kJ} \times \frac{18.02\ g}{1\ \cancel{mol\ H_2O}} = 709\ g$
CHECK Check your answer. Are the units correct? Does the answer make physical sense?	The units (g) are correct. The magnitude of the answer makes sense because each mole of water absorbs about 6 kJ of energy upon melting. Therefore 237 kJ should melt close to 40 mol of water, which is consistent with the answer (40 mol of water has a mass of about 720 g).

▶SKILLBUILDER 12.2 | Using the Heat of Fusion in Calculations

Calculate the amount of heat absorbed when a 15.5-g ice cube melts (at 0 °C).

▶SKILLBUILDER PLUS

A 5.6-g ice cube (at 0 °C) is placed into 195 g of water initially at 25 °C. If the heat absorbed for melting the ice comes only from the 195 g of water, what is the temperature change of the 195 g of water?

▶FOR MORE PRACTICE Example 12.8; Problems 55, 56, 57, 58.

CONCEPTUAL CHECKPOINT 12.2

This diagram shows a heating curve for ice beginning at −25 °C and ending at 125 °C. Correlate sections i, ii, and iii with the correct states of water.

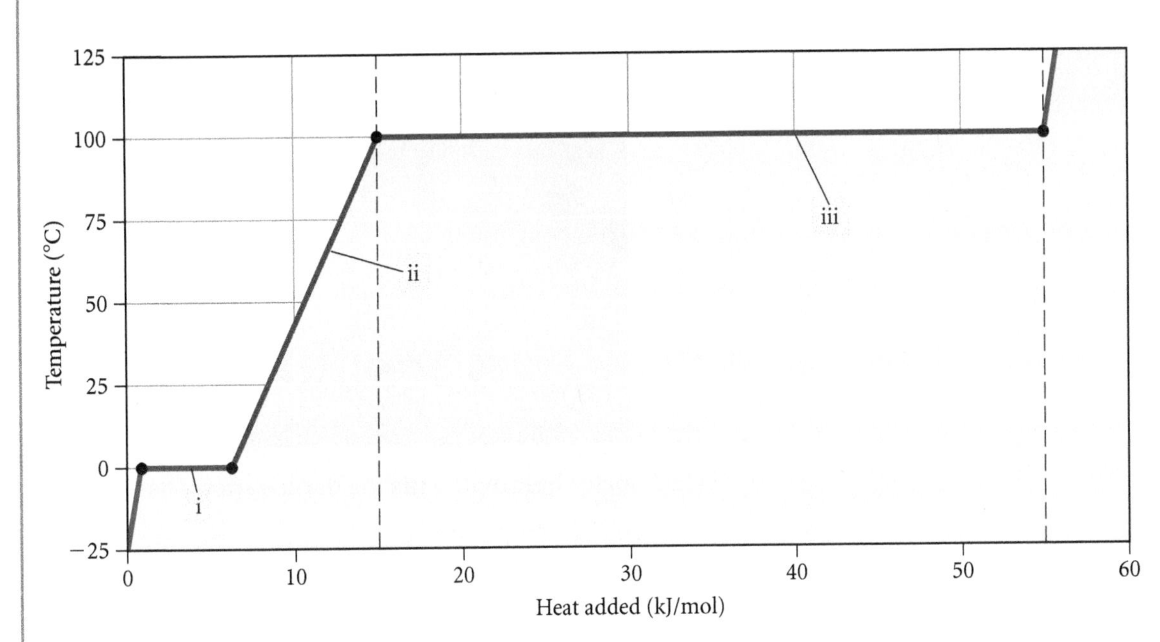

(a) i—solid, ii—liquid, iii—gas

(b) i—solid and liquid, ii—liquid, iii—liquid and gas

(c) i—liquid, ii—liquid and gas, iii—gas

(d) i—solid and liquid, ii—liquid and gas , iii—gas

▲ Dry ice is solid carbon dioxide. The solid does not melt but rather sublimes. It transforms directly from solid carbon dioxide to gaseous carbon dioxide.

SUBLIMATION

Sublimation is a physical change in which a substance changes from its solid state directly to its gaseous state. When a substance sublimes, molecules leave the surface of the solid, where they are held less tightly than in the interior, and become gaseous. For example, dry ice, which is solid carbon dioxide, does not melt under atmospheric pressure (at any temperature). At −78 °C, the CO_2 molecules have enough energy to leave the surface of the dry ice and become gaseous. Regular ice will slowly sublime at temperatures below 0 °C. You can observe the sublimation of ice in cold climates; ice or snow laying on the ground gradually disappears, even if the temperature remains below 0 °C. Similarly, ice cubes left in the freezer for a long time slowly become smaller, even though the freezer is always below 0 °C. In both cases, the ice is subliming, turning directly into water vapor.

Ice also sublimes out of frozen foods. You can clearly see this in food that is frozen in an airtight plastic bag for a long time. The ice crystals that form in the bag are water that has sublimed out of the food and redeposited on the surface of the bag. For this reason, food that remains frozen for too long becomes dried out. This can be avoided to some degree by freezing foods to colder temperatures (further below 0 °C), a process called deep-freezing. The colder temperature lowers the rate of sublimation and preserves the food longer.

CONCEPTUAL CHECKPOINT 12.3

Solid carbon dioxide (dry ice) can be depicted as follows:

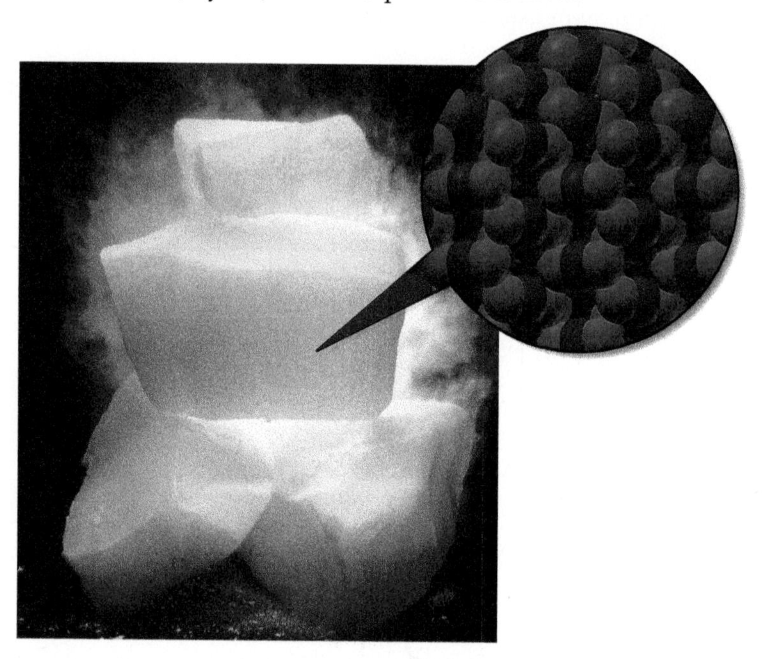

Which image best represents the dry ice after it has sublimed?

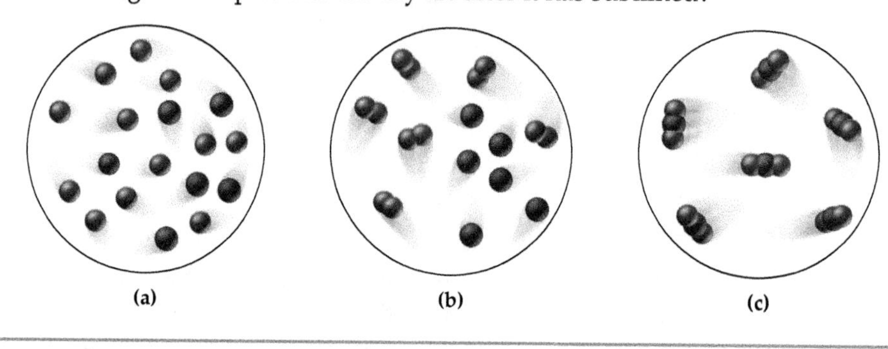

12.6 Types of Intermolecular Forces: Dispersion, Dipole–Dipole, and Hydrogen Bonding

The strength of the intermolecular forces between the molecules or atoms that compose a substance determines the state—solid, liquid, or gas—of the substance at room temperature. Strong intermolecular forces tend to result in liquids and solids (with high melting and boiling points). Weak intermolecular forces tend to result in gases (with low melting and boiling points). In this book, we focus on three fundamental types of intermolecular forces. In order of increasing strength, they are the dispersion force, the dipole–dipole force, and the hydrogen bond.

DISPERSION FORCE

The nature of dispersion forces was first recognized by Fritz W. London (1900–1954), a German-American physicist.

The default intermolecular force, present in all molecules and atoms, is the **dispersion force** (also called the *London force*). Dispersion forces are caused by fluctuations in the electron distribution within molecules or atoms. Since all atoms and molecules have electrons, they all have dispersion forces. The electrons in an atom or a molecule may, at any one instant, be unevenly distributed. For example, imagine a frame-by-frame movie of a helium atom in which each "frame" captures the position of the helium atom's two electrons (▼ Figure 12.17). In any one frame, the electrons are not symmetrically arranged around the nucleus. In Frame 3, for example, helium's two electrons are on the left side of the helium atom. The left side then acquires a slightly negative charge (δ^-). The right side of the atom, which is void of electrons, acquires a slightly positive charge (δ^+).

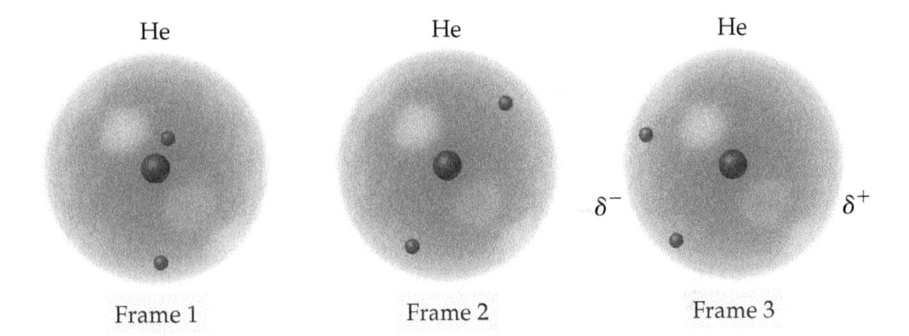

▶ FIGURE 12.17 **Instantaneous dipoles** Random fluctuations in the electron distribution of a helium atom cause instantaneous dipoles to form.

This fleeting charge separation is called an **instantaneous dipole** (or *temporary dipole*). An instantaneous dipole on one helium atom induces an instantaneous dipole on its neighboring atoms because the positive end of the instantaneous dipole attracts electrons in the neighboring atoms (▼ Figure 12.18). The dispersion force occurs as neighboring atoms attract one another—the positive end of one instantaneous dipole attracts the negative end of another. The dipoles responsible for the dispersion force are transient, constantly appearing and disappearing in response to fluctuations in electron clouds.

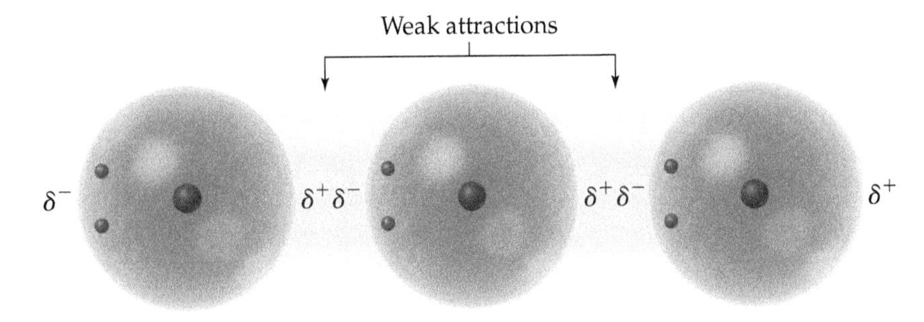

▶ FIGURE 12.18 **Dispersion force** An instantaneous dipole on any one helium atom induces instantaneous dipoles on neighboring atoms. The neighboring atoms then attract one another. This attraction is called the dispersion force.

To *polarize* means to form a dipole moment.

The magnitude of the dispersion force depends on how easily the electrons in the atom or molecule can move or *polarize* in response to an instantaneous dipole, which in turn depends on the size of the electron cloud. A larger electron cloud

TABLE 12.4 Noble Gas Boiling Points

Noble Gas	Molar Mass (g/mol)	Boiling Point (K)
He	4.00	4.2 K
Ne	20.18	27 K
Ar	39.95	87 K
Kr	83.80	120 K
Xe	131.29	165 K

results in a greater dispersion force because the electrons are held less tightly by the nucleus and therefore can polarize more easily. If all other variables are constant, the dispersion force increases with increasing molar mass. For example, consider the boiling points of the noble gases displayed in Table 12.4. As the molar mass of the noble gases increase, their boiling points increase. While molar mass alone does not determine the magnitude of the dispersion force, it can be used as a guide when comparing dispersion forces within a family of similar elements or compounds.

EXAMPLE 12.3 Dispersion Forces

Which halogen, Cl_2 or I_2, has the higher boiling point?

SOLUTION

The molar mass of Cl_2 is 70.90 g/mol, and the molar mass of I_2 is 253.80 g/mol. Since I_2 has the higher molar mass, it has stronger dispersion forces and therefore the higher boiling point.

▶SKILLBUILDER 12.3 | Dispersion Forces

Which hydrocarbon, CH_4 or C_2H_6, has the higher boiling point?

▶FOR MORE PRACTICE Problems 63, 64.

DIPOLE–DIPOLE FORCE

See Section 10.8 to review how to determine whether a molecule is polar.

The **dipole–dipole force** exists in all polar molecules. Polar molecules have **permanent dipoles** (Section 10.8) that interact with the permanent dipoles of neighboring molecules (◀ Figure 12.19). The positive end of one permanent dipole is attracted to the negative end of another; this attraction is the dipole–dipole force (◀ Figure 12.20). Polar molecules, therefore, have higher melting and boiling points than nonpolar molecules of similar molar mass. Remember that all molecules (including polar ones) have dispersion forces. In addition, polar molecules have dipole–dipole forces. These additional attractive forces raise their melting and boiling points relative to nonpolar molecules of similar molar mass. For example, consider the compounds formaldehyde and ethane:

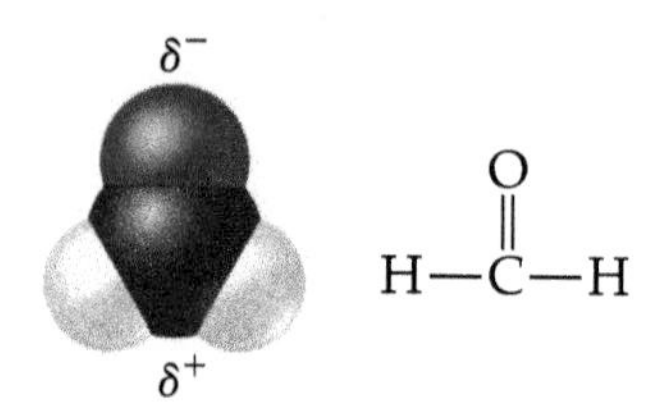

▲ **FIGURE 12.19 A permanent dipole** Molecules such as formaldehyde are polar and therefore have a permanent dipole.

Name	Formula	Molar mass (g/mol)	Structure	bp (°C)	mp (°C)
Formaldehyde	CH_2O	30.0	H—C(=O)—H	−19.5	−92
Ethane	C_2H_6	30.1	H₃C—CH₃ (H—C(H)(H)—C(H)(H)—H)	−88	−172

Formaldehyde is polar and therefore has a higher melting point and boiling point than nonpolar ethane, even though the two compounds have the same molar mass.

The polarity of molecules composing liquids is also important in determining a liquid's **miscibility**—its ability to mix without separating into two phases. In general, polar liquids are miscible with other polar liquids but are not miscible with nonpolar liquids. For example, water, a polar liquid, is not miscible with pentane (C_5H_{12}), a nonpolar liquid (▶ Figure 12.21). Similarly, water and oil (also nonpolar) do not mix. Consequently, oily hands or oily stains on clothes cannot be washed away with plain water (see Chapter 10, *Everyday Chemistry: How Soap Works*).

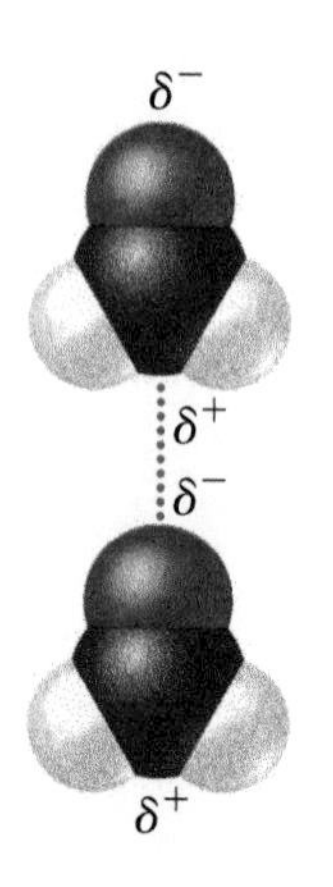

▲ **FIGURE 12.20 Dipole–dipole attraction** The positive end of a polar molecule is attracted to the negative end of its neighbor, giving rise to the dipole–dipole force.

(a)

(b)

(c)

▶ **FIGURE 12.21 Polar and nonpolar compounds** **(a)** Pentane, a nonpolar compound, does not mix with water, a polar compound. **(b)** For the same reason, the oil and vinegar (vinegar is largely a water solution of acetic acid) in salad dressing tend to separate into distinct layers. **(c)** An oil spill from a tanker demonstrates dramatically that petroleum and seawater are not miscible.

EXAMPLE 12.4 Dipole–Dipole Forces

Determine whether or not each molecule has dipole–dipole forces.

(a) CO_2 **(b)** CH_2Cl_2 **(c)** CH_4

SOLUTION

A molecule has dipole–dipole forces if it is polar. To determine whether a molecule is polar, you must:

1. determine whether the molecule contains polar bonds, and
2. determine whether the polar bonds add together to form a net dipole moment (Section 10.8).

(a) Since the electronegativities of carbon and oxygen are 2.5 and 3.5, respectively (Figure 10.2), CO_2 has polar bonds. The geometry of CO_2 is linear. Consequently, the polar bonds cancel; the molecule is not polar and does not have dipole–dipole forces.

O=C=O

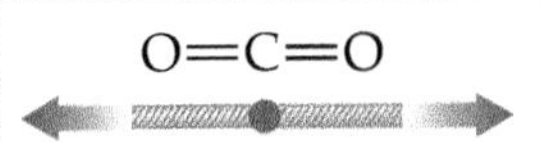

Nonpolar; no dipole–dipole forces

(b) The electronegativities of C, H, and Cl are 2.5, 2.1, and 3.5, respectively. Consequently, CH_2Cl_2 has two polar bonds (C—Cl) and two bonds that are nearly nonpolar (C—H). The geometry of CH_2Cl_2 is tetrahedral. Since the C—Cl bonds and the C—H bonds are different, they do not cancel, but sum to a net dipole moment. Therefore the molecule is polar and has dipole–dipole forces.

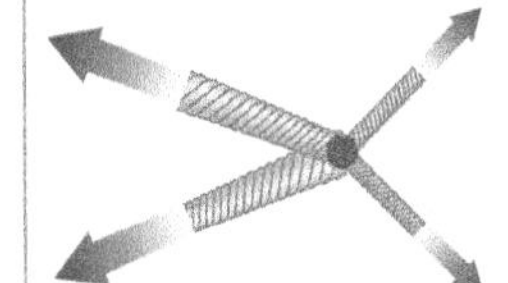

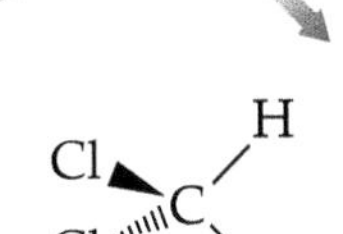

Polar; dipole–dipole forces

(c) Since the electronegativities of C and H are 2.5 and 2.1, respectively, the C—H bonds are nearly nonpolar. In addition, since the geometry of the molecule is tetrahedral, any slight polarities that the bonds might have will cancel. CH_4 is therefore nonpolar and does not have dipole–dipole forces.

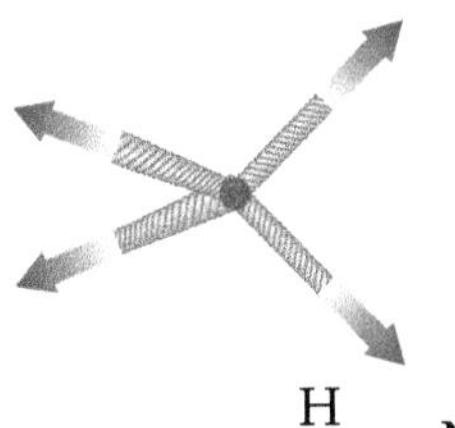

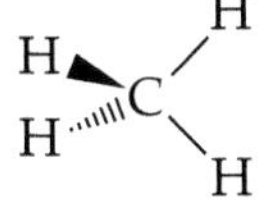

Nonpolar; no dipole–dipole forces

▶**SKILLBUILDER 12.4 | Dipole–Dipole Forces**

Determine whether or not each molecule has dipole–dipole forces.

(a) CI_4 **(b)** CH_3Cl **(c)** HCl

▶**FOR MORE PRACTICE** Problems 59, 60, 61, 62.

HYDROGEN BONDING

Polar molecules containing hydrogen atoms bonded directly to fluorine, oxygen, or nitrogen exhibit an additional intermolecular force called a **hydrogen bond.** HF, NH_3 and H_2O, for example, all undergo hydrogen bonding. A hydrogen bond is a sort of *super* dipole–dipole force. The large electronegativity difference between hydrogen and these electronegative elements, as well as the small size of these atoms (which allows neighboring molecules to get very close to each other), gives rise to a strong attraction between the hydrogen in each of these molecules and the F, O, or N on neighboring molecules. This attraction between a hydrogen atom and an electronegative atom is the hydrogen bond. For example, in HF the hydrogen is strongly attracted to the fluorine on neighboring molecules (◀ Figure 12.22).

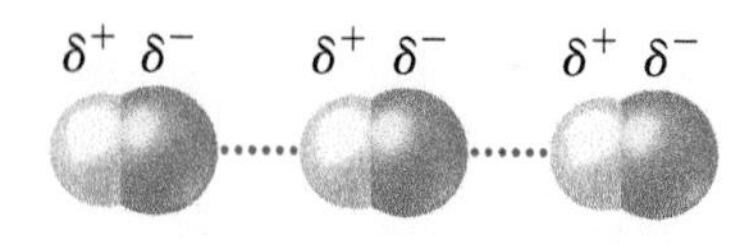

▲ **FIGURE 12.22 The hydrogen bond** In HF, the hydrogen on each molecule is strongly attracted to the fluorine on its neighbor. The intermolecular attraction of a hydrogen atom to an electronegative atom is called a *hydrogen bond.*

Do not confuse hydrogen bonds with chemical bonds. Chemical bonds occur between *individual atoms within a molecule* and are generally much stronger than hydrogen bonds. A hydrogen bond has only 2 to 5% the strength of a typical covalent chemical bond. Hydrogen bonds—like dispersion forces and dipole–dipole forces—are intermolecular forces that occur *between molecules.* In liquid water, for example, the hydrogen bonds are transient, constantly forming, breaking, and re-forming as water molecules move within the liquid. Hydrogen bonds are, however, the strongest of the three intermolecular forces. Substances composed of molecules that form hydrogen bonds have much higher melting and boiling points than you would predict based on molar mass. For example, consider the two compounds, methanol and ethane.

Name	Formula	Molar mass (g/mol)	Structure	bp (°C)	mp (°C)
Methanol	CH_3OH	32.0	H H—C—O—H H	64.7	−97.8
Ethane	C_2H_6	30.1	H H H—C—C—H H H	−88	−172

Since methanol contains hydrogen directly bonded to oxygen, its molecules have hydrogen bonding as an intermolecular force. The hydrogen that is directly bonded to oxygen is strongly attracted to the oxygen on neighboring molecules (◀ Figure 12.23). This strong attraction makes the boiling point of methanol 64.7 °C. Consequently, methanol is a liquid at room temperature. Water is another good example of a molecule with hydrogen bonding as an intermolecular force (▼ Figure 12.24). The boiling point of water (100 °C) is remarkably high for a molecule with such a low molar mass (18.02 g/mol). Hydrogen bonding is important in biological molecules. The shapes of proteins and nucleic acids are largely influenced by hydrogen bonding; for example, the two halves of DNA are held together by hydrogen bonds (see the *Chemistry and Health* box later in this section).

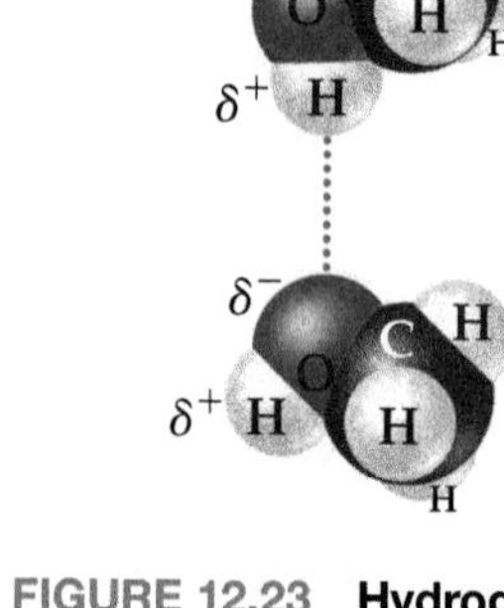

▲ **FIGURE 12.23 Hydrogen bonding in methanol** Since methanol contains hydrogen atoms directly bonded to oxygen, methanol molecules form hydrogen bonds to one another. The hydrogen atom on each methanol molecule is attracted to the oxygen atom of its neighbor.

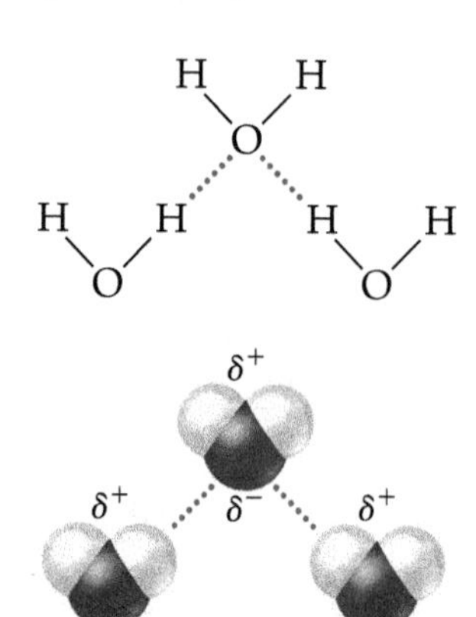

◀ **FIGURE 12.24 Hydrogen bonding in water** Water molecules form strong hydrogen bonds with one another.

EXAMPLE 12.5 Hydrogen Bonding

One of these compounds is a liquid at room temperature. Which one and why?

Formaldehyde	Fluoromethane	Hydrogen peroxide
$H{-}C({=}O){-}H$	$H{-}CH_2{-}F$	$H{-}O{-}O{-}H$

SOLUTION

The three compounds have similar molar masses.

formaldehyde	30.03 g/mol
fluoromethane	34.04 g/mol
hydrogen peroxide	34.02 g/mol

In some cases, hydrogen bonding can occur between one molecule in which H is directly bonded to F, O, or N and another molecule containing an electronegative atom. (See the box, *Chemistry and Health*, in this section for an example.)

Therefore, the strengths of their dispersion forces are similar. All three compounds are also polar, so they have dipole–dipole forces. Hydrogen peroxide, however, is the only compound that also contains H bonded directly to F, O, or N. Therefore it also has hydrogen bonding and is most likely to have the highest boiling point of the three. Since the problem stated that only one of the compounds was a liquid, we can safely assume that hydrogen peroxide is the liquid. Note that although fluoromethane *contains* both H and F, H is not *directly bonded* to F, so fluoromethane does not have hydrogen bonding as an intermolecular force. Similarly, although formaldehyde *contains* both H and O, H is not *directly bonded* to O, so formaldehyde does not have hydrogen bonding either.

▶SKILLBUILDER 12.5 | Hydrogen Bonding

Which has the higher boiling point, HF or HCl? Why?

▶FOR MORE PRACTICE Examples 12.9, 12.10; Problems 65, 66, 67, 68, 69, 70.

Table 12.5 summarizes the different types of intermolecular forces. Remember that dispersion forces, the weakest kind of intermolecular force, are present in all

TABLE 12.5 Types of Intermolecular Forces

Type of Force	Relative Strength	Present in	Example
dispersion force (or London force)	weak, but increases with increasing molar mass	all atoms and molecules	H_2 ……… H_2
dipole–dipole force	moderate	only polar molecules	HCl δ^+ δ^- ……… δ^+ δ^- HCl
hydrogen bond	strong	molecules containing H bonded directly to F, O, or N	HF δ^+ δ^- ……… δ^+ δ^- HF

CHEMISTRY AND HEALTH

Hydrogen Bonding in DNA

DNA is a long chainlike molecule that acts as a blueprint for living organisms. Copies of DNA are passed from parent to offspring, which is why we inherit traits from our parents. A DNA molecule is composed of thousands of repeating units called *nucleotides* (▶ Figure 12.25). Each nucleotide contains one of four different bases: adenine, thymine, cytosine, and guanine (abbreviated A, T, C, and G, respectively). The order of these bases along DNA encodes the instructions that specify how proteins—the workhorse molecules in living organisms—are made in each cell of the body. Proteins determine virtually all human characteristics, including how we look, how we fight infections, and even how we behave. Consequently, human DNA is a blueprint for how humans are made.

Each time a human cell divides, it must copy the blueprint—which means replicating its DNA. The replicating mechanism is related to the structure of DNA, discovered in 1953 by James Watson and Francis Crick. DNA consists of two complementary strands wrapped around each other in the now famous double helix. Each strand is held to the other by hydrogen bonds that occur between the bases on each strand. DNA replicates because each base (A, T, C, and G) has a complementary partner with which it hydrogen-bonds (▶ Figure 12.26). Adenine (A) hydrogen-bonds with thymine (T), and cytosine (C) hydrogen-bonds with guanine (G). The hydrogen bonds are so specific that each base will pair only with its complementary partner. When a cell is going to divide, the DNA unzips across the hydrogen bonds that run along its length. Then new nucleotides, containing bases complementary to the bases in each half, add along each of the halves, forming hydrogen bonds with their complement. The result is two identical copies of the original DNA (see Chapter 19).

CAN YOU ANSWER THIS? *Why would dispersion forces not work as a way to hold the two halves of DNA together? Why would covalent bonds not work?*

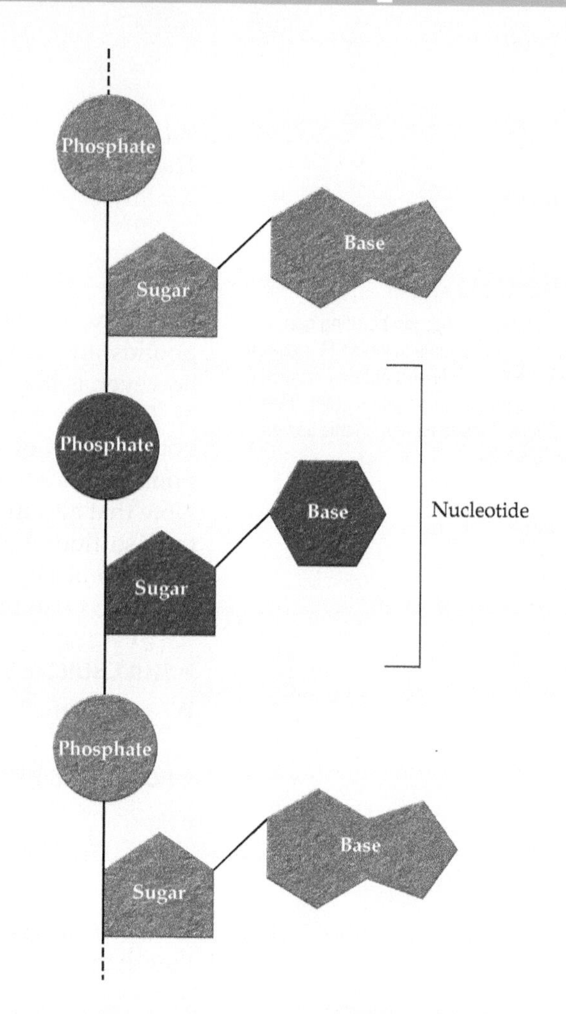

▲ **FIGURE 12.25 The structure of DNA** DNA is composed of repeating units called nucleotides. Each nucleotide is composed of a sugar, a phosphate, and a base.

molecules and atoms and increase with increasing molar mass. These forces are weak in small molecules, but they become substantial in molecules with high molar masses. Dipole–dipole forces are present in polar molecules. Hydrogen bonds, the strongest kind of intermolecular force, are present in molecules containing hydrogen bonded directly to fluorine, oxygen, or nitrogen.

CONCEPTUAL CHECKPOINT 12.4

When dry ice sublimes, what forces are overcome?

(a) chemical bonds between carbon atoms and oxygen atoms

(b) hydrogen bonds between carbon dioxide molecules

(c) dispersion forces between carbon dioxide molecules

(d) dipole–dipole forces between carbon dioxide molecules

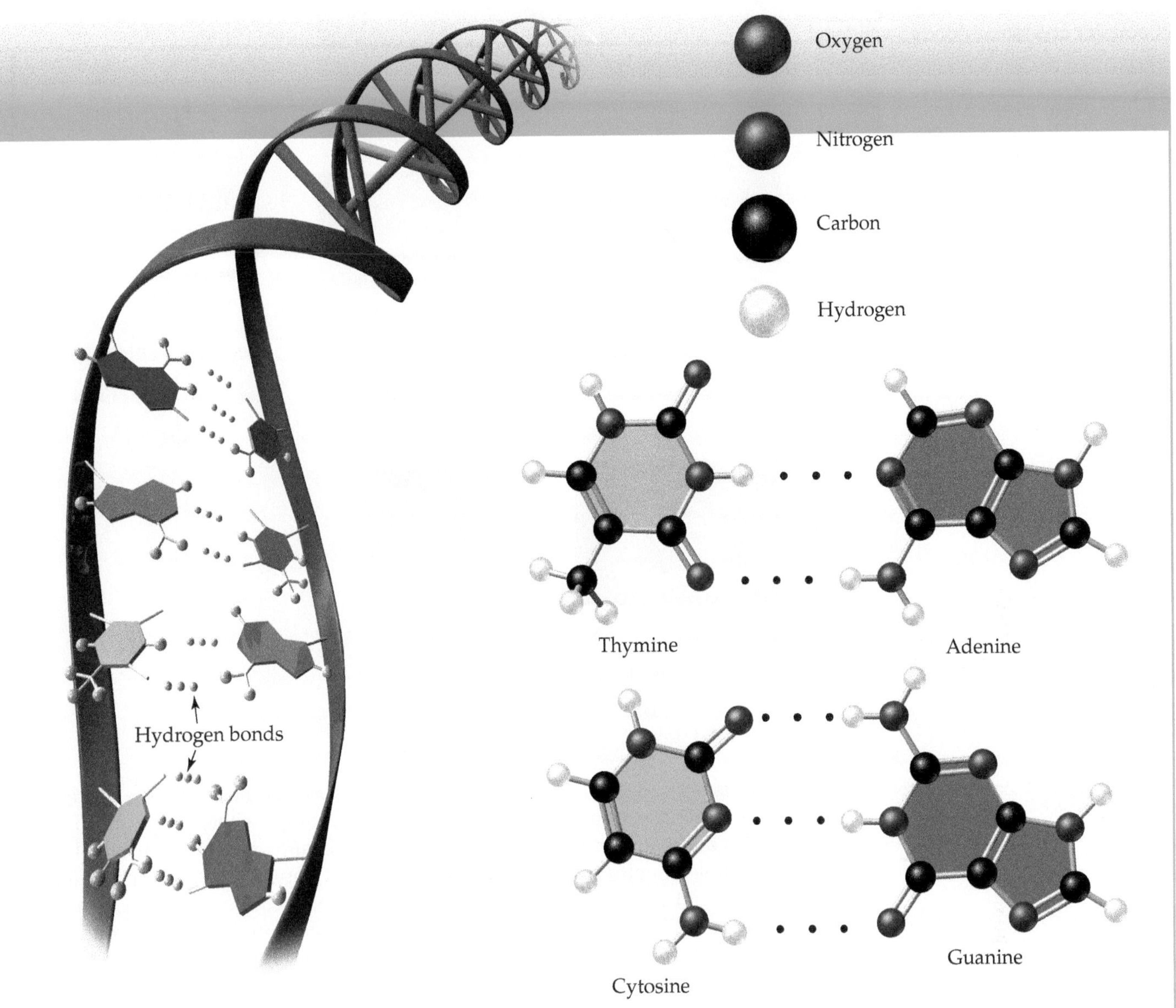

▲ **FIGURE 12.26 Hydrogen bonding in DNA** The two halves of the DNA double helix are held together by hydrogen bonds.

12.7 Types of Crystalline Solids: Molecular, Ionic, and Atomic

As we learned in Section 12.2, solids may be crystalline (a well-ordered array of atoms or molecules) or amorphous (having no long-range order). Crystalline solids can be divided into three categories—molecular, ionic, and atomic—based on the individual units that compose the solid (▶ Figure 12.27).

MOLECULAR SOLIDS

Molecular solids are solids whose composite units are *molecules*. Ice (solid H_2O) and dry ice (solid CO_2) are examples of molecular solids. Molecular solids are held together by the kinds of intermolecular forces—dispersion forces, dipole–dipole forces, and hydrogen bonding—that we just discussed in Section 12.6. For example, ice is held together by hydrogen bonds, and dry ice is held together by dispersion forces. Molecular solids as a whole tend to have low to moderately low melting points; ice melts at 0 °C and dry ice sublimes at −78.5 °C.

▶ **FIGURE 12.27 A classification scheme for crystalline solids**

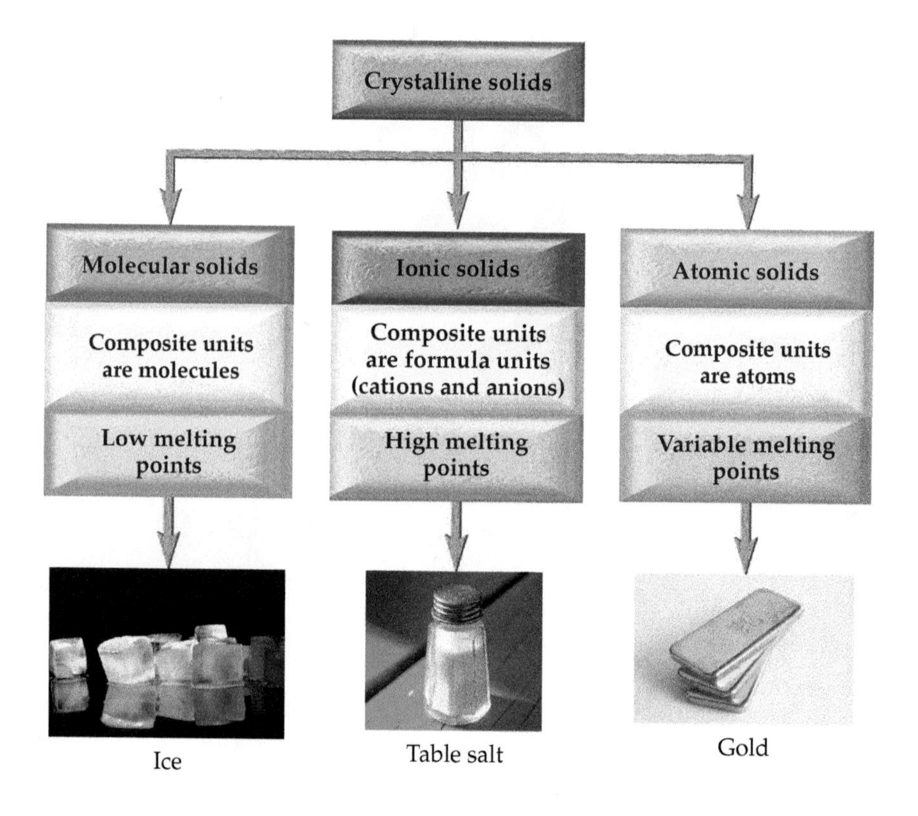

See Section 5.4 for a complete description of the formula unit.

IONIC SOLIDS

Ionic solids are solids whose composite units are *formula units*, the smallest electrically neutral collection of cations and anions that compose the compound. Table salt (NaCl) and calcium fluoride (CaF_2) are good examples of ionic solids. Ionic solids are held together by electrostatic attractions between cations and anions. For example, in NaCl, the attraction between the Na^+ cation and the Cl^- anion holds the solid lattice together because the lattice is composed of alternating Na^+ cations and Cl^- anions in a three-dimensional array. In other words, the forces that hold ionic solids together are actual ionic bonds. Since ionic bonds are much stronger than any of the intermolecular forces discussed previously, ionic solids tend to have much higher melting points than molecular solids. For example, sodium chloride melts at 801 °C, while carbon disulfide CS_2—a molecular solid with a higher molar mass—melts at −110 °C.

ATOMIC SOLIDS

Atomic solids are solids whose composite units are *individual atoms*. Diamond (C), iron (Fe), and solid xenon (Xe) are good examples of atomic solids. Atomic solids can themselves be divided into three categories—**covalent atomic solids**, **nonbonding atomic solids**, and **metallic atomic solids**—each held together by a different kind of force (▶ Figure 12.28).

Covalent atomic solids, such as diamond, are held together by covalent bonds. In diamond (▶ Figure 12.29), each carbon atom forms four covalent bonds to four other carbon atoms in a tetrahedral geometry. This structure extends throughout the entire crystal, so that a diamond crystal can be thought of as a giant molecule held together by these covalent bonds. Since covalent bonds are very strong, covalent atomic solids have high melting points. Diamond is estimated to melt at about 3800 °C.

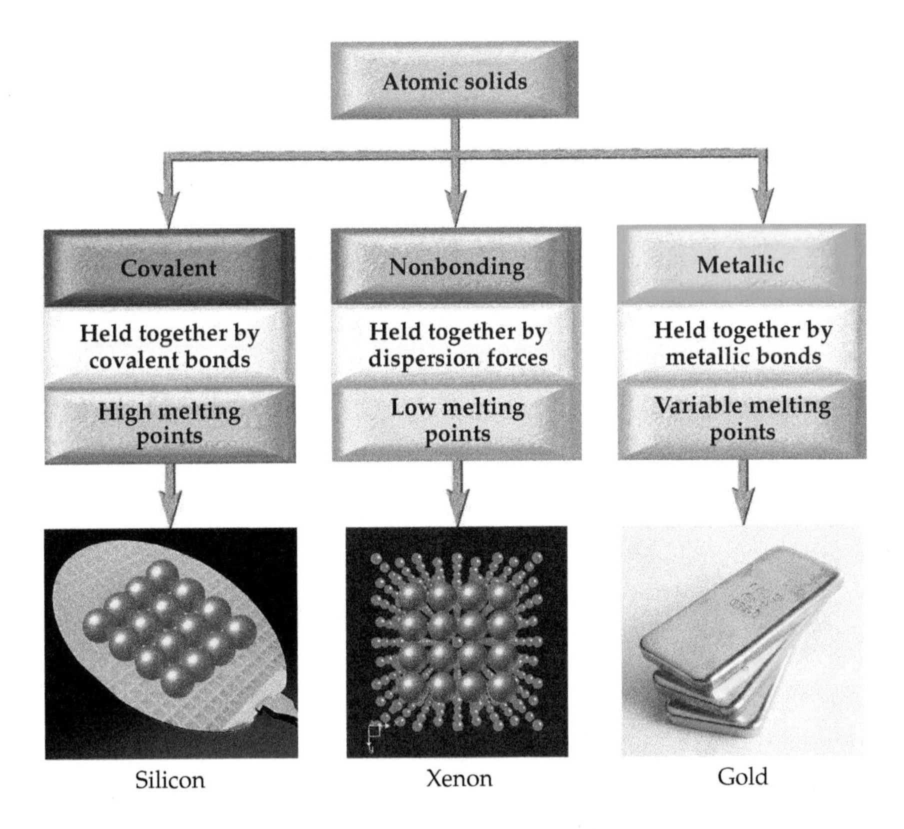

▶ **FIGURE 12.28 A classification scheme for atomic solids**

Nonbonding atomic solids, such as solid xenon, are held together by relatively weak dispersion forces. Xenon atoms have stable electron configurations and therefore do not form covalent bonds with each other. Consequently, solid xenon, like other nonbonding atomic solids, has a very low melting point (about −112 °C).

Metallic atomic solids, such as iron, have variable melting points. Metals are held together by metallic bonds that, in the simplest model, consist of positively charged ions in a sea of electrons (▼ Figure 12.30). Metallic bonds are of varying strengths, with some metals, such as mercury, having melting points below room temperature, and other metals, such as iron, having relatively high melting points (iron melts at 1809 °C).

▲ **FIGURE 12.29 Diamond: a covalent atomic solid** In diamond, carbon atoms form covalent bonds in a three-dimensional hexagonal pattern.

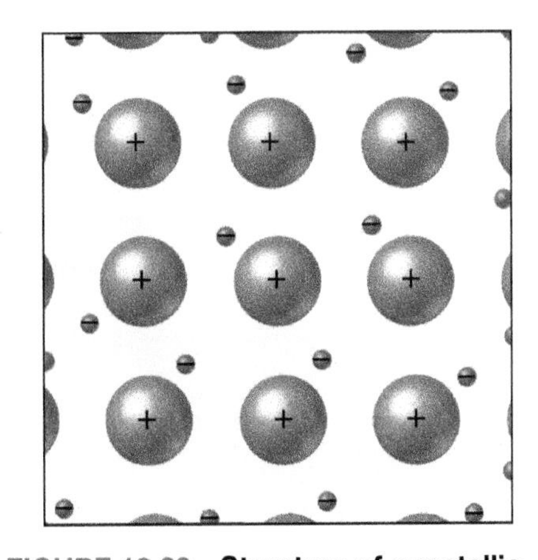

▲ **FIGURE 12.30 Structure of a metallic atomic solid** In the simplest model of a metal, each atom donates one or more electrons to an "electron sea." The metal consists of the metal cations in a negatively charged electron sea.

EXAMPLE 12.6 Identifying Types of Crystalline Solids

Identify each solid as molecular, ionic, or atomic.

(a) $CaCl_2(s)$ **(b)** $Co(s)$ **(c)** $CS_2(s)$

SOLUTION

(a) $CaCl_2$ is an ionic compound (metal and nonmetal) and therefore forms an ionic solid ($CaCl_2$ melts at 772 °C).

(b) Co is a metal and therefore forms a metallic atomic solid (Co melts at 1768 °C).

(c) CS_2 is a molecular compound (nonmetal bonded to a nonmetal) and therefore forms a molecular solid (CS_2 melts at −110 °C).

▶**SKILLBUILDER 12.6 | Identifying Types of Crystalline Solids**

Identify each solid as molecular, ionic, or atomic.

(a) $NH_3(s)$ **(b)** $CaO(s)$ **(c)** $Kr(s)$

▶**FOR MORE PRACTICE** Problems 73, 74, 75, 76.

12.8 Water: A Remarkable Molecule

Water is easily the most common and important liquid on Earth. It fills our oceans, lakes, and streams. In its solid form, it covers nearly an entire continent (Antarctica), as well as large regions around the North Pole, and caps our tallest mountains. In its gaseous form, it humidifies our air. We drink water, we sweat water, and we excrete bodily wastes dissolved in water. Indeed, the majority of our body mass *is* water. Life is impossible without water, and in most places on Earth where liquid water exists, life exists. Recent evidence of water on Mars—that existed either in the past or exists in the present—has fueled hopes of finding life or evidence of life there. Water is remarkable.

Among liquids, water is unique. It has a low molar mass (18.02 g/mol), yet is a liquid at room temperature. No other compound of similar molar mass even comes close to being a liquid at room temperature. For example, nitrogen (28.02 g/mol) and carbon dioxide (44.01 g/mol) are both gases at room temperature. Water's relatively high boiling point (for its low molar mass) can be understood by examining the structure of the water molecule (◀ Figure 12.31). The bent geometry of the water molecule and the highly polar nature of the O—H bonds result in a molecule with a significant dipole moment. Water's two O—H bonds (hydrogen directly bonded to oxygen) allow water molecules to form strong hydrogen bonds with other water molecules, resulting in a relatively high boiling point. Water's high polarity also allows it to dissolve many other polar and ionic compounds. Consequently, water is the main solvent of living organisms, transporting nutrients and other important compounds throughout the body.

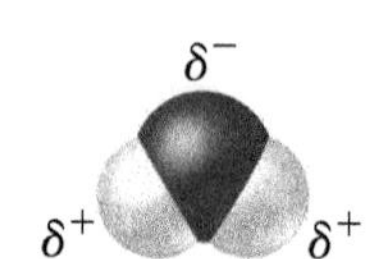

▲ **FIGURE 12.31 The water molecule**

Water reaches its maximum density at 4.0 °C.

The way water freezes is also unique. Unlike other substances, which contract upon freezing, water expands upon freezing. This seemingly trivial property has significant consequences. For example, because liquid water expands when it freezes, ice is less dense than liquid water. Consequently, ice cubes and icebergs both float. The frozen layer of ice at the surface of a winter lake insulates the water in the lake from further freezing. If this ice layer were to sink, it would kill bottom-dwelling aquatic life and possibly allow the lake to freeze solid, eliminating virtually all aquatic life in the lake.

CHEMISTRY IN THE ENVIRONMENT

Water Pollution

Water quality is critical to human health. Many human diseases—especially in developing nations—are caused by poor water quality. Several kinds of pollutants, including biological contaminants and chemical contaminants, can get into water supplies. Biological contaminants are microorganisms that cause diseases such as hepatitis, cholera, dysentery, and typhoid. Drinking water in developed nations is usually treated to kill microorganisms. Most biological contaminants can be eliminated from untreated water by boiling. Water containing biological contaminants poses an immediate danger to human health and should not be consumed.

Chemical contaminants get into drinking water from sources such as industrial dumping, pesticide and fertilizer use, and household dumping. These contaminants include organic compounds, such as carbon tetrachloride and dioxin, and inorganic elements and compounds such as mercury, lead, and nitrates. Since many chemical contaminants are neither volatile nor alive like biological contaminants, they are *not* eliminated through boiling.

The Environmental Protection Agency (EPA), under the Safe Drinking Water Act of 1974 and its amendments, sets standards that specify the maximum contamination level (MCL) for nearly 100 biological and chemical contaminants in water. Water providers that serve more than 25 people must periodically test the water they deliver to their consumers for these contaminants. If levels exceed the standards set by the EPA, the water provider must notify the consumer and take appropriate measures to remove the contaminant from the water. According to the EPA, if water comes from a provider that serves more than 25 people, it should be safe to consume over a lifetime. If it is not safe to drink for a short period of time, consumers will be notified.

▲ Safe drinking water has a major effect on public health and the spread of disease. In many parts of the world, the water supply is unsafe to drink. In the United States the Environmental Protection Agency (EPA) is charged with maintaining water safety.

CAN YOU ANSWER THIS? *Suppose a sample of water is contaminated by a nonvolatile contaminant such as lead. Why doesn't boiling eliminate the contaminant?*

The expansion of water upon freezing, however, is one reason that most organisms do not survive freezing. When the water within a cell freezes, it expands and often ruptures the cell, just as water freezing within a pipe bursts the pipe. Many foods, especially those with high water content, do not survive freezing very well either. Have you ever tried, for example, to freeze your own vegetables? Try putting lettuce or spinach in the freezer. When you defrost it, it will be limp and damaged. The frozen food industry gets around this problem by *flash-freezing* vegetables and other foods. In this process, foods are frozen instantaneously, preventing water molecules from settling into their preferred crystalline structure. Consequently, the water does not expand very much, and the food remains largely undamaged.

▶ Lettuce does not survive freezing because the expansion of water upon freezing ruptures the cells within the lettuce leaf.

CHAPTER IN REVIEW

CHEMICAL PRINCIPLES

Properties of Liquids

- High densities in comparison to gases.
- Indefinite shape; they assume the shape of their container.
- Definite volume; they are not easily compressed.

RELEVANCE

Properties of Liquids: Common liquids include water, acetone (fingernail-polish remover), and rubbing alcohol. Water is the most common and most important liquid on Earth. It is difficult to imagine life without water.

CHEMICAL PRINCIPLES

Properties of Solids

- High densities in comparison to gases.
- Definite shape; they do not assume the shape of their container.
- Definite volume; they are not easily compressed.
- May be crystalline (ordered) or amorphous (disordered).

RELEVANCE

Properties of Solids: Much of the matter we encounter is solid. Common solids include ice, dry ice, and diamond. Understanding the properties of solids involves understanding the particles that compose them and how those particles interact.

CHEMICAL PRINCIPLES

Manifestations of Intermolecular Forces: Surface tension—the tendency for liquids to minimize their surface area—is a direct result of intermolecular forces. Viscosity—the resistance of liquids to flow—is another result of intermolecular forces. Both surface tension and viscosity increase with greater intermolecular forces.

RELEVANCE

Manifestations of Intermolecular Forces: Many insects can walk on water due to surface tension. Water is drawn from roots of trees and up into the leaves because of capillary action, a direct result of intermolecular forces. The viscosity of a liquid is one of its defining properties and is important in applications such as automobile lubrication; the viscosity of a motor oil must be high enough to coat an engine's surfaces, but not so high that it can't flow to remote parts of the engine.

CHEMICAL PRINCIPLES

Evaporation and Condensation: Evaporation or vaporization—an endothermic physical change—is the conversion of a liquid to a gas. Condensation—an exothermic physical change—is the conversion of a gas to a liquid. When the rate of evaporation and condensation in a liquid/gas sample are equal, dynamic equilibrium is reached and the partial pressure of the gas at that point is called its vapor pressure. When the vapor pressure equals the external pressure, the boiling point is reached. At the boiling point, thermal energy causes molecules in the interior of the liquid, as well as those at the surface, to convert to gas, resulting in the bubbling. The heat absorbed or emitted during evaporation and condensation (respectively) can be calculated using the heat of vaporization.

RELEVANCE

Evaporation and Condensation: Evaporation is the body's natural cooling system. When we get overheated, we sweat; the sweat then evaporates and cools us. Evaporation and condensation both play roles in moderating climate. Humid areas, for example, cool less at night because as the temperature drops, water condenses out of the air, releasing heat and preventing a further temperature drop.

CHEMICAL PRINCIPLES

Melting and Freezing: Melting—an endothermic physical change—is the conversion of a solid to a liquid, and freezing—an exothermic physical change—is the conversion of liquid to a solid. The heat absorbed or emitted during melting and freezing (respectively) can be calculated using the heat of fusion.

RELEVANCE

Melting and Freezing: The melting of solid ice is used, for example, to cool drinks when we place ice cubes in them. Since melting is endothermic, it absorbs heat from the liquid and cools it.

Types of Intermolecular Forces: The three main types of intermolecular forces are:

Dispersion forces—Dispersion forces occur between all molecules and atoms due to instantaneous fluctuations in electron charge distribution. The strength of the dispersion force increases with increasing molar mass.

Dipole–dipole forces—Dipole–dipole forces exist between molecules that are polar. Consequently, polar molecules have higher melting and boiling points than nonpolar molecules of similar molar mass.

Hydrogen bonding—Hydrogen bonding exists between molecules that have H bonded directly to F, O, or N. Hydrogen bonds are the strongest of the three intermolecular forces.

Types of Intermolecular Forces: The type of intermolecular force present in a substance determines many of the properties of the substance. The stronger the intermolecular force, for example, the greater the melting and boiling points of the substance. In addition, the miscibility of liquids—their ability to mix without separating—depends on the relative kinds of intermolecular forces present within them. In general, polar liquids are miscible with other polar liquids, but not with nonpolar liquids. Hydrogen bonding is important in many biological molecules such as proteins and DNA.

Types of Crystalline Solids: Crystalline solids can be divided into three categories based on the individual units composing the solid:

Molecular solids—Molecules are the composite units of molecular solids, which are held together by dispersion forces, dipole–dipole forces, or hydrogen bonding.

Ionic solids—Formula units (the smallest electrically neutral collection of cations and anions) are the composite units of ionic solids. They are held together by the electrostatic attractions that occur between cations and anions.

Atomic solids—Atoms are the composite units of atomic solids, which are held together by different forces depending on the particular solid.

Types of Crystalline Solids: Solids have different properties depending on their individual units and the forces that hold those units together. Molecular solids tend to have low melting points. Ionic solids tend to have intermediate to high melting points. Atomic solids have varied melting points, depending on the particular solid.

Water: Water is a unique molecule. Because of its strong hydrogen bonding, water is a liquid at room temperature. Unlike most liquids, water expands when it freezes. In addition, water is highly polar, making it a good solvent for many polar substances.

Water: Water is critical to life. On Earth, wherever there is water, there is life. Water acts as a solvent and transport medium, and virtually all the chemical reactions on which life depends take place in aqueous solution. The expansion of water upon freezing allows life within frozen lakes to survive the winter. The ice on top of the lake acts as insulation, protecting the rest of the lake (and the life within it) from freezing.

CHEMICAL SKILLS

EXAMPLES

Using Heat of Vaporization in Calculations (Section 12.4)

EXAMPLE 12.7 Heat of Vaporization in Calculations

Calculate the amount of heat required to vaporize 84.8 g of water at its boiling point.

SORT

You are given the mass of water and asked to find the amount of heat required to vaporize it.

GIVEN: 84.8 g H_2O

FIND: heat (kJ)

STRATEGIZE

To calculate the amount of heat required to vaporize a given amount of a substance, first convert the given amount of the substance to moles and then use the heat of vaporization as a conversion factor to get to kilojoules. For vaporization, the heat is always absorbed. For condensation, follow the same procedure, but the heat is always emitted.

SOLUTION MAP

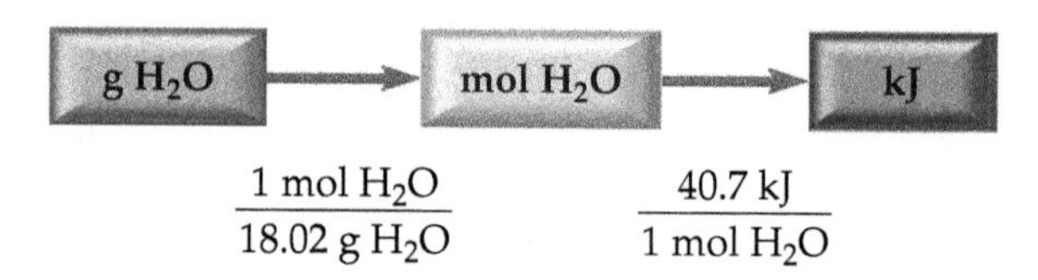

$$\frac{1 \text{ mol } H_2O}{18.02 \text{ g } H_2O} \qquad \frac{40.7 \text{ kJ}}{1 \text{ mol } H_2O}$$

RELATIONSHIPS USED

$$\Delta H_{vap} = 40.7 \text{ kJ/mol} \quad \text{at } 100\text{ °C} \quad \text{(Table 12.2)}$$

$$1 \text{ mol } H_2O = 18.02 \text{ g } H_2O \text{ (molar mass of water)}$$

SOLVE

Follow the solution map to solve the problem.

SOLUTION

$$84.8 \text{ g } H_2O \times \frac{1 \text{ mol } H_2O}{18.02 \text{ g } H_2O} \times \frac{40.7 \text{ kJ}}{1 \text{ mol } H_2O} = 192 \text{ kJ}$$

CHECK

Check your answer. Are the units correct? Does the answer make physical sense?

The units (kJ) are correct. The magnitude of the answer makes sense because each mole of water absorbs about 40 kJ of energy upon vaporization. Therefore 84.8 g (between 4 and 5 mol) should absorb between 160 and 200 kJ upon vaporization.

Using Heat of Fusion in Calculations (Section 12.5)

EXAMPLE 12.8 Using Heat of Fusion in Calculations

Calculate the amount of heat emitted when 12.4 g of water freezes to solid ice.

SORT

You are given the mass of water and asked to find the amount of heat emitted when it freezes.

GIVEN: 12.4 g H_2O

FIND: heat (kJ)

STRATEGIZE

The heat of fusion can be used as a conversion factor between moles of a substance and the amount of heat required to melt it. To calculate the amount of heat required to melt a given amount of a substance, first convert the given amount of the substance to moles and then use the heat of fusion as a conversion factor to get to kilojoules. For melting, the heat is always absorbed. For freezing, follow the same procedure, but the heat is always emitted.

SOLUTION MAP

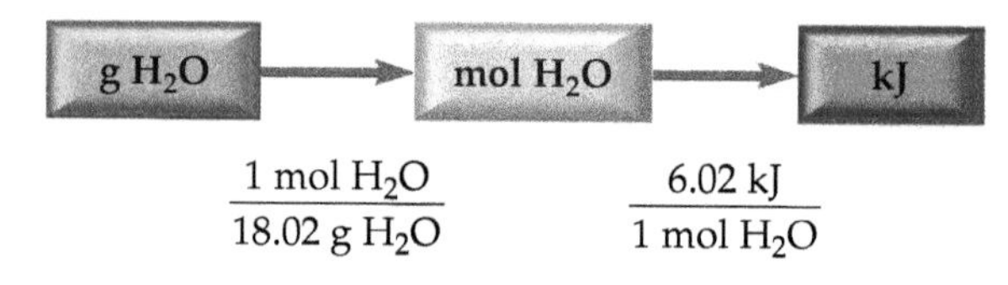

$$\frac{1 \text{ mol } H_2O}{18.02 \text{ g } H_2O} \qquad \frac{6.02 \text{ kJ}}{1 \text{ mol } H_2O}$$

RELATIONSHIPS USED

$$\Delta H_{fus} = 6.02 \text{ kJ/mol} \quad \text{(Table 12.3)}$$

$$1 \text{ mol } H_2O = 18.02 \text{ g } H_2O \text{ (molar mass of water)}$$

SOLVE

Follow the solution map to solve the problem.

SOLUTION

$$12.4 \text{ g } H_2O \times \frac{1 \text{ mol } H_2O}{18.02 \text{ g } H_2O} \times \frac{6.02 \text{ kJ}}{1 \text{ mol } H_2O} = 4.14 \text{ kJ}$$

The heat emitted is 4.14 kJ.

CHECK

Check your answer. Are the units correct? Does the answer make physical sense?

The units (kJ) are correct. The magnitude of the answer makes sense because each mole of water emits about 6 kJ of energy upon freezing. Therefore 12.2 g (less than 1 mol) should emit less than 6 kJ upon freezing.

Determining the Types of Intermolecular Forces in a Compound (Section 12.6)

EXAMPLE 12.9 Determining the Types of Intermolecular Forces in a Compound

Determine the types of intermolecular forces present in each substance.

(a) N_2
(b) CO
(c) NH_3

All substances exhibit dispersion forces. Polar substances—those whose molecules have polar bonds that add to net dipole moment—also exhibit dipole–dipole forces. Substances whose molecules contain H bonded directly to F, O, or N exhibit hydrogen bonding as well.

SOLUTION

(a) N_2 is nonpolar and therefore has only dispersion forces.
(b) CO is polar and therefore has dipole–dipole forces (in addition to dispersion forces).
(c) NH_3 has hydrogen bonding (in addition to dispersion forces and dipole–dipole forces).

Using Intermolecular Forces to Determine Melting and/or Boiling Points (Section 12.6)

EXAMPLE 12.10 Using Intermolecular Forces to Determine Melting and/or Boiling Points

Arrange each group of compounds in order of increasing boiling point.

(a) F_2, Cl_2, Br_2
(b) HF, HCl, HBr

To determine relative boiling points and melting points among compounds, you must evaluate the types of intermolecular forces that each compound exhibits. Dispersion forces are the weakest kind of intermolecular force, but they increase with increasing molar mass. Dipole–dipole forces are stronger than dispersion forces. If two compounds have similar molar mass, but one is polar, it will have higher melting and boiling points. Hydrogen bonds are the strongest type of intermolecular force. Substances that exhibit hydrogen bonding will have much higher boiling and melting points than substances without hydrogen bonding, even if the substance without hydrogen bonding is of higher molar mass.

SOLUTION

(a) Since these all have only dispersion forces, and since they are similar substances (all halogens), the strength of the dispersion force will increase with increasing molar mass. Therefore, the correct order is $F_2 < Cl_2 < Br_2$.
(b) Since HF has hydrogen bonding, it has the highest boiling point. Between HCl and HBr, HBr (because of its higher molar mass) has a higher boiling point. Therefore the correct order is HCl < HBr < HF.

KEY TERMS

atomic solid [12.7]
boiling point [12.4]
condensation [12.4]
covalent atomic solid [12.7]
dipole–dipole force [12.6]
dispersion force [12.6]
dynamic equilibrium [12.4]
evaporation [12.4]
heat of fusion (ΔH_{fus}) [12.5]
heat of vaporization (ΔH_{vap}) [12.4]
hydrogen bond [12.6]
instantaneous (temporary) dipole [12.6]
intermolecular forces [12.1]
ionic solid [12.7]
melting point [12.5]
metallic atomic solid [12.7]
miscibility [12.6]
molecular solid [12.7]
nonbonding atomic solid [12.7]
nonvolatile [12.4]
normal boiling point [12.4]
permanent dipole [12.6]
sublimation [12.5]
surface tension [12.3]
thermal energy [12.1]
vaporization [12.4]
vapor pressure [12.4]
viscosity [12.3]
volatile [12.4]

EXERCISES

QUESTIONS

1. What are intermolecular forces? Why are intermolecular forces important?
2. Why are water droplets spherical?
3. What determines whether a substance is a solid, liquid, or gas?
4. What are the properties of liquids? Explain the properties of liquids in terms of the molecules or atoms that compose them.
5. What are the properties of solids? Explain the properties of solids in terms of the molecules or atoms that compose them.
6. What is the difference between a crystalline solid and an amorphous solid?
7. What is surface tension? How does it depend on intermolecular forces?
8. What is viscosity? How does it depend on intermolecular forces?
9. What is evaporation? Condensation?
10. Why does a glass of water evaporate more slowly in the glass than if you spilled the same amount of water on a table?
11. Explain the difference between evaporation below the boiling point of a liquid and evaporation at the boiling point of a liquid.
12. What is the boiling point of a liquid? What is the normal boiling point?
13. Acetone evaporates more quickly than water at room temperature. What can you say about the relative strength of the intermolecular forces in the two compounds? Which substance is more volatile?
14. Explain condensation and dynamic equilibrium.
15. What is the vapor pressure of a substance? How does it depend on temperature and strength of intermolecular forces?
16. Explain how sweat cools the body.
17. Explain why a steam burn from gaseous water at 100 °C is worse than a water burn involving the same amount of liquid water at 100 °C.
18. Explain what happens when a liquid boils.
19. Explain why the water in a cup placed in a small ice chest (without a refrigeration mechanism) initially at −5 °C does *not* freeze.
20. Explain how ice cubes cool down beverages.
21. Is the melting of ice endothermic or exothermic? What is the sign of ΔH for the melting of ice? For the freezing of water?
22. Is the boiling of water endothermic or exothermic? What is the sign of ΔH for the boiling of water? For the condensation of steam?
23. What are dispersion forces? How does the strength of dispersion forces relate to molar mass?
24. What are dipole–dipole forces? How can you tell whether a compound has dipole–dipole forces?
25. What is hydrogen bonding? How can you tell whether a compound has hydrogen bonding?
26. What is a molecular solid? What kinds of forces hold molecular solids together?
27. How do the melting points of molecular solids relate to those of other types of solids?
28. What is an ionic solid? What kinds of forces hold ionic solids together?
29. How do the melting points of ionic solids relate to those of other types of solids?
30. What is an atomic solid? What are the properties of atomic solids?
31. In what ways is water unique?
32. How would ice be different if it were denser than water? How would that affect aquatic life in cold-climate lakes?

PROBLEMS

EVAPORATION, CONDENSATION, MELTING, AND FREEZING

33. Which will evaporate more quickly: 55 mL of water in a beaker with a diameter of 4.5 cm or 55 mL of water in a dish with a diameter of 12 cm? Why?
34. Two samples of pure water of equal volume are put into separate dishes and kept at room temperature for several days. The water in the first dish is completely vaporized after 2.8 days, while the water in the second dish takes 8.3 days to completely evaporate. What can you conclude about the two dishes?
35. One milliliter of water is poured onto one hand, and one milliliter of acetone (fingernail-polish remover) is poured onto the other. As they evaporate, they both feel cool. Which one feels cooler and why? (*Hint:* Which substance is more volatile?)
36. Spilling water over your skin on a hot day will cool you down. Spilling vegetable oil over your skin on a hot day will not. Explain the difference.

37. Several ice cubes are placed in a beaker on a lab bench, and their temperature, initially at −5.0 °C, is monitored. Explain what happens to the temperature as a function of time. Make a sketch of how the temperature might change with time. (Assume that the lab is at 25 °C.)

38. Water is put into a beaker and heated with a Bunsen burner. The temperature of the water, initially at 25 °C, is monitored. Explain what happens to the temperature as a function of time. Make a sketch of how the temperature might change with time. (Assume that the Bunsen burner is hot enough to heat the water to its boiling point.)

39. Which causes a more severe burn: spilling 0.50 g of 100 °C water on your hand, or allowing 0.50 g of 100 °C steam to condense on your hand? Why?

40. The nightly winter temperature drop in a seaside town is usually less than that in nearby towns that are farther inland. Explain.

41. When a plastic bag containing a water and ice mixture is placed in an ice chest initially at −8 °C, the temperature of the ice chest goes up. Why?

42. The refrigeration mechanism in a freezer with an automatic ice maker runs extensively each time ice forms from liquid water in the freezer. Why?

43. An ice chest is filled with 3.5 kg of ice at 0 °C. A second ice chest is filled with 3.5 kg of water at 0 °C. After several hours, which ice chest is colder? Why?

44. Why will 50 g of water initially at 0 °C warm more quickly than 50 g of an ice/water mixture initially at 0 °C?

45. In Denver, Colorado, water boils at 95 °C. Explain.

46. At the top of Mount Everest, water boils at 70 °C. Explain.

HEAT OF VAPORIZATION AND HEAT OF FUSION

47. How much heat is required to vaporize 33.8 g of water at 100 °C?

48. How much heat is required to vaporize 43.9 g of acetone at its boiling point?

49. How much heat does your body lose when 2.8 g of sweat evaporates from your skin at 25 °C? (Assume that the sweat is only water.)

50. How much heat does your body lose when 4.86 g of sweat evaporates from your skin at 25 °C? (Assume that the sweat is only water.)

51. How much heat is emitted when 4.25 g of water condenses at 25 °C?

52. How much heat is emitted when 65.6 g of isopropyl alcohol condenses at 25 °C?

53. The human body obtains 835 kJ of energy from a chocolate chip cookie. If this energy were used to vaporize water at 100 °C, how many grams of water could be vaporized? (Assume that the density of water is 1.0 g/mL.)

54. The human body obtains 1078 kJ from a candy bar. If this energy were used to vaporize water at 100 °C, how much water in liters could be vaporized? (Assume that the density of water is 1.0 g/mL.)

55. How much heat is required to melt 37.4 g of ice at 0 °C?

56. How much heat is required to melt 23.9 g of solid diethyl ether (at its melting point)?

57. How much energy is released when 34.2 g of water freezes?

58. How much energy is released when 2.55 kg of diethyl ether freezes?

INTERMOLECULAR FORCES

59. What kinds of intermolecular forces are present in each substance?
    (a) Kr
    (b) N_2
    (c) CO
    (d) HF

60. What kinds of intermolecular forces are present in each substance?
    (a) HCl
    (b) H_2O
    (c) Br_2
    (d) He

61. What kinds of intermolecular forces are present in each substance?
    (a) NCl_3 (trigonal pyramidal)
    (b) NH_3 (trigonal pyramidal)
    (c) SiH_4 (tetrahedral)
    (d) CCl_4 (tetrahedral)

62. What kinds of intermolecular forces present in each substance?
    (a) O_3
    (b) HBr
    (c) CH_3OH
    (d) I_2

63. Which substance has the highest boiling point? Why? *Hint:* They are all nonpolar.
    (a) CH_4
    (b) CH_3CH_3
    (c) $CH_3CH_2CH_3$
    (d) $CH_3CH_2CH_2CH_3$

64. Which noble gas has the highest boiling point? Why?
    (a) Kr
    (b) Xe
    (c) Rn

65. One of these two substances is a liquid at room temperature. Which one and why?

    CH_3OH CH_3SH

66. One of these two substances is a liquid at room temperature. Which one and why?

    CH_3OCH_3 CH_3CH_2OH

67. A flask containing a mixture of $NH_3(g)$ and $CH_4(g)$ is cooled. At −33.3 °C a liquid begins to form in the flask. What is the liquid?

68. Explain why CS_2 is a liquid at room temperature while CO_2 is a gas.

69. Are $CH_3CH_2CH_2CH_2CH_3$ and H_2O miscible?

70. Are CH_3OH and H_2O miscible?

71. Determine whether a homogeneous solution forms when each pair of substances is mixed.
    (a) CCl_4 and H_2O
    (b) Br_2 and CCl_4
    (c) CH_3CH_2OH and H_2O

72. Determine whether a homogeneous solution forms when each pair of substances is mixed.
    (a) $CH_3CH_2CH_2CH_2CH_3$ and $CH_3CH_2CH_2CH_2CH_2CH_3$
    (b) CBr_4 and H_2O
    (c) Cl_2 and H_2O

TYPES OF SOLIDS

73. Identify each solid as molecular, ionic, or atomic.
    (a) Ar(s)
    (b) $H_2O(s)$
    (c) $K_2O(s)$
    (d) Fe(s)

74. Identify each solid as molecular, ionic, or atomic.
    (a) $CaCl_2(s)$
    (b) $CO_2(s)$
    (c) Ni(s)
    (d) $I_2(s)$

75. Identify each solid as molecular, ionic, or atomic.
(a) $H_2S(s)$
(b) $KCl(s)$
(c) $N_2(s)$
(d) $NI_3(s)$

76. Identify each solid as molecular, ionic, or atomic.
(a) $SF_6(s)$
(b) $C(s)$
(c) $MgCl_2(s)$
(d) $Ti(s)$

77. Which solid has the highest melting point? Why?
(a) $Ar(s)$
(b) $CCl_4(s)$
(c) $LiCl(s)$
(d) $CH_3OH(s)$

78. Which solid has the highest melting point? Why?
(a) C (s, diamond)
(b) $Kr(s)$
(c) $NaCl(s)$
(d) $H_2O(s)$

79. For each pair of solids, determine which one has the higher melting point and explain why.
(a) $Ti(s)$ and $Ne(s)$
(b) $H_2O(s)$ and $H_2S(s)$
(c) $Kr(s)$ and $Xe(s)$
(d) $NaCl(s)$ and $CH_4(s)$

80. For each pair of solids, determine which one has the higher melting point and explain why.
(a) $Fe(s)$ and $CCl_4(s)$
(b) $KCl(s)$ or $HCl(s)$
(c) $TiO_2(s)$ or $HOOH(s)$

81. List these substances in order of increasing boiling point:
H_2O, Ne, NH_3, NaF, SO_2

82. List these substances in order of decreasing boiling point:
CO_2, Ne, CH_3OH, KF

CUMULATIVE PROBLEMS

83. Ice actually has negative caloric content. How much energy, in each of the following units, does your body lose from eating (and therefore melting) 78 g of ice?
(a) joules
(b) kilojoules
(c) calories (1 cal = 4.18 J)
(d) nutritional Calories or capital "C" Calories (1000 cal = 1 Cal)

84. Ice has negative caloric content. How much energy, in each of the following units, does your body lose from eating (and therefore melting) 145 g of ice?
(a) joules
(b) kilojoules
(c) calories (1 cal = 4.18 J)
(d) nutritional Calories or capital "C" calories (1000 cal = 1 Cal)

85. An 8.5-g ice cube is placed into 255 g of water. Calculate the temperature change in the water upon the complete melting of the ice. *Hint:* Determine how much heat is absorbed by the melting ice and then use $q = mC\Delta T$ to calculate the temperature change of the 255 g of water.

86. A 14.7-g ice cube is placed into 324 g of water. Calculate the temperature change in the water upon complete melting of the ice. *Hint:* Determine how much heat is absorbed by the melting ice and then use $q = mC\Delta T$ to calculate the temperature change of the 324 g of water.

87. How much ice in grams would have to melt to lower the temperature of 352 mL of water from 25 °C to 0 °C? (Assume that the density of water is 1.0 g/mL.)

88. How much ice in grams would have to melt to lower the temperature of 55.8 g of water from 55.0 °C to 0 °C? (Assume that the density of water is 1.0 g/mL.)

89. How much heat in kilojoules is evolved in converting 1.00 mol of steam at 145 °C to ice at −50.0 °C? The heat capacity of steam is 1.84 J/g °C and that of ice is 2.09 J/g °C.

90. How much heat in kilojoules is required to warm 10.0 g of ice, initially at −10.0 °C, to steam at 110.0 °C. The heat capacity of ice is 2.09 J/g °C and that of steam is 1.84 J/g °C.

91. Draw a Lewis structure for each molecule and determine its molecular geometry. What kind of intermolecular forces are present in each substance?
(a) H_2Se
(b) SO_2
(c) $CHCl_3$
(d) CO_2

92. Draw a Lewis structure for each molecule and determine its molecular geometry. What kind of intermolecular forces are present in each substance?
(a) BCl_3 (remember that B is a frequent exception to the octet rule)
(b) HCOH (carbon is central; each H and O bonded directly to C)
(c) CS_2
(d) NCl_3

93. The melting point of ionic solids depends on the magnitude of the electrostatic attractions that hold the solid together. Draw ionic Lewis structures for NaF and MgO. Which do you think has the higher melting point?

94. Draw ionic Lewis structures for KF and CaO. Use the information and the method in the previous problem to predict which of these two ionic solids has the higher melting point.

95. Explain the observed trend in the melting points of the alkyl halides. Why is HF atypical?

Compound	Melting Point
HI	−50.8 °C
HBr	−88.5 °C
HCl	−114.8 °C
HF	−83.1 °C

96. Explain the observed trend in the boiling points of the compounds listed. Why is H_2O atypical?

Compound	Boiling Point
H_2Te	−2 °C
H_2Se	−41.5 °C
H_2S	−60.7 °C
H_2O	+100 °C

97. An ice cube at 0.00 °C with a mass of 23.5 g is placed into 550.0 g of water, initially at 28.0 °C, in an insulated container. Assuming that no heat is lost to the surroundings, what is the temperature of the entire water sample after all of the ice has melted?

98. If 1.10 g of steam at 100.0 °C condenses into 38.5 g of water, initially at 27.0 °C, in an insulated container, what is the final temperature of the entire water sample? Assume no loss of heat into the surroundings.

HIGHLIGHT PROBLEMS

99. Consider the molecular view of water shown here. Pick a molecule in the interior and draw a line to each of its direct neighbors. Pick a molecule near the edge (analogous to a molecule on the surface in three dimensions) and do the same. Which molecule has the most neighbors? Which molecule is more likely to evaporate?

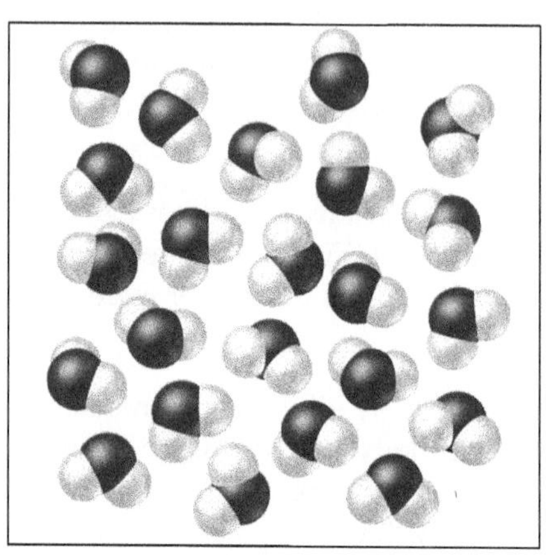

100. Water does not easily remove grease from dirty hands because grease is nonpolar and water is polar; therefore they are immiscible. The addition of soap, however, results in the removal of the grease. Examine the structure of soap shown here and explain how soap works.

$$CH_3(CH_2)_{16}\overset{\overset{\displaystyle O}{\|}}{C}—O^-Na^+$$

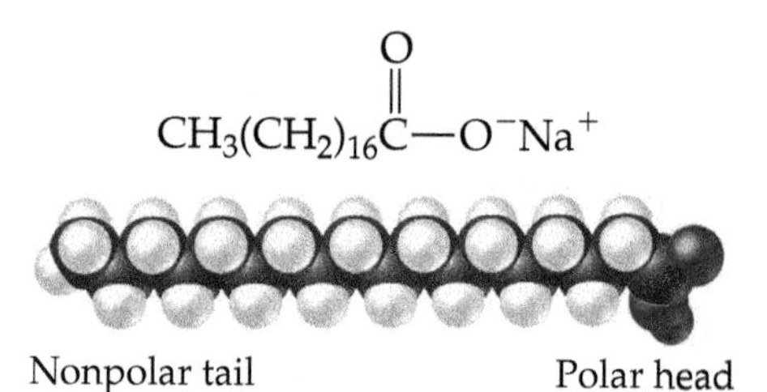

Sodium stearate
a soap

101. One prediction of global warming is the melting of global ice, which may result in coastal flooding. A criticism of this prediction is that the melting of icebergs does not increase ocean levels any more than the melting of ice in a glass of water increases the level of liquid in the glass.

   (a) Is this a valid criticism? Does the melting of an ice cube in a cup of water raise the level of the liquid in the cup? Why or why not?

   A response to this criticism is that scientists are not worried about rising ocean levels due to melting icebergs; rather, scientists are worried about rising ocean levels due to melting ice sheets that sit on the continent of Antarctica.

   (b) Would the melting of the ice sheets increase ocean levels? Why or why not?

102. Explain why rubbing alcohol feels cold when applied to the skin.

▶ANSWERS TO SKILLBUILDER EXERCISES

Skillbuilder 12.1	5.83×10^3 kJ
Skillbuilder Plus, p. 420	47 °C
Skillbuilder 12.2	5.18 kJ
Skillbuilder Plus, p. 423	−2.3 °C
Skillbuilder 12.3	C_2H_6

Skillbuilder 12.4
- **(a)** no dipole–dipole forces
- **(b)** yes, it has dipole–dipole forces
- **(c)** yes, it has dipole–dipole forces

Skillbuilder 12.5 HF, because it has hydrogen bonding as an intermolecular force

Skillbuilder 12.6
- **(a)** molecular
- **(b)** ionic
- **(c)** atomic

▶ANSWERS TO CONCEPTUAL CHECKPOINTS

12.1 (b) Since boiling is a physical rather than a chemical change, the water molecules (H_2O) undergo no chemical alteration—they merely change from the liquid to the gaseous state.

12.2 (b) the temperature remains flat during a state transition; therefore, since the water starts as ice, the first flat section (i) is the melting of the ice to liquid water. The increasing temperature section (ii) is the water warming to its boiling point. The subsequent flat section (iii) is the boiling of the liquid water to gaseous steam.

12.3 (c) Since sublimation is a physical change, the carbon dioxide molecules do not decompose into other molecules or atoms; they simply change state from the solid to the gaseous state.

12.4 (c) The chemical bonds between carbon and oxygen atoms are not broken by changes of state such as sublimation. Because carbon dioxide contains no hydrogen atoms, it cannot undergo hydrogen bonding, and because the molecule is nonpolar, it does not experience dipole–dipole interactions.

CHAPTER 13

Solutions

"The goal of science is to make sense of the diversity of nature."

JOHN BARROW (B. 1952)

13.1 Tragedy in Cameroon

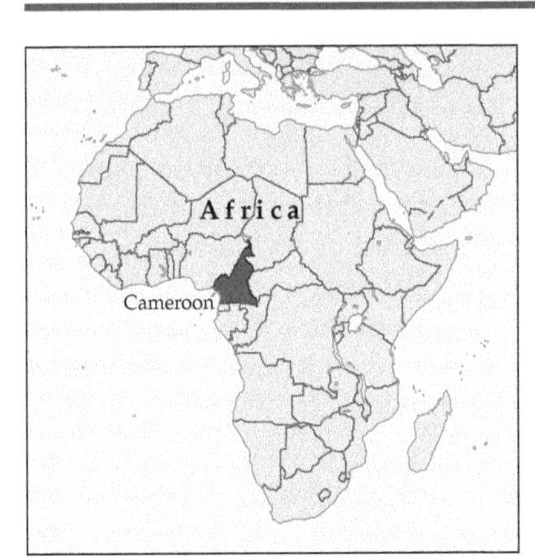

▲ Cameroon is in West Africa.

◀ Late in the summer of 1986, carbon dioxide bubbled out of Lake Nyos and flowed into the adjacent valley. The carbon dioxide came from the bottom of the lake, where it was held in solution by the pressure of the water above it. When the layers in the lake were disturbed, the carbon dioxide came out of solution due to the decrease in pressure—with lethal consequences.

On August 22, 1986, most people living near Lake Nyos in Cameroon, West Africa, began their day in an ordinary way. Unfortunately, the day ended in tragedy. On that evening, a large cloud of carbon dioxide gas, burped up from the depths of Lake Nyos, killed more than 1700 people and about 3000 head of cattle. Survivors tell of smelling rotten eggs, feeling a warm sensation, and then losing consciousness. Two years before that, a similar tragedy had occurred in Lake Monoun, just 60 miles away, killing 37 people. Today, scientists have taken steps to prevent these lakes from burping again.

Lake Nyos is a water-filled volcanic crater. Some 50 miles beneath the surface of the lake, molten volcanic rock (magma) produces carbon dioxide gas that seeps into the lake through the volcano's plumbing system. The carbon dioxide then mixes with the lake water. However, as we will see later in this chapter, the concentration of a gas (such as carbon dioxide) that can build up in water increases with increasing pressure. The great pressure at the bottom of the deep lake therefore allows the concentration of carbon dioxide to become very high (just as the pressure in a soda can allows the concentration of carbon dioxide in soda to be very high). Over time, the carbon dioxide and water mixture at the bottom of the lake became so concentrated that—either because of the high concentration itself or because of some other natural trigger, such as a landslide—some gaseous carbon dioxide escaped. The rising bubbles disrupted the stratified layers of lake water, causing the highly concentrated carbon dioxide and water mixture at the bottom of the lake to rise, which lowered the pressure on it. The drop in pressure on the mixture released

Carbon dioxide, a colorless and odorless gas, displaced the air in low-lying regions surrounding Lake Nyos, leaving no oxygen for the inhabitants to breathe. The rotten-egg smell is an indication of the presence of additional sulfur-containing gases.

more carbon dioxide bubbles just as the drop in pressure upon opening a soda can releases carbon dioxide bubbles. This in turn caused more churning and more carbon dioxide release. Since carbon dioxide is more dense than air, once freed from the lake, it traveled down the sides of the volcano and into the nearby valley, displacing air and asphyxiating many of the local residents.

In efforts to prevent these events from occurring again—by 2001, carbon dioxide concentrations had already returned to dangerously high levels—scientists built a piping system to slowly vent carbon dioxide from the lake bottom. Since 2001, this system has gradually been releasing the carbon dioxide into the atmosphere, preventing a repeat of the tragedy.

▶ Engineers watch as the carbon dioxide vented from the bottom of Lake Nyos creates a geyser. The controlled release of carbon dioxide from the lake bed is designed to prevent future catastrophes like the one that killed more than 1700 people in 1986.

13.2 Solutions: Homogeneous Mixtures

The carbon dioxide and water mixture at the bottom of Lake Nyos is an example of a **solution**, a homogeneous mixture of two or more substances. Solutions are common—most of the liquids and gases that we encounter every day are actually solutions. When most people think of a solution, they think of a solid dissolved in water. The ocean, for example, is a solution of salt and other solids dissolved in water. Blood plasma (blood that has had blood cells removed from it) is a solution of several solids (as well as some gases) dissolved in water. In addition to these, many other kinds of solutions exist. A solution may be composed of a gas and a liquid (like the carbon dioxide and water of Lake Nyos), a liquid and another liquid, a solid and a gas, or other combinations (see Table 13.1).

Aqueous comes from the Latin word *aqua*, meaning "water."

The most common solutions, however, are those containing a solid, a liquid, or a gas and water. These are *aqueous solutions*—they are critical to life and are the

TABLE 13.1 Common Types of Solutions

Solution Phase	Solute Phase	Solvent Phase	Example
gaseous solutions	gas	gas	air (mainly oxygen and nitrogen)
liquid solutions	gas	liquid	soda water (CO_2 and water)
	liquid	liquid	vodka (ethanol and water)
	solid	liquid	seawater (salt and water)
solid solutions	solid	solid	brass (copper and zinc) and other alloys

In a solid/liquid solution, the liquid is usually considered the solvent, regardless of the relative proportions of the components.

main focus of this chapter. Common examples of aqueous solutions include sugar water and salt water, both solutions of solids and water. Similarly, ethyl alcohol—the alcohol in alcoholic beverages—readily mixes with water to form a solution of a liquid with water, and we have already seen an example of a gas-and-water solution in Lake Nyos.

A solution has at least two components. The majority component is usually called the **solvent**, and the minority component is called the **solute**. In our carbon-dioxide-and-water solution, carbon dioxide is the solute and water is the solvent. In a salt-and-water solution, salt is the solute and water is the solvent. Because water is so abundant on Earth, it is a common solvent. However, other solvents are often used in the laboratory, in industry, and even in the home, especially to form solutions with nonpolar solutes. For example, you may use paint thinner, a nonpolar solvent, to remove grease from a dirty bicycle chain or from ball bearings. The paint thinner dissolves (or forms a solution with) the grease, removing it from the metal.

See Sections 10.8 and 12.6 to review the concept of polarity.

In general, polar solvents dissolve polar or ionic solutes, and nonpolar solvents dissolve nonpolar solutes. This tendency is described by the rule *like dissolves like*. Thus, similar kinds of solvents dissolve similar kinds of solutes. Table 13.2 lists some common polar and nonpolar laboratory solvents.

TABLE 13.2 Common Laboratory Solvents

Common Polar Solvents	Common Nonpolar Solvents
water (H_2O)	hexane (C_6H_{12})
acetone (CH_3COCH_3)	diethyl ether ($CH_3CH_2OCH_2CH_3$)
methyl alcohol (CH_3OH)	toluene (C_7H_8)

CONCEPTUAL CHECKPOINT 13.1

Which compound would you expect to be *least* soluble in water?

(a) CCl_4 **(b)** CH_3Cl **(c)** H_2S **(d)** KF

13.3 Solutions of Solids Dissolved in Water: How to Make Rock Candy

We have already seen several examples of solutions of a solid dissolved in water. The ocean, for example, is a solution of salt and other solids dissolved in water. A sweetened cup of coffee is a solution of sugar and other solids dissolved in water. Blood plasma is a solution of several solids (and some gases) dissolved in water. Not all solids, however, dissolve in water. We already know that nonpolar solids—such as lard and shortening—do not dissolve in water. Solids such as calcium carbonate and sand do not dissolve either.

When a solid is put into water, there is competition between the attractive forces that hold the solid together (the solute–solute interactions) and the attractive forces occurring between the water molecules and the particles that compose the solid (the solvent–solute interactions). For example, when sodium chloride is put into water, there is competition between the mutual attraction of Na^+ cations and Cl^- anions and the attraction of Na^+ and Cl^- to water molecules as shown in the margin. For sodium ions, the attraction is between the positive charge of the sodium ion and the negative side of water's dipole moment as shown in

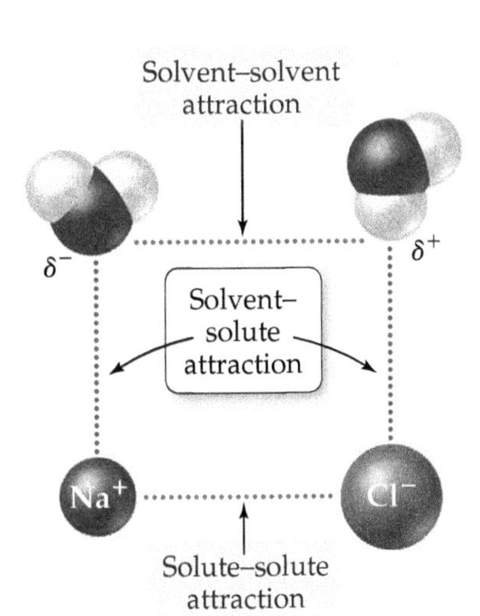

◀ When NaCl is put into water, the attraction between water molecules and Na^+ and Cl^- ions (solvent–solute attraction) overcomes the attraction between Na^+ and Cl^- ions (solute–solute attraction).

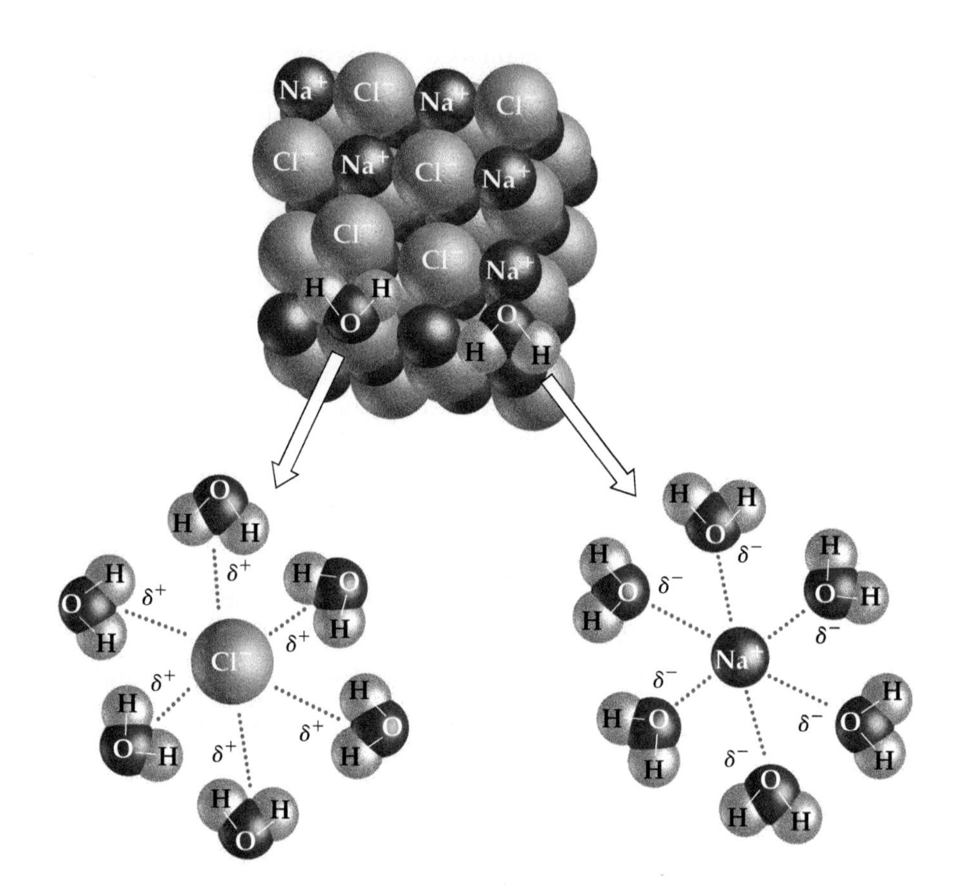

▶ **FIGURE 13.1 How a solid dissolves in water** The positive ends of the water dipoles are attracted to the negatively charged Cl^- ions, and the negative ends of the water dipoles are attracted to the positively charged Na^+ ions. The water molecules surround the ions of NaCl and disperse them in the solution.

▲ Figure 13.1 (see Section 10.8 to review dipole moment). For chloride ions, the attraction is between the negative charge of the chloride ion and the positive side of water's dipole moment. In the case of NaCl, the attraction to water wins, and sodium chloride dissolves (▼ Figure 13.2). However, in the case of calcium carbonate ($CaCO_3$), the attraction between Ca^{2+} ions and CO_3^{2-} ions wins and calcium carbonate does not dissolve in water.

SOLUBILITY AND SATURATION

The **solubility** of a compound is defined as the amount of the compound, usually in grams, that dissolves in a certain amount of liquid. For example, the solubility of sodium chloride in water at 25 °C is 36 g NaCl per 100 g water, while the solubility

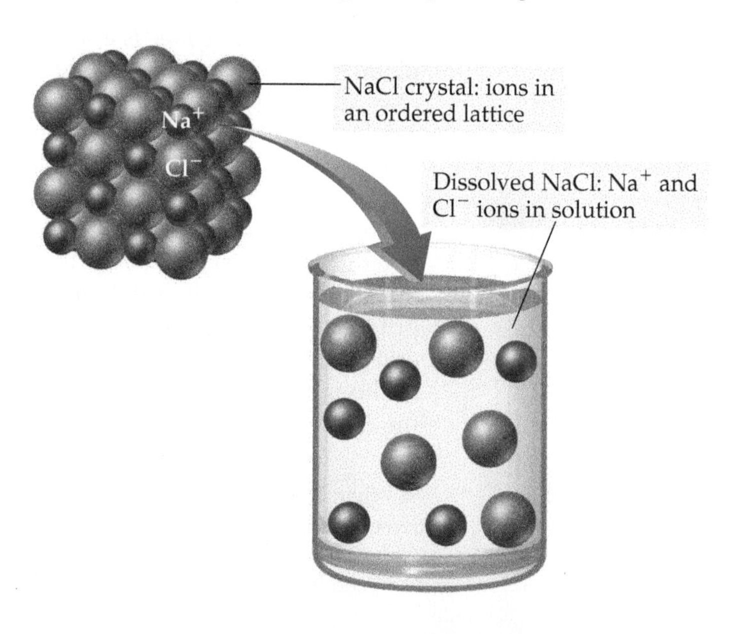

▶ **FIGURE 13.2 A sodium chloride solution** In a solution of NaCl, the Na^+ and Cl^- ions are dispersed in the water.

of calcium carbonate in water is close to zero. A solution that contains 36 g of NaCl per 100 g water is a *saturated* sodium chloride solution. A **saturated solution** holds the maximum amount of solute under the solution conditions. If additional solute is added to a saturated solution, it will not dissolve. An **unsaturated solution** is holding less than the maximum amount of solute. If additional solute is added to an unsaturated solution, it will dissolve. A **supersaturated solution** is one holding more than the normal maximum amount of solute. The solute will normally *precipitate* from (or come out of) a supersaturated solution. As the carbon dioxide and water solution rose from the bottom of Lake Nyos, for example, it became supersaturated because of the drop in pressure. The excess gas came out of the solution and rose to the surface of the lake, where it was emitted into the surrounding air.

Supersaturated solutions can form under special circumstances, such as the sudden release in pressure that occurs in a soda can when it is opened.

(a)

(b)

(c)

▶ A supersaturated solution holds more than the normal maximum amount of solute. In some cases, such as the sodium acetate solution pictured here, a supersaturated solution may be temporarily stable. Any disturbance however, such as dropping in a small piece of solid sodium acetate **(a)**, will cause the solid to come out of solution **(b, c)**.

Chapter 7 introduced the solubility rules (Section 7.5, Table 7.2), which give us a qualitative description of the solubility of ionic solids. Molecular solids may also be soluble in water depending on whether the solid is polar. Table sugar ($C_{12}H_{22}O_{11}$), for example, is polar and soluble in water. Nonpolar solids, such as lard and vegetable shortening, are usually insoluble in water.

ELECTROLYTE SOLUTIONS: DISSOLVED IONIC SOLIDS

A sugar solution (containing a molecular solid) and a salt solution (containing an ionic solid) are very different, as shown in ▼ Figure 13.3. In a salt solution the dissolved particles are ions, while in a sugar solution the dissolved particles are molecules. The ions in the salt solution are mobile charged particles and can therefore conduct electricity. As described in Section 7.5, a solution containing a solute that dissociates into ions is called an **electrolyte solution**. The sugar solution contains dissolved sugar molecules and cannot conduct electricity; it is a **nonelectrolyte solution**. In general, soluble ionic solids form electrolyte solutions, while soluble molecular solids form nonelectrolyte solutions.

NaCl forms a strong electrolyte solution (Section 7.5). Weak electrolyte solutions are covered in Chapter 14.

▶ **FIGURE 13.3 Electrolyte and nonelectrolyte solutions** Electrolyte solutions contain dissolved ions (charged particles) and therefore conduct electricity. Nonelectrolyte solutions contain dissolved molecules (neutral particles) and so do not conduct electricity.

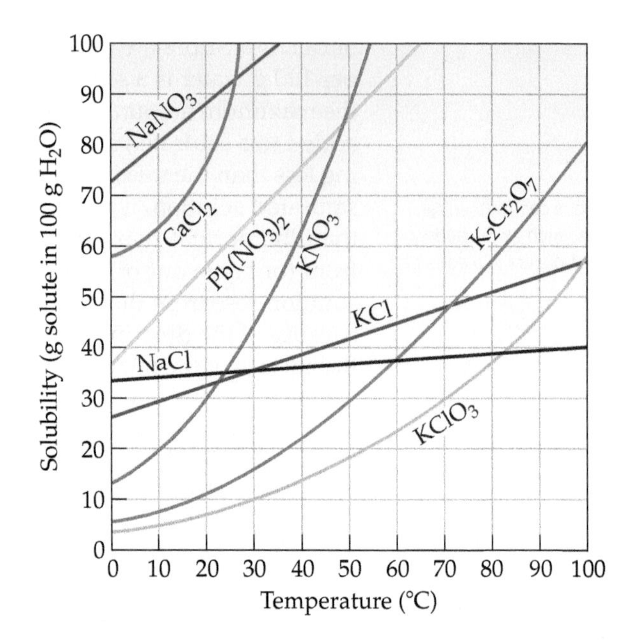

▶ **FIGURE 13.4 Solubility of some ionic solids as a function of temperature**

HOW SOLUBILITY VARIES WITH TEMPERATURE

Have you ever noticed how much easier it is to dissolve sugar in hot tea than in cold tea? The solubility of solids in water can be highly dependent on temperature. In general, the solubility of *solids* in water increases with increasing temperature (▲ Figure 13.4). For example, the solubility of potassium nitrate (KNO_3) at 20 °C is about 30 g KNO_3 per 100 g of water. However, at 50 °C, the solubility rises to 88 g KNO_3 per 100 g of water. A common way to purify a solid is a technique called **recrystallization**. Recrystallization involves putting the solid into water (or some other solvent) at an elevated temperature. Enough solid is added to the solvent to create a saturated solution at the elevated temperature. As the solution cools, the solubility decreases, causing some of the solid to precipitate from solution. If the solution cools slowly, the solid will form crystals as it comes out. The crystalline structure tends to reject impurities, resulting in a purer solid.

▲ Rock candy is composed of sugar crystals that form through recrystallization.

ROCK CANDY

Recrystallization can be used to make rock candy. To make rock candy, prepare a saturated sucrose (table sugar) solution at an elevated temperature. Dangle a string in the solution, and leave it to cool and stand for several days. As the solution cools, it becomes supersaturated and sugar crystals grow on the string. After several days, beautiful and sweet crystals, or "rocks," of sugar cover the string, ready to be admired and eaten.

13.4 Solutions of Gases in Water: How Soda Pop Gets Its Fizz

The water at the bottom of Lake Nyos and a can of soda pop are both examples of solutions in which a gas (carbon dioxide) is dissolved in a liquid (water). Most liquids exposed to air contain some dissolved gases. Lake water and seawater, for example, contain dissolved oxygen necessary for the survival of fish. Our blood contains dissolved nitrogen, oxygen, and carbon dioxide. Even tap water contains dissolved atmospheric gases.

You can see the dissolved gases in ordinary tap water by heating it on a stove. Before the water reaches its boiling point, you will see small bubbles develop in the water. These bubbles are dissolved air (mostly nitrogen and oxygen) coming out of solution. Once the water boils, the bubbling becomes more vigorous—these larger bubbles are composed of water vapor. The dissolved air comes out of solution upon heating because—unlike solids, whose solubility *increases* with increasing

Cold soda pop: carbon dioxide more likely to stay in solution

Warm soda pop: carbon dioxide more likely to bubble out of solution

▲ Warm soda pop fizzes more than cold soda pop because the solubility of the dissolved carbon dioxide decreases with increasing temperature.

temperature—the solubility of gases in water *decreases* with increasing temperature. As the temperature of the water rises, the solubility of the dissolved nitrogen and oxygen decreases and these gases come out of solution, forming small bubbles around the bottom of the pot.

The decrease in the solubility of gases with increasing temperature is the reason that warm soda pop bubbles more than cold soda pop and also the reason that warm soda goes flat faster than cold soda. The carbon dioxide comes out of solution faster (bubbles more) at room temperature than at lower temperature because it is less soluble at room temperature.

The solubility of gases also depends on pressure. The higher the pressure above a liquid, the more soluble the gas is in the liquid (▼ Figure 13.5), a relationship known as **Henry's law**.

The solubility of a gas in a liquid increases with increasing pressure.

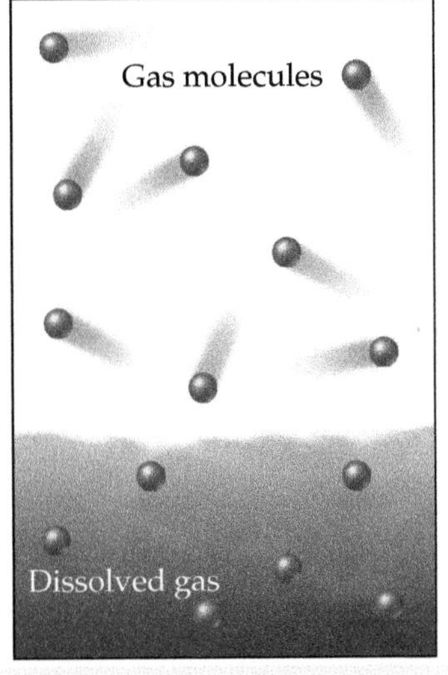

Gas at low pressure over a liquid

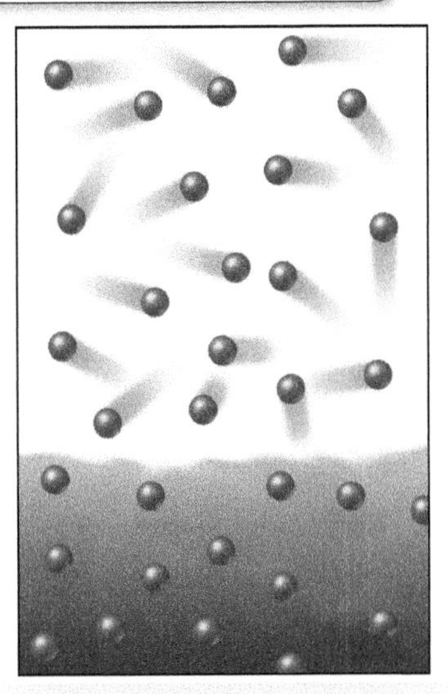

Gas at high pressure over a liquid

▶ **FIGURE 13.5 Pressure and solubility** The higher the pressure above a liquid, the more soluble the gas is in the liquid.

In a can of soda pop and at the bottom of Lake Nyos, carbon dioxide is maintained in solution by high pressure. In soda pop, the pressure is provided by a large amount of carbon dioxide gas that is pumped into the can before sealing it. When the can is opened, the pressure is released and the solubility of carbon dioxide decreases, resulting in bubbling (▼ Figure 13.6). The bubbles are formed by the carbon dioxide gas as it escapes. In Lake Nyos, the pressure is provided by the mass of the lake

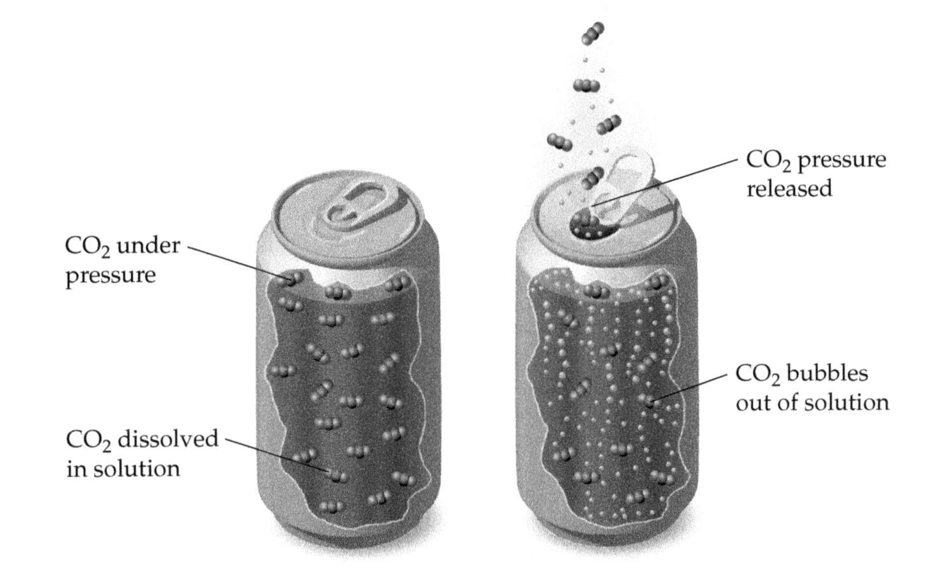

▶ **FIGURE 13.6 Pop! Fizz!** A can of soda pop is pressurized with carbon dioxide. When the can is opened, the pressure is released, lowering the solubility of carbon dioxide in the solution and causing it to come out of solution as bubbles.

water itself pushing down on the carbon-dioxide–rich water at the bottom of the lake. When the stratification (or layering) of the lake is disturbed, the pressure on the carbon dioxide solution is lowered and the solubility of carbon dioxide decreases, resulting in the release of excess carbon dioxide gas.

CONCEPTUAL CHECKPOINT 13.2

A solution is saturated in both nitrogen gas (N_2) and potassium chloride (KCl) at 75 °C. What happens when the solution is cooled to room temperature?

(a) Some nitrogen gas bubbles out of solution.

(b) Some potassium chloride precipitates out of solution.

(c) Both (a) and (c).

(d) Nothing happens.

13.5 Specifying Solution Concentration: Mass Percent

As we have seen, the amount of solute in a solution is an important property of the solution. For example, the amount of carbon dioxide in the water at the bottom of Lake Nyos is an important predictor of when the deadly event may repeat itself. A **dilute solution** is one containing small amounts of solute relative to solvent. If the water at the bottom of Lake Nyos were a dilute carbon dioxide solution, it would pose little threat. A **concentrated solution** is one containing large amounts of solute relative to solvent. If the carbon dioxide in the water at the bottom of Lake Nyos becomes concentrated (through the continual feeding of carbon dioxide from magma into the lake), it becomes a large threat. A common way to report solution concentration is *mass percent.*

MASS PERCENT

Also in common use are *parts per million* (ppm), the number of grams of solute per 1 million g of solution, and *parts per billion* (ppb), the number of grams of solute per 1 billion g of solution.

Mass percent is the number of grams of solute per 100 g of solution. So a solution with a concentration of 14% by mass, for example, contains 14 g of solute per 100 g of solution. To calculate mass percent, simply divide the mass of the solute by the mass of the solution (solute *and* solvent) and multiply by 100%.

Note that the denominator is the mass of *solution*, not the mass of solvent.

$$\text{Mass percent} = \frac{\text{Mass solute}}{\text{Mass solute} + \text{Mass solvent}} \times 100\%$$

Suppose you wanted to calculate the mass percent of NaCl in a solution containing 15.3 g of NaCl and 155.0 g of water. Begin by sorting the information in the problem statement.

GIVEN: 15.3 g NaCl

155.0 g H_2O

FIND: mass percent

SOLUTION

To solve this problem, substitute the correct values into the mass percent equation just presented.

$$\begin{aligned}\text{Mass percent} &= \frac{\text{Mass solute}}{\text{Mass solute} + \text{Mass solvent}} \times 100\% \\ &= \frac{15.3\,\text{g}}{15.3\,\text{g} + 155.0\,\text{g}} \times 100\% \\ &= \frac{15.3\,\cancel{\text{g}}}{170.3\,\cancel{\text{g}}} \times 100\% \\ &= 8.98\%\end{aligned}$$

The solution is 8.98% NaCl by mass.

EXAMPLE 13.1 Calculating Mass Percent

Calculate the mass percent of a solution containing 27.5 g of ethanol (C_2H_6O) and 175 mL of H_2O. (Assume that the density of water is 1.00 g/mL.)

Begin by setting up the problem. You are given the mass of ethanol and the volume of water and asked to find the mass percent of the solution.

GIVEN: $27.5\,g\,C_2H_6O$

$175\,mL\,H_2O$

$d_{H_2O} = \frac{1.00\,g}{mL}$

FIND: mass percent

To find the mass percent, substitute into the equation for mass percent. You need the mass of ethanol and the mass of water. Obtain the mass of water from the volume of water by using the density as a conversion factor.

SOLUTION

$$\text{Mass percent} = \frac{\text{Mass solute}}{\text{Mass solute} + \text{Mass solvent}} \times 100\%$$

$$\text{Mass } H_2O = 175\,\cancel{mL}\,H_2O \times \frac{1.00\,g}{\cancel{mL}} = 175\,g$$

Finally, substitute the correct quantities into the equation and calculate the mass percent.

$$\text{Mass percent} = \frac{\text{Mass solute}}{\text{Mass solute} + \text{Mass solvent}} \times 100\%$$

$$= \frac{27.5\,g}{27.5\,g + 175\,g}$$

$$= \frac{27.5\,g}{20\underline{2}.5\,g} \times 100\%$$

$$= 13.6\%$$

▶**SKILLBUILDER 13.1 | Calculating Mass Percent**

Calculate the mass percent of a sucrose solution containing 11.3 g of sucrose and 412.1 mL of water. (Assume that the density of water is 1.00 g/mL.)

▶**FOR MORE PRACTICE** Example 13.11; Problems 41, 42, 43, 44, 45, 46.

USING MASS PERCENT IN CALCULATIONS

We can use the mass percent of a solution as a conversion factor between mass of the solute and mass of the solution. The key to using mass percent in this way is to write it as a fraction.

$$\text{Mass percent} = \frac{\text{g solute}}{100\,\text{g solution}}$$

A solution containing 3.5% sodium chloride, for example, has the following conversion factor.

$$\frac{3.5\,g\,NaCl}{100\,g\,\text{solution}} \quad \text{converts g solution} \longrightarrow \text{g NaCl}$$

This conversion factor converts from grams of solution to grams of NaCl. If you want to go the other way, simply invert the conversion factor.

$$\frac{100\,g\,\text{solution}}{3.5\,g\,NaCl} \quad \text{converts g NaCl} \longrightarrow \text{g solution}$$

For example, to use mass percent as a conversion factor, consider a water sample from the bottom of Lake Nyos containing 8.5% carbon dioxide by mass. We can determine how much carbon dioxide in grams is contained in 28.6 L of the water solution. (Assume that the density of the solution is 1.03 g/mL.) We begin by sorting the information in the problem statement.

GIVEN: 8.5% CO_2 by mass

28.6 L solution

$$d = \frac{1.03 \text{ g}}{\text{mL}}$$

FIND: g CO_2

SOLUTION MAP

We strategize by drawing a solution map that begins with L solution and shows the conversion to mL solution and then to g solution using the density. Then we proceed from g solution to g CO_2, using the mass percent (expressed as a fraction) as a conversion factor.

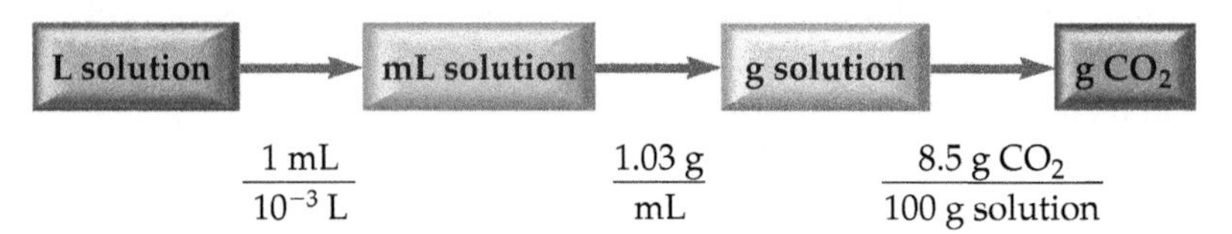

$$\frac{1 \text{ mL}}{10^{-3} \text{ L}} \qquad \frac{1.03 \text{ g}}{\text{mL}} \qquad \frac{8.5 \text{ g } CO_2}{100 \text{ g solution}}$$

RELATIONSHIPS USED

$$\frac{8.5 \text{ g } CO_2}{100 \text{ g solution}} \text{ (given mass percent, written as a fraction)}$$

$$\frac{1.03 \text{ g}}{\text{mL}} \text{ (given density of the solution)}$$

$$1 \text{ mL} = 10^{-3} \text{ L} \quad \text{(from Table 2.2)}$$

SOLUTION

We follow the solution map to calculate the answer.

$$28.6 \text{ L solution} \times \frac{1 \text{ mL}}{10^{-3} \text{ L}} \times \frac{1.03 \text{ g}}{\text{mL}} \times \frac{8.5 \text{ g } CO_2}{100 \text{ g solution}} = 2.5 \times 10^3 \text{ g } CO_2$$

In this example, we used mass percent to convert from a given amount of *solution* to the amount of *solute* present in the solution. In Example 13.2, we use mass percent to convert from a given amount of *solute* to the amount of *solution* containing that solute.

EXAMPLE 13.2 Using Mass Percent in Calculations

A soft drink contains 11.5% sucrose ($C_{12}H_{22}O_{11}$) by mass. What volume of the soft drink solution in milliliters contains 85.2 g of sucrose? (Assume a density of 1.04 g/mL.)

SORT

You are given the concentration of sucrose in a soft drink and a mass of sucrose. You are asked to find the volume of the soft drink that contains the given mass of sucrose.

GIVEN: 11.5% $C_{12}H_{22}O_{11}$ by mass

85.2 g $C_{12}H_{22}O_{11}$

$$d = \frac{1.04 \text{ g}}{\text{mL}}$$

FIND: mL solution (soft drink)

STRATEGIZE

Draw a solution map to convert from g solute ($C_{12}H_{22}O_{11}$) to g solution using the mass percent in fractional form as the conversion factor. Convert to mL using the density.

SOLUTION MAP

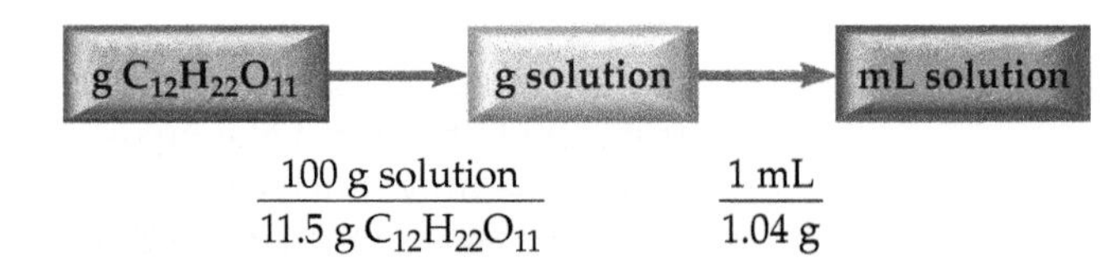

$$\frac{100 \text{ g solution}}{11.5 \text{ g } C_{12}H_{22}O_{11}} \qquad \frac{1 \text{ mL}}{1.04 \text{ g}}$$

	RELATIONSHIPS USED $\frac{11.5\text{ g } C_{12}H_{22}O_{11}}{100\text{ g solution}}$ (given mass percent,written as a fraction) $\frac{1.04\text{ g}}{\text{mL}}$ (given density of solution)
SOLVE Follow the solution map to solve the problem.	**SOLUTION** $85.2\text{ g } C_{12}H_{22}O_{11} \times \frac{100\text{ g solution}}{11.5\text{ g } C_{12}H_{22}O_{11}} \times \frac{1\text{ mL}}{1.04\text{ g}} = 712\text{ mL solution}$
CHECK Check your answer. Are the units correct? Does the answer make physical sense?	The units (mL solution) are correct. The magnitude of the answer makes sense because each 100 mL of solution contains 11.5 g sucrose; therefore 712 mL should contain a bit more than 77 g, which is close to the given amount of 85.2 g.

▶SKILLBUILDER 13.2 | Using Mass Percent in Calculations

How much sucrose ($C_{12}H_{22}O_{11}$) in grams is contained in 355 mL (12 oz) of the soft drink in Example 13.2?

▶FOR MORE PRACTICE Example 13.12; Problems 47, 48, 49, 50, 51, 52.

13.6 Specifying Solution Concentration: Molarity

Note that molarity is abbreviated with a capital M.

A second way to express solution concentration is **molarity** (M), defined as the number of moles of solute per liter of solution. We calculate the molarity of a solution as follows:

$$\textbf{Molarity}\ (\text{M}) = \frac{\text{Moles solute}}{\text{Liters solution}}$$

Note that molarity is moles of solute per liter of *solution*, not per liter of solvent. To make a solution of a specified molarity, you usually put the solute into a flask and then add water to the desired volume of solution. For example, to make 1.00 L of a 1.00 M NaCl solution, you add 1.00 mol of NaCl to a flask and then add water to make 1.00 L of solution (◀ Figure 13.7). You *do not* combine 1.00 mol of NaCl with 1.00 L of water because that would result in a total volume exceeding 1.00 L and therefore a molarity of less than 1.00 M.

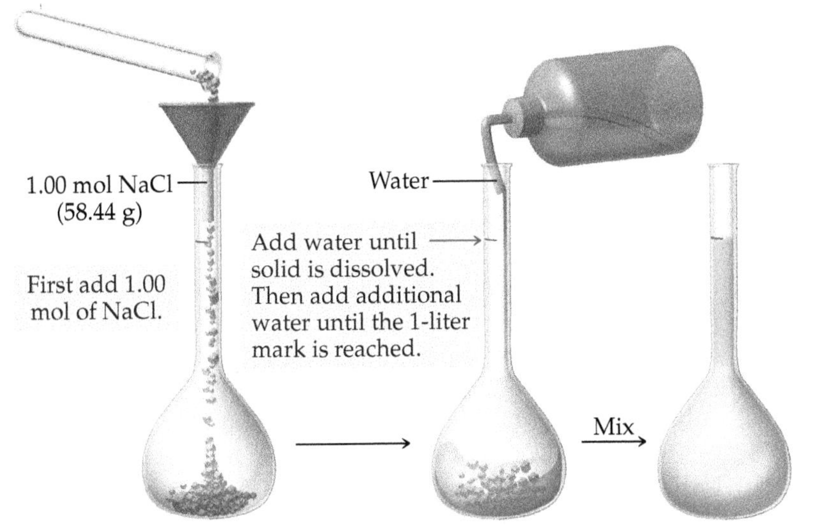
How to prepare a 1.00 molar NaCl solution.
1.00 mol NaCl
(58.44 g)
First add 1.00
mol of NaCl.
Water
Add water until
solid is dissolved.
Then add additional
water until the 1-liter
mark is reached.
Mix
A 1.00 molar NaCl solution

◀ **FIGURE 13.7 Making a solution of specific molarity** To make 1.00 L of a 1.00 M NaCl solution, you add 1.00 mol (58.44 g) of sodium chloride to a flask and then dilute to 1.00 L of total volume.
Question: What would happen if you added 1 L of water to 1 mol of sodium chloride? Would the resulting solution be 1 M?

CHEMISTRY IN THE ENVIRONMENT

The Dirty Dozen

A number of potentially harmful chemicals—such as DDT, dioxin, and polychlorinated biphenyls (PCBs)—can make their way into our water sources from industrial dumping, atmospheric emissions, agriculture, and household dumping. Since crops, livestock, and fish all rely on water, they too can accumulate these chemicals from water. Human consumption of food or water contaminated with these chemicals leads to a number of diseases and adverse health effects such as increased cancer risk, liver damage, or central nervous system damage. Governments around the world have joined forces to ban a number of these chemicals—called persistent organic pollutants or POPs—from production. The original treaty targeted 12 such substances called the dirty dozen (Table 13.3).

A difficult problem posed by these chemicals is their persistence. Once they get into the environment, they stay there for a long time. A second problem is their tendency to undergo *bioamplification.* Because these chemicals are nonpolar, they are stored and concentrated in the fatty tissues of the organisms that consume them. As larger organisms eat smaller ones that have consumed the chemical, the larger organisms consume even more of the stored chemicals. The result is an increase in the concentrations of these chemicals as they move up the food chain. Under the treaty, nearly all intentional production of these chemicals is banned. In the United States, the presence of these contaminants in water supplies is monitored under supervision of the Environmental Protection Agency (EPA). The EPA has set limits, called maximum contaminant levels (MCLs), for each of the dirty dozen in food and drinking water. Some MCLs for selected compounds in water supplies are listed in Table 13.4.

▲ Potentially dangerous chemicals can leak into the environment and contaminate water and food supplies.

TABLE 13.3 The Dirty Dozen

1. aldrin (insecticide)
2. chlordane (insecticide by-product)
3. DDT (insecticide)
4. dieldrin (insecticide)
5. dioxin (industrial by-product)
6. eldrin (insecticide)
7. furan (industrial by-product)
8. heptachlor (insecticide)
9. hexachlorobenzene (fungicide, industrial by-product)
10. mirex (insecticide, fire retardant)
11. polychlorinated biphenyls (PCBs) (electrical insulators)
12. toxaphene (insecticide)

TABLE 13.4 EPA Maximum Contaminant Level (MCL) for Several "Dirty Dozen" Chemicals

chlordane	0.002 mg/L
dioxin	0.00000003 mg/L
heptachlor	0.0004 mg/L
hexachlorobenzene	0.001 mg/L

Notice the units that the EPA uses to express the concentration of the contaminants: milligrams per liter. This unit is a conversion factor between liters of water consumed and the mass in milligrams of the pollutant. According to the EPA, as long as the contaminant concentrations are below these levels, the water is safe to drink.

CAN YOU ANSWER THIS? *Using what you know about conversion factors, calculate how much of each of the chemicals in Table 13.4 (at their MCL) would be present in 715 L of water, the approximate amount of water consumed by an adult in one year.*

To calculate molarity, divide the number of moles of the solute by the volume of the solution (solute *and* solvent) in liters. For example, to calculate the molarity of a sucrose ($C_{12}H_{22}O_{11}$) solution made with 1.58 mol of sucrose diluted to a total volume of 5.0 L of solution, we begin by sorting the information in the problem statement.

GIVEN: 1.58 mol $C_{12}H_{22}O_{11}$

5.0 L solution

FIND: molarity (M)

SOLUTION

We substitute the correct values into the equation for molarity and calculate the answer.

$$\text{Molarity (M)} = \frac{\text{Moles solute}}{\text{Liters solution}} = \frac{1.58 \text{ mol } C_{12}H_{22}O_{11}}{5.0 \text{ L solution}} = 0.32 \text{ M}$$

EXAMPLE 13.3 Calculating Molarity

Calculate the molarity of a solution made by putting 15.5 g NaCl into a beaker and adding water to make 1.50 L of NaCl solution.

You are given the mass of sodium chloride (the solute) and the volume of solution. You are asked to find the molarity of the solution.	**GIVEN:** 15.5 g NaCl 1.50 L solution **FIND:** molarity (M)
To calculate molarity, substitute the correct values into the equation and calculate the answer. You must first convert the amount of NaCl from grams to moles using the molar mass of NaCl.	**SOLUTION** $\text{mol NaCl} = 15.5 \text{ g NaCl} \times \frac{1 \text{ mol NaCl}}{58.44 \text{ g NaCl}} = 0.26\underline{5}2 \text{ mol NaCl}$ $\text{Molarity (M)} = \frac{\text{Moles solute}}{\text{Liters solution}} = \frac{0.26\underline{5}2 \text{ mol NaCl}}{1.50 \text{ L solution}} = 0.177 \text{ M}$

▶**SKILLBUILDER 13.3 | Calculating Molarity**

Calculate the molarity of a solution made by putting 55.8 g of $NaNO_3$ into a beaker and diluting to 2.50 L.

▶**FOR MORE PRACTICE** Example 13.13; Problems 59, 60, 61, 62, 63, 64.

USING MOLARITY IN CALCULATIONS

We can use the molarity of a solution as a conversion factor between moles of the solute and liters of the solution. For example, a 0.500 M NaCl solution contains 0.500 mol NaCl for every liter of solution.

$$\frac{0.500 \text{ mol NaCl}}{\text{L solution}} \quad \text{converts L solution} \longrightarrow \text{mol NaCl}$$

This conversion factor converts from liters of solution to moles of NaCl. If you want to go the other way, simply invert the conversion factor.

$$\frac{\text{L solution}}{0.500 \text{ mol NaCl}} \quad \text{converts mol NaCl} \longrightarrow \text{L solution}$$

For example, to determine how many grams of sucrose ($C_{12}H_{22}O_{11}$) are contained in 1.72 L of 0.758 M sucrose solution, begin by sorting the information in the problem statement.

GIVEN: 0.758 M $C_{12}H_{22}O_{11}$

1.72 L solution

FIND: g $C_{12}H_{22}O_{11}$

SOLUTION MAP

We strategize by drawing a solution map that begins with L solution and shows the conversion to moles of sucrose using the molarity, and then the conversion to mass of sucrose using the molar mass.

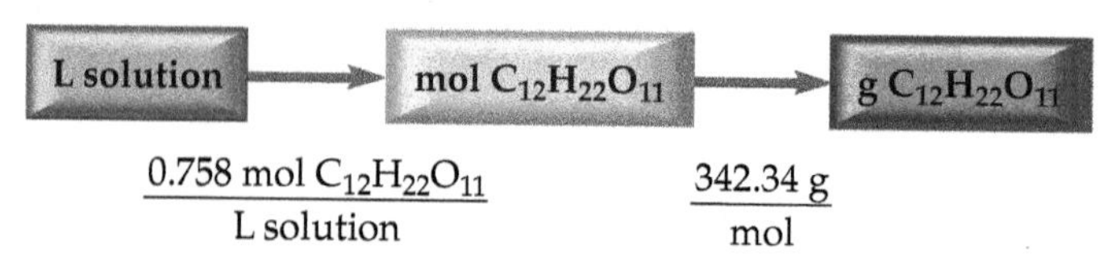

$$\frac{0.758 \text{ mol } C_{12}H_{22}O_{11}}{\text{L solution}} \qquad \frac{342.34 \text{ g}}{\text{mol}}$$

RELATIONSHIPS USED

$$\frac{0.758 \text{ mol } C_{12}H_{22}O_{11}}{\text{L solution}} \text{ (given molarity of solution, written out as a fraction)}$$

$$1 \text{ mol } C_{12}H_{22}O_{11} = 342.34 \text{ g (molar mass of sucrose)}$$

SOLUTION

We then follow the solution map to calculate the answer.

$$1.72 \text{ L solution} \times \frac{0.758 \text{ mol } C_{12}H_{22}O_{11}}{\text{L solution}} \times \frac{342.34 \text{ g } C_{12}H_{22}O_{11}}{\text{mol } C_{12}H_{22}O_{11}} = 446 \text{ g } C_{12}H_{22}O_{11}$$

In this example, we used molarity to convert from a given amount of *solution* to the amount of *solute* in that solution. In the example that follows, we use molarity to convert from a given amount of *solute* to the amount of *solution* containing that solute.

EXAMPLE 13.4 Using Molarity in Calculations

How many liters of a 0.114 M NaOH solution contains 1.24 mol of NaOH?

SORT

You are given the molarity of an NaOH solution and the number of moles of NaOH. You are asked to find the volume of solution that contains the given number of moles.

GIVEN: 0.114 M NaOH

1.24 mol NaOH

FIND: L solution

STRATEGIZE

The solution map begins with mol NaOH and shows the conversion to liters of solution using the molarity as a conversion factor.

SOLUTION MAP

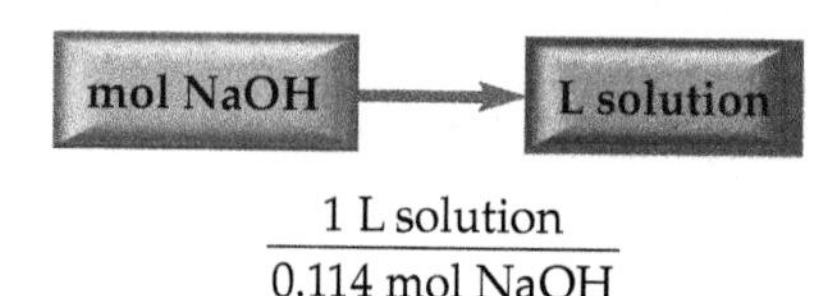

$$\frac{1 \text{ L solution}}{0.114 \text{ mol NaOH}}$$

RELATIONSHIP USED

$$\frac{0.114 \text{ mol NaOH}}{\text{L solution}} \text{ (given molarity of solution, written out as a fraction)}$$

SOLVE

Solve the problem by following the solution map.

SOLUTION

$$1.24 \text{ mol NaOH} \times \frac{1 \text{ L solution}}{0.114 \text{ mol NaOH}} = 10.9 \text{ L solution}$$

CHECK
Check your answer. Are the units correct? Does the answer make physical sense?

The units (L solution) are correct. The magnitude of the answer makes sense because each L of solution contains a little more than 0.10 moles; therefore about 10 L contains a little more than 1 mole.

▶SKILLBUILDER 13.4 | Using Molarity in Calculations
How much of a 0.225 M KCl solution contains 55.8 g of KCl?

▶FOR MORE PRACTICE Example 13.14; Problems 65, 66, 67, 68, 69, 70.

ION CONCENTRATIONS

The reported concentration of a solution containing a *molecular* compound usually reflects the concentration of the solute as it actually exists in solution. For example, a 1.0 M glucose ($C_6H_{12}O_6$) solution indicates that the solution contains 1.0 mol of $C_6H_{12}O_6$ per liter of solution. However, the reported concentration of solution containing an *ionic* compound reflects the concentration of the solute *before it is dissolved in solution*. For example, a 1.0 M $CaCl_2$ solution contains 1.0 mol of Ca^{2+} per liter and 2.0 mol of Cl^- per liter. The concentration of the individual ions present in a solution containing an ionic compound can usually be approximated from the overall concentration as shown by the following example.

When an ionic compound dissolves in solution, some of the cations and anions may pair up, so that the actual concentrations of the ions are lower than what you would expect if you assume complete dissociation occurred.

EXAMPLE 13.5 Ion Concentration

Determine the molar concentrations of Na^+ and PO_4^{3-} in a 1.50 M Na_3PO_4 solution.

You are given the concentration of an ionic solution and asked to find the concentrations of the component ions.

GIVEN: 1.50 M Na_3PO_4
FIND: molarity (M) of Na^+ and PO_4^{3-}

A formula unit of Na_3PO_4 contains 3 Na^+ ions (as indicated by the subscript), so the concentration of Na^+ is three times the concentration of Na_3PO_4. Since the same formula unit contains one PO_4^{3-} ion, the concentration of PO_4^{3-} is equal to the concentration of Na_3PO_4.

SOLUTION

$$\text{molarity of } Na^+ = 3(1.50\text{ M}) = 4.50\text{ M}$$

$$\text{molarity of } PO_4^{3-} = 1.50\text{ M}$$

▶SKILLBUILDER 13.5 | Ion Concentration
Determine the molar concentrations of Ca^{2+} and Cl^- in a 0.75 M $CaCl_2$ solution.

▶FOR MORE PRACTICE Problems 77, 78, 79, 80.

CONCEPTUAL CHECKPOINT 13.3

A solution is 0.15 M in K_2SO_4. What is the concentration of K^+ in solution?

(a) 0.075 M (b) 0.15 M (c) 0.30 M (d) 0.45 M

13.7 Solution Dilution

When diluting acids, always add the concentrated acid to the water. *Never add water to concentrated acid solutions.*

To save space in laboratory storerooms, solutions are often stored in concentrated forms called **stock solutions**. For example, hydrochloric acid is typically stored as a 12 M stock solution. However, many lab procedures call for much less concentrated hydrochloric acid solutions, so chemists must dilute the stock solution to the required concentration. This is normally done by diluting a certain amount of the stock solution with water. How do we determine how much of the stock solution to use? The easiest way to solve these problems is to use the dilution equation:

$$M_1 V_1 = M_2 V_2$$

where M_1 and V_1 are the molarity and volume of the initial concentrated solution and M_2 and V_2 are the molarity and volume of the final diluted solution. This equation works because the molarity multiplied by the volume gives the number of moles of solute ($M \times V = \text{mol}$), which is the same in both solutions. For example, suppose a laboratory procedure calls for 5.00 L of a 1.50 M KCl solution. How should we prepare this solution from a 12.0 M stock solution? We begin by sorting the information in the problem statement.

The equation $M_1 V_1 = M_2 V_2$ applies only to solution dilution, NOT to stoichiometry.

GIVEN: $M_1 = 12.0 \text{ M}$

$M_2 = 1.50 \text{ M}$

$V_2 = 5.00 \text{ L}$

FIND: V_1

SOLUTION

We solve the solution dilution equation for V_1 (the volume of the stock solution required for the dilution) and then substitute in the correct values to calculate it.

$$M_1V_1 = M_2V_2$$

$$V_1 = \frac{M_2V_2}{M_1}$$

$$= \frac{1.50 \frac{\cancel{\text{mol}}}{\cancel{\text{L}}} \times 5.00 \text{ L}}{12.0 \frac{\cancel{\text{mol}}}{\cancel{\text{L}}}}$$

$$= 0.625 \text{ L}$$

We can therefore make the solution by diluting 0.625 L of the stock solution to a total volume of 5.00 L (V_2). The resulting solution will be 1.50 M in KCl (▶ Figure 13.8).

EXAMPLE 13.6 Solution Dilution

To what volume should you dilute 0.100 L of a 15 M NaOH solution to obtain a 1.0 M NaOH solution?

You are given the initial volume and concentration of an NaOH solution and a final concentration. You are asked to find the volume required to dilute the initial solution to the given final concentration.

GIVEN: $V_1 = 0.100 \text{ L}$
$M_1 = 15 \text{ M}$
$M_2 = 1.0 \text{ M}$

FIND: V_2

Solve the solution dilution equation for V_2 (the volume of the final solution) and substitute the required quantities to calculate V_2.

SOLUTION

$$M_1V_1 = M_2V_2$$

$$V_2 = \frac{M_1V_1}{M_2}$$

$$= \frac{15 \frac{\cancel{\text{mol}}}{\cancel{\text{L}}} \times 0.100 \text{ L}}{1.0 \frac{\cancel{\text{mol}}}{\cancel{\text{L}}}}$$

$$= 1.5 \text{ L}$$

You can make the solution by diluting 0.100 L of the stock solution to a total volume of 1.5 L (V_2). The resulting solution has a concentration of 1.0 M.

▶**SKILLBUILDER 13.6 | Solution Dilution**

How much 6.0 M $NaNO_3$ solution should you use to make 0.585 L of a 1.2 M $NaNO_3$ solution?

▶**FOR MORE PRACTICE** Example 13.15; Problems 81, 82, 83, 84, 85, 86, 87, 88.

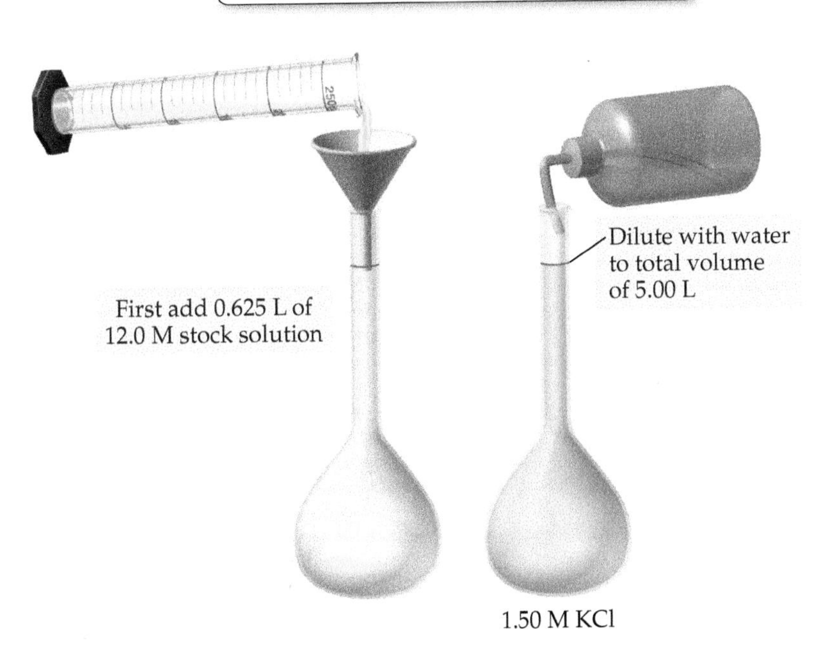
How to make 5.00 L of a 1.50 M KCl solution from a 12.0 M stock solution.
First add 0.625 L of 12.0 M stock solution
Dilute with water to total volume of 5.00 L
1.50 M KCl

$$M_1V_1 = M_2V_2$$

$$\frac{12.0\text{ mol}}{\cancel{L}} \times 0.625\cancel{L} = \frac{1.50\text{ mol}}{\cancel{L}} \times 5.00\cancel{L}$$

$$7.50\text{ mol} = 7.50\text{ mol}$$

▶ FIGURE 13.8 **Making a solution by dilution of a more concentrated solution**

CONCEPTUAL CHECKPOINT 13.4

If 25 g of salt are dissolved in 251 g of water, what is the mass of the resulting solution?

(a) 276 g (b) 251 g (c) 226 g

13.8 Solution Stoichiometry

As we discussed in Chapter 7, many chemical reactions take place in aqueous solutions. Precipitation reactions, neutralization reactions, and gas evolution reactions, for example, all occur in aqueous solutions. Chapter 8 describes how we use the coefficients in chemical equations as conversion factors between moles of reactants and moles of products in stoichiometric calculations. These conversion factors are often used to determine, for example, the amount of product obtained in a chemical reaction based on a given amount of reactant or the amount of one reactant needed to completely react with a given amount of another reactant. The general solution map for these kinds of calculations is:

See Sections 8.2 through 8.4 for a review of reaction stoichiometry.

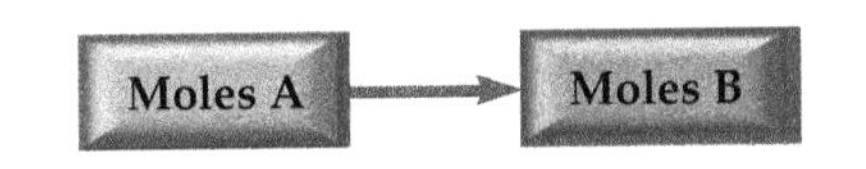
Moles A
Moles B

where A and B are two different substances involved in the reaction and the conversion factor between them comes from the stoichiometric coefficients in the balanced chemical equation.

In reactions involving aqueous reactant and products, it is often convenient to specify the amount of reactants or products in terms of their volume and concentration. We can use the volume and concentration to calculate the number of moles of reactants or products, and then use the stoichiometric coefficients to convert to other quantities in the reaction. The general solution map for these kinds of calculations is:

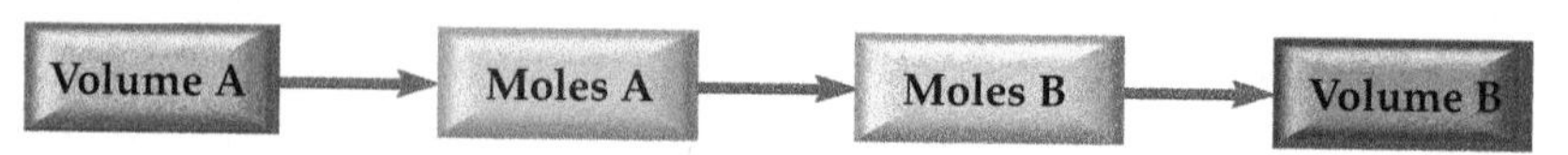

where the conversions between volume and moles are achieved using the molarities of the solutions. For example, consider the reaction for the neutralization of sulfuric acid.

$$H_2SO_4(aq) + 2\ NaOH(aq) \longrightarrow Na_2SO_4(aq) + 2\ H_2O(l)$$

How much 0.125 M NaOH solution do we need to completely neutralize 0.225 L of 0.175 M H_2SO_4 solution? Begin by sorting the information in the problem statement.

GIVEN: 0.225 L H_2SO_4 solution
0.175 M H_2SO_4
0.125 M NaOH

FIND: L NaOH solution

SOLUTION MAP

We strategize by drawing a solution map, which is similar to those for other stoichiometric problems. We first use the volume and molarity of H_2SO_4 solution to get mol H_2SO_4. Then we use the stoichiometric coefficients from the equation to convert mol H_2SO_4 to mol NaOH. Finally, we use the molarity of NaOH to get to L NaOH solution.

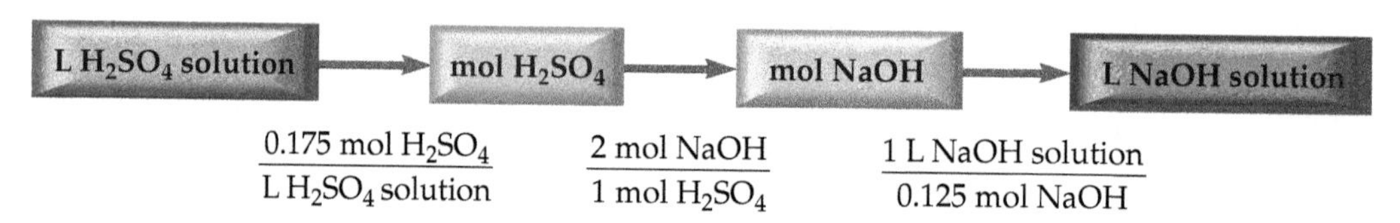

$$\frac{0.175 \text{ mol } H_2SO_4}{\text{L } H_2SO_4 \text{ solution}} \qquad \frac{2 \text{ mol NaOH}}{1 \text{ mol } H_2SO_4} \qquad \frac{1 \text{ L NaOH solution}}{0.125 \text{ mol NaOH}}$$

RELATIONSHIPS USED

$$M(H_2SO_4) = \frac{0.175 \text{ mol } H_2SO_4}{\text{L } H_2SO_4 \text{ solution}}$$ (given molarity of H_2SO_4 solution, written out as a fraction)

$$M(NaOH) = \frac{0.125 \text{ mol NaOH}}{\text{L NaOH solution}}$$ (given molarity of NaOH solution, written out as a fraction)

1 mol H_2SO_4 : 2 mol NaOH (stoichiometric relationship between H_2SO_4 and NaOH, from balanced chemical equation)

SOLUTION

To solve the problem, we follow the solution map and calculate the answer.

$$0.225 \text{ L } H_2SO_4 \text{ solution} \times \frac{0.175 \text{ mol } H_2SO_4}{\text{L } H_2SO_4 \text{ solution}} \times \frac{2 \text{ mol NaOH}}{1 \text{ mol } H_2SO_4} \times \frac{1 \text{ L NaOH solution}}{0.125 \text{ mol NaOH}} = 0.630 \text{ L NaOH solution}$$

It will take 0.630 L of the NaOH solution to completely neutralize the H_2SO_4.

EXAMPLE 13.7 Solution Stoichiometry

Consider the precipitation reaction:

$$2\ KI(aq) + Pb(NO_3)_2(aq) \longrightarrow PbI_2(s) + 2\ KNO_3(aq)$$

How much 0.115 M KI solution in liters will completely precipitate the Pb^{2+} in 0.104 L of 0.225 M $Pb(NO_3)_2$ solution?

SORT

You are given the concentration of a reactant, KI, in a chemical reaction. You are also given the volume and concentration of a second reactant, $Pb(NO_3)_2$. You are asked to find the volume of the first reactant that completely reacts with the given amount of the second.

GIVEN: 0.115 M KI

0.104 L $Pb(NO_3)_2$ solution

0.225 M $Pb(NO_3)_2$

FIND: L KI solution

STRATEGIZE

The solution map for this problem is similar to the solution maps for other stoichiometric problems. First use the volume and molarity of $Pb(NO_3)_2$ solution to get mol $Pb(NO_3)_2$ Then use the stoichiometric coefficients from the equation to convert mol $Pb(NO_3)_2$ to mol KI. Finally, use mol KI to find L KI solution.

SOLUTION MAP

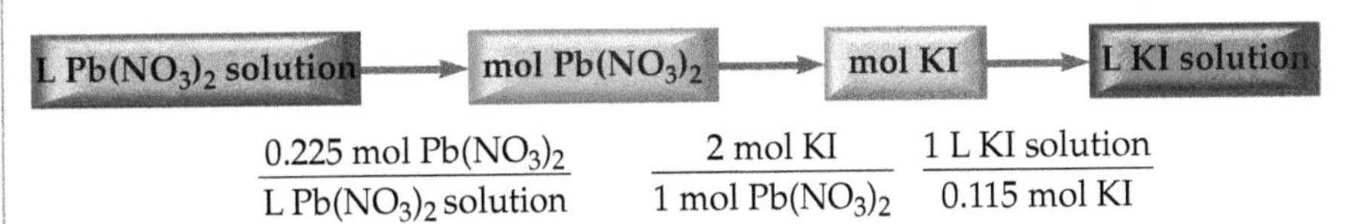

RELATIONSHIPS USED

$$M\ KI = \frac{0.115\ mol\ KI}{L\ KI\ solution}$$ (given molarity of KI solution, written out as a fraction)

$$M\ Pb(NO_3)_2 = \frac{0.225\ mol\ Pb(NO_3)_2}{L\ Pb(NO_3)_2\ solution}$$ (given molarity of $Pb(NO_3)_2$ solution, written out as a fraction)

2 mol KI ≡ 1 mol $Pb(NO_3)_2$ (stoichiometric relationship between KI and $Pb(NO_3)_2$, from balanced chemical equation)

SOLVE

Follow the solution map to solve the problem. Begin with volume of $Pb(NO_3)_2$ solution and cancel units to arrive at volume of KI solution.

SOLUTION

$$0.104\ \cancel{L\ Pb(NO_3)_2\ solution} \times \frac{0.225\ \cancel{mol\ Pb(NO_3)_2}}{\cancel{L\ Pb(NO_3)_2\ solution}} \times \frac{2\ \cancel{mol\ KI}}{\cancel{mol\ Pb(NO_3)}} \times \frac{L\ KI\ solution}{0.115\ \cancel{mol\ KI}} = 0.407\ L\ KI\ solution$$

CHECK

Check your answer. Are the units correct? Does the answer make physical sense?

The units (L KI solution) are correct. The magnitude of the answer makes sense because the lead nitrate solution is about twice as concentrated as the potassium iodide solution and 2 mol of potassium iodide are required to react with 1 mol of lead(II) nitrate. Therefore we would expect the volume of the potassium solution required to completely react with a given volume of the $Pb(NO_3)_2$ solution to be about four times as much.

▶SKILLBUILDER 13.7 | Solution Stoichiometry

How many milliliters of 0.112 M Na_2CO_3 will completely react with 27.2 mL of 0.135 M HNO_3 according to the reaction?

$$2\ HNO_3(aq) + Na_2CO_3(aq) \longrightarrow H_2O(l) + CO_2(g) + 2\ NaNO_3(aq)$$

▶SKILLBUILDER PLUS

A 25.0-mL sample of HNO_3 solution requires 35.7 mL of 0.108 M Na_2CO_3 to completely react with all of the HNO_3 in the solution. What is the concentration of the HNO_3 solution?

▶FOR MORE PRACTICE Example 13.16; Problems 89, 90, 91, 92.

13.9 Freezing Point Depression and Boiling Point Elevation: Making Water Freeze Colder and Boil Hotter

▲ Sprinkling salt on icy roads lowers the freezing point of water, so the ice melts even if the temperature is below 0 °C.

Have you ever wondered why salt is added to ice in an ice-cream maker? Or why salt is scattered on icy roads in cold climates? Salt actually lowers the melting point of ice. A salt-and-water solution will remain a liquid even below 0 °C. By adding salt to ice in the ice-cream maker, you form a mixture of ice, salt, and water that can reach a temperature of about −10 °C, cold enough to freeze the cream. On the road, the salt allows the ice to melt, even if the ambient temperature is below freezing.

Adding a nonvolatile solute—one that does not readily evaporate—to a liquid extends the temperature range over which the liquid remains a liquid. The solution has a lower melting point and a higher boiling point than the pure liquid; these effects are called **freezing point depression** and **boiling point elevation.** Freezing point depression and boiling point elevation depend only on the number of solute particles *in solution*, not on the type of solute particles. Properties such as these—which depend on the number of dissolved solute particles and not on the type of solute particles—are called **colligative properties.**

FREEZING POINT DEPRESSION

The freezing point of a solution containing a nonvolatile solute is lower than the freezing point of the pure solvent. For example, antifreeze, added to engine coolant to prevent it from freezing in cold climates, is an aqueous solution of ethylene glycol ($C_2H_6O_2$). The ethylene glycol lowers the freezing point of the aqueous solution. The more concentrated the solution is, the lower the freezing point becomes. For freezing point depression and boiling point elevation, the concentration of the solution is usually expressed in **molality (*m*)**, the number of moles of solute per kilogram of solvent.

Note that molality is abbreviated with a lowercase *m*, while molarity is abbreviated with a capital M.

$$\textbf{Molality}\ (m) = \frac{\text{Moles solute}}{\text{Kilograms slovent}}$$

Notice that molality is defined with respect to kilograms of *solvent*, not kilograms of *solution*.

EXAMPLE 13.8 Calculating Molality

Calculate the molality of a solution containing 17.2 g of ethylene glycol ($C_2H_6O_2$) dissolved in 0.500 kg of water.

You are given the mass of ethylene glycol in grams and the mass of the solvent in kilograms. You are asked to find the molality of the resulting solution.

GIVEN: 17.2 g $C_2H_6O_2$
0.500 kg H_2O

FIND: molality (m)

To calculate molality, substitute the correct values into the equation and calculate the answer. You must first convert the amount of $C_2H_6O_2$ from grams to moles using the molar mass of $C_2H_6O_2$.

SOLUTION

$$\text{mol } C_2H_6O_2 = 17.2 \text{ g } C_2H_6O_2 \times \frac{1 \text{ mol } C_2H_6O_2}{62.08 \text{ g } C_2H_6O_2} = 0.2771 \text{ mol } C_2H_6O_2$$

$$\text{Molality } (m) = \frac{\text{Moles solute}}{\text{Kilograms solvent}} = \frac{0.2771 \text{ mol } C_2H_6O_2}{0.500 \text{ kg } H_2O} = 0.554\ m$$

▶SKILLBUILDER 13.8 | Calculating Molality

Calculate the molality (m) of a sucrose ($C_{12}H_{22}O_{11}$) solution containing 50.4 g sucrose and 0.332 kg of water.

▶FOR MORE PRACTICE Example 13.17; Problems 97, 98, 99, 100.

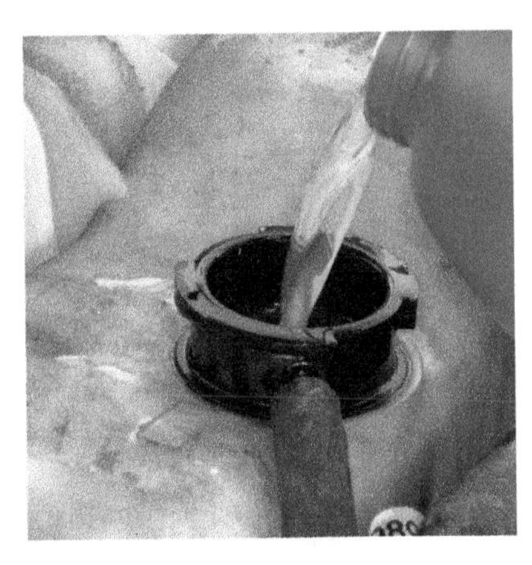

▲ Ethylene glycol is the chief component of antifreeze, which keeps engine coolant from freezing in winter or boiling over in summer.

CONCEPTUAL CHECKPOINT 13.5

A laboratory procedure calls for a 2.0 molal aqueous solution. A student accidentally makes a 2.0 molar solution. The solution made by the student is:

(a) too concentrated

(b) too dilute

(c) just right

(d) it depends on the molar mass of the solute

With an understanding of molality, we can now quantify freezing point depression. The amount that the freezing point of a solution is lowered by a particular amount of solute is given by the following equation.

The equations for freezing point depression and boiling point elevation given in this section apply only to nonelectrolyte solutions.

The freezing point depression of a solution

$$\Delta T_f = m \times K_f$$

where

- ΔT_f is the change in temperature of the freezing point in °C (from the freezing point of the pure solvent).
- m is the molality of the solution in $\dfrac{\text{mol solute}}{\text{kg solvent}}$.
- K_f is the freezing point depression constant for the solvent.

For water:

Different solvents have different values of K_f.

$$K_f = 1.86 \frac{°\text{C kg solvent}}{\text{mol solute}}$$

Calculating the freezing point of a solution involves substituting into the given equation, as the following example demonstrates.

EXAMPLE 13.9 Freezing Point Depression

Calculate the freezing point of a 1.7 m ethylene glycol solution.

You are given the molality of an aqueous solution and asked to find the freezing point depression.

You will need the freezing point depression equation provided in this section.

GIVEN: 1.7 m solution

FIND: ΔT_f

To solve this problem, simply substitute the values into the equation for freezing point depression and calculate ΔT_f.

SOLUTION

$$\Delta T_f = m \times K_f$$
$$= 1.7 \frac{\text{mol solute}}{\text{kg solvent}} \times 1.86 \frac{°\text{C kg solvent}}{\text{mol solute}}$$
$$= 3.2\ °\text{C}$$

The actual freezing point will be the freezing point of pure water (0.00 °C) − ΔT_f.

$$\text{Freezing point} = 0.00\ °\text{C} - 3.2\ °\text{C} = -3.2\ °\text{C}$$

▶SKILLBUILDER 13.9 | Freezing Point Depression

Calculate the freezing point of a 2.6 m sucrose solution.

▶FOR MORE PRACTICE Example 13.18; Problems 101, 102.

EVERYDAY CHEMISTRY

Antifreeze in Frogs

On the outside, wood frogs *(Rana sylvatica)* look like most other frogs. They are a few inches long and have characteristic greenish-brown skin. However, wood frogs survive cold winters in a remarkable way—they partially freeze. In the frozen state, the frog has no heartbeat, no blood circulation, no breathing, and no brain activity. Within 1 to 2 hours of thawing, however, these vital functions return, and the frog hops off to find food. How is this possible?

Most cold-blooded animals cannot survive freezing temperatures because the water within their cells freezes. As described in Section 12.8, when water freezes, it expands, irreversibly damaging cells. When the wood frog hibernates for the winter, however, it secretes large amounts of glucose into its blood and into the interior of its cells. When the temperature drops below freezing, extracellular bodily fluids, such as those in the abdominal cavity, freeze solid. Fluids within the frogs' cells, however, remain liquid because the high glucose concentration lowers their freezing point. In other words, the concentrated glucose solution within the cells acts as antifreeze, preventing the water within from freezing and allowing the frog to survive.

▲ The wood frog survives cold winters by partially freezing. The fluids in frog cells are protected by a high concentration of glucose that acts as antifreeze, lowering their freezing point so the intercellular fluids remain liquid to temperatures as low as −8 °C.

CAN YOU ANSWER THIS? *The wood frog can survive at body temperatures as low as −8.0 °C. Calculate the molality of a glucose solution ($C_6H_{12}O_6$) required to lower the freezing point of water to −8.0 °C.*

BOILING POINT ELEVATION

The boiling point of a solution containing a nonvolatile solute is higher than the boiling point of the pure solvent. In automobiles, antifreeze not only prevents the freezing of coolant within engine blocks in cold climates, but it also prevents the boiling of engine coolant in hot climates. The amount that the boiling point is raised for solutions is given by the following equation.

The boiling point elevation of a solution:

$$\Delta T_b = m \times K_b$$

where

- ΔT_b is change in temperature of the boiling point in °C (from the boiling point of the pure solvent).
- m is the molality of the solution in $\frac{\text{mol solute}}{\text{kg solvent}}$.
- K_b is the boiling point elevation constant for the solvent.

For water:

$$K_b = 0.512 \frac{\text{°C kg solvent}}{\text{mol solute}}$$

Different solvents have different values of K_b

The boiling point of solutions is calculated by substituting into the preceding equation as the following example demonstrates.

EXAMPLE 13.10 Boiling Point Elevation

Calculate the boiling point of a 1.7 *m* ethylene glycol solution.

You are given the molality of an aqueous solution and asked to find the boiling point.

GIVEN: 1.7 *m* solution
FIND: boiling point

To solve this problem, simply substitute the values into the equation for boiling point elevation and calculate ΔT_b.

SOLUTION

$$\Delta T_b = m \times K_b$$

$$= 1.7 \frac{\text{mol solute}}{\text{kg solvent}} \times 0.512 \frac{°\text{C kg solvent}}{\text{mol solute}}$$

$$= 0.87\,°\text{C}$$

The actual boiling point of the solution will be the boiling point of pure water (100.00 °C) plus ΔT_b.

$$\text{Boiling point} = 100.00\,°\text{C} + 0.87\,°\text{C}$$

$$= 100.87\,°\text{C}$$

▶**SKILLBUILDER 13.10 | Boiling Point Elevation**

Calculate the boiling point of a 3.5 *m* glucose solution.

▶**FOR MORE PRACTICE** Problems 103, 104, 105, 106.

CONCEPTUAL CHECKPOINT 13.6

Which solution has the highest boiling point?

(a) 0.50 M $C_{12}H_{22}O_{11}$ **(b)** 0.50 M $C_6H_{12}O_6$ **(c)** 0.50 M $C_2H_6O_2$

(d) All of these solutions will have the same boiling point.

13.10 Osmosis: Why Drinking Salt Water Causes Dehydration

Humans adrift at sea are surrounded by water, yet drinking that water would only accelerate their dehydration. Why? Salt water causes dehydration because of **osmosis**, the flow of solvent from a less concentrated solution to a more concentrated solution. Solutions containing a high concentration of solute draw solvent from solutions containing a lower concentration of solute. In other words, aqueous solutions with high concentrations of solute, such as seawater, are actually *thirsty solutions*—they draw water away from other, less concentrated solutions, including those in the human body (◀ Figure 13.9).

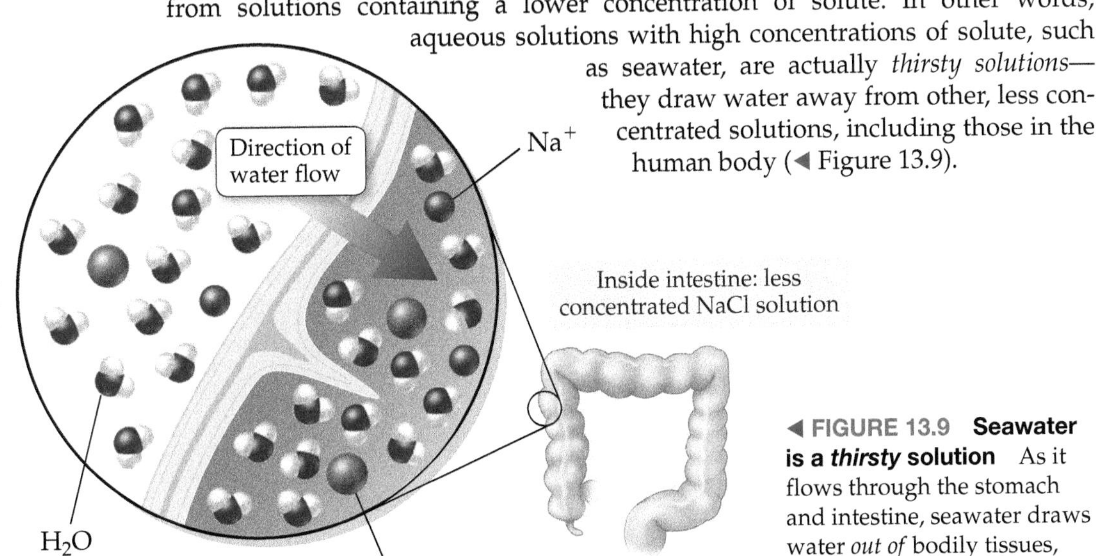

◀ **FIGURE 13.9 Seawater is a *thirsty* solution** As it flows through the stomach and intestine, seawater draws water *out of* bodily tissues, promoting dehydration.

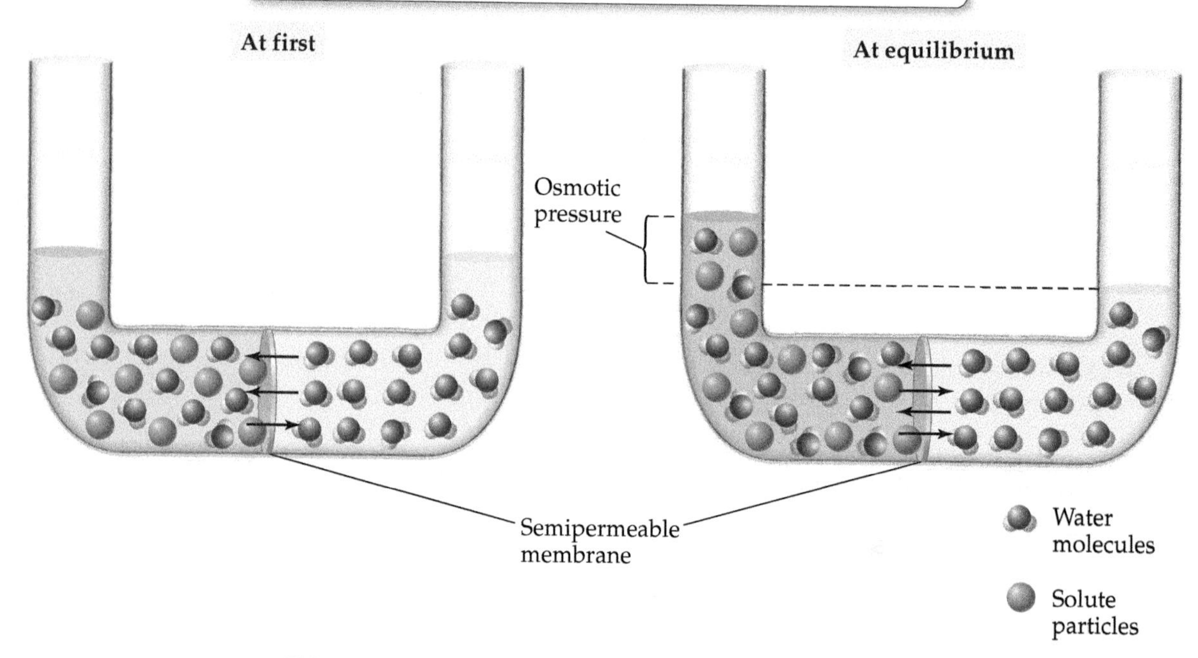

▲ **FIGURE 13.10 An osmosis cell** In an osmosis cell, water flows through a semipermeable membrane from a less concentrated solution into a more concentrated solution. As a result, fluid rises in one side of the tube until the weight of the excess fluid creates enough pressure to stop the flow. This pressure is the osmotic pressure of the solution.

▲ Figure 13.10 shows an osmosis cell. The left side of the cell contains a concentrated saltwater solution, and the right side of the cell contains pure water. A **semipermeable membrane**—a membrane that allows some substances to pass through but not others—separates the two halves of the cell. Through osmosis, water flows from the pure-water side of the cell through the semipermeable membrane into the saltwater side. Over time, the water level on the left side of the cell rises while the water level on the right side of the cell falls. This continues until the pressure created by the weight of the water on the left side is enough to stop the osmotic flow. The pressure required to stop the osmotic flow is the **osmotic pressure** of the solution. Osmotic pressure—like freezing point depression and boiling point elevation—is a colligative property; it depends only on the concentration of the solute particles, not on the type of solute. The more concentrated the solution, the greater its osmotic pressure.

The **membranes** of living cells act as semipermeable membranes. Consequently, if you put a living cell into seawater, it loses water through osmosis and becomes dehydrated. ▼ Figure 13.11 shows red blood cells in solutions of various

▶ **FIGURE 13.11 Red blood cells in solutions of different concentration** (a) When the solute concentration of the surrounding fluid is equal to that within the cell, there is no net osmotic flow, and the red blood cell exhibits its typical shape. (b) When a cell is placed in pure water, osmotic flow of water into the cell causes it to swell up. Eventually it may burst. (c) When a cell is placed in a concentrated solution, osmosis draws water out of the cell, distorting its normal shape.

Normal red blood cell

(a)

Red blood cell in pure water: water flows into cell

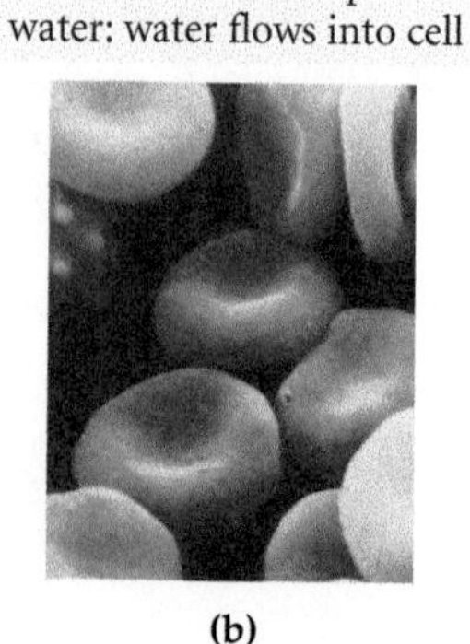

(b)

Red blood cell in concentrated solution: water flows out of cell

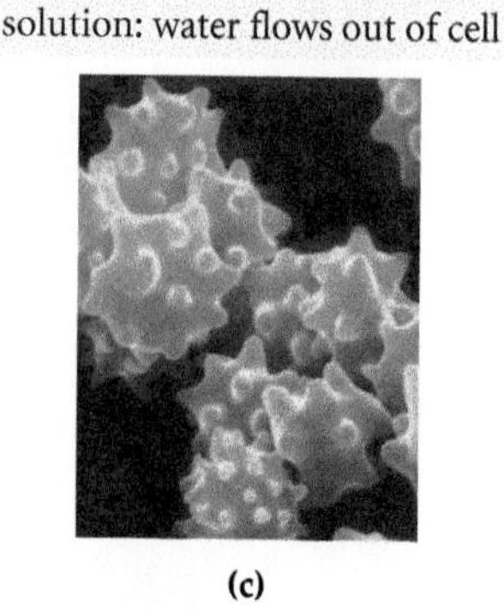

(c)

CHEMISTRY AND HEALTH

Solutions in Medicine

Doctors and others working in health fields often administer solutions to patients. The osmotic pressure of these solutions is controlled for the desired effect on the patient. Solutions having osmotic pressures less than that of bodily fluids are called *hypoosmotic*. These solutions tend to pump water into cells. When a human cell is placed in a hypoosmotic solution—such as pure water—water enters the cell, sometimes causing it to burst (Figure 13.11b). Solutions having osmotic pressures greater than that of bodily fluids are called *hyperosmotic*. These solutions tend to take water out of cells and tissues. When a human cell is placed in a hyperosmotic solution, it typically shrivels as it loses water to the surrounding solution (Figure 13.11c).

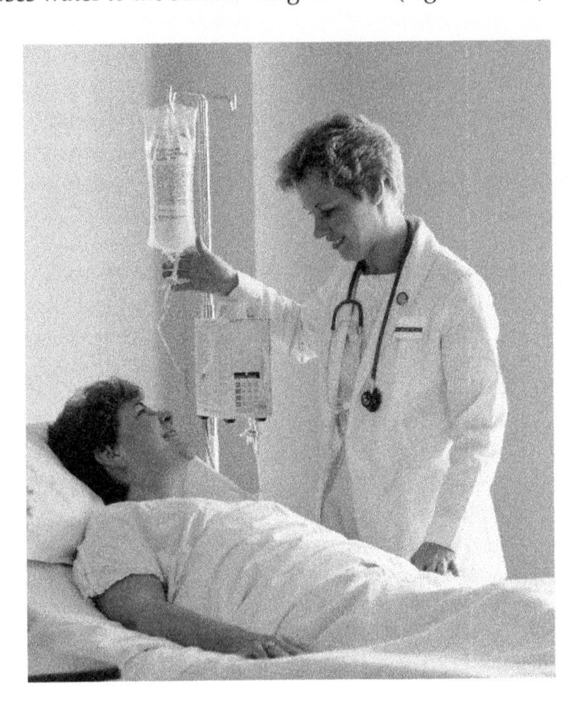

Intravenous solutions—those that are administered directly into a patient's veins—must have osmotic pressure equal to that of bodily fluids. These solutions are called *isoosmotic*. When a patient is given an IV in a hospital, the majority of the fluid is usually an isoosmotic saline solution—a solution containing 0.9 g NaCl per 100 mL of solution. In medicine and in other health-related fields, solution concentrations are often reported in units that indicate the mass of the solute in a given volume of solution. Also common is *percent mass to volume*—which is the mass of the solute in grams divided by volume of the solution in milliliters times 100%. In these units, the concentration of an isoosmotic saline solution is 0.9% mass/volume.

CAN YOU ANSWER THIS? *An isoosmotic sucrose ($C_{12}H_{22}O_{11}$) solution has a concentration of 0.30 M. Calculate its concentration in percent mass to volume.*

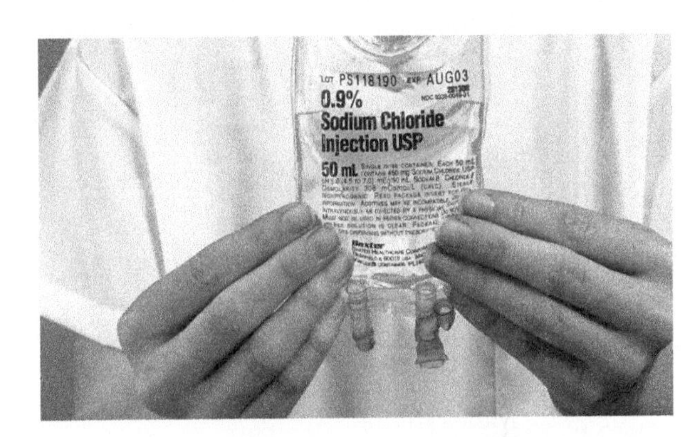

▲ Intravenous fluids consist mostly of isoosmotic saline solutions with an osmotic pressure equal to that of bodily fluids. **Question:** Why would it be dangerous to administer intravenous fluids that do not have an osmotic pressure comparable to that of bodily fluids?

concentrations. The cells in Figure 13.11a, immersed in a solution with the same solute concentration as the cell interior, have the normal red blood cell shape. The cells in Figure 13.11b, in pure water, are swollen. Because the solute concentration within the cells is higher than that of the surrounding fluid, osmosis has pulled water across the membrane *into* the cells. The cells in Figure 13.11c, in a solution more concentrated than the cell interior, are starting to shrivel as osmosis draws water *out of* the cells. Similarly, if you drink seawater, the seawater actually draws water out of your body as it passes through your stomach and intestines. All of that extra water in your intestine promotes dehydration of bodily tissues and diarrhea. Consequently, seawater should never be consumed.

CHAPTER IN REVIEW

CHEMICAL PRINCIPLES

RELEVANCE

Solutions: A solution is a homogeneous mixture with two or more components. The solvent is the majority component, and the solute is the minority component. Water is the solvent in aqueous solutions.

Solutions: Solutions are all around us—most of the fluids that we encounter every day are solutions. Common solutions include seawater (solid and liquid), soda pop (gas and liquid), alcoholic spirits such as vodka (liquid and liquid), air (gas and gas), and blood (solid, gas, and liquid).

Solid-and-Liquid Solutions: The solubility—the amount of solute that dissolves in a certain amount of solvent—of solids in liquids increases with increasing temperature. Recrystallization involves dissolving a solid into hot solvent to saturation and then allowing it to cool. As the solution cools, it becomes supersaturated and the solid crystallizes.

Solid-and-Liquid Solutions: Solutions of solids dissolved in liquids, such as seawater, coffee, and sugar water, are important both in chemistry and in everyday life. Recrystallization is used extensively in the laboratory to purify solids.

Gas-and-Liquid Solutions: The solubility of gases in liquids decreases with increasing temperature but increases with increasing pressure.

Gas-and-Liquid Solutions: The temperature and pressure dependence of gas solubility is the reason that soda pop fizzes when opened and the reason that warm soda goes flat.

Solution Concentration: Solution concentration is used to specify how much of the solute is present in a given amount of solution. Three common ways to express solution concentration are mass percent, molarity, and molality.

$$\text{Mass percent} = \frac{\text{Mass solute}}{\text{Mass solute} + \text{Mass solvent}} \times 100\%$$

$$\text{Molarity (M)} = \frac{\text{Moles solute}}{\text{Liters solution}}$$

$$\text{Molarity } (m) = \frac{\text{Moles solute}}{\text{Kilograms solvent}}$$

Solution Concentration: Solution concentration is useful in converting between amounts of solute and solution. Mass percent and molarity are the most common concentration units. Molality is used to quantify colligative properties such as freezing point depression and boiling point elevation.

Solution Dilution: Solution dilution problems are most conveniently solved using the following equation:

$$M_1V_1 = M_2V_2$$

Solution Dilution: Since many solutions are stored in concentrated form, it is often necessary to dilute them to a desired concentration.

Freezing Point Depression and Boiling Point Elevation: A nonvolatile solute will extend the liquid temperature range of a solution relative to the pure solvent. The freezing point of a solution is lower than the freezing point of the pure solvent, and the boiling point of a solution is higher than the boiling point of the pure solvent. These relationships are quantified by the following equations.

Freezing point depression:

$$\Delta T_f = m \times K_f$$

Boiling point elevation:

$$\Delta T_b = m \times K_b$$

Freezing Point Depression and Boiling Point Elevation: Salt is often added to ice in ice-cream makers and is used to melt ice on roads in frigid weather. The salt lowers the freezing point of water, allowing the cream within the ice-cream maker to freeze and the ice on icy roads to melt. Antifreeze is used in the cooling systems of cars both to lower the freezing point of the coolant in winter and to raise its boiling point in summer.

Osmosis: Osmosis is the flow of water from a low-concentration solution to a high-concentration solution through a semipermeable membrane.

Osmosis: Osmosis is the reason drinking seawater causes dehydration. As seawater goes through the stomach and intestines, it draws water away from the body through osmosis, resulting in diarrhea and dehydration. To avoid damage to body tissues, transfused fluids must always be isoosmotic with body fluids. Most transfused fluids consist in whole or part of 0.9% mass/volume saline solution.

CHEMICAL SKILLS

EXAMPLES

Calculating Mass Percent (Section 13.5)

You are given the mass of the solute and the solvent and asked to find the concentration of the solution in mass percent.

To calculate mass percent concentration, divide the mass of the solute by the mass of the solution (solute and solvent) and multiply by 100%.

EXAMPLE 13.11 Calculating Mass Percent

Find the mass percent concentration of a solution containing 19 g of solute and 158 g of solvent.

GIVEN: 19 g solute
158 g solvent

FIND: mass percent

SOLUTION

$$\text{Mass percent} = \frac{\text{mass solute}}{\text{mass solute} + \text{mass solvent}} \times 100\%$$

$$\text{Mass percent} = \frac{19\,\text{g}}{19\,\text{g} + 158\,\text{g}} \times 100\%$$

$$\text{Mass percent} = \frac{19\,\text{g}}{177\,\text{g}} \times 100\%$$

$$= 11\%$$

Using Mass Percent in Calculations (Section 13.5)

SORT
You are given the volume of a potassium chloride solution and its mass percent concentration. You are asked to find the mass of potassium chloride.

STRATEGIZE
Draw a solution map. Begin with the given volume of the solution in L and convert to mL. Then use the density to find the mass of the solution. Finally, use the mass percent to get to the mass of potassium chloride.

EXAMPLE 13.12 Using Mass Percent in Calculations

How much KCl in grams is in 0.337 L of a 5.80 % mass percent KCl solution? (Assume that the density of the solution is 1.05 g/mL.)

GIVEN: 5.80% KCl by mass
0.337 L solution

$$d = \frac{1.05\,\text{g}}{\text{mL}}$$

FIND: g KCl

SOLUTION MAP

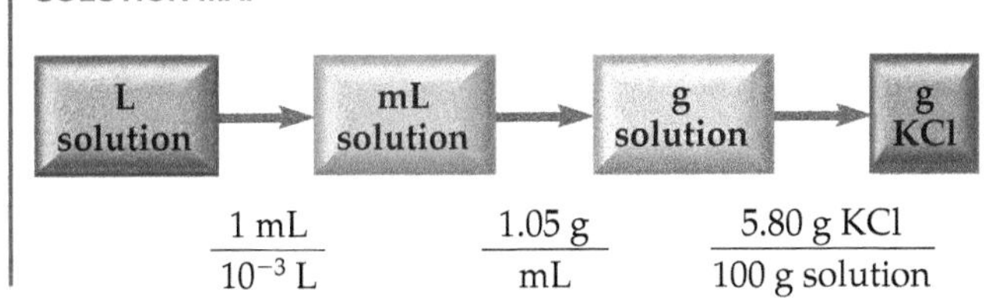

RELATIONSHIPS USED

$\frac{5.80\,\text{g KCI}}{100\,\text{g solution}}$ (given mass percent, written as a fraction)

$\frac{1.05\,\text{g}}{\text{mL}}$ (given density)

$1\,\text{mL} = 10^{-3}\,\text{L}$ (Table 2.2)

SOLVE

Follow your solution map to calculate the answer.

SOLUTION

$$0.337\ \cancel{\text{L solution}} \times \frac{1\ \cancel{\text{mL}}}{10^{-3}\ \cancel{\text{L}}} \times \frac{1.05\ \cancel{\text{g}}}{\cancel{\text{mL}}} \times \frac{5.80\ \text{g KCl}}{100\ \cancel{\text{g solution}}} = 20.5\,\text{g KCl}$$

CHECK

Check your answer. Are the units correct? Does the answer make physical sense?

The units (g KCl) are correct. The magnitude of the answer makes sense because 0.337 L is a bit more than 300 g of solution. Each 100 g of solution contains about 6 g KCl, Therefore the answer should be a bit more than 18 g.

Calculating Molarity (Section 13.6)

EXAMPLE 13.13 Calculating Molarity

Calculate the molarity of a KCl solution containing 0.22 mol of KCl in 0.455 L of solution.

You are given the number of moles of potassium chloride and the volume of solution. You are asked to find the molarity.

GIVEN: 0.22 mol KCI
0.455 L solution

FIND: molarity (M)

To calculate molarity, divide the number of moles of solute by the volume of the solution in liters.

SOLUTION

$$\text{Molarity (M)} = \frac{0.22\ \text{mol KCI}}{0.455\ \text{L solution}} = 0.48\ \text{M}$$

Using Molarity in Calculations (Section 13.6)

EXAMPLE 13.14 Using Molarity in Calculations

How much KCl in grams is contained in 0.488 L of 1.25 M KCl solution?

SORT

You are given the volume and molarity of a potassium chloride solution and asked to find the mass of potassium chloride contained in the solution.

GIVEN: 1.25 M KCI
0.488 L solution

FIND: g KCl

STRATEGIZE

Draw a solution map beginning with liters of solution and converting to moles of solute using the molarity as a conversion factor. Then convert to grams using the molar mass.

SOLUTION MAP

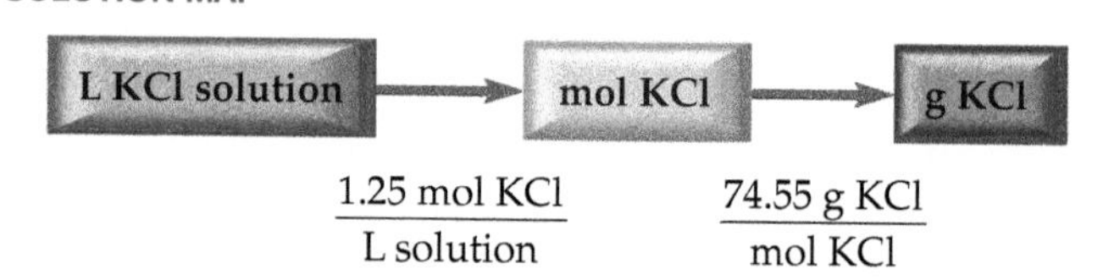

RELATIONSHIPS USED

$$\frac{1.25\text{ mol KCl}}{\text{L solution}} \text{ (given molarity, written as a fraction)}$$

$$1\text{ mol} = 74.55\text{ g (molar mass KCl)}$$

SOLVE

Follow your solution map to compute the answer.

SOLUTION

$$0.488\ \cancel{\text{L solution}} \times \frac{1.25\ \cancel{\text{mol KCl}}}{\cancel{\text{L solution}}} \times \frac{74.55\text{ g KCl}}{\cancel{\text{mol KCl}}} = 45.5\text{ g KCl}$$

CHECK

Check your answer. Are the units correct? Does the answer make physical sense?

The units (g KCl) are correct. The magnitude of the answer makes sense because if each liter of solution contains 1.25 mol, then the given amount of solution (which is about 0.5 L) should contain a bit more than 0.5 mol, which would have a mass that is bit more than about 37 g.

Solution Dilution (Section 13.7)

EXAMPLE 13.15 Solution Dilution

How much of an 8.0 M HCl solution should be used to make 0.400 L of a 2.7 M HCl solution?

You are given the initial molarity and final molarity of a solution as well as the final volume. You are asked to find the initial volume.

GIVEN: $M_1 = 8.0\text{ M}$

$M_2 = 2.7\text{ M}$

$V_2 = 0.400\text{ L}$

FIND: V_1

Most solution dilution problems will use equation $M_1V_1 = M_2V_2$.

Solve the equation for the quantity you are trying to find (in this case, V_1) and then substitute in the correct values to calculate it.

SOLUTION

$$M_1V_1 = M_2V_2$$

$$V_1 = \frac{M_2V_2}{M_1}$$

$$= \frac{2.7\,\frac{\cancel{\text{mol}}}{\cancel{\text{L}}} \times 0.400\text{ L}}{8.0\,\frac{\cancel{\text{mol}}}{\cancel{\text{L}}}}$$

$$= 0.14\text{ L}$$

Solution Stoichiometry (Section 13.8)

EXAMPLE 13.16 Solution Stoichiometry

Consider the reaction:

$$HCl(aq) + NaOH(aq) \longrightarrow NaCl(aq) + H_2O(l)$$

How much 0.113 M NaOH solution will completely neutralize 1.25 L of 0.228 M HCl solution?

SORT

You are given the volume and concentration of a hydrochloric acid solution as well as the concentration of a sodium hydroxide solution with which it reacts. You are asked to find the volume of the sodium hydroxide solution that will completely react with the hydrochloric acid.

GIVEN: 1.25 L HCl solution

0.228 M HCl

0.113 M NaOH

FIND: L NaOH solution

STRATEGIZE

Draw a solution map. Use the volume and molarity of HCl to get to mol HCl. Then use the stoichiometric coefficients to convert to mole NaOH. Finally, convert back to volume of NaOH using the molarity of NaOH.

SOLUTION MAP

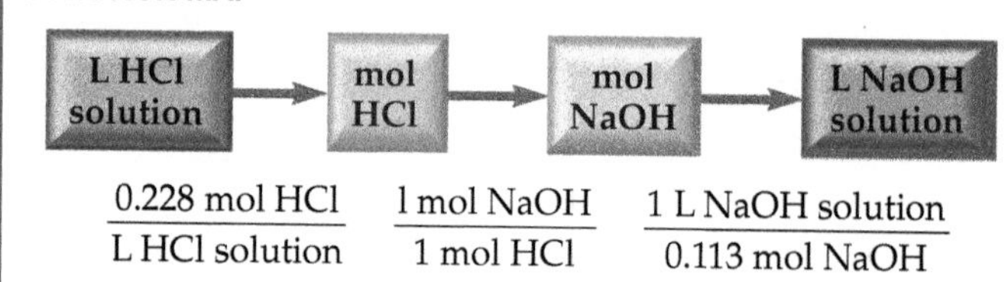

$$\frac{0.228 \text{ mol HCl}}{\text{L HCl solution}} \quad \frac{1 \text{ mol NaOH}}{1 \text{ mol HCl}} \quad \frac{1 \text{ L NaOH solution}}{0.113 \text{ mol NaOH}}$$

RELATIONSHIPS USED

$$\text{M (HCl)} = \frac{0.228 \text{ mol HCl}}{\text{L HCl solution}}$$ (given concentration of HCl solution, written as a fraction)

$$\text{M (NaOH)} = \frac{0.113 \text{ mol NaOH}}{\text{L NaOH solution}}$$ (given concentration of NaOH solution, written as a fraction)

1 mol HCl:1 mol NaOH (stoichiometric relationship between HCl and NaOH, from balanced equation)

SOLVE

Follow the solution map to calculate the answer.

SOLUTION

$$1.25 \text{ L HCl solution} \times \frac{0.228 \text{ mol HCl}}{\text{L HCl solution}} \times \frac{1 \text{ mol NaOH}}{1 \text{ mol HCl}} \times \frac{\text{L NaOH solution}}{0.113 \text{ mol NaOH}} = 2.52 \text{ L NaOH solution}$$

CHECK

Check your answer. Are the units correct? Does the answer make physical sense?

The units (L NaOH solution) are correct. The magnitude of the answer makes sense because the sodium hydroxide solution is about half as concentrated as the hydrochloric acid. Since the reaction stoichiometry is 1:1, the volume of the sodium hydroxide solution should therefore be about twice the volume of the hydrochloric acid.

Calculating Molality (Section 13.9)

EXAMPLE 13.17 Calculating Molality

Calculate the molality of a solution containing 0.183 mol of sucrose dissolved in 1.10 kg of water.

You are given the number of moles of sucrose and the mass of water into which it is dissolved. You are asked to find the molality of the resulting solution.

GIVEN: 0.183 mol of sucrose
1.10 kg H_2O

FIND: molality (m)

Substitute the correct values into the definition of molality and calculate the answer. If any of the quantities are not in the correct units, convert them into the correct units before substituting into the equation.

SOLUTION

$$\text{Molality } (m) = \frac{\text{Moles solute}}{\text{Kilograms solvent}}$$

$$\text{Molality } (m) = \frac{0.183 \text{ mol sucrose}}{1.10 \text{ kg } H_2O} = 0.166\ m$$

Freezing Point Depression and Boiling Point Elevation (Section 13.9)

EXAMPLE 13.18 Freezing Point Depression and Boiling Point Elevation

Calculate the freezing point of a 2.5 m aqueous sucrose solution.

You are given the molality of the solution and asked to find its freezing point.

GIVEN: 2.5 m solution

FIND: ΔT_f

To find ΔT_f or ΔT_b, simply substitute the values into the equation and calculate the answer.

SOLUTION

$$\Delta T_f = m \times K_f$$

$$= 2.5 \frac{\cancel{\text{mol solute}}}{\cancel{\text{kg solvent}}} \times 1.86 \frac{°\text{C} \cancel{\text{kg solvent}}}{\cancel{\text{mol solute}}}$$

$$= 4.7\ °\text{C}$$

The freezing point will be the freezing point of pure water (0.00 °C) − ΔT_f.

$$\text{Freezing point} = 0.00\ °\text{C} - 4.7\ °\text{C}$$

$$= -4.7\ °\text{C}$$

KEY TERMS

boiling point elevation [13.9]
colligative properties [13.9]
concentrated solution [13.5]
dilute solution [13.5]
electrolyte solution [13.3]
freezing point depression [13.9]
Henry's law [13.4]
mass percent [13.5]
molality (m) [13.9]
molarity (M) [13.6]
nonelectrolyte solution [13.3]
osmosis [13.10]
osmotic pressure [13.10]
recrystallization [13.3]
saturated solution [13.3]
semipermeable membrane [13.10]
solubility [13.3]
solute [13.2]
solution [13.2]
solvent [13.2]
stock solution [13.7]
supersaturated solution [13.3]
unsaturated solution [13.3]

EXERCISES

QUESTIONS

1. What is a solution? List some examples.
2. What is an aqueous solution?
3. In a solution, what is the solvent? What is the solute? List some examples.
4. Explain what "like dissolves like" means.
5. What is solubility?
6. Describe what happens when additional solute is added to:
   (a) a saturated solution
   (b) an unsaturated solution
   (c) a supersaturated solution
7. Explain the difference between a strong electrolyte solution and a nonelectrolyte solution. What kinds of solutes form strong electrolyte solutions?
8. How does gas solubility depend on temperature?
9. Explain recrystallization.
10. How is rock candy made?
11. When you heat water on a stove, bubbles form on the bottom of the pot *before* the water boils. What are these bubbles? Why do they form?
12. Explain why warm soda pop goes flat faster than cold soda pop.
13. How does gas solubility depend on pressure? How does this relationship explain why a can of soda pop fizzes when opened.
14. What is the difference between a dilute solution and a concentrated solution?
15. Define the concentration units mass percent and molarity.
16. What is a stock solution?
17. How does the presence of a nonvolatile solute affect the boiling point and melting point of a solution relative to the boiling point and melting point of the pure solvent?
18. What are colligative properties?
19. Define molality.
20. What is osmosis?

21. Two shipwreck survivors were rescued from a life raft. One had drunk seawater while the other had not. The one who had drunk the seawater was more severely dehydrated than the one who did not. Explain.

22. Why are intravenous fluids always isoosmotic saline solutions? What would happen if pure water were administered intravenously?

PROBLEMS

SOLUTIONS

23. Determine whether or not each mixture is a solution.
   (a) sand and water mixture
   (b) oil and water mixture
   (c) salt and water mixture
   (d) sterling silver cup

24. Determine whether or not each mixture is a solution.
   (a) air
   (b) carbon dioxide and water mixture
   (c) a blueberry muffin
   (d) a brass buckle

25. Identify the solute and solvent in each solution.
   (a) salt water
   (b) sugar water
   (c) soda water

26. Identify the solute and solvent in each solution.
   (a) 80-proof vodka (40% ethyl alcohol)
   (b) oxygenated water
   (c) antifreeze (ethylene glycol and water)

27. Pick an appropriate solvent from Table 13.2 to dissolve:
   (a) motor oil (nonpolar)
   (b) sugar (polar)
   (c) lard (nonpolar)
   (d) potassium chloride (ionic)

28. Pick an appropriate solvent from Table 13.2 to dissolve:
   (a) glucose (polar)
   (b) salt (ionic)
   (c) vegetable oil (nonpolar)
   (d) sodium nitrate (ionic)

SOLIDS DISSOLVED IN WATER

29. What are the dissolved particles in a solution containing an ionic solute? What is the name for this kind of solution?

30. What are the dissolved particles in a solution containing a molecular solute? What is the name for this kind of solution?

31. A solution contains 35 g of NaCl per 100 g of water at 25 °C. Is the solution unsaturated, saturated, or supersaturated? (See Figure 13.4.)

32. A solution contains 28 g of KNO_3 per 100 g of water at 25 °C. Is the solution unsaturated, saturated, or supersaturated? (See Figure 13.4.)

33. A KNO_3 solution containing 45 g of KNO_3 per 100 g of water is cooled from 40 °C to 0 °C. What happens during cooling? (See Figure 13.4.)

34. A KCl solution containing 42 g of KCl per 100 g of water is cooled from 60 °C to 0 °C. What happens during cooling? (See Figure 13.4.)

35. Refer to Figure 13.4 to determine whether each of the given amounts of solid will completely dissolve in the given amount of water at the indicated temperature.
   (a) 30.0 g $KClO_3$ in 85.0 g of water at 35 °C
   (b) 65.0 g $NaNO_3$ in 125 g of water at 15 °C
   (c) 32.0 g KCl in 70.0 g of water at 82 °C

36. Refer to Figure 13.4 to determine whether each of the given amounts of solid will completely dissolve in the given amount of water at the indicated temperature.
   (a) 45.0 g $CaCl_2$ in 105 g of water at 5 °C
   (b) 15.0 g $KClO_3$ in 115 g of water at 25 °C
   (c) 50.0 g $Pb(NO_3)_2$ in 95.0 g of water at 10 °C

GASES DISSOLVED IN WATER

37. Some laboratory procedures involving oxygen-sensitive reactants or products call for using preboiled (and then cooled) water. Explain why this is so.

38. A person preparing a fish tank uses preboiled (and then cooled) water to fill it. When the fish is put into the tank, it dies. Explain.

39. Scuba divers breathing air at increased pressure can suffer from nitrogen narcosis—a condition resembling drunkenness—when the partial pressure of nitrogen exceeds about 4 atm. What property of gas/water solutions causes this to happen? How could the diver reverse this effect?

40. Scuba divers breathing air at increased pressure can suffer from oxygen toxicity—too much oxygen in the bloodstream—when the partial pressure of oxygen exceeds about 1.4 atm. What happens to the amount of oxygen in a diver's bloodstream when he or she breathes oxygen at elevated pressures? How can this be reversed?

MASS PERCENT

41. Calculate the concentration of each solution in mass percent.
    (a) 41.2 g $C_{12}H_{22}O_{11}$ in 498 g H_2O
    (b) 178 mg $C_6H_{12}O_6$ in 4.91 g H_2O
    (c) 7.55 g NaCl in 155 g H_2O

42. Calculate the concentration of each solution in mass percent.
    (a) 132 g KCl in 598 g H_2O
    (b) 22.3 mg KNO_3 in 2.84 g H_2O
    (c) 8.72 g C_2H_6O in 76.1 g H_2O

43. A soft drink contains 42 g of sugar in 311 g of H_2O. What is the concentration of sugar in the soft drink in mass percent?

44. A soft drink contains 32 mg of sodium in 309 g of H_2O. What is the concentration of sodium in the soft drink in mass percent?

45. Complete the table:

Mass Solute	Mass Solvent	Mass Solution	Mass Percent
15.5 g	238.1 g	______	______
22.8 g	______	______	12.0%
______	183.3 g	212.1 g	______
______	315.2 g	______	15.3%

46. Complete the table:

Mass Solute	Mass Solvent	Mass Solution	Mass Percent
2.55 g	25.0 g	______	______
______	45.8 g	______	3.8%
1.38 g	______	27.2 g	______
23.7 g	______	______	5.8%

47. Ocean water contains 3.5% NaCl by mass. How much salt can be obtained from 254 g of seawater?

48. A saline solution contains 1.1% NaCl by mass. How much NaCl is present in 96.3 g of this solution?

49. Determine the amount of sucrose in each solution.
    (a) 48 g of a solution containing 3.7% sucrose by mass
    (b) 103 mg of a solution containing 10.2% sucrose by mass
    (c) 3.2 kg of a solution containing 14.3% sucrose by mass

50. Determine the amount of potassium chloride in each solution.
    (a) 19.7 g of a solution containing 1.08% KCl by mass
    (b) 23.2 kg of a solution containing 18.7% KCl by mass
    (c) 38 mg of a solution containing 12% KCl by mass

51. Determine the mass (in g) of each NaCl solution that contains 1.5 g of NaCl.
    (a) 0.058% NaCl by mass
    (b) 1.46% NaCl by mass
    (c) 8.44% NaCl by mass

52. Determine the mass (in g) of each sucrose solution that contains 12 g of sucrose.
    (a) 4.1% sucrose by mass
    (b) 3.2% sucrose by mass
    (c) 12.5% sucrose by mass

53. $AgNO_3$ solutions are often used to plate silver onto other metals. What is the maximum amount of silver in grams that can be plated out of 4.8 L of an $AgNO_3$ solution containing 3.4% Ag by mass? (Assume that the density of the solution is 1.01 g/mL.)

54. A dioxin-contaminated water source contains 0.085% dioxin by mass. How much dioxin is present in 2.5 L of this water? (Assume that the density of the solution is 1.01 g/mL.)

55. Ocean water contains 3.5% NaCl by mass. What mass of ocean water in grams contains 45.8 g of NaCl?

56. A hard water sample contains 0.0085% Ca by mass (in the form of Ca^{2+} ions). What mass of water in grams contains 1.2 g of Ca? (1.2 g of Ca is the recommended daily allowance of calcium for 19- to 24-year-olds.)

57. Lead is a toxic metal that affects the central nervous system. A Pb-contaminated water sample contains 0.0011% Pb by mass. What volume of the water in milliliters contains 115 mg of Pb? (Assume that the density of the solution is 1.0 g/mL.)

58. Benzene is a carcinogenic (cancer-causing) compound. A benzene-contaminated water sample contains 0.000037% benzene by mass. What volume of the water in liters contains 175 mg of benzene? (Assume that the density of the solution is 1.0 g/mL.)

MOLARITY

59. Calculate the molarity of each solution.
(a) 0.127 mol of sucrose in 655 mL of solution
(b) 0.205 mol of KNO_3 in 0.875 L of solution
(c) 1.1 mol of KCl in 2.7 L of solution

60. Calculate the molarity of each solution.
(a) 1.54 mol of LiCl in 22.2 L of solution
(b) 0.101 mol of $LiNO_3$ in 6.4 L of solution
(c) 0.0323 mol of glucose in 76.2 mL of solution

61. Calculate the molarity of each solution.
(a) 22.6 g of $C_{12}H_{22}O_{11}$ in 0.442 L of solution
(b) 42.6 g of NaCl in 1.58 L of solution
(c) 315 mg of $C_6H_{12}O_6$ in 58.2 mL of solution

62. Calculate the molarity of each solution.
(a) 33.2 g of KCl in 0.895 L of solution
(b) 61.3 g of C_2H_6O in 3.4 L of solution
(c) 38.2 mg of KI in 112 mL of solution

63. A 205-mL sample of ocean water contains 6.8 g of NaCl. What is the molarity of the solution with respect to NaCl?

64. A 355-mL can of soda pop contains 41 g of sucrose ($C_{12}H_{22}O_{11}$). What is the molarity of the solution with respect to sucrose?

65. How many moles of NaCl are contained in each solution?
(a) 1.5 L of a 1.2 M NaCl solution
(b) 0.448 L of a 0.85 M NaCl solution
(c) 144 mL of a 1.65 M NaCl solution

66. How many moles of sucrose are contained in each solution?
(a) 3.4 L of a 0.100 M sucrose solution
(b) 0.952 L of a 1.88 M sucrose solution
(c) 21.5 mL of a 0.528 M sucrose solution

67. What volume of each solution contains 0.15 mol of KCl?
(a) 0.255 M KCl
(b) 1.8 M KCl
(c) 0.995 M KCl

68. What volume of each solution contains 0.325 mol of NaI?
(a) 0.152 M NaI
(b) 0.982 M NaI
(c) 1.76 M NaI

69. Complete the table:

Solute	Solute Mass	Mol Solute	Volume Solution	Molarity
KNO_3	22.5 g	______	125.0 mL	______
$NaHCO_3$	______	______	250.0 mL	0.100 M
$C_{12}H_{22}O_{11}$	55.38 g	______	______	0.150 M

70. Complete the table:

Solute	Solute Mass	Mol Solute	Volume Solution	Molarity
$MgSO_4$	0.588 g	______	25.0 mL	______
NaOH	______	______	100.0 mL	1.75 M
CH_3OH	12.5 g	______	______	0.500 M

71. Calculate the mass of NaCl in a 35-mL sample of a 1.3 M NaCl solution.

72. Calculate the mass of glucose ($C_6H_{12}O_6$) in a 105-mL sample of a 1.02 M glucose solution.

73. A chemist wants to make 2.5 L of a 0.100 M KCl solution. How much KCl in grams should the chemist use?

74. A laboratory procedure calls for making 500.0 mL of a 1.4 M KNO_3 solution. How much KNO_3 in grams is needed?

75. How many liters of a 0.500 M sucrose ($C_{12}H_{22}O_{11}$) solution contain 1.5 kg of sucrose?

76. What volume of a 0.35 M $Mg(NO_3)_2$ solution contains 87 g of $Mg(NO_3)_2$?

77. Determine the concentration of Cl^- in each aqueous solution. (Assume complete dissociation of each compound.)
   (a) 0.15 M NaCl
   (b) 0.15 M $CuCl_2$
   (c) 0.15 M $AlCl_3$

78. Determine the concentration of NO_3^- in each aqueous solution. (Assume complete dissociation of each compound.)
   (a) 0.10 M KNO_3
   (b) 0.10 M $Ca(NO_3)_2$
   (c) 0.10 M $Cr(NO_3)_3$

79. Determine the concentration of the cation and anion in each aqueous solution. (Assume complete dissociation of each compound.)
   (a) 0.12 M Na_2SO_4
   (b) 0.25 M K_2CO_3
   (c) 0.11 M RbBr

80. Determine the concentration of the cation and anion in each aqueous solution. (Assume complete dissociation of each compound.)
   (a) 0.20 M $SrSO_4$
   (b) 0.15 M $Cr_2(SO_4)_3$
   (c) 0.12 M SrI_2

SOLUTION DILUTION

81. A 122-mL sample of a 1.2 M sucrose solution is diluted to 500.0 mL. What is the molarity of the diluted solution?

82. A 3.5-L sample of a 5.8 M NaCl solution is diluted to 55 L. What is the molarity of the diluted solution?

83. Describe how you would make 2.5 L of a 0.100 M KCl solution from a 5.5 M stock KCl solution.

84. Describe how you would make 500.0 mL of a 0.200 M NaOH solution from a 15.0 M stock NaOH solution.

85. To what volume should you dilute 25 mL of a 12 M stock HCl solution to obtain a 0.500 M HCl solution?

86. To what volume should you dilute 75 mL of a 10.0 M H_2SO_4 solution to obtain a 1.75 M H_2SO_4 solution?

87. How much of a 12.0 M HNO_3 solution should you use to make 850.0 mL of a 0.250 M HNO_3 solution?

88. How much of a 5.0 M sucrose solution should you use to make 85.0 mL of a 0.040 M solution?

SOLUTION STOICHIOMETRY

89. Determine the volume of 0.150 M NaOH solution required to neutralize each sample of hydrochloric acid. The neutralization reaction is:

$$NaOH(aq) + HCl(aq) \longrightarrow H_2O(l) + NaCl(aq)$$

(a) 25 mL of a 0.150 M HCl solution

(b) 55 mL of a 0.055 M HCl solution

(c) 175 mL of a 0.885 M HCl solution

90. Determine the volume of 0.225 M KOH solution required to neutralize each sample of sulfuric acid. The neutralization reaction is:

$$H_2SO_4(aq) + 2\,KOH(aq) \longrightarrow K_2SO_4(aq) + 2\,H_2O(l)$$

(a) 45 mL of 0.225 M H_2SO_4

(b) 185 mL of 0.125 M H_2SO_4

(c) 75 mL of 0.100 M H_2SO_4

91. Consider the reaction:

$$2\,K_3PO_4(aq) + 3\,NiCl_2(aq) \longrightarrow Ni_3(PO_4)_2(s) + 6\,KCl(aq)$$

What volume of 0.225 M K_3PO_4 solution is necessary to completely react with 134 mL of 0.0112 M $NiCl_2$?

92. Consider the reaction:

$$K_2S(aq) + Co(NO_3)_2(aq) \longrightarrow 2\,KNO_3(aq) + CoS(s)$$

What volume of 0.225 M K_2S solution is required to completely react with 175 mL of 0.115 M $Co(NO_3)_2$?

93. A 10.0-mL sample of an unknown H_3PO_4 solution requires 112 mL of 0.100 M KOH to completely react with the H_3PO_4. What was the concentration of the unknown H_3PO_4 solution?

$$H_3PO_4(aq) + 3\,KOH(aq) \longrightarrow 3\,H_2O(l) + K_3PO_4(aq)$$

94. A 25.0-mL sample of an unknown $HClO_4$ solution requires 45.3 mL of 0.101 M NaOH for complete neutralization. What was the concentration of the unknown $HClO_4$ solution? The neutralization reaction is:

$$HClO_4(aq) + NaOH(aq) \longrightarrow H_2O(l) + NaClO_4(aq)$$

95. What is the minimum amount of 6.0 M H_2SO_4 necessary to produce 15.0 g of $H_2(g)$ according to the reaction:

$$2\,Al(s) + 3\,H_2SO_4(aq) \longrightarrow Al_2(SO_4)_3(aq) + 3\,H_2(g)$$

96. What is the molarity of $ZnCl_2(aq)$ that forms when 15.0 g of zinc completely reacts with $CuCl_2(aq)$ according to the following reaction? (Assume a final volume of 175 mL.)

$$Zn(s) + CuCl_2(aq) \longrightarrow ZnCl_2 + Cu(s)$$

MOLALITY, FREEZING POINT DEPRESSION, AND BOILING POINT ELEVATION

97. Calculate the molality of each solution.

(a) 0.25 mol solute; 0.250 kg solvent

(b) 0.882 mol solute; 0.225 kg solvent

(c) 0.012 mol solute; 23.1 g solvent

98. Calculate the molality of each solution.

(a) 0.455 mol solute; 1.97 kg solvent

(b) 0.559 mol solute; 1.44 kg solvent

(c) 0.119 mol solute; 488 g solvent

99. Calculate the molality of a solution containing 12.5 g of ethylene glycol ($C_2H_6O_2$) dissolved in 135 g of water.

100. Calculate the molality of a solution containing 257 g glucose ($C_6H_{12}O_6$) dissolved in 1.62 L of water. (Assume a density of 1.00 g/mL for water.)

101. Calculate the freezing point of a water solution at each concentration.

(a) 0.85 m

(b) 1.45 m

(c) 4.8 m

(d) 2.35 m

102. Calculate the freezing point of a water solution at each concentration.

(a) 0.100 m

(b) 0.469 m

(c) 1.44 m

(d) 5.89 m

103. Calculate the boiling point of a water solution at each concentration.

(a) 0.118 *m*

(b) 1.94 *m*

(c) 3.88 *m*

(d) 2.16 *m*

104. Calculate the boiling point of a water solution at each concentration.

(a) 0.225 *m*

(b) 2.58 *m*

(c) 4.33 *m*

(d) 6.77 *m*

105. A glucose solution contains 55.8 g of glucose ($C_6H_{12}O_6$) in 455 g of water. Calculate the freezing point and boiling point of the solution. (Assume a density of 1.00 g/mL for water.)

106. An ethylene glycol solution contains 21.2 g of ethylene glycol ($C_2H_6O_2$) in 85.4 mL of water. Calculate the freezing point and boiling point of the solution. (Assume a density of 1.00 g/mL for water.)

CUMULATIVE PROBLEMS

107. An NaCl solution is made using 133 g of NaCl and diluting to a total solution volume of 1.00 L. Calculate the molarity and mass percent of the solution. (Assume a density of 1.08 g/mL for the solution.)

108. A KNO_3 solution is made using 88.4 g of KNO_3 and diluting to a total solution volume of 1.50 L. Calculate the molarity and mass percent of the solution. (Assume a density of 1.05 g/mL for the solution.)

109. A 125-mL sample of an 8.5 M NaCl solution is diluted to 2.5 L. What volume of the diluted solution contains 10.8 g of NaCl?

110. A 45.8-mL sample of a 5.8 M KNO_3 solution is diluted to 1.00 L. What volume of the diluted solution contains 15.0 g of KNO_3?

111. To what final volume should you dilute 50.0 mL of a 5.00 M KI solution so that 25.0 mL of the diluted solution contains 3.25 g of KI?

112. To what volume should you dilute 125 mL of an 8.00 M $CuCl_2$ solution so that 50.0 mL of the diluted solution contains 5.9 g $CuCl_2$?

113. What is the molarity of an aqueous solution that is 5.88% NaCl by mass? (Assume a density of 1.02 g/mL for the solution.)

114. What is the molarity of an aqueous solution that is 6.75% glucose ($C_6H_{12}O_6$) by mass? (Assume a density of 1.03 g/mL for the solution.)

115. Consider the reaction:

$$2\,Al(s) + 3\,H_2SO_4(aq) \longrightarrow Al_2(SO_4)_3(aq) + 3\,H_2(g)$$

What minimum volume of 4.0 M H_2SO_4 is required to produce 15.0 L of H_2 at STP?

116. Consider the reaction:

$$Mg(s) + 2\,HCl(aq) \longrightarrow MgCl_2(aq) + H_2(g)$$

What minimum amount of 1.85 M HCl is necessary to produce 28.5 L of H_2 at STP?

117. How much of a 1.25 M sodium chloride solution in milliliters is required to completely precipitate all of the silver in 25.0 mL of a 0.45 M silver nitrate solution?

118. How much of a 1.50 M sodium sulfate solution in milliliters is required to completely precipitate all of the barium in 150.0 mL of a 0.250 M barium nitrate solution?

119. Nitric acid is usually purchased in concentrated form with a 70.3% HNO_3 concentration by mass and a density of 1.41 g/mL. How much of the concentrated stock solution in milliliters should you use to make 2.5 L of 0.500 M HNO_3?

120. Hydrochloric acid is usually purchased in concentrated form with a 37.0% HCl concentration by mass and a density of 1.20 g/mL. How much of the concentrated stock solution in milliliters should you use to make 2.5 L of 0.500 M HCl?

121. An ethylene glycol solution is made using 58.5 g of ethylene glycol ($C_2H_6O_2$) and diluting to a total volume of 500.0 mL. Calculate the freezing point and boiling point of the solution. (Assume a density of 1.09 g/mL for the solution.)

122. A sucrose solution is made using 144 g of sucrose ($C_{12}H_{22}O_{11}$) and diluting to a total volume of 1.00 L. Calculate the freezing point and boiling point of the solution. (Assume a density of 1.06 g/mL for the final solution.)

123. A 250.0-mL sample of a 5.00 M glucose ($C_6H_{12}O_6$) solution is diluted to 1.40 L. What are the freezing and boiling points of the final solution? (Assume a density of 1.06 g/mL for the final solution.)

124. A 135-mL sample of a 10.0 M ethylene glycol ($C_2H_6O_2$) solution is diluted to 1.50 L. What are the freezing and boiling points of the final solution? (Assume a density of 1.05 g/mL for the final solution.)

125. An aqueous solution containing 17.5 g of an unknown molecular (nonelectrolyte) compound in 100.0 g of water has a freezing point of −1.8 °C. Calculate the molar mass of the unknown compound.

126. An aqueous solution containing 35.9 g of an unknown molecular (nonelectrolyte) compound in 150.0 g of water has a freezing point of −1.3 °C. Calculate the molar mass of the unknown compound.

127. What is the boiling point of an aqueous solution that freezes at −6.7 °C?

128. What is the freezing point of an aqueous solution that boils at 102.1 °C?

129. A 125-g sample contains only glucose ($C_6H_{12}O_6$) and sucrose ($C_{12}H_{22}O_{11}$). When the sample is added to 0.500 kg of pure water, the resulting solution has a freezing point of −1.75 °C. What were the masses of glucose and sucrose in the original sample?

130. A 13.03-g sample contains only ethylene glycol ($C_2H_6O_2$) and propylene glycol ($C_3H_8O_2$). When the sample is added to 100.0 g of pure water, the resulting solution has a freezing point of −3.50 °C. What was the percent composition of ethylene glycol and propylene glycol in the original sample?

HIGHLIGHT PROBLEMS

131. Consider the molecular views of osmosis cells. For each cell, determine the direction of water flow.

(a)

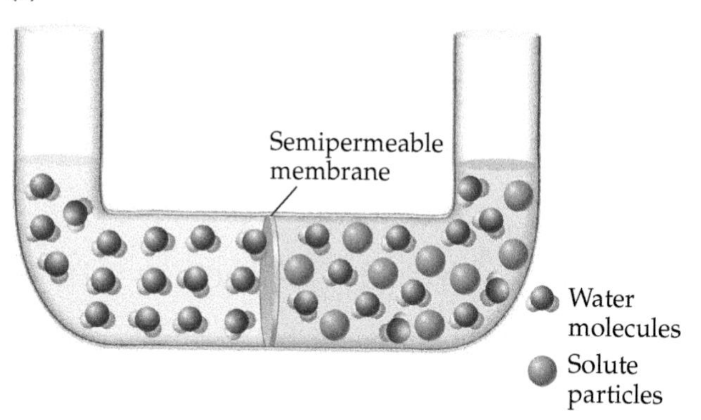

(b)

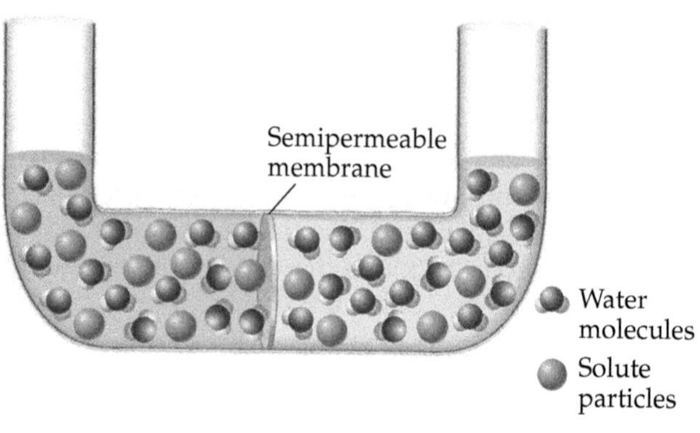

(c)

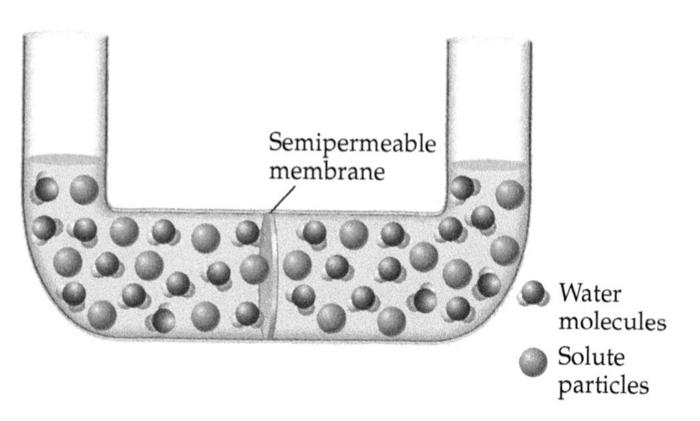

132. What is wrong with this molecular view of a sodium chloride solution? What would make the picture correct?

133. The Safe Drinking Water Act (SDWA) sets a limit for mercury—a toxin to the central nervous system—at 0.002 mg/L. Water suppliers must periodically test their water to ensure that mercury levels do not exceed 0.002 mg/L. Suppose water became contaminated with mercury at twice the legal limit (0.004 mg/L). How much of this water would have to be consumed to ingest 0.100 g of mercury?

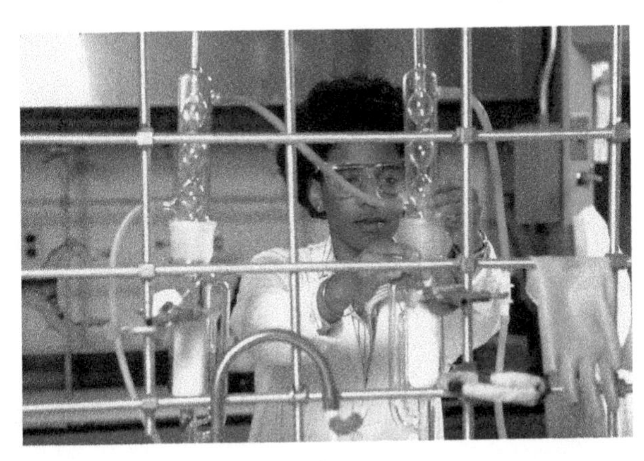

134. Water softeners often replace calcium ions in hard water with sodium ions. Since sodium compounds are soluble, the presence of sodium ions in water does not result in the white, scaly residues caused by calcium ions. However, calcium is more beneficial to human health than sodium. Calcium is a necessary part of the human diet, while high levels of sodium intake are linked to increases in blood pressure. The Food and Drug Administration (FDA) recommends that adults ingest less than 2.4 g of sodium per day. How many liters of softened water, containing a sodium concentration of 0.050% sodium by mass, have to be consumed to exceed the FDA recommendation? (Assume a density of 1.0 g/mL for water.)

◀ Drinking water must be tested for the presence of various pollutants, including mercury compounds that can damage the nervous system.

▶ANSWERS TO SKILLBUILDER EXCERISES

Skillbuilder 13.1	2.67%	**Skillbuilder 13.7**	16.4 mL
Skillbuilder 13.2	42.5 g sucrose	**Skillbuilder Plus, p. 465**	0.308 M
Skillbuilder 13.3	0.263 M	**Skillbuilder 13.8**	0.443 *m*
Skillbuilder 13.4	3.33 L	**Skillbuilder 13.9**	−4.8 °C
Skillbuilder 13.5	0.75 M Ca^{2+} and 1.5 M Cl^-	**Skillbuilder 13.10**	101.8 °C
Skillbuilder 13.6	0.12 L		

▶ANSWERS TO CONCEPTUAL CHECKPOINTS

13.1 (a) CH_3Cl and H_2S are both polar compounds, and KF is ionic. All three would therefore interact more strongly with water molecules (which are polar) than CCl_4, which is nonpolar.

13.2 (b) Some potassium chloride precipitates out of solution. The solubility of most solids decreases with decreasing temperature. However, the solubility of gases increases with decreasing temperature. Therefore, the nitrogen becomes more soluble and will not bubble out of solution.

13.3 (c) The solution is 0.30 M in K^+ because the compound K_2SO_4 forms two moles of K^+ in solution for each mole of K_2SO_4 that dissolves.

13.4 (a) The mass of a solution is equal to the mass of the solute plus the mass of the solvent. Although the solute seems to disappear, it does not, and its mass becomes part of the mass of the solution, in accordance with the law of conservation of mass.

13.5 (a) A 2.0 *m* solution would be made by adding 2 mol of solute to 1 kg of solvent. 1 kg of water has a volume of 1 L, but because of the dissolved solute, the final solution would have a volume of slightly *more than* 1 L. A 2.0 M solution, by contrast, would consist of 2 mol of solute in a solution of *exactly* 1 L. Therefore, a 2 M aqueous solution would be slightly more concentrated than a 2 *m* solution.

13.6 (d) Since boiling point elevation depends only on the *concentration* of the dissolved particles, and not on the *kind* of dissolved particles, all of these solutions have the same boiling point.

REALEMON
LEMON JUICE
BEST YET

CHAPTER 14

Acids and Bases

"The differences between the various acid–base concepts are not concerned with which is 'right,' but which is most convenient to use in a particular situation."

JAMES E. HUHEEY

14.1 Sour Patch Kids and International Spy Movies

Gummy candies have a sweet taste and chewy texture that both children and adults can enjoy. From the original classic gummy bear to the gummy worm to the gummy just-about-any-shape-you-can-imagine, these candies are incredibly popular. A common variation is the *sour* gummy candy, whose best-known incarnation is the Sour Patch Kid. Sour Patch Kids are gummy candies shaped like children and coated with a white powder. When you first put a Sour Patch Kid in your mouth, it tastes incredibly sour. The taste is caused by the white powder coating, a mixture of citric acid and tartaric acid. Like all acids, citric and tartaric acid taste sour.

A number of other foods contain acids as well. The taste of lemons and limes, the bite of sourdough bread, and the tang of a tomato are all caused by acids. Acids are substances that—by one definition that we will elaborate on later—produce H^+ ions in solution. When the citric and tartaric acids from a Sour Patch Kid combine with saliva in your mouth, they produce H^+ ions. Those H^+ ions react with protein molecules on your tongue. The protein molecules then change shape, sending an electrical signal to your brain that you experience as a sour taste (▶ Figure 14.1).

When we say that acids dissolve metals, we mean that acids react with metals in a way that causes them to go into solution as metal cations. Bond's pen is made of gold because gold is one of the few metals that is not dissolved by most acids (see Section 16.5).

◀ Acids are found in many common foods. The molecules shown here are citric acid (upper left), the acid found in lemon and limes; acetic acid (upper right), the acid present in vinegar; and tartaric acid (lower left), one of the acids used to coat sour gummy candies.

Acids have also been made famous by their use in spy movies. James Bond, for example, often carries an acid-filled gold pen. When Bond is captured and imprisoned—as inevitably happens at least one time in each movie—he squirts some acid out of his pen and onto the iron bars of his cell. The acid quickly dissolves the metal, allowing Bond to escape. Although acids do not dissolve iron bars with the ease depicted in the movies, they do dissolve metals. A small piece of aluminum placed in hydrochloric acid, for example, dissolves away in about

◀ **FIGURE 14.1 Acids taste sour** When a person eats a sour food, H^+ ions from the acid in the food react with protein molecules in the taste cells of the tongue. This interaction causes the protein molecules to change shape, triggering a nerve impulse to the brain that the person experiences as a sour taste.

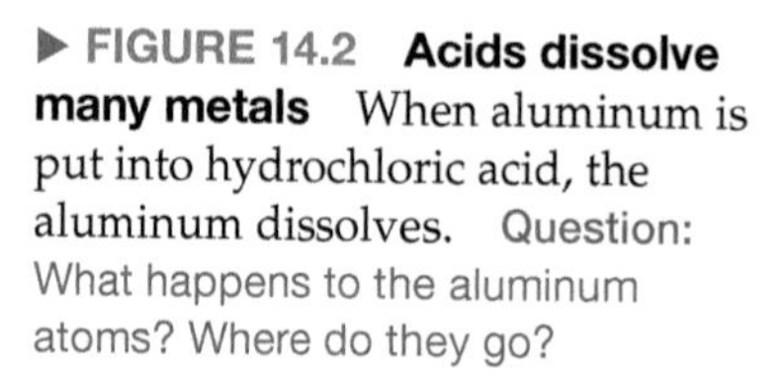

▶ **FIGURE 14.2 Acids dissolve many metals** When aluminum is put into hydrochloric acid, the aluminum dissolves. Question: What happens to the aluminum atoms? Where do they go?

10 minutes (▲ Figure 14.2). With enough acid, it would be possible to dissolve the iron bars of a prison cell, but it would take more acid than the amount that fits in a pen.

14.2 Acids: Properties and Examples

NEVER taste or touch laboratory chemicals.

Acids have the following properties:

- Acids have a sour taste.
- Acids dissolve many metals.
- Acids turn blue litmus paper red.

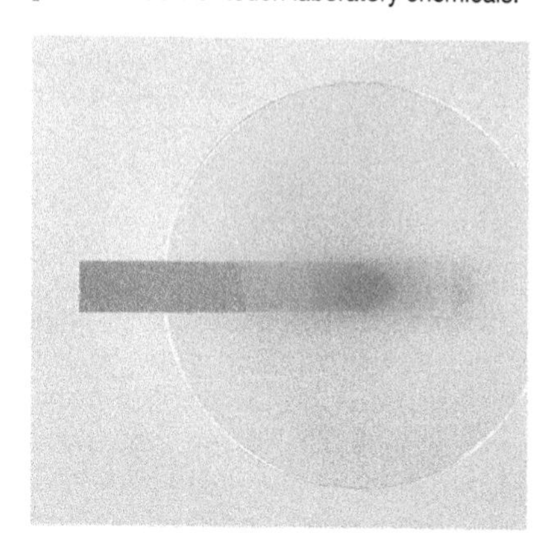

▲ **FIGURE 14.3 Acids turn blue litmus paper red.**

We have just discussed examples of the sour taste of acids (Sour Patch Kids) and their ability to dissolve metals (spy movies). Acids also turn blue litmus paper red. Litmus paper contains a dye that turns red in acidic solutions (◀ Figure 14.3). In the laboratory, litmus paper is used routinely to test the acidity of solutions.

Some common acids are listed in Table 14.1. Hydrochloric acid is found in most chemistry laboratories. It is used in industry to clean metals, to prepare and process some foods, and to refine metal ores.

For a review of naming acids, see Section 5.9.

Hydrochloric acid is also the main component of stomach acid. In the stomach, hydrochloric acid helps break down food and kills harmful bacteria that might enter the body through food. The sour taste sometimes associated with

TABLE 14.1 Some Common Acids

Name	Uses
hydrochloric acid (HCl)	metal cleaning; food preparation; ore refining; main component of stomach acid
sulfuric acid (H_2SO_4)	fertilizer and explosive manufacturing; dye and glue production; automobile batteries
nitric acid (HNO_3)	fertilizer and explosive manufacturing; dye and glue production
acetic acid ($HC_2H_3O_2$)	plastic and rubber manufacturing; food preservation; active component of vinegar
carbonic acid (H_2CO_3)	found in carbonated beverages due to the reaction of carbon dioxide with water
hydrofluoric acid (HF)	metal cleaning; glass frosting and etching

indigestion is caused by the stomach's hydrochloric acid refluxing up into the esophagus (the tube that joins the stomach and the mouth) and throat.

Annual U.S. production of sulfuric acid exceeds 36 million tons.

Sulfuric acid—the most widely produced chemical in the United States—and nitric acid are commonly used in the laboratory. In addition, they are used in the manufacture of fertilizers, explosives, dyes, and glue. Sulfuric acid is contained in most automobile batteries.

H_2SO_4

Sulfuric acid

HNO_3

Nitric acid

Acetic acid is found in most people's homes as the active component of vinegar. It is also produced in improperly stored wines. The word *vinegar* originates from the French *vin aigre*, which means "sour wine." The presence of vinegar in wines is considered a serious fault, making the wine taste like salad dressing.

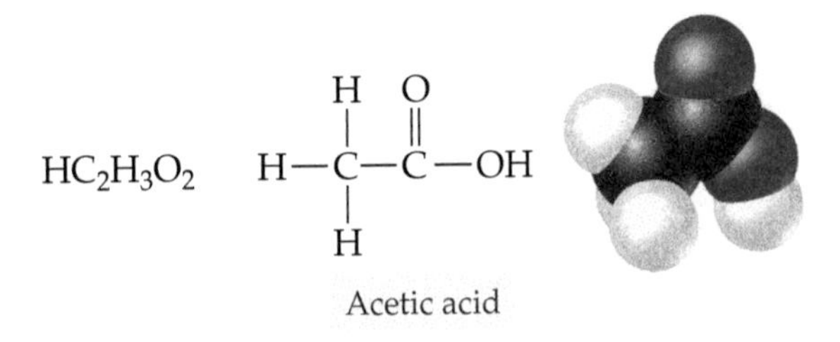

▲ Acetic acid is the active component in vinegar.

Acetic acid is an example of a **carboxylic acid**, an acid containing the grouping of atoms known as the carboxylic acid group.

—COOH

Carboxylic acid group

We often find carboxylic acids (covered in more detail in Chapter 18, Section 18.15), in substances derived from living organisms. Other carboxylic acids include citric acid, the main acid in lemons and limes, and malic acid, an acid found in apples, grapes, and wine.

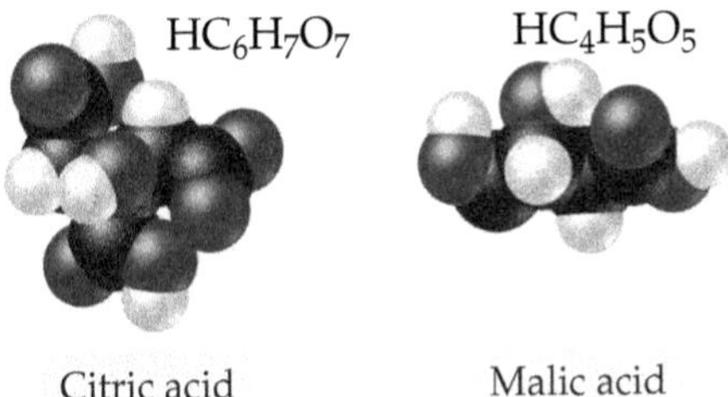

14.3 Bases: Properties and Examples

NEVER taste or touch laboratory chemicals.

Bases have the following properties:

- Bases have a bitter taste.
- Bases have a slippery feel.
- Bases turn red litmus paper blue.

Coffee is acidic overall, but bases present in coffee—such as caffeine—impart a bitter flavor.

▲ All these consumer products contain bases.

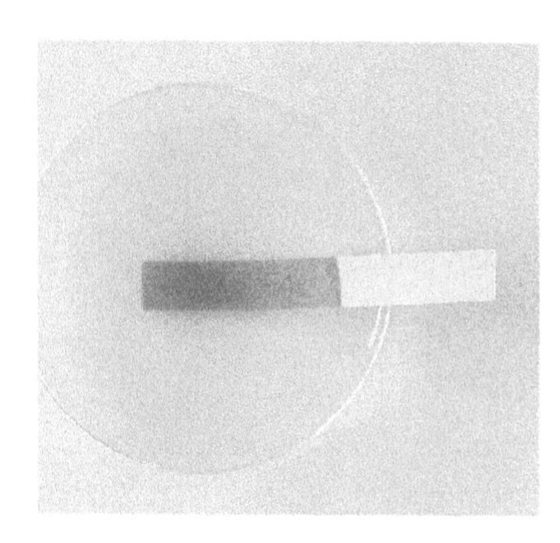

▲ FIGURE 14.4 **Bases turn red litmus paper blue.**

Bases are less common in foods than acids because of their bitter taste. A Sour Patch Kid coated with a base would never sell. Our aversion to the taste of bases is probably an adaptation to protect us against **alkaloids**, organic bases found in plants (see the Chemistry and Health box in Section 14.9). Alkaloids are often poisonous—the active component of hemlock, for example, is the alkaloid coniine—and their bitter taste warns us against eating them. Nonetheless, some foods, such as coffee, contain small amounts of base (caffeine is a base). Many people enjoy the bitterness, but only after acquiring the taste over time.

$C_8H_{17}N$

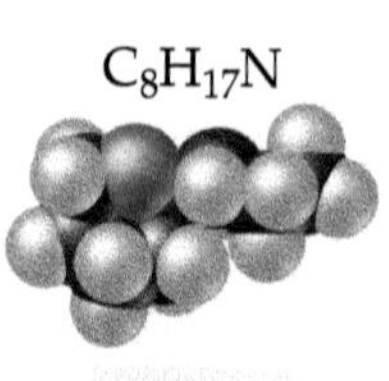

Coniine

$C_8H_{10}N_4O_2$

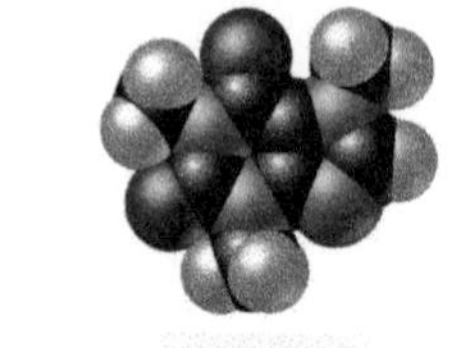

Caffeine

Bases feel slippery because they react with oils on your skin to form soaplike substances. Soap itself is basic, and its slippery feel is characteristic of bases. Some household cleaning solutions, such as ammonia, are also basic and have the typical slippery feel of a base. Bases turn red litmus paper blue (◀ Figure 14.4). In the laboratory, litmus paper is routinely used to test the basicity of solutions.

Table 14.2 lists some common bases. Sodium hydroxide and potassium hydroxide are found in most chemistry laboratories. They are also used in processing petroleum and cotton and in soap and plastic manufacturing. Sodium hydroxide is the active ingredient in products such as Drano that work to unclog drains. Sodium bicarbonate can be found in most homes as baking soda and is also an active ingredient in many antacids. When taken as an antacid, sodium bicarbonate neutralizes stomach acid (see Section 14.5), relieving heartburn and sour stomach.

TABLE 14.2 Some Common Bases

Name	Uses
sodium hydroxide (NaOH)	petroleum processing; soap and plastic manufacturing
potassium hydroxide (KOH)	cotton processing; electroplating; soap production
sodium bicarbonate ($NaHCO_3$)*	antacid; ingredient of baking soda; source of CO_2
ammonia (NH_3)	detergent; fertilizer and explosive manufacturing; synthetic fiber production

*Sodium bicarbonate is a salt whose anion (HCO_3^-) is the conjugate base of a weak acid (see Section 14.4) and acts as a base.

14.4 Molecular Definitions of Acids and Bases

We have just seen some of the properties of acids and bases. In this section we examine two different models that explain the molecular basis for acid and base behavior: the Arrhenius model and the Brønsted–Lowry model. The Arrhenius model, which was developed earlier, is more limited in its scope. The Brønsted–Lowry model was developed later and is more broadly applicable.

THE ARRHENIUS DEFINITION

In the 1880s, the Swedish chemist Svante Arrhenius proposed the following molecular definitions of acids and bases.

The Arrhenius definition

Acid—An acid produces $\mathbf{H^+}$ ions in aqueous solution.
Base—A base produces $\mathbf{OH^-}$ ions in aqueous solution.

For example, according to the **Arrhenius definition**, HCl is an **Arrhenius acid** because it produces H^+ ions in solution (◀ Figure 14.5).

$$HCl(aq) \longrightarrow H^+(aq) + Cl^-(aq)$$

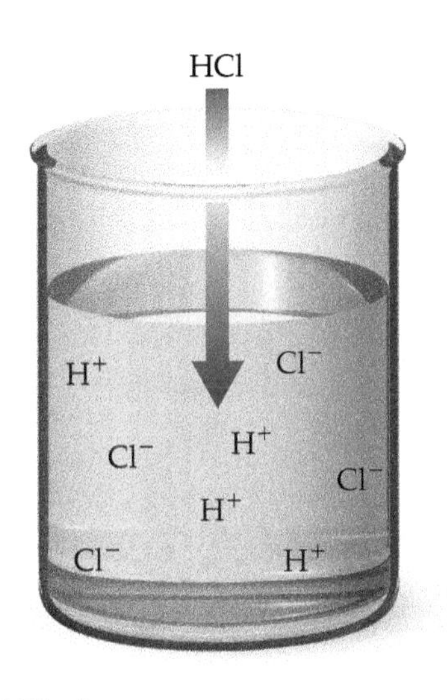

$$HCl(aq) \longrightarrow H^+(aq) + Cl^-(aq)$$

▲ **FIGURE 14.5 Arrhenius definition of an acid** The Arrhenius definition states that an acid is a substance that produces H^+ ions in solution. These H^+ ions associate with H_2O to form H_3O^+ ions.

HCl is a covalent compound and does not contain ions. However, in water it **ionizes** to form $H^+(aq)$ ions and $Cl^-(aq)$ ions. The H^+ ions are highly reactive. In aqueous solution, they bond to water molecules according to the reaction.

$$H^+ + :\ddot{\underset{\cdot\cdot}{O}}:H \ (\text{with H above O}) \longrightarrow \left[H:\ddot{\underset{\cdot\cdot}{O}}:H \ (\text{with H above O}) \right]^+$$

The H_3O^+ ion is the **hydronium ion**. In water, H^+ ions *always* associate with H_2O molecules. Chemists often use $H^+(aq)$ and $H_3O^+(aq)$ interchangeably, however, to refer to the same thing—a hydronium ion.

In the molecular formula for an acid, we often write the ionizable hydrogen first. For example, we write the formula for formic acid as follows:

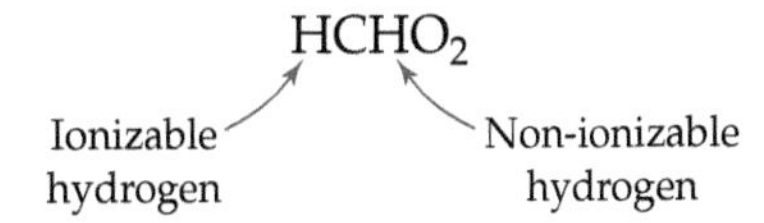

The structure of formic acid, however, is not indicated by the molecular formula in the preceding figure. We represent the *structure* of formic acid with its structural formula:

$$\overset{\displaystyle O}{\overset{\|}{HC}}—OH \quad \leftarrow \text{Ionizable hydrogen}$$

Notice that the structural formula indicates how the atoms are bonded together; the molecular formula, by contrast, simply indicates the number of each type of atom.

NaOH is an **Arrhenius base** because it produces OH^- ions in solution (◀ Figure 14.6).

$$NaOH(aq) \longrightarrow Na^+(aq) + OH^-(aq)$$

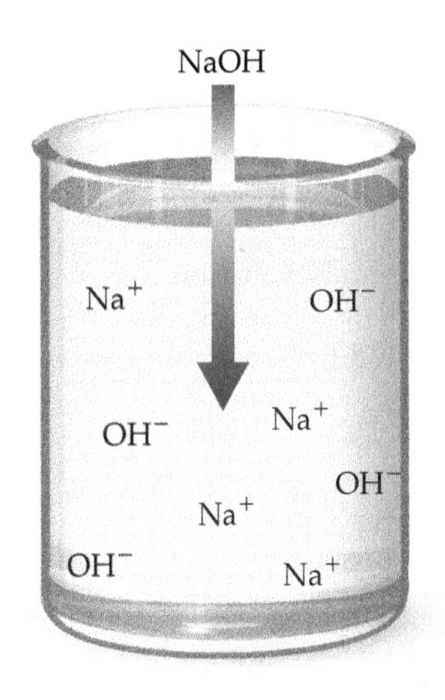

$$NaOH(aq) \longrightarrow Na^+(aq) + OH^-(aq)$$

▲ **FIGURE 14.6 Arrhenius definition of a base** The Arrhenius definition states that a base is a substance that produces OH^- ions in solution.

> Ionic compounds such as NaOH are composed of positive and negative ions. In solution, soluble ionic compounds dissociate into their component ions. Molecular compounds containing an OH group, such as methanol CH_3OH, do not dissociate and therefore do not act as bases.

NaOH is an ionic compound and therefore contains Na^+ and OH^- ions. When NaOH is added to water, it **dissociates**, or breaks apart into its component ions.

Under the Arrhenius definition, acids and bases naturally combine to form water, neutralizing each other in the process.

$$H^+(aq) + OH^-(aq) \longrightarrow H_2O(l)$$

THE BRØNSTED–LOWRY DEFINITION

Although the Arrhenius definition of acids and bases works in many cases, it cannot easily explain why some substances act as bases even though they do not contain OH^-. The Arrhenius definition also does not apply to nonaqueous solvents. A second definition of acids and bases, called the **Brønsted–Lowry definition**, introduced in 1923, applies to a wider range of acid–base phenomena. This definition focuses on the *transfer* of H^+ ions in an acid–base reaction. Since an H^+ ion is a proton—a hydrogen atom with its electron taken away—this definition focuses on the idea of a proton donor and a proton acceptor.

Brønsted–Lowry definition

Acid—An acid is a proton (**H^+ ion**) *donor*.
Base—A base is a proton (**H^+ ion**) *acceptor*.

According to this definition, HCl is a **Brønsted–Lowry acid** because, in solution, it donates a proton to water.

Johannes Brønsted, working in Denmark, and Thomas Lowry, working in England, developed the concept of proton transfer in acid–base behavior independently and simultaneously.

$$HCl(aq) + H_2O(l) \longrightarrow H_3O^+(aq) + Cl^-(aq)$$

This definition more clearly accounts for what happens to the H^+ ion from an acid: it associates with a water molecule to form H_3O^+ (a hydronium ion). The Brønsted–Lowry definition also works well with bases (such as NH_3) that do not inherently contain OH^- ions but that still produce OH^- ions in solution. NH_3 is a **Brønsted–Lowry base** because it accepts a proton from water.

The double arrows in this equation indicate that the reaction does not go to completion. We discuss this concept in more detail in Section 14.7.

$$NH_3(aq) + H_2O(l) \rightleftharpoons NH_4^+(aq) + OH^-(aq)$$

In the Brønsted–Lowry definition, acids (proton donors) and bases (proton acceptors) always occur together. In the reaction between HCl and H_2O, HCl is the proton donor (acid), and H_2O is the proton acceptor (base).

$$\underset{\substack{\text{Acid}\\\text{(Proton donor)}}}{HCl(aq)} + \underset{\substack{\text{Base}\\\text{(Proton acceptor)}}}{H_2O(l)} \longrightarrow H_3O^+(aq) + Cl^-(aq)$$

In the reaction between NH_3 and H_2O, H_2O is the proton donor (acid) and NH_3 is the proton acceptor (base).

$$\underset{\substack{\text{Base}\\\text{(Proton acceptor)}}}{NH_3(aq)} + \underset{\substack{\text{Acid}\\\text{(Proton donor)}}}{H_2O(l)} \rightleftharpoons NH_4^+(aq) + OH^-(aq)$$

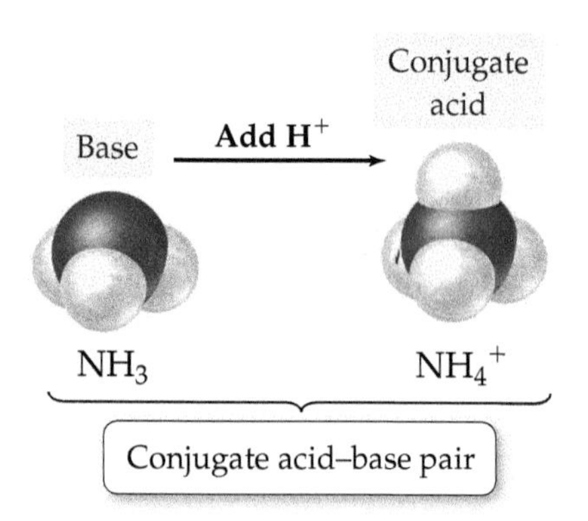

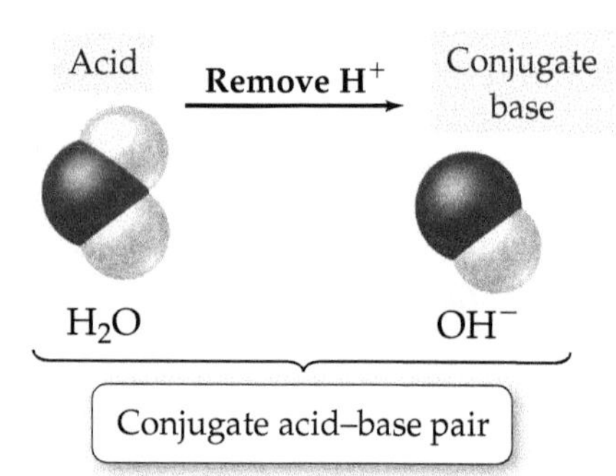

▲ **FIGURE 14.7 A conjugate acid–base pair** Any two substances related to each other by the transfer of a proton can be considered a conjugate acid–base pair.

Notice that under the Brønsted–Lowry definition, some substances—such as water in the previous two equations—can act as acids *or* bases. Substances that can act as acids or bases are **amphoteric**. Notice also what happens when an equation representing Brønsted–Lowry acid–base behavior is reversed.

$$\underset{\substack{\text{Acid}\\\text{(Proton donor)}}}{NH_4^+(aq)} + \underset{\substack{\text{Base}\\\text{(Proton acceptor)}}}{OH^-(aq)} \rightleftharpoons NH_3(aq) + H_2O(l)$$

In this reaction, NH_4^+ is the proton donor (acid) and OH^- is the proton acceptor (base). What was the base (NH_3) has become the acid (NH_4^+), and vice versa. NH_4^+ and NH_3 are often referred to as a **conjugate acid–base pair**, two substances related to each other by the transfer of a proton (◀ Figure 14.7). Going back to the original forward reaction, we can identify the conjugate acid–base pairs as follows:

$$\underset{\text{Base}}{NH_3(aq)} + \underset{\text{Acid}}{H_2O(l)} \rightleftharpoons \underset{\substack{\text{Conjugate}\\\text{acid}}}{NH_4^+(aq)} + \underset{\substack{\text{Conjugate}\\\text{base}}}{OH^-(aq)}$$

In an acid–base reaction, a base accepts a proton and becomes a conjugate acid. An acid donates a proton and becomes a conjugate base.

EXAMPLE 14.1 Identifying Brønsted–Lowry Acids and Bases and Their Conjugates

In each reaction, identify the Brønsted–Lowry acid, the Brønsted–Lowry base, the conjugate acid, and the conjugate base.

(a) $H_2SO_4(aq) + H_2O(l) \longrightarrow H_3O^+(aq) + HSO_4^-(aq)$
(b) $HCO_3^-(aq) + H_2O(l) \rightleftharpoons H_2CO_3(aq) + OH^-(aq)$

SOLUTION

(a) Since H_2SO_4 donates a proton to H_2O in this reaction, it is the acid (the proton donor). After H_2SO_4 donates the proton, it becomes HSO_4^-, the conjugate base. Since H_2O accepts a proton, it is the base (the proton acceptor). After H_2O accepts the proton, it becomes H_3O^+, the conjugate acid.

$$\underset{\text{Acid}}{H_2SO_4(aq)} + \underset{\text{Base}}{H_2O(l)} \longrightarrow \underset{\text{Conjugate base}}{HSO_4^-(aq)} + \underset{\text{Conjugate acid}}{H_3O^+(aq)}$$

(b) Since H_2O donates a proton to HCO_3^- in this reaction, it is the acid (the proton donor). After H_2O donates the proton, it becomes OH^-, the conjugate base. Since HCO_3^- accepts a proton, it is the base (the proton acceptor). After HCO_3^- accepts the proton, it becomes H_2CO_3, the conjugate acid.

$$\underset{\text{Base}}{HCO_3^-(aq)} + \underset{\text{Acid}}{H_2O(l)} \longrightarrow \underset{\text{Conjugate acid}}{H_2CO_3(aq)} + \underset{\text{Conjugate base}}{OH^-(aq)}$$

▶SKILLBUILDER 14.1 | Identifying Brønsted–Lowry Acids and Bases and Their Conjugates

In each reaction, identify the Brønsted–Lowry acid, the Brønsted–Lowry base, the conjugate acid, and the conjugate base.

(a) $C_5H_5N(aq) + H_2O(l) \rightleftharpoons C_5H_5NH^+(aq) + OH^-(aq)$
(b) $HNO_3(aq) + H_2O(l) \longrightarrow NO_3^-(aq) + H_3O^+(aq)$

▶FOR MORE PRACTICE Example 14.11; Problems 35, 36, 37, 38.

CONCEPTUAL CHECKPOINT 14.1

Which species is the conjugate base of H_2SO_3?

(a) $H_3SO_3^+$ **(b)** HSO_3^- **(c)** SO_3^{2-}

14.5 Reactions of Acids and Bases

NEUTRALIZATION REACTIONS

The reaction between HCl and KOH is also a double-displacement reaction (see Section 7.10).

Neutralization reactions are covered in Section 7.8.

One of the most important reactions of acids and bases is **neutralization**, first introduced in Chapter 7. When an acid and a base are mixed, the $H^+(aq)$ from the acid combines with the $OH^-(aq)$ from the base to form H_2O(l). For example, consider the reaction between hydrochloric acid and potassium hydroxide.

$$\underset{\text{Acid}}{HCl(aq)} + \underset{\text{Base}}{KOH(aq)} \longrightarrow \underset{\text{Water}}{H_2O(l)} + \underset{\text{Salt}}{KCl(aq)}$$

Acid–base reactions generally form water and a **salt**—an ionic compound—that usually remains dissolved in the solution. The salt contains the cation from the base and the anion from the acid.

$$\text{Acid} + \text{Base} \longrightarrow \text{Water} + \text{Salt}$$

Ionic compound that contains the cation from the base and the anion from the acid

The net ionic equation for many neutralization reactions is:

$$H^+(aq) + OH^-(aq) \longrightarrow H_2O(l)$$

Net ionic equations are explained in Section 7.7.

A slightly different but common type of neutralization reaction involves an acid reacting with carbonates or bicarbonates (compounds containing CO_3^{2-} or HCO_3^-). This type of neutralization reaction produces water, gaseous carbon dioxide, and a salt. As an example, consider the reaction of hydrochloric acid and sodium bicarbonate.

$$HCl(aq) + NaHCO_3(aq) \longrightarrow H_2O(l) + CO_2(g) + NaCl(aq)$$

$HCl(aq) + NaHCO_3(aq) \longrightarrow H_2O(l) + CO_2(g) + NaCl(aq)$

▲ The reaction of carbonates or bicarbonates with acids produces water, gaseous carbon dioxide, and a salt.

Since this reaction produces gaseous CO_2, it is also called a *gas evolution reaction* (Section 7.8).

EXAMPLE 14.2 Writing Equations for Neutralization Reactions

Write a molecular equation for the reaction between aqueous HCl and aqueous $Ca(OH)_2$.

SOLUTION	
First identify the acid and the base and write the skeletal reaction showing the production of water and the salt. The formulas for the ionic compounds in the equation must be charge neutral (see Section 5.5).	$HCl(aq) + Ca(OH)_2(aq) \longrightarrow H_2O(l) + CaCl_2(aq)$
Balance the equation. Notice that $Ca(OH)_2$ contains 2 mol of OH^- for every 1 mol of $Ca(OH)_2$ and will therefore require 2 mol of H^+ to neutralize it.	$2\,HCl(aq) + Ca(OH)_2(aq) \longrightarrow 2\,H_2O(l) + CaCl_2(aq)$

▶SKILLBUILDER 14.2 | Writing Equations for Neutralization Reactions

Write a molecular equation for the reaction that occurs between aqueous H_3PO_4 and aqueous NaOH. *Hint:* H_3PO_4 is a triprotic acid, meaning that 1 mol of H_3PO_4 requires 3 mol of OH^- to completely react with it.

▶FOR MORE PRACTICE Example 14.12; Problems 43, 44.

ACID REACTIONS

$2\,HCl(aq) + Mg(s) \longrightarrow H_2(g) + MgCl_2(aq)$

▲ The reaction between an acid and a metal usually produces hydrogen gas and a dissolved salt containing the metal ion.

In Section 14.1, we learned that acids dissolve metals, or more precisely, that acids react with metals in a way that causes metals to go into solution. The reaction between an acid and a metal usually produces hydrogen gas and a dissolved salt containing the metal ion as the cation. For example, hydrochloric acid reacts with magnesium metal to form hydrogen gas and magnesium chloride.

$$\underset{\text{Acid}}{2HCl(aq)} + \underset{\text{Metal}}{Mg(s)} \longrightarrow \underset{\text{Hydrogen gas}}{H_2(g)} + \underset{\text{Salt}}{MgCl_2(aq)}$$

Similarly, sulfuric acid reacts with zinc to form hydrogen gas and zinc sulfate.

$$\underset{\text{Acid}}{H_2SO_4(aq)} + \underset{\text{Metal}}{Zn(s)} \longrightarrow \underset{\text{Hydrogen gas}}{H_2(g)} + \underset{\text{Salt}}{ZnSO_4(aq)}$$

It is through reactions such as these that the acid from James Bond's pen in our earlier example dissolves the metal bars that imprison him. For example, if the bars were made of iron and the acid in the pen were hydrochloric acid, the reaction would be:

$$\underset{\text{Acid}}{2\,HCl(aq)} + \underset{\text{Metal}}{Fe(s)} \longrightarrow \underset{\text{Hydrogen gas}}{H_2(g)} + \underset{\text{Salt}}{FeCl_2(aq)}$$

Some metals, however, do not readily react with acids. If the bars that imprisoned James Bond were made of gold, for example, a pen filled with hydrochloric acid would not dissolve the bars. We will discuss the way to determine whether a particular metal dissolves in an acid in Section 16.5.

Acids also react with metal oxides to produce water and a dissolved salt. For example, hydrochloric acid reacts with potassium oxide to form water and potassium chloride.

$$\underset{\text{Acid}}{2\,HCl(aq)} + \underset{\text{Metal oxide}}{K_2O(s)} \longrightarrow \underset{\text{Water}}{H_2O(l)} + \underset{\text{Salt}}{2\,KCl(aq)}$$

Similarly, hydrobromic acid reacts with magnesium oxide to form water and magnesium bromide.

$$\underset{\text{Acid}}{2\,HBr(aq)} + \underset{\text{Metal oxide}}{MgO(s)} \longrightarrow \underset{\text{Water}}{H_2O(l)} + \underset{\text{Salt}}{MgBr_2(aq)}$$

EXAMPLE 14.3 Writing Equations for Acid Reactions

Write an equation for:

(a) The reaction of hydroiodic acid with potassium metal
(b) The reaction of hydrobromic acid with sodium oxide

SOLUTION

(a) The reaction of hydroiodic acid with potassium metal forms hydrogen gas and a salt. The salt contains the ionized form of the metal (K^+) as the cation and the anion of the acid (I^-). Write the skeletal equation and then balance it.	$HI(aq) + K(s) \longrightarrow H_2(g) + KI(aq)$ $2\ HI(aq) + 2\ K(s) \longrightarrow H_2(g) + 2\ KI(aq)$
(b) The reaction of hydrobromic acid with sodium oxide forms water and a salt. The salt contains the cation from the metal oxide (Na^+) and the anion of the acid (Br^-). Write the skeletal equation and then balance it.	$HBr(aq) + Na_2O(s) \longrightarrow H_2O(l) + NaBr(aq)$ $2\ HBr(aq) + Na_2O(s) \longrightarrow H_2O(l) + 2\ NaBr(aq)$

▶SKILLBUILDER 14.3 | Writing Equations for Acid Reactions

Write an equation for:

(a) The reaction of hydrochloric acid with strontium metal
(b) The reaction of hydroiodic acid with barium oxide

▶FOR MORE PRACTICE Example 14.13; Problems 45, 46, 47, 48.

EVERYDAY CHEMISTRY

What Is in My Antacid?

Heartburn, a burning sensation in the lower throat and above the stomach, is caused by the reflux or backflow of stomach acid into the esophagus (the tube that joins the stomach to the throat). In most individuals, this occurs only occasionally, typically after large meals. Physical activity—such as bending, stooping, or lifting—after meals also aggravates heartburn. In some people, the flap between the esophagus and the stomach that normally prevents acid reflux becomes damaged, in which case heartburn becomes a regular occurrence.

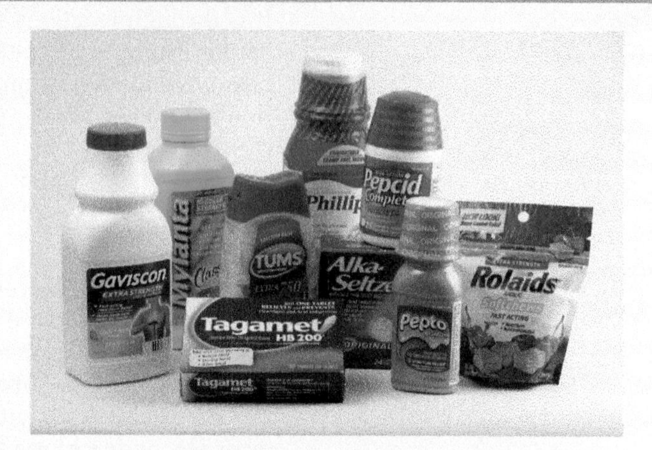

Gaviscon
Mylanta
TUMS
Pepcid
Alka-
Tagamet
HB 200
Pepto
Rolaids

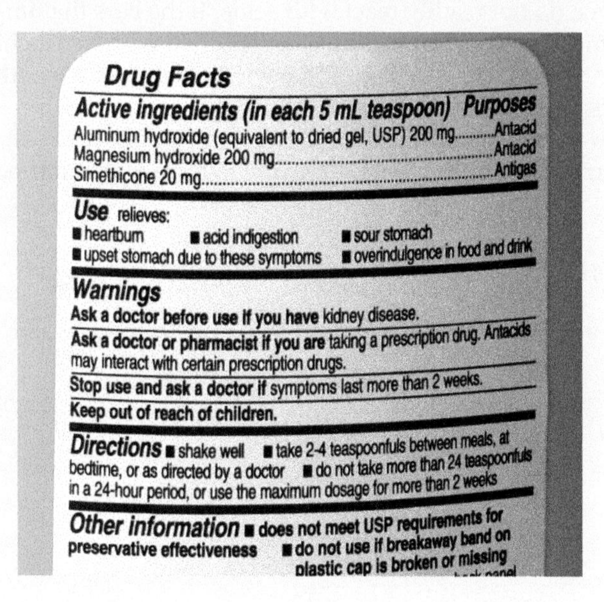

Drug Facts
Active ingredients (in each 5 mL teaspoon) Purposes
Aluminum hydroxide (equivalent to dried gel, USP) 200 mg..........Antacid
Magnesium hydroxide 200 mg..........Antacid
Simethicone 20 mg..........Antigas
Use relieves:
■ heartburn ■ acid indigestion ■ sour stomach
■ upset stomach due to these symptoms ■ overindulgence in food and drink
Warnings
Ask a doctor before use if you have kidney disease.
Ask a doctor or pharmacist if you are taking a prescription drug. Antacids may interact with certain prescription drugs.
Stop use and ask a doctor if symptoms last more than 2 weeks.
Keep out of reach of children.
Directions ■ shake well ■ take 2-4 teaspoonfuls between meals, at bedtime, or as directed by a doctor ■ do not take more than 24 teaspoonfuls in a 24-hour period, or use the maximum dosage for more than 2 weeks
Other information ■ does not meet USP requirements for preservative effectiveness ■ do not use if breakaway band on plastic cap is broken or missing

Drugstores carry many products that either reduce the secretion of stomach acid or neutralize the acid that is produced. Antacids such as Mylanta or Phillips' milk of magnesia contain bases that neutralize the refluxed stomach acid, alleviating heartburn.

CAN YOU ANSWER THIS? *Look at the label of Mylanta shown in the photograph. Can you identify the bases responsible for the antacid action? Write chemical equations showing the reactions of these bases with stomach acid (HCl).*

BASE REACTIONS

The most important base reactions are those in which a base neutralizes an acid (see the beginning of this section). The only other kind of base reaction that we cover in this book is the reaction of sodium hydroxide with aluminum and water.

$$2\ NaOH(aq) + 2\ Al(s) + 6\ H_2O(l) \longrightarrow 2\ NaAl(OH)_4(aq) + 3\ H_2(g)$$

Aluminum is one of the few metals that dissolves in a base. Consequently, it is safe to use NaOH (the main ingredient in many drain-opening products) to unclog your drain as long as your pipes are not made of aluminum, which is generally the case as the use of aluminum pipe is forbidden in most building codes.

14.6 Acid–Base Titration: A Way to Quantify the Amount of Acid or Base in a Solution

The principles we learned in Chapter 13 (Section 13.8) on solution stoichiometry can be applied to a common laboratory procedure called a titration. In a **titration**, a substance in a solution of known concentration is reacted with another substance in a solution of unknown concentration. For example, consider the acid–base reaction between hydrochloric acid and sodium hydroxide:

$$HCl(aq) + NaOH(aq) \longrightarrow H_2O(l) + NaCl(aq)$$

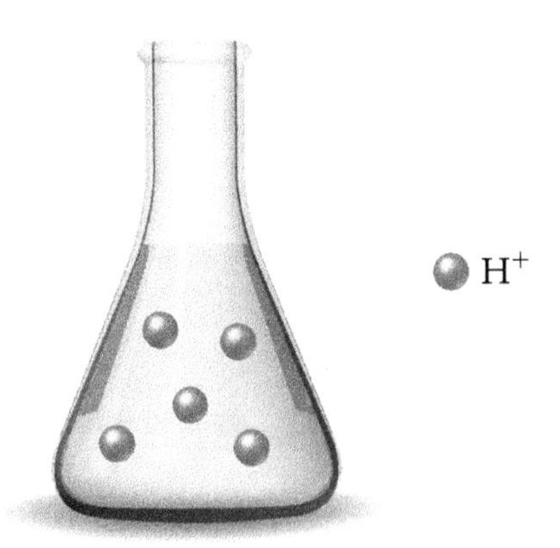

The net ionic equation for this reaction is:

$$H^+(aq) + OH^-(aq) \longrightarrow H_2O(l)$$

Suppose you have an HCl solution represented by the molecular diagram at left. (The Cl^- ions and the H_2O molecules not involved in the reaction have been omitted from this representation for clarity.)

In titrating this sample, we slowly add a solution of known OH^- concentration as represented by the following molecular diagrams.

The OH^- solution also contains Na^+ cations that are not shown in this figure for clarity.

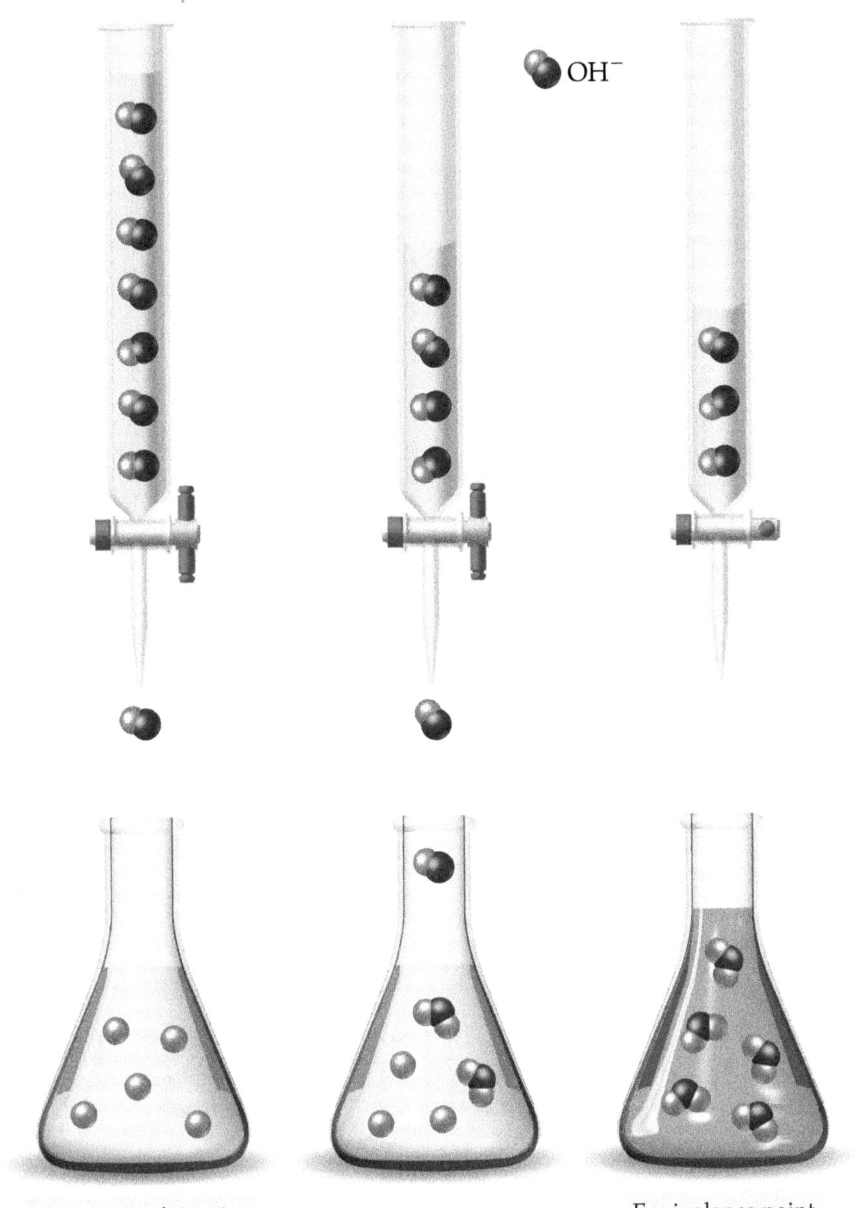

At the equivalence point, neither reactant is present in excess, and both are limiting. The number of moles of the reactants are related by the reaction stoichiometry (see Chapter 8).

As the OH^- is added, it reacts with and neutralizes the H^+, forming water. At the **equivalence point**—*the point in the titration when the number of moles of OH^- added equals the number of moles of H^+ originally in solution*—the titration is complete. The equivalence point is usually signaled by an **indicator**, a dye whose color depends on the acidity of the solution (▶ Figure 14.8). In most laboratory titrations, the concentration of one of the reactant solutions is unknown, and the concentration of the other is precisely known. By carefully measuring the volume of each solution required to reach the equivalence point, the concentration of the unknown solution can be determined, as demonstrated in Example 14.4.

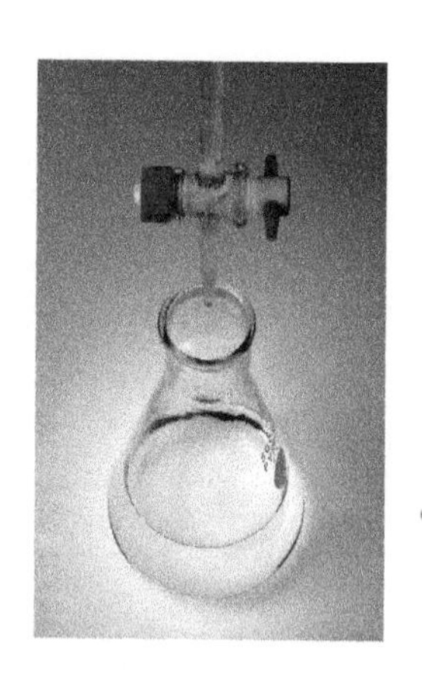

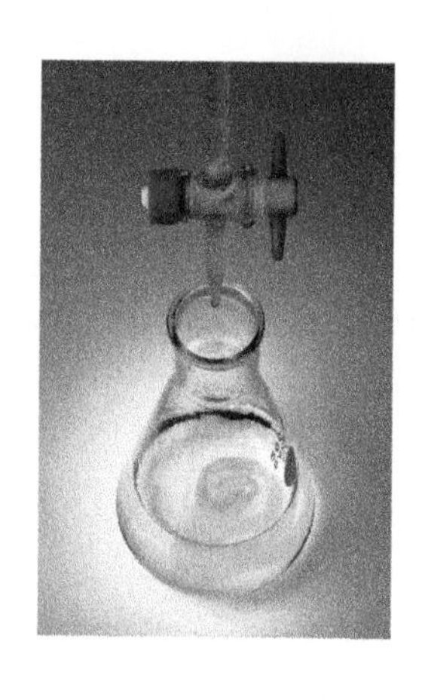

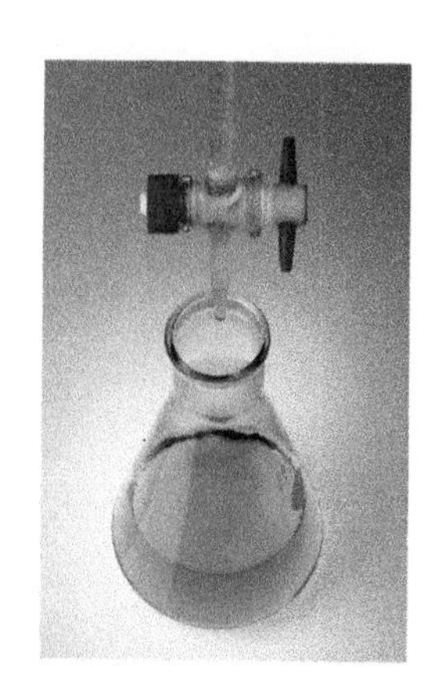

▶ **FIGURE 14.8 Acid–base titration** In this titration, NaOH is added to an HCl solution. When the NaOH and HCl reach stoichiometric proportions (1 mol of OH^- for every 1 mol of H^+), the indicator (phenolphthalein) changes to pink, signaling the equivalence point of the titration. (Phenolphthalein is an indicator that is colorless in acidic solution and pink in basic solution.)

EXAMPLE 14.4 Acid–Base Titration

The titration of 10.00 mL of an HCl solution of unknown concentration requires 12.54 mL of a 0.100 M NaOH solution to reach the equivalence point. What is the concentration of the unknown HCl solution?

SORT

You are given the volume of an unknown HCl solution and the volume of a known NaOH solution required to titrate the unknown solution. You are asked to find the concentration of the unknown solution.

GIVEN: 10.00 mL HCl solution

12.54 mL of a 0.100 M NaOH solution

FIND: concentration of HCl solution (mol/L)

STRATEGIZE

You must first write the balanced chemical equation for the reaction between the acid and the base (see Example 14.2).

The solution map then has two parts. In the first part, use the volume of NaOH required to reach the equivalence point to calculate the number of moles of HCl in the solution. The final conversion factor comes from the balanced neutralization equation.

In the second part, use the number of moles of HCl and the volume of HCl solution to determine the molarity of the HCl solution.

SOLUTION MAP

$$HCl(aq) + NaOH(aq) \longrightarrow H_2O(l) + NaCl(aq)$$

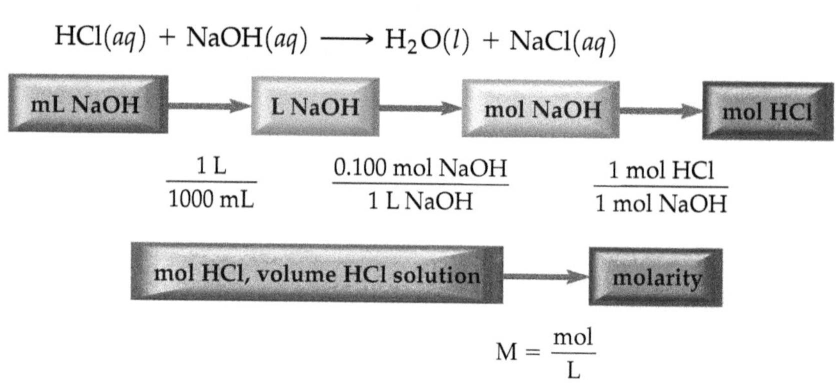

RELATIONSHIPS USED

1 mol HCl : 1 mol NaOH (from balanced chemical equation)

$$\text{Molarity (M)} = \frac{\text{mol solute}}{\text{L solution}}$$ (definition of molarity, from Section 13.6)

SOLVE

Calculate the moles of HCl in the unknown solution by following the first part of the solution map.

To get the concentration of the solution, divide the number of moles of HCl by the volume of the HCl solution in L. (Note that 10.00 mL is equivalent to 0.01000 L.)

The unknown HCl solution therefore has a concentration of 0.125 M.

SOLUTION

$$12.54\ \text{mL NaOH} \times \frac{1\ \text{L}}{1000\ \text{mL}} \times \frac{0.100\ \text{mol NaOH}}{1\ \text{L NaOH}} \times \frac{1\ \text{mol HCl}}{1\ \text{mol NaOH}} = 1.25 \times 10^{-3}\ \text{mol HCl}$$

$$\text{Molarity} = \frac{1.25 \times 10^{-3}\ \text{mol HCl}}{0.01000\ \text{L}} = 0.125\ \text{M}$$

CHECK

Check your answer. Are the units correct? Does the answer make physical sense?

The units (M) are correct. The magnitude of the answer makes sense because the reaction has a one-to-one stoichiometry and the volumes of the two solutions are similar; therefore, their concentrations should also be similar.

▶**SKILLBUILDER 14.4 | Acid–Base Titration**

The titration of a 20.0-mL sample of an H_2SO_4 solution of unknown concentration requires 22.87 mL of a 0.158 M KOH solution to reach the equivalence point. What is the concentration of the unknown H_2SO_4 solution?

▶**FOR MORE PRACTICE** Example 14.14; Problems 51, 52, 53, 54, 55, 56.

14.7 Strong and Weak Acids and Bases

STRONG ACIDS

Hydrochloric acid (HCl) and hydrofluoric acid (HF) appear to be similar, but there is an important difference between these two acids. HCl is an example of a **strong acid**, one that completely ionizes in solution.

Single arrow indicates complete ionization

$$HCl(aq) + H_2O(l) \longrightarrow H_3O^+(aq) + Cl^-(aq)$$

[X] means "molar concentration of X."

Strong electrolyte solutions were first defined in Section 7.5.

We show the *complete* ionization of HCl with a single arrow pointing to the right in the equation. An HCl solution contains almost no intact HCl; virtually all the HCl has reacted with water to form $H_3O^+(aq)$ and $Cl^-(aq)$ (◀ Figure 14.9). A 1.0 M HCl solution will therefore have an H_3O^+ concentration of 1.0 M. The concentration of H_3O^+ is often abbreviated as $[H_3O^+]$. Using this notation, a 1.0-M HCl solution has $[H_3O^+] = 1.0$ M.

A strong acid is an example of a **strong electrolyte**, a substance whose aqueous solutions are good conductors of electricity (▼ Figure 14.10). Aqueous solutions require the presence of charged particles to conduct electricity. Strong acid solutions are also strong electrolyte solutions because each acid molecule

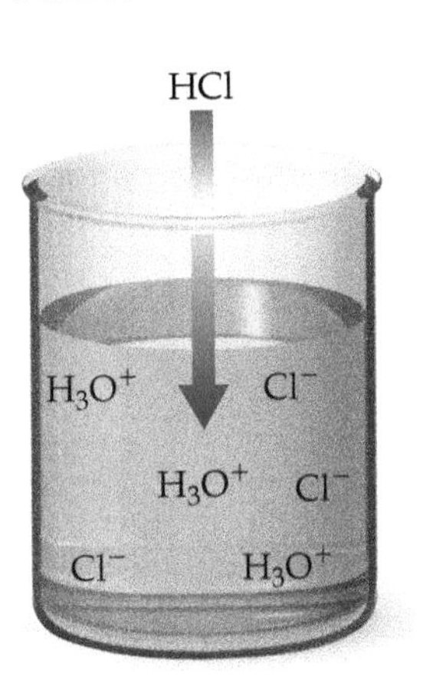

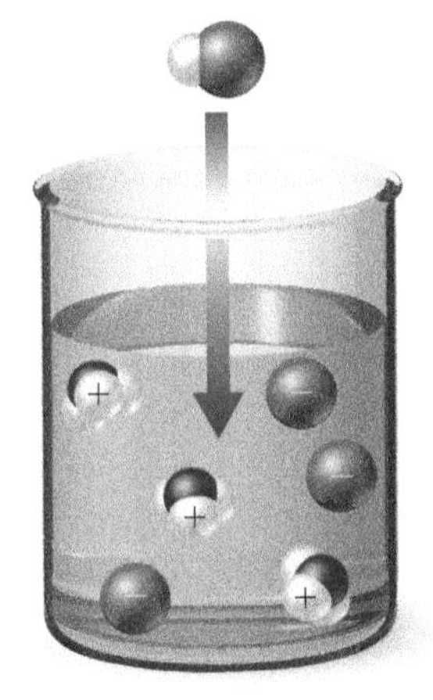

◀ **FIGURE 14.9 A strong acid** When HCl dissolves in water, it completely ionizes into H_3O^+ and Cl^- ions. The solution contains no intact HCl.

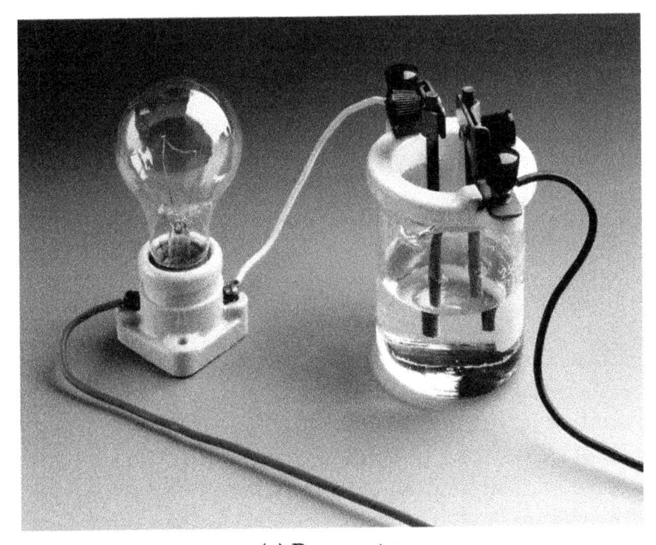

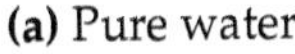

(a) Pure water

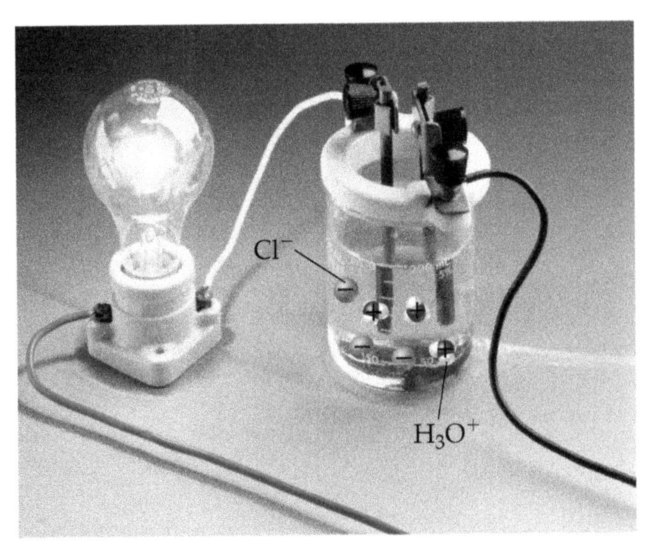

(b) HCl solution

▲ **FIGURE 14.10 Conductivity of a strong electrolyte solution** (a) Pure water will not conduct electricity. (b) The presence of ions in an HCl solution results in the conduction of electricity, causing the lightbulb to light. Solutions such as these are called strong electrolyte solutions.

ionizes into positive and negative ions. These mobile ions are good conductors of electricity. Pure water is not a good conductor of electricity because it has relatively few charged particles. The danger of using electrical devices—such as a hair dryer—while sitting in the bathtub is that water is seldom pure and often contains dissolved ions. If the device were to come in contact with the water, dangerously high levels of electricity could flow through the water and through your body.

An ionizable proton is one that becomes an H^+ ion in solution.

Table 14.3 lists the six strong acids. The first five acids in the table are **monoprotic acids**, acids containing only one ionizable proton. Sulfuric acid is an example of a **diprotic acid**, an acid that contains two ionizable protons.

TABLE 14.3 Strong Acids

hydrochloric acid (HCl)	nitric acid (HNO_3)
hydrobromic acid (HBr)	perchloric acid ($HClO_4$)
hydroiodic acid (HI)	sulfuric acid (H_2SO_4) *(diprotic)*

WEAK ACIDS

It is a common mistake to confuse the terms *strong* and *weak acids* with the terms *concentrated* and *dilute acids*. Can you state the difference between these terms?

In contrast to HCl, HF is a **weak acid**, one that does not completely ionize in solution.

Double arrow indicates partial ionization

$$HF(aq) + H_2O(l) \rightleftharpoons H_3O^+(aq) + F^-(aq)$$

To show that HF does not completely ionize in solution, the equation for its ionization has two opposing arrows, indicating that the reverse reaction occurs to some degree. An HF solution contains a lot of intact HF; it also contains some $H_3O^+(aq)$ and $F^-(aq)$ (▼ Figure 14.11). In other words, a 1.0 M HF solution has $[H_3O^+] < 1.0$ M because only some of the HF molecules ionize to form H_3O^+.

Calculating exact $[H_3O^+]$ for weak acids is beyond the scope of this text.

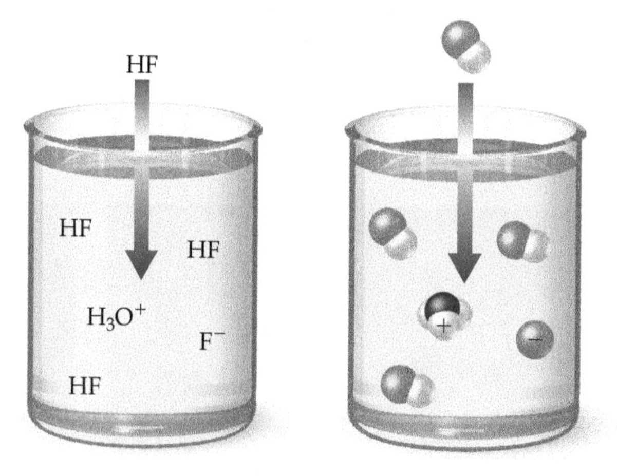

▶ **FIGURE 14.11 A weak acid** When HF dissolves in water, only a fraction of the dissolved molecules ionize into H_3O^+ and F^- ions. The solution contains many intact HF molecules.

A weak acid is an example of a **weak electrolyte**, a substance whose aqueous solutions are poor conductors of electricity (▶ Figure 14.12). Weak acid solutions contain few charged particles because only a small fraction of the acid molecules ionize into positive and negative ions.

Notice that the strength of a conjugate base is related to its attraction to H^+ in solution.

The degree to which an acid is strong or weak depends in part on the attraction between the anion of the acid (the conjugate base) and the hydrogen ion. Suppose HA is a generic formula for an acid. Then, the degree to which the following reaction proceeds in the forward direction depends in part on the strength of the attraction between H^+ and A^-.

$$\underset{\text{Acid}}{HA(aq)} + H_2O(l) \longrightarrow H_3O^+(aq) + \underset{\text{Conjugate base}}{A^-(aq)}$$

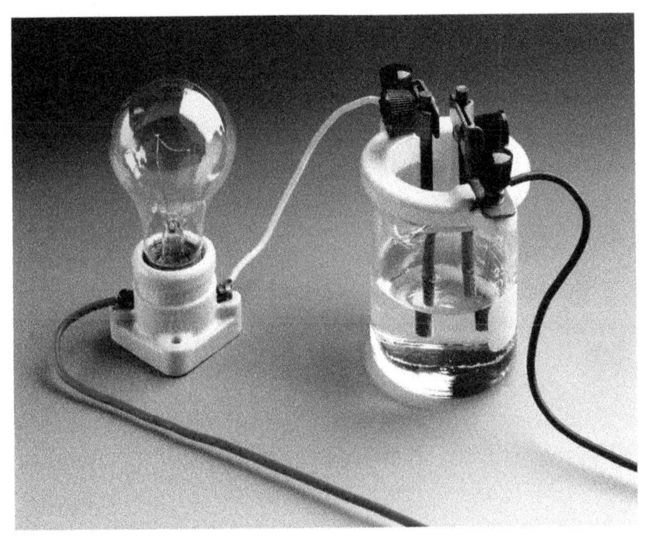

(a) Pure water

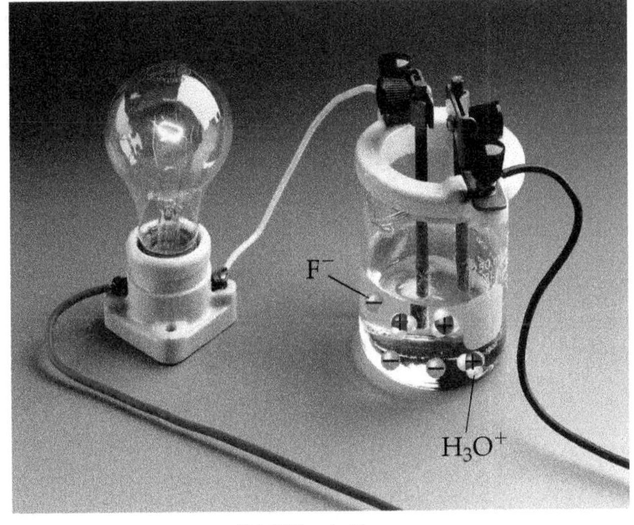

(b) HF solution

▲ **FIGURE 14.12 Conductivity of a weak electrolyte solution** **(a)** Pure water will not conduct electricity. **(b)** An HF solution contains some ions, but most of the HF is intact. The light glows only dimly. Solutions such as these are called weak electrolyte solutions.

Notice that the strength of a conjugate base is related to its attraction to H^+ in solution.

If the attraction between H^+ and A^- is *weak*, then the reaction favors the forward direction and the acid is *strong* (◀ Figure 14.13a). If the attraction between H^+ and A^- is *strong*, then the reaction favors the reverse direction and the acid is *weak* (Figure 14.13b).

For example, in HCl, the conjugate base (Cl^-) has a relatively weak attraction to H^+, meaning that the reverse reaction does not occur to any significant extent. In HF, on the other hand, the conjugate base (F^-) has a greater attraction to H^+, meaning that the reverse reaction occurs to a significant degree. *In general, the stronger the acid, the weaker the conjugate base and vice versa.* This means that if the forward reaction (that of the acid) has a high tendency to occur, then the reverse reaction (that of the conjugate base) has a low tendency to occur. Table 14.4 lists some common weak acids.

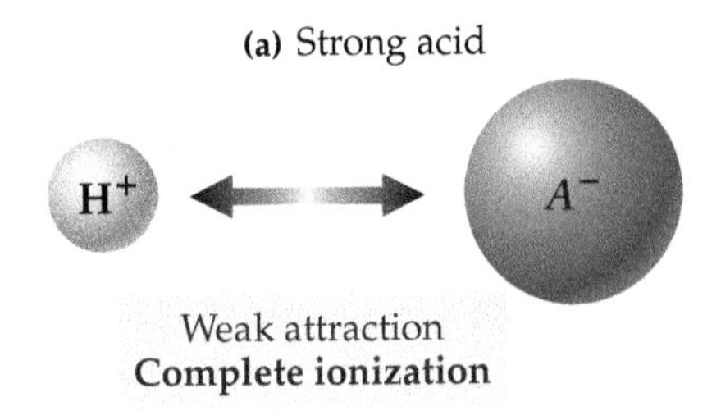

(b) Weak acid

H^+ ⟷ A^-

Strong attraction
Partial ionization

▲ **FIGURE 14.13 Strong and weak acids** **(a)** In a strong acid, the attraction between H^+ and A^- is low, resulting in complete ionization. **(b)** In a weak acid, the attraction between H^+ and A^- is high, resulting in partial ionization.

TABLE 14.4 Some Weak Acids

hydrofluoric acid (HF)	sulfurous acid (H_2SO_3) *(diprotic)*
acetic acid ($HC_2H_3O_2$)	carbonic acid (H_2CO_3) *(diprotic)*
formic acid ($HCHO_2$)	phosphoric acid (H_3PO_4) *(triprotic)*

Notice that two of the weak acids in Table 14.4 are diprotic (meaning they have two ionizable protons) and one is triprotic (meaning that it has three ionizable protons). Let us return to sulfuric acid for a moment. Sulfuric acid is a diprotic acid that is strong in its first ionizable proton:

$$H_2SO_4(aq) + H_2O(l) \longrightarrow H_3O^+(aq) + HSO_4^-(aq)$$

but weak in its second ionizable proton.

$$HSO_4^-(aq) + H_2O(l) \rightleftharpoons H_3O^+(aq) + SO_4^{2-}(aq)$$

Sulfurous acid and carbonic acid are weak in both of their ionizable protons, and phosphoric acid is weak in all three of its ionizable protons.

EXAMPLE 14.5 Determining $[H_3O^+]$ in Acid Solutions

What is the H_3O^+ concentration in each solution?

(a) 1.5 M HCl
(b) 3.0 M $HC_2H_3O_2$
(c) 2.5 M HNO_3

SOLUTION

(a) Since HCl is a strong acid, it completely ionizes. The concentration of H_3O^+ will be 1.5 M.

$$[H_3O^+] = 1.5 \text{ M}$$

(b) Since $HC_2H_3O_2$ is a weak acid, it partially ionizes. The calculation of the exact concentration of H_3O^+ is beyond the scope of this text, but we know that it will be less than 3.0 M.

$$[H_3O^+] < 3.0 \text{ M}$$

(c) Since HNO_3 is a strong acid, it completely ionizes. The concentration of H_3O^+ will be 2.5 M.

$$[H_3O^+] = 2.5 \text{ M}$$

▶SKILLBUILDER 14.5 | Determining $[H_3O^+]$ in Acid Solutions

What is the H_3O^+ concentration in each solution?

(a) 0.50 M $HCHO_2$
(b) 1.25 M HI
(c) 0.75 M HF

▶FOR MORE PRACTICE Example 14.15; Problems 59, 60.

CONCEPTUAL CHECKPOINT 14.2

Examine the molecular views of three different acid solutions shown here. Based on these views, which one of these acids is a weak acid?

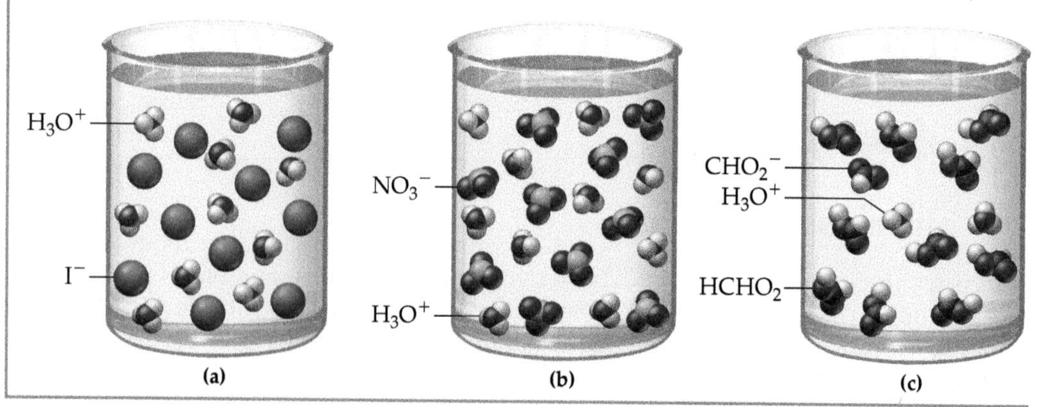

STRONG BASES

In analogy to the definition of a strong acid, a **strong base** is one that completely dissociates in solution. NaOH, for example, is a strong base.

$$NaOH(aq) \longrightarrow Na^+(aq) + OH^-(aq)$$

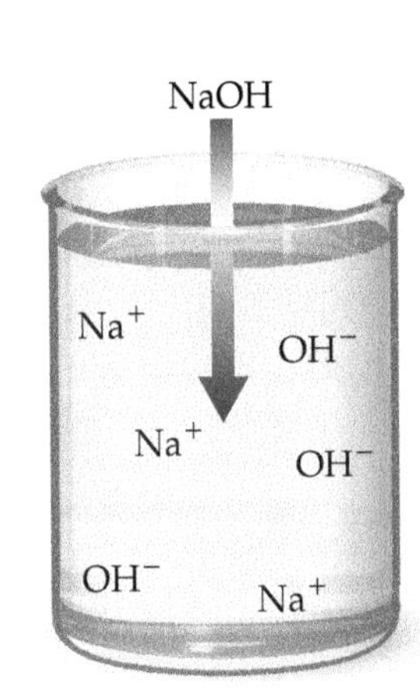

▶ **FIGURE 14.14 A strong base** When NaOH dissolves in water, it completely dissociates into Na^+ and OH^-. **Question:** The solution contains no intact NaOH. Is NaOH a strong or weak electrolyte?

An NaOH solution contains no intact NaOH—it has all dissociated to form $Na^+(aq)$ and $OH^-(aq)$ (▲ Figure 14.14), and a 1.0 M NaOH solution has $[OH^-] = 1.0$ M and $[Na^+] = 1.0$ M. Some common strong bases are listed in Table 14.5.

TABLE 14.5 Strong Bases

lithium hydroxide (LiOH)	strontium hydroxide ($Sr(OH)_2$)
sodium hydroxide (NaOH)	calcium hydroxide ($Ca(OH)_2$)
potassium hydroxide (KOH)	barium hydroxide ($Ba(OH)_2$)

Unlike diprotic acids, which ionize in two steps, bases containing 2 OH^- ions dissociate in one step.

Some strong bases, such as $Sr(OH)_2$, contain two OH^- ions. These bases completely dissociate, producing two moles of OH^- per mole of base. For example, $Sr(OH)_2$ dissociates as follows:

$$Sr(OH)_2(aq) \longrightarrow Sr^{2+}(aq) + 2\,OH^-(aq)$$

WEAK BASES

A **weak base** is analogous to a weak acid. Unlike strong bases that contain OH^- and dissociate in water, the most common weak bases produce OH^- by accepting a proton from water, ionizing water to form OH^-.

$$B(aq) + H_2O(l) \rightleftharpoons BH^+(aq) + OH^-(aq)$$

In this equation, B is generic for a weak base. Ammonia, for example, ionizes water according to the reaction:

Calculating exact $[OH^-]$ for weak bases is beyond the scope of this text.

$$NH_3(aq) + H_2O(l) \rightleftharpoons NH_4^+(aq) + OH^-(aq)$$

The double arrow indicates that the ionization is not complete. An NH_3 solution contains NH_3, NH_4^+, and OH^- (◀ Figure 14.15). A 1.0 M NH_3 solution has $[OH^-] < 1.0$ M. Table 14.6 lists some common weak bases.

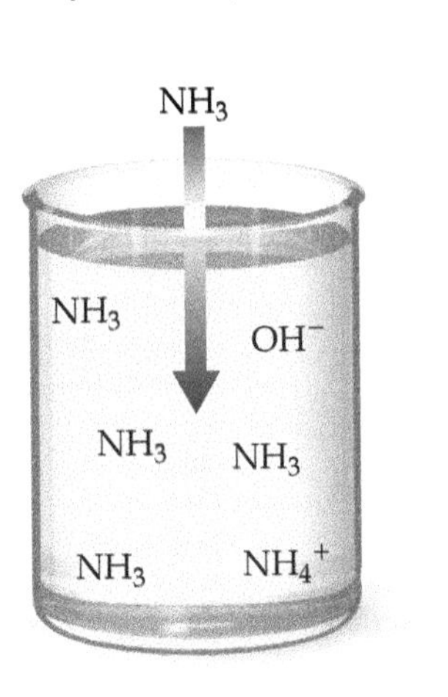

◀ **FIGURE 14.15 A weak base** When NH_3 dissolves in water, it partially ionizes to form NH_4^+ and OH^-. However, only a fraction of the molecules ionize. Most NH_3 molecules remain as NH_3. **Question:** Is NH_3 a strong or weak electrolyte?

TABLE 14.6 Some Weak Bases

Base	Ionization Reaction
ammonia (NH_3)	$NH_3(aq) + H_2O(l) \rightleftharpoons NH_4^+(aq) + OH^-(aq)$
pyridine (C_5H_5N)	$C_5H_5N(aq) + H_2O(l) \rightleftharpoons C_5H_5NH^+(aq) + OH^-(aq)$
methylamine (CH_3NH_2)	$CH_3NH_2(aq) + H_2O(l) \rightleftharpoons CH_3NH_3^+(aq) + OH^-(aq)$
ethylamine ($C_2H_5NH_2$)	$C_2H_5NH_2(aq) + H_2O(l) \rightleftharpoons C_2H_5NH_3^+(aq) + OH^-(aq)$
bicarbonate ion (HCO_3^-)*	$HCO_3^-(aq) + H_2O(l) \rightleftharpoons H_2CO_3(aq) + OH^-(aq)$

*The bicarbonate ion must occur with a positively charged ion such as Na^+ that serves to balance the charge but does not have any part in the ionization reaction. It is the bicarbonate ion that makes sodium bicarbonate ($NaHCO_3$) basic.

EXAMPLE 14.6 Determining [OH^-] in Base Solutions

What is the OH^- concentration in each solution?

(a) 2.25 M KOH
(b) 0.35 M CH_3NH_2
(c) 0.025 M $Sr(OH)_2$

SOLUTION

(a) Since KOH is a strong base, it completely dissociates into K^+ and OH^- in solution. The concentration of OH^- is 2.25 M.

$$[OH^-] = 2.25 \text{ M}$$

(b) Since CH_3NH_2 is a weak base, it only partially ionizes water. We cannot calculate the exact concentration of OH^-, but we know it is less than 0.35 M.

$$[OH^-] < 0.35 \text{ M}$$

(c) Since $Sr(OH)_2$ is a strong base, it completely dissociates into $Sr^{2+}(aq)$ and $2\,OH^-(aq)$. $Sr(OH)_2$ forms 2 mol of OH^- for every 1 mol of $Sr(OH)_2$. Consequently, the concentration of OH^- is twice the concentration of $Sr(OH)_2$.

$$[OH^-] = 2(0.025 \text{ M}) = 0.050 \text{ M}$$

▶SKILLBUILDER 14.6 | Determining [OH^-] in Base Solutions

What is the OH^- concentration in each solution?

(a) 0.055 M $Ba(OH)_2$
(b) 1.05 M C_5H_5N
(c) 0.45 M NaOH

▶FOR MORE PRACTICE Example 14.16; Problems 63, 64.

14.8 Water: Acid and Base in One

We saw earlier that water acts as a base when it reacts with HCl and as an acid when it reacts with NH_3.

Water acting as a base

$$\underset{\substack{\text{Acid} \\ \text{(Proton donor)}}}{HCl(aq)} + \underset{\substack{\text{Base} \\ \text{(Proton acceptor)}}}{H_2O(l)} \longrightarrow H_3O^+(aq) + Cl^-(aq)$$

Water acting as an acid

$$\underset{\substack{\text{Base} \\ \text{(Proton acceptor)}}}{NH_3(aq)} + \underset{\substack{\text{Acid} \\ \text{(Proton donor)}}}{H_2O(l)} \rightleftharpoons NH_4^+(aq) + OH^-(aq)$$

Water is *amphoteric*; it can act as either an acid or a base. Even in pure water, water acts as an acid and a base with itself, a process called self-ionization.

Water acting as both an acid and a base

$$\underset{\substack{\text{Acid} \\ \text{(Proton donor)}}}{H_2O(l)} + \underset{\substack{\text{Base} \\ \text{(Proton acceptor)}}}{H_2O(l)} \rightleftharpoons H_3O^+(aq) + OH^-(aq)$$

In pure water, at 25 °C, the preceding reaction occurs only to a very small extent, resulting in equal and small concentrations of H_3O^+ and OH^-.

$$[H_3O^+] = [OH^-] = 1.0 \times 10^{-7}\ \text{M} \qquad \text{(in pure water at 25 °C)}$$

where $[H_3O^+]$ = the concentration of H_3O^+ in M
and $[OH^-]$ = the concentration of OH^- in M

So all samples of water contain some hydronium ions and some hydroxide ions. The *product* of the concentration of these two ions in aqueous solutions is called the **ion product constant for water (K_w)**.

$$K_w = [H_3O^+][OH^-]$$

The units of K_w are normally dropped.

We can find the value of K_w at 25 °C by multiplying the hydronium and hydroxide concentrations for pure water listed earlier.

$$\begin{aligned} K_w &= [H_3O^+][OH^-] \\ &= (1.0 \times 10^{-7})(1.0 \times 10^{-7}) \\ &= (1.0 \times 10^{-7})^2 \\ &= 1.0 \times 10^{-14} \end{aligned}$$

The preceding equation holds true for all aqueous solutions at 25 °C. The concentration of H_3O^+ times the concentration of OH^- will be 1.0×10^{-14}. In pure water, since H_2O is the only source of these ions, there is one H_3O^+ ion for every OH^- ion. Consequently, the concentrations of H_3O^+ and OH^- are equal. Such a solution is a **neutral solution**.

In a neutral solution, $[H_3O^+] = [OH^-]$.

$$[H_3O^+] = [OH^-] = \sqrt{K_w} = 1.0 \times 10^{-7}\ \text{M (in pure water)}$$

An **acidic solution** contains an acid that creates additional H_3O^+ ions, causing $[H_3O^+]$ to increase. However, the *ion product constant still applies*.

$$[H_3O^+][OH^-] = K_w = 1.0 \times 10^{-14}$$

In an acidic solution, $[H_3O^+] > [OH^-]$.

If $[H_3O^+]$ increases, then $[OH^-]$ must decrease for the ion product to remain 1.0×10^{-14}. For example, suppose $[H_3O^+] = 1.0 \times 10^{-3}$ M; then $[OH^-]$ can be found by solving the ion product expression for $[OH^-]$.

$$(1.0 \times 10^{-3})[OH^-] = 1.0 \times 10^{-14}$$

$$[OH^-] = \frac{1.0 \times 10^{-14}}{1.0 \times 10^{-3}} = 1.0 \times 10^{-11}\ \text{M}$$

In an acidic solution, $[H_3O^+]$ is greater than 1.0×10^{-7} M, and $[OH^-]$ is less than 1.0×10^{-7} M.

In a basic solution, $[H_3O^+] < [OH^-]$.

A **basic solution** contains a base that creates additional OH^- ions, causing the $[OH^-]$ to increase and the $[H_3O^+]$ to decrease. For example, suppose $[OH^-] = 1.0 \times 10^{-2}$ M; then $[H_3O^+]$ can be found by solving the ion product expression for $[H_3O^+]$.

$$[H_3O^+](1.0 \times 10^{-2}) = 1.0 \times 10^{-14}$$

$$[H_3O^+] = \frac{1.0 \times 10^{-14}}{1.0 \times 10^{-2}} = 1.0 \times 10^{-12}\ \text{M}$$

In a basic solution, $[OH^-]$ is greater than 1.0×10^{-7} M and $[H_3O^+]$ is less than 1.0×10^{-7} M.

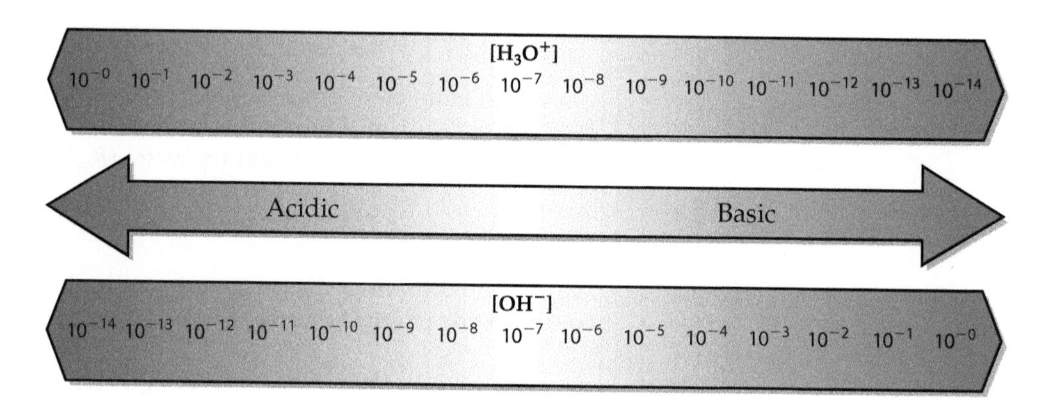

▶ FIGURE 14.16 **Acidic and basic solutions**

To summarize, at 25 °C (see ▲ Figure 14.16):

- In a neutral solution, $[H_3O^+] = [OH^-] = 1.0 \times 10^{-7}$ M
- In an acidic solution, $[H_3O^+] > 1.0 \times 10^{-7}$ M $[OH^-] < 1.0 \times 10^{-7}$ M
- In a basic solution, $[H_3O^+] < 1.0 \times 10^{-7}$M $[OH^-] > 1.0 \times 10^{-7}$ M
- In all aqueous solutions, $[H_3O^+][OH^-] = K_w = 1.0 \times 10^{-14}$

EXAMPLE 14.7 Using K_w in Calculations

Calculate $[OH^-]$ in each solution and determine whether the solution is acidic, basic, or neutral.

(a) $[H_3O^+] = 7.5 \times 10^{-5}$ M
(b) $[H_3O^+] = 1.5 \times 10^{-9}$ M
(c) $[H_3O^+] = 1.0 \times 10^{-7}$ M

	SOLUTION
To find $[OH^-]$ use the ion product constant, K_w. Substitute the given value for $[H_3O^+]$ and solve the equation for $[OH^-]$. Since $[H_3O^+] > 1.0 \times 10^{-7}$ M and $[OH^-] < 1.0 \times 10^{-7}$ M, the solution is acidic.	**(a)** $[H_3O^+][OH^-] = K_w = 1.0 \times 10^{-14}$ $[7.5 \times 10^{-5}][OH^-] = K_w = 1.0 \times 10^{-14}$ $[OH^-] = \frac{1.0 \times 10^{-14}}{7.5 \times 10^{-5}} = 1.3 \times 10^{-10}$ M acidic solution
Substitute the given value for $[H_3O^+]$ into the ion product constant equation and solve the equation for $[OH^-]$. Since $[H_3O^+] < 1.0 \times 10^{-7}$ M and $[OH^-] > 1.0 \times 10^{-7}$ M, the solution is basic.	**(b)** $[H_3O^+][OH^-] = K_w = 1.0 \times 10^{-14}$ $[1.5 \times 10^{-9}][OH^-] = 1.0 \times 10^{-14}$ $[OH^-] = \frac{1.0 \times 10^{-14}}{1.5 \times 10^{-9}} = 6.7 \times 10^{-6}$ M basic solution

Substitute the given value for $[H_3O^+]$ into the ion product constant equation and solve the equation for $[OH^-]$. Since $[H_3O^+] = 1.0 \times 10^{-7}$ M and $[OH^-] = 1.0 \times 10^{-7}$ M, the solution is neutral.

(c) $[H_3O^+][OH^-] = K_w = 1.0 \times 10^{-14}$

$[1.0 \times 10^{-7}][OH^-] = 1.0 \times 10^{-14}$

$$[OH^-] = \frac{1.0 \times 10^{-14}}{1.0 \times 10^{-7}} = 1.0 \times 10^{-7}\text{ M}$$

neutral solution

▶SKILLBUILDER 14.7 | Using K_w in Calculations

Calculate $[H_3O^+]$ in each solution and determine whether the solution is acidic, basic, or neutral.

(a) $[OH^-] = 1.5 \times 10^{-2}$ M
(b) $[OH^-] = 1.0 \times 10^{-7}$ M
(c) $[OH^-] = 8.2 \times 10^{-10}$ M

▶FOR MORE PRACTICE Example 14.17; Problems 67, 68, 69, 70.

CONCEPTUAL CHECKPOINT 14.3

Which substance would be least likely to act as a base?

(a) H_2O
(b) OH^-
(c) NH_3
(d) NH_4^+

14.9 The pH and pOH Scales: Ways to Express Acidity and Basicity

TABLE 14.7 The pH of Some Common Substances

Substance	pH
gastric (human stomach) acid	1.0–3.0
limes	1.8–2.0
lemons	2.2–2.4
soft drinks	2.0–4.0
plums	2.8–3.0
wine	2.8–3.8
apples	2.9–3.3
peaches	3.4–3.6
cherries	3.2–4.0
beer	4.0–5.0
rainwater (unpolluted)	5.6
human blood	7.3–7.4
egg whites	7.6–8.0
milk of magnesia	10.5
household ammonia	10.5–11.5
4% NaOH solution	14

Notice that an increase of 1 in pH corresponds to a tenfold *decrease* in $[H_3O^+]$.

Chemists have devised a scale based on the hydrogen ion concentration to compactly express the acidity or basicity of solutions. The scale is called the **pH** scale and at 25 °C has these general characteristics:

- $\text{pH} < 7$ ***acidic*** solution
- $\text{pH} > 7$ ***basic*** solution
- $\text{pH} = 7$ ***neutral*** solution

Strongly acidic | Weakly acidic | Neutral | Weakly basic | Strongly basic

pH 1 2 3 4 5 6 7 8 9 10 11 12 13 14

Table 14.7 lists the pH of some common substances. Notice that, as we discussed in Section 14.1, many foods, especially fruits, are acidic and therefore have low pH values. The foods with the lowest pH values are limes and lemons, and they are among the sourest. Relatively few foods, however, are basic.

The pH scale is a **logarithmic scale**; therefore, a change of 1 pH unit corresponds to a tenfold change in H_3O^+ concentration. For example, a lime with a pH of 2.0 is 10 times more acidic than a plum with a pH of 3.0 and 100 times more acidic than a cherry with a pH of 4.0. Each change of 1 in pH scale corresponds to a change of 10 in $[H_3O^+]$ (▶ Figure 14.17).

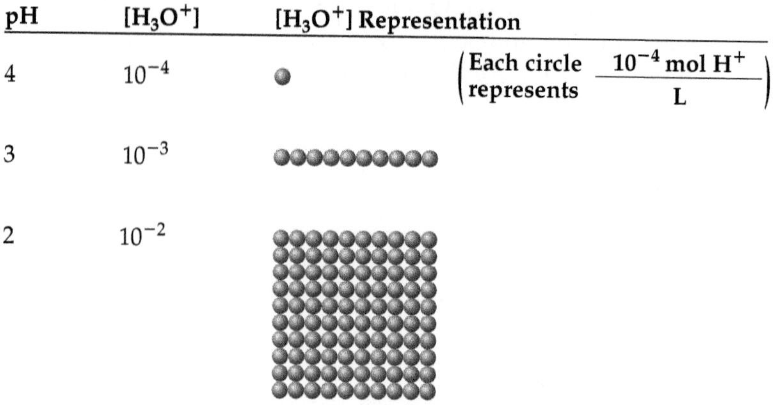

pH	$[H_3O^+]$	$[H_3O^+]$ Representation
4	10^{-4}	● (Each circle represents $\frac{10^{-4}\text{ mol H}^+}{\text{L}}$)
3	10^{-3}	●●●●●●●●●●
2	10^{-2}	10 × 10 circles

▶ **FIGURE 14.17 The pH scale is a logarithmic scale** A *decrease* of 1 unit on the pH scale corresponds to an *increase* in $[H_3O^+]$ concentration by a factor of 10. Each circle stands for 10^{-4} mol H^+/L, or 6.022×10^{19} H^+ ions per liter.
Question: How much of an increase in H_3O^+ concentration corresponds to a decrease of 2 pH units?

CALCULATING pH FROM $[H_3O^+]$

The pH of a solution is defined as the negative of the log of the hydronium ion concentration:

Note that pH is defined using the log function (base ten), which is different from the natural log (abbreviated ln).

$$pH = -\log[H_3O^+]$$

To calculate pH, you must be able to calculate logarithms. Recall that the log of a number is the exponent to which 10 must be raised to obtain that number, as shown in these examples:

$$\log 10^1 = 1;\ \log 10^2 = 2;\ \log 10^3 = 3$$

$$\log 10^{-1} = -1;\ \log 10^{-2} = -2;\ \log 10^{-3} = -3$$

In the next example, we calculate the log of 1.5×10^{-7}. A solution having an $[H_3O^+] = 1.5 \times 10^{-7}$ M (acidic) has a pH of:

$$\begin{aligned} pH &= -\log[H_3O^+] \\ &= -\log(1.5 \times 10^{-7}) \\ &= -(-6.82) \\ &= 6.82 \end{aligned}$$

Notice that the pH is reported to two decimal places here. This is because only the numbers to the right of the decimal place are significant in a log. Since our original value for the concentration had two significant figures, the log of that number has two decimal places.

When you take the log of a quantity, the result should have the same number of decimal places as the number of significant figures in the original quantity.

$$\log 1.0 \times 10^{-3} = 3.00 \quad \text{(2 decimal places)}$$

If the original number had three significant figures, the log would be reported to three decimal places:

$$-\log 1.00 \times 10^{-3} = 3.000 \quad \text{(3 decimal places)}$$

A solution having $[H_3O^+] = 1.0 \times 10^{-7}$ M (neutral) has a pH of:

$$\begin{aligned} pH &= -\log[H_3O^+] \\ &= -\log 1.0 \times 10^{-7} \\ &= -(-7.00) \\ &= 7.00 \end{aligned}$$

EXAMPLE 14.8 Calculating pH from $[H_3O^+]$

Calculate the pH of each solution and indicate whether the solution is acidic or basic.

(a) $[H_3O^+] = 1.8 \times 10^{-4}$ M
(b) $[H_3O^+] = 7.2 \times 10^{-9}$ M

SOLUTION

To calculate pH, substitute the given $[H_3O^+]$ into the pH equation. Since the pH < 7, this solution is acidic.	(a) $\text{pH} = -\log[H_3O^+]$ $= -\log 1.8 \times 10^{-4}$ $= -(-3.74)$ $= 3.74$
Again, substitute the given $[H_3O^+]$ into the pH equation. Since the pH > 7, this solution is basic.	(b) $\text{pH} = -\log[H_3O^+]$ $= -\log(7.2 \times 10^{-9})$ $= -(-8.14)$ $= 8.14$

▶**SKILLBUILDER 14.8 | Calculating pH from $[H_3O^+]$**

Calculate the pH of each solution and indicate whether the solution is acidic or basic.

(a) $[H_3O^+] = 9.5 \times 10^{-9}$ M
(b) $[H_3O^+] = 6.1 \times 10^{-3}$ M

▶**SKILLBUILDER PLUS**

Calculate the pH of a solution with $[OH^-] = 1.3 \times 10^{-2}$ M and indicate whether the solution is acidic or basic. *Hint:* Begin by using K_w to find $[H_3O^+]$.

▶**FOR MORE PRACTICE** Example 14.18; Problems 73, 74.

CALCULATING $[H_3O^+]$ FROM pH

Ten raised to the log of a number is equal to that number: $10^{\log x} = x$.

To calculate $[H_3O^+]$ from a pH value, you must *undo* the log. The log can be undone using the inverse log function *(Method 1)* on most calculators or using the 10^x key *(Method 2)*. Both methods do the same thing; the one you use depends on your calculator.

The invlog function "undoes" log: $\text{invlog}(\log x) = x$.

Method 1: Inverse Log Function	Method 2: 10^x Function
$\text{pH} = -\log[H_3O^+]$	$\text{pH} = -\log[H_3O^+]$
$-\text{pH} = \log[H_3O^+]$	$-\text{pH} = \log[H_3O^+]$
$\text{invlog}(-\text{pH}) = \text{invlog}(\log[H_3O^+])$	$10^{-\text{pH}} = 10^{\log[H_3O^+]}$
$\text{invlog}(-\text{pH}) = [H_3O^+]$	$10^{-\text{pH}} = [H_3O^+]$

The inverse log is sometimes called the antilog.

So, to calculate $[H_3O^+]$ from a pH value, take the inverse log of the negative of the pH value *(Method 1)* or raise 10 to the negative of the pH value *(Method 2)*.

EXAMPLE 14.9 Calculating $[H_3O^+]$ from pH

Calculate the H_3O^+ concentration for a solution with a pH of 4.80.

SOLUTION

To find the $[H_3O^+]$ from pH, we must undo the log function. Use either Method 1 or Method 2.

The number of significant figures in the inverse log of a number is equal to the number of decimal places in the number.

Method 1: Inverse Log Function	Method 2: 10^x function
$pH = -\log[H_3O^+]$	$pH = -\log[H_3O^+]$
$4.80 = -\log[H_3O^+]$	$4.80 = -\log[H_3O^+]$
$-4.80 = \log[H_3O^+]$	$-4.80 = \log[H_3O^+]$
$\text{invlog}(-4.80) = \text{invlog}(\log[H_3O^+])$	$10^{-4.80} = 10^{\log[H_3O^+]}$
$\text{invlog}(-4.80) = [H_3O^+]$	$10^{-4.80} = [H_3O^+]$
$[H_3O^+] = 1.6 \times 10^{-5}$ M	$[H_3O^+] = 1.6 \times 10^{-5}$ M

▶**SKILLBUILDER 14.9 | Calculating $[H_3O^+]$ from pH**

Calculate the H_3O^+ concentration for a solution with a pH of 8.37.

▶**SKILLBUILDER PLUS**

Calculate the OH^- concentration for a solution with a pH of 3.66.

▶**FOR MORE PRACTICE** Example 14.19; Problems 75, 76.

CONCEPTUAL CHECKPOINT 14.4

Solution A has a pH of 13. Solution B has a pH of 10. The concentration of H_3O^+ in solution B is ______ times that in solution A.

(a) 0.001

(b) $\frac{1}{3}$

(c) 3

(d) 1000

THE pOH SCALE

The **pOH** scale is analogous to the pH scale, but is defined with respect to $[OH^-]$ instead of $[H_3O^+]$.

Notice that *p* is the mathematical function $-\log$; thus, $pX = -\log X$.

$$pOH = -\log\,[OH^-]$$

A solution having an $[OH^-]$ of 1.0×10^{-3}M (basic) has a pOH of 3.00. On the pOH scale, a pOH less than 7 is basic and a pOH greater than 7 is acidic. A pOH of 7 is neutral. The $[OH^-]$ concentration can be found from the pOH just as the $[H_3O^+]$ concentration is found from the pH, as shown in the following example.

EXAMPLE 14.10 Calculating $[OH^-]$ from pOH

Calculate the $[OH^-]$ concentration for a solution with a pOH of 8.55.

SOLUTION

To find the $[OH^-]$ from pOH, we must undo the log function. Use either Method 1 or Method 2.

Method 1: Inverse Log Function	Method 2: 10^x function
$pOH = -\log[OH^-]$	$pOH = -\log[OH^-]$
$8.55 = -\log[OH^-]$	$8.55 = -\log[OH^-]$
$-8.55 = \log[OH^-]$	$-8.55 = \log[OH^-]$
$\text{invlog}(-8.55) = \text{invlog}(\log[OH^-])$	$10^{-8.55} = 10^{\log[OH^-]}$
$\text{invlog}(-8.55) = [OH^-]$	$10^{-8.55} = [OH^-]$
$[OH^-] = 2.8 \times 10^{-9}$ M	$[OH^-] = 2.8 \times 10^{-9}$ M

▶**SKILLBUILDER 14.10 | Calculating OH^- from pOH**

Calculate the OH^- concentration for a solution with a pOH of 4.25.

▶**SKILLBUILDER PLUS**

Calculate the H_3O^+ concentration for a solution with a pOH of 5.68.

▶**FOR MORE PRACTICE** Problems 83, 84, 85, 86.

We can derive a relationship between pH and pOH at 25 °C from the expression for K_w.

$$[H_3O^+][OH^-] = 1.0 \times 10^{-14}$$

log (AB) = log A + log B

Taking the log of both sides, we get

$$\begin{aligned} \log\{[H_3O^+][OH^-]\} &= \log(1.0 \times 10^{-14}) \\ \log[H_3O^+] + \log[OH^-] &= -14.00 \\ -\log[H_3O^+] - \log[OH^-] &= 14.00 \\ pH + pOH &= 14.00 \end{aligned}$$

The sum of pH and pOH is always equal to 14.00 at 25 °C. Therefore, a solution with a pH of 3 has a pOH of 11.

CONCEPTUAL CHECKPOINT 14.5

A solution has a pH of 5. What is the pOH of the solution?

(a) 5 **(b)** 10 **(c)** 14 **(d)** 9

14.10 Buffers: Solutions That Resist pH Change

Most solutions rapidly become more acidic (lower pH) upon addition of an acid or more basic (higher pH) upon addition of a base. A **buffer**, however, resists pH change by neutralizing added acid or added base. Human blood, for example, is a buffer. Acid or base that is added to blood gets neutralized by components within blood, resulting in a nearly constant pH. In healthy individuals, blood pH is between 7.36 and 7.40. If blood pH were to drop below 7.0 or rise above 7.8, death would result.

How does blood maintain such a narrow pH range? Like all buffers, blood contains *significant* amounts of *both a weak acid and its conjugate base.* When additional base is added to blood, the weak acid reacts with the base, neutralizing it. When additional acid is added to blood, the conjugate base reacts with the acid, neutralizing it. In this way, blood maintains a constant pH.

Buffers can also be composed of a weak base and its conjugate acid.

CHEMISTRY AND HEALTH

Alkaloids

Alkaloids are organic bases that occur naturally in many plants (see Section 14.3) that often have medicinal qualities. Morphine, for example, is a powerful alkaloid drug that occurs in the opium poppy (▶ Figure 14.18) and is used to relieve severe pain. Morphine is an example of a *narcotic*, a drug that dulls the senses and induces sleep. It produces relief from and indifference to pain. Morphine can also produce feelings of euphoria and contentment, which leads to its abuse. Morphine is highly addictive, both psychologically and physically. A person who abuses morphine over long periods of time becomes physically dependent on the drug and suffers severe withdrawal symptoms upon termination of use.

▲ **FIGURE 14.18 Opium poppy** The opium poppy contains the alkaloids morphine and codeine.

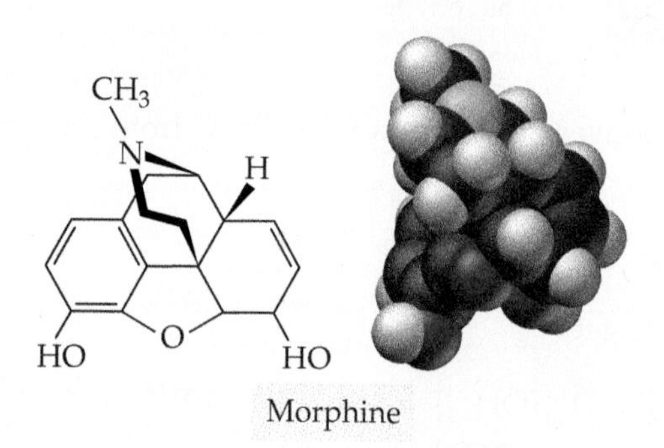

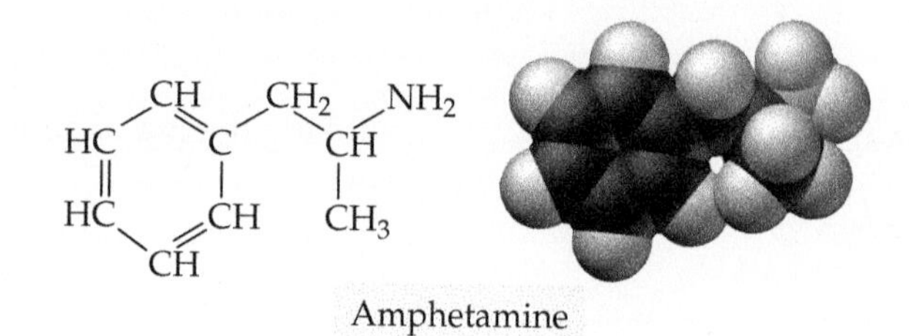

Amphetamine is another powerful drug related to the alkaloid ephedrine. Whereas morphine slows down nerve signal transmissions, amphetamine enhances them. Amphetamine is an example of a *stimulant*, a drug that increases alertness and wakefulness. Amphetamine is widely used to treat Attention-Deficit Hyperactivity Disorder (ADHD) and is prescribed under the trade name Adderall. Patients suffering from ADHD find that amphetamine helps them to focus and concentrate more effectively. However, because amphetamine produces alertness and increased stamina, it, too, is often abused.

Other common alkaloids include caffeine and nicotine, both of which are stimulants. Caffeine is found in the coffee bean, and nicotine is found in tobacco. Although both have some addictive qualities, nicotine is by far the most addictive. A nicotine addiction is among the most difficult to break, as any smoker can attest.

CAN YOU ANSWER THIS? *What part of the amphetamine and morphine molecules makes them bases?*

A simple buffer can be made by mixing both acetic acid ($HC_2H_3O_2$) and its conjugate base, sodium acetate ($NaC_2H_3O_2$) in water (▶ Figure 14.19). (The sodium in sodium acetate is just a spectator ion and does not contribute to buffering action.) Since $HC_2H_3O_2$ is a weak acid and since $C_2H_3O_2^-$ is its conjugate base, a solution containing both of these is a buffer. Note that a weak acid by itself, even though it partially ionizes to form some of its conjugate base, does not contain sufficient base to be a buffer. A buffer must contain *significant* amounts of *both* a weak acid and its conjugate base. Suppose that we add more base, in the form of NaOH, to the buffer solution containing acetic acid and sodium acetate. The acetic acid would neutralize the base according to the reaction:

$$\underset{\text{Base}}{NaOH(aq)} + \underset{\text{Acid}}{HC_2H_3O_2(aq)} \longrightarrow H_2O(l) + NaC_2H_3O_2(aq)$$

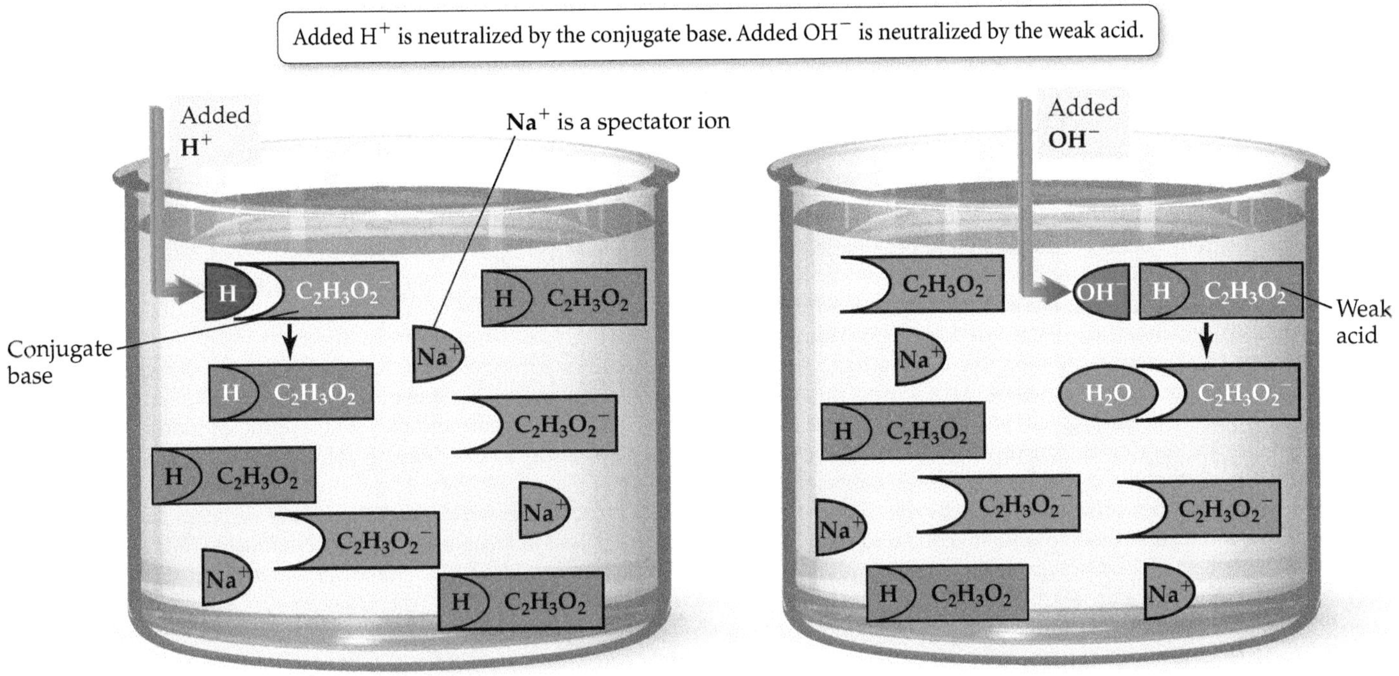

Added H^+ is neutralized by the conjugate base. Added OH^- is neutralized by the weak acid.

▲ **FIGURE 14.19 Buffers** A buffer contains significant amounts of a weak acid and its conjugate base. The acid consumes any added base, and the base consumes any added acid. In this way, a buffer resists pH change.

As long as the amount of NaOH that we add is less than the amount of $HC_2H_3O_2$ in solution, the solution neutralizes the NaOH, and the resulting pH change is small. Suppose, on the other hand, that we add more acid, in the form of HCl, to the solution. Then the conjugate base, $NaC_2H_3O_2$, neutralizes the added HCl according to the reaction:

$$\underset{\text{Acid}}{HCl(aq)} + \underset{\text{Base}}{NaC_2H_3O_2(aq)} \longrightarrow HC_2H_3O_2(aq) + NaCl(aq)$$

As long as the amount of HCl that we add is less than the amount of $NaC_2H_3O_2$ in solution, the solution will neutralize the HCl and the resulting pH change is small.

To summarize:

- Buffers resist pH change.
- Buffers contain significant amounts of both a weak acid and its conjugate base.
- The weak acid neutralizes added base.
- The conjugate base neutralizes added acid.

CONCEPTUAL CHECKPOINT 14.6

Which of the following is a buffer solution?

(a) $H_2SO_4(aq)$ and $H_2SO_3(aq)$

(b) $HF(aq)$ and $NaF(aq)$

(c) $HCl(aq)$ and $NaCl(aq)$

(d) $NaCl(aq)$ and $NaOH(aq)$

CHEMISTRY AND HEALTH

The Danger of Antifreeze

Most types of antifreeze used in cars are solutions of ethylene glycol. Every year, thousands of dogs and cats die from ethylene glycol poisoning because they consume improperly stored antifreeze or antifreeze that has leaked out of a radiator. The antifreeze has a somewhat sweet taste, which attracts a curious dog or cat. Young children are also at risk for ethylene glycol poisoning.

The first stage of ethylene glycol poisoning is a drunken state. Ethylene glycol is an alcohol, and it affects the brain of a dog or cat much as an alcoholic beverage would. Once ethylene glycol begins to metabolize, however, the second and more deadly stage begins. Ethylene glycol is metabolized in the liver into glycolic acid ($HC_2H_3O_3$), which enters the bloodstream. If the original quantities of consumed antifreeze are significant, the glycolic acid overwhelms the blood's natural buffering system, causing blood pH to drop to dangerously low levels. At this point, the cat or dog may begin hyperventilating in an effort to overcome the acidic blood's reduced ability to carry oxygen. If no treatment is administered, the animal will eventually go into a coma and die.

One treatment for ethylene glycol poisoning is the administration of ethyl alcohol (the alcohol found in alcoholic beverages). The liver enzyme that metabolizes ethylene glycol is the same one that metabolizes ethyl alcohol, but it has a higher affinity for ethyl alcohol than for ethylene glycol. Consequently, the enzyme preferentially metabolizes ethyl alcohol, allowing the unmetabolized ethylene glycol to escape through the urine. If administered early, this treatment can save the life of a dog or cat that has consumed ethylene glycol.

CAN YOU ANSWER THIS? *One of the main buffering systems found in blood consists of carbonic acid (H_2CO_3) and bicarbonate ion (HCO_3^-). Write an equation showing how this buffering system could neutralize glycolic acid ($HC_2H_3O_3$) that might enter the blood from ethylene glycol poisoning. Suppose a cat has 0.15 mol of HCO_3^- and 0.15 mol of H_2CO_3 in its bloodstream. How many grams of $HC_2H_3O_3$ could be neutralized before the buffering system in the cat's blood is overwhelmed?*

14.11 Acid Rain: An Environmental Problem Related to Fossil Fuel Combustion

About 90% of U.S. energy comes from fossil fuel combustion. Fossil fuels include petroleum, natural gas, and coal. Some fossil fuels, especially coal, contain significant amounts of sulfur impurities. During combustion, these impurities react with oxygen to form SO_2. In addition, during combustion of any fossil fuel, nitrogen from the air reacts with oxygen to form NO_2. The SO_2 and NO_2 emitted from fossil fuel combustion react with water in the atmosphere to form sulfuric acid and nitric acid.

These equations represent simplified versions of the reactions that actually occur.

$$2\ SO_2 + O_2 + 2\ H_2O \longrightarrow 2\ H_2SO_4$$

$$4\ NO_2 + O_2 + 2\ H_2O \longrightarrow 4\ HNO_3$$

These acids combine with rain to form **acid rain**. In the United States, the problem is greatest in the northeastern portion of the country because many midwestern power plants burn coal. The sulfur and nitrogen oxides produced from coal combustion in the Midwest are carried toward the Northeast by natural air currents, making rain in that portion of the country significantly acidic.

Rain is naturally somewhat acidic because of atmospheric carbon dioxide. Carbon dioxide combines with rainwater to form carbonic acid.

$$CO_2 + H_2O \longrightarrow H_2CO_3$$

However, carbonic acid is a relatively weak acid. Even rain that is saturated with CO_2 has a pH of only about 5.6, which is mildly acidic. However, when nitric acid and sulfuric acid mix with rain, the pH of the rain can fall as low as 4.4 (▶ Figure 14.20). Remember that, because of the logarithmic nature of the pH scale, rain with a pH of 4.4 has an $[H_3O^+]$ about 16 times greater than that of rain with a pH of 5.6. Rain that is this acidic has negative consequences for the environment.

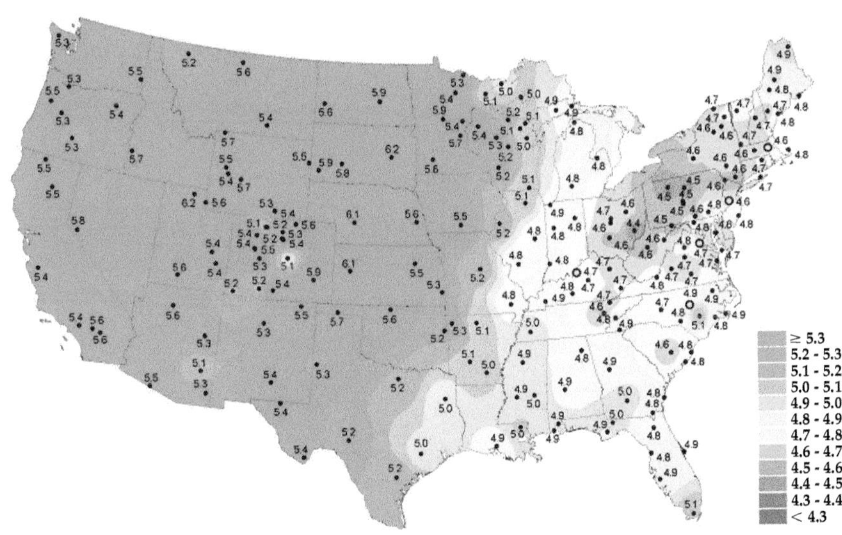

National Atmospheric Deposition Program/National Trends Network
http://nadp.sws.uiuc.edu

▶ **FIGURE 14.20 Acid rain in the United States** Average pH of precipitation in the United States for 2008.

ACID RAIN DAMAGE

Because acids dissolve metals, acid rain damages metal structures. Bridges, railroads, and even automobiles can be damaged by acid rain. Since acids also react with carbonates (CO_3^{2-}), acid rain damages building materials that contain carbonates, including marble, cement, and limestone. Statues, buildings, and pathways in the Northeast show significant signs of acid rain damage (▼ Figure 14.21).

Acid rain can also accumulate in lakes and rivers and affect aquatic life. In the northeastern United States, more than 2000 lakes and streams have increased acidity levels due to acid rain. Aquatic plants, frogs, salamanders, and some species of fish are sensitive to acid levels and cannot live in the acidified lakes. Trees can also be affected by acid rain because the acid removes nutrients from the soil, making it more difficult for trees to survive.

▶ **FIGURE 14.21 Acid rain damage** Many monuments and statues, such as this one of George Washington in New York's Washington Square Park, have suffered severe deterioration caused by acid rain. The photo at left was taken in 1935, the one at right some 60 years later. (The statue has recently undergone restoration.)

ACID RAIN LEGISLATION

The Clean Air Act, and its 1990 amendments, have provisions that target acid rain. These provisions force electrical utilities—which are the most significant source of SO_2—to lower their SO_2 emissions gradually over time (▶ Figure 14.22). The decrease in SO_2 emissions has been significant, and the acidity of rain in the Northeast has already stabilized and should decrease in the coming years. Scientists expect most lakes, streams, and forests to recover once the pH of the rain returns to normal levels.

See Section 7.8 for the reaction between acids and carbonates.

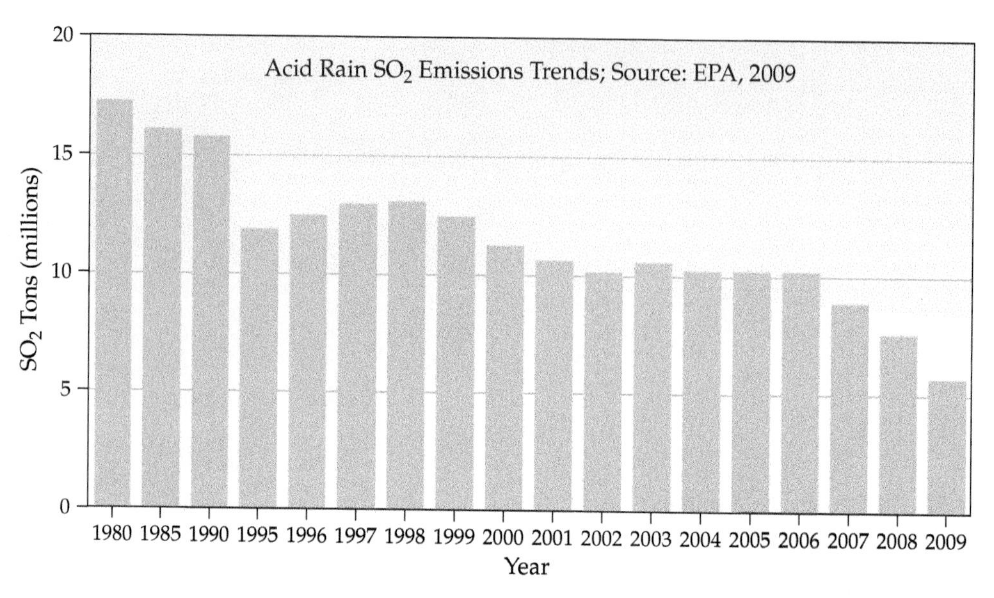

▲ FIGURE 14.22 **Emissions of SO_2 from 1980 to 2009** The height of each bar represents annual SO_2 emissions for the year noted. Under the Clean Air Act and its amendments, SO_2 emissions have been decreasing significantly in the last 30 years.

CHAPTER IN REVIEW

CHEMICAL PRINCIPLES

Acid Properties:

- Acids have a sour taste.
- Acids dissolve many metals.
- Acids turn blue litmus paper red.

Base Properties:

- Bases have a bitter taste.
- Bases have a slippery feel.
- Bases turn red litmus paper blue.

Molecular Definitions of Acids and Bases:

Arrhenius definition

Acid—substance that produces H^+ ions in solution

Base—substance that produces OH^- ions in solution

Brønsted–Lowry definition

Acid—proton donor

Base—proton acceptor

RELEVANCE

Acid Properties: Acids are responsible for the sour taste in many foods such as lemons, limes, and vinegar. They are also often used in the laboratory and in industry.

Base Properties: Bases are less common in foods, but their presence in some foods—such as coffee and beer—is enjoyed by many as an acquired taste. Bases also have widespread use in the laboratory and in industry.

Molecular Definitions of Acids and Bases: The Arrhenius definition is simpler and easier to use. It also shows how an acid and a base neutralize each other to form water ($H^+ + OH^- \longrightarrow H_2O$). The more generally applicable Brønsted–Lowry definition helps us see that, in water, H^+ ions usually associate with water molecules to form H_3O^+. It also shows how bases that do not contain OH^- ions can still act as bases by accepting a proton from water.

Reactions of Acids and Bases:
Neutralization Reactions In a neutralization reaction, an acid and a base react to form water and a salt.

$$\underset{\text{Acid}}{HCl(aq)} + \underset{\text{Base}}{KOH(aq)} \longrightarrow \underset{\text{Water}}{H_2O(l)} + \underset{\text{Salt}}{KCl(aq)}$$

Acid–Metal Reactions Acids react with many metals to form hydrogen gas and a salt.

$$2\,\underset{\text{Acid}}{HCl(aq)} + \underset{\text{Metal}}{Mg(s)} \longrightarrow \underset{\text{Hydrogen gas}}{H_2(g)} + \underset{\text{Salt}}{MgCl_2(aq)}$$

Acid–Metal Oxide Reactions Acids react with many metal oxides to form water and a salt.

$$2\,\underset{\text{Acid}}{HCl(aq)} + \underset{\text{Metal oxide}}{K_2O(s)} \longrightarrow \underset{\text{Water}}{H_2O(l)} + 2\,\underset{\text{Salt}}{KCl(aq)}$$

Reactions of Acids and Bases: Neutralization reactions are common in our everyday lives. Antacids, for example, are bases that react with acids from the stomach to alleviate heartburn and sour stomach.
Acid–metal and acid–metal oxide reactions show the corrosive nature of acids. In both of these reactions, the acid dissolves the metal or the metal oxide. Some of the effects of these kinds of reactions can be seen in the damage to building materials caused by acid rain. Since acids dissolve metals and metal oxides, any building materials composed of these substances are susceptible to acid rain.

Acid–Base Titration: In an acid–base titration, an acid (or base) of known concentration is added to a base (or acid) of unknown concentration. The two reactants are combined until they are in exact stoichiometric proportions (moles of H^+ = moles of OH^-), which marks the equivalence point of the titration. In titration, since you know the moles of H^+ (or OH^-) that you added, you can determine the moles of OH^- (or H^+) in the unknown solution.

Acid–Base Titration: An acid–base titration is a laboratory procedure often used to determine the unknown concentration of an acid or a base.

Strong and Weak Acids and Bases: Strong acids completely ionize, and strong bases completely dissociate in aqueous solutions. For example:

$$HCl(aq) + H_2O(l) \longrightarrow H_3O^+(aq) + Cl^-(aq)$$

$$NaOH(aq) \longrightarrow Na^+(aq) + OH^-(aq)$$

A 1 M HCl solution has $[H_3O^+]$ = 1 M and a 1 M NaOH solution has $[OH^-]$ = 1 M.

Weak acids only partially ionize in solution. Most weak bases partially ionize water in solution. For example:

$$HF(aq) + H_2O(l) \rightleftharpoons H_3O^+(aq) + F^-(aq)$$

$$NH_3(aq) + H_2O(l) \rightleftharpoons NH_4^+(aq) + OH^-(aq)$$

A 1 M HF solution has $[H_3O^+] < 1$ M, and a 1 M NH_3 solution has $[OH^-] < 1$ M.

Strong and Weak Acids and Bases: Whether an acid is strong or weak depends on the conjugate base: The stronger the conjugate base, the weaker the acid. Since the acidity or basicity of a solution depends on $[H_3O^+]$ and $[OH^-]$, we must know whether an acid is strong or weak to know the degree of acidity or basicity.

Self-Ionization of Water: Water can act as both an acid and a base with itself.

$$\underset{\text{Acid}}{H_2O(l)} + \underset{\text{Base}}{H_2O(l)} \rightleftharpoons H_3O^+(aq) + OH^-(aq)$$

The product of $[H_3O^+]$ and $[OH^-]$ in aqueous solutions will always be equal to the ion product constant, $K_w(10^{-14})$.

$$[H_3O^+][OH^-] = K_w = 1.0 \times 10^{-14}$$

Self-Ionization of Water: The self-ionization of water occurs because aqueous solutions always contain some H_3O^+ and some OH^-. In a neutral solution, the concentrations of these are equal (1.0×10^{-7} M). When an acid is added to water, $[H_3O^+]$ increases and $[OH^-]$ decreases. When a base is added to water, the opposite happens. The ion product constant, however, still equals 1.0×10^{-14}, allowing us to calculate $[H_3O^+]$ given $[OH^-]$ and vice versa.

pH and pOH Scales:

$$pH = -\log[H_3O^+]$$
$$pH > 7\,(\text{basic})$$
$$pH < 7\,(\text{acidic})$$
$$pH = 7\,(\text{neutral})$$
$$pOH = -\log[OH^-]$$

pH and pOH Scales: pH is a convenient way to specify acidity or basicity. Since the pH scale is logarithmic, a change of one on the pH scale corresponds to a tenfold change in the $[H_3O^+]$. The pOH scale, defined with respect to $[OH^-]$ instead of $[H_3O^+]$, is less commonly used.

Buffers: Buffers are solutions containing significant amounts of both a weak acid and its conjugate base. Buffers resist pH change by neutralizing added acid or base.

Buffers: Buffers are important in blood chemistry because blood must stay within a narrow pH range in order to carry oxygen.

Acid Rain: Acid rain is the result of sulfur oxides and nitrogen oxides emitted by fossil fuel combustion. These oxides react with water to form sulfuric acid and nitric acid, which then fall as acid rain.

Acid Rain: Since acids are corrosive, acid rain damages building materials. Because many aquatic plants and animals cannot survive in acidic water, acid rain also affects lakes and rivers, making them too acidic for the survival of some species.

CHEMICAL SKILLS

EXAMPLES

Identifying Brønsted–Lowry Acids and Bases and Their Conjugates (Section 14.4)

The substance that donates the proton is the acid (proton donor) and becomes the conjugate base (as a product). The substance that accepts the proton (proton acceptor) is the base and becomes the conjugate acid (as a product).

EXAMPLE 14.11 Identifying Brønsted–Lowry Acids and Bases and Their Conjugates

Identify the Brønsted–Lowry acid, the Brønsted–Lowry base, the conjugate acid, and the conjugate base in this reaction:

$$HNO_3(aq) + H_2O(l) \longrightarrow H_3O^+(aq) + NO_3^-(aq)$$

SOLUTION

$$\underset{\text{Acid}}{HNO_3(aq)} + \underset{\text{Base}}{H_2O(l)} \longrightarrow \underset{\text{Conjugate acid}}{H_3O^+(aq)} + \underset{\text{Conjugate base}}{NO_3^-(aq)}$$

Writing Equations for Neutralization Reactions (Section 14.5)

In a neutralization reaction, an acid and a base usually react to form water and a salt (ionic compound).

$$\text{Acid} + \text{Base} \longrightarrow \text{Water} + \text{Salt}$$

Write the skeletal equation first, making sure to write the formula of the salt so that it is charge-neutral. Then balance the equation.

EXAMPLE 14.12 Writing Equations for Neutralization Reactions

Write a molecular equation for the reaction between aqueous HBr and aqueous $Ca(OH)_2$.

SOLUTION

Skeletal equation:

$$HBr(aq) + Ca(OH)_2(aq) \longrightarrow H_2O(l) + CaBr_2(aq)$$

Balanced equation:

$$2\,HBr(aq) + Ca(OH)_2(aq) \longrightarrow 2\,H_2O(l) + CaBr_2(aq)$$

Writing Equations for the Reactions of Acids with Metals and with Metal Oxides (Section 14.5)

Acids react with many metals to form hydrogen gas and a salt.

$$\text{Acid} + \text{Metal} \longrightarrow \text{Hydrogen gas} + \text{Salt}$$

Write the skeletal equation first, making sure to write the formula of the salt so that it is charge-neutral. Then balance the equation.

Acids react with many metal oxides to form water and a salt.

$$\text{Acid} + \text{Metal oxide} \longrightarrow \text{Water} + \text{Salt}$$

Write the skeletal equation first, making sure to write the formula of the salt so that it is charge-neutral. Then balance the equation.

EXAMPLE 14.13 Writing Equations for the Reactions of Acids with Metals and with Metal Oxides

Write equations for the reaction of hydrobromic acid with calcium metal and for the reaction of hydrobromic acid with calcium oxide.

SOLUTION

Skeletal equation:

$$HBr(aq) + Ca(s) \longrightarrow H_2(g) + CaBr_2(aq)$$

Balanced equation:

$$2\ HBr(aq) + Ca(s) \longrightarrow H_2(g) + CaBr_2(aq)$$

Skeletal equation:

$$HBr(aq) + CaO(s) \longrightarrow H_2O(l) + CaBr_2(aq)$$

Balanced equation:

$$2\ HBr(aq) + CaO(s) \longrightarrow H_2O(l) + CaBr_2(aq)$$

Acid–Base Titrations (Section 14.6)

EXAMPLE 14.14 Acid–Base Titrations

A 15.00-mL sample of a NaOH solution of unknown concentration requires 17.88 mL of a 0.1053 M H_2SO_4 solution to reach the equivalence point in a titration. What is the concentration of the NaOH solution?

SORT

You are given the volume of a sodium hydroxide solution and the volume and concentration of the sulfuric acid solution required for its titration. You are asked to find the concentration of the sodium hydroxide solution.

GIVEN: 15.00-mL NaOH

17.88 mL of a 0.1053 M H_2SO_4 solution

FIND: concentration of NaOH solution mol/L

STRATEGIZE

Begin by writing the balanced equation for the neutralization reaction (see Example 14.12).

Next draw a solution map. Use the volume and concentration of the known reactant to determine moles of the known reactant. (You have to convert from milliliters to liters first.) Then use the stoichiometric ratio from the balanced equation to get moles of the unknown reactant.

Then add a second part to the solution map indicating how moles and volume can be used to determine molarity.

SOLUTION MAP

$$H_2SO_4(aq) + 2\ NaOH(aq) \longrightarrow 2\ H_2O(l) + Na_2SO_4(aq)$$

mL H_2SO_4 → L H_2SO_4 → mol H_2SO_4 → mol NaOH

$$\frac{1\ \text{L}}{1000\ \text{mL}} \qquad \frac{0.1053\ \text{mol}\ H_2SO_4}{1\ \text{L}\ H_2SO_4} \qquad \frac{2\ \text{mol NaOH}}{1\ \text{mol}\ H_2SO_4}$$

mol NaOH, volume NaOH solution → molarity

$$M = \frac{\text{mol}}{\text{L}}$$

RELATIONSHIPS USED

2 mol NaOH : 1 mol H_2SO_4 (from balanced equation)

$$\text{Molarity}(M) = \frac{\text{mol solute}}{\text{L solution}}$$

SOLVE

Follow the solution map to solve the problem. The first part of the solution gives you moles of the unknown reactant. In the second part of the solution, divide the moles from the first part by the volume to obtain molarity.

SOLUTION

$$17.88\ \cancel{mL}\ \cancel{H_2SO_4} \times \frac{1\ \cancel{L}}{1000\ \cancel{mL}} \times \frac{0.1053\ \cancel{mol\ H_2SO_4}}{\cancel{L}\ \cancel{H_2SO_4}} \times \frac{2\ mol\ NaOH}{1\ \cancel{mol\ H_2SO_4}} = 3.7655 \times 10^{-3}\ mol\ NaOH$$

$$M = \frac{mol}{L} = \frac{3.7655 \times 10^{-3}\ mol\ NaOH}{0.01500\ L\ NaOH} = 0.2510\ M$$

The unknown NaOH solution has a concentration of 0.2510 M.

CHECK

Check your answer. Are the units correct? Does the answer make physical sense?

The units (M) are correct. The magnitude of the answer makes sense because the reaction has a two-to-one stoichiometry and the volumes of the two solutions are similar; therefore, the concentration of the NaOH solution must be approximately twice the concentration of the H_2SO_4 solution.

Determining $[H_3O^+]$ in Acid Solutions (Section 14.7)

In a strong acid, $[H_3O^+]$ will be equal to the concentration of the acid. In a weak acid, $[H_3O^+]$ will be less than the concentration of the acid.

EXAMPLE 14.15 Determining $[H_3O^+]$ in Acid Solutions

What is the H_3O^+ concentration in a 0.25 M HCl solution and in a 0.25 M HF solution?

SOLUTION

In the 0.25 M HCl solution (strong acid), $[H_3O^+] = 0.25$ M. In the 0.25 M HF solution (weak acid), $[H_3O^+] < 0.25$ M.

Determining $[OH^-]$ in Base Solutions (Section 14.7)

In a strong base, $[OH^-]$ is equal to the concentration of the base times the number of hydroxide ions in the base. In a weak base, $[OH^-]$ is less than the concentration of the base.

EXAMPLE 14.16 Determining $[OH^-]$ in Base Solutions

What is the OH^- concentration in a 0.25 M NaOH solution, in a 0.25 M $Sr(OH)_2$ solution, and in a 0.25 M NH_3 solution?

SOLUTION

In the 0.25 M NaOH solution (strong base), $[OH^-] = 0.25$ M. In the 0.25 M $Sr(OH)_2$ solution (strong base),

$[OH^-] = 0.50$ M. In the 0.25 M NH_3 solution (weak base),

$[OH^-] < 0.25$ M.

Finding the Concentration of $[H_3O^+]$ or $[OH^-]$ from K_w (Section 14.8)

To find $[H_3O^+]$ or $[OH^-]$, use the ion product constant expression.

$$[H_3O^+][OH^-] = 1.0 \times 10^{-14}$$

Substitute the known quantity into the equation ($[H_3O^+]$ or $[OH^-]$) and solve for the unknown quantity.

EXAMPLE 14.17 Finding the Concentration of $[H_3O^+]$ or $[OH^-]$ from K_w

Calculate $[OH^-]$ in a solution with

$$[H_3O^+] = 1.5 \times 10^{-4}\ M.$$

SOLUTION

$$[H_3O^+][OH^-] = 1.0 \times 10^{-14}$$

$$[1.5 \times 10^{-4}][OH^-] = 1.0 \times 10^{-14}$$

$$[OH^-] = \frac{1.0 \times 10^{-14}}{1.5 \times 10^{-4}} = 6.7 \times 10^{-11}\ M$$

Calculating pH from $[H_3O^+]$ (Section 14.9)

To calculate the pH of a solution from $[H_3O^+]$, simply take the negative log of $[H_3O^+]$.

$$pH = -\log[H_3O^+]$$

EXAMPLE 14.18 Calculating pH from $[H_3O^+]$

Calculate the pH of a solution with $[H_3O^+] = 2.4 \times 10^{-5}$ M.

SOLUTION

$$\begin{aligned} pH &= -\log[H_3O^+] \\ &= -\log(2.4 \times 10^{-5}) \\ &= -(-4.62) \\ &= 4.62 \end{aligned}$$

Calculating $[H_3O^+]$ from pH (Section 14.9)

You can calculate $[H_3O^+]$ from pH by taking the inverse log of the negative of the pH value (Method 1):

$$[H_3O^+] = \text{invlog}(-pH)$$

You can also calculate $[H_3O^+]$ from pH by raising 10 to the negative of the pH (Method 2):

$$[H_3O^+] = 10^{-pH}$$

EXAMPLE 14.19 Calculating $[H_3O^+]$ from pH

Calculate the $[H_3O^+]$ for a solution with a pH of 6.22.

SOLUTION

Method 1: Inverse Log Function

$$\begin{aligned} [H_3O^+] &= \text{invlog}(-pH) \\ &= \text{invlog}(-6.22) \\ &= 6.0 \times 10^{-7} \end{aligned}$$

Method 2: 10^x Function

$$\begin{aligned} [H_3O^+] &= 10^{-pH} \\ &= 10^{-6.22} \\ &= 6.0 \times 10^{-7} \end{aligned}$$

KEY TERMS

acid **[14.2]**
acid rain **[14.11]**
acidic solution **[14.8]**
alkaloid **[14.3]**
amphoteric **[14.4]**
Arrhenius acid **[14.4]**
Arrhenius base **[14.4]**
Arrhenius definition **[14.4]**
base **[14.3]**
basic solution **[14.8]**
Brønsted–Lowry acid **[14.4]**
Brønsted–Lowry base **[14.4]**
Brønsted–Lowry definition **[14.4]**
buffer **[14.10]**
carboxylic acid **[14.2]**
conjugate acid–base pair **[14.4]**
diprotic acid **[14.7]**
dissociation **[14.4]**
equivalence point **[14.6]**
hydronium ion **[14.4]**
indicator **[14.6]**
ion product constant for water (K_w) **[14.8]**
ionize **[14.4]**
logarithmic scale **[14.9]**
monoprotic acid **[14.7]**
neutral solution **[14.8]**
neutralization **[14.5]**
pH **[14.9]**
pOH **[14.9]**
salt **[14.5]**
strong acid **[14.7]**
strong base **[14.7]**
strong electrolyte **[14.7]**
titration **[14.6]**
weak acid **[14.7]**
weak base **[14.7]**
weak electrolyte **[14.7]**

EXERCISES

QUESTIONS

1. What makes tart gummy candies, such as Sour Patch Kids, sour?
2. What are the properties of acids? List some examples of foods that contain acids.
3. What is the main component of stomach acid? Why do we have stomach acid?
4. What are organic acids? List two examples of organic acids.
5. What are the properties of bases? Provide some examples of common substances that contain bases.
6. What are alkaloids?
7. Give the Arrhenius definition of an acid and demonstrate the definition with a chemical equation.
8. Give the Arrhenius definition of a base and demonstrate the definition with a chemical equation.
9. Give the Brønsted–Lowry definitions of acids and bases and demonstrate each with a chemical equation.
10. According to the Brønsted–Lowry definition of acids and bases, what is a conjugate acid–base pair? Provide an example.

11. What is an acid–base neutralization reaction? Provide an example.
12. Provide an example of a reaction between an acid and a metal.
13. List an example of a reaction between an acid and a metal oxide.
14. Name a metal that dissolves in a base and write an equation for the reaction.
15. What is a titration? What is the equivalence point?
16. If a solution contains 0.85 mol of OH^-, how many moles of H^+ would be required to reach the equivalence point in a titration?
17. What is the difference between a strong acid and a weak acid?
18. How is the strength of an acid related to the strength of its conjugate base?
19. What are monoprotic and diprotic acids?
20. What is the difference between a strong base and a weak base?
21. Does pure water contain any H_3O^+ ions? Explain.
22. What happens to $[OH^-]$ in an aqueous solution when $[H_3O^+]$ increases?
23. Give a possible value of $[OH^-]$ and $[H_3O^+]$ in a solution that is:

    (a) acidic (b) basic (c) neutral
24. How is pH defined? A change of 1.0 pH unit corresponds to how much of a change in $[H_3O^+]$?
25. How is pOH defined? A change of 2.0 pOH units corresponds to how much of a change in $[OH^-]$?
26. In any aqueous solution at 25 °C, the sum of pH and pOH is 14.0. Explain why this is so.
27. What is a buffer?
28. What are the main components in a buffer?
29. What is the cause of acid rain?
30. Write equations for the chemical reactions by which acid rain forms in the atmosphere.
31. What are the effects of acid rain?
32. How is the problem of acid rain being addressed in the United States?

PROBLEMS

ACID AND BASE DEFINITIONS

33. Identify each substance as an acid or a base and write a chemical equation showing how it is an acid or a base according to the Arrhenius definition.

    (a) $H_2SO_4(aq)$
    (b) $Sr(OH)_2(aq)$
    (c) $HBr(aq)$
    (d) $NaOH(aq)$

34. Identify each substance as an acid or a base and write a chemical equation showing how it is an acid or a base according to the Arrhenius definition.

    (a) $Ca(OH)_2(aq)$
    (b) $HC_2H_3O_2(aq)$
    (c) $KOH(aq)$
    (d) $HNO_3(aq)$

35. For each reaction, identify the Brønsted–Lowry acid, the Brønsted–Lowry base, the conjugate acid, and the conjugate base.

    (a) $HBr(aq) + H_2O(l) \longrightarrow H_3O^+(aq) + Br^-(aq)$
    (b) $NH_3(aq) + H_2O(l) \rightleftharpoons NH_4^+(aq) + OH^-(aq)$
    (c) $HNO_3(aq) + H_2O(l) \longrightarrow H_3O^+(aq) + NO_3^-(aq)$
    (d) $C_5H_5N(aq) + H_2O(l) \rightleftharpoons C_5H_5NH^+(aq) + OH^-(aq)$

36. For each reaction, identify the Brønsted–Lowry acid, the Brønsted–Lowry base, the conjugate acid, and the conjugate base.

    (a) $HI(aq) + H_2O(l) \longrightarrow H_3O^+(aq) + I^-(aq)$
    (b) $CH_3NH_2(aq) + H_2O(l) \rightleftharpoons CH_3NH_3^+(aq) + OH^-(aq)$
    (c) $CO_3^{2-}(aq) + H_2O(l) \rightleftharpoons HCO_3^-(aq) + OH^-(aq)$
    (d) $H_2CO_3(aq) + H_2O(l) \rightleftharpoons H_3O^+(aq) + HCO_3^-(aq)$

37. Determine whether each pair is a conjugate acid–base pair.

    (a) NH_3, NH_4^+
    (b) HCl, HBr
    (c) $C_2H_3O_2^-$, $HC_2H_3O_2$
    (d) HCO_3^-, NO_3^-

38. Determine whether each pair is a conjugate acid–base pair

    (a) HI, I^-
    (b) $HCHO_2$, SO_4^{2-}
    (c) PO_4^{3-}, HPO_4^{2-}
    (d) CO_3^{2-}, HCl

39. Write the formula for the conjugate base of each acid.

    (a) HCl (b) H_2SO_3
    (c) $HCHO_2$ (d) HF

40. Write the formula for the conjugate base of each acid.

    (a) HBr (b) H_2CO_3
    (c) $HClO_4$ (d) $HC_2H_3O_2$

41. Write the formula for the conjugate acid of each base.
(a) NH_3
(b) ClO_4^-
(c) HSO_4^-
(d) CO_3^{2-}

42. Write the formula for the conjugate acid of each base.
(a) CH_3NH_2
(b) C_5H_5N
(c) Cl^-
(d) F^-

ACID–BASE REACTIONS

43. Write a neutralization reaction for each acid and base pair.
(a) $HI(aq)$ and $NaOH(aq)$
(b) $HBr(aq)$ and $KOH(aq)$
(c) $HNO_3(aq)$ and $Ba(OH)_2(aq)$
(d) $HClO_4(aq)$ and $Sr(OH)_2(aq)$

44. Write a neutralization reaction for each acid and base pair.
(a) $HF(aq)$ and $Ba(OH)_2(aq)$
(b) $HClO_4(aq)$ and $NaOH(aq)$
(c) $HBr(aq)$ and $Ca(OH)_2(aq)$
(d) $HCl(aq)$ and $KOH(aq)$

45. Write a balanced chemical equation showing how each metal reacts with HBr.
(a) Rb
(b) Mg
(c) Ba
(d) Al

46. Write a balanced chemical equation showing how each metal reacts with HCl.
(a) K
(b) Ca
(c) Na
(d) Sr

47. Write a balanced chemical equation showing how each metal oxide reacts with HI.
(a) MgO
(b) K_2O
(c) Rb_2O
(d) CaO

48. Write a balanced chemical equation showing how each metal oxide reacts with HCl.
(a) SrO
(b) Na_2O
(c) Li_2O
(d) BaO

49. Predict the products of each reaction:
(a) $HClO_4(aq) + Fe_2O_3(s) \longrightarrow$
(b) $H_2SO_4(aq) + Sr(s) \longrightarrow$
(c) $H_3PO_4(aq) + KOH(aq) \longrightarrow$

50. Predict the products of each reaction:
(a) $HI(aq) + Al(s) \longrightarrow$
(b) $H_2SO_4(aq) + TiO_2(s) \longrightarrow$
(c) $H_2CO_3(aq) + LiOH(aq) \longrightarrow$

ACID–BASE TITRATIONS

51. Four solutions of unknown HCl concentration are titrated with solutions of NaOH. The following table lists the volume of each unknown HCl solution, the volume of NaOH solution required to reach the equivalence point, and the concentration of each NaOH solution. Calculate the concentration (in M) of the unknown HCl solution in each case.

HCl Volume (mL)	NaOH Volume (mL)	[NaOH] (M)
(a) 25.00 mL	28.44 mL	0.1231 M
(b) 15.00 mL	21.22 mL	0.0972 M
(c) 20.00 mL	14.88 mL	0.1178 M
(d) 5.00 mL	6.88 mL	0.1325 M

52. Four solutions of unknown NaOH concentration are titrated with solutions of HCl. The following table lists the volume of each unknown NaOH solution, the volume of HCl solution required to reach the equivalence point, and the concentration of each HCl solution. Calculate the concentration (in M) of the unknown NaOH solution in each case.

NaOH Volume (mL)	HCl Volume (mL)	[HCl] (M)
(a) 5.00 mL	9.77 mL	0.1599 M
(b) 15.00 mL	11.34 mL	0.1311 M
(c) 10.00 mL	10.55 mL	0.0889 M
(d) 30.00 mL	36.18 mL	0.1021 M

53. A 25.00-mL sample of an H_2SO_4 solution of unknown concentration is titrated with a 0.1322 M KOH solution. A volume of 41.22 mL of KOH was required to reach the equivalence point. What is the concentration of the unknown H_2SO_4 solution?

54. A 5.00-mL sample of an H_3PO_4 solution of unknown concentration is titrated with a 0.1090 M NaOH solution. A volume of 7.12 mL of the NaOH solution was required to reach the equivalence point. What is the concentration of the unknown H_3PO_4 solution?

55. What volume in milliliters of a 0.121 M sodium hydroxide solution is required to reach the equivalence point in the complete titration of a 10.0-mL sample of 0.102 M sulfuric acid?

56. What volume in milliliters of 0.0985 M sodium hydroxide solution is required to reach the equivalence point in the complete titration of a 15.0-mL sample of 0.124 M phosphoric acid?

STRONG AND WEAK ACIDS AND BASES

57. Classify each acid as strong or weak.

(a) HCl

(b) HF

(c) HBr

(d) H_2SO_3

58. Classify each acid as strong or weak.

(a) $HCHO_2$

(b) H_2SO_4

(c) HNO_3

(d) H_2CO_3

59. Determine $[H_3O^+]$ in each acid solution. If the acid is weak, indicate the value that $[H_3O^+]$ is less than.

(a) 1.7 M HBr

(b) 1.5 M HNO_3

(c) 0.38 M H_2CO_3

(d) 1.75 M $HCHO_2$

60. Determine $[H_3O^+]$ in each acid solution. If the acid is weak, indicate the value that $[H_3O^+]$ is less than.

(a) 0.125 M $HClO_2$

(b) 1.25 M H_3PO_4

(c) 2.77 M HCl

(d) 0.95 M H_2SO_3

61. Classify each base as strong or weak.

(a) LiOH

(b) NH_4OH

(c) $Ca(OH)_2$

(d) NH_3

62. Classify each base as strong or weak.

(a) C_5H_5N

(b) NaOH

(c) $Ba(OH)_2$

(d) KOH

63. Determine $[OH^-]$ in each base solution. If the acid is weak, indicate the value that $[OH^-]$ is less than.

(a) 0.25 M NaOH

(b) 0.25 M NH_3

(c) 0.25 M $Sr(OH)_2$

(d) 1.25 M KOH

64. Determine $[OH^-]$ in each base solution. If the acid is weak, indicate the value that $[OH^-]$ is less than.

(a) 2.5 M KOH

(b) 1.95 M NH_3

(c) 0.225 M $Ba(OH)_2$

(d) 1.8 M C_5H_5N

ACIDITY, BASICITY, AND K_W

65. Determine whether each solution is acidic, basic, or neutral.

(a) $[H_3O^+] = 1 \times 10^{-5}$ M; $[OH^-] = 1 \times 10^{-9}$ M

(b) $[H_3O^+] = 1 \times 10^{-6}$ M; $[OH^-] = 1 \times 10^{-8}$ M

(c) $[H_3O^+] = 1 \times 10^{-7}$ M; $[OH^-] = 1 \times 10^{-7}$ M

(d) $[H_3O^+] = 1 \times 10^{-8}$ M; $[OH^-] = 1 \times 10^{-6}$ M

66. Determine whether each solution is acidic, basic, or neutral.

(a) $[H_3O^+] = 1 \times 10^{-9}$ M; $[OH^-] = 1 \times 10^{-5}$ M

(b) $[H_3O^+] = 1 \times 10^{-10}$ M; $[OH^-] = 1 \times 10^{-4}$ M

(c) $[H_3O^+] = 1 \times 10^{-2}$ M; $[OH^-] = 1 \times 10^{-12}$ M

(d) $[H_3O^+] = 1 \times 10^{-13}$ M; $[OH^-] = 1 \times 10^{-1}$ M

67. Calculate $[OH^-]$ given $[H_3O^+]$ in each aqueous solution and classify the solution as acidic or basic.
(a) $[H_3O^+] = 1.5 \times 10^{-9}$ M
(b) $[H_3O^+] = 9.3 \times 10^{-9}$ M
(c) $[H_3O^+] = 2.2 \times 10^{-6}$ M
(d) $[H_3O^+] = 7.4 \times 10^{-4}$ M

68. Calculate $[OH^-]$ given $[H_3O^+]$ in each aqueous solution and classify the solution as acidic or basic.
(a) $[H_3O^+] = 1.3 \times 10^{-3}$ M
(b) $[H_3O^+] = 9.1 \times 10^{-12}$ M
(c) $[H_3O^+] = 5.2 \times 10^{-4}$ M
(d) $[H_3O^+] = 6.1 \times 10^{-9}$ M

69. Calculate $[H_3O^+]$ given $[OH^-]$ in each aqueous solution and classify each solution as acidic or basic.
(a) $[OH^-] = 2.7 \times 10^{-12}$ M
(b) $[OH^-] = 2.5 \times 10^{-2}$ M
(c) $[OH^-] = 1.1 \times 10^{-10}$ M
(d) $[OH^-] = 3.3 \times 10^{-4}$ M

70. Calculate $[H_3O^+]$ given $[OH^-]$ in each aqueous solution and classify each solution as acidic or basic.
(a) $[OH^-] = 2.1 \times 10^{-11}$ M
(b) $[OH^-] = 7.5 \times 10^{-9}$ M
(c) $[OH^-] = 2.1 \times 10^{-4}$ M
(d) $[OH^-] = 1.0 \times 10^{-2}$ M

pH

71. Classify each solution as acidic, basic, or neutral according to its pH value.
(a) pH = 8.0
(b) pH = 7.0
(c) pH = 3.5
(d) pH = 6.1

72. Classify each solution as acidic, basic, or neutral according to its pH value.
(a) pH = 4.0
(b) pH = 3.5
(c) pH = 13.0
(d) pH = 0.85

73. Calculate the pH of each solution.
(a) $[H_3O^+] = 1.7 \times 10^{-8}$ M
(b) $[H_3O^+] = 1.0 \times 10^{-7}$ M
(c) $[H_3O^+] = 2.2 \times 10^{-6}$ M
(d) $[H_3O^+] = 7.4 \times 10^{-4}$ M

74. Calculate the pH of each solution.
(a) $[H_3O^+] = 2.4 \times 10^{-10}$ M
(b) $[H_3O^+] = 7.6 \times 10^{-2}$ M
(c) $[H_3O^+] = 9.2 \times 10^{-13}$ M
(d) $[H_3O^+] = 3.4 \times 10^{-5}$ M

75. Calculate $[H_3O^+]$ for each solution.
(a) pH = 8.55
(b) pH = 11.23
(c) pH = 2.87
(d) pH = 1.22

76. Calculate $[H_3O^+]$ for each solution.
(a) pH = 1.76
(b) pH = 3.88
(c) pH = 8.43
(d) pH = 12.32

77. Calculate the pH of each solution.
(a) $[OH^-] = 1.9 \times 10^{-7}$ M
(b) $[OH^-] = 2.6 \times 10^{-8}$ M
(c) $[OH^-] = 7.2 \times 10^{-11}$ M
(d) $[OH^-] = 9.5 \times 10^{-2}$ M

78. Calculate the pH of each solution.
(a) $[OH^-] = 2.8 \times 10^{-11}$ M
(b) $[OH^-] = 9.6 \times 10^{-3}$ M
(c) $[OH^-] = 3.8 \times 10^{-12}$ M
(d) $[OH^-] = 6.4 \times 10^{-4}$ M

79. Calculate $[OH^-]$ for each solution.
(a) pH = 4.25
(b) pH = 12.53
(c) pH = 1.50
(d) pH = 8.25

80. Calculate $[OH^-]$ for each solution.
(a) pH = 1.82
(b) pH = 13.28
(c) pH = 8.29
(d) pH = 2.32

81. Calculate the pH of each solution:
(a) 0.0155 M HBr
(b) 1.28×10^{-3} M KOH
(c) 1.89×10^{-3} M HNO_3
(d) 1.54×10^{-4} M $Sr(OH)_2$

82. Calculate the pH of each solution:
(a) 1.34×10^{-3} M $HClO_4$
(b) 0.0211 M NaOH
(c) 0.0109 M HBr
(d) 7.02×10^{-5} M $Ba(OH)_2$

pOH

83. Detemine the pOH of each solution and classify it as acidic, basic, or neutral.
(a) $[OH^-] = 1.5 \times 10^{-9}$ M
(b) $[OH^-] = 7.0 \times 10^{-5}$ M
(c) $[OH^-] = 1.0 \times 10^{-7}$ M
(d) $[OH^-] = 8.8 \times 10^{-3}$ M

84. Detemine the pOH of each solution and classify it as acidic, basic, or neutral.
(a) $[OH^-] = 4.5 \times 10^{-2}$ M
(b) $[OH^-] = 3.1 \times 10^{-12}$ M
(c) $[OH^-] = 5.4 \times 10^{-5}$ M
(d) $[OH^-] = 1.2 \times 10^{-2}$ M

85. Determine the pOH of each solution.
(a) $[H_3O^+] = 1.2 \times 10^{-8}$ M
(b) $[H_3O^+] = 5.5 \times 10^{-2}$ M
(c) $[H_3O^+] = 3.9 \times 10^{-9}$ M
(d) $[OH^-] = 1.88 \times 10^{-13}$ M

86. Determine the pOH of each solution.
(a) $[H_3O^+] = 8.3 \times 10^{-10}$ M
(b) $[H_3O^+] = 1.6 \times 10^{-7}$ M
(c) $[H_3O^+] = 7.3 \times 10^{-2}$ M
(d) $[OH^-] = 4.32 \times 10^{-4}$ M

87. Determine the pH of each solution and classify it as acidic, basic, or neutral.
(a) pOH = 8.5
(b) pOH = 4.2
(c) pOH = 1.7
(d) pOH = 7.0

88. Determine the pH of each solution and classify it as acidic, basic, or neutral.
(a) pOH = 12.5
(b) pOH = 5.5
(c) pOH = 0.55
(d) pOH = 7.98

BUFFERS AND ACID RAIN

89. Determine your location on the map in Figure 14.20. What is the pH of rain where you live? What is the $[H_3O^+]$?

90. Identify the area of the United States with the most acidic rainfall on the map in Figure 14.20. What is the pH of the rain? What is the $[H_3O^+]$?

91. Determine whether or not each mixture is a buffer.
(a) HCl and HF
(b) NaOH and NH_3
(c) HF and NaF
(d) $HC_2H_3O_2$ and $KC_2H_3O_2$

92. Determine whether or not each mixture is a buffer.
(a) HBr and NaCl
(b) $HCHO_2$ and $NaCHO_2$
(c) HCl and HBr
(d) KOH and NH_3

93. Write reactions showing how each of the buffers in Problem 91 would neutralize added HCl.

94. Write reactions showing how each of the buffers in Problem 92 would neutralize added NaOH.

95. What substance could you add to each solution to make it a buffer solution?
(a) 0.100 M $NaC_2H_3O_2$
(b) 0.500 M H_3PO_4
(c) 0.200 M $HCHO_2$

96. What substance could you add to each solution to make it a buffer solution?
(a) 0.050 M $NaHSO_3$
(b) 0.150 M HF
(c) 0.200 M $KCHO_2$

CUMULATIVE PROBLEMS

97. How much 0.100 M HCl is required to completely neutralize 20.0 mL of 0.250 M NaOH?

98. How much 0.200 M KOH is required to completely neutralize 25.0 mL of 0.150 M $HClO_4$?

99. What is the minimum volume of 5.0 M HCl required to completely dissolve 10.0 g of magnesium metal?

100. What is the minimum volume of 3.0 M HBr required to completely dissolve 15.0 g of potassium metal?

101. When 18.5 g of $K_2O(s)$ is completely dissolved by $HI(aq)$, how many grams of $KI(aq)$ are formed in solution?

102. When 5.88 g of $CaO(s)$ is completely dissolved by $HBr(aq)$, how many grams of $CaBr_2(aq)$ are formed in solution?

103. A 0.125-g sample of a monoprotic acid of unknown molar mass is dissolved in water and titrated with 0.1003 M NaOH. The equivalence point is reached after adding 20.77 mL of base. What is the molar mass of the unknown acid?

104. A 0.105-g sample of a diprotic acid of unknown molar mass is dissolved in water and titrated with 0.1288 M NaOH. The equivalence point is reached after adding 15.2 mL of base. What is the molar mass of the unknown acid?

105. Antacids, such as milk of magnesia, are often taken to reduce the discomfort of acid stomach or heartburn. The recommended dose of milk of magnesia is 1 teaspoon, which contains 400 mg of $Mg(OH)_2$. What volume of HCl solution with a pH of 1.1 can be neutralized by 1 dose of milk of magnesia? (Assume two significant figures in your calculations.)

106. An antacid tablet requires 25.82 mL of 0.200 M HCl to titrate to its equivalence point. What volume in milliliters of stomach acid can be neutralized by the antacid tablet? Assume that stomach acid has a pH of 1.1. (Assume two significant figures in your calculations.)

107. For each $[H_3O^+]$, determine the pH and state whether the solution is acidic or basic.

(a) $[H_3O^+] = 0.0025$ M

(b) $[H_3O^+] = 1.8 \times 10^{-12}$ M

(c) $[H_3O^+] = 9.6 \times 10^{-9}$ M

(d) $[H_3O^+] = 0.0195$ M

108. For each $[OH^-]$, determine the pH and state whether the solution is acidic or basic.

(a) $[OH^-] = 1.8 \times 10^{-5}$ M

(b) $[OH^-] = 8.9 \times 10^{-12}$ M

(c) $[OH^-] = 3.1 \times 10^{-2}$ M

(d) $[OH^-] = 1.96 \times 10^{-9}$ M

109. Complete the table. (The first row is completed for you.)

$[H_3O^+]$	$[OH^-]$	pOH	pH	Acidic or Basic
1.0×10^{-4}	1.0×10^{-10}	10.00	4.00	acidic
5.5×10^{-3}	______	______	______	______
______	3.2×10^{-6}	______	______	______
4.8×10^{-9}	______	______	______	______
______	______	______	7.55	______

110. Complete the table. (The first row is completed for you.)

$[H_3O^+]$	$[OH^-]$	pOH	pH	Acidic or Basic
1.0×10^{-8}	1.0×10^{-6}	6.00	8.00	basic
______	______	______	3.55	______
1.7×10^{-9}	______	______	______	______
______	______	______	13.5	______
______	8.6×10^{-11}	______	______	______

111. For each strong acid solution, determine $[H_3O^+]$, $[OH^-]$, and pH.

(a) 0.0088 M $HClO_4$

(b) 1.5×10^{-3} M HBr

(c) 9.77×10^{-4} M HI

(d) 0.0878 M HNO_3

112. For each strong acid solution, determine $[H_3O^+]$, $[OH^-]$, and pH.

(a) 0.0150 M HCl

(b) 1.9×10^{-4} M HI

(c) 0.0226 M HBr

(d) 1.7×10^{-3} M HNO_3

113. For each strong base solution, determine $[OH^-]$, $[H_3O^+]$, pH, and pOH.
(a) 0.15 M NaOH
(b) 1.5×10^{-3} M $Ca(OH)_2$
(c) 4.8×10^{-4} M $Sr(OH)_2$
(d) 8.7×10^{-5} M KOH

114. For each strong base solution, determine $[OH^-]$, $[H_3O^+]$, pH, and pOH.
(a) 8.77×10^{-3} M LiOH
(b) 0.0112 M $Ba(OH)_2$
(c) 1.9×10^{-4} M KOH
(d) 5.0×10^{-4} M $Ca(OH)_2$

115. As described in Section 14.1, jailed spies on the big screen often use acid stored in a pen to dissolve jail bars and escape. What minimum volume of 12.0 M hydrochloric acid would be required to completely dissolve a 500.0-g iron bar? Would this amount of acid fit into a pen?

116. A popular classroom demonstration consists of filing notches into a new penny and soaking the penny in hydrochloric acid overnight. Since new pennies are made of zinc coated with copper, and since hydrochloric acid dissolves zinc and not copper, the inside of the penny is dissolved by the acid, while the outer copper shell remains. Suppose the penny contains 2.5 g of zinc and is soaked in 20.0 mL of 6.0 M HCl. Calculate the concentration of the HCl solution after all of the zinc has dissolved. *Hint:* The Zn from the penny is oxidized to Zn^{2+}.

117. What is the pH of a solution formed by mixing 125.0 mL of 0.0250 M HCl with 75.0 mL of 0.0500 M NaOH?

118. What is the pH of a solution formed by mixing 175.0 mL of 0.0880 M HI with 125.0 mL of 0.0570 M KOH?

119. How many H^+ (or H_3O^+) ions are present in one drop (0.050 mL) of pure water at 25 °C?

120. Calculate the number of H^+ (or H_3O^+) ions and OH^- ions in 1.0 mL of 0.100 M HCl.

121. A 4.00-L base solution contains 0.100 mol total of NaOH and $Sr(OH)_2$. The pOH of the solution is 1.51. Determine the amounts (in moles) of NaOH and $Sr(OH)_2$ in the solution.

122. A 1.50-L acid solution contains 0.35 g total of HCl and HBr. The pH of the solution is 2.40. What are the masses of HCl and HBr in the solution?

HIGHLIGHT PROBLEMS

123. Based on the molecular view of each acid solution, determine whether the acid is weak or strong.

(a)
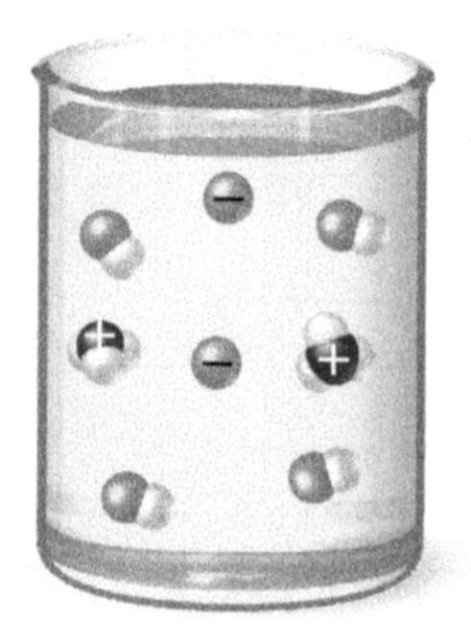

(b)

(c)

(d)

124. Lakes that have been acidified by acid rain can be neutralized by liming, the addition of limestone ($CaCO_3$). How much limestone in kilograms is required to completely neutralize a 3.8×10^9 L lake with a pH of 5.5?

125. Acid rain over the Great Lakes has a pH of about 4.5. Calculate the $[H_3O^+]$ of this rain and compare that value to the $[H_3O^+]$ of rain over the West Coast that has a pH of 5.4. How many times more concentrated is the acid in rain over the Great Lakes?

▸ANSWERS TO SKILLBUILDER EXERCISES

Skillbuilder 14.1

(a) $C_5H_5N(aq)$ + $H_2O(l)$ $\rightleftharpoons$ $C_5H_5NH^+(aq)$ + $OH^-(aq)$

Base, Acid, Conjugate acid, Conjugate base

(b) $HNO_3(aq)$ + $H_2O(l)$ $\longrightarrow$ $H_3O^+(aq)$ + $NO_3^-(aq)$

Acid, Base, Conjugate acid, Conjugate base

Skillbuilder 14.2

$H_3PO_4(aq) + 3\,NaOH(aq) \longrightarrow 3\,H_2O(l) + Na_3PO_4(aq)$

Skillbuilder 14.3

(a) $2\,HCl(aq) + Sr(s) \longrightarrow H_2(g) + SrCl_2(aq)$

(b) $2\,HI(aq) + BaO(s) \longrightarrow H_2O(l) + BaI_2(aq)$

Skillbuilder 14.4 9.03×10^{-2} M H_2SO_4

Skillbuilder 14.5

(a) $[H_3O^+] < 0.50$ M

(b) $[H_3O^+] = 1.25$ M

(c) $[H_3O^+] < 0.75$ M

Skillbuilder 14.6

(a) $[OH^-] = 0.11$ M

(b) $[OH^-] < 1.05$ M

(c) $[OH^-] = 0.45$ M

Skillbuilder 14.7

(a) $[H_3O^+] = 6.7 \times 10^{-13}$ M; basic

(b) $[H_3O^+] = 1.0 \times 10^{-7}$ M; neutral

(c) $[H_3O^+] = 1.2 \times 10^{-5}$ M; acidic

Skillbuilder 14.8

(a) pH = 8.02; basic

(b) pH = 2.21 acidic

Skillbuilder Plus, p. 509 pH = 12.11; basic

Skillbuilder 14.9 4.3×10^{-9} M

Skillbuilder Plus, p. 510 4.6×10^{-11} M

Skillbuilder 14.10 5.6×10^{-5} M

Skillbuilder Plus, p. 511 4.8×10^{-9} M

▸ANSWERS TO CONCEPTUAL CHECKPOINTS

14.1 (b) The conjugate base of an acid always has one fewer proton and is one charge unit lower (more negative) than the acid.

14.2 (c) Both (a) and (b) show complete ionization and are therefore strong acids. Only the acid depicted in (c) undergoes partial ionization and is therefore a weak acid.

14.3 (d) Each of the others can accept a proton and thus acts as a base. NH_4^+, however, is the conjugate acid of NH_3 and therefore acts as an acid and not as a base.

14.4 (d) Because pH is the *negative* log of the H_3O^+ concentration, a higher pH corresponds to a lower $[H_3O^+]$, and each unit of pH represents a tenfold change in concentration.

14.5 (d) Since the pH is 5, the pOH = 14 − 5 = 9.

14.6 (b) A buffer solution consists of a weak acid and its conjugate base. Of the compounds listed, HF is the only weak acid, and F^- (from NaF in solution) is its conjugate base.

National Blvd

Chemical Equilibrium

"A system is in equilibrium when the forces constituting it are arranged in such a way as to compensate each other, like the two weights pulling at the arms of a pair of scales."

Rudolf Arnheim (1904–2007)

15.1 Life: Controlled Disequilibrium

◀ Dynamic equilibrium involves two opposing processes occurring at the same rate. This image draws an analogy between a chemical equilibrium ($N_2O_4 \rightleftharpoons 2NO_2$), in which the two opposing reactions occur at the same rate, and a freeway with traffic moving in opposing directions at the same rate.

Have you ever tried to define life? If you have, you know that life is not easy to define. How are living things different from nonliving things? You may try to define living things as those things that can move. But of course many living things do not move—many plants, for example, do not move very much—and some nonliving things, such as glaciers and Earth itself, do move. So motion is neither unique to nor definitive of life. You may try to define living things as those things that can reproduce. But again, many living things, such as mules or sterile humans, cannot reproduce; yet they are alive. In addition, some nonliving things—such as crystals—reproduce (in some sense). So what is unique about living things?

The concept of equilibrium underlies one definition of life. We define *chemical* equilibrium more carefully soon. For now, we can think generally of equilibrium as *sameness and constancy*. When an object is in equilibrium with its surroundings, some property of the object has reached sameness with the surroundings and is no longer changing. For example, a cup of hot water is not in equilibrium with its surroundings with respect to temperature. If left undisturbed, the cup of hot water will slowly cool until it reaches equilibrium with its surroundings. At that point, the temperature of the water is the *same as* that of the surroundings (sameness) and *no longer changes* (constancy).

So equilibrium involves sameness and constancy. Part of a definition for living things, then, is that living things *are not* in equilibrium with their surroundings. Our body temperature, for example, is not the same as the temperature of our surroundings. When we jump into a swimming pool, the pH of our blood does not become the same as the pH of the surrounding water. Living things, even the simplest ones, maintain some measure of *disequilibrium* with their environment.

We must add one more concept, however, to complete our definition of life with respect to equilibrium. A cup of hot water is in disequilibrium with its environment, yet it is not alive. However, the cup of hot water has no control over its disequilibrium and will slowly come to equilibrium with its environment. In contrast, living things—as long as they are alive—maintain and *control* their disequilibrium. Your body temperature, for example, is not only in disequilibrium with your surroundings—it is in controlled disequilibrium. Your body maintains your temperature within a specific range that is not in equilibrium with the surrounding temperature.

So one definition for life is that living things are in *controlled disequilibrium* with their environment. A living thing comes into equilibrium with its surroundings only after it dies. In this chapter, we examine the concept of equilibrium, especially chemical equilibrium—the state that involves sameness and constancy.

15.2 The Rate of a Chemical Reaction

Reaction rates are related to chemical equilibrium because, as we will see in Section 15.3, a chemical system is at equilibrium when the rate of the forward reaction equals the rate of the reverse reaction.

Before we probe more deeply into the concept of chemical equilibrium, we must first understand something about the rates of chemical reactions. The **rate of a chemical reaction**—a measure of how fast the reaction proceeds—is defined as the amount of reactant that changes to product in a given period of time. A reaction with a fast rate proceeds quickly; a large amount of reactant is converted to product in a certain period of time (▶ Figure 15.1a). A reaction with a slow rate proceeds slowly; only a small a small amount of reactant is converted to product in the same period of time (▶ Figure 15.1b).

A reaction rate can also be defined as the amount of a product that forms in a given period of time.

Chemists seek to control reaction rates for many chemical reactions. For example, the space shuttle is propelled by the reaction of hydrogen and oxygen to form water. If the reaction proceeds too slowly, the shuttle will not lift off the ground. If, however, the reaction proceeds too quickly, the shuttle can explode. Reaction rates can be controlled if we understand the factors that influence them.

COLLISION THEORY

According to **collision theory**, chemical reactions occur through collisions between molecules or atoms. For example, consider the gas-phase chemical reaction between $H_2(g)$ and $I_2(g)$ to form $HI(g)$.

$$H_2(g) + I_2(g) \longrightarrow 2\ HI(g)$$

The gas-phase reaction between hydrogen and iodine can proceed by other mechanisms, but this mechanism is valid for the low-temperature thermal reaction.

Whether a collision leads to a reaction also depends on the *orientation* of the colliding molecules, but this topic is beyond the scope of this text.

The reaction begins when an H_2 molecule collides with an I_2 molecule. If the collision occurs with enough energy—that is, if the colliding molecules are moving fast enough—the reaction can proceed to form the products. If the collision occurs with insufficient energy, the reactant molecules (H_2 and I_2) simply bounce off of one another. Since gas-phase molecules have a wide distribution of velocities, collisions occur with a wide distribution of energies. High-energy collisions lead to products, and low-energy collisions do not.

Higher-energy collisions are more likely to lead to products because most chemical reactions have an *activation energy* (or an activation barrier). The activation energy for chemical reactions is discussed in more detail in Section 15.12. For now, we can think of the activation energy as an energy barrier that must be overcome for the reaction to proceed. For example, in the case of H_2 reacting with I_2 to form HI, the product (HI) can begin to form only after the H—H bond and the I—I bond each begin to break. The activation energy is the energy required to begin to break these bonds.

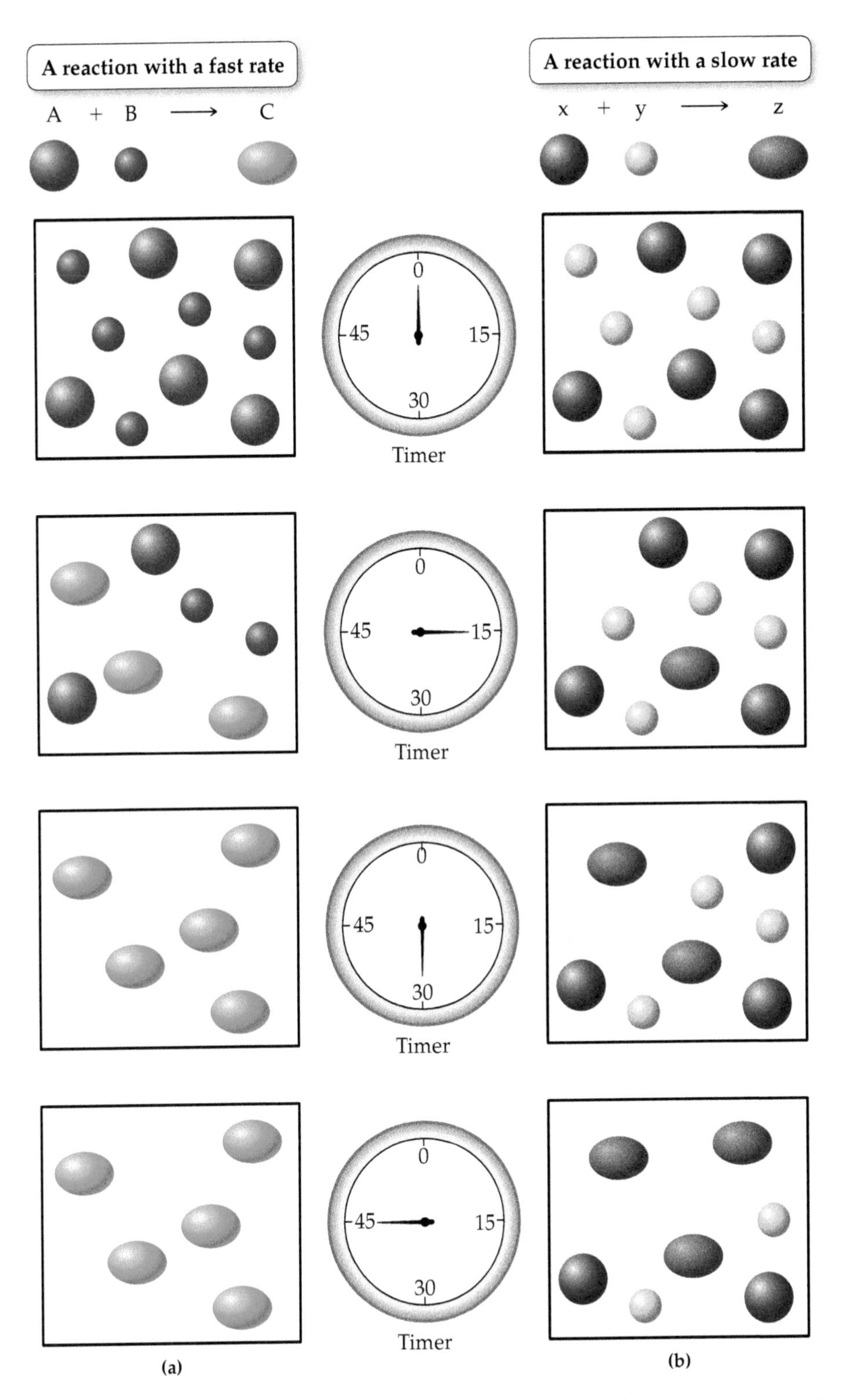

▲ FIGURE 15.1 **Reaction rates** **(a)** In a reaction with a fast rate, the reactants react to form products in a short period of time. **(b)** In a reaction with a slow rate, the reactants react to form products over a long period of time.

If molecules react via high-energy collisions, then the factors that influence the rate of a reaction must be the same factors that affect the number of high-energy collisions that occur per unit time. Here, we focus on the two most important factors: the *concentration* of the reacting molecules and the *temperature* of the reaction mixture.

HOW CONCENTRATION AFFECTS THE RATE OF A REACTION

▼ Figure 15.2a through 15.2c shows various mixtures of H_2 and I_2 at the same temperature but different concentrations. If H_2 and I_2 react via collisions to form HI, which mixture do you think will have the highest reaction rate? Since Figure 15.2c has the highest concentration of H_2 and I_2, it will have the most collisions per unit time and therefore the fastest reaction rate. This idea holds true for most chemical reactions.

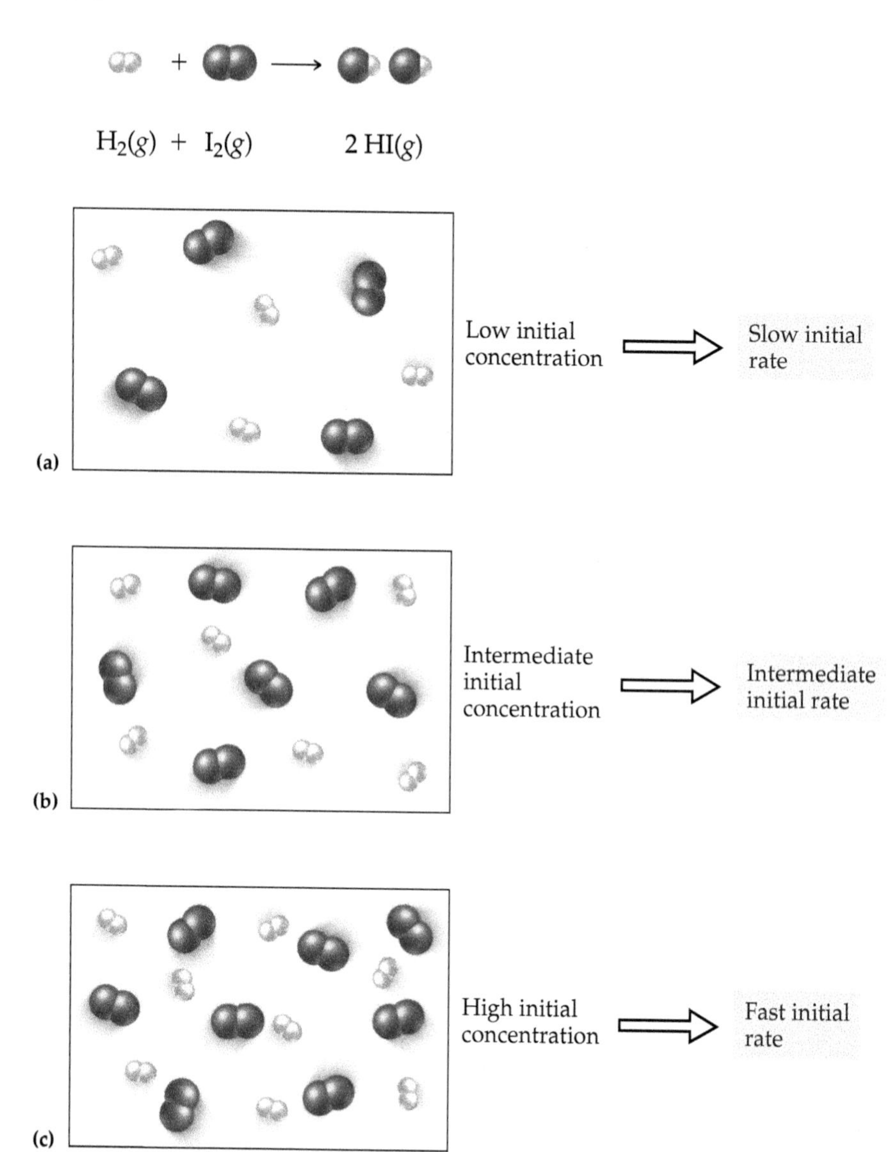

▶ **FIGURE 15.2 Effect of concentration on reaction rate**
Question: Which reaction mixture will have the fastest initial rate? The mixture in (c) is fastest because it has the highest concentration of reactants and therefore the highest rate of collisions.

The rate of a chemical reaction generally increases with increasing concentration of the reactants.

The exact relationship between increases in concentration and increases in reaction rate varies for different reactions and is beyond the scope of this text. For our purposes, it will suffice to know that for most reactions the reaction rate increases with increasing reactant concentration.

Armed with this knowledge, what can we say about the rate of a reaction as the reaction proceeds? Since reactants turn into products in the course of a reaction, their concentration decreases. Consequently, the reaction rate decreases as well. In other words, as a reaction proceeds, there are fewer reactant molecules (because they have turned into products), and the reaction slows down.

HOW TEMPERATURE AFFECTS THE RATE OF A REACTION

Reaction rates also depend on temperature. ▼ Figure 15.3a through 15.3c show various mixtures of H_2 and I_2 at the same concentration, but different temperatures. Which will have the fastest rate? Raising the temperature makes the molecules move faster (Section 3.10). They therefore experience more collisions per unit time, resulting in a faster reaction rate. In addition, a higher temperature results in more collisions that are (on average) of higher energy. Since it is the high-energy collisions that result in products, this also produces a faster rate. Consequently, Figure 15.3c (which has the highest temperature) has the fastest reaction rate. This relationship holds true for most chemical reactions.

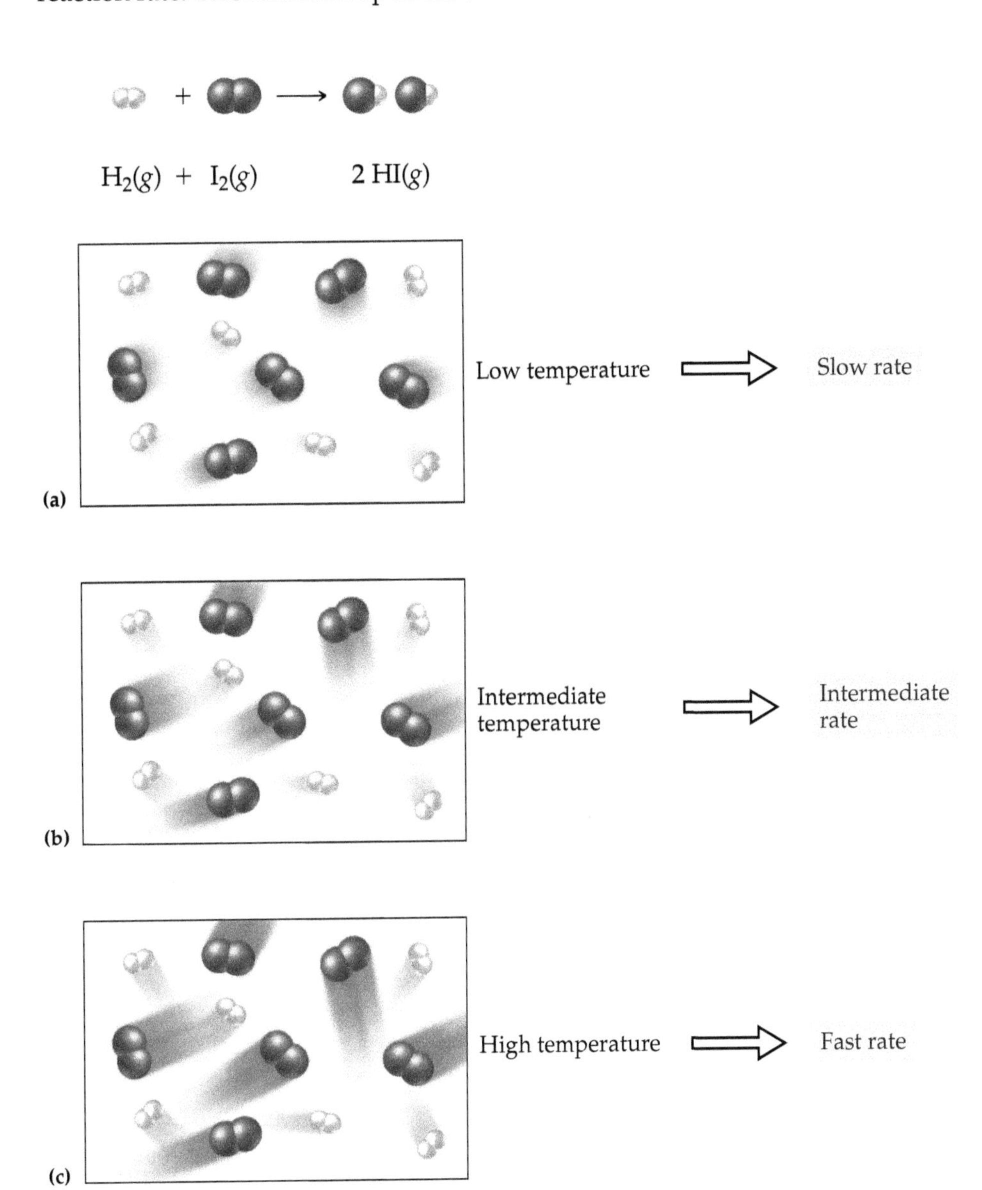

▶ **FIGURE 15.3 Effect of temperature on reaction rate**
Question: Which reaction mixture will have the fastest initial rate? The mixture in (c) is fastest because it has the highest temperature.

The rate of a chemical reaction generally increases with increasing temperature of the reaction mixture.

The temperature dependence of reaction rates is the reason that cold-blooded animals become more sluggish at lower temperatures. The reactions required for them to think and move become slower, resulting in the sluggish behavior.

To summarize:

- Reaction rates generally increase with increasing reactant concentration.
- Reaction rates generally increase with increasing temperature.
- Reaction rates generally decrease as a reaction proceeds.

CONCEPTUAL CHECKPOINT 15.1

In a chemical reaction between two gases, you would expect that increasing the pressure of the gases would probably

(a) increase the reaction rate.

(b) decrease the reaction rate.

(c) not affect the reaction rate.

15.3 The Idea of Dynamic Chemical Equilibrium

What would happen if our reaction between H_2 and I_2 to form HI were able to proceed in both the forward and reverse directions?

$$H_2(g) + I_2(g) \rightleftharpoons 2HI(g)$$

Now, H_2 and I_2 collide and react to form 2 HI molecules, but the 2 HI molecules also collide and react to reform H_2 and I_2. A reaction that can proceed in both the forward and reverse directions is a **reversible reaction.**

Suppose we begin with only H_2 and I_2 in a container (▶ Figure 15.4a). What happens initially? The H_2 and I_2 molecules begin to react to form HI (Figure 15.4b). However, as H_2 and I_2 react, their concentration decreases, which in turn decreases the rate of the forward reaction. At the same time, HI begins to form. As the concentration of HI increases, the reverse reaction begins to occur at an increasingly faster rate because there are more HI collisions with other HI molecules. Eventually, the rate of the reverse reaction (which is increasing) equals the rate of the forward reaction (which is decreasing). At that point, **dynamic equilibrium** is reached (Figure 15.4c and Figure 15.4d).

> **Dynamic equilibrium**—In a chemical reaction, the condition in which the rate of the forward reaction equals the rate of the reverse reaction.

This condition is not static—it is dynamic because the forward and reverse reactions are still occurring but at the same constant rate. When dynamic equilibrium is reached, the concentrations of H_2, I_2, and HI no longer change. They remain the same because the reactants and products are being depleted at the same rate at which they are being formed.

Notice that dynamic equilibrium includes the concepts of sameness and constancy that we discussed in Section 15.1. When dynamic equilibrium is reached, the forward reaction rate is the same as the reverse reaction rate (sameness). Because the reaction rates are the same, the concentrations of the reactants and products no longer change (constancy). However, just because the concentrations of reactants and products no longer change at equilibrium does *not* imply that the concentrations of reactants and products are *equal* to one another at equilibrium. Some reactions reach equilibrium only after most of the reactants have formed products. (Recall strong acids from Chapter 14.) Others reach equilibrium when only a small fraction of the reactants have formed products. (Recall weak acids from Chapter 14.) It depends on the reaction.

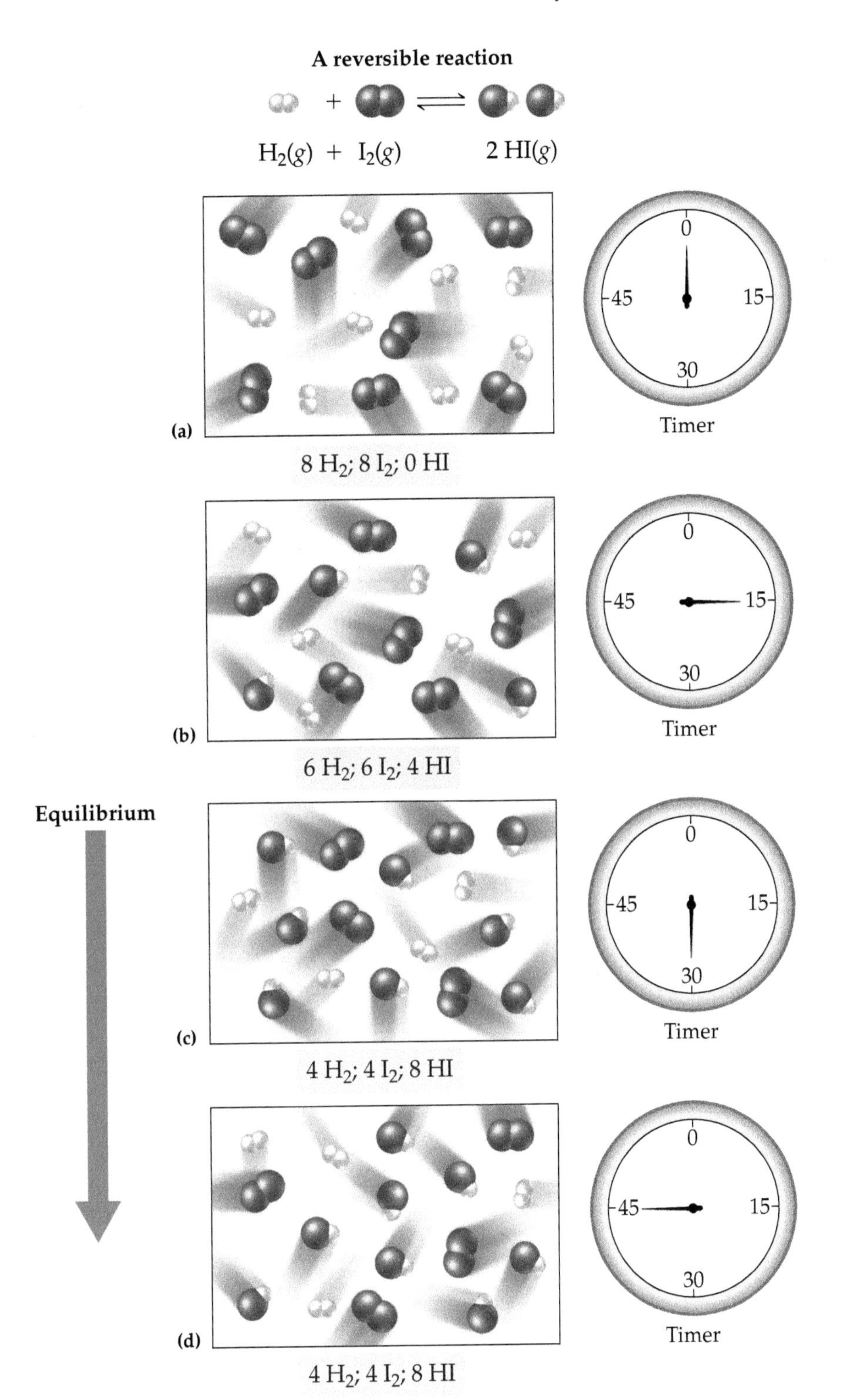

▶ FIGURE 15.4 **Equilibrium**
When the concentrations of the reactants and products no longer change, equilibrium has been reached.

Narnia is the fictitious world featured in C.S. Lewis's *The Chronicles of Narnia*, and Middle Earth is the fictitious world featured in J.R.R. Tolkien's *The Lord of the Rings.*

We can better understand dynamic equilibrium with a simple analogy. Imagine that Narnia and Middle Earth are two neighboring kingdoms (▶ Figure 15.5). Narnia is overpopulated, and Middle Earth is underpopulated. One day, however, the border between the two kingdoms opens, and people immediately begin to leave Narnia for Middle Earth (call this the forward reaction).

$$\text{Narnia} \longrightarrow \text{Middle Earth} \quad \text{(forward reaction)}$$

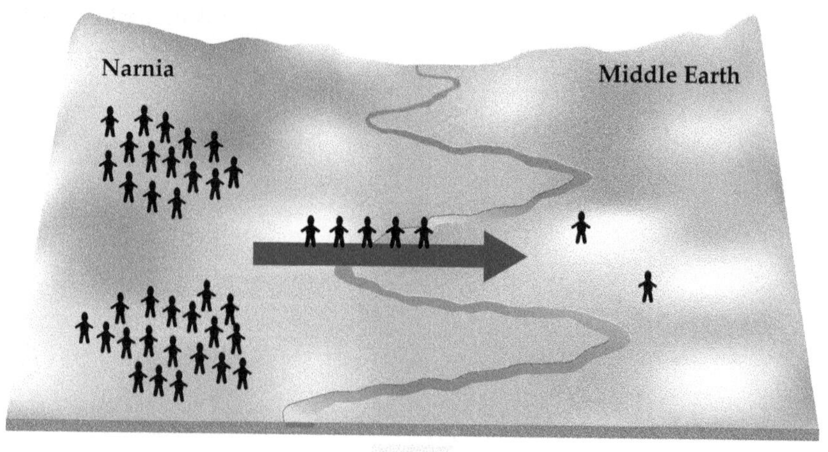

Initial

Represents population

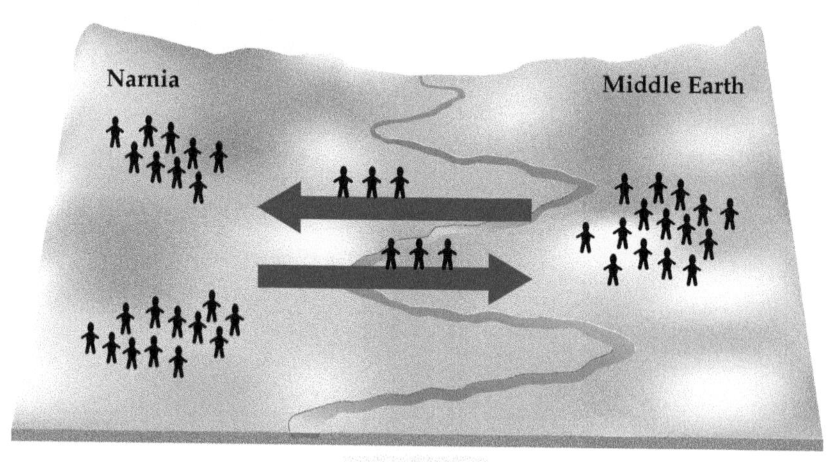

Equilibrium

▶ **FIGURE 15.5 Population analogy for a chemical reaction proceeding to equilibrium**

The population of Narnia decreases as the population of Middle Earth increases. As people leave Narnia, however, the *rate* at which they leave begins to slow down (because Narnia becomes less crowded). On the other hand, as people move into Middle Earth, some decide it was not for them and begin to move back (call this the reverse reaction).

$$\text{Narnia} \longleftarrow \text{Middle Earth} \quad \text{(reverse reaction)}$$

As Middle Earth fills, the rate of people moving back to Narnia accelerates. Eventually, the *rate* of people moving out of Narnia (which has been slowing down as people leave) equals the *rate* of people moving back to Narnia (which has been increasing as Middle Earth gets more crowded). Dynamic equilibrium has been reached.

$$\text{Narnia} \rightleftharpoons \text{Middle Earth}$$

Notice that when the two kingdoms reach dynamic equilibrium, their populations no longer change because the number of people moving out equals the number of people moving in. However, one kingdom—because of its charm, or the character of its leader, or a lower tax rate, or whatever other reason—may have a higher population than the other kingdom, even when dynamic equilibrium is reached.

Similarly, when a chemical reaction reaches dynamic equilibrium, the rate of the forward reaction (analogous to people moving out of Narnia) equals the rate of the reverse reaction (analogous to people moving back into Narnia), and the relative concentrations of reactants and products (analogous to the relative populations of the two kingdoms) become constant. Also, like our two kingdoms, the concentrations of reactants and products will not necessarily be equal at equilibrium, just as the populations of the two kingdoms are not equal at equilibrium.

15.4 The Equilibrium Constant: A Measure of How Far a Reaction Goes

We have just learned that the *concentrations* of reactants and products are not equal at equilibrium; rather, it is the *rates* of the forward and reverse reactions that are equal. But what about the concentrations? What can we know about them? The equilibrium constant (K_{eq}) is a way to quantify the relative concentrations of the reactants and products at equilibrium. Consider the generic chemical reaction:

$$aA + bB \rightleftharpoons cC + dD$$

where A and B are reactants, C and D are products, and a, b, c, and d are the respective stoichiometric coefficients in the chemical equation. The **equilibrium constant (K_{eq})** for the reaction is defined as the ratio—at equilibrium—of the concentrations of the products raised to their stoichiometric coefficients divided by the concentrations of the reactants raised to their stoichiometric coefficients.

$$K_{eq} = \frac{[C]^c [D]^d}{[A]^a [B]^b}$$

Products

Reactants

Notice that the equilibrium constant is a measure of the relative concentrations of reactants and products at equilibrium; the larger the equilibrium constant, the greater the concentration of products relative to reactants at equilibrium.

WRITING EQUILIBRIUM EXPRESSIONS FOR CHEMICAL REACTIONS

To write an equilibrium expression for a chemical reaction, examine the chemical equation and follow the preceding definition. For example, suppose we want to write an equilibrium expression for the reaction:

$$2\,N_2O_5(g) \rightleftharpoons 4\,NO_2(g) + O_2(g)$$

The equilibrium constant is $[NO_2]$ raised to the fourth power multiplied by $[O_2]$ raised to the first power divided by $[N_2O_5]$ raised to the second power.

$$K_{eq} = \frac{[NO_2]^4[O_2]}{[N_2O_5]^2}$$

Notice that the *coefficients* in the chemical equation become the *exponents* in the equilibrium expression.

$$2\,N_2O_5(g) \rightleftharpoons 4\,NO_2(g) + O_2(g)$$

Implied 1

$$K_{eq} = \frac{[NO_2]^4\,[O_2]}{[N_2O_5]^2}$$

EXAMPLE 15.1 Writing Equilibrium Expressions for Chemical Reactions

Write an equilibrium expression for the chemical equation:

$$CO(g) + 2H_2(g) \rightleftharpoons CH_3OH(g)$$

SOLUTION

The equilibrium expression is the concentration of the products raised to their stoichiometric coefficients divided by the concentration of the reactants raised to their stoichiometric coefficients. Notice that the expression is a ratio of products over reactants. Notice also that the coefficients in the chemical equation are the exponents in the equilibrium expression.

$$K_{eq} = \frac{[CH_3OH]}{[CO][H_2]^2}$$

Product (numerator); Reactants (denominator)

▶ SKILLBUILDER 15.1 | Writing Equilibrium Expressions for Chemical Reactions

Write an equilibrium expression for the chemical equation:

$$H_2(g) + F_2(g) \rightleftharpoons 2HF(g)$$

▶ FOR MORE PRACTICE Example 15.10; Problems 43, 44.

THE SIGNIFICANCE OF THE EQUILIBRIUM CONSTANT

Given this definition of an equilibrium constant, what does it tell us? For example, what does a large equilibrium constant ($K_{eq} \gg 1$) imply about a reaction? It means that the forward reaction is largely favored and that there will be more products than reactants when equilibrium is reached. For example, consider the reaction:

$$H_2(g) + Br_2(g) \rightleftharpoons 2HBr(g) \quad K_{eq} = 1.9 \times 10^{19} \text{ at } 25\,°C$$

The equilibrium constant is large, meaning that at equilibrium the reaction lies far to the right—high concentrations of products, tiny concentrations of reactants (▼ Figure 15.6).

$$H_2(g) + Br_2(g) \rightleftharpoons 2\,HBr(g)$$

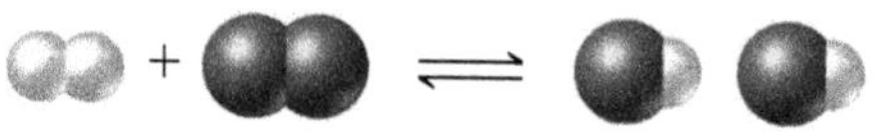

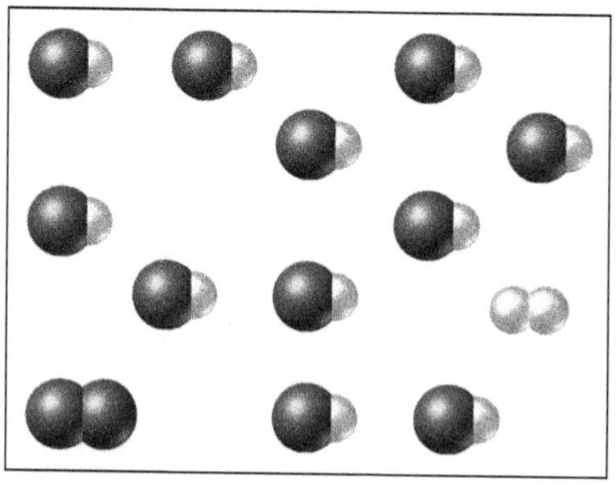

$$K_{eq} = \frac{[HBr]^2}{[H_2][Br_2]} = \text{Large Number}$$

▶ **FIGURE 15.6 The meaning of a large equilibrium constant** A large equilibrium constant means that there will be a high concentration of products and a low concentration of reactants at equilibrium.

Conversely, what does a *small* equilibrium constant ($K_{eq} \ll 1$) mean? It means that the reverse reaction is favored and that there will be more reactants than products when equilibrium is reached. For example, consider the reaction:

$$N_2(g) + O_2(g) \rightleftharpoons 2NO(g) \quad K_{eq} = 4.1 \times 10^{-31} \text{ at } 25\,°C$$

The equilibrium constant is very small, meaning that at equilibrium the reaction lies far to the left—high concentrations of reactants, low concentrations of products

$$N_2(g) + O_2(g) \rightleftharpoons 2\,NO(g)$$

$$K_{eq} = \frac{[NO]^2}{[N_2][O_2]} = \textbf{Small Number}$$

▲ **FIGURE 15.7 The meaning of a small equilibrium constant** A small equilibrium constant means that there will be a high concentration of reactants and a low concentration of products at equilibrium.

(▲ Figure 15.7). This is fortunate because N_2 and O_2 are the main components of air. If this equilibrium constant were large, much of the N_2 and O_2 in air would react to form NO, a toxic gas.

The symbol ≈ means "approximately equal to."

To summarize:

- $K_{eq} \ll 1$ Reverse reaction is favored; forward reaction does not proceed very far.
- $K_{eq} \approx 1$ Neither direction is favored; forward reaction proceeds about halfway (significant amounts of both reactants and products are present at equilibrium).
- $K_{eq} \gg 1$ Forward reaction is favored; forward reaction proceeds virtually to completion.

CONCEPTUAL CHECKPOINT 15.2

Consider a generic chemical reaction in which the reactant, A, simply turns directly into the product, B.

$$A(g) \rightleftharpoons B(g)$$

The reaction is allowed to come to equilibrium at three different temperatures as represented below. At which temperature is the equilibrium constant the largest?

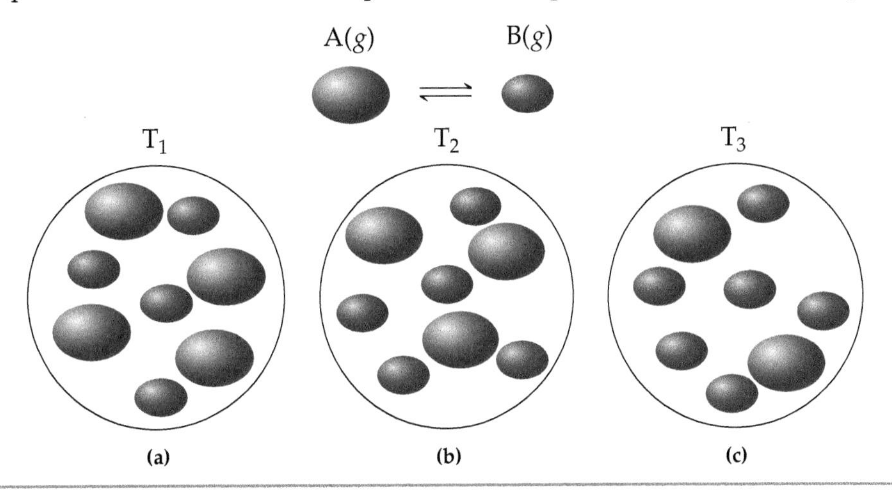

15.5 Heterogeneous Equilibria: The Equilibrium Expression for Reactions Involving a Solid or a Liquid

Consider the chemical reaction:

$$2\,CO(g) \rightleftharpoons CO_2(g) + C(s)$$

We might expect the expression for the equilibrium constant to be:

$$K_{eq} = \frac{[CO_2][C]}{[CO]^2} \quad \text{(incorrect)}$$

However, since carbon is a solid, its concentration is constant—it does not change. Adding more or less carbon to the reaction mixture does not change the concentration of carbon. The concentration of a solid does not change because a solid does not expand to fill its container. The concentration of a solid, therefore, depends only on its density, which (except for slight variations due to temperature) is constant as long as *some solid is present*. Consequently, pure solids—those reactants or products labeled in the chemical equation with an (*s*)—are not included in the equilibrium expression. The correct equilibrium expression is:

The concentrations of pure solids and pure liquids are excluded from equilibrium expressions because they are constant.

$$K_{eq} = \frac{[CO_2]}{[CO]^2} \quad \text{(correct)}$$

Similarly, the concentration of a pure liquid does not change. Consequently, pure liquids—those reactants or products labeled in the chemical equation with an (*l*)—are also excluded from the equilibrium expression. For example, what is the equilibrium expression for the following reaction?

$$CO_2(g) + H_2O(l) \rightleftharpoons H^+(aq) + HCO_3^-(aq)$$

Since $H_2O(l)$ is pure liquid, it is omitted from the equilibrium expression.

$$K_{eq} = \frac{[H^+][HCO_3^-]}{[CO_2]}$$

EXAMPLE 15.2 Writing Equilibrium Expressions for Reactions Involving a Solid or a Liquid

Write an equilibrium expression for the chemical equation:

$$CaCO_3(s) \rightleftharpoons CaO(s) + CO_2(g)$$

SOLUTION

Since $CaCO_3(s)$ and $CaO(s)$ are both solids, they are omitted from the equilibrium expression.

$$K_{eq} = [CO_2]$$

▶SKILLBUILDER 15.2 | Writing Equilibrium Expressions for Reactions Involving a Solid or a Liquid

Write an equilibrium expression for the chemical equation:

$$4\,HCl(g) + O_2(g) \rightleftharpoons 2\,H_2O(l) + 2\,Cl_2(g)$$

▶FOR MORE PRACTICE Problems 45, 46.

15.6 Calculating and Using Equilibrium Constants

CALCULATING EQUILIBRIUM CONSTANTS

The most direct way to obtain a value for the equilibrium constant of a reaction is to measure the concentrations of the reactants and products in a reaction mixture at equilibrium. For example, consider the reaction:

$$H_2(g) + I_2(g) \rightleftharpoons 2\,HI(g)$$

Equilibrium constants depend on temperature, so temperatures will often be included with equilibrium data. However, the temperature is not a part of the equilibrium expression.

Suppose a mixture of H_2 and I_2 is allowed to come to equilibrium at 445 °C. The measured equilibrium concentrations are $[H_2] = 0.11\,M$, $[I_2] = 0.11\,M$, and $[HI] = 0.78\,M$. What is the value of the equilibrium constant? We begin by sorting the information in the problem statement.

GIVEN: $[H_2] = 0.11\,M$

$[I_2] = 0.11\,M$

$[HI] = 0.78\,M$

FIND: K_{eq}

SOLUTION

The expression for K_{eq} can be written from the balanced equation.

$$K_{eq} = \frac{[HI]^2}{[H_2][I_2]}$$

To calculate the value of K_{eq}, substitute the correct equilibrium concentrations into the expression for K_{eq}.

$$K_{eq} = \frac{[HI]^2}{[H_2][I_2]} = \frac{[0.78]^2}{[0.11][0.11]} = 5.0 \times 10^1$$

The concentrations in an equilibrium expression should always be in units of molarity (M), but the units themselves are normally dropped.

The concentrations within K_{eq} must always be written in moles per liter (M); however, the units are normally dropped in expressing the equilibrium constant.

The *particular concentrations* of reactants and products for a reaction at equilibrium will *not* always be the same for a given reaction; they will depend on the initial concentrations. However, the *equilibrium constant* will always be the same at a given temperature, regardless of the initial concentrations. For example, Table 15.1

TABLE 15.1 Initial and Equilibrium Concentrations at 445 °C for the Reaction $H_2(g) + I_2(g) \rightleftharpoons 2\,HI(g)$.

Initial			Equilibrium			Equilibrium Constant
$[H_2]$	$[I_2]$	$[HI]$	$[H_2]$	$[I_2]$	$[HI]$	$K_{eq} = \frac{[HI]^2}{[H_2][I_2]}$
0.50	0.50	0.0	0.11	0.11	0.78	$\frac{[0.78]^2}{[0.11][0.11]} = 50$
0.0	0.0	0.50	0.055	0.055	0.39	$\frac{[0.39]^2}{[0.055][0.055]} = 50$
0.50	0.50	0.50	0.165	0.165	1.17	$\frac{[1.17]^2}{[0.165][0.165]} = 50$
1.0	0.5	0.0	0.53	0.033	0.934	$\frac{[0.934]^2}{[0.53][0.033]} = 50$

A reaction can approach equilibrium from either direction, depending on the initial concentrations, but its K_{eq} at a given temperature will always be the same.

shows several different equilibrium concentrations of H_2, I_2, and HI, each from a different set of initial concentrations. Notice that the equilibrium constant is always the same, regardless of the initial concentrations. In other words, no matter what the initial concentrations are, the reaction will always go in a direction so that the equilibrium concentrations—when substituted into the equilibrium expression—give the same constant, K_{eq}.

EXAMPLE 15.3 Calculating Equilibrium Constants

Consider the reaction:

$$2\,CH_4(g) \rightleftharpoons C_2H_2(g) + 3\,H_2(g)$$

A mixture of CH_4, C_2H_2, and H_2 is allowed to come to equilibrium at 1700 °C. The measured equilibrium concentrations are $[CH_4] = 0.0203$ M, $[C_2H_2] = 0.0451$ M, and $[H_2] = 0.112$ M. What is the value of the equilibrium constant at this temperature?

You are given the concentrations of the reactants and products of a reaction at equilibrium. You are asked to find the equilibrium constant.

GIVEN: $[CH_4] = 0.0203$ M

$[C_2H_2] = 0.0451$ M

$[H_2] = 0.112$ M

FIND: K_{eq}

Write the expression for K_{eq} from the balanced equation. To calculate the value of K_{eq}, substitute the correct equilibrium concentrations into the expression for K_{eq}.

SOLUTION

$$K_{eq} = \frac{[C_2H_2][H_2]^3}{[CH_4]^2}$$

$$K_{eq} = \frac{[0.0451][0.112]^3}{[0.0203]^2}$$

$$= 0.154$$

▶SKILLBUILDER 15.3 | Calculating Equilibrium Constants

Consider the reaction:

$$CO(g) + 2\,H_2(g) \rightleftharpoons CH_3OH(g)$$

A mixture of CO, H_2, and CH_3OH is allowed to come to equilibrium at 225 °C. The measured equilibrium concentrations are $[CO] = 0.489$ M, $[H_2] = 0.146$ M, and $[CH_3OH] = 0.151$ M. What is the value of the equilibrium constant at this temperature?

▶SKILLBUILDER PLUS

Suppose that the preceding reaction is carried out at a different temperature and that the initial concentrations of the reactants are $[CO] = 0.500$ M and $[H_2] = 1.00$ M. Assuming that there is no product at the beginning of the reaction and that at equilibrium $[CO] = 0.15$ M, find the equilibrium constant at this new temperature. *Hint:* Use the stoichiometric relationships from the balanced equation to find the equilibrium concentrations of H_2 and CH_3OH.

▶FOR MORE PRACTICE Example 15.11; Problems 51, 52, 53, 54, 55, 56.

USING EQUILIBRIUM CONSTANTS IN CALCULATIONS

We can also use the equilibrium constant to calculate the equilibrium concentration of one of the reactants or products, given the equilibrium concentrations of the others. For example, consider the reaction:

$$2\,COF_2(g) \rightleftharpoons CO_2(g) + CF_4(g) \quad K_{eq} = 2.00 \text{ at } 1000\,°C$$

In an equilibrium mixture, the concentration of COF_2 is 0.255 M and the concentration of CF_4 is 0.118 M. What is the equilibrium concentration of CO_2? We begin by sorting the information in the problem statement.

GIVEN: $[COF_2] = 0.255\ M$
$[CF_4] = 0.118\ M$
$K_{eq} = 2.00$

FIND: $[CO_2]$

SOLUTION MAP

We then draw a solution map showing how the expression for the equilibrium constant provides the equation that gets us from the given quantities to the quantity we are trying to find.

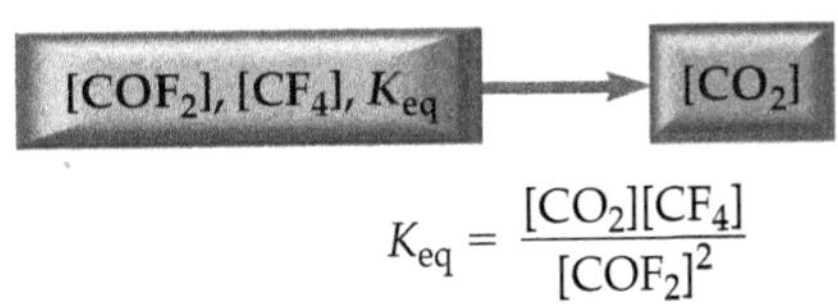

$$K_{eq} = \frac{[CO_2][CF_4]}{[COF_2]^2}$$

SOLUTION

We write the equilibrium expression for the reaction, and then we solve it for the quantity we are trying to find ($[CO_2]$).

$$K_{eq} = \frac{[CO_2][CF_4]}{[COF_2]^2}$$

$$[CO_2] = K_{eq}\frac{[COF_2]^2}{[CF_4]}$$

Now we substitute the appropriate values and calculate $[CO_2]$.

$$[CO_2] = 2.00\frac{[0.255]^2}{[0.118]}$$
$$= 1.10\ M$$

EXAMPLE 15.4 Using Equilibrium Constants in Calculations

Consider the reaction:

$$H_2(g) + I_2(g) \rightleftharpoons 2\ HI(g) \quad K_{eq} = 69 \text{ at } 340\ ^\circ C$$

In an equilibrium mixture, the concentrations of H_2 and I_2 are both 0.020 M. What is the equilibrium concentration of HI?

SORT

You are given the equilibrium concentrations of the reactants in a chemical reaction and also the value of the equilibrium constant. You are asked to find the concentration of the product.

GIVEN: $[H_2] = [I_2] = 0.020\ M$
$K_{eq} = 69$

FIND: $[HI]$

STRATEGIZE

Draw a solution map showing how the equilibrium constant expression gives the relationship between the given concentrations and the concentration you are asked to find.

SOLUTION MAP

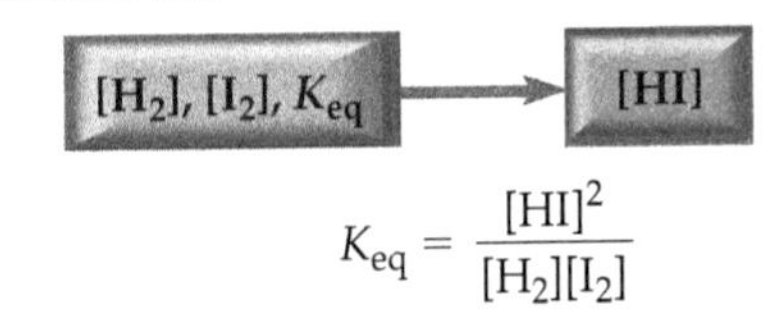

$$K_{eq} = \frac{[HI]^2}{[H_2][I_2]}$$

SOLVE

Solve the equilibrium expression for [HI] and then substitute in the appropriate values to calculate it.

Since the value of [HI] is squared, you must take the square root of both sides of the equation to solve for [HI] because $\sqrt{[HI]^2} = [HI]$.

SOLUTION

$$K_{eq} = \frac{[HI]^2}{[H_2][I_2]}$$
$$[HI]^2 = K_{eq}[H_2][I_2]$$
$$\sqrt{[HI]^2} = \sqrt{K_{eq}[H_2][I_2]}$$
$$[HI] = \sqrt{69(0.020)(0.020)}$$
$$= 0.17\ M$$

CHECK

You can check your answer by substituting it back into the expression for K_{eq}.

$$K_{eq} = \frac{[HI]^2}{[H_2][I_2]}$$

$$= \frac{(0.17)^2}{(0.020)(0.020)}$$

$$= 72$$

The calculated value of K_{eq} is about equal to the given value of K_{eq} (which was 69), indicating that your answer is correct. The slight difference is due to rounding error, which is common in problems like these.

▶SKILLBUILDER 15.4 | Using Equilibrium Constants in Calculations

Diatomic iodine (I_2) decomposes at high temperature to form I atoms according to the reaction:

$$I_2(g) \rightleftharpoons 2\,I(g) \quad K_{eq} = 0.011 \text{ at } 1200\,°C$$

In an equilibrium mixture, the concentration of I_2 is 0.10 M. What is the equilibrium concentration of I?

▶FOR MORE PRACTICE Example 15.12; Problems 57, 58, 59, 60.

CONCEPTUAL CHECKPOINT 15.3

When the reaction $A(aq) \rightleftharpoons B(aq) + C(aq)$ is at equilibrium, each of the three compounds has a concentration of 2 M. The equilibrium constant for this reaction is:

(a) 4 **(b)** 2 **(c)** 1 **(d)** 1/2

15.7 Disturbing a Reaction at Equilibrium: Le Châtelier's Principle

| Pronounced "le-sha-te-lyay"

We have seen that a chemical system not in equilibrium tends to go toward equilibrium and that the concentrations of the reactants and products at equilibrium correspond to the equilibrium constant, K_{eq}. What happens, however, when a chemical system already at equilibrium is disturbed? **Le Châtelier's principle** states that the chemical system will respond to minimize the disturbance.

> **Le Châtelier's principle**—When a chemical system at equilibrium is disturbed, the system shifts in a direction that minimizes the disturbance.

In other words, a system at equilibrium tries to maintain that equilibrium—it fights back when disturbed.

We can understand Le Châtelier's principle by returning to our Narnia and Middle Earth analogy. Suppose the populations of Narnia and Middle Earth are at equilibrium. This means that the rate of people moving out of Narnia (and into Middle Earth) is equal to the rate of people moving into Narnia (and out of Middle Earth). It also means that the populations of the two kingdoms are stable. Now imagine disturbing that balance (▶ Figure 15.8). Suppose we add extra people to Middle Earth. What happens? Since Middle Earth suddenly becomes more crowded, the rate of people leaving Middle Earth increases. The net flow of people is *out of Middle Earth and into Narnia.* Notice what happened. We disturbed the equilibrium by adding more people to Middle Earth. The system responded by moving people out of Middle Earth—it shifted in the direction that minimized the disturbance.

On the other hand, what happens if we add extra people to Narnia? Since Narnia suddenly gets more crowded, the rate of people leaving Narnia goes up. The net flow of people is out of Narnia and into Middle Earth. We added people to Narnia,

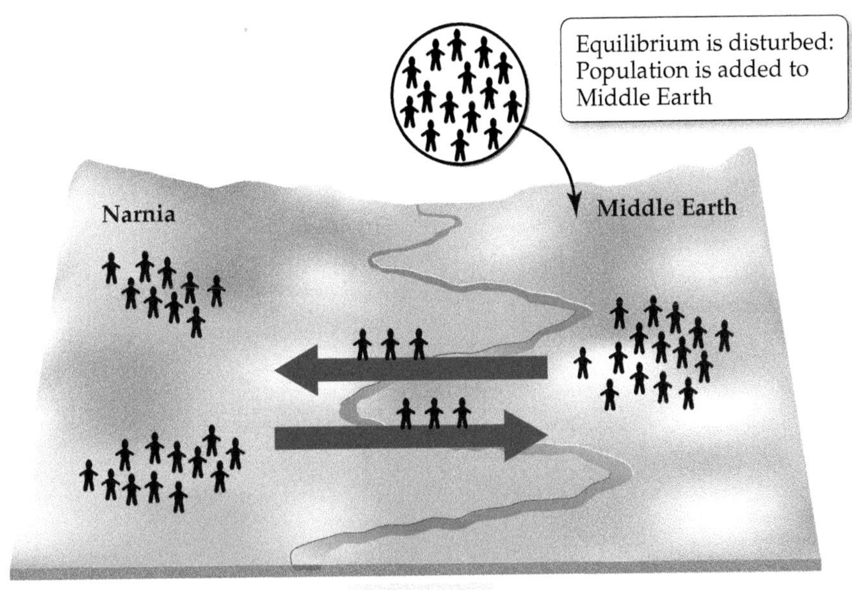

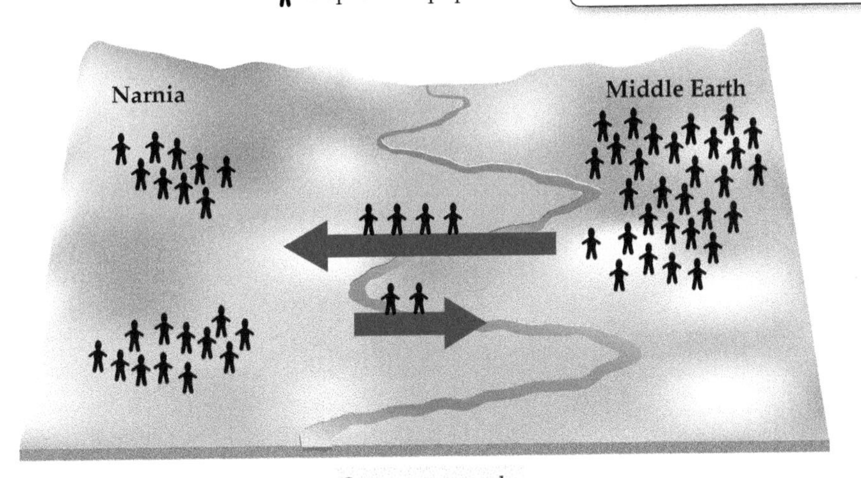

▶ **FIGURE 15.8 Population analogy for Le Châtelier's principle** When a system at equilibrium is disturbed, it shifts to minimize the disturbance. In this case, adding population to Middle Earth (the disturbance) causes population to move out of Middle Earth (minimizing the disturbance). Question: What would happen if you disturbed the equilibrium by taking population out of Middle Earth? In which direction would the population move to minimize the disturbance?

and the system responded by moving people out of Narnia. When systems at equilibrium are disturbed, they react to counter the disturbance. Chemical systems behave similarly. There are several ways to disturb a system in chemical equilibrium. We consider each of these separately in the next three sections of the chapter.

15.8 The Effect of a Concentration Change on Equilibrium

Consider the following reaction at chemical equilibrium:

$$N_2O_4(g) \rightleftharpoons 2\ NO_2(g)$$

Suppose we disturb the equilibrium by adding NO_2 to the equilibrium mixture (▶ Figure 15.9). In other words, we increase the concentration of NO_2. What happens? According to Le Châtelier's principle, the system shifts in a direction to minimize the disturbance. The shift is caused by the increased concentration of NO_2, which in turn increases the rate of the reverse reaction because reaction rates generally increase with increasing concentration (as we discussed in Section 15.2).

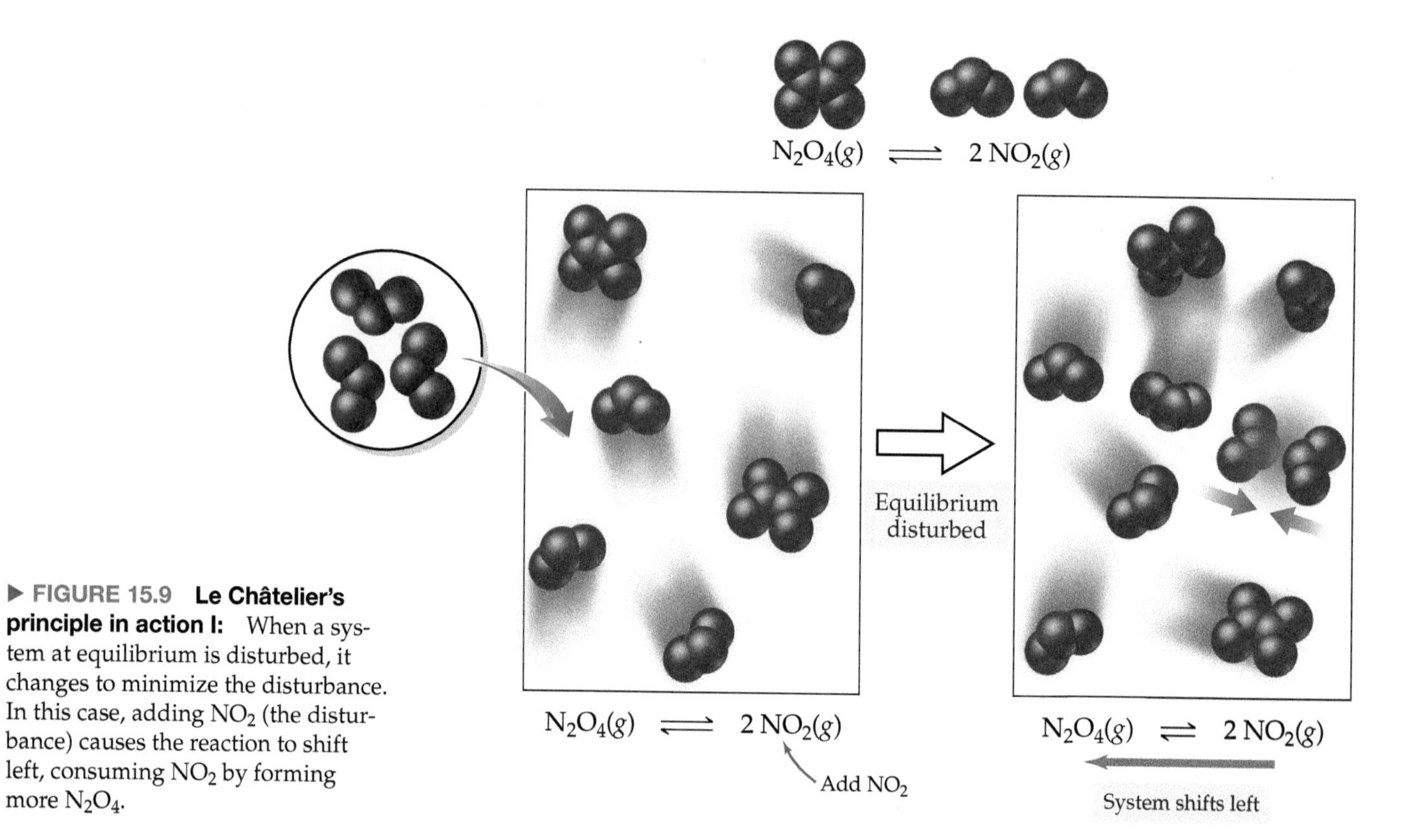

▶ **FIGURE 15.9 Le Châtelier's principle in action I:** When a system at equilibrium is disturbed, it changes to minimize the disturbance. In this case, adding NO_2 (the disturbance) causes the reaction to shift left, consuming NO_2 by forming more N_2O_4.

When we say that a reaction *shifts to the left* we mean that it proceeds in the reverse direction, consuming products and forming reactants.

The reaction shifts to the left (it proceeds in the reverse direction), consuming some of the added NO_2 and bringing its concentration back down.

$$N_2O_4(g) \rightleftharpoons 2\,NO_2(g)$$

Reaction shifts left ← Add NO_2

On the other hand, what happens if we add extra N_2O_4, increasing its concentration? In this case, the rate of the forward reaction increases and the reaction shifts to the right, consuming some of the added N_2O_4 and bringing *its* concentration back down (▶ Figure 15.10).

$$N_2O_4(g) \rightleftharpoons 2\,NO_2(g)$$

Add N_2O_4 → Reaction shifts right

When we say that a reaction *shifts to the right*, we mean that it proceeds in the forward direction, consuming reactants and forming products.

In each case, the system shifts in a direction that minimizes the disturbance.

To summarize, if a chemical system is at equilibrium:

- Increasing the concentration of one or more of the reactants causes the reaction to shift to the right (in the direction of the products).
- Increasing the concentration of one or more of the products causes the reaction to shift to the left (in the direction of the reactants).

EXAMPLE 15.5 The Effect of a Concentration Change on Equilibrium

Consider the following reaction at equilibrium:

$$CaCO_3(s) \rightleftharpoons CaO(s) + CO_2(g)$$

What is the effect of adding additional CO_2 to the reaction mixture? What is the effect of adding additional $CaCO_3$?

SOLUTION

Adding more CO_2 increases the concentration of CO_2 and causes the reaction to shift to the left. Adding more $CaCO_3$ does not increase the concentration of $CaCO_3$ because $CaCO_3$ is a solid and thus has a constant concentration. It is therefore not included in the equilibrium expression and has no effect on the position of the equilibrium.

▶SKILLBUILDER 15.5 | The Effect of a Concentration Change on Equilibrium

Consider the following reaction in chemical equilibrium.

$$2\ BrNO(g) \rightleftharpoons 2\ NO(g) + Br_2(g)$$

What is the effect of adding more Br_2 to the reaction mixture? What is the effect of adding more BrNO?

▶SKILLBUILDER PLUS

What is the effect of removing some Br_2 from the preceding reaction mixture?

▶FOR MORE PRACTICE Example 15.13a, b; Problems 63, 64, 65, 66.

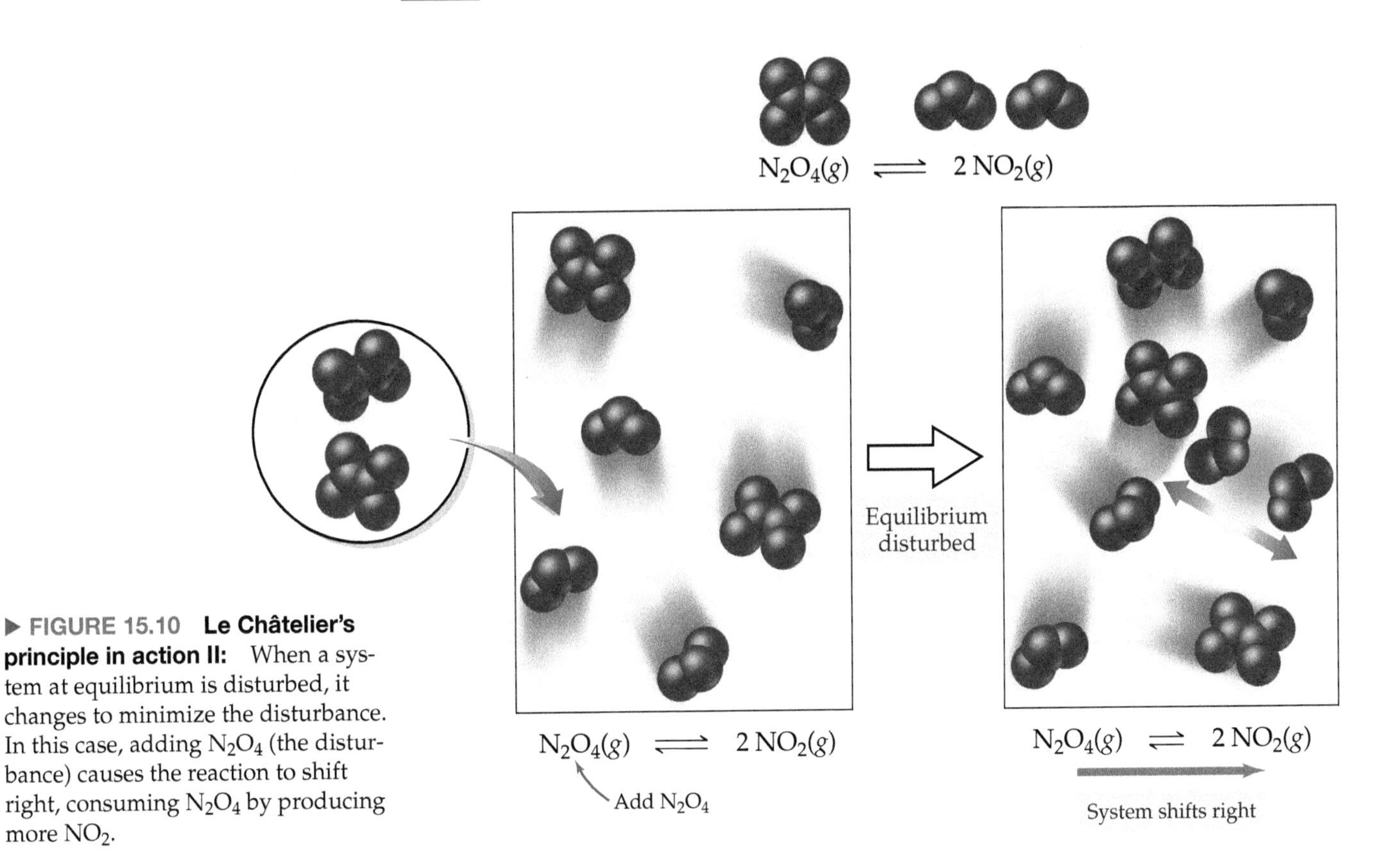

▶ **FIGURE 15.10 Le Châtelier's principle in action II:** When a system at equilibrium is disturbed, it changes to minimize the disturbance. In this case, adding N_2O_4 (the disturbance) causes the reaction to shift right, consuming N_2O_4 by producing more NO_2.

CONCEPTUAL CHECKPOINT 15.4

Consider the equilibrium reaction between carbon monoxide and hydrogen gas to form methanol:

$$CO(g) + 2\ H_2(g) \rightleftharpoons CH_3OH(g)$$

Suppose you have a reaction mixture of these three substances at equilibrium. Which would cause a greater shift toward products: doubling the carbon monoxide concentration or doubling the hydrogen gas concentration?

15.9 The Effect of a Volume Change on Equilibrium

See Section 11.4 for a complete description of Boyle's law.

How does a system in chemical equilibrium respond to a volume change? Remember from Chapter 11 that changing the volume of a gas (or a gas mixture) results in a change in pressure. Remember also that pressure and volume are inversely related: a *decrease* in volume causes an *increase* in pressure, and an *increase* in volume causes a *decrease* in pressure. So, if the volume of a gaseous reaction mixture at chemical equilibrium is changed, the pressure changes and the system will shift in a direction to minimize that change. For example, consider the following reaction at equilibrium in a cylinder equipped with a moveable piston:

$$N_2(g) + 3\,H_2(g) \rightleftharpoons 2\,NH_3(g)$$

What happens if we push down on the piston, lowering the volume and raising the pressure (▶ Figure 15.11)? How can the chemical system bring the pressure back down? Look carefully at the reaction coefficients in the balanced equation. If the reaction shifts to the right, 4 mol of gas particles (1 mol of N_2 and 3 mol of H_2) are converted to 2 mol of gas particles (2 mol of NH_3). Therefore, as the reaction shifts toward products, the pressure is lowered (because the reaction mixture contains fewer gas particles). So the system then shifts to the right, bringing the pressure back down and minimizing the disturbance.

From the ideal gas law ($PV = nRT$), we can see that lowering the number of moles of a gas (n) results in a lower pressure (P) at constant temperature and volume.

Consider the same reaction mixture at equilibrium again. What happens if, this time, we pull *up* on the piston, *increasing* the volume (▶ Figure 15.12)? The higher volume results in a lower pressure, and the system responds by trying to bring the pressure back up. It can do this by shifting to the left, converting 2 mol of gas particles into 4 mol of gas particles. As the reaction shifts toward reactants, the pressure increases again (because the reaction mixture contains more gas particles) minimizing the disturbance.

To summarize, if a chemical system is at equilibrium:

- Decreasing the volume causes the reaction to shift in the direction that has fewer moles of gas particles.
- Increasing the volume causes the reaction to shift in the direction that has more moles of gas particles.

Notice that if a chemical reaction has an equal number of moles of gas particles on both sides of the chemical equation, a change in volume has no effect. For example, consider the following reaction:

$$H_2(g) + I_2(g) \rightleftharpoons 2\,HI(g)$$

Both the left and the right sides of the equation contain 2 mol of gas particles, so a change in volume has no effect on this reaction. In addition, a change in volume has no effect on a reaction that has no gaseous reactants or products.

EXAMPLE 15.6 The Effect of a Volume Change on Equilibrium

Consider the reaction at chemical equilibrium:

$$2\,KClO_3(s) \rightleftharpoons 2\,KCl(s) + 3\,O_2(g)$$

What is the effect of decreasing the volume of the reaction mixture? Increasing the volume of the reaction mixture?

SOLUTION

The chemical equation has 3 mol of gas on the right and 0 mol of gas on the left. Decreasing the volume of the reaction mixture increases the pressure and causes the reaction to shift to the left (toward the side with fewer moles of gas particles). Increasing the volume of the reaction mixture decreases the pressure and causes the reaction to shift to the right (toward the side with more moles of gas particles).

▶SKILLBUILDER 15.6 | The Effect of a Volume Change on Equilibrium

Consider the reaction at chemical equilibrium:

$$2\,SO_2(g) + O_2(g) \rightleftharpoons 2\,SO_3(g)$$

What is the effect of decreasing the volume of the reaction mixture? Increasing the volume of the reaction mixture?

▶FOR MORE PRACTICE Example 15.13c; Problems 67, 68, 69, 70.

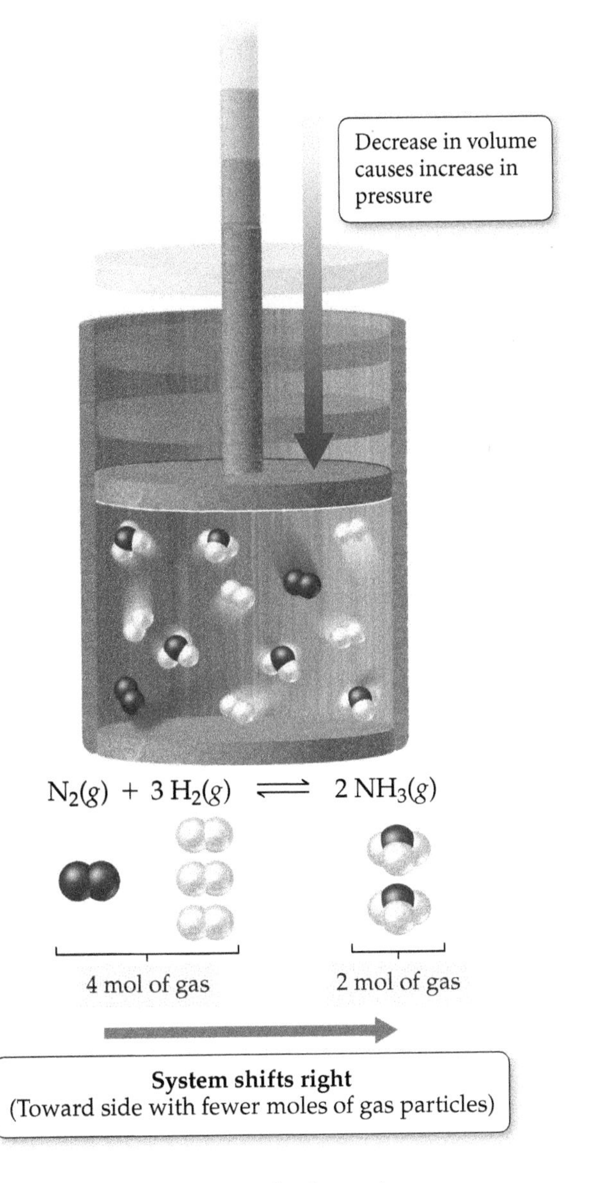

▲ **FIGURE 15.11 Effect of volume decrease on equilibrium** When the volume of an equilibrium mixture decreases, the pressure increases. The system responds (to bring the pressure back down) by shifting to the right, the side of the reaction with the fewest moles of gas particles.

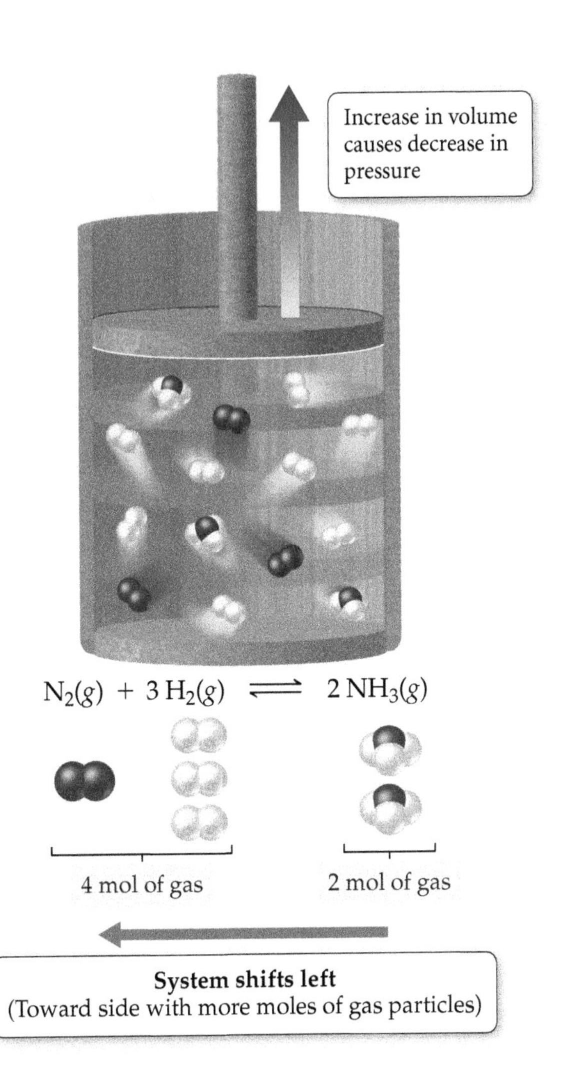

▲ **FIGURE 15.12 Effect of volume increase on equilibrium** When the volume of an equilibrium mixture increases, the pressure decreases. The system responds (to raise the pressure) by shifting to the left, the side of the reaction with the most moles of gas particles.

CHEMISTRY AND HEALTH

How a Developing Fetus Gets Oxygen from Its Mother

Have you ever wondered how a baby in the womb gets oxygen? Unlike you and me, a fetus cannot breathe. Yet like you and me, a fetus needs oxygen. Where does that oxygen come from? In adults, oxygen is absorbed in the lungs and carried in the blood by a protein molecule called hemoglobin, which is abundantly present in red blood cells. Hemoglobin (Hb) reacts with oxygen according to the equilibrium equation:

$$\text{Hb} + \text{O}_2 \rightleftharpoons \text{HbO}_2$$

The equilibrium constant for this reaction is neither large nor small, but intermediate. Consequently, the reaction shifts toward the right or the left, depending on the concentration of oxygen. As blood flows through the lungs, where oxygen concentrations are high, the equilibrium shifts to the right—hemoglobin loads oxygen.

Lung $[\text{O}_2]$ high

$$\text{Hb} + \text{O}_2 \rightleftharpoons \text{HbO}_2$$

Reaction shifts right

As blood flows through muscles and organs that are using oxygen (where oxygen concentrations have been depleted), the equilibrium shifts to the left—hemoglobin unloads oxygen.

Muscle $[\text{O}_2]$ low

$$\text{Hb} + \text{O}_2 \rightleftharpoons \text{HbO}_2$$

Reaction shifts left

A fetus has its own blood circulatory system. The mother's blood never flows into the fetus's body, and the fetus cannot get any air in the womb. So how does the fetus get oxygen?

The answer lies in fetal hemoglobin (HbF), which is slightly different from adult hemoglobin. Like adult hemoglobin, fetal hemoglobin is in equilibrium with oxygen.

$$\text{HbF} + \text{O}_2 \rightleftharpoons \text{HbFO}_2$$

However, the equilibrium constant for fetal hemoglobin is larger than the equilibrium constant for adult hemoglobin. In other words, fetal hemoglobin will load oxygen at a lower oxygen concentration than adult hemoglobin. So, when the mother's hemoglobin flows through the placenta, it unloads oxygen into the placenta. The baby's blood also flows into the placenta, and even though the baby's blood never mixes with the mother's blood, the fetal hemoglobin within the baby's blood loads the oxygen (that the mother's hemoglobin unloaded) and carries it to the baby. Nature has thus engineered a chemical system where the mother's hemoglobin can in effect *hand off* oxygen to the baby's hemoglobin.

CAN YOU ANSWER THIS? *What would happen if fetal hemoglobin had the same equilibrium constant for the reaction with oxygen as adult hemoglobin?*

▲ A human fetus. **Question:** How does the fetus get oxygen?

CONCEPTUAL CHECKPOINT 15.5

Consider the reaction:

$$\text{H}_2(g) + \text{I}_2(g) \rightleftharpoons 2\,\text{HI}(g)$$

Which change would cause the reaction to shift to the right (toward products)?

(a) decreasing the volume

(b) increasing the volume

(c) increasing the concentration of hydrogen gas

(d) decreasing the concentration of hydrogen gas

15.10 The Effect of a Temperature Change on Equilibrium

According to Le Châtelier's principle, if the temperature of a system at equilibrium is changed, the system should shift in a direction to counter that change. So if the temperature is increased, the reaction should shift in the direction that attempts to lower the temperature and vice versa. Recall from Section 3.9 that energy changes are often associated with chemical reactions. If we want to predict the direction in which a reaction will shift upon a temperature change, we must understand how a shift in the reaction affects the temperature.

In Section 3.9, we classify chemical reactions according to whether they absorb or emit heat energy in the course of the reaction. Recall that an *exothermic reaction* (one with a negative ΔH_{rxn}) emits heat.

Exothermic reaction: $A + B \rightleftharpoons C + D + \text{Heat}$

In an exothermic reaction, we can think of heat as a product. Consequently, raising the temperature of an exothermic reaction—think of this as adding heat—causes the reaction to shift left. For example, the reaction of nitrogen with hydrogen to form ammonia is exothermic.

$$N_2(g) + 3\,H_2(g) \rightleftharpoons 2\,NH_3(g) + \text{Heat}$$

Reaction shifts left (←) — Add heat (↑)

Raising the temperature of an equilibrium mixture of these three gases causes the reaction to shift left, absorbing some of the added heat. Conversely, lowering the temperature of an equilibrium mixture of these three gases causes the reaction to shift right, releasing heat.

$$N_2(g) + 3\,H_2(g) \rightleftharpoons 2\,NH_3(g) + \text{Heat}$$

Reaction shifts right (→) — Remove heat (↓)

In contrast, an *endothermic reaction* (one with a positive ΔH_{rxn}) absorbs heat.

Endothermic reaction: $A + B + \text{Heat} \rightleftharpoons C + D$

In an endothermic reaction, we can think of heat as a reactant. Consequently, raising the temperature (or adding heat) causes an endothermic reaction to shift right. For example, the following reaction is endothermic:

$$\underset{\text{Colorless}}{N_2O_4(g)} + \text{Heat} \rightleftharpoons \underset{\text{Brown}}{2\,NO_2(g)}$$

Add heat (↑) — Reaction shifts right (→)

Raising the temperature of an equilibrium mixture of these two gases causes the reaction to shift right, absorbing some of the added heat. Since N_2O_4 is colorless and NO_2 is brown, we can easily see the effects of changing the temperature of this reaction (▶ Figure 15.13). On the other hand, lowering the temperature of a reaction mixture of these two gases causes the reaction to shift left, releasing heat.

$$\underset{\text{Colorless}}{N_2O_4(g)} + \text{Heat} \rightleftharpoons \underset{\text{Brown}}{2\,NO_2(g)}$$

Remove heat (↓) — Reaction shifts left (←)

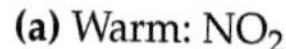

(a) Warm: NO_2

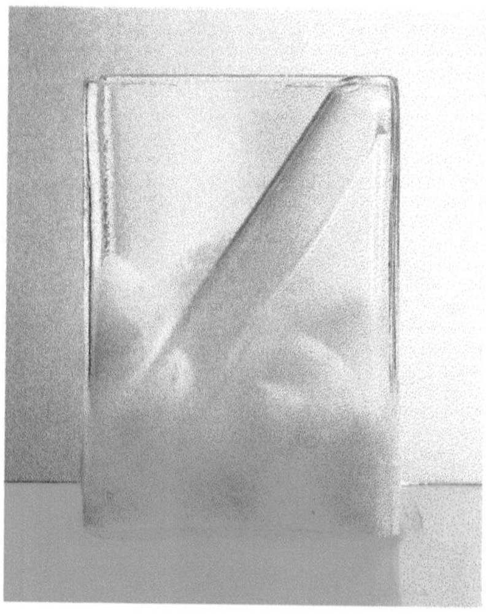

(b) Cool: N_2O_4

▶ **FIGURE 15.13 Equilibrium as a function of temperature** Since the reaction $N_2O_4(g) \rightleftharpoons 2NO_2(g)$ is endothermic, warm temperatures **(a)** cause a shift to the right, toward the production of brown NO_2. Cool temperatures **(b)** cause a shift to the left, to colorless N_2O_4.

To summarize:

In an exothermic chemical reaction, heat is a product and:

- Increasing the temperature causes the reaction to shift left (in the direction of the reactants).
- Decreasing the temperature causes the reaction to shift right (in the direction of the products).

In an endothermic chemical reaction, heat is a reactant and:

- Increasing the temperature causes the reaction to shift right (in the direction of the products).
- Decreasing the temperature causes the reaction to shift left (in the direction of the reactants).

EXAMPLE 15.7 The Effect of a Temperature Change on Equilibrium

The following reaction is endothermic.

$$CaCO_3(s) \rightleftharpoons CaO(s) + CO_2(g)$$

What is the effect of increasing the temperature of the reaction mixture? Decreasing the temperature?

SOLUTION

Since the reaction is endothermic, we can think of heat as a reactant.

$$\text{Heat} + CaCO_3(s) \rightleftharpoons CaO(s) + CO_2(g)$$

Raising the temperature is adding heat, causing the reaction to shift to the right. Lowering the temperature is removing heat, causing the reaction to shift to the left.

▶**SKILLBUILDER 15.7 | The Effect of a Temperature Change on Equilibrium**

The following reaction is exothermic.

$$2\ SO_2(g) + O_2(g) \rightleftharpoons 2\ SO_3(g)$$

What is the effect of increasing the temperature of the reaction mixture? Decreasing the temperature?

▶**FOR MORE PRACTICE** Example 15.13d; Problems 71, 72, 73, 74.

CONCEPTUAL CHECKPOINT 15.6

Consider the endothermic reaction:

$$Cl_2(g) \rightleftharpoons 2\,Cl(g)$$

If a reaction mixture is at equilibrium, which disturbances will increase the amount of product the most?

(a) increasing the temperature and increasing the volume
(b) increasing the temperature and decreasing the volume
(c) decreasing the temperature and increasing the volume
(d) decreasing the temperature and decreasing the volume

15.11 The Solubility-Product Constant

Recall from Section 7.5 that a compound is considered soluble if it dissolves in water and insoluble if it does not. Recall also that, by applying the *solubility rules* (Table 7.2), we can classify many ionic compounds as soluble or insoluble. We can better understand the solubility of an ionic compound with the concept of equilibrium. The process by which an ionic compound dissolves is an equilibrium process. For example, we can represent the dissolving of calcium fluoride in water with the chemical equation:

$$CaF_2(s) \rightleftharpoons Ca^{2+}(aq) + 2\,F^-(aq)$$

The equilibrium expression for a chemical equation that represents the dissolving of an ionic compound is the **solubility-product constant (K_{sp})**. For CaF_2, the solubility-product constant is:

$$K_{sp} = [Ca^{2+}][F^-]^2$$

Notice that, as we discussed in Section 15.5, solids are omitted from the equilibrium expression.

The K_{sp} value is therefore a measure of the solubility of a compound. A large K_{sp} (forward reaction favored) means that the compound is very soluble. A small K_{sp} (reverse reaction favored) means that the compound is not very soluble. Table 15.2 lists the value of K_{sp} for a number of ionic compounds.

TABLE 15.2 Selected Solubility-Product Constants (K_{sp})

Compound	Formula	K_{sp}
barium sulfate	$BaSO_4$	1.07×10^{-10}
calcium carbonate	$CaCO_3$	4.96×10^{-9}
calcium fluoride	CaF_2	1.46×10^{-10}
calcium hydroxide	$Ca(OH)_2$	4.68×10^{-6}
calcium sulfate	$CaSO_4$	7.10×10^{-5}
copper(II) sulfide	CuS	1.27×10^{-36}
iron(II) carbonate	$FeCO_3$	3.07×10^{-11}
iron(II) hydroxide	$Fe(OH)_2$	4.87×10^{-17}
lead(II) chloride	$PbCl_2$	1.17×10^{-5}
lead(II) sulfate	$PbSO_4$	1.82×10^{-8}
lead(II) sulfide	PbS	9.04×10^{-29}
magnesium carbonate	$MgCO_3$	6.82×10^{-6}
magnesium hydroxide	$Mg(OH)_2$	2.06×10^{-13}
silver chloride	$AgCl$	1.77×10^{-10}
silver chromate	Ag_2CrO_4	1.12×10^{-12}
silver iodide	AgI	8.51×10^{-17}

EXAMPLE 15.8 Writing Expressions for K_{sp}

Write expressions for K_{sp} for each ionic compound.

(a) $BaSO_4$ (b) $Mn(OH)_2$ (c) Ag_2CrO_4

SOLUTION

To write the expression for K_{sp}, first write the chemical reaction showing the solid compound in equilibrium with its dissolved aqueous ions. Then write the equilibrium expression based on this equation.

(a) $BaSO_4(s) \rightleftharpoons Ba^{2+}(aq) + SO_4^{2-}(aq)$

$$K_{sp} = [Ba^{2+}][SO_4^{2-}]$$

(b) $Mn(OH)_2(s) \rightleftharpoons Mn^{2+}(aq) + 2OH^-(aq)$

$$K_{sp} = [Mn^{2+}][OH^-]^2$$

(c) $Ag_2CrO_4(s) \rightleftharpoons 2Ag^+(aq) + CrO_4^{2-}(aq)$

$$K_{sp} = [Ag^+]^2[CrO_4^{2-}]$$

▶**SKILLBUILDER 15.8 | Writing Expressions for K_{sp}**

Write expressions for K_{sp} for each ionic compound.

(a) AgI (b) $Ca(OH)_2$

▶**FOR MORE PRACTICE** Example 15.14; Problems 77, 78.

USING K_{sp} TO DETERMINE MOLAR SOLUBILITY

Recall from Section 13.3 that the solubility of a compound is the amount of the compound that dissolves in a certain amount of liquid. The **molar solubility** is the solubility in units of moles per liter. The molar solubility of a compound can be calculated directly from K_{sp}. For example, consider silver chloride.

$$AgCl(s) \rightleftharpoons Ag^+(aq) + Cl^-(aq) \quad K_{sp} = 1.77 \times 10^{-10}$$

How can we find the molar solubility of AgCl from K_{sp}? First, notice that K_{sp} is *not* the molar solubility; it is the solubility-product constant.

Second, notice that the concentration of either Ag^+ or Cl^- at equilibrium will be equal to the amount of AgCl that dissolved. We know this from the relationship of the stoichiometric coefficients in the balanced equation.

$$1 \text{ mol AgCl} : 1 \text{ mol } Ag^+ : 1 \text{ mol } Cl^-$$

Consequently, to find the solubility, we simply need to find $[Ag^+]$ or $[Cl^-]$ at equilibrium. We can do this by writing the expression for the solubility-product constant.

$$K_{sp} = [Ag^+][Cl^-]$$

Because both Ag^+ and Cl^- come from AgCl, their concentrations must be equal. Since the solubility of AgCl is equal to the equilibrium concentration of either dissolved ion, we write:

$$\text{Solubility} = S = [Ag^+] = [Cl^-]$$

Substituting this into the expression for the solubility constant, we get:

$$\begin{aligned} K_{sp} &= [Ag^+][Cl^-] \\ &= S \times S \\ &= S^2 \end{aligned}$$

EVERYDAY CHEMISTRY

Hard Water

Many areas of the United States obtain their water from lakes or reservoirs that have significant concentrations of $CaCO_3$ and $MgCO_3$. These salts dissolve into rainwater as it flows through soils rich in $CaCO_3$ and $MgCO_3$. Water containing these salts is known as hard water. Hard water is not a health hazard because both calcium and magnesium are part of a healthy diet, but their presence in water can be annoying. For example, because of their relatively low solubility-product constants, water can easily become saturated with $CaCO_3$ and $MgCO_3$. A drop of water, for example, becomes saturated with $CaCO_3$ and $MgCO_3$ as it evaporates. A saturated solution such as this precipitates some of its dissolved ions. These precipitates show up as scaly deposits on faucets, sinks, or cookware. Washing cars or dishes with hard water leaves spots of $CaCO_3$ and $MgCO_3$ as these precipitate out of drying drops of water.

◀ Hard water leaves scaly deposits on plumbing fixtures.

CAN YOU ANSWER THIS? *Is the water in your community hard or soft? Use the solubility-product constants from Table 15.2 to calculate the molar solubility of $CaCO_3$ and $MgCO_3$. How many moles of $CaCO_3$ are in 5 L of water that is saturated with $CaCO_3$? How many grams?*

In this text, we limit the calculation of molar solubility to ionic compounds whose chemical formulas have one cation and one anion.

Therefore,

$$S = \sqrt{K_{sp}}$$
$$= \sqrt{1.77 \times 10^{-10}}$$
$$= 1.33 \times 10^{-5}\,\text{M}$$

So the molar solubility of AgCl is 1.33×10^{-5} mol/L.

EXAMPLE 15.9 Calculating Molar Solubility from K_{sp}

Calculate the molar solubility of $BaSO_4$.

SOLUTION	
Begin by writing the reaction by which solid $BaSO_4$ dissolves into its constituent aqueous ions.	$BaSO_4(s) \rightleftharpoons Ba^{2+}(aq) + SO_4^{2-}(aq)$
Next, write the expression for K_{sp}.	$K_{sp} = [Ba^{2+}][SO_4^{2-}]$
Define the molar solubility (S) as $[Ba^{2+}]$ or $[SO_4^{2-}]$ at equilibrium.	$S = [Ba^{2+}] = [SO_4^{2-}]$
Substitute S into the equilibrium expression and solve for it.	$K_{sp} = [Ba^{2+}][SO_4^{2-}]$ $= S \times S$ $= S^2$ Therefore $S = \sqrt{K_{sp}}$
Finally, look up the value of K_{sp} in Table 15.2 and calculate S. The molar solubility of $BaSO_4$ is 1.03×10^{-5} mol/L.	$S = \sqrt{K_{sp}}$ $= \sqrt{1.07 \times 10^{-10}}$ $= 1.03 \times 10^{-5}$ M

▶SKILLBUILDER 15.9 | Calculating Molar Solubility from K_{sp}

Calculate the molar solubility of $CaSO_4$.

▶FOR MORE PRACTICE Example 15.15; Problems 85, 86, 87, 88.

15.12 The Path of a Reaction and the Effect of a Catalyst

Warning: Hydrogen gas is explosive and should never be handled without proper training.

In this chapter, we have learned that the equilibrium constant describes the ultimate fate of a chemical reaction. Large equilibrium constants mean that the reaction favors the products. Small equilibrium constants mean that the reaction favors the reactants. But the equilibrium constant by itself does not tell the whole story. For example, consider the reaction between hydrogen gas and oxygen gas to form water:

$$2H_2(g) + O_2(g) \rightleftharpoons 2H_2O(g) \quad K_{eq} = 3.2 \times 10^{81} \text{ at } 25\ °C$$

The equilibrium constant is huge, meaning that the forward reaction is heavily favored. Yet you can mix hydrogen and oxygen in a balloon at room temperature, and no reaction occurs. Hydrogen and oxygen peacefully coexist together inside of the balloon and form virtually no water. Why?

The equilibrium constant describes *how far* a chemical reaction will go. The reaction rate describes *how fast* it will get there.

The activation energy is sometimes called the *activation barrier.*

To answer this question, we revisit a topic from the beginning of this chapter—*the reaction rate.* At 25 °C, the reaction rate between hydrogen gas and oxygen gas is virtually zero. Even though the equilibrium constant is large, the reaction rate is small and no reaction occurs. The reaction rate between hydrogen and oxygen is slow because the reaction has a large *activation energy.* The **activation energy** (or activation barrier) for a reaction is the energy barrier that must be overcome in order for the reactants to be converted into products. Activation energies exist for most chemical reactions because the original bonds must begin to break before new bonds begin to form, and this requires energy. For example, for H_2 and O_2 to react to form H_2O, the H—H and O=O bonds must begin to break before the new bonds can form. The initial weakening of H_2 and O_2 bonds takes energy—this is the activation energy of the reaction.

HOW ACTIVATION ENERGIES AFFECT REACTION RATES

We can illustrate how activation energies affect reaction rates with a graph showing the energy progress of a reaction (▼ Figure 15.14). We see in the figure that the products have less energy than the reactants, so the reaction is exothermic (it releases energy when it occurs). However, before the reaction can take place, some energy must first be *added*—the energy of the reactants must be raised by an amount that we call the activation energy. The activation energy is a kind of "energy hump" that normally exists between the reactants and products.

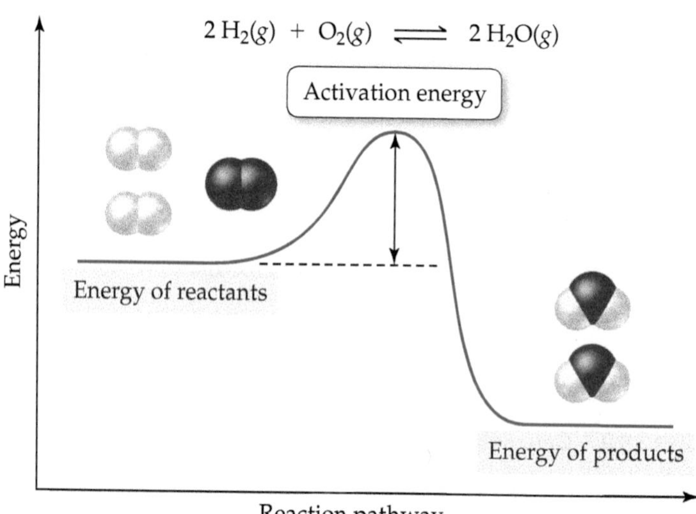

▶ **FIGURE 15.14 Activation energy** This plot represents the energy of the reactants and products along the reaction pathway (as the reaction occurs). Notice that the energy of the products is lower than the energy of the reactants, so this is an exothermic reaction. However, notice that the reactants must get over an energy hump—called the *activation energy*—to proceed from reactants to products.

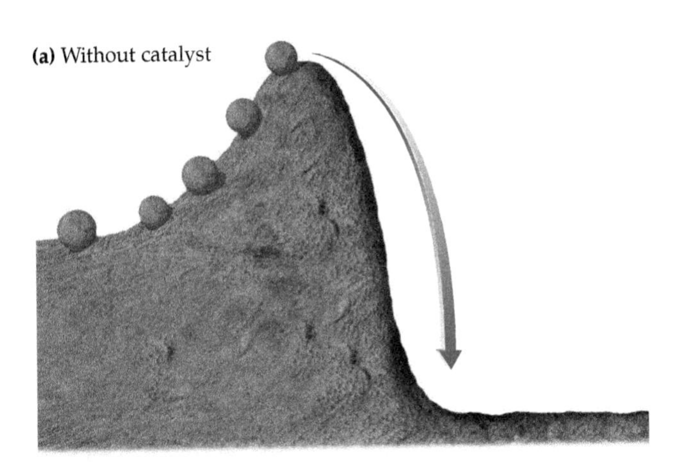

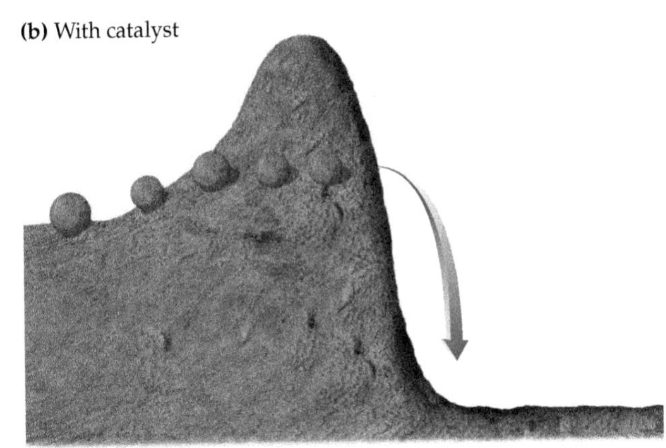

▲ **FIGURE 15.15 Hill analogy for activation energy** There are several ways to get these boulders over the hill as fast as possible. **(a)** One way is simply to push them harder—this is analogous to an increase in temperature for a chemical reaction. **(b)** Another way is to find a path that goes *around* the hill—this is analogous to the role of a catalyst for a chemical reaction.

We can understand this concept better by means of a simple analogy—getting a chemical reaction to occur is much like trying to push a bunch of boulders over a hill (▲ Figure 15.15a). We can think of each collision that occurs between reactant molecules as an attempt to roll a boulder over the hill. We can think of a successful collision between two molecules (one that leads to product) as a successful attempt to roll a boulder over the hill and down the other side.

For rolling boulders, the higher the hill is, the harder it will be to get the boulders over the hill, and the fewer the number of boulders that make it over the hill in a given period of time. Similarly, for chemical reactions, the higher the activation energy, the fewer the number of reactant molecules that make it over the barrier, and the slower the reaction rate. In general:

> At a given temperature, the higher the activation energy for a chemical reaction, the slower the reaction rate.

Are there any ways to speed up a slow reaction (one with a high activation barrier)? In Section 15.2 we talked of two ways to increase reaction rates. The first way is to increase the concentrations of the reactants, which results in more collisions per unit time. This is analogous to simply pushing more boulders toward the hill in a given period of time. The second way is to increase the temperature. This results in more collisions per unit time, and also in higher energy collisions. Higher-energy collisions are analogous to pushing the boulders harder (with more force), which will result in more boulders making it over the hill per unit time—a faster reaction rate. There is, however, a third way to speed up a slow chemical reaction: by using a *catalyst*.

CATALYSTS LOWER THE ACTIVATION ENERGY

A catalyst does not change the *position* of equilibrium, only *how fast* equilibrium is reached.

A **catalyst** is a substance that increases the rate of a chemical reaction but is not consumed by the reaction. A catalyst works by lowering the activation energy for the reaction, making it easier for reactants to get over the energy barrier (▶ Figure 15.16). In our boulder analogy, a catalyst creates another path for the boulders to travel—a path with a smaller hill (see Figure 15.15b). For example, consider the noncatalytic destruction of ozone in the upper atmosphere.

Upper-atmospheric ozone forms a shield against harmful ultraviolet light that would otherwise enter Earth's atmosphere. See the *Chemistry in the Environment* box in Chapter 6.

$$O_3 + O \longrightarrow 2\,O_2$$

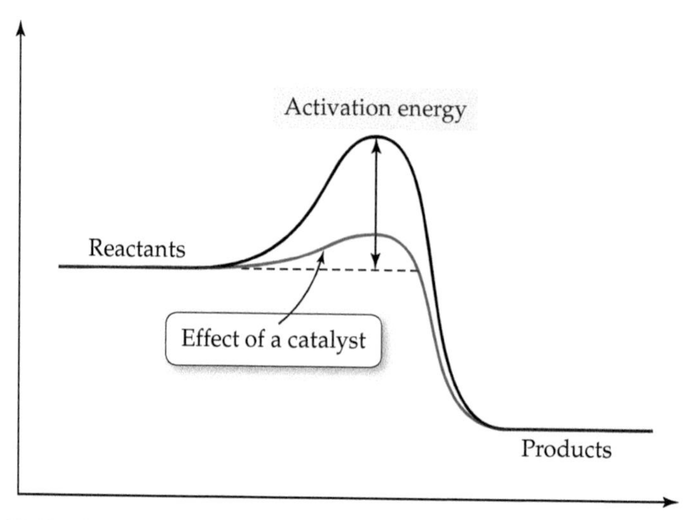

▲ **FIGURE 15.16 Function of a catalyst** A catalyst provides an alternate pathway with a lower activation energy barrier for the reaction.

We have a protective ozone layer because this reaction has a fairly high activation barrier and therefore proceeds at a fairly slow rate. The ozone layer does not rapidly decompose into O_2.

However, the addition of Cl (from synthetic chlorofluorocarbons) to the upper atmosphere has resulted in another pathway by which O_3 can be destroyed. The first step in this pathway—called the *catalytic* destruction of ozone—is the reaction of Cl with O_3 to form ClO and O_2.

$$Cl + O_3 \longrightarrow ClO + O_2$$

This is followed by a second step in which ClO reacts with O, regenerating Cl.

$$ClO + O \longrightarrow Cl + O_2$$

Notice that, if we add the two reactions, the overall reaction is identical to the noncatalytic reaction.

$$\begin{array}{l} \cancel{Cl} + O_3 \longrightarrow \cancel{ClO} + O_2 \\ \cancel{ClO} + O \longrightarrow \cancel{Cl} + O_2 \\ \hline O_3 + O \longrightarrow 2\,O_2 \end{array}$$

However, the activation energies for the two reactions in this pathway are much smaller than for the first, uncatalyzed pathway, and therefore the reaction occurs at a much faster rate. Note that the Cl is not consumed in the overall reaction; this is characteristic of a catalyst.

In the case of the catalytic destruction of ozone, the catalyst speeds up a reaction that we do *not* want to happen. Most of the time, however, catalysts are used to speed up reactions that we *do* want to happen. For example, your car most likely has a catalytic converter in its exhaust system. The catalytic converter contains a catalyst that converts exhaust pollutants (such as carbon monoxide) into less harmful substances (such as carbon dioxide). These reactions occur only with the help of a catalyst because they are too slow to occur otherwise.

A catalyst cannot change the value of K_{eq} for a reaction—it affects only the *rate* of the reaction.

The role of catalysis in chemistry cannot be overstated. Without catalysts, chemistry would be a different field. For many reactions, increasing the reaction rate in another way—such as raising the temperature—is simply not feasible. Many reactants are thermally sensitive—increasing the temperature often destroys them. The only way to carry out many reactions is to use catalysts.

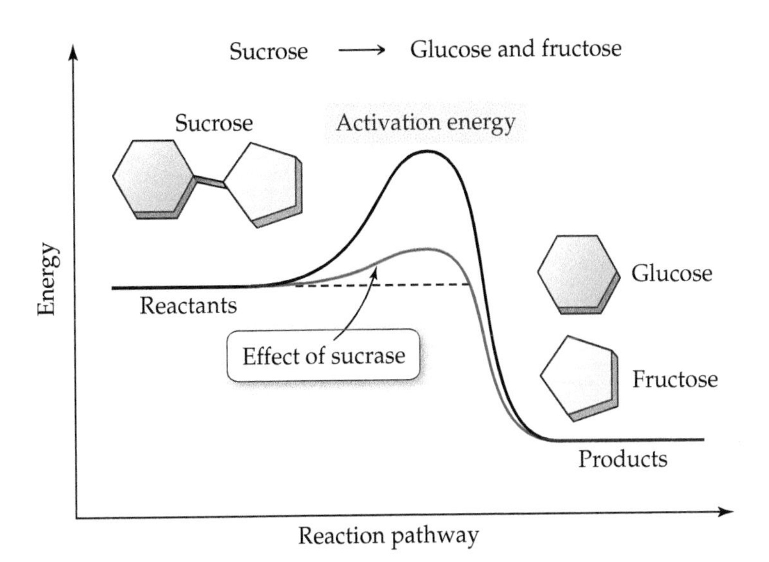

▶ **FIGURE 15.17 An enzyme catalyst** The enzyme sucrase creates a pathway with a lower activation energy for the conversion of sucrose to glucose and fructose.

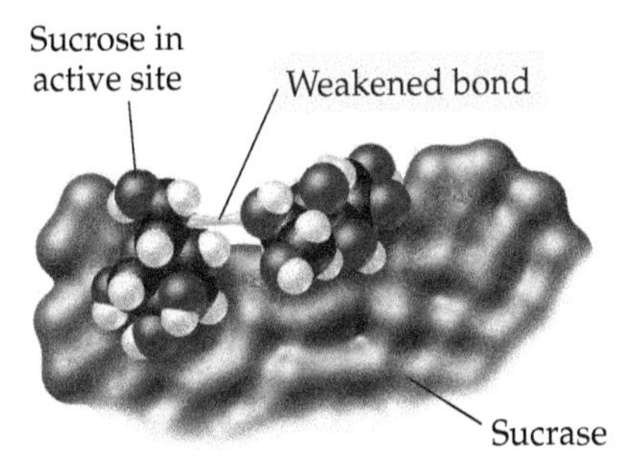

▲ **FIGURE 15.18 How an enzyme works** Sucrase has a pocket called the active site where sucrose binds. When a molecule of sucrose enters the active site, the bond between glucose and fructose is weakened, lowering the activation energy for the reaction.

ENZYMES: BIOLOGICAL CATALYSTS

Perhaps the best example of chemical catalysis is found in living organisms. Most of the thousands of reactions that must occur for a living organism to survive would be too slow at normal temperatures. So living organisms use **enzymes**, biological catalysts that increase the rates of biochemical reactions. For example, when we eat sucrose (table sugar), our bodies must break it into two smaller molecules called glucose and fructose. The equilibrium constant for this reaction is large, favoring the products. However, at room temperature, or even at body temperature, the sucrose does not break down into glucose and fructose because the activation energy is high, resulting in a slow reaction rate. In other words, table sugar remains table sugar at room temperature, even though the equilibrium constant for its reaction to glucose and fructose is relatively large (▲ Figure 15.17). In the body, however, an enzyme called *sucrase* catalyzes the conversion of sucrose to glucose and fructose. Sucrase has a pocket—called the active site—into which sucrose snugly fits (like a key into a lock). When sucrose is in the active site, the bond between the glucose and fructose units weakens, lowering the activation energy for the reaction and increasing the reaction rate (◀ Figure 15.18). The reaction can then proceed toward equilibrium—which favors the products—at a much lower temperature.

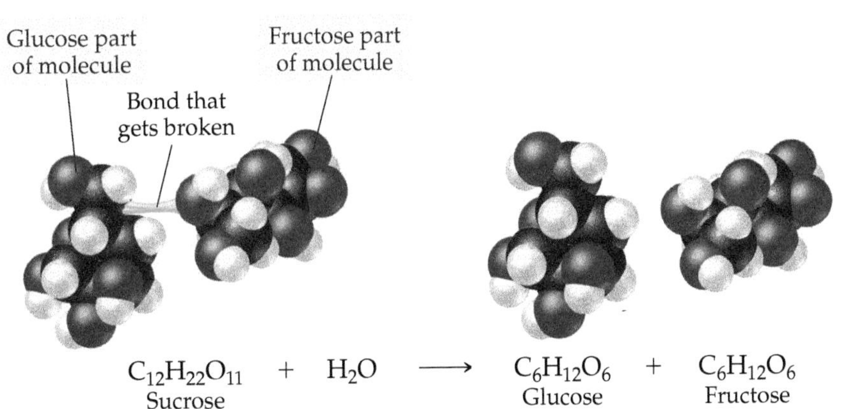

Not only do enzymes allow otherwise slow reactions to occur at a reasonable rate, they also allow living organisms to have tremendous control over which reactions occur and when. Enzymes are extremely specific—each enzyme catalyzes only a single reaction. So to turn a particular reaction on, a living organism simply needs to produce or activate the correct enzyme to catalyze that reaction.

CHAPTER IN REVIEW

CHEMICAL PRINCIPLES / RELEVANCE

The Concept of Equilibrium: Equilibrium involves the ideas of sameness and constancy. When a system is in equilibrium, some property of the system remains the same and does not change.

The Concept of Equilibrium: The equilibrium concept explains many phenomena such as the human body's oxygen delivery system. Life itself can be defined as controlled disequilibrium with the environment.

Rates of Chemical Reactions: The rate of a chemical reaction is the amount of reactant(s) that goes to product(s) in a given period of time. In general, reaction rates increase with increasing reactant concentration and increasing temperature. Since reaction rates depend on the concentration of reactants, and since the concentration of reactants decreases as a reaction proceeds, reaction rates usually slow down as a reaction proceeds.

Rates of Chemical Reactions: The rate of a chemical reaction determines how fast a reaction will reach its equilibrium. Chemists want to understand the factors that influence reaction rates so that they can control them.

Dynamic Chemical Equilibrium: Dynamic chemical equilibrium occurs when the rate of the forward reaction equals the rate of the reverse reaction.

Dynamic Chemical Equilibrium: When dynamic chemical equilibrium is reached, the concentrations of the reactants and products become constant.

The Equilibrium Constant: For the generic reaction

$$aA + bB \rightleftharpoons cC + dD$$

the equilibrium constant (K_{eq}) is defined as:

$$K_{eq} = \frac{[C]^c[D]^d}{[A]^a[B]^b}$$

Only the concentrations of gaseous or aqueous reactants and products are included in the equilibrium constant—the concentrations of solid or liquid reactants or products are omitted.

The Equilibrium Constant: The equilibrium constant is a measure of how far a reaction will proceed. A large K_{eq} means the forward reaction is favored (lots of products at equilibrium). A small K_{eq} means the reverse reaction is favored (lots of reactants at equilibrium). An intermediate K_{eq} means that there will be significant amounts of both reactants and products at equilibrium.

Le Châtelier's Principle: Le Châtelier's principle states that when a chemical system at equilibrium is disturbed, the system shifts in a direction that minimizes the disturbance.

Le Châtelier's Principle: Le Châtelier's principle helps us predict what happens to a chemical system at equilibrium when the conditions are changed. This allows chemists to modify the conditions of a chemical reaction to obtain a desired result.

Effect of a Concentration Change on Equilibrium:

- Increasing the concentration of one or more of the ***reactants*** causes the reaction to shift to the ***right***.
- Increasing the concentration of one or more of the ***products*** causes the reaction to shift to the ***left***.

Effect of a Concentration Change on Equilibrium: There are many cases when a chemist may want to drive a reaction in one direction or another. For example, suppose a chemist is carrying out a reaction to make a desired compound. The reaction can be pushed to the right by continuously removing the product from the reaction mixture as it forms, thus maximizing the amount of product that can be made.

Effect of a Volume Change on Equilibrium:

- Decreasing the volume causes the reaction to shift in the direction that has *fewer* moles of gas particles.
- Increasing the volume causes the reaction to shift in the direction that has more moles of gas particles.

Effect of a Volume Change on Equilibrium: Like the effect of concentration, the effect of pressure on equilibrium allows a chemist to choose the best conditions under which to carry out a chemical reaction. Some reactions are favored in the forward direction by high pressure (those with fewer moles of gas particles in the products), and others (those with fewer moles of gas particles in the reactants) are favored in the forward direction by low pressure.

Effect of a Temperature Change on Equilibrium:
Exothermic chemical reaction (heat is a product):

- ***Increasing*** the temperature causes the reaction to shift ***left***.
- ***Decreasing*** the temperature causes the reaction to shift ***right***.

Endothermic chemical reaction (heat is a reactant):

- ***Increasing*** the temperature causes the reaction to shift ***right***.
- ***Decreasing*** the temperature causes the reaction to shift ***left***.

Effect of a Temperature Change on Equilibrium: Again, the effect of temperature on a reaction allows chemists to choose conditions that will favor desired reactions. Higher temperatures favor endothermic reactions, while lower temperatures favor exothermic reactions. Most reactions will occur *faster* at higher temperature, so the effect of temperature on the rate, not just on the equilibrium constant, must be considered.

The Solubility-Product Constant, K_{sp}: The solubility-product constant of an ionic compound is the equilibrium constant for the chemical equation that describes the dissolving of the compound.

The Solubility-Product Constant, K_{sp}: The solubility-product constant reflects the solubility of a compound. The greater the solubility-product constant, the greater the solubility of the compound.

Reaction Paths and Catalysts: Most chemical reactions must overcome an energy hump, called the *activation energy*, as they proceed from reactants to products. Increasing the temperature of a reaction mixture increases the fraction of reactant molecules that make it over the energy hump, therefore increasing the rate. A catalyst—a substance that increases the rate of the reaction but is not consumed by it—lowers the activation energy so that it is easier to get over the energy hump *without* increasing the temperature.

Reaction Paths and Catalysts: Catalysts are used in many chemical reactions to increase the rates. Without catalysts, many reactions occur too slowly to be of any value. The thousands of reactions that occur in living organisms are controlled by biological catalysts called *enzymes*.

CHEMICAL SKILLS

Writing Equilibrium Expressions for Chemical Reactions (Section 15.5)

Examine the definition of the equilibrium constant in the Chemical Principles section (page 562). To write the equilibrium expression for a reaction, write the concentrations of the products raised to their stoichiometric coefficients divided by the concentrations of the reactants raised to their stoichiometric coefficients. Remember that if the reaction contains reactants or products that are liquids or solids, these are omitted from the equilibrium expression.

EXAMPLES

EXAMPLE 15.10 Writing Equilibrium Expressions for Chemical Reactions

Write an equilibrium expression for the chemical equation:

$$2\,NO(g) + Br_2(g) \rightleftharpoons 2\,NOBr(g)$$

SOLUTION

$$K_{eq} = \frac{[NOBr]^2}{[NO]^2[Br_2]}$$

Calculating Equilibrium Constants (Section 15.6)

EXAMPLE 15.11 Calculating Equilibrium Constants

An equilibrium mixture of the following reaction had

$[I] = 0.075\,M$ and $[I_2] = 0.88\ M$.

What is the value of the equilibrium constant?

$$I_2(g) \rightleftharpoons 2\ I(g)$$

Begin by setting up the problem in the usual way.

GIVEN:

$$[I] = 0.075\ M$$
$$[I_2] = 0.88\ M$$

FIND: K_{eq}

Then write the expression for K_{eq} from the balanced equation. To calculate the value of K_{eq}, substitute the correct equilibrium concentrations into the expression for K_{eq}. The concentrations within K_{eq} should always be written in moles per liter, M. Units are normally dropped in expressing the equilibrium constant so that K_{eq} is unitless.

SOLUTION

$$K_{eq} = \frac{[I]^2}{[I_2]} = \frac{[0.075]^2}{[0.88]} = 0.0064$$

Using the Equilibrium Constant to Find the Concentration of a Reactant or Product at Equilibrium (Section 15.6)

EXAMPLE 15.12 Using the Equilibrium Constant to Find the Concentration of a Reactant or Product at Equilibrium

Consider the reaction:

$$N_2(g) + 3\,H_2(g) \rightleftharpoons 2\,NH_3(g)$$

$$K_{eq} = 152 \text{ at } 225\ °C$$

In an equilibrium mixture, $[N_2] = 0.110\ M$ and $[H_2] = 0.0935\ M$. What is the equilibrium concentration of NH_3?

SORT

You are given the initial concentrations of nitrogen and hydrogen as well as the equilibrium constant for their reaction to form ammonia. You are asked to find the equilibrium concentration of ammonia.

GIVEN:

$$[N_2] = 0.110\ M$$
$$[H_2] = 0.0935\ M$$
$$K_{eq} = 152$$

FIND: $[NH_3]$

STRATEGIZE

Write a solution map that shows how you can use the given concentrations and the equilibrium constant to get to the unknown concentration.

SOLUTION MAP

$[N_2], [H_2], K_{eq}$ → $[NH_3]$

$$K_{eq} = \frac{[NH_3]^2}{[N_2][H_2]^3}$$

SOLVE

Next, solve the equilibrium expression for the quantity you are trying to find and substitute in the appropriate values to calculate the unknown quantity.

SOLUTION

$$K_{eq} = \frac{[NH_3]^2}{[N_2][H_2]^3}$$

$$[NH_3]^2 = K_{eq}[N_2][H_2]^3$$

$$[NH_3] = \sqrt{K_{eq}[N_2][H_2]^3}$$

$$= \sqrt{(152)(0.110)(0.0935)^3}$$

$$= 0.117\,M$$

CHECK

You can check your answer by substituting it back into the expression for K_{eq}.

$$K_{eq} = \frac{[NH_3]^2}{[N_2][H_2]^3}$$

$$= \frac{(0.117)^2}{(0.119)(0.0935)^3}$$

$$= 141$$

The calculated value of K_{eq} is about equal to the given value of K_{eq} (which was 152) indicating that your answer is correct. The slight difference is due to rounding, which is common in problems like these.

Using Le Châtelier's Principle (Sections 15.8, 15.9, 15.10)

To apply Le Châtelier's principle, review the effects of concentration, volume, and temperature in the Chemical Principles section (pages 562–563). For each disturbance, predict how the reaction will change to counter the disturbance.

EXAMPLE 15.13 Using Le Châtelier's Principle

Consider the *endothermic* chemical reaction:

$$C(s) + H_2O(g) \rightleftharpoons CO(g) + H_2(g)$$

Predict the effect of:

(a) increasing [CO]
(b) increasing $[H_2O]$
(c) increasing the reaction volume
(d) increasing the temperature

SOLUTION

(a) Shift left
(b) Shift right
(c) Shift right (more moles of gas on right)
(d) Shift right (heat is a reactant)

Writing an Expression for the Solubility-Product Constant (Section 15.11)

To write the expression for K_{sp}, first write the chemical reaction showing the solid compound in equilibrium with its dissolved aqueous ions. Then write the equilibrium expression as the product of the concentrations of the aqueous ions raised to their stoichiometric coefficients.

EXAMPLE 15.14 Writing an Expression for the Solubility-Product Constant

Write an expression for K_{sp} for $PbCl_2$.

SOLUTION

$$PbCl_2(s) \rightleftharpoons Pb^{2+}(aq) + 2\,Cl^-(aq)$$

$$K_{sp} = [Pb^{2+}][Cl^-]^2$$

Using K_{sp} to Determine Molar Solubility (Section 15.11)

Begin by writing the reaction by which the solid dissolves into its constituent aqueous ions.

Next, write the expression for K_{sp}.

For the problems assigned in this book, the concentration of individual aqueous ions is equal to the solubility, S.

Substitute S into the equilibrium expression and solve the expression for S.

Finally, look up the value of K_{sp} in Table 15.2 and calculate S.

EXAMPLE 15.15 Using K_{sp} to Determine Molar Solubility

Calculate the molar solubility of AgI.

SOLUTION

$$AgI(s) \rightleftharpoons Ag^+(aq) + I^-(aq)$$

$$K_{sp} = [Ag^+][I^-]$$

$$S = [Ag^+] = [I^-]$$

$$K_{sp} = [Ag^+][I^-] = S \times S = S^2$$

$$S = \sqrt{K_{sp}}$$

$$S = \sqrt{8.51 \times 10^{-17}} = 9.22 \times 10^{-9}\,M$$

KEY TERMS

activation energy **[15.12]**
catalyst **[15.12]**
collision theory **[15.2]**
dynamic equilibrium **[15.3]**
enzyme **[15.12]**
equilibrium constant (K_{eq}) **[15.4]**
Le Châtelier's principle **[15.7]**
molar solubility **[15.11]**
rate of a chemical reaction (reaction rate) **[15.2]**
reversible reaction **[15.3]**
solubility-product constant (K_{sp}) **[15.11]**

EXERCISES

QUESTIONS

1. What are the two *general* concepts involved in equilibrium?
2. What is the rate of a chemical reaction? What is the difference between a chemical reaction with a fast rate and one with a slow rate?
3. Why do chemists seek to control reaction rates?
4. How do most chemical reactions occur?
5. What factors influence reaction rates? How?
6. What normally happens to the rate of the forward reaction as a reaction proceeds?
7. What is dynamic chemical equilibrium?
8. Explain how dynamic chemical equilibrium involves the concepts of sameness and constancy.
9. Explain why the concentrations of reactants and products are not necessarily the same at equilibrium.
10. Devise your own analogy—like the Narnia and Middle Earth analogy in the chapter—to explain chemical equilibrium.
11. What is the equilibrium constant? Why is it significant?
12. Write the expression for the equilibrium constant for the following generic chemical equation.

$$aA + bB \rightleftharpoons cC + dD$$

13. What does a small equilibrium constant tell you about a reaction? A large equilibrium constant?
14. Why are solids and liquids omitted from the equilibrium expression?
15. Will the concentrations of reactants and products always be the same in every equilibrium mixture of a particular reaction at a given temperature? Explain.
16. What is Le Châtelier's principle?
17. Apply Le Châtelier's principle to your analogy from Question 12.
18. What is the effect of *increasing* the concentration of a reactant in a reaction mixture at equilibrium?
19. What is the effect of *decreasing* the concentration of a reactant in a reaction mixture at equilibrium?
20. What is the effect of *increasing* the concentration of a product in a reaction mixture at equilibrium?
21. What is the effect of *decreasing* the concentration of a product in a reaction mixture at equilibrium?
22. What is the effect of increasing the pressure of a reaction mixture at equilibrium if the reactant side has fewer moles of gas particles than the product side?

23. What is the effect of increasing the pressure of a reaction mixture at equilibrium if the product side has fewer moles of gas particles than the reactant side?
24. What is the effect of decreasing the pressure of a reaction mixture at equilibrium if the reactant side has fewer moles of gas particles than the product side?
25. What is the effect of decreasing the pressure of a reaction mixture at equilibrium if the product side has fewer moles of gas particles than the reactant side?
26. What is the effect of increasing the temperature of an endothermic reaction mixture at equilibrium? Of decreasing the temperature?
27. What is the effect of increasing the temperature of an exothermic reaction mixture at equilibrium? Of decreasing the temperature?
28. What is the solubility-product constant? What does it signify?
29. Write an expression for the solubility-product constant of $AB_2(s)$. Assume that an ion of B has a charge of -1 (that is, B^-).
30. Write an expression for the solubility-product constant of $A_2B(s)$. Assume that an ion of B has charge of -2 (that is, B^{2-}).
31. What are solubility and molar solubility?
32. What is activation energy for a chemical reaction?
33. Explain why two reactants with a large K_{eq} for a particular reaction might not react immediately when combined.
34. What is the effect of a catalyst on reaction? Why are catalysts so important to chemistry?
35. Does a catalyst affect the value of the equilibrium constant?
36. What are enzymes?

PROBLEMS

THE RATE OF REACTION

37. Two gaseous reactants are allowed to react in a 1-L flask, and the reaction rate is measured. The experiment is repeated with the same amount of each reactant and at the same temperature, but now in a 2-L flask (so the concentration of each reactant is now less). What is likely to happen to the measured reaction rate in the second experiment compared to the first?

38. The rate of phosphorus pentachloride decomposition is measured at a PCl_5 pressure of 0.015 atm and then again at a PCl_5 pressure of 0.30 atm. The temperature is identical in both measurements. Which rate is likely to be faster?

39. The body temperature of cold-blooded animals varies with the ambient temperature. From the point of view of reaction rates, explain why cold-blooded animals are more sluggish at cold temperatures.

40. The rate of a reaction doubles when the temperature increases from 25 °C to 35 °C. Explain why this is so.

41. The initial rate of a chemical reaction was measured, and one of the reactants was found to be reacting at a rate of 0.0011 mol/L s. The reaction was allowed to proceed for 15 minutes, and the rate was measured again. What would you predict about the second measured rate relative to the first?

42. When vinegar is added to a solution of sodium bicarbonate, the mixture immediately begins to bubble furiously. As time passes, however, the bubbling becomes less and less. Explain.

THE EQUILIBRIUM CONSTANT

43. Write an equilibrium expression for each chemical equation.
(a) $2\ NO_2(g) \rightleftharpoons N_2O_4(g)$
(b) $2\ BrNO(g) \rightleftharpoons 2\ NO(g) + Br_2(g)$
(c) $H_2O(g) + CO(g) \rightleftharpoons H_2(g) + CO_2(g)$
(d) $CH_4(g) + 2\ H_2S(g) \rightleftharpoons CS_2(g) + 4\ H_2(g)$

44. Write an equilibrium expression for each chemical equation.
(a) $2\ CO(g) + O_2(g) \rightleftharpoons 2\ CO_2(g)$
(b) $N_2(g) + O_2(g) \rightleftharpoons 2\ NO(g)$
(c) $SbCl_5(g) \rightleftharpoons SbCl_3(g) + Cl_2(g)$
(d) $CO(g) + Cl_2(g) \rightleftharpoons COCl_2(g)$

45. Write an equilibrium expression for each chemical equation involving one or more solid or liquid reactants or products.

(a) $PCl_5(g) \rightleftharpoons PCl_3(l) + Cl_2(g)$
(b) $2\ KClO_3(s) \rightleftharpoons 2\ KCl(s) + 3\ O_2(g)$
(c) $HF(aq) + H_2O(l) \rightleftharpoons H_3O^+(aq) + F^-(aq)$
(d) $NH_3(aq) + H_2O(l) \rightleftharpoons NH_4^+(aq) + OH^-(aq)$

46. Write an equilibrium expression for each chemical equation involving one or more solid or liquid reactants or products.

(a) $HCHO_2(aq) + H_2O(l) \rightleftharpoons H_3O^+(aq) + CHO_2^-(aq)$
(b) $CO_3^{2-}(aq) + H_2O(l) \rightleftharpoons HCO_3^-(aq) + OH^-(aq)$
(c) $2\ C(s) + O_2(g) \rightleftharpoons 2\ CO(g)$
(d) $C(s) + CO_2(g) \rightleftharpoons 2\ CO(g)$

47. Consider the reaction:

$$2\ H_2S(g) \rightleftharpoons 2\ H_2(g) + S_2(g)$$

Find the mistakes in the equilibrium expression and fix them.

$$K_{eq} = \frac{[H_2][S_2]}{[H_2S]}$$

48. Consider the reaction:

$$CO(g) + Cl_2(g) \rightleftharpoons COCl_2(g)$$

Find the mistake in the equilibrium expression and fix it.

$$K_{eq} = \frac{[CO][Cl_2]}{[COCl_2]}$$

49. For each equilibrium constant, indicate whether you would expect an equilibrium reaction mixture to be dominated by reactants, to be dominated by products, or to contain significant amounts of both.

(a) $K_{eq} = 5.2 \times 10^{17}$
(b) $K_{eq} = 1.24$
(c) $K_{eq} = 3.22 \times 10^{-21}$
(d) $K_{eq} = 0.47$

50. For each equilibrium constant, indicate whether you would expect an equilibrium reaction mixture to be dominated by reactants, to be dominated by products, or to contain significant amounts of both.

(a) $K_{eq} = 0.75$
(b) $K_{eq} = 8.5 \times 10^{-7}$
(c) $K_{eq} = 1.4 \times 10^{19}$
(d) $K_{eq} = 4.7 \times 10^{-9}$

CALCULATING AND USING EQUILIBRIUM CONSTANTS

51. Consider the reaction:

$$COCl_2(g) \rightleftharpoons CO(g) + Cl_2(g)$$

An equilibrium mixture of this reaction at a certain temperature was found to have $[COCl_2] = 0.225$ M, $[CO] = 0.105$ M, and $[Cl_2] = 0.0844$ M. What is the value of the equilibrium constant at this temperature?

52. Consider the reaction:

$$CO(g) + 2\ H_2(g) \rightleftharpoons CH_3OH(g)$$

An equilibrium mixture of this reaction at a certain temperature was found to have $[CO] = 0.105$ M, $[H_2] = 0.114$ M, and $[CH_3OH] = 0.185$ M. What is the value of the equilibrium constant at this temperature?

53. Consider the reaction:

$$2\ H_2S(g) \rightleftharpoons 2\ H_2(g) + S_2(g)$$

An equilibrium mixture of this reaction at a certain temperature was found to have $[H_2S] = 0.562$ M, $[H_2] = 2.74 \times 10^{-2}$ M, and $[S_2] = 7.54 \times 10^{-3}$ M. What is the value of the equilibrium constant at this temperature?

54. Consider the reaction:

$$CO(g) + H_2O(g) \rightleftharpoons CO_2(g) + H_2(g)$$

An equilibrium mixture of this reaction at a certain temperature was found to have $[CO] = 0.0233$ M, $[H_2O] = 0.0115$ M, $[CO_2] = 0.175$ M, and $[H_2] = 0.0274$ M. What is the value of the equilibrium constant at this temperature?

55. Consider the reaction:

$$NH_4HS(s) \rightleftharpoons NH_3(g) + H_2S(g)$$

An equilibrium mixture of this reaction at a certain temperature was found to have $[NH_3] = 0.278\,M$ and $[H_2S] = 0.355\,M$. What is the value of the equilibrium constant at this temperature?

56. Consider the reaction:

$$CaCO_3(s) \rightleftharpoons CaO(s) + CO_2(g)$$

An equilibrium mixture of this reaction at a certain temperature was found to have $[CO_2] = 0.548\,M$. What is the value of the equilibrium constant at this temperature?

57. An equilibrium mixture of the following reaction was found to have $[SbCl_3] = 0.0255\,M$ and $[Cl_2] = 0.135\,M$ at 248 °C. What is the concentration of $SbCl_5$?

$$SbCl_5(g) \rightleftharpoons SbCl_3(g) + Cl_2(g)$$

$$K_{eq} = 4.9 \times 10^{-4} \text{ at } 248\ ^\circ C$$

58. An equilibrium mixture of the following reaction was found to have $[I_2] = 0.0205\,M$ at 1200 °C. What is the concentration of I?

$$I_2(g) \rightleftharpoons 2\,I(g)$$

$$K_{eq} = 1.1 \times 10^{-2} \text{ at } 1200\ ^\circ C$$

59. An equilibrium mixture of the following reaction was found to have $[I_2] = 0.0112\,M$ and $[Cl_2] = 0.0155\,M$ at 25 °C. What is the concentration of ICl?

$$I_2(g) + Cl_2(g) \rightleftharpoons 2\,ICl(g)$$

$$K_{eq} = 81.9 \text{ at } 25\ ^\circ C$$

60. An equilibrium mixture of the following reaction was found to have $[SO_3] = 0.391\,M$ and $[O_2] = 0.125\,M$ at 600 °C. What is the concentration of SO_2?

$$N_2(g) + 3\,H_2(g) \rightleftharpoons 2\,NH_3(g)$$

$$K_{eq} = 4.34 \text{ at } 600\ ^\circ C$$

61. Consider the reaction:

$$N_2(g) + 3\,H_2(g) \rightleftharpoons 2\,NH_3(g)$$

Complete the table. Assume that all concentrations are equilibrium concentrations in moles per liter, M.

T (K)	$[N_2]$	$[H_2]$	$[NH_3]$	K_{eq}
500	0.115	0.105	0.439	_____
575	0.110	_____	0.128	9.6
775	0.120	0.140	_____	0.0584

62. Consider the reaction:

$$H_2(g) + I_2(g) \rightleftharpoons 2\,HI(g)$$

Complete the table. Assume that all concentrations are equilibrium concentrations in moles per liter, M.

T (°C)	$[H_2]$	$[I_2]$	$[HI]$	K_{eq}
25	0.355	0.388	0.0922	_____
340	_____	0.0455	0.387	9.6
445	0.0485	0.0468	_____	50.2

LE CHÂTELIER'S PRINCIPLE

63. Consider this reaction at equilibrium.

$$CO(g) + Cl_2(g) \rightleftharpoons COCl_2(g)$$

Predict the effect (shift right, shift left, or no effect) of

(a) adding Cl_2 to the reaction mixture.

(b) adding $COCl_2$ to the reaction mixture.

(c) adding CO to the reaction mixture.

64. Consider this reaction at equilibrium.

$$2\,BrNO(g) \rightleftharpoons 2\,NO(g) + Br_2(g)$$

Predict the effect (shift right, shift left, or no effect) of

(a) adding BrNO to the reaction mixture.

(b) adding NO the reaction mixture.

(c) adding Br_2 to the reaction mixture.

65. Consider this reaction at equilibrium.

$$C(s) + H_2O(g) \rightleftharpoons CO(g) + H_2(g)$$

Predict the effect (shift right, shift left, or no effect) of

(a) adding C to the reaction mixture.

(b) condensing H_2O and removing it from the reaction mixture.

(c) adding CO to the reaction mixture.

(d) removing H_2 from the reaction mixture.

66. Consider this reaction at equilibrium.

$$2\,KClO_3(s) \rightleftharpoons 2\,KCl(s) + 3\,O_2(g)$$

Predict the effect (shift right, shift left, or no effect) of

(a) adding KCl to the reaction mixture.

(b) adding $KClO_3$ to the reaction mixture.

(c) adding O_2 to the reaction mixture.

(d) removing O_2 from the reaction mixture.

67. Consider the effect of a volume change on this reaction at equilibrium.

$$I_2(g) \rightleftharpoons 2I(g)$$

Predict the effect (shift right, shift left, or no effect) of

(a) increasing the reaction volume.

(b) decreasing the reaction volume.

68. Consider the effect of a volume change on this reaction at equilibrium.

$$2H_2S(g) \rightleftharpoons 2H_2(g) + S_2(g)$$

Predict the effect (shift right, shift left, or no effect) of

(a) increasing the reaction volume.

(b) decreasing the reaction volume.

69. Consider the effect of a volume change on this reaction at equilibrium.

$$I_2(g) + Cl_2(g) \rightleftharpoons 2ICl(g)$$

Predict the effect (shift right, shift left, or no effect) of

(a) increasing the reaction volume.

(b) decreasing the reaction volume.

70. Consider the effect of a volume change on this reaction at equilibrium.

$$CO(g) + H_2O(g) \rightleftharpoons CO_2(g) + H_2(g)$$

Predict the effect (shift right, shift left, or no effect) of

(a) increasing the reaction volume.

(b) decreasing the reaction volume.

71. This reaction is endothermic.

$$C(s) + CO_2(g) \rightleftharpoons 2CO(g)$$

Predict the effect (shift right, shift left, or no effect) of

(a) increasing the reaction temperature.

(b) decreasing the reaction temperature.

72. This reaction is endothermic.

$$I_2(g) \rightleftharpoons 2I(g)$$

Predict the effect (shift right, shift left, or no effect) of

(a) increasing the reaction temperature.

(b) decreasing the reaction temperature.

73. This reaction is exothermic.

$$C_6H_{12}O_6(s) + 6O_2(g) \rightleftharpoons 6CO_2(g) + 6H_2O(g)$$

Predict the effect (shift right, shift left, or no effect) of

(a) increasing the reaction temperature.

(b) decreasing the reaction temperature.

74. The following reaction is exothermic.

$$C_2H_4(g) + Br_2(g) \rightleftharpoons C_2H_4Br_2(g)$$

Predict the effect (shift right, shift left, or no effect) of

(a) increasing the reaction temperature.

(b) decreasing the reaction temperature.

75. Coal, which is primarily carbon, can be converted to natural gas, primarily CH_4, by the following exothermic reaction.

$$C(s) + 2H_2(g) \rightleftharpoons CH_4(g)$$

If this reaction mixture is at equilibrium, predict the effect (shift right, shift left, or no effect) of

(a) adding more C to the reaction mixture.

(b) adding more H_2 to the reaction mixture.

(c) raising the temperature of the reaction mixture.

(d) lowering the volume of the reaction mixture.

(e) adding a catalyst to the reaction mixture.

76. Coal can be used to generate hydrogen gas (a potential fuel) by this endothermic reaction.

$$C(s) + H_2O(g) \rightleftharpoons CO(g) + H_2(g)$$

If this reaction mixture is at equilibrium, predict the effect (shift right, shift left, or no effect) of

(a) adding more C to the reaction mixture.

(b) adding more $H_2O(g)$ to the reaction mixture.

(c) raising the temperature of the reaction mixture.

(d) increasing the volume of the reaction mixture.

(e) adding a catalyst to the reaction mixture.

THE SOLUBILITY-PRODUCT CONSTANT

77. For each compound, write an equation showing how the compound dissolves in water and write an expression for K_{sp}.

(a) $CaSO_4$

(b) $AgCl$

(c) CuS

(d) $FeCO_3$

78. For each compound, write an equation showing how the compound dissolves in water and write an expression for K_{sp}.

(a) $Mg(OH)_2$

(b) $FeCO_3$

(c) PbS

(d) $PbSO_4$

79. Determine what is wrong with the following K_{sp} expression for $Fe(OH)_2$ and correct it.

$$K_{sp} = [Fe^{2+}][OH^-]$$

80. Determine what is wrong with the following K_{sp} expression for $Ba(OH)_2$ and correct it.

$$K_{sp} = \frac{[Ba(OH)_2]}{[Ba^{2+}][OH^-]^2}$$

81. A saturated solution of MgF_2 has $[Mg^{2+}] = 2.6 \times 10^{-4}$ M and $[F^-] = 5.2 \times 10^{-4}$ M. What is the value of K_{sp} for MgF_2?

82. A saturated solution of AgI has $[Ag^+] = 9.2 \times 10^{-9}$ M and $[I^-] = 9.2 \times 10^{-9}$ M. What is the value of K_{sp} for AgI?

83. A saturated solution of $PbSO_4$ has $[Pb^{2+}] = 1.35 \times 10^{-4}$ M. What is the concentration of SO_4^{2-}?

84. A saturated solution of $PbCl_2$ has $[Cl^-] = 2.86 \times 10^{-2}$ M. What is the concentration of Pb^{2+}?

85. Calculate the molar solubility of $CaCO_3$.

86. Calculate the molar solubility of PbS.

87. Calculate the molar solubility of $MgCO_3$.

88. Calculate the molar solubility of CuI ($K_{sp} = 1.27 \times 10^{-12}$).

89. Complete the table. Assume that all concentrations are equilibrium concentrations in moles per liter, M.

Compound	[Cation]	[Anion]	K_{sp}
$SrCO_3$	2.4×10^{-5}	2.4×10^{-5}	______
SrF_2	1.0×10^{-3}	______	4.0×10^{-9}
Ag_2CO_3	______	1.3×10^{-4}	8.8×10^{-12}

90. Complete the table. Assume that all concentrations are equilibrium concentrations in moles per liter, M.

Compound	[Cation]	[Anion]	K_{sp}
CdS	3.7×10^{-15}	3.7×10^{-15}	______
BaF_2	______	7.2×10^{-3}	1.9×10^{-7}
Ag_2SO_4	2.8×10^{-2}	______	1.1×10^{-5}

CUMULATIVE PROBLEMS

91. Consider the reaction:

$$Fe^{3+}(aq) + SCN^-(aq) \rightleftharpoons FeSCN^{2+}(aq)$$

A solution is made containing initial $[Fe^{3+}] = 1.0 \times 10^{-3}$ M and initial $[SCN^-] = 8.0 \times 10^{-4}$ M. At equilibrium, $[FeSCN^{2+}] = 1.7 \times 10^{-4}$. Calculate the value of the equilibrium constant. *Hint:* Use the chemical reaction stoichiometry to calculate the equilibrium concentrations of Fe^{3+} and SCN^-.

92. Consider the reaction:

$$SO_2Cl_2(g) \rightleftharpoons SO_2(g) + Cl_2(g)$$

A solution is made containing initial $[SO_2Cl_2] = 0.020$ M. At equilibrium, $[Cl_2] = 1.2 \times 10^{-2}$ M. Calculate the value of the equilibrium constant. *Hint:* Use the chemical reaction stoichiometry to calculate the equilibrium concentrations of SO_2Cl_2 and SO_2.

93. Consider the reaction:

$$CO(g) + Cl_2(g) \rightleftharpoons COCl_2(g)$$

$$K_{eq} = 6.17 \times 10^{-2} \text{ at } 25\ °C$$

A 3.67-L flask containing an equilibrium reaction mixture has $[H_2] = 0.104$ M and $[I_2] = 0.0202$ M. How much HI in grams is in the equilibrium mixture?

94. Consider the reaction:

$$H_2(g) + I_2(g) \rightleftharpoons 2\ HI(g)$$

$$K_{eq} = 2.9 \times 10^{10} \text{ at } 25\ °C$$

A 5.19-L flask containing an equilibrium reaction mixture has $[CO] = 1.8 \times 10^{-6}$ M and $[Cl_2] = 7.3 \times 10^{-7}$ M. How much $COCl_2$ in grams is in the equilibrium mixture?

95. This reaction is exothermic.

$$C_2H_4(g) + Cl_2(g) \rightleftharpoons C_2H_4Cl_2(g)$$

If you were a chemist trying to maximize the amount of $C_2H_4Cl_2$ produced, which of the following might you try? Assume that the reaction mixture reaches equilibrium.

(a) increasing the reaction volume

(b) removing $C_2H_4Cl_2$ from the reaction mixture as it forms

(c) lowering the reaction temperature

(d) adding Cl_2

96. This reaction is endothermic.

$$C_2H_4(g) + I_2(g) \rightleftharpoons C_2H_4I_2(g)$$

If you were a chemist trying to maximize the amount of $C_2H_4I_2$ produced, which of the following might you try? Assume that the reaction mixture reaches equilibrium.

(a) decreasing the reaction volume

(b) removing I_2 from the reaction mixture

(c) raising the reaction temperature

(d) adding C_2H_4 to the reaction mixture

97. Calculate the molar solubility of CuS. How many grams of CuS are present in 15.0 L of a saturated CuS solution?

98. Calculate the molar solubility of $FeCO_3$. How many grams of $FeCO_3$ are present in 15.0 L of a saturated $FeCO_3$ solution?

99. A sample of tap water is found to be 0.025 M in Ca^{2+}. If 105 mg of Na_2SO_4 is added to 100.0 mL of the tap water, will any $CaSO_4$ precipitate out of solution?

100. If 50.0 mg of Na_2CO_3 are added to 150.0 mL of a solution that is 1.5×10^{-3} M in Mg^{2+}, will any $MgCO_3$ precipitate from the solution?

101. The solubility of $CaCrO_4$ at 25 °C is 4.15 g/L. Calculate K_{sp} for $CaCrO_4$.

102. The solubility of nickel(II) carbonate at 25 °C is 0.042 g/L. Calculate K_{sp} for nickel(II) carbonate.

103. Consider the reaction:

$$CaCO_3 \rightleftharpoons CaO(s) + CO_2(g)$$

A sample of $CaCO_3$ is placed into a sealed 0.500-L container and heated to 550 K at which the equilibrium constant is 4.1×10^{-4}. When the reaction has come to equilibrium, what mass of solid CaO will be in the container? (Assume that the sample of $CaCO_3$ was large enough that equilibrium could be achieved.)

104. Consider the reaction:

$$NH_4HS(s) \rightleftharpoons NH_3(g) + H_2S(g)$$

A sample of pure NH_4HS is placed in a sealed 2.0-L container and heated to 550 K at which the equilibrium constant is 3.5×10^{-3}. Once the reaction reaches equilibrium, what mass of NH_3 is present in the container? (Assume that the sample of $CaCO_3$ was large enough that equilibrium could be achieved.)

105. A 2.55-L solution is 0.115 M in Mg^{2+}. If K_2CO_3 were added to the solution in order to precipitate the magnesium, what minimum mass of K_2CO_3 would be required to get a precipitate?

106. A 75.0-L solution is 0.0251 M in Ca^{2+}. If Na_2SO_4 were added to the solution in order to precipitate the calcium, what minimum mass of Na_2SO_4 would be required to get a precipitate?

HIGHLIGHT PROBLEMS

107. H_2 and I_2 are combined in a flask and allowed to react according to the reaction:

$$H_2(g) + I_2(g) \rightleftharpoons 2\,HI(g)$$

Examine the following figures (sequential in time) and determine which figure represents the point where equilibrium is reached.

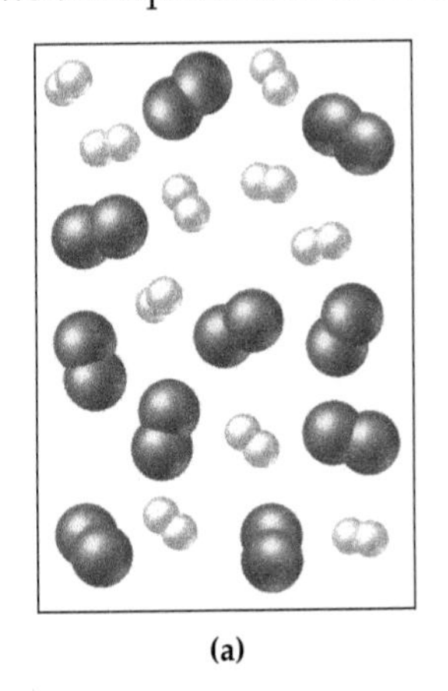

(a)

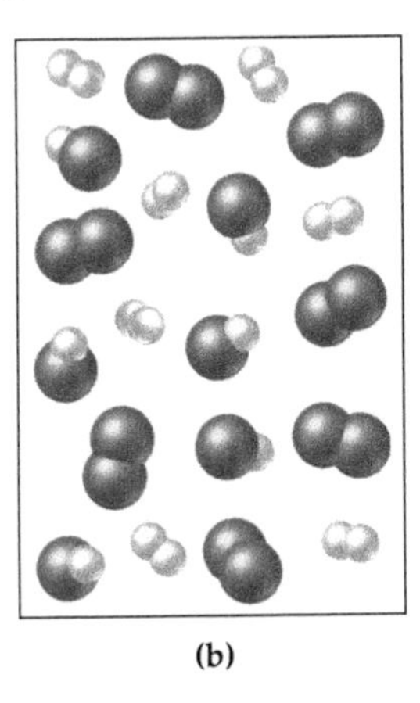

(b)

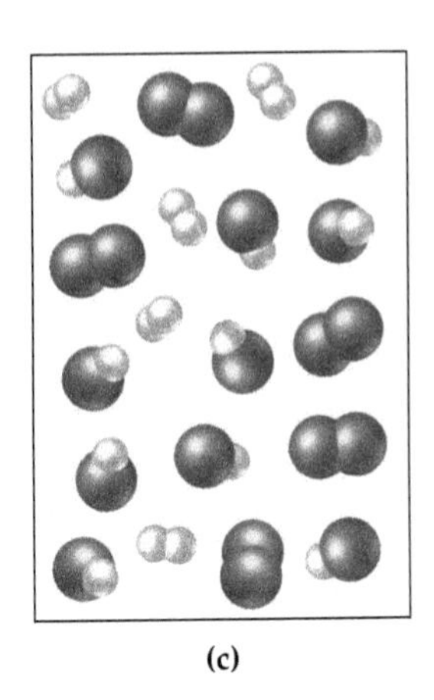

(c)

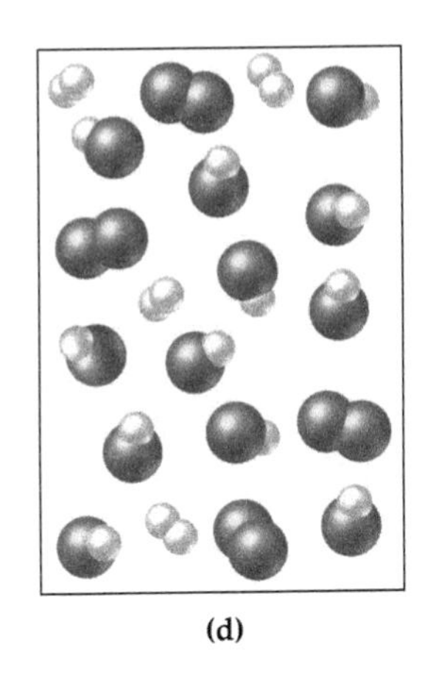

(d)

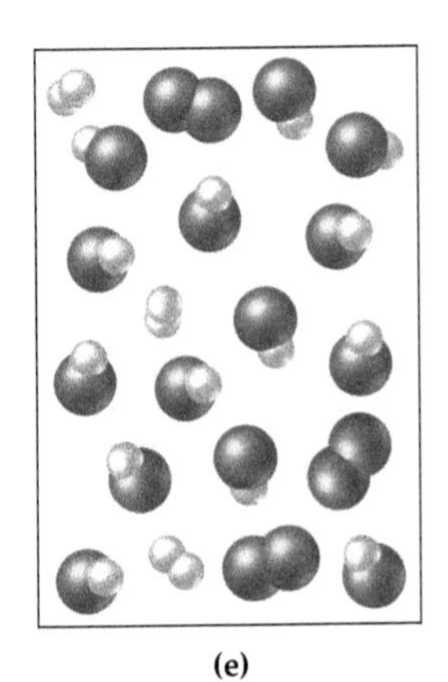

(e)

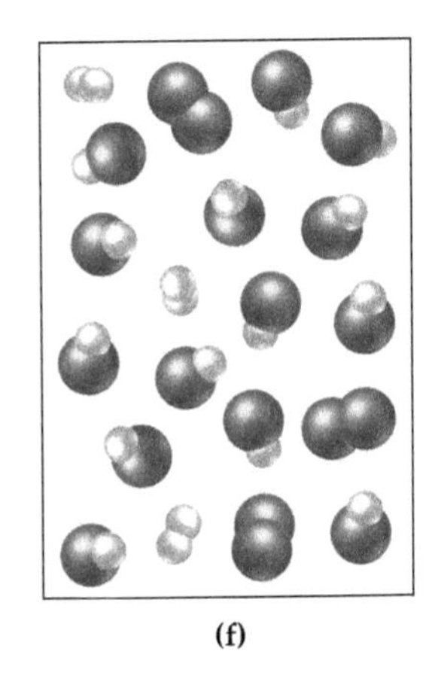

(f)

108. Ethene (C_2H_4) can be halogenated by the reaction:

$$C_2H_4(g) + X_2(g) \rightleftharpoons C_2H_4X_2(g)$$

where X_2 can be Cl_2, Br_2, or I_2. Examine the figures representing equilibrium concentrations of this reaction at the same temperature for the three different halogens. Rank the equilibrium constants for these three reactions from largest to smallest.

$$C_2H_4 + Cl_2 \rightleftharpoons C_2H_4Cl_2$$

(a)

$$C_2H_4 + Br_2 \rightleftharpoons C_2H_4Br_2$$

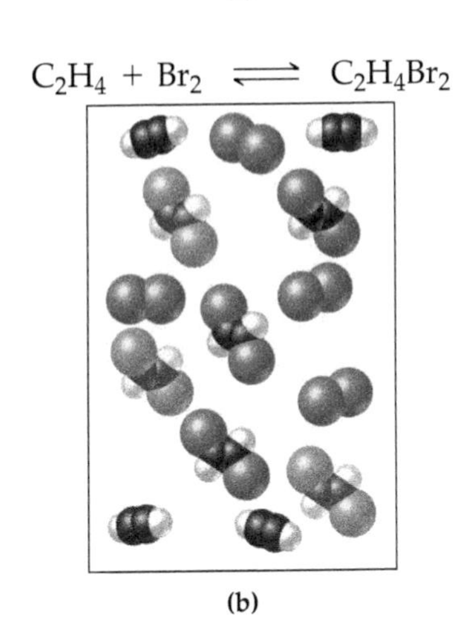

(b)

$$C_2H_4 + I_2 \rightleftharpoons C_2H_4I_2$$

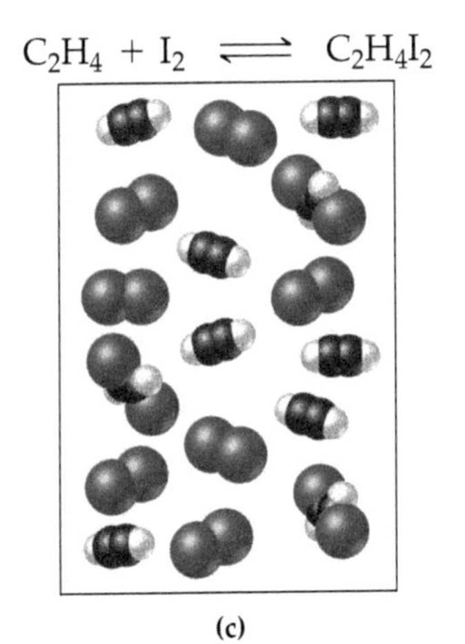

(c)

109. One of the main components of hard water is $CaCO_3$. When hard water evaporates, some of the $CaCO_3$ is left behind as a white mineral deposit. Plumbing fixtures in homes with hard water often acquire these deposits over time. Toilets, for example, may develop these deposits at the water line as the water in the toilet slowly evaporates away. If water is saturated with $CaCO_3$, how much of it has to evaporate to deposit 0.250 g of $CaCO_3$? *Hint:* Begin by using K_{sp} for $CaCO_3$ to determine its solubility.

110. Consider the following generic equilibrium in which a solid reactant is in equilibrium with a gaseous product:

$$A(s) \rightleftharpoons B(g)$$

The following diagrams represent the reaction mixture at the following points: (a) initially; (b) after a short period of time has passed; and (c) at equilibrium.

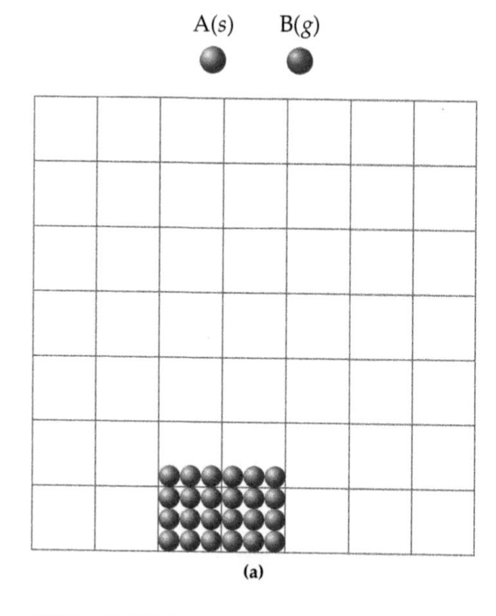

(a)

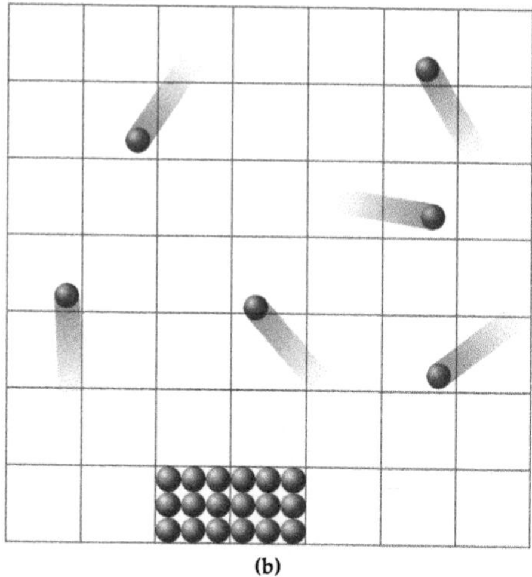
(b)

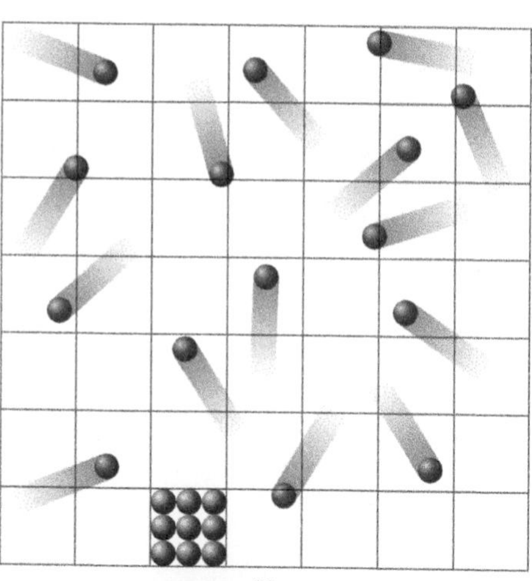
(c)

For each diagram, calculate the concentrations of the spheres representing A(*s*) and B(*g*). Assume that each block in the grid has an area of 1 cm^2 and report your answer in units of spheres/cm^2. (Since the spheres in the solid are not free to move, the solid only occupies the area that it covers. The spheres in the solid, however, are free to move and therefore occupy the entire grid.) What do you notice about the concentrations of A(*s*) and B(*g*) in these representations? Write an equilibrium expression for the generic reaction and use the results of your calculations to explain why A(*s*) is not included in the expression.

▶ANSWERS TO SKILLBUILDER EXERCISES

Skillbuilder 15.1 $K_{eq} = \dfrac{[HF]^2}{[H_2][F_2]}$

Skillbuilder 15.2 $K_{eq} = \dfrac{[Cl_2]^2}{[HCl]^4[O_2]}$

Skillbuilder 15.3 $K_{eq} = 14.5$

Skillbuilder Plus, p. 544 $K_{eq} = 26$

Skillbuilder 15.4 0.033 M

Skillbuilder 15.5 Adding Br_2 causes a shift to the left; adding BrNO causes a shift to the right.

Skillbuilder Plus, p. 549 Removing Br_2 causes a shift to the right

Skillbuilder 15.6 Decreasing volume causes a shift to the right; increasing volume causes a shift to the left.

Skillbuilder 15.7 Increasing the temperature shifts the reaction to the left; decreasing the temperature shifts the reaction to the right.

Skillbuilder 15.8 **(a)** $K_{sp} = [Ag^+][I^-]$
(b) $K_{sp} = [Ca^{2+}][OH^-]^2$

Skillbuilder 15.9 8.43×10^{-3} M

▶ANSWERS TO CONCEPTUAL CHECKPOINTS

15.1 (a) In accordance with the gas laws (Chapter 11), increasing the pressure would increase the temperature, decrease the volume, or both. Increasing the temperature would increase the reaction rate. Decreasing the volume would increase the concentration of the reactants, which would also increase the reaction rate. Therefore, we would expect that increasing the pressure would speed up the reaction.

15.2 (c) Since the image in (c) has the greatest amount of product, the equilibrium constant must be largest at T_3.

15.3 (b) For this reaction, $K_{eq} = [B][C]/[A] = (2 \times 2)/2 = 2$.

15.4 Doubling the hydrogen concentration leads to a larger shift toward products because the concentration of hydrogen in the denominator is squared.

15.5 (c) Increasing the concentration of a reactant causes the reaction to shift right. For this reaction, changing the volume has no effect because the number of gas particles on both sides of the equation is equal.

15.6 (a) Since the reaction is endothermic, increasing the temperature drives it to the right (toward the product). Since the reaction has 1 mol particles on the left and 2 mol particles on the right, increasing the volume drives it to the right. Therefore, increasing the temperature and increasing the volume will create the greatest amount of product.

APPENDIX: Mathematics Review

Basic Algebra

In chemistry, you often have to solve an equation for a particular variable. For example, suppose you want to solve the following equation for V.

$$PV = nRT$$

To solve an equation for a particular variable, you must isolate that variable on one side of the equation. The rest of the variables or numbers will then be on the other side of the equation. To solve the above equation for V, simply divide both sides by P.

$$\frac{PV}{P} = \frac{nRT}{P}$$

$$V = \frac{nRT}{P}$$

The Ps cancel, and we are left with an expression for V. For another example, consider solving the following equation for °F.

$$°C = \frac{(°F - 32)}{1.8}$$

First, eliminate the 1.8 in the denominator of the right side by multiplying both sides by 1.8.

$$(1.8)\ °C = \frac{(°F - 32)}{1.8}(1.8)$$

$$(1.8)\ °C = (°F - 32)$$

Then eliminate the -32 on the right by adding 32 to both sides.

$$(1.8)\ °C + 32 = (°F - 32) + 32$$

$$(1.8)\ °C + 32 = °F$$

We are now left with an expression for °F.

In general, solve equations by following these guidelines:

- Cancel numbers or symbols in the denominator (bottom part of a fraction) by multiplying by the number or symbol to be canceled.
- Cancel numbers or symbols in the numerator (upper part of a fraction) by dividing by the number or symbol to be canceled.
- Eliminate numbers or symbols that are added by subtracting the same number or symbol.
- Eliminate numbers or symbols that are subtracted by adding the same number or symbol.
- Whether you add, subtract, multiply, or divide, **always perform the same operation for both sides of a mathematical equation**. (Otherwise, the two sides will no longer be equal.)

For a final example, solve the following equation for x.

$$\frac{67x - y + 3}{6} = 2z$$

Cancel the 6 in the denominator by multiplying both sides by 6.

$$(6)\frac{67x - y + 3}{6} = (6)2z$$

$$67x - y + 3 = 12z$$

Eliminate the +3 by subtracting 3 from both sides.

$$67x - y + 3 - 3 = 12z - 3$$

$$67x - y = 12z - 3$$

Eliminate the $-y$ by adding y to both sides.

$$67x - y + y = 12z - 3 + y$$

$$67x = 12z - 3 + y$$

Cancel the 67 by dividing both sides by 67.

$$\frac{67x}{67} = \frac{12z - 3 + y}{67}$$

$$x = \frac{12z - 3 + y}{67}$$

FOR PRACTICE Using Algebra to Solve Equations

Solve each of the following for the indicated variable.

(a) $P_1V_1 = P_2V_2$; solve for V_2

(b) $\frac{V_1}{T_1} = \frac{V_2}{T_2}$; solve for T_1

(c) $PV = nRT$; solve for n

(d) K = °C + 273; solve for °C

(e) $\frac{3x + 7}{2} = y$; solve for x

(f) $\frac{32}{y + 3} = 8$; solve for y

ANSWERS

(a) $V_2 = \frac{P_1V_1}{P_2}$

(b) $T_1 = \frac{V_1T_2}{V_2}$

(c) $n = \frac{PV}{RT}$

(d) °C = K − 273

(e) $x = \frac{2y - 7}{3}$

(f) $y = 1$

Mathematical Operations with Scientific Notation

Writing numbers in scientific notation is covered in detail in Section 2.2. Briefly, a number written in scientific notation consists of a **decimal part,** a number that is usually between 1 and 10, and an **exponential part,** 10 raised to an **exponent,** n.

Each of the following numbers is written in both scientific and decimal notation.

$$1.0 \times 10^5 = 100{,}000 \qquad 1.0 \times 10^{-6} = 0.000001$$

$$6.7 \times 10^3 = 6700 \qquad 6.7 \times 10^{-3} = 0.0067$$

MULTIPLICATION AND DIVISION

To multiply numbers expressed in scientific notation, multiply the decimal parts and add the exponents.

$$(A \times 10^m)\,(B \times 10^n) = (A \times B) \times 10^{m+n}$$

To divide numbers expressed in scientific notation, divide the decimal parts and subtract the exponent in the denominator from the exponent in the numerator.

$$\frac{(A \times 10^m)}{(B \times 10^n)} = \left(\frac{A}{B}\right) \times 10^{m-n}$$

Consider the following example involving multiplication.

$$\begin{aligned}(3.5 \times 10^4)(1.8 \times 10^6) &= (3.5 \times 1.8) \times 10^{4+6}\\ &= 6.3 \times 10^{10}\end{aligned}$$

Consider the following example involving division.

$$\begin{aligned}\frac{(5.6 \times 10^7)}{(1.4 \times 10^3)} &= \left(\frac{5.6}{1.4}\right) \times 10^{7-3}\\ &= 4.0 \times 10^4\end{aligned}$$

ADDITION AND SUBTRACTION

To add or subtract numbers expressed in scientific notation, rewrite all the numbers so that they have the same exponent, and then add or subtract the decimal parts of the numbers. The exponents remained unchanged.

$$\begin{array}{r} A \times 10^n \\ \pm\, B \times 10^n \\ \hline (A \pm B) \times 10^n \end{array}$$

Notice that the numbers *must have* the same exponent.

Consider the following example involving addition.

$$\begin{array}{r} 4.82 \times 10^7 \\ +3.4 \times 10^6 \\ \hline \end{array}$$

First, express both numbers with the same exponent. In this case, we rewrite the lower number and perform the addition as follows:

$$\begin{array}{r} 4.82 \times 10^7 \\ +0.34 \times 10^7 \\ \hline 5.16 \times 10^7 \end{array}$$

Consider the following example involving subtraction.

$$\begin{array}{r} 7.33 \times 10^5 \\ -1.9 \times 10^4 \\ \hline \end{array}$$

First, express both numbers with the same exponent. In this case, we rewrite the lower number and perform the subtraction as follows:

$$\begin{array}{r} 7.33 \times 10^5 \\ -0.19 \times 10^5 \\ \hline 7.14 \times 10^5 \end{array}$$

FOR PRACTICE Mathematical Operations with Scientific Notation

Perform each of the following operations.

(a) $(2.1 \times 10^7)(9.3 \times 10^5)$

(b) $(5.58 \times 10^{12})(7.84 \times 10^{-8})$

(c) $\dfrac{(1.5 \times 10^{14})}{(5.9 \times 10^8)}$

(d) $\dfrac{(2.69 \times 10^7)}{(8.44 \times 10^{11})}$

(e) $\begin{array}{r} 1.823 \times 10^9 \\ +1.11 \times 10^7 \\ \hline \end{array}$

(f) $\begin{array}{r} 3.32 \times 10^{-5} \\ +3.400 \times 10^{-7} \\ \hline \end{array}$

(g) $\begin{array}{r} 6.893 \times 10^9 \\ -2.44 \times 10^8 \\ \hline \end{array}$

(h) $\begin{array}{r} 1.74 \times 10^4 \\ -2.9 \times 10^3 \\ \hline \end{array}$

ANSWERS

(a) 2.0×10^{13}

(b) 4.37×10^5

(c) 2.5×10^5

(d) 3.19×10^{-5}

(e) 1.834×10^9

(f) 3.35×10^{-5}

(g) 6.649×10^9

(h) 1.45×10^4

Logarithms

The logarithm (or log) of a number is the exponent to which 10 must be raised to obtain that number. For example, the log of 100 is 2 because 10 must be raised to the 2nd power to get 100. Similarly, the log of 1000 is 3 because 10 must be raised to the 3rd power to get 1000. The logs of several multiples of 10 are shown on the following page.

$$\log 10 = 1$$
$$\log 100 = 2$$
$$\log 1000 = 3$$
$$\log 10{,}000 = 4$$

Because $10^0 = 1$ by definition, $\log 1 = 0$.

The log of a number smaller than 1 is negative because 10 must be raised to a negative exponent to get a number smaller than 1. For example, the log of 0.01 is −2 because 10 must be raised to the power of −2 to get 0.01. Similarly, the log of 0.001 is −3 because 10 must be raised to the power of −3 to get 0.001. The logs of several fractional numbers are as follows.

$$\log 0.1 = -1$$
$$\log 0.01 = -2$$
$$\log 0.001 = -3$$
$$\log 0.0001 = -4$$

The logs of numbers that are not multiples of 10 can be computed on your calculator. See your calculator manual for specific instructions.

INVERSE LOGARITHMS

The inverse logarithm or invlog function (sometimes called antilog) is exactly the opposite of the log function. For example, the log of 100 is 2 and the inverse log of 2 is 100. The log function and the invlog function undo one another.

$$\log 1000 = 3$$
$$\text{invlog } 3 = 1000$$
$$\text{invlog } (\log 1000) = 1000$$

The inverse log of a number is simply 10 raised to that number.

$$\text{invlog } x = 10^x$$
$$\text{invlog } 3 = 10^3 = 1000$$

The inverse logs of numbers can be computed on your calculator. See your calculator manual for specific instructions.

FOR PRACTICE Logarithms and Inverse Logarithms

Perform each of the following operations.

(a) $\log 1.0 \times 10^5$

(b) $\log 59$

(c) $\log 1.0 \times 10^{-5}$

(d) $\log 0.068$

(e) invlog 7.0

(f) invlog 1.44

(g) invlog −6.0

(h) invlog −0.250

(i) invlog (log 88)

ANSWERS

(a) 5.00

(b) 1.77

(c) −5.00

(d) −1.17

(e) 1×10^7

(f) 28

(g) 1×10^{-6}

(h) 0.56

(i) 88

GLOSSARY

absolute zero The coldest temperature possible. Absolute zero (0 K or −273 °C or −459 °F) is the temperature at which molecular motion stops. Lower temperatures do not exist.

acid A molecular compound that dissolves in solution to form H^+ ions. Acids have the ability to dissolve some metals and will turn litmus paper red.

acid rain Acidic precipitation in the form of rain; created when fossil fuels are burned, which releases SO_2 and NO_2, which then react with water in the atmosphere to form sulfuric acid and nitric acid.

acid–base reaction A reaction that forms water and typically a salt.

acidic solution A solution containing a concentration of H_3O^+ ions greater than 1.0×10^{-7} M (pH < 7).

activation energy The amount of energy that must be absorbed by reactants before a reaction can occur; an energy hump that normally exists between the reactants and products.

activity series of metals A listing of metals (and hydrogen) in order of decreasing activity, decreasing ability to oxidize, and decreasing tendency to lose electrons.

actual yield The amount of product actually produced by a chemical reaction.

addition polymer A polymer formed by addition of monomers to one another without elimination of any atoms.

alcohol An organic compound containing an —OH functional group bonded to a carbon atom and having the general formula *R*OH.

aldehyde An organic compound with the general formula *R*CHO.

alkali metals The Group 1A elements, which are highly reactive metals.

alkaline battery A dry cell employing half-reactions that use a base.

alkaline earth metals The Group 2A elements, which are fairly reactive metals.

alkaloids Organic compounds that are typically found in plants and act as bases.

alkanes Hydrocarbons in which all carbon atoms are connected by single bonds. Noncyclic alkanes have the general formula C_nH_{2n+2}.

alkene A hydrocarbon that contains at least one double bond between carbon atoms. Noncyclic alkenes have the general formula C_nH_{2n}.

alkyl group In an organic molecule, any group containing only singly bonded carbon atoms and hydrogen atoms.

alkyne A hydrocarbon that contains at least one triple bond between carbon atoms. Noncyclic alkynes have the general formula C_nH_{2n-2}.

alpha particle A particle consisting of two protons and two neutrons (a helium nucleus), represented by the symbol $^4_2$He.

alpha (α) radiation Radiation emitted by an unstable nucleus, consisting of alpha particles.

alpha (α)-helix The most common secondary protein structure. The amino acid chain is wrapped into a tight coil from which the side chains extend outward. The structure is maintained by hydrogen bonding interactions between NH and CO groups along the peptide backbone of the protein.

amine An organic compound that contains nitrogen and has the general formula NR_3, where *R* may be an alkyl group or a hydrogen atom.

amino acid A molecule containing an amine group, a carboxylic acid group, and an *R* group (also called a side chain). Amino acids are the building blocks of proteins.

amorphous A type of solid matter in which atoms or molecules do not have long-range order (e.g., glass and plastic).

amphoteric In Brønsted–Lowry terminology, able to act as either an acid or a base.

anion A negatively charged ion.

anode The electrode where oxidation occurs in an electrochemical cell.

aqueous solution A homogeneous mixture of a substance with water.

aromatic ring A ring of carbon atoms containing alternating single and double bonds; another name for the benzene ring.

Arrhenius acid A substance that produces H^+ ions in aqueous solution.

Arrhenius base A substance that produces OH^- ions in aqueous solution.

atmosphere (atm) The average pressure at sea level, 101,325 Pa (760 mmHg).

atom The smallest identifiable unit of an element.

atomic element An element that exists in nature with single atoms as the basic unit.

atomic mass A weighted average of the masses of each naturally occurring isotope of an element; atomic mass is the average mass of the atoms of an element.

atomic mass unit (amu) The unit commonly used to express the masses of protons, neutrons, and nuclei. 1 amu = 1.66×10^{-24} g.

atomic number (Z) The number of protons in the nucleus of an atom.

atomic size The size of atom, which is determined by how far the outermost electrons are from the nucleus.

atomic solid A solid whose component units are individual atoms (e.g., diamond, C; iron, Fe).

atomic theory A theory stating that all matter is composed of tiny particles called atoms.

Avogadro's law A law stating that the volume (*V*) of a gas and the amount of the gas in moles (*n*) are directly proportional.

Avogadro's number The number of entities in a mole, 6.022×10^{23}.

balanced equation A chemical equation in which the numbers of each type of atom on both sides of the equation are equal.

base A molecular compound that dissolves in solution to form OH^- ions. Bases have a slippery feel and turn litmus paper blue.

base chain The longest continuous chain of carbon atoms in an organic compound.

basic solution A solution containing a concentration of OH^- ions greater than 1.0×10^{-7} M (pH > 7).

bent The molecular geometry in which 3 atoms are not in a straight line. This geometry occurs when the central atoms contain 4 electron groups (2 bonding and 2 nonbonding) or 3 electron groups (2 bonding and 1 nonbonding).

benzene (C_6H_6) A particularly stable organic compound consisting of six carbon atoms joined by alternating single and double bonds in a ring structure.

beta particle A form of radiation consisting of an energetic electron and represented by the symbol ${}^{0}_{-1}e$.

beta (β) radiation Energetic electrons emitted by an unstable nucleus.

beta (β)-pleated sheet A common pattern in the secondary structure of proteins. The protein chain is extended in a zigzag pattern, and the peptide backbones of adjacent strands interact with one another through hydrogen bonding to form sheets.

binary acid An acid containing only hydrogen and a nonmetal.

binary compound A compound containing only two different kinds of elements.

biochemistry The study of the chemical substances and processes that occur in living organisms.

Bohr model A model for the atom in which electrons travel around the nucleus in circular orbits at specific, fixed distances from the nucleus.

boiling point The temperature at which the vapor pressure of a liquid is equal to the pressure above it.

boiling point elevation The increase in the boiling point of a solution caused by the presence of the solute.

bonding pair Electrons that are shared between two atoms in a chemical bond.

bonding theory A model that predicts how atoms bond together to form molecules.

Boyle's law A law maintaining that the volume (V) of a gas and its pressure (P) are inversely proportional.

branched alkane An alkane composed of carbon atoms bonded in chains containing branches.

Brønsted–Lowry acid A proton (H^+ ion) donor.

Brønsted–Lowry base A proton (H^+ ion) acceptor.

buffer A solution that resists pH change by neutralizing added acid or added base.

Calorie (Cal) An energy unit equivalent to 1000 little-*c* calories.

calorie (cal) The amount of energy required to raise the temperature of 1 g of water by 1 °C.

carbohydrates Polyhydroxyl aldehydes or ketones or their derivatives, containing multiple —OH groups and often having the general formula $(CH_2O)_n$.

carbonyl group A carbon atom double bonded to an oxygen atom.

carboxylic acid An organic compound with the general formula *RCOOH*.

catalyst A substance that increases the rate of a chemical reaction but is not consumed by the reaction.

cathode The electrode where reduction occurs in an electrochemical cell.

cation A positively charged ion.

cell The smallest structural unit of living organisms that has the properties associated with life.

cell membrane The structure that bounds the cell and holds the contents of the cell together.

cellulose A common polysaccharide composed of repeating glucose units linked together.

Celsius (°C) scale A temperature scale often used by scientists. On this scale, water freezes at 0 °C and boils at 100 °C at 1 atm pressure. Room temperature is approximately 22 °C.

chain reaction A self-sustaining chemical or nuclear reaction yielding energy or products that cause further reactions of the same kind.

charge A fundamental property of protons and electrons. Charged particles experience forces such that like charges repel and unlike charges attract.

Charles's law A law stating that the volume (V) of a gas and its temperature (T) expressed in kelvins are directly proportional.

chemical bond The sharing or transfer of electrons to attain stable electron configurations among the bonding atoms.

chemical change A change in which matter changes its composition.

chemical energy The energy associated with chemical changes.

chemical equation An equation that represents a chemical reaction; the reactants are on the left side of the equation and the products are on the right side.

chemical formula A way to represent a compound. At a minimum, the chemical formula indicates the elements present in the compound and the relative number of atoms of each element.

chemical properties Properties that a substance can display only through changing its composition.

chemical reaction The process by which one or more substances transform into different substances via a chemical change. Chemical reactions often emit or absorb energy.

chemical symbol A one- or two-letter abbreviation for an element. Chemical symbols are listed directly below the atomic number in the periodic table.

chemistry The science that seeks to understand the behavior of matter by studying what atoms and molecules do.

chromosome A biological structure containing genes, located within the nucleus of a cell.

codon A sequence of three bases in a nucleic acid that codes for one amino acid.

colligative properties Physical properties of solutions that depend on the number of solute particles present but not the type of solute particles.

collision theory A theory of reaction rates stating that effective collisions between reactant molecules must take place in order for the reaction to occur.

color change One type of evidence of a chemical reaction, involving the change in color of a substance after a reaction.

combined gas law A law that combines Boyle's law and Charles's law; it is used to calculate how a property of a gas (*P*, *V*, or *T*) changes when two other properties are changed at the same time.

combustion reaction A reaction in which a substance reacts with oxygen, emitting heat and forming one or more oxygen-containing compounds.

complementary base In DNA, a base capable of precise pairing with a specific other DNA base.

complete ionic equation A chemical equation showing all the species as they are actually present in solution.

complex carbohydrate A carbohydrate composed of many repeating saccharide units.

compound A substance composed of two or more elements in fixed, definite proportions.

compressible Able to occupy a smaller volume when subjected to increased pressure. Gases are compressible because, in the gas phase, atoms or molecules are widely separated.

concentrated solution A solution containing large amounts of solute.

condensation A physical change in which a substance is converted from its gaseous form to its liquid form.

condensation polymer A class of polymers that expel atoms, usually water, during their formation or polymerization.

condensed structural formula A shorthand way of writing a structural formula.

conjugate acid–base pair In Brønsted–Lowry terminology, two substances related to each other by the transfer of a proton.

conservation of energy, law of A law stating that energy can be neither created nor destroyed. The total amount of energy is constant and cannot change; it can only be transferred from one object to another or converted from one form to another.

conservation of mass, law of A law stating that in a chemical reaction, matter is neither created nor destroyed.

constant composition, law of A law stating that all samples of a given compound have the same proportions of their constituent elements.

conversion factor A factor used to convert between two separate units; a conversion factor is constructed from any two quantities known to be equivalent.

copolymers Polymers that are composed of two different kinds of monomers and result in chains composed of alternating units rather than a single repeating unit.

core electrons The electrons that are not in the outermost principal shell of an atom.

corrosion The oxidation of metals (e.g., rusting of iron).

covalent atomic solid An atomic solid, such as diamond, that is held together by covalent bonds.

covalent bond The bond that results when two nonmetals combine in a chemical reaction. In a covalent bond, the atoms share their electrons.

critical mass The mass of uranium or plutonium required for a nuclear reaction to be self-sustaining.

crystalline A type of solid matter with atoms or molecules arranged in a well-ordered, three-dimensional array with long-range, repeating order (e.g., salt and diamond).

cytoplasm In a cell, the region between the nucleus and the cell membrane.

Dalton's law of partial pressure A law stating that the sum of the partial pressures of each component in a gas mixture equals the total pressure.

daughter nuclide The nuclide product of a nuclear decay.

decimal part One part of a number expressed in scientific notation.

decomposition A reaction in which a complex substance decomposes to form simpler substances; $AB \longrightarrow A + B$.

density (*d*) A fundamental property of materials that relates mass and volume and differs from one substance to another. The units of density are those of mass divided by volume, most commonly expressed in g/cm^3, g/mL, or g/L.

derived unit A unit formed from the combination of other units.

dilute solution A solution containing small amounts of solute.

dimer A molecule formed by the joining together of two smaller molecules.

dipeptide Two amino acids linked together via a peptide bond.

dipole moment A measure of the separation of charge in a bond or in a molecule.

diprotic acid An acid containing two ionizable protons.

disaccharide A carbohydrate that can be decomposed into two simpler carbohydrates.

dispersion force The intermolecular force present in all molecules and atoms. Dispersion forces are caused by fluctuations in the electron distribution within molecules or atoms.

displacement A reaction in which one element displaces another in a compound; $A + BC \longrightarrow AC + B$.

dissociation In aqueous solution, the process by which a solid ionic compound separates into its ions.

disubstituted benzene A benzene in which two hydrogen atoms have been replaced by an atom or group of atoms.

DNA (deoxyribonucleic acid) Long chainlike molecules that occur in the nucleus of cells and act as blueprints for the construction of proteins.

dot structure A drawing that represents the valence electrons in atoms as dots; it shows a chemical bond as the sharing or transfer of electron dots.

double bond The bond that exists when two electron pairs are shared between two atoms. In general, double bonds are shorter and stronger than single bonds.

double displacement A reaction in which two elements or groups of elements in two different compounds exchange places to form two new compounds; $AB + CD \longrightarrow AD + CB$.

dry cell An ordinary battery (voltaic cell); it does not contain large amounts of liquid water.

duet The name for the two electrons corresponding to a stable Lewis structure in hydrogen and helium.

dynamic equilibrium In a chemical reaction, the condition in which the rate of the forward reaction equals the rate of the reverse reaction.

electrical current The flow of electric charge—for example, electrons flowing through a wire or ions through a solution.

electrical energy Energy associated with the flow of electric charge.

electrochemical cell A device that creates electrical current from a redox reaction.

electrolysis A process in which electrical current is used to drive an otherwise nonspontaneous redox reaction.

electrolytic cell An electrochemical cell used for electrolysis.

electromagnetic radiation A type of energy that travels through space at a constant speed of 3.0×10^8 m/s (186,000 miles/s) and exhibits both wavelike and particlelike behavior. Light is a form of electromagnetic radiation.

electromagnetic spectrum A spectrum that includes all wavelengths of electromagnetic radiation.

electron A negatively charged particle that occupies most of the atom's volume but contributes almost none of its mass.

electron configuration A representation that shows the occupation of orbitals by electrons for a particular element.

electron geometry The geometrical arrangement of the electron groups in a molecule.

electron group A general term for a lone pair, single bond, or multiple bond in a molecule.

electron spin A fundamental property of all electrons that causes them to have magnetic fields associated with them. The spin of an electron can either be oriented up $\left(+\frac{1}{2}\right)$ or down $\left(-\frac{1}{2}\right)$.

electronegativity The ability of an element to attract electrons within a covalent bond.

element A substance that cannot be broken down into simpler substances.

emission spectrum A spectrum associated with the emission of electromagnetic radiation by elements or compounds.

empirical formula A formula for a compound that gives the smallest whole-number ratio of each type of atom.

empirical formula molar mass The sum of the molar masses of all the atoms in an empirical formula.

endothermic Describes a process that absorbs heat energy.

endothermic reaction A chemical reaction that absorbs energy from the surroundings.

energy The capacity to do work.

English system A unit system commonly used in the United States.

enzymes Biological catalysts that increase the rates of biochemical reactions; enzymes are abundant in living organisms.

equilibrium constant (K_{eq}) The ratio, at equilibrium, of the concentrations of the products raised to their stoichiometric coefficients divided by the concentrations of the reactants raised to their stoichiometric coefficients.

equivalence point The point in a reaction at which the reactants are in exact stoichiometric proportions.

equivalent The stoichiometric proportions of elements and compounds in a chemical equation.

ester An organic compound with the general formula *RCOOR*.

ester linkage A type of bond with the general structure —COO—. Ester linkages join glycerol to fatty acids.

ether An organic compound with the general formula *ROR*.

evaporation A process in which molecules of a liquid, undergoing constant random motion, acquire enough energy to overcome attractions to neighbors and enter the gas phase.

excited state An unstable state for an atom or a molecule in which energy has been absorbed but not reemitted, raising an electron from the ground state into a higher energy orbital.

exothermic Describes a process that releases heat energy.

exothermic reaction A chemical reaction that releases energy to the surroundings.

experiment A procedure that attempts to measure observable predictions to test a theory or law.

exponent A number that represents the number of times a term is multiplied by itself. For example, in 2^4 the exponent is 4 and represents $2 \times 2 \times 2 \times 2$.

exponential part One part of a number expressed in scientific notation; it represents the number of places the decimal point has moved.

Fahrenheit (°F) scale The temperature scale that is most familiar in the United States; water freezes at 32 °F and boils at 212 °F at 1 atm prssure.

family (of elements) A group of elements that have similar outer electron configurations and therefore similar properties. Families occur in vertical columns in the periodic table.

family (of organic compounds) A group of organic compounds with the same functional group.

fatty acid A type of lipid consisting of a carboxylic acid with a long hydrocarbon tail.

film badge dosimeter Badges used to measure radiation exposure, consisting of photographic film held in a small case that is pinned to clothing.

fission, nuclear The process by which a heavy nucleus is split into nuclei of smaller masses and energy is emitted.

formula mass The average mass of the molecules (or formula units) that compose a compound.

formula unit The basic unit of ionic compounds; the smallest electrically neutral collection of cations and anions that compose the compound.

freezing point depression The decrease in the freezing point of a solvent caused by the presence of a solute.

frequency The number of wave cycles or crests that pass through a stationary point in one second.

fuel cell A voltaic cell in which the reactants are constantly replenished.

functional group A set of atoms that characterize a family of organic compounds.

fusion, nuclear The combination of light atomic nuclei to form heavier ones with emission of large amounts of energy.

galvanic (voltaic) cell An electrochemical cell that spontaneously produces electrical current.

gamma radiation High-energy, short-wavelength electromagnetic radiation emitted by an atomic nucleus.

gamma rays The shortest-wavelength, most energetic form of electromagnetic radiation. Gamma ray photons are represented by the symbol ${}^{0}_{0}\gamma$.

gas A state of matter in which atoms or molecules are widely separated and free to move relative to one another.

gas-evolution reaction A reaction that occurs in solution and forms a gas as one of the products.

gas formation One type of evidence of a chemical reaction, a gas forms when two substances are mixed together.

Geiger-Müller counter A radioactivity detector consisting of a chamber filled with argon gas that discharges electrical signals when high-energy particles pass through it.

gene A sequence of codons within a DNA molecule that codes for a single protein. Genes vary in length from hundreds to thousands of codons.

genetic material The inheritable blueprint for making organisms.

glycogen A type of polysaccharide; it has a structure similar to that of starch, but the chain is highly branched.

glycolipid A biological molecule composed of a nonpolar fatty acid and hydrocarbon chain and a polar section composed of a sugar molecule such as glucose.

glycoside linkage The link between monosaccharides in a polysaccharide.

ground state The state of an atom or molecule in which the electrons occupy the lowest possible energy orbitals available.

group (of elements) Elements that have similar outer electron configurations and therefore similar properties. Groups occur in vertical columns in the periodic table.

half-cell A compartment in which the oxidation or reduction half-reaction occurs in a galvanic or voltaic cell.

half-life The time it takes for one-half of the parent nuclides in a radioactive sample to decay to the daughter nuclides.

half-reaction Either the oxidation part or the reduction part of a redox reaction.

halogens The Group 7A elements, which are very reactive nonmetals.

heat absorption One type of evidence of a chemical reaction, involving the intake of energy.

heat capacity The quantity of heat energy required to change the temperature of a given amount of a substance by 1 °C.

heat emission One type of evidence of a chemical reaction, involving the evolution of thermal energy.

heat of fusion The amount of heat required to melt one mole of a solid at its melting point with no change in temperature.

heat of vaporization The amount of heat required to vaporize one mole of a liquid at its boiling point with no change in temperature.

heterogeneous mixture A mixture, such as oil and water, that has two or more regions with different compositions.

homogeneous mixture A mixture, such as salt water, that has the same composition throughout.

human genome All of the genetic material of a human being; the total DNA of a human cell.

Hund's rule A rule stating that when filling orbitals of equal energy, electrons will occupy empty orbitals singly before pairing with other electrons.

hydrocarbon A compound that contains only carbon and hydrogen atoms.

hydrogen bond A strong dipole–dipole interaction between molecules containing hydrogen directly bonded to a small, highly electronegative atom, such as N, O, or F.

hydrogenation The chemical addition of hydrogen to a compound.

hydronium ion The H_3O^+ ion. Chemists often use $H^+(aq)$ and $H_3O^+(aq)$ interchangeably to mean the same thing—a hydronium ion.

hypothesis A theory or law before it has become well established; a tentative explanation for an observation or a scientific problem that can be tested by further investigation.

hypoxia A shortage of oxygen in the tissues of the body.

ideal gas law A law that combines the four properties of a gas—pressure (P), volume (V), temperature (T), and number of moles (n) in a single equation showing their interrelatedness: $PV = nRT$ (R = ideal gas constant).

indicator A substance that changes color with acidity level, often used to detect the endpoint of a titration.

infrared (IR) light The fraction of the electromagnetic spectrum between visible light and microwaves. Infrared light is invisible to the human eye.

insoluble Not soluble in water.

instantaneous dipole A type of intermolecular force resulting from transient shifts in electron density within an atom or molecule.

intermolecular forces Attractive forces that exist between molecules.

International System (SI) The standard set of units for science measurements, based on the metric system.

ion An atom (or group of atoms) that has gained or lost one or more electrons, so that it has an electric charge.

ion product constant (K_w) The product of the H_3O^+ ion concentration and the OH^- ion concentration in an aqueous solution. At room temperature, $K_w = 1.0 \times 10^{-14}$.

ionic bond The bond that results when a metal and a nonmetal combine in a chemical reaction. In an ionic bond, the metal transfers one or more electrons to the nonmetal.

ionic compound A compound formed between a metal and one or more nonmetals.

ionic solid A solid compound composed of metals and nonmetals joined by ionic bonds.

ionization The forming of ions.

ionization energy The energy required to remove an electron from an atom in the gaseous state.

ionizing power The ability of radiation to ionize other molecules and atoms.

isomers Molecules with the same molecular formula but different structures.

isoosmotic Describes solutions having equal osmotic pressure.

isotope scanning The use of radioactive isotopes to identify disease in the body.

isotopes Atoms with the same number of protons but different numbers of neutrons.

Kelvin (K) scale The temperature scale that assigns 0 K to the coldest temperature possible, absolute zero (−273 °C or −459 °F), the temperature at which molecular motion stops. The size of the kelvin is identical to that of the Celsius degree.

ketone An organic compound with the general formula *RCOR*.

kilogram (kg) The SI standard unit of mass.

kilowatt-hour (kWh) A unit of energy equal to 3.6 million joules.

kinetic energy Energy associated with the motion of an object.

kinetic molecular theory A simple model for gases that predicts the behavior of most gases under many conditions.

Le Châtelier's principle A principle stating that when a chemical system at equilibrium is disturbed, the system shifts in a direction that minimizes the disturbance.

lead-acid storage battery An automobile battery consisting of six electrochemical cells wired in series. Each cell produces 2 volts for a total of 12 volts.

Lewis structure A drawing that represents chemical bonds between atoms as shared or transferred electrons; the valence electrons of atoms are represented as dots.

Lewis theory A simple theory for chemical bonding involving diagrams showing bonds between atoms as lines or dots. In this theory, atoms bond together to obtain stable octets (8 valence electrons).

light emission One type of evidence of a chemical reaction, involving the giving off of electromagnetic radiation.

limiting reactant The reactant that determines the amount of product formed in a chemical reaction.

linear Describes the molecular geometry of a molecule containing two electron groups (two bonding groups and no lone pairs).

linearly related A relationship between two variables such that, when they are plotted one against the other, the graph produced is a straight line.

lipid A cellular component that is insoluble in water but soluble in nonpolar solvents.

lipid bilayer A structure formed by lipids in the cell membrane.

liquid A state of matter in which atoms or molecules are packed close to each other (about as closely as in a solid) but are free to move around and by each other.

logarithmic scale A scale involving logarithms. A logarithm entails an exponent that indicates the power to which a number is raised to produce a given number (e.g., the logarithm of 100 to the base 10 is 2).

lone pair Electrons that are only on one atom in a Lewis structure.

main-group elements Groups 1A–8A on the periodic table. These groups have properties that tend to be predictable based on their position in the periodic table.

mass A measure of the quantity of matter within an object.

mass number (A) The sum of the number of neutrons and protons in an atom.

mass percent composition (or mass percent) The percentage, by mass, of each element in a compound.

matter Anything that occupies space and has mass. Matter exists in three different states: solid, liquid, and gas.

melting point The temperature at which a solid turns into a liquid.

messenger RNA (mRNA) Long chainlike molecules that act as blueprints for the construction of proteins.

metallic atomic solid An atomic solid, such as iron, which is held together by metallic bonds that, in the simplest model, consist of positively charged ions in a sea of electrons.

metallic character The properties typical of a metal, especially the tendency to lose electrons in chemical reactions. Elements become more metallic as you move from right to left across the periodic table.

metalloids Those elements that fall along the boundary between the metals and the nonmetals in the periodic table; their properties are intermediate between those of metals and those of nonmetals.

metals Elements that tend to lose electrons in chemical reactions. They are found at the left side and in the center of the periodic table.

meter (m) The SI standard unit of length.

metric system The unit system commonly used throughout most of the world.

microwaves The part of the electromagnetic spectrum between the infrared region and the radio wave region. Microwaves are efficiently absorbed by water molecules and can therefore be used to heat water-containing substances.

millimeter of mercury (mmHg) A unit of pressure that originates from the method used to measure pressure with a barometer. Also called a *torr*.

miscibility The ability of two liquids to mix without separating into two phases, or the ability of one liquid to mix with (dissolve in) another liquid.

mixture A substance composed of two or more different types of atoms or molecules combined in variable proportions.

molality (m) A common unit of solution concentration, defined as the number of moles of solute per kilogram of solvent.

molar mass The mass of one mole of atoms of an element or one mole of molecules (or formula units) for a compound. An element's molar mass in grams per mole is numerically equivalent to the element's atomic mass in amu.

molar solubility The solubility of a substance in units of moles per liter (mol/L).

molar volume The volume occupied by one mole of gas. Under standard temperature and pressure conditions the molar volume of ideal gas is 22.5 L.

molarity (M) A common unit of solution concentration, defined as the number of moles of solute per liter of solution.

mole Avogadro's number (6.022×10^{23}) of particles—especially, of atoms, ions, or molecules. A mole of any element has a mass in grams that is numerically equivalent to its atomic mass in amu.

molecular compound A compound formed from two or more nonmetals. Molecular compounds have distinct molecules as their simplest identifiable units.

molecular element An element that does not normally exist in nature with single atoms as the basic unit. These elements usually exist as diatomic molecules—2 atoms of that element bonded together—as their basic units.

molecular equation A chemical equation showing the complete, neutral formulas for every compound in a reaction.

molecular formula A formula for a compound that gives the specific number of each type of atom in a molecule.

molecular geometry The geometrical arrangement of the atoms in a molecule.

molecular solid A solid whose composite units are molecules.

molecule Two or more atoms joined in a specific arrangement by chemical bonds. A molecule is the smallest identifiable unit of a molecular compound.

monomer An individual repeating unit that makes up a polymer.

monoprotic acid An acid containing only one ionizable proton.

monosaccharide A carbohydrate that cannot be decomposed into simpler carbohydrates.

monosubstituted benzene A benzene in which one of the hydrogen atoms has been replaced by another atom or group of atoms.

net ionic equation An equation that shows only the species that actually participate in a reaction.

neutral solution A solution in which the concentrations of H_3O^+ and OH^- are equal (pH = 7).

neutralization A reaction that takes place when an acid and a base are mixed; the $H^+(aq)$ from the acid combines with the $OH^-(aq)$ from the base to form $H_2O(l)$.

neutron A nuclear particle with no electrical charge and nearly the same mass as a proton.

nitrogen narcosis An increase in nitrogen concentration in bodily tissues and fluids that results in feelings of drunkenness.

noble gases The Group 8A elements, which are chemically unreactive.

nonbonding atomic solid An atomic solid that is held together by relatively weak dispersion forces.

nonelectrolyte solution A solution containing a solute that dissolves as molecules; therefore, the solution does not conduct electricity.

nonmetals Elements that tend to gain electrons in chemical reactions. They are found at the upper right side of the periodic table.

nonpolar molecule A molecule that does not have a net dipole moment.

nonvolatile Describes a compound that does not vaporize easily.

normal alkane (or *n*-alkane) An alkane composed of carbon atoms bonded in a straight chain with no branches.

normal boiling point The boiling point of a liquid at a pressure of 1 atmosphere.

nuclear equation An equation that represents the changes that occur during radioactivity and other nuclear processes.

nuclear radiation The energetic particles emitted from the nucleus of an atom when it is undergoing a nuclear process.

nuclear theory of the atom A theory stating that most of the atom's mass and all of its positive charge is contained in a small, dense nucleus. Most of the volume of the atom is empty space occupied by negatively charged electrons.

nucleic acids Biological molecules, such as deoxyribonucleic acid (DNA) and ribonucleic acid (RNA), that store and transmit genetic information.

nucleotide An individual unit of a nucleic acid. Nucleic acids are polymers of nucleotides.

nucleus (of a cell) The part of the cell that contains the genetic material.

nucleus (of an atom) The small core containing most of the atom's mass and all of its positive charge. The nucleus is made up of protons and neutrons.

observation Often the first step in the scientific method. An observation must measure or describe something about the physical world.

octet The number of electrons, eight, around atoms with stable Lewis structures.

octet rule A rule that states that an atom will give up, accept, or share electrons in order to achieve a filled outer electron shell, which usually consists of 8 electrons.

orbital The region around the nucleus of an atom where an electron is most likely to be found.

orbital diagram An electron configuration in which electrons are represented as arrows in boxes corresponding to orbitals of a particular atom.

organic chemistry The study of carbon-containing compounds and their reactions.

organic molecule A molecule whose main structural component is carbon.

osmosis The flow of solvent from a lower-concentration solution through a semipermeable membrane to a higher-concentration solution.

osmotic pressure The pressure produced on the surface of a semipermeable membrane by osmosis or the pressure required to stop osmotic flow.

oxidation The gain of oxygen, the loss of hydrogen, or the loss of electrons (the most fundamental definition).

oxidation state (or oxidation number) A number that can be used as an aid in writing formulas and balancing equations. It is computed for each element based on the number of electrons assigned to it in a scheme where the most electronegative element is assigned all of the bonding electrons.

oxidation–reduction (redox) reaction A reaction in which electrons are transferred from one substance to another.

oxidizing agent In a redox reaction, the substance being reduced. Oxidizing agents tend to gain electrons easily.

oxyacid An acid containing hydrogen, a nonmetal, and oxygen.

oxyanion An anion containing oxygen. Most polyatomic ions are oxyanions.

oxygen toxicity The result of increased oxygen concentration in bodily tissues.

parent nuclide The original nuclide in a nuclear decay.

partial pressure The pressure due to any individual component in a gas mixture.

pascal (Pa) The SI unit of pressure, defined as 1 newton per square meter.

Pauli exclusion principle A principle stating that no more than two electrons can occupy an orbital and that the two electrons must have opposite spins.

penetrating power The ability of a radioactive particle to penetrate matter.

peptide bond The bond between the amine end of one amino acid and the carboxylic acid end of another. Amino acids link together via peptide bonds to form proteins.

percent natural abundance The percentage amount of each isotope of an element in a naturally occurring sample of the element.

percent yield In a chemical reaction, the percentage of the theoretical yield that was actually attained.

period A horizontal row of the periodic table.

periodic law A law that states that when the elements are arranged in order of increasing relative mass, certain sets of properties recur periodically.

periodic table An arrangement of the elements in which atomic number increases from left to right and elements with similar properties fall in columns called families or groups.

permanent dipole A separation of charge resulting from the unequal sharing of electrons between atoms.

pH scale A scale used to quantify acidity or basicity. A pH of 7 is neutral; a pH lower than 7 is acidic, and a pH greater than 7 is basic. The pH is defined as follows: $pH = -\log[H_3O^+]$.

phenyl group The term for a benzene ring when other substituents are attached to it.

phospholipid A lipid with the same basic structure as a triglyceride, except that one of the fatty acid groups is replaced with a phosphate group.

phosphorescence The slow, long-lived emission of light that sometimes follows the absorption of light by some atoms and molecules.

photon A particle of light or a packet of light energy.

physical change A change in which matter does not change its composition, even though its appearance might change.

physical properties Those properties that a substance displays without changing its composition.

polar covalent bond A covalent bond between atoms of different electronegativities. Polar covalent bonds have a dipole moment.

polar molecule A molecule with polar bonds that add together to create a net dipole moment.

polyatomic ion An ion composed of a group of atoms with an overall charge.

polymer A molecule with many similar units, called monomers, bonded together in a long chain.

polypeptide A short chain of amino acids joined by peptide bonds.

polysaccharide A long, chainlike molecule composed of many linked monosaccharide units. Polysaccharides are polymers of monosaccharides.

positron A nuclear particle that has the mass of an electron but carries a +1 charge.

positron emission Expulsion of a positron from an unstable atomic nucleus. In positron emission, a proton is transformed into a neutron.

potential energy The energy of a body that is associated with its position or the arrangement of its parts.

precipitate An insoluble product formed through the reaction of two solutions containing soluble compounds.

precipitation reaction A reaction that forms a solid or precipitate when two aqueous solutions are mixed.

prefix multipliers Prefixes used by the SI system with the standard units. These multipliers change the value of the unit by powers of 10.

pressure The force exerted per unit area by gaseous molecules as they collide with the surfaces around them.

primary protein structure The sequence of amino acids in a protein's chain. Primary protein structure is maintained by the covalent peptide bonds between individual amino acids.

principal quantum number A number that indicates the shell that an electron occupies.

principal shell The shell indicated by the principal quantum number.

products The final substances produced in a chemical reaction; represented on the right side of a chemical equation.

properties The characteristics we use to distinguish one substance from another.

protein A biological molecule composed of a long chain of amino acids joined by peptide bonds. In living organisms, proteins serve many varied and important functions.

proton A positively charged nuclear particle. A proton's mass is approximately 1 amu.

pure substance A substance composed of only one type of atom or molecule.

quantification The assigning of a number to an observation so as to specify a quantity or property precisely.

quantum (*pl.* quanta) The precise amount of energy possessed by a photon; the difference in energy between two atomic orbitals.

quantum number (*n*) An integer that specifies the energy of an orbital. The higher the quantum number n, the greater the distance between the electron and the nucleus and the higher its energy.

quantum-mechanical model The foundation of modern chemistry; explains how electrons exist in atoms, and how they affect the chemical and physical properties of elements.

quaternary structure In a protein, the way that individual chains fit together to compose the protein. Quaternary structure is maintained by interactions between the R groups of amino acids on the different chains.

R group (side chain) An organic group attached to the central carbon atom of an amino acid.

radio waves The longest wavelength and least energetic form of electromagnetic radiation.

radioactive Describes a substance that emits tiny, invisible, energetic particles from the nuclei of its component atoms.

radioactivity The emission of tiny, invisible, energetic particles from the unstable nuclei of atoms. Many of these particles can penetrate matter.

radiocarbon dating A technique used to estimate the age of fossils and artifacts through the measurement of natural radioactivity of carbon atoms in the environment.

radiotherapy Treatment of disease with radiation, such as the use of gamma rays to kill rapidly dividing cancer cells.

random coil The name given to an irregular pattern of a secondary protein structure.

rate of a chemical reaction (reaction rate) The amount of reactant that changes to product in a given period of time. Also defined as the amount of a product that forms in a given period of time.

reactants The initial substances in a chemical reaction, represented on the left side of a chemical equation.

recrystallization A technique used to purify a solid; involves dissolving the solid in a solvent at high temperature, creating a saturated solution, then cooling the solution to cause the crystallization of the solid.

reducing agent In a redox reaction, the substance being oxidized. Reducing agents tend to lose electrons easily.

reduction The loss of oxygen, the gain of hydrogen, or the gain of electrons (the most fundamental definition).

rem Stands for *roentgen equivalent man;* a weighted measure of radiation exposure that accounts for the ionizing power of the different types of radiation.

resonance structures Two or more Lewis structures that are necessary to describe the bonding in a molecule or ion.

reversible reaction A reaction that is able to proceed in both the forward and reverse directions.

RNA (ribonucleic acid) Long chainlike molecules that occur throughout cells and take part in the construction of proteins.

salt An ionic compound that usually remains dissolved in a solution after an acid–base reaction has occurred.

salt bridge An inverted, U-shaped tube containing a strong electrolyte; completes the circuit in an electrochemical cell by allowing the flow of ions between the two half-cells.

saturated fat A triglyceride composed of saturated fatty acids. Saturated fat tends to be solid at room temperature.

saturated hydrocarbon A hydrocarbon that contains no double or triple bonds between the carbon atoms.

saturated solution A solution that holds the maximum amount of solute under the solution conditions. If additional solute is added to a saturated solution, it will not dissolve.

scientific law A statement that summarizes past observations and predicts future ones. Scientific laws are usually formulated from a series of related observations.

scientific method The way that scientists learn about the natural world. The scientific method involves observations, laws, hypotheses, theories, and experimentation.

scientific notation A system used to write very big or very small numbers, often containing many zeros, more compactly and precisely. A number written in scientific notation consists of a decimal part and an exponential part (10 raised to a particular exponent).

scintillation counter A device used to detect radioactivity in which energetic particles traverse a material that emits ultraviolet or visible light when excited by their passage. The light is detected and turned into an electrical signal.

second (s) The SI standard unit of time.

secondary protein structure Short-range periodic or repeating patterns often found in proteins. Secondary protein structure is maintained by interactions between amino acids that are fairly close together in the linear sequence of the protein chain or adjacent to each other on neighboring chains.

semiconductor A compound or element exhibiting intermediate electrical conductivity that can be changed and controlled.

semipermeable membrane A membrane that selectively allows some substances to pass through but not others.

SI units The most convenient system of units for science measurements, based on the metric system. The set of standard units agreed on by scientists throughout the world.

significant digits (figures) The non-place-holding digits in a reported measurement; they represent the precision of a measured quantity.

simple carbohydrate (simple sugar) A monosaccharide or disaccharide.

single bond A chemical bond in which one electron pair is shared between two atoms.

solid A state of matter in which atoms or molecules are packed close to each other in fixed locations.

solid formation One type of evidence of a chemical reaction, involving the formation of a solid.

solubility The amount of a compound, usually in grams, that will dissolve in a certain amount of solvent.

solubility rules A set of empirical rules used to determine whether an ionic compound is soluble.

solubility-product constant (K_{sp}) The equilibrium expression for a chemical equation that represents the dissolving of an ionic compound in solution.

soluble Dissolves in solution.

solute The minority component of a solution.

solution A homogeneous mixture of two or more substances.

solvent The majority component of a solution.

specific heat capacity (or specific heat) The heat capacity of a substance in joules per gram degree celsius (J/g °C).

spectator ions Ions that do not participate in a reaction; they appear unchanged on both sides of a chemical equation.

standard temperature and pressure (STP) Conditions often assumed in calculations involving gases: $T = 0\,°C$ (273 K) and $P = 1$ atm.

starch A common polysaccharide composed of repeating glucose units.

states of matter The three forms in which matter can exist: solid, liquid, and gas.

steroid A biological compound containing a 17-carbon 4-ring system.

stock solution A concentrated form in which solutions are often stored.

stoichiometry The numerical relationships among chemical quantities in a balanced chemical equation. Stoichiometry allows us to predict the amounts of products that form in a chemical reaction based on the amounts of reactants.

strong acid An acid that completely ionizes in solution.

strong base A base that completely dissociates in solution.

strong electrolyte A substance whose aqueous solutions are good conductors of electricity.

strong electrolyte solution A solution containing a solute that dissociates into ions; therefore, a solution that conducts electricity well.

structural formula A two-dimensional representation of molecules that not only shows the number and type of atoms, but also how the atoms are bonded together.

sublimation A physical change in which a substance is converted from its solid form directly into its gaseous form.

subshell In quantum mechanics, specifies the shape of the orbital and is represented by different letters (*s*, *p*, *d*, *f*).

substituent An atom or a group of atoms that has been substituted for a hydrogen atom in an organic compound.

substitution reaction A reaction in which one or more atoms are replaced by one or more different atoms.

supersaturated solution A solution holding more than the normal maximum amount of solute.

surface tension The tendency of liquids to minimize their surface area, resulting in a "skin" on the surface of the liquid.

synthesis A reaction in which simpler substances combine to form more complex substances; $A + B \longrightarrow AB$.

temporary dipole A type of intermolecular force resulting from transient shifts in electron density within an atom or molecule.

terminal atom An atom that is located at the end of a molecule or chain.

tertiary structure A protein's structure that consists of the large-scale bends and folds due to interactions between the *R* groups of amino acids that are separated by large distances in the linear sequence of the protein chain.

tetrahedral The molecular geometry of a molecule containing four electron groups (four bonding groups and no lone pairs).

theoretical yield The maximum amount of product that can be made in a chemical reaction based on the amount of limiting reactant.

theory A proposed explanation for observations and laws. A theory presents a model of the way nature works and predicts behavior that extends well beyond the observations and laws from which it was formed.

titration A laboratory procedure used to determine the amount of a substance in solution. In a titration, a reactant in a solution of known concentration is reacted with another reactant in a solution of unknown concentration until the reaction reaches the endpoint.

torr A unit of pressure named after the Italian physicist Evangelista Torricelli; also called a millimeter of mercury.

transition metals The elements in the middle of the periodic table whose properties tend to be less predictable based simply on their position in the periodic table. Transition metals lose electrons in their chemical reactions, but do not necessarily acquire noble gas configurations.

triglyceride A fat or oil; a tryglyceride is a tri-ester composed of glycerol with three fatty acids attached.

trigonal planar The molecular geometry of a molecule containing three electron groups, three bonding groups, and no lone pairs.

trigonal pyramidal The molecular geometry of a molecule containing four electron groups, three bonding groups, and one lone pair.

triple bond A chemical bond consisting of three electron pairs shared between two atoms. In general, triple bonds are shorter and stronger than double bonds.

Type I compounds Compounds containing metals that always form cations with the same charge.

Type II compounds Compounds containing metals that can form cations with different charges.

ultraviolet (UV) light The fraction of the electromagnetic spectrum between the visible region and the X-ray region. UV light is invisible to the human eye.

units Previously agreed-on quantities used to report experimental measurements. Units are vital in chemistry.

unsaturated fat (or oil) A triglyceride composed of unsaturated fatty acids. Unsaturated fats tend to be liquids at room temperature.

unsaturated hydrocarbon A hydrocarbon that contains one or more double or triple bonds between its carbon atoms.

unsaturated solution A solution holding less than the maximum possible amount of solute under the solution conditions.

valence electrons The electrons in the outermost principal shell of an atom; they are involved in chemical bonding.

valence shell electron pair repulsion (VSEPR) A theory that allows prediction of the shapes of molecules based on the idea that electrons—either as lone pairs or as bonding pairs—repel one another.

vapor pressure The partial pressure of a vapor in dynamic equilibrium with its liquid.

vaporization The phase transition between a liquid and a gas.

viscosity The resistance of a liquid to flow; manifestation of intermolecular forces.

visible light The fraction of the electromagnetic spectrum that is visible to the human eye, bounded by wavelengths of 400 nm (violet) and 780 nm (red).

vital force A mystical or supernatural power that, it was once believed, was possessed only by living organisms and allowed them to produce organic compounds.

vitalism The belief that living things contain a nonphysical "force" that allows them to synthesize organic compounds.

volatile Tending to vaporize easily.

voltage The potential difference between two electrodes; the driving force that causes electrons to flow.

volume A measure of space. Any unit of length, when cubed, becomes a unit of volume.

wavelength The distance between adjacent wave crests in a wave.

weak acid An acid that does not completely ionize in solution.

weak base A base that does not completely dissociate in solution.

weak electrolyte A substance whose aqueous solutions are poor conductors of electricity.

X-rays The portion of the electromagnetic spectrum between the ultraviolet (UV) region and the gamma-ray region.

ANSWERS TO ODD-NUMBERED EXERCISES

Note: Answers in the Questions section are written as briefly as possible. Student answers may vary and still be correct.

CHAPTER 1

QUESTIONS

1. Soda fizzes due to the interactions between carbon dioxide and water under high pressure. At room temperature, carbon dioxide is a gas and water is a liquid. Through the use of pressure, the makers of soda force the carbon dioxide gas to dissolve in the water. When the can is sealed, the solution remains mixed. When the can is opened, the pressure is released and the carbon dioxide molecules escape in bubbles of gas.
3. Chemists study molecules and interactions at the molecular level to learn about and explain macroscopic events. Chemists attempt to explain why ordinary things are as they are.
5. Chemistry is the science that seeks to understand what matter does by studying what atoms and molecules do.
7. The scientific method is the way chemists investigate the chemical world. The first step consists of observing the natural world. Later observations can be combined to create a scientific law, which summarizes and predicts behavior. Theories are models that strive to explain the cause of the observed phenomenon. Theories are tested through experiment. When a theory is not well established, it is sometimes referred to as a hypothesis.
9. A law is simply a general statement that summarizes and predicts observed behavior. Theories seek to explain the causes of observed behavior.
11. To say "It is just a theory" makes it seem as if theories are easily discardable. However, many theories are very well established and are as close to truth as we get in science. Established theories are backed up with years of experimental evidence, and they are the pinnacle of scientific understanding.
13. The atomic theory states that all matter is composed of small, indestructible particles called atoms. John Dalton formulated this theory.

PROBLEMS

15. Carbon dioxide contains one carbon atom and two oxygen atoms. Water contains one oxygen atom and two hydrogen atoms.
17. **a.** observation **b.** theory **c.** law **d.** observation
19. Mass (g) Volume (L) Ratio (g/L)
22.5 1.6 14
35.8 2.55 14.0
70.2 5.00 14.0
98.5 7.01 14.1
The ratio of mass to volume is constant.
21. **a.** All atoms contain a degree of chemical reactivity. The larger the size of an atom, the higher the chemical reactivity of that atom.
b. There are many correct answers. One example is: Conceivably, when the size of an atom is increased, the surface area of the atom is also increased; an atom with a greater surface area is more likely to react chemically.

CHAPTER 2

QUESTIONS

1. Without units, the results are unclear and it is hard to keep track of what each separate measurement entails.
3. Often scientists work with very large or very small numbers that contain a lot of zeros. Scientific notation allows these numbers to be written more compactly, and the information is more organized.
5. Zeros count as significant digits when they are interior zeros (zeros between two numbers) and when they are trailing zeros (zeros after a decimal point). Zeros are **not** significant digits when they are leading zeros, which are zeros to the left of the first nonzero number.
7. For calculations involving only multiplication and division, the result carries the same number of significant figures as the factor with the fewest significant figures.
9. In calculations involving both multiplication/division and addition/subtraction, do the steps in parentheses first; determine the correct number of significant figures in the intermediate answer; then do the remaining steps.
11. The basic SI unit of length is the meter. The kilogram is the SI unit of mass. Lastly, the second is the SI unit of time.
13. For measuring a Frisbee, the unit would be the meter and the prefix multiplier would be *centi-*. The final measurement would be in centimeters.
15. **a.** 2.42 cm **b.** 1.79 cm **c.** 21.58 cm **d.** 21.85 cm
17. Units act as a guide in the calculation and are able to show if the calculation is off track. The units must be followed in the calculation, so that the answer is correctly written and understood.
19. A conversion factor is a quantity used to relate two separate units. They are constructed from any two quantities known to be equivalent.
21. The conversion factor is $\frac{1\text{ ft}}{12\text{ in.}}$. For a feet-to-inches conversion, the conversion factor must be inverted $\left(\frac{12\text{ in.}}{1\text{ ft}}\right)$.

23. **a.** Sort the information into the **given** information (the starting point for the problem) and the **find** information (the end point).

b. Create a solution map to get from the given information to the information you are trying to find. This will likely include conversion factors or equations.

c. Follow the solution map to solve the problem. Carry out mathematical operations and cancel units as needed.

d. Ask, does this answer make physical sense? Are the units correct? Is the number of significant figures correct?

25. The solution map for converting grams to pounds is:

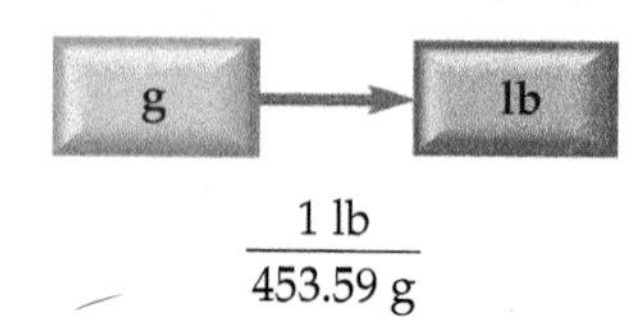

$$\frac{1\ \text{lb}}{453.59\ \text{g}}$$

27. The solution map for converting meters to feet is:

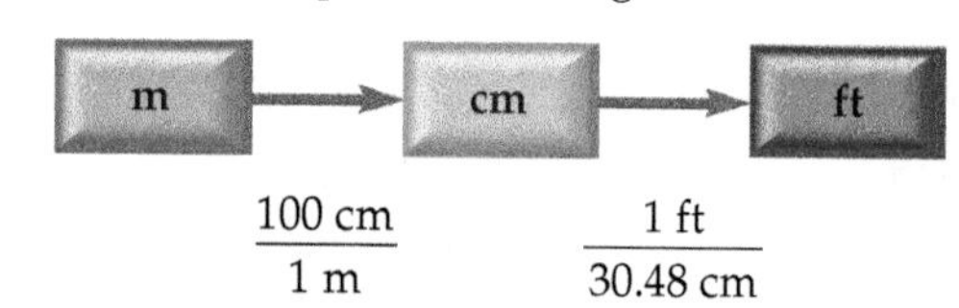

$$\frac{100\ \text{cm}}{1\ \text{m}} \qquad \frac{1\ \text{ft}}{30.48\ \text{cm}}$$

29. The density of a substance is the ratio of its mass to its volume. Density is a fundamental property of materials and differs from one substance to another. Density can be used to relate two separate units, thus working as a conversion factor. Density is a conversion factor between mass and volume.

PROBLEMS

31. **a.** 3.6756×10^7 **b.** 1.288×10^6
c. 1.949×10^7 **d.** 5.32×10^5

33. **a.** 7.461×10^{-11} m **b.** 1.58×10^{-5} mi
c. 6.32×10^{-7} m **d.** 1.5×10^{-5} m

35. **a.** 602,200,000,000,000,000,000,000
b. 0.00000000000000000016 C
c. 299,000,000 m/s
d. 344 m/s

37. **a.** 32,000,000 **b.** 0.0072
c. 118,000,000,000 **d.** 0.00000943

39.

2,000,000,000	2×10^9
1,211,000,000	1.211×10^9
0.000874	8.74×10^{-4}
320,000,000,000	3.2×10^{11}

41. **a.** 54.9 mL **b.** 48.7 °C
c. 46.83 °C **d.** 64 mL

43. **a.** Ø.ØØ5$\underline{0}$5$\underline{0}$ **b.** Ø.ØØØØØØØØØØØØØØ6$\underline{0}$
c. 22$\underline{0}$,1$\underline{0}$3 **d.** Ø.ØØ1$\underline{0}$8

45. **a.** 4 **b.** 4
c. 6 **d.** 5

47. **a.** correct **b.** 3
c. 7 **d.** correct

49. **a.** 256.0 **b.** 0.0004893
c. 2.901×10^{-4} **d.** 2.231×10^{-6}

51. **a.** 2.3 **b.** 2.4
c. 2.3 **d.** 2.4

53. **a.** 42.3 **b.** correct
c. correct **d.** 0.0456

55.

8.32466	8.325	8.3	8
84.57225	84.57	85	8×10^1
132.5512	132.6	1.3×10^2	1×10^2

57. **a.** 0.054 **b.** 0.619
c. 1.2×10^8 **d.** 6.6

59. **a.** 4.22×10^3 **b.** correct
c. 3.9969 **d.** correct

61. **a.** 110.6 **b.** 41.4
c. 183.3 **d.** 1.22

63. **a.** correct **b.** 1.0982
c. correct **d.** 3.53

65. **a.** 3.9×10^3 **b.** 632
c. 8.93×10^4 **d.** 6.34

67. **a.** 3.15×10^3 **b.** correct
c. correct **d.** correct

69. **a.** 3.55×10^3 g **b.** 8.944 m
c. 4.598×10^{-3} kg **d.** 18.7 mL

71. **a.** 0.588 L **b.** 34.1 μg
c. 10.1 ns **d.** 2.19×10^{-12} m

73. **a.** 57.2 cm **b.** 38.4 m
c. 0.754 km **d.** 61 mm

75. **a.** 15.7 in **b.** 91.2 ft
c. 6.21 mi **d.** 8478 lb

77.

5.08×10^8 m	5.08×10^5 km	508 Mm
5.08×10^{-1} Gm	5.08×10^{-4} Tm	
2.7976×10^{10} m	2.7976×10^7 km	27,976 Mm
2.7976×10^1 Gm	2.7976×10^{-2} Tm	
1.77×10^{12} m	1.77×10^9 km	1.77×10^6 Mm
1.77×10^3 Gm	1.77 Tm	
1.5×10^8 m	1.5×10^5 km	1.5×10^2 Mm
0.15 Gm	1.5×10^{-4} Tm	
4.23×10^{11} m	4.23×10^8 km	4.23×10^5 Mm
423 Gm	0.423 Tm	

79. **a.** 2.255×10^7 kg **b.** 2.255×10^4 Mg
c. 2.255×10^{13} mg **d.** 2.255×10^4 metric tons

81. 1.5×10^3 g

83. 5.0×10^1 min

85. 4.7×10^3 cm^3

87. **a.** 1.0×10^6 m^2 **b.** 1.0×10^{-6} m^3
c. 1.0×10^{-9} m^3

89. **a.** 6.2×10^5 pm^3 **b.** 6.2×10^{-4} nm^3 **c.** 6.2×10^{-1} Å^3

91. **a.** 2.15×10^{-4} km^2 **b.** 2.15×10^4 dm^2 **c.** 2.15×10^6 cm^2

93. 1.49×10^6 mi^2

95. 11.4 g/cm^3, lead

97. 1.26 g/cm^3

99. Yes, the density of the crown is 19.3 g/cm^3.

101. **a.** 4.30×10^2 g **b.** 3.12 L

103. **a.** 3.38×10^4 g (gold); 5.25×10^3 g (sand)

b. Yes, the mass of the bag of sand is different from the mass of the gold vase; thus, the weight-sensitive pedestal will sound the alarm.

105. 10.6 g/cm^3

107. $2.7 \times 10^3 \dfrac{\text{kg}}{\text{m}^3}$

109. 2.5×10^5 lbs

111. 1.19×10^5 kg

113. 18 km/L

115. 768 mi

117. Metal A is denser than metal B.

119. 2.26 g/cm^3

121. 108 km; 47.2 km

123. 9.1×10^{10} g/cm^3

CHAPTER 3

QUESTIONS

1. Matter is defined as anything that occupies space and possesses mass. It can be thought of as the physical material that makes up the universe.

3. The three states of matter are solid, liquid, and gas.

5. In a crystalline solid, the atoms/molecules are arranged in geometric patterns with repeating order. In amorphous solids, the atoms/molecules do not have long-range order.

7. The atoms/molecules in gases are not in contact with each other and are free to move relative to one another. The spacing between separate atoms/molecules is very far apart. A gas has no fixed volume or shape; rather, it assumes both the shape and the volume of the container it occupies.

9. A mixture is two or more pure substances combined in variable proportions.

11. Pure substances are those composed of only one type of atom or molecule.

13. A mixture is formed when two or more pure substances are mixed together; however, a new substance is not formed. A compound is formed when two or more elements are bonded together and form a new substance.

15. In a physical change, the composition of the substance does not change, even though its appearance might change. However, in a chemical change, the substance undergoes a change in its composition.

17. Energy is defined as the capacity to do work.

19. Kinetic energy is the energy associated with the motion of an object. Potential energy is the energy associated with the position or composition of an object.

21. Three common units for energy are joules, calories, and kilowatt-hour.

23. An endothermic reaction is one that absorbs energy from the surroundings. The products have more energy than the reactants in an endothermic reaction.

25. Heat is the transfer of thermal energy caused by a temperature difference, whereas temperature is a measure of the thermal energy of matter.

27. Heat capacity is the quantity of heat energy required to change the temperature of a given amount of the substance by 1 °C.

29. $°\text{F} = \frac{9}{5}(°\text{C}) + 32$

PROBLEMS

31. **a.** element **b.** element **c.** compound **d.** compound

33. **a.** homogeneous **b.** heterogeneous **c.** homogeneous **d.** homogeneous

35. **a.** pure substance-element
b. mixture-homogeneous
c. mixture-heterogeneous
d. mixture-heterogeneous

37. **a.** chemical **b.** physical **c.** physical **d.** chemical

39. physical–colorless; odorless; gas at room temperature; one liter has a mass of 1.260 g under standard conditions; mixes with acetone; chemical–flammable; polymerizes to form polyethylene

41. **a.** chemical **b.** physical **c.** chemical **d.** chemical

43. **a.** physical **b.** chemical

45. 2.10×10^2 kg

47. **a.** Yes **b.** No

49. 15.1 g of water

51. **a.** 2.46×10^3 J **b.** 4.16×10^{-3} Cal **c.** 32.0 Cal **d.** 2.35×10^5 J

53. **a.** 9.0×10^7 J **b.** 0.249 Cal **c.** 1.31×10^{-4} kWh **d.** 1.1×10^4 cal

55.

J	cal	Cal	kWh
225	53.8	5.38×10^{-2}	6.25×10^{-5}
3.44×10^6	8.21×10^5	8.21×10^2	9.54×10^{-1}
1.06×10^9	2.54×10^8	2.54×10^5	295
6.49×10^5	1.55×10^5	155	1.80×10^{-1}

57. 3.697×10^9 J

59. 8×10^2 kJ; 17 days

61. Exothermic.

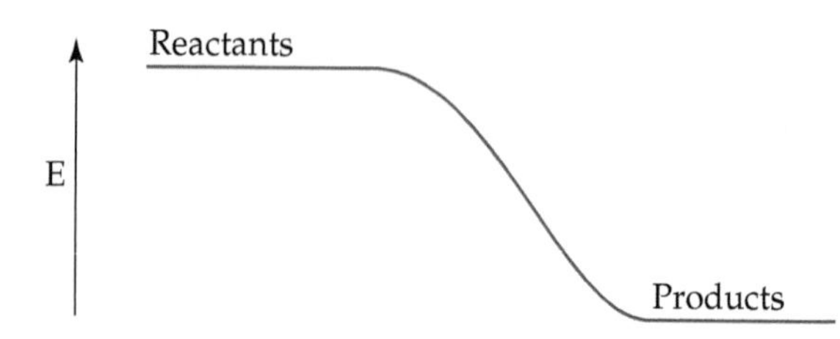

63. **a.** exothermic, $-\Delta H$ **b.** endothermic, $+\Delta H$
c. exothermic, $-\Delta H$

65. **a.** 1.00×10^2 °C **b.** -3.2×10^2 °F
c. 298 K **d.** 3.10×10^2 K

67. −62 °C, 211 K

69. 159 K, −173 °F

71. −75.5 °F

73.

0.0 K	−459.4 °F	−273.0 °C
301 K	82.5 °F	28.1 °C
282 K	47 °F	8.5 °C

75. 9.0×10^3 J

77. 8.7×10^5 J

79. 58 °C

81. 31 °C

83. 1.0×10^1 °C

85. 0.24 J/g°C; silver

87. 2.2 J/g°C

89. When warm drinks are placed into the ice, they release heat, which then melts the ice. The prechilled drinks, on the other hand, are already cold, so they do not release much heat.

91. 49 °C

93. 70.2 J

95. 1.7×10^4 kJ

97. 67 °C

99. 6.0 kWh

101. 22 g of fuel

103. 78 g

105. 27.2 °C

107. 5.96×10^5 kJ; \$25

109. −40°

111. **a.** pure substance **b.** pure substance
c. pure substance **d.** mixture

113. physical change

115. Small temperature changes in the ocean have a great impact on global weather because of the high heat capacity of water.

117. **a.** Sacramento is farther inland than San Francisco, so Sacramento is not as close to the ocean. The ocean water has a high heat capacity and will be able to keep San Francisco cooler in the hot days of summer. However, Sacramento is away from the ocean in a valley, so it will experience high temperatures in the summer.
b. San Francisco is located right next to the ocean, so the high heat capacity of the seawater keeps the temperature in the city from dropping. In the winter, the ocean actually helps to keep the city warmer, compared to an inland city like Sacramento.

CHAPTER 4

QUESTIONS

1. Democritus theorized that matter was ultimately composed of small, indivisible particles called atoms. Upon dividing matter, one would find tiny, indestructible atoms.

3. Rutherford's gold foil experiment involved sending positively charged alpha-particles through a thin sheet of gold foil and detecting if there was any deflection of the particles. He found that most passed straight through, yet some particles showed some deflection. This result contradicts the plum-pudding model of the atom because the plum-pudding model does not explain the deflection of the alpha-particles.

5.

Particle	Mass (kg)	Mass (amu)	Charge
Proton	1.67262×10^{-27}	1	+1
Neutron	1.67493×10^{-27}	1	0
Electron	0.00091×10^{-27}	0.00055	−1

7. Matter is usually charge-neutral due to protons and electrons having opposite charges. If matter were not charge neutral, many unnatural things would occur, such as objects repelling or attracting each other.

9. A chemical symbol is a unique one- or two-letter abbreviation for an element. It is listed below the atomic number for that element on the periodic table.

11. Mendeleev noticed that many patterns were evident when elements were organized by increasing mass; from this observation he formulated the periodic law. He also organized the elements based on this law and created the basis for the periodic table being used today.

13. The periodic table is organized by listing the elements in order of increasing atomic number.

15. Nonmetals have varied properties (solid, liquid, or gas at room temperature); however, as a whole they tend to be poor conductors of heat and electricity, and they all tend to gain electrons when they undergo chemical changes. They are located toward the upper right side of the periodic table.

17. Each column within the main group elements in the periodic table is labeled as a family or group of elements. The elements within a group usually have similar chemical properties.

19. An ion is an atom or group of atoms that has lost or gained electrons and has become charged.

21. **a.** ion charge = +1 **b.** ion charge = +2
c. ion charge = +3 **d.** ion charge = −2
e. ion charge = −1

23. The percent natural abundance of isotopes is the relative amount of each different isotope in a naturally occurring sample of a given element.

25. Isotopes are noted in this manner: ${}^{A}_{Z}X$. X represents the chemical symbol, A represents the mass number, and Z represents the atomic number.

PROBLEMS

27. **a.** Correct.
    b. False; different elements contain different types of atoms according to Dalton.
    c. False; one cannot have 1.5 hydrogen atoms; combinations must be in simple, whole-number ratios.
    d. Correct.
29. **a.** Correct.
    b. False; most of the volume of the atom is empty space occupied by tiny, negatively charged electrons.
    c. False, the number of negatively charged particles outside the nucleus equals the number of positively charged particles inside the nucleus.
    d. False, the majority of the mass of an atom is found in the nucleus.
31. Solid matter seems to have no empty space within it because electromagnetic forces hold the atoms in a tight arrangement and the variation in density is too small to perceive with our eyes.
33. a, b, d
35. b, d
37. approximately 1.8×10^3 electrons
39. 5.4×10^{-4} g
41. **a.** 87 **b.** 36
    c. 91 **d.** 32
    e. 13
43. **a.** 18 **b.** 50
    c. 54 **d.** 8
    e. 81
45. **a.** C, 6 **b.** N, 7
    c. Na, 11 **d.** K, 19
    e. Cu, 29
47. **a.** manganese, 25 **b.** silver, 47
    c. gold, 79 **d.** lead, 82
    e. sulfur, 16
49.

Element Name	Element Symbol	Atomic Number
Gold	Au	79
Tin	Sn	50
Arsenic	As	33
Copper	Cu	29
Iron	Fe	26
Mercury	Hg	80

51. **a.** metal **b.** metal
    c. nonmetal **d.** nonmetal
    e. metalloid
53. a, d, e
55. a, b
57. c, d
59. b, e
61. **a.** halogen **b.** noble gas
    c. halogen **d.** neither
    e. noble gas
63. **a.** 6A **b.** 3A
    c. 4A **d.** 4A
    e. 5A
65. b, oxygen; it is in the same group or family.
67. b, chlorine and fluorine; they are in the same family or group.
69.

Chemical Symbol	Group Number	Group Name	Metal or Nonmetal
K	1A	Alkali Metals	Metals
Br	7A	Halogens	Nonmetal
Sr	2A	Alkaline Earth	Metal
He	8A	Noble Gas	Nonmetal
Ar	8A	Noble Gas	Nonmetal

71. **a.** e^- **b.** O^{2-}
    c. $2e^-$ **d.** Cl^-
73. **a.** 2− **b.** 3+
    c. 4+ **d.** 1−
75. **a.** 11 protons, 10 electrons
    b. 56 protons, 54 electrons
    c. 8 protons, 10 electrons
    d. 27 protons, 24 electrons
77. **a.** False; Ti^{2+} has 22 protons and 20 electrons.
    b. True
    c. False; Mg^{2+} has 12 protons and 10 electrons
    d. True
79. **a.** Rb^+ **b.** K^+
    c. Al^{3+} **d.** O^{2-}
81. **a.** 3 electrons lost **b.** 1 electron lost
    c. 1 electron gained **d.** 2 electrons gained
83.

Symbol	Ion Commonly Formed	Number of Electrons in Ion	Number of Protons in Ion
Te	Te^{2-}	54	52
In	In^{3+}	46	49
Sr	Sr^{2+}	36	38
Mg	Mg^{2+}	10	12
Cl	Cl^-	18	17

85. **a.** Z = 1, A = 3 **b.** Z = 24, A = 52
    c. Z = 20, A = 42 **d.** Z = 73, A = 182
87. **a.** ${}^{16}_{8}O$ **b.** ${}^{19}_{9}F$
    c. ${}^{23}_{11}Na$ **d.** ${}^{27}_{13}Al$
89. **a.** ${}^{60}_{27}Co$ **b.** ${}^{22}_{10}Ne$
    c. ${}^{131}_{53}I$ **d.** ${}^{244}_{94}Pu$

91. **a.** 11 protons, 12 neutrons
b. 88 protons, 178 neutrons
c. 82 protons, 126 neutrons
d. 7 protons, 7 neutrons

93. 6 protons, 8 neutrons, ${}^{14}_{6}C$

95. 85.47 amu

97. **a.** 49.31% **b.** 78.91 amu

99. 121.8 amu, Sb

101. 7.8×10^{17} electrons

103. 4.2×10^{-45} m^3; 6.2×10^{-31} m^3; 6.7×10^{-13} %

105.

Number Symbol	Number of Protons	Number of Neutrons	A (Mass Number)	Natural Abundance
Sr-84 or ${}^{84}_{38}Sr$	38	46	84	0.56%
Sr-86 or ${}^{86}_{38}Sr$	38	48	86	9.86%
Sr-87 or ${}^{87}_{38}Sr$	38	49	87	7.00%
Sr-88 or ${}^{88}_{38}Sr$	38	50	88	82.58%

Atomic mass of Sr = 87.62 amu

107.

Symbol	Z	A	Number of Protons	Number of Electrons	Number of Neutrons	Charge
Zn^{+}	30	64	30	29	34	1+
Mn^{3+}	25	55	25	22	30	3+
P	15	31	15	15	16	0
O^{2-}	8	16	8	10	8	2−
S^{2-}	16	34	16	18	18	2−

109. 153 amu, 52.2%

111. The atomic theory and nuclear model of the atom are both theories because they attempt to provide a broader understanding and model behavior of chemical systems.

113. Atomic mass is measured as the mean value of masses of all isotopes in a sample. In the case of fluorine, only the 19.00 amu isotope is naturally occurring. In the case of chlorine, about 76% of naturally occurring atoms are 35 amu, and 24% are 37 amu.

115. 69.3% Cu-63, 30.7% Cu-65

117. **a.** Nt − 304 = 72%; Nt − 305 = 4%; Nt − 306 = 24%

b.

120
Nt
304.5

CHAPTER 5

QUESTIONS

1. Yes; when elements combine with other elements, a compound is created. Each compound is unique and contains properties different from those of the elements that compose it.

3. The law of constant composition states that all samples of a given compound have the same proportions of their constituent elements. Joseph Proust formulated this law.

5. The more metallic element is generally listed first in a chemical formula.

7. The empirical formula gives the relative number of atoms of each element in a compound. The molecular formula gives the actual number of atoms of each element in a molecule of the compound.

9. An atomic element is one that exists in nature with a single atom as the basic unit. A molecular element is one that exists as a diatomic molecule as the basic unit. Molecular elements include H_2, N_2, O_2, F_2, Cl_2, Br_2, and I_2.

11. The systematic name can be directly derived by looking at the compound's formula. The common name for a compound acts like a nickname and can only be learned through familiarity.

13. The block that contains the elements for Type II compounds is known as the transition metals.

15. The basic form for the names of Type II ionic compounds is to have the name of the metal cation first, followed by the charge of the metal cation (in parentheses, using Roman numerals), and finally the base name of the nonmetal anion with *-ide* attached to the end.

17. For compounds containing a polyatomic anion, the name of the cation is first, followed by the name for the polyatomic anion. Also, if the compound contains both a polyatomic cation and a polyatomic anion, one would just use the names of both polyatomic ions.

19. The form for naming molecular compounds is to have the first element preceded by a prefix to indicate the number of atoms present. This is then followed by the second element with its corresponding prefix and *-ide* placed on the end of the second element.

21. To correctly name a binary acid, one must begin the first word with *hydro-*, which is followed by the base name of the nonmetal plus *-ic* added on the end. Finally, the word *acid* follows the first word.

23. To name an acid with oxyanions ending with *-ite*, one must take the base name of the oxyanion and attach *-ous* to it; the word *acid* follows this.

PROBLEMS

25. Yes; the ratios of sodium to chlorine in both samples were equal.

27. 2.06×10^3 g

29.

	Mass N_2O	Mass N	Mass O
Sample A	2.85	1.82	1.03
Sample B	4.55	2.91	1.64
Sample C	3.74	2.39	1.35
Sample D	1.74	1.11	0.63

31. NI_3

33. **a.** Fe_3O_4 **b.** PCl_3
c. PCl_5 **d.** Ag_2O

35. **a.** 4 **b.** 4
c. 6 **d.** 4

37. **a.** magnesium, 1; chlorine, 2
b. sodium, 1; nitrogen, 1; oxygen, 3
c. calcium, 1; nitrogen, 2; oxygen, 4
d. strontium, 1; oxygen, 2; hydrogen, 2

39.

Formula	Number of $C_2H_3O_2$	Number of C Atoms	Number of H Atoms	Number of O Atoms	Number of Metal Atoms
$Mg(C_2H_3O_2)_2$	2	4	6	4	1
$NaC_2H_3O_2$	1	2	3	2	1
$Cr_2(C_2H_3O_2)_4$	4	8	12	8	2

41. **a.** CH_3 **b.** NO_2
c. C_2H_3O **d.** NH_3

43. **a.** molecular **b.** atomic
c. atomic **d.** molecular

45. **a.** molecular **b.** ionic
c. ionic **d.** molecular

47. helium ⟶ single atoms
CCl_4 ⟶ molecules
K_2SO_4 ⟶ formula units
bromine ⟶ diatomic molecules

49. **a.** formula units **b.** single atoms
c. molecules **d.** molecules

51. **a.** ionic; forms only one type of ion
b. molecular
c. molecular
d. ionic; forms only one type of ion

53. **a.** Na_2S **b.** SrO
c. Al_2S_3 **d.** $MgCl_2$

55. **a.** $KC_2H_3O_2$ **b.** K_2CrO_4
c. K_3PO_4 **d.** KCN

57. **a.** Li_3N, Li_2O, LiF **b.** Ba_3N_2, BaO, BaF_2
c. AlN, Al_2O_3, AlF_3

59. **a.** cesium chloride **b.** strontium bromide
c. potassium oxide **d.** lithium fluoride

61. **a.** chromium(II) chloride **b.** chromium(III) chloride
c. tin(IV) oxide **d.** lead(II) iodide

63. **a.** forms more than one type of ion, chromium(III) oxide
b. forms only one type of ion, sodium iodide
c. forms only one type of ion, calcium bromide
d. forms more than one type of ion, tin(II) oxide

65. **a.** barium nitrate **b.** lead(II) acetate
c. ammonium iodide **d.** potassium chlorate
e. cobalt(II) sulfate **f.** sodium perchlorate

67. **a.** hypobromite ion **b.** bromite ion
c. bromate ion **d.** perbromate ion

69. **a.** $CuBr_2$ **b.** $AgNO_3$
c. KOH **d.** Na_2SO_4
e. $KHSO_4$ **f.** $NaHCO_3$

71. **a.** sulfur dioxide
b. nitrogen triiodide
c. bromine pentafluoride
d. nitrogen monoxide
e. tetranitrogen tetraselenide

73. **a.** CO **b.** S_2F_4
c. Cl_2O **d.** PF_5
e. BBr_3 **f.** P_2S_5

75. **a.** PBr_5 phosphorus pentabromide
b. P_2O_3 diphosphorus trioxide
c. SF_4 sulfur tetraflouride
d. correct

77. **a.** oxyacid, nitrous acid, nitrite
b. binary acid, hydroiodic acid
c. oxyacid, sulfuric acid, sulfate
d. oxyacid, nitric acid, nitrate

79. **a.** hypochlorous acid **b.** chlorous acid
c. chloric acid **d.** perchloric acid

81. **a.** H_3PO_4 **b.** HBr
c. H_2SO_3

83. **a.** 63.02 amu **b.** 199.88 amu
c. 153.81 amu **d.** 211.64 amu

85. PBr_3, Ag_2O, PtO_2, $Al(NO_3)_3$

87. **a.** CH_4 **b.** SO_3
c. NO_2

89. **a.** 12 **b.** 4
c. 12 **d.** 7

91. **a.** 8 **b.** 12
c. 12

93.

Formula	Type	Name
N_2H_4	molecular	dinitrogen tetrahydride
KCl	ionic	potassium chloride
H_2CrO_4	acid	chromic acid
$Co(CN)_3$	ionic	cobalt(III) cyanide

95. **a.** calcium nitrite
b. potassium oxide
c. phosphorus trichloride
d. correct
e. potassium iodite

97. **a.** $Sn(SO_4)_2$ 310.9 amu **b.** HNO_2 47.02 amu
c. $NaHCO_3$ 84.01 amu **d.** PF_5 125.97 amu

99. **a.** platinum(IV) oxide 227.08 amu
b. dinitrogen pentoxide 108.02 amu
c. aluminum chlorate 277.33 amu
d. phosphorus pentabromide 430.47 amu

101. C_2H_4

103. 10 different isotopes can exist. 151.88 amu, 152.88 amu, 153.88 amu, 154.88 amu, 155.88 amu, 156.88 amu, 157.88 amu, 158.88 amu, 159.88 amu, and 160.88 amu.

105. **a.** molecular element **b.** atomic element
c. ionic compound **d.** molecular compound

107. **a.** NaOCl; NaOH **b.** $Al(OH)_3$; $Mg(OH)_2$
c. $CaCO_3$
d. $NaHCO_3$, $Ca_3(PO_4)_2$, $NaAl(SO_4)_2$

CHAPTER 6

QUESTIONS

1. Chemical composition lets us determine how much of a particular element is contained within a particular compound.
3. There are 6.022×10^{23} atoms in 1 mole of atoms.
5. One mole of any element has a mass equal to its atomic mass in grams.
7. **a.** 30.97 g **b.** 195.08 g **c.** 12.01 g **d.** 52.00 g
9. Each element has a different atomic mass number. So, the subscripts that represent mole ratios cannot be used to represent the ratios of grams of a compound. The grams per mole of one element always differ from the grams per mole of a different element.
11. **a.** 11.19 g H≡100 g H_2O **b.** 53.29 g O≡100 g fructose **c.** 84.12 g C≡100 g octane **d.** 52.14 g C≡100 g ethanol
13. The empirical formula gives the smallest whole-number ratio of each type of atom. The molecular formula gives the specific number of each type of atom in the molecule. The molecular formula is always a multiple of the empirical formula.
15. The empirical formula mass of a compound is the sum of the masses of all the atoms in the empirical formula.

PROBLEMS

17. 3.5×10^{24} atoms
19. **a.** 2.0×10^{24} atoms **b.** 5.8×10^{21} atoms. **c.** 1.38×10^{25} atoms **d.** 1.29×10^{23} atoms
21.

Element	Moles	Number of Atoms
Ne	0.552	3.32×10^{23}
Ar	5.40	3.25×10^{24}
Xe	1.78	1.07×10^{24}
He	1.79×10^{-4}	1.08×10^{20}

23. **a.** 72.7 dozen **b.** 6.06 gross **c.** 1.74 reams **d.** 1.45×10^{-21} moles
25. 0.321 mol
27. 28.6 g
29. **a.** 2.05×10^{-2} mol **b.** 0.623 mol **c.** 0.401 mol **d.** 3.21×10^{-3} mol
31.

Element	Moles	Mass
Ne	1.11	22.5 g
Ar	0.117	4.67 g
Xe	7.62	1.00 kg
He	1.44×10^{-4}	5.76×10^{-4} g

33. 8.07×10^{18} atoms
35. 8.44×10^{22} atoms
37. **a.** 1.16×10^{23} atoms **b.** 2.81×10^{23} atoms **c.** 2.46×10^{22} atoms **d.** 7.43×10^{23} atoms
39. 1.9×10^{21} atoms
41. 1.61×10^{25} atoms
43.

Element	Mass	Moles	Number of Atoms
Na	38.5 mg	1.67×10^{-3}	1.01×10^{21}
C	13.5 g	1.12	6.74×10^{23}
V	1.81×10^{-20} g	3.55×10^{-22}	214
Hg	1.44 kg	7.18	4.32×10^{24}

45. b
47. **a.** 0.654 mol **b.** 1.22 mol **c.** 96.6 mol **d.** 1.76×10^{-5} mol
49.

Compound	Mass	Moles	Molecules
H_2O	112 kg	6.22×10^{3}	3.74×10^{27}
N_2O	6.33 g	0.144	8.66×10^{22}
SO_2	156	2.44	1.47×10^{24}
CH_2Cl_2	5.46	0.0643	3.87×10^{22}

51. 6.20×10^{21} molecules
53. **a.** 1.2×10^{23} molecules **b.** 1.21×10^{24} molecules **c.** 3.5×10^{23} molecules **d.** 6.4×10^{22} molecules
55. 0.10 mg
57. $\$6.022 \times 10^{21}$ total. $\$9.1 \times 10^{11}$ per person. Each person would be a billionaire.
59. 5.4 mol Cl
61. d, 3 mol O
63. **a.** 2.5 mol C **b.** 0.230 mol C **c.** 22.7 mol C **d.** 201 mol C
65. **a.** 2 moles H per mole of molecules; 8 H atoms present **b.** 4 moles H per mole of molecules; 20 H atoms present **c.** 3 moles H per mole of molecules; 9 H atoms present
67. **a.** 22.3 g **b.** 29.4 g **c.** 21.6 g **d.** 12.9 g
69. **a.** 1.4×10^{3} kg **b.** 1.4×10^{3} kg **c.** 2.1×10^{3} kg
71. 84.8% Sr
73. 36.1% Ca; 63.9% Cl
75. 10.7 g
77. 6.6 mg
79. **a.** 63.65% **b.** 46.68% **c.** 30.45% **d.** 25.94%
81. **a.** 39.99% C; 6.73% H; 53.28% O **b.** 26.09% C; 4.39% H; 69.52% O **c.** 60.93% C; 15.37% H; 23.69% N **d.** 54.48% C; 13.74% H; 31.78% N
83. Fe_3O_4, 72.36% Fe; Fe_2O_3, 69.94% Fe; $FeCO_3$, 48.20% Fe; magnetite
85. NO_2
87. **a.** NiI_2 **b.** $SeBr_4$ **c.** $BeSO_4$
89. C_2H_6N

91. a. C_3H_6O b. $C_5H_{10}O_2$
c. $C_9H_{10}O_2$

93. P_2O_3

95. NCl_3

97. C_4H_8

99. a. C_6Cl_6 b. C_2HCl_3
c. $C_6H_3Cl_3$

101. 2.43×10^{23} atoms

103. 2×10^{21} molecules

105.

Substance	Mass	Moles	Number of Particles
Ar	0.018 g	4.5×10^{-4}	2.7×10^{20}
NO_2	8.33×10^{-3} g	1.81×10^{-4}	1.09×10^{20}
K	22.4 mg	5.73×10^{-4}	3.45×10^{20}
C_8H_{18}	3.76 kg	32.9	1.98×10^{25}

107. a. CuI_2: 20.03% Cu; 79.97% I
b. $NaNO_3$: 27.05% Na; 16.48% N; 56.47% O
c. $PbSO_4$:68.32% Pb; 10.57% S; 21.10% O
d. CaF_2: 51.33% Ca; 48.67% F

109. 1.8×10^3 kg rock

111. 59 kg Cl

113. 1.1×10^2 g H

115.

Formula	Molar Mass	%C (by mass)	%H (by mass)
C_2H_4	28.06	85.60%	14.40%
C_4H_{10}	58.12	82.66%	17.34%
C_4H_8	56.12	85.60%	14.40%
C_3H_8	44.09	81.71%	18.29%

117. $C_4H_6O_2$

119. $C_{10}H_{14}N_2$

121. 70.4% KBr, 29.6% KI

123. 29.6 g SO_2

125. 2.66 kg Fe

127. a. 1×10^{57} atoms per star
b. 1×10^{68} atoms per galaxy
c. 1×10^{79} atoms in the universe

129. $C_{16}H_{10}$

CHAPTER 7

QUESTIONS

1. A chemical reaction is the change of one or more substances into different substances, for example, burning wood, rusting iron, and protein synthesis.

3. The main evidence of a chemical reaction includes a color change, the formation of a solid, the formation of a gas, the emission of light, and the emission or absorption of heat.

5. a. gas b. liquid
c. solid d. aqueous

7. a. reactants: 4 Ag, 2 O, 1 C products: 4 Ag, 2 O, 1 C balanced: yes
b. reactants: 1 Pb, 2 N, 6 O, 2 Na, 2 Cl products: 1 Pb, 2 N, 6 O, 2 Na, 2 Cl balanced: yes
c. reactants: 3 C, 8 H, 2 O products: 3 C, 8 H, 10 O balanced: no

9. If a compound dissolves in water, then it is soluble. If it does not dissolve in water, it is insoluble.

11. When ionic compounds containing polyatomic ions dissolve in water, the polyatomic ions usually dissolve as intact units.

13. The solubility rules are a set of empirical rules for ionic compounds that were deduced from observations on many compounds. The rules help us determine whether particular compounds will be soluble or insoluble.

15. The precipitate will always be insoluble; it is the solid that forms upon mixing two aqueous solutions.

17. Acid–base reactions involve an acid and a base reacting to form water and an ionic compound. An example is the reaction between hydrobromic acid and sodium hydroxide:
$HBr + NaOH \longrightarrow H_2O + NaBr$

19. Gas evolution reactions are reactions that evolve a gas. An example is the reaction between hydrochloric acid and sodium bicarbonate:
$HCl + NaHCO_3 \longrightarrow H_2O + CO_2 + NaCl$

21. Combustion reactions are a type of redox reaction and are characterized by the exothermic reaction of a substance with O_2. An example is the reaction between methane and oxygen: $CH_4 + 2\,O_2 \longrightarrow CO_2 + 2\,H_2O$

23. A synthesis reaction combines simpler substances to form more complex substances. An example is the reaction between elemental potassium and chloride: $2\,K + Cl_2 \longrightarrow 2\,KCl$. A decomposition decomposes a more complex substance into simpler substances. An example is the decomposition of water: $2\,H_2O \longrightarrow 2\,H_2 + O_2$

PROBLEMS

25. a. Yes; there is a color change showing a chemical reaction
b. No; the state of the compound changes, but no chemical reaction takes place.
c. Yes; there is a formation of a solid in a previously clear solution.
d. Yes; there is a formation of a gas when the yeast was added to the solution.

27. Yes; a chemical reaction has occurred, for the presence of the bubbles is evidence for the formation of a gas.

29. Yes; a chemical reaction has occurred. We know this due to the color change of the hair.

31. Placing a subscript 2 after H_2O would change the compound from water to hydrogen peroxide (H_2O_2). To balance chemical reactions, one must add coefficients, not subscripts.
$2\,H_2O(l) \longrightarrow 2\,H_2(g) + O_2(g)$

33. a. $PbS + 2HCl \longrightarrow PbCl_2 + H_2S$
b. $CO + 3H_2 \longrightarrow CH_4 + H_2O$
c. $Fe_2O_3 + 3H_2 \longrightarrow 2Fe + 3H_2O$
d. $4NH_3 + 5O_2 \longrightarrow 4NO + 6H_2O$

35. a. $Mg(s) + 2\,CuNO_3(aq) \longrightarrow 2\,Cu(s) + Mg(NO_3)_2(aq)$
b. $2\,N_2O_5(g) \longrightarrow 4\,NO_2(g) + O_2(g)$
c. $Ca(s) + 2\,HNO_3(aq) \longrightarrow H_2(g) + Ca(NO_3)_2(aq)$
d. $2\,CH_3OH(l) + 3\,O_2(g) \longrightarrow 2\,CO_2(g) + 4\,H_2O(g)$

37. $2\,H_2(g) + O_2(g) \longrightarrow 2\,H_2O(l)$;
$Cl(g) + O_3(g) \longrightarrow ClO(g) + O_2(g)$

39. $2\,Na(s) + 2\,H_2O(l) \longrightarrow H_2(g) + 2\,NaOH(aq)$

41. $2\,SO_2(g) + O_2(g) + 2\,H_2O(l) \longrightarrow 2\,H_2SO_4(aq)$

43. $V_2O_5(s) + 2\,H_2(g) \longrightarrow V_2O_3(s) + 2\,H_2O(l)$

45. $C_{12}H_{22}O_{11}(aq) + H_2O(l) \longrightarrow 4\,CO_2(g) + 4\,C_2H_5OH(aq)$

47. a. $Na_2S(aq) + Cu(NO_3)_2(aq) \longrightarrow 2\,NaNO_3(aq) + CuS(s)$
b. $4\,HCl(aq) + O_2(g) \longrightarrow 2\,H_2O(l) + 2\,Cl_2(g)$
c. $2\,H_2(g) + O_2(g) \longrightarrow 2\,H_2O(l)$
d. $FeS(s) + 2\,HCl(aq) \longrightarrow FeCl_2(aq) + H_2S(g)$

49. a. $BaO_2(s) + H_2SO_4(aq) \longrightarrow BaSO_4(s) + H_2O_2(aq)$
b. $2\,Co(NO_3)_3(aq) + 3\,(NH_4)_2S(aq) \longrightarrow Co_2S_3(s) + 6\,NH_4NO_3(aq)$
c. $Li_2O(s) + H_2O(l) \longrightarrow 2\,LiOH(aq)$
d. $Hg_2(C_2H_3O_2)_2(aq) + 2\,KCl(aq) \longrightarrow Hg_2Cl_2(s) + 2\,KC_2H_3O_2(aq)$

51. a. $2\,Rb(s) + 2\,H_2O(l) \longrightarrow 2\,RbOH(aq) + H_2(g)$
b. Equation is balanced
c. $2\,NiS(s) + 3\,O_2(g) \longrightarrow 2\,NiO(s) + 2\,SO_2(g)$
d. $3\,PbO(s) + 2\,NH_3(g) \longrightarrow 3\,Pb(s) + N_2(g) + 3\,H_2O(l)$

53. $C_6H_{12}O_6(aq) + 6\,O_2(g) \longrightarrow 6\,CO_2(g) + 6\,H_2O(l)$

55. $2\,NO(g) + 2\,CO(g) \longrightarrow N_2(g) + 2\,CO_2(g)$

57. a. soluble; Na^+, $C_2H_3O_2^-$
b. soluble; Sn^{2+}, NO_3^-
c. insoluble
d. soluble; Na^+, PO_4^{3-}

59. $AgCl$; $BaSO_4$; $CuCO_3$; Fe_2S_3

61.

Soluble	Insoluble
K_2S	Hg_2I_2
BaS	$Cu_3(PO_4)_2$
NH_4Cl	MgS
Na_2CO_3	$CaSO_4$
K_2SO_4	$PbSO_4$
SrS	$PbCl_2$
Li_2S	Hg_2Cl_2

63. a. NO REACTION
b. $K_2SO_4(aq) + BaBr_2(aq) \longrightarrow BaSO_4(s) + 2\,KBr(aq)$
c. $2\,NaCl(aq) + Hg_2(C_2H_3O_2)_2(aq) \longrightarrow Hg_2Cl_2(s) + 2\,NaC_2H_3O_2(aq)$
d. NO REACTION

65. a. $Na_2CO_3(aq) + Pb(NO_3)_2(aq) \longrightarrow PbCO_3(s) + 2\,NaNO_3(aq)$
b. $K_2SO_4(aq) + Pb(CH_3CO_2)_2(aq) \longrightarrow PbSO_4(s) + 2\,KC_2H_3O_2$
c. $Cu(NO_3)_2(aq) + BaS(aq) \longrightarrow CuS(s) + Ba(NO_3)_2(aq)$
d. NO REACTION

67. a. correct
b. NO REACTION
c. correct
d. $Pb(NO_3)_2(aq) + 2\,LiCl(aq) \longrightarrow PbCl_2(s) + 2\,LiNO_3(aq)$

69. K^+, NO_3^-

71. a. $Ag^+(aq) + NO_3^-(aq) + K^+(aq) + Cl^-(aq) \longrightarrow AgCl(s) + K^+(aq) + NO_3^-(aq)$
$Ag^+(aq) + Cl^-(aq) \longrightarrow AgCl(s)$
b. $Ca^{2+}(aq) + S^{2-}(aq) + Cu^{2+}(aq) + 2\,Cl^-(aq) \longrightarrow CuS(s) + Ca^{2+}(aq) + 2\,Cl^-(aq)$
$Cu^{2+}(aq) + S^{2-}(aq) \longrightarrow CuS(s)$
c. $Na^+(aq) + OH^-(aq) + H^+(aq) + NO_3^-(aq) \longrightarrow H_2O(l) + Na^+(aq) + NO_3^-(aq)$
$H^+(aq) + OH^-(aq) \longrightarrow H_2O(l)$
d. $6\,K^+(aq) + 2\,PO_4^{3-}(aq) + 3\,Ni^{2+}(aq) + 6\,Cl^-(aq) \longrightarrow Ni_3(PO_4)_2(s) + 6\,K^+(aq) + 6\,Cl^-(aq)$
$3\,Ni^{2+}(aq) + 2\,PO_4^{3-}(aq) \longrightarrow Ni_3(PO_4)_2(s)$

73. $Hg_2^{2+}(aq) + 2\,NO_3^-(aq) + 2\,Na^+(aq) + 2\,Cl^-(aq) \longrightarrow Hg_2Cl_2(s) + 2\,Na^+(aq) + 2\,NO_3^-(aq)$
$Hg_2^{2+}(aq) + 2\,Cl^-(aq) \longrightarrow Hg_2Cl_2(s)$

75. a. $2\,Na^+(aq) + CO_3^{2-}(aq) + Pb^{2+}(aq) + 2\,NO_3^-(aq) \longrightarrow PbCO_3(s) + 2\,Na^+(aq) + 2\,NO_3^-(aq)$
$Pb^{2+}(aq) + CO_3^{2-}(aq) \longrightarrow PbCO_3(s)$
b. $2\,K^+(aq) + SO_4^{2-}(aq) + Pb^{2+}(aq) + 2\,CH_3CO_2^-(aq) \longrightarrow PbSO_4(s) + 2\,K^+(aq) + 2\,CH_3CO_2^-(aq)$
$Pb^{2+}(aq) + SO_4^{2-}(aq) \longrightarrow PbSO_4(s)$
c. $Cu^{2+}(aq) + 2\,NO_3^-(aq) + Ba^{2+}(aq) + S^{2-}(aq) \longrightarrow CuS(s) + Ba^{2+}(aq) + 2\,NO_3^-(aq)$
$Cu^{2+}(aq) + S^{2-}(aq) \longrightarrow CuS(s)$
d. NO REACTION

77. $HCl(aq) + KOH(aq) \longrightarrow H_2O(l) + KCl(aq)$
$H^+(aq) + OH^-(aq) \longrightarrow H_2O(l)$

79. a. $2\,HCl(aq) + Ba(OH)_2(aq) \longrightarrow 2\,H_2O(l) + BaCl_2(aq)$
b. $H_2SO_4(aq) + 2\,KOH(aq) \longrightarrow 2\,H_2O(l) + K_2SO_4(aq)$
c. $HClO_4(aq) + NaOH(aq) \longrightarrow H_2O(l) + NaClO_4(aq)$

81. a. $HBr(aq) + NaHCO_3(aq) \longrightarrow H_2O(l) + CO_2(g) + NaBr(aq)$
b. $NH_4I(aq) + KOH(aq) \longrightarrow H_2O(l) + NH_3(g) + KI(aq)$
c. $2\,HNO_3(aq) + K_2SO_3(aq) \longrightarrow H_2O(l) + SO_2(g) + 2\,KNO_3(aq)$
d. $2\,HI(aq) + Li_2S(aq) \longrightarrow H_2S(g) + 2\,LiI(aq)$

83. b and d are redox reactions; a and c are not.

85. a. $2\,C_2H_6(g) + 7\,O_2(g) \longrightarrow 4\,CO_2(g) + 6\,H_2O(g)$
b. $2\,Ca(s) + O_2(g) \longrightarrow 2\,CaO(s)$
c. $2\,C_3H_8O(l) + 9\,O_2(g) \longrightarrow 6\,CO_2(g) + 8\,H_2O(g)$
d. $2\,C_4H_{10}S(l) + 15\,O_2(g) \longrightarrow 8\,CO_2(g) + 10\,H_2O(g) + 2\,SO_2(g)$

87. a. $2\ Ag(s) + Br_2(g) \longrightarrow 2\ AgBr(s)$
b. $2\ K(s) + Br_2(g) \longrightarrow 2\ KBr(s)$
c. $2\ Al(s) + 3\ Br_2(g) \longrightarrow 2\ AlBr_3(s)$
d. $Ca(s) + Br_2(g) \longrightarrow CaBr_2(s)$

89. a. double displacement
b. synthesis or combination
c. single displacement
d. decomposition

91. a. synthesis
b. decomposition
c. synthesis

93. a. $2\ Na^+(aq) + 2\ I^-(aq) + Hg_2^+(aq) + 2\ NO_3^-(aq) \longrightarrow Hg_2I_2(s) + 2\ Na^+(aq) + 2\ NO_3^-(aq)$
b. $2\ H^+(aq) + 2\ ClO_4^-(aq) + Ba^{2+}(aq) + 2\ OH^-(aq) \longrightarrow 2\ H_2O(l) + Ba^{2+}(aq) + 2\ ClO_4^-(aq)$

$H^+(aq) + OH^-(aq) \longrightarrow H_2O(s)$

c. NO REACTION
d. $2\ H^+(aq) + 2\ Cl^-(aq) + 2\ Li^+(aq) + CO_3^{2-}(aq) \longrightarrow H_2O(l) + CO_2(g) + 2\ Li^+(aq) + 2\ Cl^-(aq)$

$2\ H^+(aq) + CO_3^{2-}(aq) \longrightarrow H_2O(l) + CO_2(g)$

95. a. NO REACTION
b. NO REACTION
c. $K^+(aq) + HSO_3^-(aq) + H^+(aq) + NO_3^-(aq) \longrightarrow H_2O(l) + SO_2(g) + K^+(aq) + NO_3^-(aq)$

$H^+(aq) + HSO_3^-(aq) \longrightarrow H_2O(l) + SO_2(g)$

d. $Mn^{3+}(aq) + 3\ Cl^-(aq) + 3\ K^+(aq) + PO_4^{3-}(aq) \longrightarrow MnPO_4(s) + 3\ K^+(aq) + 3\ Cl^-(aq)$

$Mn^{3+}(aq) + PO_4^{3-}(aq) \longrightarrow MnPO_4(s)$

97. a. acid–base; $KOH(aq) + HC_2H_3O_2(aq) \longrightarrow H_2O(l) + KC_2H_3O_2(aq)$
b. gas evolution; $2\ HBr(aq) + K_2CO_3(aq) \longrightarrow H_2O(l) + CO_2(g) + 2\ KBr(aq)$
c. synthesis; $2\ H_2(g) + O_2(g) \longrightarrow 2\ H_2O(l)$
d. precipitation; $2\ NH_4Cl(aq) + Pb(NO_3)_2(aq) \longrightarrow PbCl_2(s) + 2\ NH_4NO_3(aq)$

99. a. oxidation–reduction; single displacement
b. gas evolution; acid–base
c. gas evolution; double displacement
d. precipitation; double displacement

101. $3\ CaCl_2(aq) + 2\ Na_3PO_4(aq) \longrightarrow Ca_3(PO_4)_2(s) + 6\ NaCl(aq)$

$3\ Ca^{2+}(aq) + 6\ Cl^-(aq) + 6\ Na^+(aq) + 2\ PO_4^{3-}(aq) \longrightarrow Ca_3(PO_4)_2(s) + 6\ Na^+(aq) + 6\ Cl^-(aq)$

$3\ Ca^{2+}(aq) + 2\ PO_4^{3-}(aq) \longrightarrow Ca_3(PO_4)_2(s)$

$3\ Mg(NO_3)_2(aq) + 2\ Na_3PO_4(aq) \longrightarrow Mg_3(PO_4)_2(s) + 6\ NaNO_3(aq)$

$3\ Mg^{2+}(aq) + 6\ NO_3^-(aq) + 6\ Na^+(aq) + 2\ PO_4^{3-}(aq) \longrightarrow Mg_3(PO_4)_2(s) + 6\ Na^+(aq) + 6\ NO_3^-(aq)$

$3\ Mg^{2+}(aq) + 2\ PO_4^{3-}(aq) \longrightarrow Mg_3(PO_4)_2(s)$

103. *Correct answers may vary; representative correct answers are:
a. addition of a solution containing SO_4^{2-}; $Pb^{2+}(aq) + SO_4^{2-}(aq) \longrightarrow PbSO_4(s)$
b. addition of a solution containing SO_4^{2-}; $Ca^{2+}(aq) + SO_4^{2-}(aq) \longrightarrow CaSO_4(s)$
c. addition of a solution containing SO_4^{2-}; $Ba^{2+}(aq) + SO_4^{2-}(aq) \longrightarrow BaSO_4(s)$
d. addition of a solution containing Cl^-; $Hg_2^{2+}(aq) + 2\ Cl^-(aq) \longrightarrow Hg_2Cl_2(s)$

105. $Ca^{2+}$and Cu^{2+} were present in the original solution.
1st: $Ca^{2+}(aq) + SO_4^{2-}(aq) \longrightarrow CaSO_4(s)$
2nd: $Cu^{2+}(aq) + CO_3^{2-}(aq) \longrightarrow CuCO_3(s)$

107. 0.168 mol Ca; 6.73 g Ca

109. 0.00128 mol NaCl, 0.0750 g NaCl

111. a. chemical
b. physical

CHAPTER 8

QUESTIONS

1. Reaction stoichiometry is very important to chemistry. It gives us a numerical relationship between the reactants and products that allows chemists to plan and carry out chemical reactions to obtain products in the desired quantities.

   For example, how much CO_2 is produced when a given amount of C_8H_{10} is burned?

   How much $H_2(g)$ is produced when a given amount of water decomposes?

3. 1 mol $Cl_2 \equiv 2$ mol NaCl

5. mass A $\longrightarrow$ moles A $\longrightarrow$ moles B $\longrightarrow$ mass B (A = reactant, B = product)

7. The limiting reactant is the reactant that limits the amount of product in a chemical reaction.

9. The actual yield is the amount of product actually produced by a chemical reaction. The percent yield is the percentage of the theoretical yield that was actually attained.

11. d

13. The enthalpy of reaction is the total amount of heat generated or absorbed by a particular chemical reaction. The quantity is important because it quantifies the change in heat for the chemical reaction. It is useful for determining the necessary starting conditions and predicting the outcome of various reactions.

PROBLEMS

15. a. 2 mol C
b. 1 mol C
c. 3 mol C
d. 1.5 mol C

17. a. 2.6 mol NO_2
b. 11.6 mol NO_2
c. 8.90×10^3 mol NO_2
d. 2.012×10^{-3} mol NO_2

19. c

21. a. 3.50 mol HCl
b. 3.50 mol H_2O
c. 0.875 mol Na_2O_2
d. 1.17 mol SO_3

23. a. 2.4 mol $PbO(s)$, 2.4 mol $SO_2(g)$
b. 1.6 mol $PbO(s)$, 1.6 mol $SO_2(g)$
c. 5.3 mol $PbO(s)$, 5.3 mol $SO_2(g)$
d. 3.5 mol $PbO(s)$, 3.5 mol $SO_2(g)$

25.

mol N_2H_4	mol N_2O_4	mol N_2	mol H_2O
4	2	6	8
6	3	9	12
4	2	6	8
11	5.5	16.5	22
3	1.5	4.5	6
8.26	4.13	12.4	16.5

27. $2\ C_4H_{10}(g) + 13\ O_2(g) \longrightarrow 8\ CO_2(g) + 10\ H_2O(g)$; 32 mol O_2

29. a. $Pb(s) + 2\ AgNO_3(aq) \longrightarrow Pb(NO_3)_2(aq) + 2\ Ag(s)$
b. 19 mol $AgNO_3$ c. 56.8 mol Ag

31. a. 0.157 g O_2 b. 0.500 g O_2
c. 114 g O_2 d. 2.86×10^{-4} g O_2

33. a. 4.0 g NaCl b. 4.3 g $CaCO_3$
c. 4.0 g MgO d. 3.1 g NaOH

35. a. 8.9 g Al_2O_3, 9.7 g Fe b. 3.0 g Al_2O_3, 3.3 g Fe

37.

Mass CH_4	Mass O_2	Mass CO_2	Mass H_2O
0.645 g	2.57 g	1.77 g	1.45 g
22.32 g	89.00 g	61.20 g	50.09 g
5.044 g	20.11 g	13.83 g	11.32 g
1.07 g	4.28 g	2.94 g	2.41 g
3.18 kg	12.7 kg	8.72 kg	7.14 kg
8.57×10^2 kg	3.42×10^3 kg	2.35×10^3 kg	1.92×10^3 kg

39. a. 2.3 g HCl b. 4.3 g HNO_3
c. 2.2 g H_2SO_4

41. 123 g H_2SO_4, 2.53 g H_2

43. a. 2 mol A b. 1.8 mol A
c. 4 mol B d. 40 mol B

45. a. 1.5 mol C b. 3 mol C
c. 3 mol C d. 96 mol C

47. a. 1 mol K b. 1.8 mol K
c. 1 mol Cl_2 d. 14.6 mol K

49. a. 1.3 mol MnO_3 b. 4.8 mol MnO_3
c. 0.107 mol MnO_3 d. 27.5 mol MnO_3

51. 3 mol A, 0 mol B, 4 mol C

53. a. 2 Cl_2 b. 3 Cl_2
c. 2 Cl_2

55. a. 1.0 g F_2 b. 10.5 g Li
c. 6.79×10^3 g F_2

57. a. 1.3 g $AlCl_3$ b. 24.8 g $AlCl_3$
c. 2.17 g $AlCl_3$

59. 74.6%

61. CaO; 25.7 g $CaCO_3$; 75.5%

63. O_2; 5.07 g NiO; 95.9%

65. Pb^{2+}; 262.7 g $PbCl_2$; 96.09%

67. TiO_2: 0 g, C: 7.0 g, Ti: 5.99 g, CO: 7.00 g

69. a. exothermic, $-\Delta H$ b. endothermic, $+\Delta H$
c. exothermic, $-\Delta H$

71. a. 55 kJ b. 110 kJ
c. 28 kJ d. 55 kJ

73. 4.78×10^3 kJ

75. 34.9 g C_8H_{18}

77. N_2

79. 0.152 g Ba^{2+}

81. 1.5 g HCl

83. 3.1 kg CO_2

85. 4.7 g Na_3PO_4

87. 469 g Zn

89. $2\ NH_4NO_3(s) \longrightarrow 2\ N_2(g) + O_2(g) + 4\ H_2O(l)$; 2.00×10^2 g O_2

91. salicylic acid ($C_7H_6O_3$); 2.71 g $C_9H_8O_4$; 74.1%

93. NH_3; 120 kg (CH_4N_2O); 72.9%

95. 2.4 mg $C_4H_6O_4S_2$

97. 1.0×10^3 g CO_2

99. b; the loudest explosion will occur when the ratio is 2 hydrogen to 1 oxygen, for that is the ratio that occurs in water.

101. 2.8×10^{13} kg CO_2 per year; 1.1×10^2 years

CHAPTER 9

QUESTIONS

1. Both the Bohr model and the quantum-mechanical model for the atom were developed in the early 1900s. These models serve to explain how electrons are arranged within the atomic structure and how the electrons affect the chemical and physical properties of each element.

3. White light contains a spectrum of wavelengths and therefore a spectrum of color. Colored light is produced by a single wavelength and is therefore a single color.

5. Energy carried per photon is greater for shorter wavelengths than for longer wavelengths. Wavelength and frequency are inversely related—the shorter the wavelength, the higher the frequency.

7. X-rays pass through many substances that block visible light and are therefore used to image bones and organs.

9. Ultraviolet light contains enough energy to damage biological molecules, and excessive exposure increases the risk of skin cancer and cataracts.

11. Microwaves can only heat things containing water, and therefore the food, which contains water, becomes hot, but the plate does not.

13. The Bohr model is a representation for the atom in which electrons travel around the nucleus in circular orbits with a fixed energy at specific, fixed distances from the nucleus.

15. The Bohr orbit describes the path of an electron as an orbit or trajectory (a specified path). A quantum-mechanical orbital describes the path of an electron using a probability map.

17. The e^- has wave particle duality, which means the path of an electron is not predictable. The motion of a baseball is predictable. A probability map shows a statistical, reproducible pattern of where the electron is located.

19. The subshells are *s* (1 orbital, which contains a maximum of 2 electrons); *p* (3 orbitals, which contain a maximum of 6 electrons); *d* (5 orbitals, which contain a maximum of 10 electrons); and *f* (7 orbitals, which contain a maximum of 14 electrons).

21. The Pauli exclusion principle states that separate orbitals may hold no more than 2 electrons, and when 2 electrons are present in a single orbital, they must have opposite spins. When writing electron configurations, the principle means that no box can have more than 2 arrows, and the arrows will point in opposite directions.

23. [Ne] represents $1s^2 2s^2 2p^6$.
[Kr] represents $1s^2 2s^2 2p^6 3s^2 3p^6 4s^2 3d^{10} 4p^6$.

25.

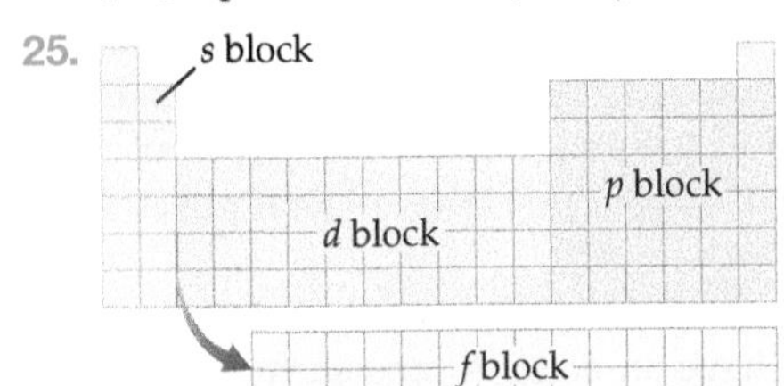

27. Group 1 elements form 1+ ions because they lose one valence electron in the outer *s* shell to obtain a noble gas configuration. Group 7 elements form 1− ions because they gain an electron to fill their outer *p* orbital to obtain a noble gas configuration.

PROBLEMS

29. **a.** 1.0 ns
b. 13.21 ms
c. 4 hrs 10 min

31. infrared

33. radiowaves < microwaves < infrared < ultraviolet

35. gamma, ultraviolet, or X-rays

37. **a.** radio waves < infrared < X-rays
b. radio waves < infrared < X-rays
c. X-rays < infrared < radio waves

39. energies, distances

41. $n = 6 \longrightarrow n = 2$: 410 nm
$n = 5 \longrightarrow n = 2$: 434 nm

43.

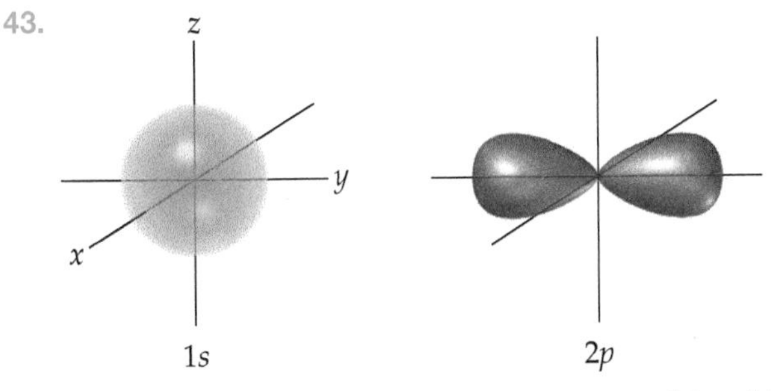

The 2*s* and 3*p* orbitals are bigger than the 1*s* and 2*p* orbitals.

45. Electron in the 2*s* orbital

47. $2p \longrightarrow 1s$

49. **a.** $1s^2\, 2p^2\, 2p^6\, 3s^2\, 3p^6\, 4s^2\, 3d^{10}\, 4p^6\, 5s^2$
b. $1s^2\, 2s^2\, 2p^6\, 3s^2\, 3p^6\, 4s^2\, 3d^{10}\, 4p^2$
c. $1s^2\, 2s^1$
d. $1s^2\, 2s^2\, 2p^6\, 3s^2\, 3p^6\, 4s^2\, 3d^{10}\, 4p^6$

51. **a.** He [↑↓] [ ]
1s 2s

b. B [↑↓] [↑↓] [↑ | |]
1s 2s 2p

c. Li [↑↓] [↑] [| |]
1s 2s 2p

d. N [↑↓] [↑↓] [↑↓ | ↓ | ↓]
1s 2s 2p

53. **a.** $[\text{Ar}]4s^2 3d^{10} 4p^1$ **b.** $[\text{Ar}]4s^2 3d^{10} 4p^3$
c. $[\text{Kr}]5s^1$ **d.** $[\text{Kr}]5s^2 4d^{10} 5p^2$

55. **a.** $[\text{Ar}]4s^2 3d^{10}$ **b.** $[\text{Ar}]4s^1 3d^{10}$
c. $[\text{Kr}]5s^2 4d^2$ **d.** $[\text{Ar}]4s^2 3d^6$

57. Valence electrons are underlined
a. $1s^2\, 2s^2\, 2p^6\, 3s^2\, 3p^6\, \underline{4s^2}\, 3d^{10}\, \underline{4p^6}$
b. $1s^2\, 2s^2\, 2p^6\, 3s^2\, 3p^6\, \underline{4s^2}\, 3d^{10}\, \underline{4p^2}$
c. $1s^2\, 2s^2\, 2p^6\, \underline{3s^2}\, \underline{3p^5}$
d. $1s^2\, 2s^2\, 2p^6\, 3s^2\, 3p^6\, 4s^2\, 3d^{10}\, 4p^6\, \underline{5s^2}$

59. **a.** Br [↑↓] [↑↓ | ↑↓ | ↑], 1 unpaired electron
4s 4p

b. Kr [↑↓] [↑↓ | ↑↓ | ↑↓], 0 unpaired electron
4s 4p

c. Na [↑], 1 unpaired electron
3s

d. In [↑↓] [↑ | |], 1 unpaired electron
5s 5p

61. **a.** 6 **b.** 6
c. 7 **d.** 1

63. **a.** ns^1 **b.** ns^2
c. ns^2np^3 **d.** ns^2np^5

65. **a.** $[\text{Ne}]3s^2 3p^1$ **b.** $[\text{He}]2s^2$
c. $[\text{Kr}]5s^2 4d^{10} 5p^1$ **d.** $[\text{Kr}]5s^2 4d^2$

67. **a.** $[\text{Kr}]5s^2$ **b.** $[\text{Kr}]5s^2 4d^1$
c. $[\text{Ar}]4s^2 3d^2$
d. $[\text{Kr}]5s^2 4d^{10} 5p^4$

69. **a.** 2 **b.** 3
c. 5 **d.** 6

71. Period 1 has two elements. Period 2 has eight elements. The number of subshells is equal to the principal quantum number. For Period 1, $n = 1$ and the *s* subshell contains only two elements. For Period 2, $n = 2$ and contains *s* and *p* subshells that have a total of 8 elements.

73. **a.** Al **b.** S **c.** Ar **d.** Mg

75. **a.** Cl **b.** Ga **c.** Fe **d.** Rb

77. **a.** As **b.** Br **c.** cannot tell **d.** S

79. Pb < Sn < Te < S < Cl

81. **a.** In **b.** Si **c.** Pb **d.** C

83. F < S < Si < Ge < Ca < Rb

85. **a.** Sr **b.** Bi **c.** cannot tell **d.** As

87. S < Se < Sb < In < Ba < Fr

89. 18 e^-

91. Alkaline earth metals have the general electron configuration of ns^2. If they lose their two *s* electrons, they will obtain the stable electron configuration of a noble gas. This loss of electrons will give the metal a +2 charge.

93. **a.** $1s^22s^22p^63s^23p^6$
b. $1s^22s^22p^63s^23p^6$
c. $1s^22s^22p^63s^23p^6$
d. $1s^22s^22p^63s^23p^64s^23d^{10}4p^6$
They all have noble gas electron configurations.

95. Metals tend to form positive ions because they tend to lose electrons. Elements on the left side of the periodic table have only a few extra electrons, which they will lose to gain a noble gas configuration. Metalloids tend to be elements with 3 to 5 valence electrons; they could lose or gain electrons to obtain a noble gas configuration. Nonmetals tend to gain electrons to fill their almost full valence shell, so they tend to form negative ions and are on the right side of the table.

97. **a.** Can only have 2 in the *s* shell and 6 in the *p* shell: $1s^22s^22p^63s^23p^3$.
b. There is no 2*d* subshell: $1s^22s^22p^63s^23p^2$.
c. There is no 1*p* subshell: $1s^22s^22p^3$.
d. Can only have 6 in the *p* shell: $1s^22s^22p^63s^23p^3$.

99. Bromine is highly reactive because it reacts quickly to gain an electron and obtain a stable valence shell. Krypton is a noble gas because it already has a stable valence shell.

101. K

103. 660 nm

105. 8 min, 19 sec

107. The quantum-mechanical model provided the ability to understand and predict chemical bonding, which is the basic level of understanding of matter and how it interacts. This model was critical in the areas of lasers, computers, semiconductors, and drug design. The quantum-mechanical model for the atom is considered the foundation of modern chemistry.

109. **a.** 1.5×10^{-34} m **b.** 1.88×10^{-10} m
Electrons have wave-particle duality, whereas golf balls do not.

111. The ionization energy dips at column 3A because removing an electron from one of those atoms leaves the atom with a fairly stable, filled *s*-orbital as its valence shell. For the group 6A elements, special stability occurs when those elements lose an electron and achieve a half-filled *p*-orbital as their valence shell.

113. Ultraviolet light is the only one of these three types of light that contains enough energy to break chemical bonds in biological molecules.

CHAPTER 10

QUESTIONS

1. Bonding theories predict how atoms bond together to form molecules, and they also predict what combinations of atoms form molecules and what combinations do not. Likewise, bonding theories explain the shapes of molecules, which in turn determine many of their physical and chemical properties.

3. Atoms with eight valence electrons are particularly stable and are said to have an octet. Atoms such as hydrogen, helium, lithium, and beryllium are exceptions to the octet rule as they achieve stability when their outermost shell contains two electrons—a duet. A chemical bond is the sharing or transfer of electrons to attain stable electron configurations among the bonding atoms.

5. The Lewis structure for potassium has 1 valence electron, whereas the Lewis structure for monatomic chlorine has 7 valence electrons. From these structures we can determine that if potassium gives up its one valence electron to chlorine, K^+ and Cl^- are formed; therefore the formula must be KCl.

7. Double and triple bonds are shorter and stronger than single bonds.

9. You determine the number of electrons that go into the Lewis structure of a molecule by summing the valence electrons of each atom in the molecule.

11. The octet rule is not sophisticated enough to be correct every time. For example, some molecules that exist in nature have an odd number of valence electrons and thus will not have octets on all their constituent atoms. Some elements tend to form compounds in nature in which they have more (sulfur) or less (boron) than 8 valence electrons.

13. VSEPR theory predicts the shape of molecules using the idea that electron groups repel each other.

15. **a.** 180° **b.** 120° **c.** 109.5°

17. Electronegativity is the ability of an element to attract electrons within a covalent bond.

19. A polar covalent bond is a covalent bond that has a dipole moment.

21. If a polar liquid and a nonpolar liquid are mixed they will separate into distinct regions because the polar molecules will be attracted to one another and will exclude the nonpolar molecules.

PROBLEMS

23. a. $1s^22s^22p^3$, ·N̈:
 b. $1s^22s^22p^2$, ·Ċ·
 c. $1s^22s^22p^63s^23p^5$, :C̈l·
 d. $1s^22s^22p^63s^23p^6$, :Är:

25. a. :Ï: b. ·S̈:
 c. ·Ġe· d. ·Ca·

27. :Ẍ: Halogens tend to gain one electron in a chemical reaction.

29. M: Alkaline earth metals tend to lose two electrons in a chemical reaction.

31. a. Al^{3+} b. Mg^{2+}
 c. $[:\ddot{Se}:]^{2-}$ d. $[:\ddot{N}:]^{3-}$

33. a. Kr b. Ne
 c. Kr d. Xe

35. a. covalent b. ionic
 c. covalent d. ionic

37. a. $Na^+[:\ddot{F}:]^-$ b. $Ca^{2+}[:\ddot{O}:]^{2-}$
 c. $[:\ddot{Br}:]^-Sr^{2+}[:\ddot{Br}:]^-$ d. $K^+[:\ddot{O}:]^{2-}K^+$

39. a. CaS b. $MgBr_2$
 c. CsI d. Ca_3N_2

41. a. $[:\ddot{F}:]^-Mg^{2+}[:\ddot{F}:]^-$ b. $Mg^{2+}[:\ddot{O}:]^{2-}$
 c. $Mg^{2+}[:\ddot{N}:]^{3-}Mg^{2+}[:\ddot{N}:]^{3-}Mg^{2+}$

43. a. $Cs^+[:\ddot{Cl}:]^-$ b. $Ba^{2+}[:\ddot{O}:]^{2-}$
 c. $[:\ddot{I}:]^-Ca^{2+}[:\ddot{I}:]^-$

45. a. Hydrogen exists as a diatomic molecule because two hydrogen molecules achieve a stable duet when they share their electrons and form a single covalent bond.
 b. Iodine achieves a stable octet when two atoms share electrons and form a single bond.
 c. Nitrogen achieves a stable octet when two atoms share electrons and form a triple bond.
 d. Oxygen achieves a stable octet when two atoms share electrons and form a double bond.

47. a. H—P̈—H (with H bonded below P) b. :C̈l—S̈—C̈l:
 c. :F̈—F̈: d. H—Ï:

49. a. Ö=Ö b. :C≡O:
 c. H—Ö—N̈=Ö d. :Ö=S̈—Ö:

51. a. H—C≡C—H b. H—C=C—H (each C bonded to an H below)
 c. H—N̈=N̈—H d. H—N̈—N̈—H (each N bonded to an H below)

53. a. :N≡N: b. S̈=Si=S̈
 c. H—Ö—H d. :Ï—N̈—Ï: (with :Ï: bonded below N)

55. a. Ö=S̈e—Ö: ⟷ :Ö—S̈e=Ö
 b. $[\ddot{O}=C(-:\ddot{O}:)-\ddot{O}:]^{2-}$ ⟷ $[:\ddot{O}-C(-:\ddot{O}:)=\ddot{O}]^{2-}$ ⟷ $[:\ddot{O}-C(=\ddot{O}:)-\ddot{O}:]^{2-}$
 c. $[:\ddot{Cl}-\ddot{O}:]^-$ d. $[:\ddot{O}-\ddot{Cl}-\ddot{O}:]^-$

57. a. $[:\ddot{O}-P(-:\ddot{O}:)(-:\ddot{O}:)-\ddot{O}:]^{3-}$ (:Ö: above and below P) b. $[:C\equiv N:]^-$
 c. $[:\ddot{O}=\ddot{N}-\ddot{O}:]^-$ ⟷ $[:\ddot{O}-\ddot{N}=\ddot{O}:]^-$
 d. $[:\ddot{O}-\ddot{S}(-:\ddot{O}:)-\ddot{O}:]^{2-}$

59. a. :C̈l—B—C̈l: (with :C̈l: bonded below B)
 b. Ö=N̈—Ö: ⟷ :Ö—N̈=Ö
 c. H—B—H (with H bonded below B)

61. a. 4 b. 4
 c. 2 d. 4

63. a. 3 bonding groups, 1 lone pair
 b. 2 bonding groups, 2 lone pairs
 c. 4 bonding groups, 0 lone pairs
 d. 2 bonding groups, 0 lone pairs

65. a. tetrahedral b. trigonal planar
 c. linear d. trigonal planar

67. a. 109.5° b. 120°
 c. 180° d. 120°

69. a. linear, linear
 b. trigonal planar, bent
 c. tetrahedral, bent
 d. tetrahedral, trigonal pyramidal

71. a. 180° b. 120°
 c. 109.5° d. 109.5°

73. a. linear, linear
 b. trigonal planar, bent (about both nitrogen atoms)
 c. tetrahedral, trigonal pyramidal (about both nitrogen atoms)

75. a. trigonal planar b. bent
 c. trigonal planar d. tetrahedral

77. a. 1.2 b. 1.8
 c. 2.8

79. Cl > Si > Ga > Ca > Rb

81. **a.** polar covalent **b.** ionic
c. pure covalent **d.** polar covalent

83. $H_2 < ICl < HBr < CO$

85. **a.** polar **b.** nonpolar
c. nonpolar **d.** polar

87. **a.** $(+)$:C≡O:$(-)$
b. nonpolar
c. nonpolar
d. $(+)$H—Br:$(-)$

89. **a.** nonpolar **b.** polar
c. nonpolar **d.** polar

91. **a.** nonpolar **b.** polar
c. nonpolar **d.** polar

93. **a.** $1s^22s^22p^63s^23p^6\underline{4s^2}$, Ca: (underlined electrons are the ones included)
b. $1s^22s^22p^33s^23p^6\underline{4s^2}3d^{10}\underline{4p^1}$, Ga:
c. $[Ar]\underline{4s^2}3d^{10}\underline{4p^3}$, ·As:
d. $[Kr]\underline{5s^2}4d^{10}\underline{5p^5}$, :I:

95. **a.** ionic, $K^+[:S:]^{2-}K^+$
b. covalent, H—C(=O:)—F:
c. ionic, $Mg^{2+}[:Se:]^{2-}$
d. covalent, :Br—P(—Br:)—Br:

97. :Cl—C(=O)—Cl: polar, Cl—C(=O)—Cl

99. H—C(H)(H)—C(=O:)—OH; H‖‖‖C(H)(H)—C(=O)OH

101. H:Cl: + $Na^+[:O:H]^-$ ⟶ H:O:H + $Na^+[:Cl:]^-$

103. K·, :Cl—Cl:, $K^+[:Cl:]^-$, Cl reduced, K oxidized

105. **a.** $K^+[:O:H]^-$
b. $K^+[O=N(:O:)—O:]^-$ ⟷ $K^+[:O:N(=O):O:]^-$ ⟷ $K^+[:O:N(:O:)=O:]^-$
c. $Li^+[:I:O:]^-$
d. $Ba^{2+}[C(=O)(O)(O)]^{2-}$ ⟷ $Ba^{2+}[C(O)(=O)(O)]^{2-}$ ⟷ $Ba^{2+}[C(O)(O)(=O)]^{2-}$

107. **a.** PF_5 (P bonded to five :F:) **b.** SF_4 (:S bonded to four :F:)
c. SeF_4 (:Se bonded to four :F:)

109. CH_2O_2 or H—C(=O:)—O—H

111. H—O—O· HOO is not stable because one oxygen atom does not have an octet. The geometry for HOO is *bent*.

113. **a.** $[:O—O·]^-$ **b.** $[:O·]^-$
c. ·O—H **d.** H—C(H)(H)—O—O·

115. **a.** The structure has 2 bonding electron pairs and 2 lone pairs. The Lewis structure is analogous to that of water, and the molecular geometry is bent.
b. Correct
c. The structure has 3 bonding electron pairs and 1 lone pair. The Lewis structure is analogous to that of NH_3, and the geometry is trigonal pyramidal.
d. Correct

CHAPTER 11

QUESTIONS

1. Pressure is the push (or force) exerted per unit area by gaseous molecules as they collide with the surfaces around them.

3. The kinetic molecular theory makes four main assumptions. The first is that the gas is a collection of molecules in constant motion. Secondly, there is no attraction or repulsion between the particles and collisions are perfectly elastic. Thirdly, there is a lot of space in between the particles relative to the particle size. Lastly, the speed of the particles increases with temperature.

5. The pain we experience in our ears during a change in altitude is due to a pressure difference between the cavities inside of our ears and the surrounding air.

7. Boyle's Law states that the volume of a gas and its pressure are inversely proportional. This relationship can be explained by the kinetic molecular theory. If the volume of a sample is decreased, the same number of particles are crowded into a smaller space, causing more collisions with the walls of the container. This causes the pressure to increase.

9. When an individual is more than a couple of meters underwater, the air pressure in the lungs is greater than the air pressure at the water's surface. If a snorkel were used, it would move the air from the lungs to the surface, making it very difficult to breathe.

11. Increasing the temperature of the air in the balloon causes it to expand. As the volume of the air increases, the density decreases allowing it to float in the cooler, more dense air surrounding it.
13. Avogadro's law states that the volume of a gas is directly proportional to the amount of gas in moles. Kinetic molecular theory predicts that if the number of gas particles increases at a constant pressure and temperature, the volume increases.
15. The ideal gas law is most accurate when the volume of gas particles is small compared to the space between them. It is also accurate when the forces between particles are not important. The ideal gas law breaks down at high pressures and low temperatures. This breakdown occurs because the gases are no longer acting according to the kinetic molecular theory.
17. Dalton's law states that the sum of the partial pressures in a gas mixture must equal the total pressure. $P_{tot} = P_A + P_B + P_C + \ldots$
19. Deep-sea divers breathe helium with oxygen because helium, unlike nitrogen, does not have physiological effects under high-pressure conditions. The oxygen concentration in the mixture is low to avoid oxygen toxicity.
21. Vapor pressure is the partial pressure of a gas above its liquid. Partial pressure increases with increasing temperature.

PROBLEMS

23. a. 1.680 atm b. 2.35 atm c. 8.64 atm d. .599 atm
25. a. 1.7×10^3 torr b. 36 mmHg c. 1.28×10^3 mmHg d. 834.2 torr
27.

Pascals	Atmospheres	mmHg	Torr	PSI
882	0.00871	6.62	6.62	0.128
5.65×10^4	0.558	424	424	8.20
1.71×10^5	1.69	1.28×10^3	1.28×10^3	24.8
1.02×10^5	1.01	764	764	14.8
3.32×10^4	0.328	249	249	4.82

29. a. 0.832 atm b. 632 mmHg c. 12.2 psi d. 8.43×10^4 Pa
31. a. 809.0 mmHg b. 1.065 atm c. 809.0 torr d. 107.9 kPa
33. 518 mmHg
35. 1.8 L
37.

P_1	V_1	P_2	V_2
755 mmHg	2.85 L	885 mmHg	2.43 L
9.35 atm	1.33 L	4.32 atm	2.88 L
192 mmHg	382 mL	152 mmHg	482 mL
2.11 atm	226 mL	3.82 atm	125 mL

39. 4.0 L
41. 58.9 mL
43.

V_1	T_1	V_2	T_2
1.08 L	25.4 °C	1.33 L	94.5 °C
58.9 mL	77 K	228 mL	298 K
115 cm^3	12.5 °C	119 cm^3	22.4 °C
232 L	18.5 °C	294 L	96.2 °C

45. 6.8 L
47. 4.33 L
49.

V_1	n_1	V_2	n_2
38.5 mL	1.55×10^{-3}	49.4 mL	1.99×10^{-3}
8.03 L	1.37	26.8 L	4.57
11.2 L	0.628	15.7 L	0.881
422 mL	0.0109	671 mL	0.0174

51. 1.71×10^3 mmHg
53. 0.76 L
55. 877 mmHg
57.

P_1	V_1	T_1	P_2	V_2	T_2
121 atm	1.58 L	12.2 °C	1.54 torr	1.33 L	32.3 °C
721 torr	141 mL	135 K	801 torr	152 mL	162 K
5.51 atm	0.879 L	22.1 °C	4.87 atm	1.05 L	38.3 °C

59. 5.11 L
61. 2.1 mol
63. 1.42 mol
65.

P	V	n	T
1.05 atm	1.19 L	0.112 mol	136 K
112 torr	40.8 L	0.241 mol	304 K
1.50 atm	28.5 mL	1.74×10^{-3} mol	25.4 °C
0.559 atm	0.439 L	0.0117 mol	255 K

67. 0.23 mol
69. 44.0 g/mol
71. 4.00 g/mol
73. 571 torr
75. 10.7 atm
77. 7.00×10^2 mmHg
79. 0.87 atm N_2; 0.25 atm O_2
81. 0.34 atm
83. a. 504 L b. 81 L c. 49 L d. 6.0×10^2
85. a. 59.1 L b. 30.0 L c. 72.1 L d. 0.125 L
87. a. 0.350 g b. 0.221 g c. 8.15 g
89. 28 L
91. 33 L H_2; 16 L CO
93. 8.82 L
95. 12.6 g

97. 0.5611 g

99. $V = \frac{nRT}{P}$

$$= \frac{1.00 \text{ mol}\left(0.0821 \frac{\text{L} \cdot \text{atm}}{\text{mol} \cdot \text{K}}\right)(273 \text{ K})}{1.00 \text{ atm}} = 22.4 \text{ L}$$

101. 27.8 g/mol

103. C_4H_{10}

105. 0.828 g

107. 0.128 g

109. 0.935 L

111. $HCl + NaHCO_3 \longrightarrow CO_2 + H_2O + NaCl$;
1.11×10^{-3} mol

113. **a.** SO_2, 0.0127 mol **b.** 65.6%

115. **a.** NO_2, 24.0 g **b.** 61.6%

117. 11.7 L

119. 356 torr

121. 0.15 atm

123. **c.** From the ideal gas law, we see that pressure is directly proportional to the number of moles of gas per unit volume (n/V). The gas in (c) contains the greatest concentration of particles and thus has the highest pressure.

125. 22.8 g

127. $V_2 = 0.76$ L, actual volume is 0.61 L. Difference is due to the fact that the ideal gas law is not ideal, especially at low temperatures.

CHAPTER 12

QUESTIONS

1. Intermolecular forces are attractive forces that occur between molecules. Intermolecular forces are what living organisms depend on for many physiological processes. Intermolecular forces are also responsible for the existence of liquids and solids.

3. The magnitude of intermolecular forces relative to the amount of thermal energy in the sample determines the state of the matter.

5. Properties of solids:
   a. Solids have high densities in comparison to gases.
   b. Solids have a definite shape.
   c. Solids have a definite volume.
   d. Solids may be crystalline or amorphous.

7. Surface tension is the tendency of liquids to minimize their surface area. Molecules at the surface have few neighbors to interact with via intermolecular forces.

9. Evaporation is a physical change in which a substance is converted from its liquid form to its gaseous form. Condensation is a physical change in which a substance is converted from its gaseous form to its liquid form.

11. Evaporation below the boiling point occurs because molecules on the surface of the liquid experience fewer attractions to the neighboring molecules and can therefore break away. At the boiling point, evaporation occurs faster because more of the molecules have sufficient thermal energy to break away (including internal molecules).

13. Acetone has weaker intermolecular forces than water. Acetone is more volatile than water.

15. Vapor pressure is the partial pressure of a gas in dynamic equilibrium with its liquid. It increases with increasing temperature, and it also increases with decreasing strength of intermolecular forces.

17. A steam burn is worse than a water burn at the same temperature (100 °C), because when the steam condenses on the skin, it releases large amounts of additional heat.

19. As the first molecules freeze, they release heat, making it harder for other molecules to freeze without the aid of a refrigeration mechanism, which would draw heat out.

21. The melting of ice is endothermic. ΔH for melting is positive (+), whereas ΔH for freezing is negative (−).

23. Dispersion forces are the default intermolecular force present in all molecules and atoms. Dispersion forces are caused by fluctuations in the electron distribution within molecules or atoms. Dispersion forces are the weakest type of intermoleculr force and increase with increasing molar mass.

25. Hydrogen bonding is an intermolecular force and is sort of a super dipole–dipole force. Hydrogen bonding occurs in compounds containing hydrogen atoms bonded directly to fluorine, oxygen, or nitrogen.

27. Molecular solids as a whole tend to have low to moderately low melting points relative to other types of solids; however, strong molecular forces can increase their melting points relative to each other.

29. Ionic solids tend to have much higher melting points relative to the melting points of other types of solids.

31. Water is unique for a couple of reasons. Water has a low molar mass, yet it is still liquid at room temperature and has a relatively high boiling point. Unlike other substances, which contract upon freezing, water expands upon freezing.

PROBLEMS

33. The 55 mL of water in a dish with a diameter of 12 cm will evaporate more quickly because it has a larger surface area.

35. Acetone feels cooler while evaporating from one's hand, for it is more volatile than water and evaporates much faster.

37. The ice's temperature will increase from −5 °C to 0 °C, where it will then stay constant while the ice completely melts. After the melting process is complete, the water will continue to rise steadily in temperature until it reaches room temperature (25 °C).

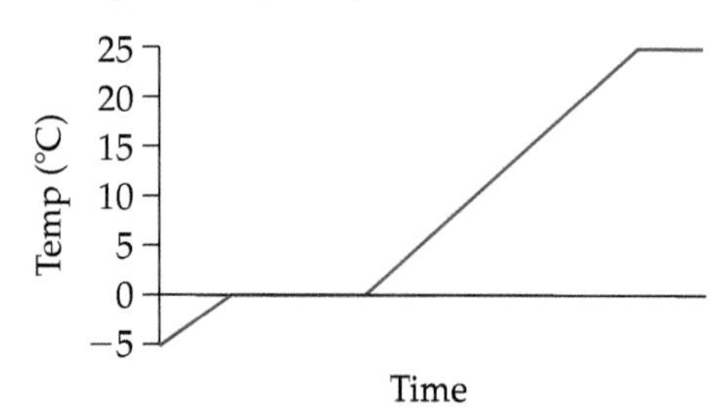

39. Allowing 0.50 g of 100 °C steam to condense on your hand would cause a more severe burn than spilling 0.50 g of 100 °C water on your hand. When the steam condenses on the skin, it releases large amounts of additional heat.
41. The −8 °C ice chest will cause the water in the watery bag of ice to freeze, which is an exothermic process. The freezing process of the water will release heat, and the temperature of the ice chest will increase.
43. The ice chest filled with ice at 0 °C will be colder after a couple of hours than the ice chest filled with water at 0 °C. This is because the ice can absorb additional heat as it melts.
45. Denver is a mile above sea level and thus has a lower air pressure. Due to this low pressure, the point at which the vapor pressure of water equals the external pressure will occur at a lower temperature.
47. 76.3 kJ
49. 6.8 kJ
51. 10.4 kJ
53. 3.70×10^2 g
55. 12.5 kJ
57. 11.4 kJ
59. **a.** dispersion
    b. dispersion
    c. dispersion, dipole–dipole
    d. dispersion, dipole–dipole, hydrogen bonding
61. **a.** dispersion, dipole–dipole
    b. dispersion, dipole–dipole, hydrogen bonding
    c. dispersion
    d. dispersion
63. d, because it has the highest molecular weight
65. CH_3OH, due to strong hydrogen bonding
67. NH_3, because it has the ability to form hydrogen bonds
69. These two substances are not miscible, for H_2O is polar and $CH_3CH_2CH_2CH_2CH_3$ is nonpolar.
71. **a.** no **b.** yes
    c. yes
73. **a.** atomic **b.** molecular
    c. ionic **d.** atomic
75. **a.** molecular **b.** ionic
    c. molecular **d.** molecular
77. **c.** LiCl(*s*); it is an ionic solid and possesses ionic bonds resulting in a higher melting point.
79. **a.** Ti(*s*); Ti is a covalent atomic solid, and Ne is a nonbonding atomic solid.
    b. H_2O(*s*); while both are molecular solids, water has strong hydrogen bonding.
    c. Xe(*s*); both are nonbonding atomic solids, but Xe has a higher molar mass.
    d. NaCl(*s*); NaCl(*s*) is an ionic solid, and CH_4(*s*) is a molecular solid.
81. Ne < SO_2 < NH_3 < H_2O < NaF
83. **a.** 2.6×10^4 J **b.** 26 kJ
    c. 6.2×10^3 cal **d.** 6.2 Cal
85. 2.7 °C
87. 1.1×10^2 g
89. 57.5 kJ
91. **a.** H—S̤̈e—H Bent: Dispersion and dipole–dipole
    b. Ö̤=S̈—Ö̤: Bent: Dispersion and dipole–dipole
    c. H—C(—:C̈l:)(—:C̤l:)—C̤̈l: Tetrahedral: Dispersion and dipole–dipole
    d. :Ö=C=Ö: Linear: Dispersion
93. $Na^+[:\ddot{F}:]^-$; $Mg^{2+}[:\ddot{O}:]^{2-}$; MgO has a higher melting point, because the magnitude of the charges on the ions is greater.
95. As the molecular weight increases from Cl to I, the greater the London dispersion forces present, which will increase the boiling point as observed. However, HF is the only compound listed that has the ability to form hydrogen bonds, which explains the anomaly in the trend.
97. 23.6 °C
99. The molecule in the interior has the most neighbors. The molecule on the surface is more likely to evaporate. In three dimensions, the molecules that make up the surface area have the fewest neighbors and are more likely to evaporate than the molecules in the interior.
101. **a.** Yes, if the focus is on the melting of icebergs. No, the melting of an ice cube in a cup of water will *not* raise the level of the liquid in the cup; when the ice cube melts, the volume of the water created will be less than the volume of the initial ice cube.
    b. Yes, for the ice sheets that sit on the continent of Antarctica are above sea level, and if some melted, the water created would be added to the ocean without decreasing the amount of ice below the ocean's surface.

CHAPTER 13

QUESTIONS

1. A solution is a homogeneous mixture of two or more substances. Some examples are air, seawater, soda water, and brass.
3. In a solution, the solvent is the majority component of the mixture, and the solute is the minority component. For example, in a seawater solution, the water is the solvent, and the salt content is the solute.
5. Solubility is the amount of the compound, usually in grams, that will dissolve in a specified amount of solvent.
7. In solutions with solids, soluble ionic solids form strong electrolyte solutions, while soluble molecular solids form nonelectrolyte solutions. Strong electrolyte solutions are solutions containing solutes that dissociate into ions, for example, $BaCl_2$ and NaOH.
9. Recrystallization is a common way to purify a solid. In recrystallization, enough solid is put into high-temperature water until a saturated solution is created. Then the solution cools slowly, and crystals result from the solution. The crystalline structure tends to reject impurities, resulting in a purer solid.

11. The bubbles formed on the bottom of a pot of heated water (before boiling) are dissolved air coming out of the solution. These gases come out of solution because the solubility of the dissolved nitrogen and oxygen decreases as the temperature of the water rises.

13. The solubility of gases increases with increasing pressure. When a soda can is opened, the pressure is lowered, decreasing the solubility of carbon dioxide. This causes bubbles of carbon dioxide to come out of the solution.

15. Mass percent is the number of grams of solute per 100 grams of solution. Molarity is defined as the number of moles of solute per liter of solution.

17. The boiling point of a solution containing a nonvolatile solute is higher than the boiling point of the pure solvent. The melting point of the solution, however, is lower.

19. Molality is a common unit of concentration of a solution expressed as number of moles of solute per kilogram of solvent.

21. Water tends to move from lower concentrations to higher concentrations, and when the salt water is being passed through the human body, the salt content draws the water out of the body, causing dehydration.

PROBLEMS

23. c and d are solutions

25. **a.** solute: salt, solvent: water
b. solute: sugar, solvent: water
c. solute: CO_2, solvent: water

27. **a.** hexane **b.** water
c. ethyl ether **d.** water

29. ions, strong electrolyte solution

31. unsaturated

33. recrystallization

35. **a.** no
b. yes
c. yes

37. At room temperature water contains some dissolved oxygen gas; however, the boiling of the water will remove dissolved gases.

39. Under higher pressure, the gas (nitrogen) will be more easily dissolved in the blood. To reverse this process, the diver should ascend to relieve the pressure.

41. **a.** 7.64%
b. 3.50%
c. 4.64%

43. 12%

45.

Mass Solute	Mass Solvent	Mass Solution	Mass%
15.5	238.1	253.6	6.11%
22.8	167.2	190.0	12.0%
28.8	183.3	212.1	13.6%
56.9	315.2	372.1	15.3%

47. 8.9 g NaCl

49. **a.** 1.8 g **b.** 10.5 mg
c. 0.46 kg

51. **a.** 2.6 kg **b.** 1.0×10^2 g
c. 18 g

53. 1.6×10^2 g

55. 1.3×10^3 g

57. 11 L

59. **a.** 0.194 M **b.** 0.234 M
c. 0.41 M

61. **a.** 0.149 M **b.** 0.461 M
c. 3.00×10^{-2} M

63. 0.57 M

65. **a.** 1.8 mol **b.** 0.38 mol
c. 0.238 mol

67. **a.** 0.59 L **b.** 0.083 L
c. 0.15 L

69.

Solute	Mass Solute	Mol Solute	Volume Solution	Molarity
KNO_3	22.5 g	0.223	125 mL	1.78 M
$NaHCO_3$	2.10 g	0.0250	250.0 mL	0.100 M
$C_{12}H_{22}O_{11}$	55.38 g	0.162	1.08 L	0.150 M

71. 2.7 g

73. 19 g

75. 8.8 L

77. **a.** 0.15 M **b.** 0.30 M
c. 0.45 M

79. **a.** 0.24 M Na^+, 0.12 M SO_4^{2-}
b. 0.50 M K^+, 0.25 M CO_3^{2-}
c. 0.11 M Rb^+, 0.11 M Br^-

81. 0.29 M

83. Dilute 0.045 L of the stock solution to 2.5 L.

85. 6.0×10^2 mL

87. 17.7 mL

89. **a.** 0.025 L **b.** 0.020 L
c. 1.03 L

91. 4.45 mL

93. 0.373 M

95. 1.2 L

97. **a.** 1.0 m **b.** 3.92 m
c. 0.52 m

99. 1.49 m

101. **a.** −1.6 °C **b.** −2.70 °C
c. −8.9 °C **d.** −4.37 °C

103. **a.** 100.060 °C **b.** 100.993 °C
c. 101.99 °C **d.** 101.11 °C

105. −1.27 °C, 100.348 °C

107. 2.28 M, 12.3%

109. 0.43 L

111. 319 mL

113. 1.03 M

115. 0.17 L

117. 9.0 mL
119. 8.0×10^2 mL
121. −3.60 °C, 100.992 °C
123. −1.86 °C, 100.508 °C
125. 1.8×10^2 g/mol
127. 101.8 °C
129. 39.8 g glucose, 85.2 g sucrose
131. **a.** Water will flow from left to right.
b. Water will flow from right to left.
c. Water won't flow between the two.
133. 3×10^4 L

CHAPTER 14

QUESTIONS

1. Sour gummy candies are coated with a white powder that is a mixture of citric acid and tartaric acid. The combination of these two acids creates the sour taste.
3. The main component of stomach acid is hydrochloric acid. Its purpose is to help break down food and kill harmful bacteria.
5. The properties of bases are bitter taste, slippery feel, and the ability to turn red litmus paper blue. Some common substances that contain bases are ammonia, Drano, baking soda, and antacids.
7. The Arrhenius definition of an acid is a substance that produces H^+ ions in aqueous solution. An example:

$$HCl(aq) \longrightarrow H^+(aq) + Cl^-(aq)$$

9. The Brønsted–Lowry definition states that an acid is a proton donor and a base is a proton acceptor. The following is an example of a chemical equation demonstrating this definition:

$$\underset{\text{acid}}{HCl(aq)} + \underset{\text{base}}{H_2O(l)} \longrightarrow H_3O^+(aq) + Cl^-(aq)$$

11. An acid–base neutralization reaction occurs when an acid and a base are mixed and the $H^+(aq)$ from the acid combines with the $OH^-(aq)$ from the base to form $H_2O(l)$. An example follows.

$$HCl(aq) + KOH(aq) \longrightarrow H_2O(l) + KCl(aq)$$

13. $2\,HCl(aq) + K_2O(s) \longrightarrow H_2O(l) + 2\,KCl(aq)$
15. A titration is a laboratory procedure in which a reactant in a solution of known concentration is reacted with another reactant in a solution of unknown concentration until the reaction has reached the equivalence point. The equivalence point is the point at which the reactants are in exact stoichiometric proportions.
17. A strong acid is one that will completely dissociate in solution, while a weak acid does not completely dissociate in solution.
19. Monoprotic acids (such as HCl) contain only one hydrogen ion that will dissociate in solution, while diprotic acids (such as H_2SO_4) contain two hydrogen ions that will dissociate in solution.
21. Yes, pure water contains H_3O^+ ions. Through self-ionization, water acts as an acid and a base with itself; water is amphoteric.
23. **a.** $[H_3O^+] > 1.0 \times 10^{-7}$ M; $[OH^-] < 1.0 \times 10^{-7}$ M
b. $[H_3O^+] < 1.0 \times 10^{-7}$ M; $[OH^-] > 1.0 \times 10^{-7}$ M
c. $[H_3O^+] = 1.0 \times 10^{-7}$ M; $[OH^-] = 1.0 \times 10^{-7}$ M
25. The pOH of a solution is the negative base-10 logarithm of the concentration of OH^- ions ($-\log[OH^-]$). A change of 2.0 pOH units corresponds to a 100-fold change in $[OH^-]$.
27. A buffer is a solution that resists pH change by neutralizing added acid or added base.
29. The cause of acid rain is the formation of SO_2, NO, and NO_2 during the combustion of fossil fuels.
31. Acid rain damages structures made out of metal, marble, cement, and limestone, as well as harming and possibly killing aquatic life and trees.

PROBLEMS

33. **a.** acid; $H_2SO_4(aq) \longrightarrow H^+(aq) + HSO_4^-(aq)$
b. base; $Sr(OH)_2(aq) \longrightarrow Sr^{2+}(aq) + 2\,OH^-(aq)$
c. acid; $HBr(aq) \longrightarrow H^+(aq) + Br^-(aq)$
d. base; $NaOH(aq) \longrightarrow Na^+(aq) + OH^-(aq)$

35.

B-L Acid	B-L Base	Conjugate Acid	Conjugate Base
a. HBr	H_2O	H_3O^+	Br^-
b. H_2O	NH_3	NH_4^+	OH^-
c. HNO_3	H_2O	H_3O^+	NO_3^-
d. H_2O	C_5H_5N	$C_5H_5NH^+$	OH^-

37. a, c
39. **a.** Cl^- **b.** HSO_3^-
c. CHO_2^- **d.** F^-
41. **a.** NH_4^+ **b.** $HClO_4$
c. H_2SO_4 **d.** HCO_3^-
43. **a.** $HI(aq) + NaOH(aq) \longrightarrow H_2O(l) + NaI(aq)$
b. $HBr(aq) + KOH(aq) \longrightarrow H_2O(l) + KBr(aq)$
c. $2\,HNO_3(aq) + Ba(OH)_2(aq) \longrightarrow 2\,H_2O(l) + Ba(NO_3)_2(aq)$
d. $2\,HClO_4(aq) + Sr(OH)_2(aq) \longrightarrow 2\,H_2O(l) + Sr(ClO_4)_2(aq)$
45. **a.** $2\,HBr(aq) + 2\,Rb(s) \longrightarrow 2\,RbBr(aq) + H_2(g)$
b. $2\,HBr(aq) + Mg(s) \longrightarrow MgBr_2(aq) + H_2(g)$
c. $2\,HBr(aq) + 2\,Ba(s) \longrightarrow 2\,BaBr(aq) + H_2(g)$
d. $6\,HBr(aq) + 2\,Al(s) \longrightarrow 2\,AlBr_3(aq) + 3\,H_2(g)$
47. **a.** $MgO(aq) + 2\,HI(aq) \longrightarrow H_2O(l) + MgI_2(aq)$
b. $K_2O(aq) + 2\,HI(aq) \longrightarrow H_2O(l) + 2\,KI(aq)$
c. $Rb_2O(aq) + 2\,HI(aq) \longrightarrow H_2O(l) + 2\,RbI(aq)$
d. $CaO(aq) + 2\,HI(aq) \longrightarrow H_2O(l) + CaI_2(aq)$
49. **a.** $6\,HClO_4(aq) + Fe_2O_3(s) \longrightarrow 2\,Fe(ClO_4)_3(aq) + 3\,H_2O(l)$
b. $H_2SO_4(aq) + Sr(s) \longrightarrow SrSO_4(aq) + H_2(g)$
c. $H_3PO_4(aq) + 3\,KOH(aq) \longrightarrow 3\,H_2O(l) + K_3PO_4(aq)$
51. **a.** 0.1400 M **b.** 0.138 M
c. 0.08764 M **d.** 0.182 M

53. 0.1090 M H_2SO_4

55. 16.9 mL

57. **a.** strong **b.** weak
c. strong **d.** weak

59. **a.** $[H_3O^+] = 1.7$ M **b.** $[H_3O^+] = 1.5$ M
c. $[H_3O^+] < 0.38$ M **d.** $[H_3O^+] < 1.75$ M

61. **a.** strong **b.** weak
c. strong **d.** weak

63. **a.** $[OH^-] = 0.25$ M **b.** $[OH^-] < 0.25$ M
c. $[OH^-] = 0.50$ M **d.** $[OH^-] = 1.25$ M

65. **a.** acidic **b.** acidic
c. neutral **d.** basic

67. **a.** 6.7×10^{-6} M, basic **b.** 1.1×10^{-6} M, basic
c. 4.5×10^{-9} M, acidic **d.** 1.4×10^{-11} M, acidic

69. **a.** 3.7×10^{-3} M, acidic **b.** 4.0×10^{-13} M, basic
c. 9.1×10^{-5} M, acidic **d.** 3.0×10^{-11} M, basic

71. **a.** basic **b.** neutral
c. acidic **d.** acidic

73. **a.** 7.77 **b.** 7.00
c. 5.66 **d.** 3.13

75. **a.** 2.8×10^{-9} M **b.** 5.9×10^{-12} M
c. 1.3×10^{-3} M **d.** 6.0×10^{-2} M

77. **a.** 7.28 **b.** 6.42
c. 3.86 **d.** 12.98

79. **a.** 1.8×10^{-10} M **b.** 3.4×10^{-2} M
c. 3.2×10^{-13} M **d.** 1.8×10^{-6} M

81. **a.** 1.810 **b.** 11.107
c. 2.724 **d.** 10.489

83. **a.** pOH = 8.82, acidic **b.** pOH = 4.15, basic
c. pOH = 7.00, neutral **d.** pOH = 2.06, basic

85. **a.** pOH = 6.08, basic **b.** pOH = 12.74, acidic
c. pOH = 5.59, basic **d.** pOH = 1.274, basic

87. **a.** pH = 5.5, acidic **b.** pH = 9.8, basic
c. pH = 12.3, basic **d.** pH = 7.0, neutral

89. various answers

91. c and d are buffers

93. $HCl(aq) + NaF(aq) \longrightarrow HF(aq) + NaCl(aq)$
$HCl(aq) + KC_2H_3O_2(aq) \longrightarrow HC_2H_3O_2(aq) + KCl(aq)$

95. **a.** $HC_2H_3O_2$ **b.** NaH_2PO_4
c. NaCHOO

97. 50.0 mL

99. 0.16 L

101. 65.2 g

103. 60.0 g/mol

105. 0.17 L

107. **a.** 2.60, acidic
b. 11.75, basic
c. 8.02, basic
d. 1.710, acidic

109.

$[H_3O^+]$	$[OH^-]$	pH	Acidic or Basic
1.0×10^{-4}	1.0×10^{-10}	4.00	acidic
5.5×10^{-3}	1.8×10^{-12}	2.26	acidic
3.1×10^{-9}	3.2×10^{-6}	8.50	basic
4.8×10^{-9}	2.1×10^{-6}	8.32	basic
2.8×10^{-8}	3.5×10^{-7}	7.55	basic

111. a. $[H_3O^+] = 0.0088$ M
$[OH^-] = 1.1 \times 10^{-12}$ M
pH = 2.06

b. $[H_3O^+] = 1.5 \times 10^{-3}$ M
$[OH^-] = 6.7 \times 10^{-12}$ M
pH = 2.82

c. $[H_3O^+] = 9.77 \times 10^{-4}$ M
$[OH^-] = 1.02 \times 10^{-11}$ M
pH = 3.010

d. $[H_3O^+] = 0.0878$ M
$[OH^-] = 1.14 \times 10^{-13}$ M
pH = 1.057

113. a.$[OH^-] = 0.15$ M
$[H_3O^+] = 6.7 \times 10^{-14}$ M
pH = 13.18

b. $[OH^-] = 3.0 \times 10^{-3}$ M
$[H_3O^+] = 3.3 \times 10^{-12}$ M
pH = 11.48

c. $[OH^-] = 9.6 \times 10^{-4}$ M
$[H_3O^+] = 1.0 \times 10^{-11}$ M
pH = 10.98

d. $[OH^-] = 8.7 \times 10^{-5}$ M
$[H_3O^+] = 1.1 \times 10^{-10}$ M
pH = 9.94

115. 1.49 L

117. 11.495

119. 3.0×10^{12} H^+ ions

121. 0.024 mol $Sr(OH)_2$, 0.076 mol NaOH

123. **a.** weak
b. strong
c. weak
d. strong

125. approximately 8 times more concentrated

CHAPTER 15

QUESTIONS

1. The two general concepts involved in equilibrium are sameness and changelessness.

3. By controlling reaction rates, chemists can control the amount of a product that forms in a given period of time and have control of the outcome.

5. The two factors that influence reaction rates are concentration and temperature. The rate of a reaction increases with increasing concentration. The rate of a reaction increases with increasing temperature.

7. In a chemical reaction, dynamic equilibrium is the condition in which the rate of the forward reaction equals the rate of the reverse reaction.

9. Because the rate of the forward and reverse reactions is the same at equilibrium, the relative concentrations of reactants and products become constant.

11. The equilibrium constant is a measure of how far a reaction goes; it is significant because it is a way to quantify the concentrations of the reactants and products at equilibrium.

13. A small equilibrium constant shows that a reverse reaction is favored and that when equilibrium is reached, there will be more reactants than products. A large equilibrium constant shows that a forward reaction is favored and that when equilibrium is reached, there will be more products than reactants.

15. No, the particular concentrations of reactants and products at equilibrium will not always be the same for a given reaction—they will depend on the initial concentrations.

17. Various answers depending on the answer for Question 12.

19. Decreasing the concentration of a reactant in a reaction mixture at equilibrium causes the reaction to shift to the left.

21. Decreasing the concentration of a product in a reaction mixture at equilibrium causes the reaction to shift to the right.

23. Increasing the pressure of a reaction mixture at equilibrium if the product side has fewer moles of gas particles than the reactant side causes the reaction to shift to the right.

25. Decreasing the pressure of a reaction mixture at equilibrium if the product side has fewer moles of gas particles than the reactant side causes the reaction to shift to the left.

27. Increasing the temperature of an exothermic reaction mixture at equilibrium causes the reaction to shift left, absorbing some of the added heat. Decreasing the temperature of an exothermic reaction mixture at equilibrium causes the reaction to shift right, releasing heat.

29. $K_{sp} = [A^{2+}][B^-]^2$

31. The solubility of a compound is the amount of the compound that dissolves in a certain amount of liquid, and the molar solubility is the solubility in units of moles per liter.

33. Two reactants with a large K_{eq} for a particular reaction might not react immediately when combined because of a large activation energy, which is an energy hump that normally exists between the reactants and products. The activation energy must be overcome before the system will undergo a reaction.

35. No, a catalyst does not affect the value of the equilibrium constant; it simply lowers the activation energy and increases the rate of a chemical reaction.

PROBLEMS

37. Rate would decrease because the effective concentration of the reactants has been decreased, which lowers the rate of a reaction.

39. Reaction rates tend to decrease with decreasing temperature, so all life processes (chemical reactions) would have decreased rates.

41. The rate would be lower because the concentration of reactants decreases as they are consumed in the reaction.

43. **a.** $K_{eq} = \dfrac{[N_2O_4]}{[NO_2]^2}$ **b.** $K_{eq} = \dfrac{[NO]^2[Br_2]}{[BrNO]^2}$

c. $K_{eq} = \dfrac{[H_2][CO_2]}{[H_2O][CO]}$ **d.** $K_{eq} = \dfrac{[CS_2][H_2]^4}{[CH_4][H_2S]^2}$

45. **a.** $K_{eq} = \dfrac{[Cl_2]}{[PCl_5]}$ **b.** $K_{eq} = [O_2]^3$

c. $K_{eq} = \dfrac{[H_3O^+][F^-]}{[HF]}$ **d.** $K_{eq} = \dfrac{[NH_4^+][OH^-]}{[NH_3]}$

47. $K_{eq} = \dfrac{[H_2]^2[S_2]}{[H_2S]^2}$

49. **a.** products **b.** both
c. reactants **d.** both

51. 0.0394

53. 1.79×10^{-5}

55. 0.0987

57. 7.0 M

59. 0.119 M

61.

T(K)	$[N_2]$	$[H_2]$	$[NH_3]$	K_{eq}
500	0.115	0.105	0.439	1.45×10^3
575	0.110	0.25	0.128	9.6
775	0.120	0.140	0.00439	0.0584

63. **a.** shift right **b.** shift left
c. shift right

65. **a.** no effect **b.** shift left
c. shift left **d.** shift right

67. **a.** shift right **b.** shift left

69. **a.** no effect **b.** no effect

71. **a.** shift right **b.** shift left

73. **a.** shift left **b.** shift right

75. **a.** no effect **b.** shift right
c. shift left **d.** shift right
e. no effect

77. **a.** $CaSO_4(s) \longrightarrow Ca^{2+}(aq) + SO_4^{2-}(aq)$
$K_{sp} = [Ca^{2+}][SO_4^{2-}]$

b. $AgCl(s) \longrightarrow Ag^+(aq) + Cl^-(aq)$
$K_{sp} = [Ag^+][Cl^-]$

c. $CuS(s) \longrightarrow Cu^{2+}(aq) + S^{2-}(aq)$
$K_{sp} = [Cu^{2+}][S^{2-}]$

d. $FeCO_3(s) \longrightarrow Fe^{2+}(aq) + CO_3^{2-}(aq)$
$K_{sp} = [Fe^{2+}][CO_3^{2-}]$

79. $K_{sp} = [Fe^{2+}][OH^-]^2$

81. 7.0×10^{-11}

83. 1.35×10^{-4} M

85. 7.04×10^{-5} M

87. 2.61×10^{-3} M

89.

Compound	[Cation]	[Anion]	K_{sp}
$SrCO_3$	2.4×10^{-5}	2.4×10^{-5}	5.8×10^{-10}
SrF_2	1.0×10^{-3}	2.0×10^{-3}	4.0×10^{-9}
Ag_2CO_3	2.6×10^{-4}	1.3×10^{-4}	8.8×10^{-12}

91. 3.3×10^{2}

93. 5.34 g

95. b, c, d

97. 1.13×10^{-18} M, 1.62×10^{-15} g

99. Yes

101. 7.07×10^{-4}

103. 1.2×10^{-2} g

105. 0.021 g K_2CO_3

107. e

109. 35.5 L

CHAPTER 16

QUESTIONS

1. A fuel-cell electric vehicle is an automobile running on an electric motor that is powered by hydrogen. The fuel cells use the electron-gaining tendency of oxygen and the electron-losing tendency of hydrogen to force electrons to move through a wire, creating the electricity that powers the car.

3. **a.** Oxidation is the gaining of oxygen, and reduction is the losing of oxygen.

   b. Oxidation is the loss of electrons, and reduction is the gain of electrons.

   c. Oxidation is an increase in oxidation state, and reduction is a decrease in oxidation state.

5. gain

7. The oxidization state of a free element is zero. The oxidization state of a monoatomic ion equals its charge.

9. For an ion, the sum of the oxidation states of the individual atoms must add up to *the charge of the ion*.

11. In a redox reaction, an atom that undergoes an increase in oxidation state is *oxidized*. An atom that undergoes a decrease in oxidation state is *reduced*.

13. When balancing redox equations, the number of electrons lost in the oxidation half-reaction must *equal* the number of electrons gained in the reduction half-reaction.

15. When balancing aqueous redox reactions, charge is balanced using *electrons*.

17. The metals at the top of the activity series are the most reactive.

19. The metals at the bottom of the activity series are least likely to lose electrons.

21. If the metal is listed above H_2 on the activity series, it will dissolve in acids such as HCl or HBr.

23. Oxidation occurs at the *anode* of an electrochemical cell.

25. The salt bridge joins the two half-cells or completes the circuit; it allows the flow of ions between the two half-cells.

27. The common dry cell battery does not contain large amounts of liquid water and is composed of a zinc case that acts as the anode. The cathode is a carbon rod immersed in a moist paste of MnO_2 that also contains NH_4Cl. The anode and cathode reactions that occur produce a voltage of about 1.5 volts.

    anode reaction:

    $$Zn(s) \longrightarrow Zn^{2+}(aq) + 2\,e^-$$

    cathode reaction:

    $$2\,MnO_2(s) + 2\,NH_2^{+}(aq) + 2\,e^- \longrightarrow 2\,Mn_2O_3(s) + 2\,NH_3(g) + H_2O(l)$$

29. Fuel cells are like batteries, but the reactants are constantly replenished. The reactants constantly flow through the battery, generating electrical current as they undergo a redox reaction.

    anode reaction:

    $$2\,H_2(g) + 4\,OH^-(aq) \longrightarrow 4\,H_2O(g) + 4\,e^-$$

    cathode reaction:

    $$O_2(g) + 2\,H_2O(l) + 4\,e^- \longrightarrow 4\,OH^-(aq)$$

31. Corrosion is the oxidation of metals; the most common example is rusting of iron.

    oxidation:

    $$2\,Fe(s) \longrightarrow 2\,Fe^{2+}(aq) + 4\,e^-$$

    reduction:

    $$O_2(g) + 2\,H_2O(l) + 4\,e^- \longrightarrow 4\,OH^-(aq)$$

    overall:

    $$2\,Fe(s) + O_2(g) + 2\,H_2O(l) \longrightarrow 2\,Fe(OH)_2(s)$$

PROBLEMS

33. **a.** H_2 **b.** Al

    c. Al

35. **a.** Sr is oxidized, O_2 is reduced.

    b. Ca is oxidized, Cl_2 is reduced.

    c. Mg is oxidized, Ni^{2+} is reduced.

37. **a.** Sr is the reducing agent; O_2 is the oxidizing agent.

    b. Ca is the reducing agent; Cl_2 is the oxidizing agent.

    c. Mg is the reducing agent; Ni^{2+} is the oxidizing agent.

39. b (F_2), d (Cl_2)

41. a (K), c (Fe)

43. **a.** N_2 is oxidized and is the reducing agent.
    O_2 is reduced and is the oxidizing agent.

    b. C is oxidized and is the reducing agent.
    O_2 is reduced and is the oxidizing agent.

    c. Sb is oxidized and is the reducing agent.
    Cl_2 is reduced and is the oxidizing agent.

    d. K is oxidized and is the reducing agent.
    Pb^{2+} is reduced and is the oxidizing agent.

45. a. 0 b. +2
c. +3 d. 0

47. a. Na: +1; Cl: −1 b. Ca: +2; F: −1
c. S: +4; O: −2 d. H: +1; S: −2

49. a. +2 b. +4
c. +1

51. a. C: +4; O: −2 b. O: −2; H: +1
c. N: +5; O: −2 d. N: +3; O: −2

53. a. +1 b. +3
c. +5 d. +7

55. a. Cu, +2; N, +5; O, −2
b. Sr, +2; O, −2; H, +1
c. K, +1; O, −2; Cr, +6
d. Na, +1; H, +1; O, −2; C, +4

57. a. Sb + 5 ⟶ +3, reduced
Cl − 1 ⟶ 0, oxidized
b. C + 2 ⟶ +4, oxidized
Cl 0 ⟶ −1, reduced
c. N + 2 ⟶ +3, oxidized
Br 0 ⟶ −1, reduced
d. H 0 ⟶ +1, oxidized
C + 4 ⟶ +2, reduced

59. Na is the reducing agent.
H is the oxidizing agent.

61. a. $3\,K(s) + Cr^{3+}(aq) \longrightarrow Cr(s) + 3\,K^{+}(aq)$
b. $Mg(s) + 2\,Ag^{+}(aq) \longrightarrow Mg^{2+}(aq) + 2\,Ag(s)$
c. $2\,Al(s) + 3\,Fe^{2+}(aq) \longrightarrow 2\,Al^{3+}(aq) + 3\,Fe(s)$

63. a. reduction, $5\,e^{-} + MnO_4^{-}(aq) + 8\,H^{+}(aq) \longrightarrow Mn^{2+}(aq) + 4\,H_2O(l)$
b. oxidation, $2\,H_2O(l) + Pb^{2+}(aq) \longrightarrow PbO_2(s) + 4\,H^{+}(aq) + 2e^{-}$
c. reduction, $10\,e^{-} + 2\,IO_3^{-}(aq) + 12\,H^{+}(aq) \longrightarrow I_2(s) + 6\,H_2O(l)$
d. oxidation, $SO_2(g) + 2\,H_2O(l) \longrightarrow SO_4^{2-}(aq) + 4\,H^{+}(aq) + 2\,e^{-}$

65. a. $PbO_2(s) + 4\,H^{+}(aq) + 2\,I^{-}(aq) \longrightarrow I_2(s) + Pb^{2+}(aq) + 2\,H_2O(l)$
b. $5\,SO_3^{2-}(aq) + 6\,H^{+}(aq) + 2\,MnO_4^{-}(aq) \longrightarrow 5\,SO_4^{2-}(aq) + 2\,Mn^{2+}(aq) + 3\,H_2O(l)$
c. $S_2O_3^{2-}(aq) + 4\,Cl_2(g) + 5\,H_2O(l) \longrightarrow 2\,SO_4^{2-}(aq) + 8\,Cl^{-}(aq) + 10\,H^{+}(aq)$

67. a. $ClO_4^{-}(aq) + 2\,H^{+}(aq) + 2\,Cl^{-}(aq) \longrightarrow ClO_3^{-}(aq) + Cl_2(aq) + H_2O(l)$
b. $3\,MnO_4^{-}(aq) + 24\,H^{+}(aq) + 5\,Al(s) \longrightarrow 3\,Mn^{2+}(aq) + 5\,Al^{3+}(aq) + 12\,H_2O(l)$
c. $Br_2(aq) + Sn(s) \longrightarrow Sn^{2+}(aq) + 2\,Br^{-}(aq)$

69. a. $3\,ClO^{-}(aq) + 2\,Cr(OH)_4^{-}(aq) + 2\,OH^{-}(aq) \rightarrow 3\,Cl^{-}(aq) + 2\,CrO_4^{2-}(aq) + 5\,H_2O(l)$
b. $2\,MnO_4^{-}(aq) + Br(aq) + H_2O(l) \longrightarrow 2\,MnO_2(s) + BrO_3^{-}(aq) + 2\,OH^{-}(aq)$

71. a, Ag

73. b, Cu^{2+}

75. b, Al

77. b and c occur spontaneously in the forward direction

79. Fe, Cr, Zn, Mn, Al, Mg, Na, Ca, K, Li

81. Mg

83. a. no reaction
b. $2\,HCl(aq) + Fe(s) \longrightarrow H_2(g) + FeCl_2(aq)$
c. no reaction
d. $6\,HCl(aq) + 2\,Al(s) \longrightarrow 3\,H_2(g) + 2\,AlCl_3(aq)$

85.

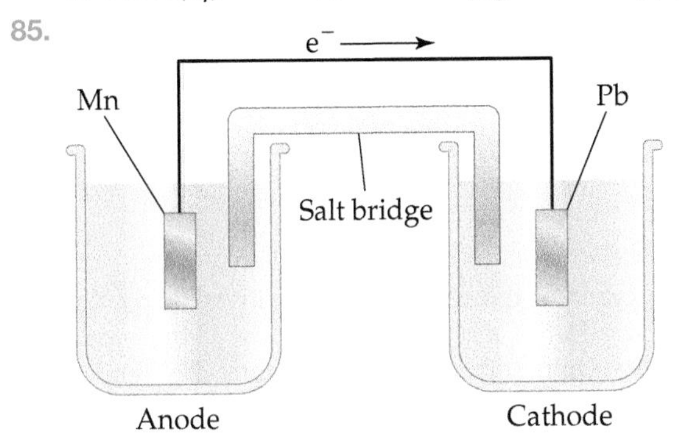

87. d

89. $Zn(s) + 2\,MnO_2(s) + 2\,H_2O(l) \longrightarrow Zn(OH)_2(s) + 2\,MnO(OH)(s)$

91.

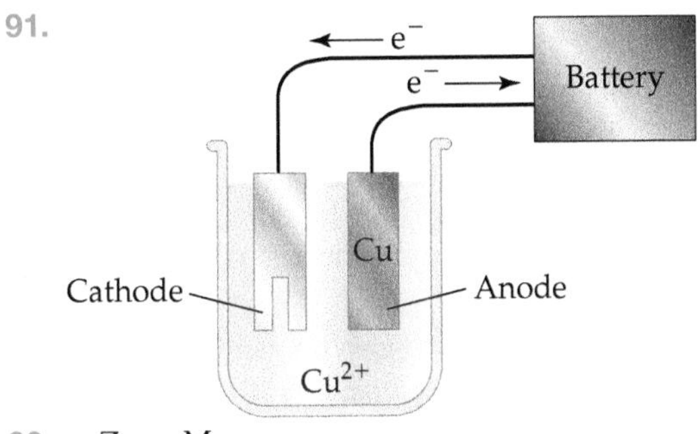

93. a, Zn; c, Mn

95. a. redox; Zn is oxidized; Co is reduced.
b. not redox
c. not redox
d. redox; K is oxidized; Br is reduced.

97. $16\,H^{+}(aq) + 2\,MnO_4^{-}(aq) + 5\,Zn(s) \longrightarrow 2\,Mn^{2+}(aq) + 5\,Zn^{2+}(aq) + 8\,H_2O(l)$; 34.9 mL

99. Yes, the reaction will occur spontaneously.
$Mg(s) \longrightarrow Mg^{2+}(aq) + 2\,e^{-}$
$Ag^{+}(aq) + e^{-} \longrightarrow Ag(s)$
$2\,Ag^{+}(aq) + Mg(s) \longrightarrow Mg^{2+}(aq) + 2\,Ag(s)$

101. 2.95%

103. 0.054 mol

105. a. $2\,Cr(s) + 6\,HI(aq) \longrightarrow 2\,Cr^{3+}(aq) + 6\,I^{-}(aq) + 3\,H_2(g)$, 98 mL HI
b. $2\,Al(s) + 6\,HI(aq) \longrightarrow 2\,Al^{3+}(aq) + 6\,I^{-}(aq) + 3\,H_2(g)$, 68 mL HI
c. no
d. no

107. 0.67 cm

109. 8.9×10^3 s or 2.5 hrs

111.

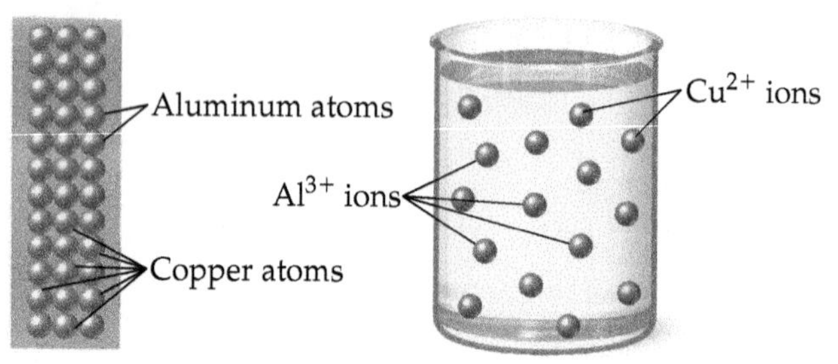

113. Many of the Zn atoms on the electrode would become Zn^{2+} ions in solution. Many Ni^{2+} ions in solution would become Ni atoms on the electrode.

CHAPTER 17

QUESTIONS

1. Radioactivity is the emission of tiny, invisible particles by disintegration of atomic nuclei. Many of these particles can pass right through matter. Atoms that emit these particles are radioactive.

3. Uranic rays were the name given by Henri Becquerel to the radiation emitted by crystals that contained uranium.

5. X: chemical symbol, used to identify the element.

   A: mass number, which is the sum of the number of protons and number of neutrons in the nucleus.

   Z: atomic number, which is the number of protons in the nucleus.

7. Alpha radiation occurs when an unstable nucleus emits a small piece of itself composed of 2 protons and 2 neutrons. The symbol for an alpha particle is ${}^4_2\text{He}$.

9. Alpha particles have high ionizing power and low penetrating power compared to beta and gamma particles.

11. When an atom emits a beta particle, its atomic number increases by one because it now has an additional proton. The mass of an atom does not change as a result of beta emission.

13. Gamma radiation is electromagnetic radiation, and the symbol for a gamma ray is ${}^0_0\gamma$.

15. Gamma particles have low ionizing power and high penetrating power compared to alpha and beta particles.

17. When an atom emits a positron, its atomic number decreases by one because it now has one less proton. The mass of an atom does not change when it emits a positron.

19. A nuclear equation represents the changes that occur during radioactivity and other nuclear processes. For a nuclear equation to be balanced, the sum of the atomic numbers on both sides of the equation must be equal, and the sum of the mass numbers on both sides of the equation must be equal.

21. A film-badge dosimeter is a badge that consists of photographic film held in a small case that is pinned to clothing. It is used to monitor a person's exposure to radiation. The more exposed the film has become in a given period of time, the more the person has been exposed to radioactivity.

23. In a scintillation counter, the radioactive particles pass through a material that emits ultraviolet or visible light in response to excitation by radioactive particles. The light is detected and turned into an electrical signal.

25. The half-life is the time it takes for one-half of the parent nuclides in a radioactive sample to decay to the daughter nuclides. One can relate the half-life of objects to find their radioactive decay rates.

27. The decaying of uranium in the ground is the source of radon in our environment. Radon increases the risk of lung cancer because it is a gas that can be inhaled.

29. When an organism dies, it stops incorporating carbon-14 into its tissues, and the amount present at its death will decay with a half-life of 5730 years. Using this information, one can determine the age of the organism by the amount of carbon-14 still present in the remains.

31. Fermi believed that if a neutron could be incorporated into the nucleus of an atom, the nucleus might undergo beta decay and convert a neutron into a proton. The nuclear equation for this process is:

    $${}^{238}_{92}\text{U} + {}^1_0\text{n} \longrightarrow {}^{239}_{93}\text{U} \longrightarrow {}^{239}_{93}\text{X} + {}^{0}_{-1}\text{e}$$

33. Fission can be used in a bomb because it is a self amplifying reaction (fission of one atom induces fission of another) which can produce great amounts of energy.

35. The main goal of the Manhattan Project was to build an atomic bomb before the Germans did. Its project leader was J.R. Oppenheimer.

37. In nuclear reactors control rods control the amount of fission that can occur. When the control rods are inserted into the fuel assembly, they absorb neutrons, preventing them from inducing fission in the fuel rods.

39. No, a nuclear reactor cannot detonate the way a nuclear bomb can, because the uranium fuel used in electricity generation is not sufficiently enriched in U-235 to produce a nuclear detonation.

41. Modern nuclear weapons use both fission and fusion. In the hydrogen bomb, a small fission bomb is detonated first to create a high enough temperature for the fusion reaction to proceed.

43. Radiation can affect the molecules in living organisms by ionizing them.

45. Lower doses of radiation over extended periods of time can increase cancer risk by damaging DNA. Occasionally a change in DNA can cause cells to grow abnormally and to become cancerous.

47. The main unit of radiation exposure is the rem, which stands for *roentgen equivalent man*. The average American is exposed to 1/3 of a rem of radiation per year.

49. Isotope scanning can be used in the medical community to detect and identify cancerous tumors. Likewise, isotope scanning can produce necessary images of several different internal organs.

PROBLEMS

51. ${}^{128}_{82}\text{Pb}$

53. 81 protons, 126 neutrons

55. **a.** beta particle **b.** neutron
    c. gamma ray

57.

Chemical Symbol	Atomic Number (Z)	Mass Number (A)	Number of Protons	Number of Neutrons
Tc	43	95	43	52
Ba	56	128	56	72
Eu	63	145	63	82
Fr	87	223	87	136

59. a. ${}^{234}_{92}\text{U} \longrightarrow {}^{230}_{90}\text{Th} + {}^{4}_{2}\text{He}$
b. ${}^{230}_{90}\text{Th} \longrightarrow {}^{226}_{88}\text{Ra} + {}^{4}_{2}\text{He}$
c. ${}^{226}_{88}\text{Ra} \longrightarrow {}^{222}_{86}\text{Rn} + {}^{4}_{2}\text{He}$
d. ${}^{222}_{86}\text{Rn} \longrightarrow {}^{218}_{84}\text{Po} + {}^{4}_{2}\text{He}$

61. a. ${}^{214}_{82}\text{Pb} \longrightarrow {}^{214}_{83}\text{Bi} + {}^{0}_{-1}\text{e}$
b. ${}^{214}_{83}\text{Bi} \longrightarrow {}^{214}_{84}\text{Po} + {}^{0}_{-1}\text{e}$
c. ${}^{231}_{90}\text{Th} \longrightarrow {}^{231}_{91}\text{Pa} + {}^{0}_{-1}\text{e}$
d. ${}^{227}_{89}\text{Ac} \longrightarrow {}^{227}_{90}\text{Th} + {}^{0}_{-1}\text{e}$

63. a. ${}^{11}_{6}\text{C} \longrightarrow {}^{11}_{5}\text{B} + {}^{0}_{+1}\text{e}$
b. ${}^{13}_{7}\text{N} \longrightarrow {}^{13}_{6}\text{C} + {}^{0}_{+1}\text{e}$
c. ${}^{15}_{8}\text{O} \longrightarrow {}^{15}_{7}\text{N} + {}^{0}_{+1}\text{e}$

65. ${}^{241}_{94}\text{Pu} \longrightarrow {}^{241}_{95}\text{Am} + {}^{0}_{-1}\text{e}$
${}^{241}_{95}\text{Am} \longrightarrow {}^{237}_{93}\text{Np} + {}^{4}_{2}\text{He}$
${}^{237}_{93}\text{Np} \longrightarrow {}^{233}_{91}\text{Pa} + {}^{4}_{2}\text{He}$
${}^{233}_{91}\text{Pa} \longrightarrow {}^{233}_{92}\text{U} + {}^{0}_{-1}\text{e}$

67. ${}^{232}_{90}\text{Th} \longrightarrow {}^{228}_{88}\text{Ra} + {}^{4}_{2}\text{He}$
${}^{228}_{88}\text{Ra} \longrightarrow {}^{228}_{89}\text{Ac} + {}^{0}_{-1}\text{e}$
${}^{228}_{89}\text{Ac} \longrightarrow {}^{228}_{90}\text{Th} + {}^{0}_{-1}\text{e}$
${}^{228}_{90}\text{Th} \longrightarrow {}^{224}_{88}\text{Ra} + {}^{4}_{2}\text{He}$

69. 3.1×10^3

71. 18 hrs

73. 1.2×10^6 yrs

75. 0.31 g

77. Ga-67 > P-32 > Cr-51 > Sr-89

79. 5,730 yrs

81. 34,380 yrs

83. ${}^{235}_{92}\text{U} + {}^{1}_{0}\text{n} \longrightarrow {}^{144}_{54}\text{Xe} + {}^{90}_{38}\text{Sr} + 2\,{}^{1}_{0}\text{n}$; 2 neutrons

85. ${}^{2}_{1}\text{H} + {}^{2}_{1}\text{H} \longrightarrow {}^{3}_{2}\text{He} + {}^{1}_{0}\text{n}$

87. a. ${}^{6}_{3}\text{Li}$
b. ${}^{64}_{28}\text{Ni}$
c. ${}^{179}_{73}\text{Ta}$

89. ${}^{238}_{92}\text{U} + {}^{1}_{0}\text{n} \longrightarrow {}^{239}_{92}\text{U}$; ${}^{239}_{92}\text{U} \longrightarrow {}^{0}_{-1}\text{e} + {}^{239}_{93}\text{Np}$;
${}^{239}_{93}\text{NP} \longrightarrow {}^{0}_{-1}\text{e} + {}^{239}_{94}\text{Pu}$

91. per mole $= 1.9 \times 10^{13}$ J
per kg $= 8.1 \times 10^{13}$ J

93. $1.7 \times 10^{21}\,\beta$ emissions

95. 68.4%

97. 8.7×10^{-6} L

99. nucleus with 9 protons and 7 neutrons

101. nucleus with 5 protons and 5 neutrons

CHAPTER 18

QUESTIONS

1. Organic molecules are often involved in smell.

3. At the end of the eighteenth century, it was believed that organic compounds came from living things and were easily decomposed, while inorganic compounds came from the earth and were more difficult to decompose. A final difference is that many inorganic compounds could be easily synthesized, but organic compounds could not be.

5. Carbon is unique because it has four valence electrons and can form covalent bonds. Also it can combine with itself to form chains, branches, and rings.

7. Hydrocarbons are compounds that contain only carbon and hydrogen. Hydrocarbons are commonly used for fuels and are also the starting materials in the synthesis of many different consumer products.

9. A saturated hydrocarbon contains no double or triple bonds between the carbon atoms; however, an unsaturated hydrocarbon contains one or more double or triple bonds between the carbon atoms.

11. Alkanes composed of carbon atoms bonded in a straight chain with no branches are called *n*-alkanes. Alkanes composed of carbon atoms forming branched structures are called branched alkanes.

13. Alkenes are hydrocarbons containing at least one double bond between carbon atoms, whereas alkanes contain only single bonds.

15. Hydrocarbon combustion reactions involve the burning of hydrocarbons in the presence of oxygen. An example is:

$$CH_2{=}CHCH_2CH_3(g) + 6\,O_2(g) \longrightarrow 4\,CO_2(g) + 4\,H_2O(g)$$

17. An alkene addition reaction occurs when atoms add across the double bond. For example:

$$CH_2{=}CH_2(g) + Cl_2(g) \longrightarrow CH_2ClCH_2Cl(g)$$

19. The structure of benzene is 6 carbon atoms connected together in a circle, with each bonded to a hydrogen atom. Here are two ways that benzene is often represented.

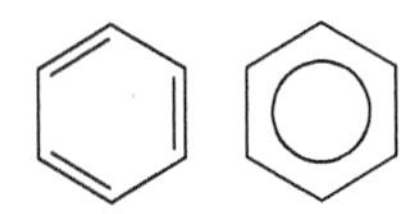

21. The generic structure of alcohols is $R{-}OH$. The structure of methanol is CH_3OH, and the structure of ethanol is CH_3CH_2OH.

23. The generic structure of ethers is $R{-}O{-}R$. The structure of dimethyl ether is CH_3OCH_3, and the structure of diethyl ether is $CH_3CH_2OCH_2CH_3$.

25. The generic structure of an aldehyde is $R{-}CHO$; for example, propanal is CH_3CH_2CHO. The generic structure of a ketone is $R{-}CO{-}R$; for example, acetone is CH_3COCH_3.

27. The generic structure of a carboxylic acid is $R{-}COOH$; for example, acetic acid is CH_3COOH. The generic structure of an ester is $R{-}COO{-}R$; for example, ethyl propanoate is $CH_3CH_2COOCH_2CH_3$.

29. An amine is an organic compound containing nitrogen, the structure being NR_X. Two examples are methylamine, CH_3NH_2, and ethylamine, $CH_3CH_2NH_2$.

31. A polymer is a long chainlike molecule composed of repeating units called *monomers*. A copolymer consists of two different kinds of monomers.

PROBLEMS

33. c and d are hydrocarbons

35. **a.** alkyne **b.** alkane
c. alkyne **d.** alkene

37. **a.**

```
    H  H  H  H  H  H  H
    |  |  |  |  |  |  |
 H—C—C—C—C—C—C—C—H
    |  |  |  |  |  |  |
    H  H  H  H  H  H  H
```

$CH_3CH_2CH_2CH_2CH_2CH_2CH_3$

b.

```
    H  H  H  H  H  H  H  H
    |  |  |  |  |  |  |  |
 H—C—C—C—C—C—C—C—C—H
    |  |  |  |  |  |  |  |
    H  H  H  H  H  H  H  H
```

$CH_3CH_2CH_2CH_2CH_2CH_2CH_2CH_3$

c.

```
    H  H  H  H  H  H
    |  |  |  |  |  |
 H—C—C—C—C—C—C—H
    |  |  |  |  |  |
    H  H  H  H  H  H
```

$CH_3CH_2CH_2CH_2CH_2CH_3$

d.

```
    H  H
    |  |
 H—C—C—H
    |  |
    H  H
```

39. $H_3C—CH_2—CH_2—CH_3$

```
H3C—CH—CH3
     |
     CH3
```

41.

```
    H  H  H  H  H  H  H  H
    |  |  |  |  |  |  |  |
 H—C—C—C—C—C—C—C—C—H
    |  |  |  |  |  |  |  |
    H  H  H  H  H  H  H  H
```

```
    H  H  H  H  H  H  H
    |  |  |  |  |  |  |
 H—C—C—C—C—C—C—C—H
    |  |  |  |  |  |  |
    H  |  H  H  H  H  H
     H—C—H
       |
       H
```

```
    H  H  H  H  H  H  H
    |  |  |  |  |  |  |
 H—C—C—C—C—C—C—C—H
    |  |  |  |  |  |  |
    H  H  |  H  H  H  H
        H—C—H
          |
          H
```

```
    H  H  H  H  H  H  H
    |  |  |  |  |  |  |
 H—C—C—C—C—C—C—C—H
    |  |  |  |  |  |  |
    H  H  H  |  H  H  H
           H—C—H
             |
             H
```

```
    H  H  H  H  H  H
    |  |  |  |  |  |
 H—C—C—C—C—C—C—H
    |  |  |  |  |  |
    H  H  |  H  H  H
        H—C—H
          |
        H—C—H
          |
          H
```

43. **a.** *n*-pentane **b.** 2-methylbutane
c. 4-ethyl-2-methylhexane
d. 3,3-dimethylpentane

45. **a.**

```
H3C—CH—CH2—CH3
     |
     CH3
```

b.

```
          CH3
          |
          CH2
          |
H3C—CH—CH—CH2—CH2—CH3
     |
     CH3
```

c.

```
H3C—CH2—CH—CH2—CH2—CH2—CH3
          |
          HC—CH3
          |
          CH3
```

d.

```
H3C—CH—CH2—CH2—CH—CH2—CH2—CH3
     |              |
     CH3            CH3
```

47. **a.** *n*-pentane **b.** 3-methylhexane
c. 2,3-dimethylpentane

49.

Name	Molecular Formula	Structural Formula	Condensed Structural Formula
2,2,3-trimethylpentane	C_8H_{18}	$\begin{array}{ccccccccc} & & CH_3 & & CH_3 & & & & \\ & & \vert & & \vert & & & & \\ CH_3 & - & C & - & CH & - & CH_2 & - & CH_3 \\ & & \vert & & & & & & \\ & & CH_3 & & & & & & \end{array}$	$CH_3C(CH_3)_2CH(CH_3)CH_2CH_3$
2-methyl-3-propylhexane	$C_{10}H_{22}$	$\begin{array}{ccccccccccc} & & CH_3 & & & & & & & & \\ & & \vert & & & & & & & & \\ CH_3 & - & CH & - & CH & - & CH_2 & - & CH_2 & - & CH_3 \\ & & & & \vert & & & & & & \\ & & & & CH_2 & & & & & & \\ & & & & \vert & & & & & & \\ & & & & CH_2 & & & & & & \\ & & & & \vert & & & & & & \\ & & & & CH_3 & & & & & & \end{array}$	$CH_3CH(CH_3)CH(CH_2CH_2CH_3)CH_2CH_2CH_3$
2,2,3,3-tetramethylhexane	$C_{10}H_{22}$	$\begin{array}{ccccccccccc} & & CH_3 & & CH_3 & & & & & & \\ & & \vert & & \vert & & & & & & \\ CH_3 & - & C & - & C & - & CH_2 & - & CH_2 & - & CH_3 \\ & & \vert & & \vert & & & & & & \\ & & CH_3 & & CH_3 & & & & & & \end{array}$	$CH_3C(CH_3)_2C(CH_3)_2CH_2CH_2CH_3$
4,4-diethyl 2,3-dimethylhexane	$C_{12}H_{26}$	$\begin{array}{ccccccccccc} & & & & & & CH_3 & & & & \\ & & & & & & \vert & & & & \\ & & CH_3 & & CH_3 & & CH_2 & & & & \\ & & \vert & & \vert & & \vert & & & & \\ CH_3 & - & CH & - & CH & - & C & - & CH_2 & - & CH_3 \\ & & & & & & \vert & & & & \\ & & & & & & CH_2 & & & & \\ & & & & & & \vert & & & & \\ & & & & & & CH_3 & & & & \end{array}$	$CH_3CH(CH_3)CH(CH_3)CH(CH_2CH_3)_2CH_2CH_3$

51.

$$\begin{array}{ccc} H & & H \\ & \diagdown\;\diagup & \\ & C{=}C & \\ & \diagup\;\diagdown & \\ H & & H \end{array} \qquad \begin{array}{ccccc} H & & H & & H \\ & \diagdown & \vert & & \vert \\ & & C{=}C & - & C-H \\ & \diagup & & & \vert \\ H & & & & H \end{array}$$

$CH_2{=}CH_2$ $\qquad$ $CH_2{=}CHCH_3$

53. $H_2C{=}CH-CH_2-CH_2-CH_3$

$H_3C-CH{=}CH-CH_2-CH_3$

55. **a.** 2-pentene
b. 4-methyl-2-pentene
c. 3,3-dimethyl-1-butene
d. 3,4-dimethyl-1-hexene

57. **a.** 2-butyne
b. 4-methyl-2-pentyne
c. 4,4-dimethyl-2-hexyne
d. 3-ethyl-3-methyl-1-pentyne

59. **a.** $H_3C-CH{=}CH-CH_2-CH_2-CH_3$
b. $H_3C-CH_2-C{\equiv}C-CH_2-CH_2-CH_3$
c. $\begin{array}{ccccccc} & & & & CH_3 & & \\ & & & & \vert & & \\ HC{\equiv}C & - & & & CH & - & CH_2-CH_3 \end{array}$
d. $\begin{array}{ccccccc} & & & & CH_3 & & \\ & & & & \vert & & \\ H_3C-CH{=}CH & - & & & C & - & CH_2-CH_3 \\ & & & & \vert & & \\ & & & & CH_3 & & \end{array}$

61. $H_2C{=}CH-CH_2-CH_2-CH_3$ 1-pentene

$H_3C-CH{=}CH-CH_2-CH_3$ 2-pentene

$\begin{array}{ccccc} & & CH_3 & & \\ & & \vert & & \\ H_2C & = & C & - & CH_2-CH_3 \end{array}$ 2-methyl-1-butene

$\begin{array}{ccccc} & & CH_3 & & \\ & & \vert & & \\ H_3C & - & CH & - & CH{=}CH_2 \end{array}$ 3-methyl-1-butene

$\begin{array}{ccccc} & & CH_3 & & \\ & & \vert & & \\ H_3C & - & C & = & CH-CH_3 \end{array}$ 2-methyl-2-butene

63.

Name	Molecular Formula	Structural Formula	Condensed Structural Formula
2,2-dimethyl-3-hexene	C_8H_{16}	CH_3 (above C) $CH_3-C-CH=CH-CH_2-CH_3$ CH_3 (below C)	$CH_3C(CH_3)_2CH=CHCH_2CH_3$
4,4-diethyl-5,5-dimethyl-2-hexyne	$C_{12}H_{22}$	CH_3 H_3C CH_2 $CH_3-C-C-C\equiv C-CH_3$ H_3C CH_2 CH_3	$CH_3C(CH_3)_2C(CH_2CH_3)_2C\equiv CCH_3$
3,4-dimethyl-1-octyne	$C_{10}H_{18}$	$HC\equiv C-CH-CH-CH_2-CH_2-CH_2-CH_3$ CH_3 CH_3	$CH\equiv CCH(CH_3)CH(CH_3)CH_2CH_2CH_2CH_3$
4,4-diethyl-5,5-dimethyl-2-hexene	$C_{12}H_{24}$	CH_3 H_3C CH_2 $CH_3-C-C-CH=CH-CH_3$ H_3C CH_2 CH_3	$CH_3C(CH_3)_2C(CH_2CH_3)_2CH=CHCH_3$

65. a. $CH_3CH_3(g) + 7\,O_2(g) \longrightarrow 4\,CO_2(g) + 6\,H_2O(g)$

b. $2\,CH_2=CHCH_3(g) + 9\,O_2(g) \longrightarrow 6\,CO_2(g) + 6\,H_2O(g)$

c. $2\,CH=CH(g) + 5\,O_2(g) \longrightarrow 4\,CO_2(g) + 2\,H_2O(g)$

67. $CH_4(g) + Br_2(g) \longrightarrow CH_3Br(g) + HBr(g)$

69. $CH_3CH=CHCH_3(g) + Cl_2(g) \longrightarrow CH_3CHClCHClCH_3(g)$

71. $CH_2=CH_2(g) + H_2(g) \longrightarrow CH_3CH_3(g)$

73. (Two resonance structures of benzene, C_6H_6, each carbon bearing one H, with alternating double bonds shifted) $\longleftrightarrow$

75. a. fluorobenzene

b. isopropylbenzene

c. ethylbenzene

77. a. 4-phenyloctane

b. 5-phenyl-3-heptene

c. 7-phenyl-2-heptyne

79. a. 1-bromo-2-chlorobenzene

b. 1,2-diethylbenzene or orthodiethylbenzene

c. 1,3-difluorobenzene or metadifluorobenzene

81. a. (benzene ring)$-CH_2-CH_2-CH_2-CH_3$

b. (benzene ring with H_3C-CH_2 and, on the adjacent carbon, I)

c. (benzene ring with CH_3 at top and CH_3 at bottom, para)

83. a. ether = $R-O-R$

b. aldehyde = $R-\overset{O}{\overset{\|}{C}}-H$

c. amine = $R-\overset{R}{\overset{|}{N}}-R$

d. ketone = $R-\overset{O}{\overset{\|}{C}}-R$

85. a. $H_3C-CH_2-CH_2-$(NH)$-CH_3$ amine

b. $H_3C-CH_2-CH_2-$($\overset{O}{\overset{\|}{C}}H$) aldehyde

c. $H_3C-C(CH_3)_2-C(CH_3)_2-$(OH) alcohol

d. $H_3C-C(CH_3)_2-$(O)$-CH_2-CH_3$ ether

87. a. 2-butanol

b. 2-methyl-1-propanol

c. 3-ethyl-1-hexanol

d. 3-methyl-3-pentanol

89. a. $CH_3-CH_2-\overset{OH}{\overset{|}{C}H}-CH_2-CH_3$

b. $\overset{OH}{\overset{|}{C}H_2}-\overset{CH_3}{\overset{|}{C}H}-CH_2-CH_3$

c.
$$\begin{array}{c} \ \ \ OH\ \ CH_3CH_2 \\ CH_3-\overset{|}{C}H-\overset{|}{C}H-CH_2-CH_2-CH_3 \end{array}$$

d. CH_3-CH_2-OH

91. a. $CH_3-CH_2-CH_2-CH_2-O-CH_2-CH_2-CH_2-CH_3$

b. ethyl propyl ether

c. dipropyl ether

d. $CH_3-O-CH_2-CH_2-CH_2-CH_2-CH_3$

93. a. $CH_3-CH_2-CH_2-CH_2-CH_2-CH_2-CH_2-\overset{O}{\overset{\|}{C}}H$

b. butanal

c. 4-heptanone

d. $CH_3-CH_2-\overset{O}{\overset{\|}{C}}-CH_2-CH_2-CH_3$

95. a. $CH_3-CH_2-CH_2-CH_2-CH_2-CH_2-CH_2-\overset{O}{\overset{\|}{C}}-OH$

b. methyl ethanoate

c. $H_3C-CH_2-CH_2-\overset{O}{\overset{\|}{C}}-O-CH_2-CH_3$

d. heptanoic acid

97. a. $CH_3-CH_2-\underset{H}{\underset{|}{N}}-CH_2-CH_3$

b. triethylamine

c. butylpropylamine

99. $\left[-CH_2-\underset{CH_3}{\underset{|}{\overset{CH_3}{\overset{|}{C}}}}-\right]_n$

101. $HO-\overset{O}{\overset{\|}{C}}-C_6H_4-\overset{O}{\overset{\|}{C}}-O-CH_2-CH_2-OH$ (ester group circled)

103. a. alcohol b. amine

c. alkane d. carboxylic acid

e. ether f. alkene

105. a. 3-methyl-4-tert-butylheptane

b. 3-methyl butanal

c. 4-isopropyl-3-methyl-2-heptene

d. propyl butanoate

107. a. same molecule b. isomers

c. same molecule

109. $CH_2{=}CH_2 + HCl \longrightarrow CH_3CH_2Cl$

111. 558 g H_2

113. 4.63×10^4 L

115. a. alcohol b. amine

c. carboxylic acid d. ester

e. alkane f. ether

CHAPTER 19

QUESTIONS

1. The human genome project is a 15-year project to map all of the genetic material of a human being. Scientists were surprised to discover that humans have only 20,000–25,000 genes, which is not much more than the number of genes in many simpler organisms.

3. A cell is the smallest structural unit of life. The main chemical components of a cell are carbohydrates, lipids, proteins, and nucleic acids.

5. Glucose is soluble in water due to its many —OH groups. This is important because glucose is the primary fuel of cells and can be easily transported in the bloodstream.

7. During digestion the links in disaccharides and polysaccharides are broken, allowing individual monosaccharides to pass through the intestinal wall and enter the bloodstream.

9. Starch and cellulose are both polysaccharides, but the bond between saccharide units is slightly different. Consequently, humans can digest starch and use it for energy, whereas cellulose cannot be digested and passes directly through humans.

11. Fatty acids are carboxylic acids with long hydrocarbon tails. The general structure of a fatty acid is $R-\overset{O}{\overset{\|}{C}}-OH$, where R is 3 to 19 carbon atoms long.

13. A triglyceride is a triester composed of glycerol with three fatty acids attached as shown here.

$$\begin{array}{l} H_2C-O-\overset{O}{\overset{\|}{C}}-R \\ \ \ | \\ HC-O-\overset{O}{\overset{\|}{C}}-R \\ \ \ | \\ H_2C-O-\overset{O}{\overset{\|}{C}}-R \end{array}$$

15. A phospholipid is similar to a triglyceride except instead of one of the fatty acid groups it has a phosphate group. A glycolipid has a nonpolar section made of a fatty acid chain and hydrocarbon chain, and a polar section made of a sugar molecule. Phospholipids and glycolipids both have a polar and nonpolar section.

17. Steroids are lipids that contain a four-ring structure. Cholesterol is a steroid that is part of cell membranes and also serves as a starting material for the body to synthesize other steroids. Also, steroids serve as male and female hormones in the body.

19. Proteins serve as catalysts; structural units of muscle, skin, and cartilage; transporters of oxygen; disease-fighting antibodies; and as hormones.

21. Amino acids differ from each other only in their R group or side chain.

23. $H_2N-CH(R_1)-C(=O)-OH + H_2N-CH(R_2)-C(=O)-OH \longrightarrow H_2N-CH(R_1)-C(=O)-NH-CH(R_2)-C(=O)-OH + H_2O$

25. Primary protein structure refers to the sequence of amino acids in the protein's chain. Primary protein structure is maintained by the covalent peptide bonds between individual amino acids.

27. Tertiary protein structure refers to the large-scale twists and folds within the protein. These are maintained by interactions between the *R* groups of amino acids that are separated by long distances in the chain sequence.

29. In the α-helix structure, the amino acid chain is wound into a tight coil by hydrogen bonding between C=O and N—H groups at different locations along the backbone. The side chains extend outward. In the β-pleated sheet structure, the amino acid chain doubles back on itself repeatedly in a zig-zag pattern, with adjacent sections held together by hydrogen bonding between C=O and N—H groups along the backbone. The resulting structure is an undulating sheet with the side chains extending above and below it.

31. Nucleic acids contain a chemical code that specifies the correct amino acid sequences for proteins.

33. The four different bases that occur within DNA are adenine (A), cytosine (C), guanine (G), and thymine (T).

35. The genetic code is the code that links a specific codon to an amino acid.

37. A gene is a sequence of codons within a DNA molecule that codes for a single protein. Genes vary in length from 50 to thousands of codons.

39. Chromosomes located within the nuclei of cells are structures containing genes.

41. No; most cells in the human body only synthesize proteins that are important to their function.

43. **a.** The complementary base of adenine (A) is thymine (T).

b. The complementary base of thymine (T) is adenine (A).

c. The complementary base of cytosine (C) is guanine (G).

d. The complementary base of guanine (G) is cytosine (C).

PROBLEMS

45. **a.** monosaccharide
b. not a carbohydrate
c. not a carbohydrate
d. disaccharide

47. **a.** hexose **b.** tetrose
c. pentose **d.** tetrose

49. Open-chain: $HC(=O)$; $H-C-OH$; $HO-C-H$; $H-C-OH$; $H-C-OH$; H_2C-OH (top to bottom). Ring form: six-membered ring (H_2C-OH on ring carbon; ring O; ring carbons bearing H, OH, HO, H, OH as drawn).

51. Glucose (ring, H_2C-OH) —O— Fructose (ring, HO–H_2C, CH_2–OH)

Glucose Fructose

53. **a.** fatty acid, saturated **b.** steroid
c. triglyceride, unsaturated
d. not a lipid

55. Glycerol — Fatty acid; Fatty acid; Fatty acid

Triglyceride

57.

$$H_2C-O-C(=O)-(CH_2)_{12}-CH_3$$
$$HC-O-C(=O)-(CH_2)_{12}-CH_3$$
$$H_2C-O-C(=O)-(CH_2)_{12}-CH_3\text{, fat}$$

59. b, d

61. $H_2N-CH(CH(CH_3)CH_2CH_3)-C(=O)-OH + H_2N-CH(CH_2OH)-C(=O)-OH \longrightarrow H_2N-CH(CH(CH_3)CH_2CH_3)-C(=O)-NH-CH(CH_2OH)-C(=O)-OH$

Isoleucine Serine

63. a.

```
      H  O       H  O       H  O
      |  ‖       |  ‖       |  ‖
H2N—C—C—NH—C—C—NH—C—C—OH
      |          |          |
      CH2        CH3        H
      |
  H3C—CH
      |
      CH3
```

b.

```
      H  O       H  O       H  O
      |  ‖       |  ‖       |  ‖
H2N—C—C—NH—C—C—NH—C—C—OH
      |          |          |
  H3C—CH     HO—CH          CH2
      |          |          |
      CH3        CH3        CH2
                            |
                            CH2
                            |
                            CH2
                            |
                            NH2
```

c.

```
      H  O       H  O       H  O
      |  ‖       |  ‖       |  ‖
H2N—C—C—NH—C—C—NH—C—C—OH
      |          |          |
      H          CH2        CH2
                 |          |
               (C6H5)       OH
```

65. tertiary

67. primary

69. a. nucleotide, G

b. not a nucleotide

c. not a nucleotide

d. not a nucleotide

71.

73.

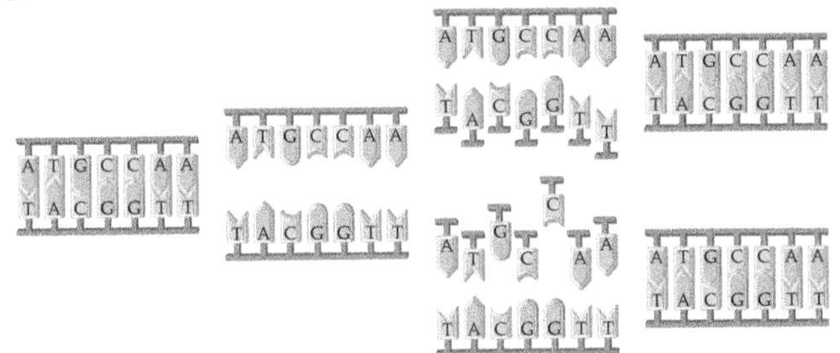

75. a. glycoside linkage—carbohydrates

b. peptide bonds—proteins

c. ester linkage—triglycerides

77. a. glucose—short-term energy storage

b. DNA—blueprint for proteins

c. phospholipids—compose cell membranes

d. triglycerides—long-term energy storage

79. a. codon—codes for a single amino acid

b. gene—codes for a single protein

c. genome—all of the genetic material of an organism

d. chromosome—structure that contains genes

81. Nitrogen: tetrahedral electron geometry, trigonal pyramidal molecular geometry

1st Carbon: tetrahedral electron geometry, tetrahedral molecular geometry

2nd Carbon: trigonal planar electron geometry, trigonal planar molecular geometry

```
 H
  \      H
   N.    ▼     O
  /   .  |   //
 H      C—C
       ◢     \
      H       OH
```

83.

```
   H  O       H  O                    H  O       H  O
   |  ‖       |  ‖                    |  ‖       |  ‖
H2N—C—C—NH—C—C—OH              H2N—C—C—NH—C—C—OH
   |          |                       |          |
   H      H3C—CH                  H3C—CH         H
              |                       |
              CH3                     CH3
        gly-val                            val-gly
```

The difference lies in the end groups. In gly-val, glycine has the amine end and valine has the carboxyl end. For val-gly, the reverse is true.

85. gly-arg-ala-ser-phe-gly-asn-lys-trp-glu-val

87. 153 base pairs

89. 6.07×10^3 g/mol

91. The actual thymine-containing nucleotide uses the —OH end to bond and replicate; however, with the fake nucleotide having a nitrogen-based end instead, the possibility of replication is halted.

PHOTO CREDITS

Chapter 1 Page 2: Richard Megna/Fundamental Photographs. Page 3 (Tl): Maxwellartandphoto.com. Page 3 (Tr): De Visu/Shutterstock. Page 3 center: Jaroslav74/Shutterstock. Page 3 bottom: Kevin Fleming/Corbis. Page 5 (Tr): Jacques-Louis David (French, 1748-1825), "Antoine-Laurent Lavoisier (1743-1794) and His Wife (Marie-Anne-Pierrette Paulze, 1758-1836)", 1788; Oil on canvas, 102-1/4 in. x 76-5/8 in. (259.7 x 194.6 cm). Page 5 (Tl): Corbis. Page 5 (B): IBM Research, Almaden Research Center. Page 7: bonniej/Istockphoto.com. Page 6: SPL/Photo Researchers. **Chapter 2** Page 12: Getty. Page 14 (T): Maxwellartandphoto.com. Page 14 (C): Paul Silverman/Fundamental Photographs. Page 14 (Bl & R): Richard Megna/Fundamental Photographs. Page 15 (T): tzara/Istockphoto.com. Page 15 (B): Richard Megna/Fundamental Photographs. Page 18: NASA. Page 22: Richard Megna/Fundamental Photographs. Page 23 (Tl): National Institute of Standards and Technology. Page 23 (Tc): Bureau International des Poids et Mesures. Page 23 (Tr): National Institute of Standards and Technology. Page 23 (B): Richard Megna/Fundamental Photographs. Page 24: David Mager/Pearson Education. Page 32: Maxwellartandphoto.com. Page 34: Litespeed Titanium. Page 40: Richard Megna/Fundamental Photographs. Page 52 (L): NASA. Page 52 (R): NASA Ozone Watch. **Chapter 3** Page 56 (Tl): Getty Images. Page 56 (Tr): Ken Liska. Page 56 (Bl): IBM Research, Almaden Research Center. Page 56 (Br): Driscoll, Youngquist, & Baldeschwieler, Caltech/SPL/Photo Researchers. Page 57 (Tl): Marek CECH/Shutterstock. Page 57 (Tc): Getty Images. Page 57 (Tr): Getty Images. Page 57 (B): Natural History Museum, London/Alamy. Page 59 (Tl): Shutterstock. Page 60: Getty Images. Page 59 (Tr): Getty Images. Page 59 (B1, 2): Richard Megna/Fundamental Photographs. Page 59 (B3): DenisLarkin/Istockphoto.com. Page 59 (B4): Kip Peticolas/Fundamental Photographs. Page 61: istockphoto.com. Page 63: Richard Megna/Fundamental Photographs. Page 64: Etienne du Preez/Shutterstock. Page 66: JLGutierrez/istockphoto.com. Page 74, 75: Getty Images. Page 90 (T): International Research Institute for Climate and Society. Page 90 (B): peeterv/istockphoto.com. **Chapter 4** Page 94 (B): Library of Congress. Page 94 (Tl): Getty Images. Page 94 (Tr): Corbis. Page 95: IBM Communications Media Relations. Page 97: Maxwellartandphoto.com. Page 99 (T): Getty Images. Page 99 (Bl): Photos.com/Jupiter Images. Page 99 (Br): Getty Images. Page 101 (T): Charles D. Winters/Photo Researchers. Page 101 (B): Library of Congress. Page 102: Stamp from the private collection of Professor C. M. Lang, photography by Gary J. Shulfer, University of Wisconsin, Stevens Point. "Russia: #3607 (1969)"; Scott Standard Postage Stamp Catalogue, Scott Pub. Co., Sidney, Ohio. Page 103: Corbis RF. Page 104 (T): Getty Images. Page 104 (B): Graeme Dawes/Shutterstock. Page 105 (Tlt): Richard Megna/Fundamental Photographs. Page 105 (Tlb): sciencephotos/Alamy. Page 105 (Bl): Richard Megna/Fundamental Photographs. Page 105 (Trt): Charles D. Winters/Photo Researchers. Page 105 (Trb): Pearson Education. Page 109: Getty Images. Page 112: U.S. Department of Energy. **Chapter 5** Page 127 (Bl): Pearson Education/PH College. Page 127 (Br NIP): Charles D. Winters/Photo Researchers. Page 128 (T): Diane Diederich/Istockphoto.com. Page 128 (T Bl): Getty Images. Page 128 (T Br): Mike Kemp/Rubberball/Alamy. Page 132 (NIP): Istockphoto.com. Page 133 (C): Harry Taylor/Dorling Kindersly Media Library. Page 133 (B NIP): Charles D. Winters/Photo Researchers. Page 134 (T): Ken Karp/Omni-Photo Communication. Page 134 (B): Paul Silverman/Fundamental Photographs. Page 141: Maxwellartandphoto.com. Page 146 (L): Photoshot/Alamy. Page 146 (R): Nickos/Istockphoto.com. Page 160 (L): Charles D. Winters/Photo Researchers. Page 160 (R): Richard Megna/Fundamental Photographs. Page 161 (T): Richard Megna/Fundamental Photographs. Page 161 (Bl): Getty Images. Page 161 (Br): Ken Eward/Photo Researchers. Page 162: Maxwellartandphoto.com. **Chapter 6** Page 166 (Tl): Richard Kittenberger/Shutterstock. Page 166 (Tr): Joseph P. Sinnot. Page 166 (C & B): Richard Megna/Fundamental Photographs. Page 167 (T): Maxwellartandphoto.com. Page 167 (B): Getty Images. Page 175, 176: Getty Images. Page 169 (T): Maxwellartandphoto.com. Page 169 (B): Richard Megna/Fundamental Photographs. Page 179: Tom Pantages. Page 181: Maxwellartandphoto.com. Page 184: Charles D. Winters/Photo Researchers. Page 202 (Bc & L): Getty Images. Page 202 (Br): NASA. Page 203: NASA Johnson Space Center. **Chapter 7** Page 206: Maxwellartandphoto.com. Page 207 (Bl): Maxwellartandphoto.com. Page 207 (Tl): Richard Megna/Fundamental Photographs. Page 207 (Tr): Charles D. Winters/Photo Researchers. Page 207 (Bl): Tom Bochsler/Pearson Education/PH College. Page 208 (Tl): Magnascan/Istockphoto.com. Page 208 (B1, 2, 3 from left): Richard Megna/Fundamental Photographs. Page 208 (B4): Jeff Daly/Fundamental Photographs. Page 208 (B5): ayazad/Shutterstock. Page 211: Getty Images. Page 215: Photodisc. Page 218: Richard Megna/Fundamental Photographs. Page 223: Maxwellartandphoto.com. Page 224: Fundamental Photographs. Page 225: Maxwellartandphoto.com. Page 226 (L): Renn SMinkey/Creative Digital Visions/Pearson. Page 226 (R): Tom McCarthy/PhotoEdit. Pages 229, 230, 246: Richard Megna/Fundamental Photographs. **Chapter 8** Pages 250, 251, 254, 258: Maxwellartandphoto.com. Page 265: Richard Megna/Fundamental Photographs. Page 282 (L): Getty Images. Page 282 (R): Katrina Leigh/Shutterstock. **Chapter 9** Page 285: Associated Press. Page 286 (L): Burgess Companies. Page 286 (R): American Institute of Physics/Emilio Segre Visual Archives. Page 287: Martin Barraud/Getty Images. Page 288: zooropa/Shutterstock. Page 289: [copyright] Sierra Pacific Innovations. All rights reserved. SPI CORP, www.x20.org. Page 290: Larry Mulvehill/Photo Researchers. Page 291 (Tl): Getty Images. Page 291 (B): Richard Megna/Fundamental Photographs. Page 295 (R): Joe Sohm/Photo Researchers. Page 295 (L): Associated Press. Page 322 (L): Getty Images. Page 322 (R): Library of Congress. **Chapter 10** Page 341: Kip Peticolas/Fundamental Photographs. Page 340: Maxwellartandphoto.com. Page 345: Richard Megna/Fundamental Photographs. Page 356: Tom Grundy/Shutterstock. **Chapter 11** Page 370: Getty Images. Page 365: Jerry Driendl/Getty Images. Page 372: Richard Megna/Fundamental Photographs. Page 377: Matka Wariatka/Shutterstock. Page 387: Hiro Kuraoka/Corbis. Page 394: Getty Images. Page 407: Don Johnston/Getty Images. Page 408: Tom Bochsler/Pearson Education/PH College. **Chapter 12** Page 413: Getty Images. Page 414 (T NIP): Anthony West/Corbis. Page 414 (C): Richard Megna/Fundamental Photographs. Page 414 (B): LauriPatterson/Istockphoto.com. Page 415 (Tl): lostbear/Istockphoto.com. Page 415 (Bl): NASA/Johnson Space Center. Page 415 (Br): Richard Megna/Fundamental Photographs. Page 417 (T): Richard Megna/Fundamental Photographs. Page 417 (B): Magnascan/Istockphoto.com. Page 421: Richard Megna/Fundamental Photographs. Page 424 (B): Ken Karp/Omni-photo communications. Page 424 (T): Charles Winters/Photo Researchers. Page 427 (L): Richard Megna/Fundamental Photographs. Page 427 (C): Richard

Haynes/Prentice Hall School Division. Page 427 (R): John Caps III/Associated Press. Page 432 (L): KieselUndStein/Istockphoto.com. Page 432 (C): Matejay/Istockphoto.com. Page 432 (R): Shutterstock. Page 433 (L): Getty Images. Page 433 (C): Dr. Mark J. Winter. Page 433 (R): Shutterstock. Page 433 (B): Maciej Toporowicz/Getty Images. Page 435 (B): Kristen Brochmann/Fundamental Photographs. Page 435 (T): Lisa F. Young/Shutterstock. **Chapter 13** Page 448: University of Savoie. Page 451: Richard Megna/Fundamental Photographs. Page 452: bodhihill/Istockphoto.com. Page 453: Maxwellartandphoto.com. Page 458: Don B. Stevenson/Alamy. Page 466: Dennis McDonald/PhotoEdit. Page 467: jane/Istockphoto.com. Page 468: Masonjar /Shutterstock. Page 471 (L): David Kamm/Alamy. Page 471 (R): Al Dodge. Page 485: Ken Lax/Photo Researchers. Page 470: Sam Singer/Pearson Education. **Chapter 14** Page 488 (Tl): George Goodwin/SuperStock. Page 488 (Tr, B): Richard Megna/Fundamental Photographs. Page 489: Ivaylo Ivanov/Shutterstock. Page 490 (T): Maxwellartandphoto.com. Page 490 (B): Richard Megna/ Fundamental Photographs. Page 494 (T): Paul Silverman/ Fundamental Photographs. Page 494 (B): Richard Megna/ Fundamental Photographs. Page 496: Maxwellartandphoto.com. Page 498: Richard Megna/Fundamental Photographs. Page 499: Richard Megna/Fundamental Photographs. Page 501: Richard Megna/ Fundamental Photographs. Page 512: Vera Bogaerts/Shutterstock. Page 515: NYC Parks Photo Archive/Fundamental Photographs. Page 515: Spencer Platt/Getty Images. **Chapter 15** Page 552: Claude Edelmann/Petit Format/Photo Researchers. Page 554: Richard Megna/ Fundamental Photographs. Page 557: Alamy Images. **Chapter 16** Page 577: American Honda Motor Co. Inc. Page 578: Ron Zmiri/ Shutterstock. Page 578: Getty Images. Page 579: Pearson Education/ PH College. Page 583: John-Francis Bourke/Digital Vision/Getty Images. Page 589: Yellowj/Shutterstock. Page 590: Richard Megna/ Fundamental Photographs. Page 591: Chris Cheadle/Getty Images. Page 592: Richard Megna/Fundamental Photographs. Page 595 (L): Kim Steele/Getty Images. Page 595 (R): Edmond Van Hoorick/Getty Images. Page 598 (T): Charles Winters/Photo Researchers. Page 598 (B): Angus Beare/Dorling Kindersly Media Library. Page 599: Draeger Safety, Inc. Page 610: Tony McNicol/Alamy. **Chapter 17** Page 614: Southern Illinois State University/Photo Researchers. Page 615 (L): Getty Images. Page 615 (R): Richard Megna/Fundamental Photographs. Page 622 (T): Hank Morgan/Photo Researchers. Page 622 (B): Scott Peterson/Liaison/Getty Images. Page 628: Associated Press. Page 627: "Otto Hahn, A Scientific Autobiography", Charles Scribner's Sons, New York, Page 1966, courtesy AIP Emilio Segre Visual Archives. Page 629 (T): Getty Images. Page 629 (B): H. Mark Weidman Photography/Alamy. Page 630: Istockphoto.com. Page 633 (T): Roger Tully/Getty Images. Page 633 (B): Peter Arnold/Alamy. **Chapter 18** Page 644 (L): Alex L. Fradkin/Getty Images. Page 644 (R): Emma Lee/Getty Images. Page 645 (T): Ryan McVey/Getty Images. Page 645 (T): C Squared Studios/Getty Images. Page 646: Science Photo Library/Photo Researchers. Page 649: jdjana/Istockphoto.com. Page 648: David Toase/Getty Images. Page 652 (1 from top): ayazad/ Shutterstock. Page 652 (2 from top): Maxwellartandphoto.com. Page 652 (3 from top): David Buffington/Getty Images. Page 652 (4 from top): PhotoEdit. Page 652 (5 from top): Getty Images. Page 652 (6 from top): David Toase/Getty Images. Page 657: Melissa Brandes/ Shutterstock. Page 658: Arthur S. Aubry/Getty Images. Page 661: Maxwellartandphoto.com. Page 666 (T): Todd Taulman/Shutterstock. Page 666 (B): Maxwellartandphoto.com. Page 669 (L): Spencer Jones/Getty Images. Page 669 (R): Maxwellartandphoto.com. Page 670 (L): GrigoryL/Shutterstock. Page 670 (R): C Squared Studios/Getty Images. Page 671: Getty Images. Page 672 (T): Getty Images. Page 672 (B): Lawrence Lawry/Getty Images. Page 674: Mary Kay Denney/ PhotoEdit. Page 675: Maxwellartandphoto.com. Page 676: Professor Nivaldo Jose Tro. **Chapter 19** Page 694: Huntstock/Subjects/Getty Images. Page 698 (T): Spencer Jones/Getty Images. Page 698 (B): Geostock/Getty Images. Page 706: Maxwellartandphoto.com. Page 713: Oliver Meckes & Nicole Ottawa/Photo Researchers. Page 714: Professor Nivaldo Jose Tro. Page 720: Kenneth Eward/Photo Researchers.

INDEX

F

Fundamental Physical Constants

Atomic mass unit	1 amu = 1.660539×10^{-27} kg 1 g = 6.022142×10^{23} amu
Avogadro's number	$N_A = 6.022142 \times 10^{23}$/mol
Electron charge	$e = 1.602176 \times 10^{-19}$ C
Gas constant	$R = 8.314472$ J/(mol · K) = 0.0820582 (L · atm)/(mol · K)
Mass of electron	$m_e = 5.485799 \times 10^{-4}$ amu $= 9.109382 \times 10^{-31}$ kg
Mass of neutron	$m_n = 1.008665$ amu $= 1.674927 \times 10^{-27}$ kg
Mass of proton	$m_p = 1.007276$ amu $= 1.672622 \times 10^{-27}$ kg
Pi	$\pi = 3.1415926536$
Planck's constant	$h = 6.626069 \times 10^{-34}$ J · s
Speed of light in vacuum	$c = 2.99792458 \times 10^{8}$ m/s

Useful Geometric Formulas

Perimeter of a rectangle = $2l + 2w$

Circumference of a circle = $2\pi r$

Area of a triangle = (1/2)(base × height)

Area of a circle = πr^2

Surface area of a sphere = $4\pi r^2$

Volume of a sphere = $(4/3)\pi r^3$

Volume of a cylinder or prism = area of base × height

Important Conversion Factors

Length: SI unit = meter (m)

- 1 m = 39.37 in.
- 1 in. = 2.54 cm (exactly)
- 1 mile = 5280 ft = 1.609 km
- 1 angstrom (Å) = 10^{-10} m

Volume: SI unit = cubic meter (m^3)

- 1 L = 1000 cm^3 = 1.057 qt (U.S.)
- 1 gal (U.S.) = 4 qt = 8 pt
= 128 fluid ounces
= 3.785 L

Mass: SI unit = kilogram (kg)

- 1 kg = 2.205 lb
- 1 lb = 16 oz = 453.6 g
- 1 ton = 2000 lb
- 1 metric ton = 1000 kg = 1.103 tons
- 1 g = 6.022×10^{23} atomic mass units (amu)

Pressure: SI unit = pascal (Pa)

- 1 Pa = 1 N/m^2
- 1 bar = 10^5 Pa
- 1 atm = 1.01325×10^5 Pa (exactly)
= 1.01325 bar
= 760 mmHg
= 760 torr (exactly)

Energy: SI unit = joule (J)

- 1 J = 1 N · m
- 1 cal = 4.184 J (exactly)
- 1 L · atm = 101.33 J

Temperature: SI unit = kelvin (K)

- K = °C + 273.15
- °C = (5/9) (°F − 32°)
- °F = (9/5) (°C) + 32°